TEXTBOOK OF
MODERN BIOLOGY

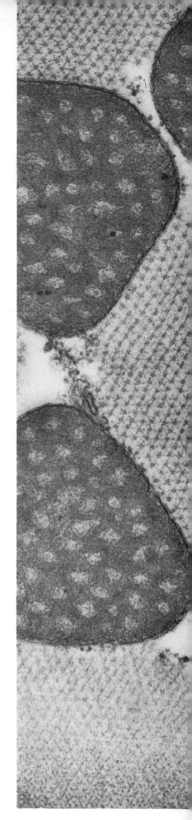

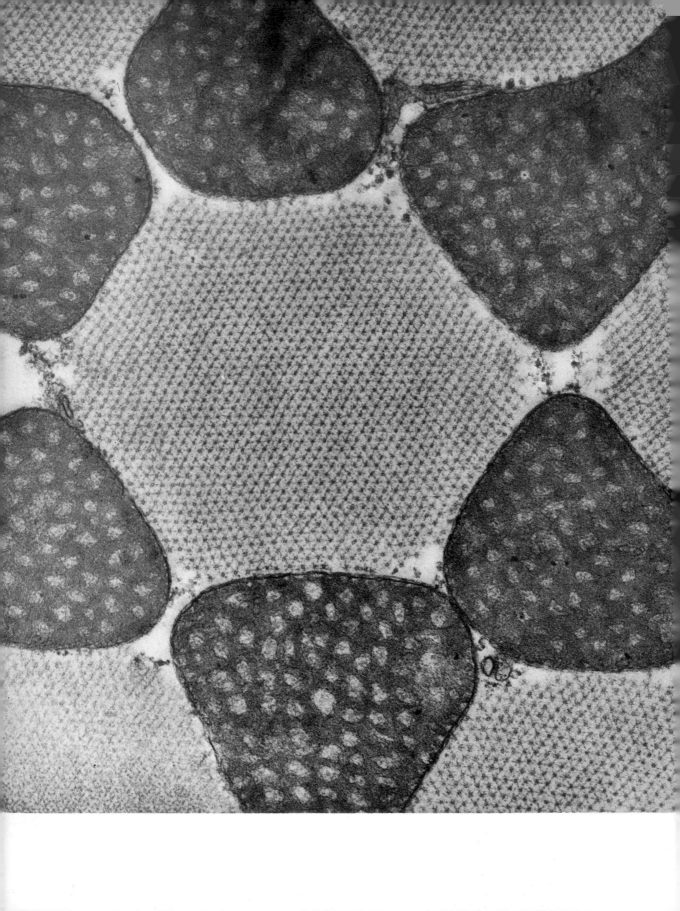

TEXTBOOK OF
MODERN BIOLOGY

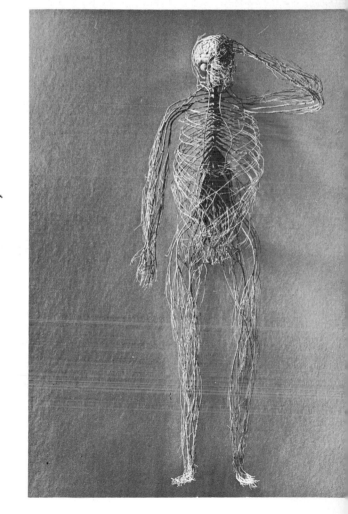

ALVIN NASON

Professor of Biology
Associate Director, McCollum-Pratt Institute
The Johns Hopkins University

JOHN WILEY & SONS, INC.
NEW YORK · LONDON · SYDNEY

The painting on the cover is by Kandinsky, "Penetrating Green," Baltimore Museum of Art, Bequest of Mrs. Sadie A. May.

The picture facing the title page is a transverse section of *Calliphora* flight muscle, magnification 48,500X. Courtesy of Dr. David S. Smith.

The pictures on the title page are Figures 18.1 and 21.3. At the top is a glass model of a member of the *Foraminifer, Globigerina bulloides*. Below is a wire model of the nervous system. Both are used by courtesy of the American Museum of Natural History.

Library of Congress Catalog Card Number: 64-25884
Printed in the United States of America

To the Memory of My Parents

Preface

We are very fortunate to be living in a wonderful age of progress. The rapid march of science today borders on the revolutionary. It will not be necessary for future historians to look back at our era and designate it as a period of great change for we can see these advances taking place before our very eyes on an almost day-to-day basis, and we are aware that they are the most exciting that mankind has ever experienced. The marvels of atomic energy already have been superseded in our imaginations by the breathtaking vistas of the space age. Artificial planets orbiting around the sun, space ships with astronauts revolving about the earth, and rockets arriving at the moon make it quite clear that travel to our nearest neighbors in the solar system—the moon, Mars, and Venus—will almost certainly be accomplished within a decade. We are passing a boundary of history and all of us already have an inkling of the momentous character of the breakthrough.

But what has all this to do with biology? The answer—a revolution of similar proportions, and no less exciting, has been occurring in the biological sciences and at an ever-accelerating pace. It has been brought to the attention of the general public to a limited extent by such spectacular medical accomplishments as antibiotics, polio vaccine, and open heart surgery, to name but a few. But far greater and more fundamental conquests have been quietly and inexorably taking place, unaccompanied by the blare of publicity, paving the way for these invaluable applications of pure research. Consider, for example, the formulation and documentation more than a century ago of two fundamental concepts in biology: the cell theory and the Darwinian theory of evolution. The latter with certain modifications has since emerged as one of the most important unifying principles in biology.

Modern biology can no longer be regarded as a collection of descriptive information of living forms. Broad principles have been emerging and crystallizing from the vast compilation of biological facts, reflecting the shift in emphasis from the descriptive to the experimental and the interpretive. The modern biologist no longer is occupied chiefly with "what is this." He now concentrates more than ever on the "hows" and "whys."

In virtually all areas there has been a marked tendency to analyze biological phenomena in terms of the laws of chemistry and physics. The remarkably successful application of biochemistry and biophysics has been most striking in the fields of metabolism, genetics, and evolution. In genetics, for example, the last two decades have witnessed a growing interest in the mechanism of gene action rather than in the mechanics of heredity alone. As a result the behavior of the gene has been increasingly related to its physical and chemical nature. This has revealed, among other things, the close relationship between genes and somewhat similar particles, the viruses. In turn the mechanism of evolution is being examined increasingly in the light of metabolic and genetic changes at the molecular level.

These concepts, together with the interpretation of cellular activities in terms of biochemical reactions and concomitant energy relationships, have led to the projection of reasonable theories, based on purely scientific criteria, regarding the origin of life on the planet earth and its evolution to present-day forms. The discoveries of modern biochemistry and biophysics have had an impact on all areas of biology including cytology, embryology, taxonomy, immunology, physiology, and evolution. These are the facts of life!

This book, in presenting a course in *modern biology,* of necessity seeks to include an evaluation of many biological phenomena in biochemical terms. It is also essential, however, to include the broad concepts of classic descriptive biology. It would be an incomplete treatment to favor one phase to the exclusion of the other. The guiding concept has been to expose the student to the broad principles of modern biology from both the molecular and classically descriptive views with the ultimate aim of demonstrating the intimate relationship between the two. The main objectives are to analyze critically the structural and functional features of living things (and their interrelationships) from various aspects ranging from the molecular level to the whole organism. In all cases the major emphasis will be to examine the broad unifying principles of biology, as we know them today, and the detailed facts and information from which they are derived. The areas of biological ignorance as well as knowledge will be indicated.

The book has been written for both one-semester and two-semester introductory courses in undergraduate biology, with a decided effort to omit technical nomenclature wherever feasible. It does not presuppose a previous knowledge of chemistry, and, in fact, hopes to fill this gap as far as some of the basic principles of chemistry and biochemistry are concerned. In order to give the student an appreciation of the biochemical influence in biology, a number of optional chapters have been devoted to a broad and comprehensive treatment of chemical and biochemical principles, more so than is usually found in biology textbooks. A decided effort has been made to present these chemical and physical concepts along lines that allow the student to visualize their meaning and significance when applied to biological phenomena. It has been my experience that students lacking a formal background in chemistry find themselves at a distinct disadvantage in an up-to-date introductory college biology course. Their efforts to gain this background on their own by referring to chemistry textbooks are usually unrewarding. For those students who have been exposed to some formal course work in chemistry, it is hoped that the chapters on chemistry and biochemistry will serve not only as a helpful review but also as a suitable orientation for the biology that follows in the main body of the book.

It should be pointed out, however, that the design of the book is such that the presentation of the biological material does not depend on the preceding chemistry and biochemistry chapters. Whether or not these chapters are used is left to the discretion of the instructor and student. The chemical and biochemical material may be omitted or utilized, depending on the level at which the course is being given. Although these chapters will aid in understanding many biological phenomena, they are not absolutely essential for the utilization of the book.

The attempt has been made to integrate the biochemical aspects of various biological phenomena and the classical descriptive views with the appropriate subject matter. Wherever feasible brief narrations of some of the experiments that led to momentous discoveries have also been incorporated. These narrations are intended to illustrate the significant roles played by the scientific method, original and often unorthodox ideas, keen observation, and, sometimes, sheer good luck. In addition, the application of basic discoveries to practice has been indicated. Finally, an effort has been made during the presentation of subject material to point out the unsolved problems and controversial areas in biology with a view to stimulating the student.

In addition to the more extensive treatment of the basic relevant chemical and biochemical concepts, a number of other departures have been made from the format common to most introductory biology textbooks. Two early chapters are devoted to a broad nontechnical description of the concepts of the origin and evolution of the universe for both inanimate and living components. The primary motivations were, first, to offer an overall view of the setting and relationship of life in the immense background of the universe, and, second, to illustrate in general terms the operation of the fundamental principles of evolution not only in biology but in the inanimate world (e.g., astronomy, geology) as well. This seemed especially worthwhile before considering the detailed aspects of biology in the chapters that follow. Various phases of the origin and evolution of living things are treated again in the later chapters, but in greater detail with the accent on genetic and biochemical aspects.

Another departure has been to handle the chapters on heredity and genetics, usually reserved for the latter portion of most textbooks, as basic subject material by presenting them immediately after the sections on cell structure, cell physiology, and biochemistry.

For several reasons emphasis has been placed on the human body. Biological phenomena, especially when abstract concepts are involved, have considerably more meaning (and interest) for the beginning student when presented in reference to *Homo sapiens*. This approach in addition fills an unexpectedly large gap in the student's background of general information by providing him with knowledge about human anatomy and physiology of which he often knows surprisingly little.

Judging from my experience in teaching this course to science and non-science students at The Johns Hopkins University during the past fourteen years, the response to this approach has been most gratifying. It has aroused interest and curiosity and, most of all, it has imparted to the student a picture of modern biology as we know it today.

I am grateful for the expert advice of Dr. Howard A. Bern who read and critized the manuscript in its entirety, and to the following persons for their suggestions and criticisms of various chapters: Dr. Maurice J. Bessman, Dr. David Bodian, Dr. John W. Gryder, Dr. William F. Harrington, Dr. Philip E. Hartman, Dr. Thomas R. Hendrix, Dr. André T. Jagendorf,

Dr. Julius R. Krevans, Dr. Martin G. Larrabee, Dr. Joseph D. Lichtenberg, Dr. Edward F. MacNichol, Jr., Dr. Clement L. Markert, Dr. William M. Mitchell, Dr. Alex Nickon, Dr. Alex B. Novikoff, Dr. Abraham G. Osler, Dr. Solbert Permutt, Dr. David Rabinowitz, Dr. Howard L. Sanders, Dr. Howard H. Seliger, Dr. William L. Straus, Jr., Dr. Sigmund R. Suskind, Dr. Rowland W. Taylor, Dr. Harry A. Teitelbaum, Dr. W. Gordon Walker, Dr. Theodore R. F. Wright, Dr. Michael D. Young, Dr. William J. Young, and Dr. Kenneth L. Zierler. I also wish to acknowledge the invaluable advice and encouragement of my colleagues Dr. Carl P. Swanson and Dr. William D. McElroy, and Mr. Reuben Shiling. It is a pleasure to express my appreciation to Mr. Charles Halgren and Mr. Joseph B. Whitton and their staff at the CARU Studios for the fine art work, to the Marine Biological Laboratory at Woods Hole, Mass., for the use of its excellent library, and to Mrs. Jean Gadziola and Mr. Reginald H. Garret for their general assistance and cooperation. I also wish to thank my present and former students and associates for their numerous suggestions.

In particular I am deeply indebted to my wife, Thelma, for many things. Her patience, comfort, interest, and understanding made the writing of this book possible.

Alvin Nason

Baltimore, Md.
January 1965

Contents

CREATION

All was calm and quiet
Before *it* began,
But God had decided
To act on a well-thought-out plan,
He had decided
To create earth and man.

Deborah R. Nason (age 10)

ONE
THE BEGINNINGS

This telescopic photograph shows the Milky Way, which, according to the latest astronomical findings, is a vast assemblage or galaxy of an estimated one hundred billion stars containing our sun as one of its ordinary stars. The Milky Way is one of at least a billion galaxies that compose the universe. Earth is only a minor one of the nine planets known to revolve about the sun. The laws of physics and chemistry operating on our planet also apply throughout the entire universe. It is conceivable that the conditions suitable for the origin and existence of life as we know it could occur on an estimated one hundred million other planets. This number would represent only an infinitesimally small fraction of the total number of planets of the universe.

The Milky Way (courtesy of Lick Observatory, U. of California).

Chapter 1   Introduction:

Biology and the World of Ideas

THE SCIENCE OF BIOLOGY

Life

Biology is the study of living things. As a body of organized knowledge of natural phenomena and their relationships, biology is a science. It is the science of life. The term originates from two Greek roots, *bios* meaning life, and *logos* meaning thought or, in a broader sense, study or science. The major problem under consideration is what is meant by life. What are living things and how do we distinguish them from nonliving systems? The answer to this question is the underlying theme of this book.

A definition of life from the biological viewpoint (or from any viewpoint for that matter), if indeed such a definition can be made at this time, cannot be presented in just a few words with any real understanding. It involves first a careful examination of fundamental biological concepts and the critical evidence on which they are based. The definition must concern itself not only with the apparent characteristics displayed by organisms but even more important with the underlying principles and mechanisms that account for these characteristics. This necessarily calls for an analysis of biological phenomena not only in terms of structure and function of the whole organism and its component parts, but at the molecular level as well in terms of the established laws of chemistry and physics. Living forms, as highly organized and uniquely self-directing and self-reproducing systems of energy and matter, are subject to the same chemical and physical principles that govern inanimate systems.

Old Definition

Most of us in the course of our everyday experiences have no difficulty in distinguishing between living and nonliving things. Even when occasionally confronted with a completely unfamiliar object we can usually discriminate whether or not it is alive. Living things display certain typical characteristics. These include the phenomena of *growth* (and self-repair), *reproduction*, *metabolism* (a collective term designating the many chemical and physical reactions and accompanying energy changes that occur in all organisms), *responsiveness* (capacity to react to stimuli), *movement*, *complexity*, and *adaptation* (capacity to adjust to environmental changes). These classic criteria of the more important features and activities associated with most organisms do not, of course, constitute a definition of life. They simply describe the more important characteristics of living forms.

New Definition

In light of our present-day knowledge, it is no longer sufficient to describe life by simply listing the obvious characteristics commonly exhibited by living forms. We now have evidence of some of the common basic features and mechanisms that account for the foregoing biological phenomena.

The last two decades have witnessed tremendous strides in the analysis and interpretation of biological structure and function in terms of chemistry and physics. This approach has produced two very powerful disciplines, biochemistry (or biological chemistry) and biophysics, which have been successfully applied to the many areas of biology. They are concerned primarily with the analysis at the molecular level of biological structure and function as well as the interrelationships between the two; and they have been inevitably leading to an exposure of some of the fundamental phenomena responsible for the foregoing life characteristics. As a result, from the vast welter of detailed biological data, a number of basic patterns at the molecular level which appear to be common to all living things have crystallized.

We know, for example, that all organisms are not only basically alike in their chemical and physical make-up, but they are essentially similar in their metabolism as well. The great array of chemical and physical reactions carried out by organisms are fundamentally similar and often identical to those occurring in inanimate systems. They involve the same atoms and frequently the same substances; and they are universally governed by the same principles of chemistry and physics which are the basis for all reactions of matter and energy. In one sense living forms can be regarded as a more extensive development of a now-extinct primeval nonliving system which in the course of evolution acquired the unique features of growth and self-duplication that we associate with living things. We believe this gradual transition of an inanimate system to a living one, which was finally attained an estimated two billion years ago, constitutes the origin of life on our planet (see Chapter 3).

On the basis of our present-day knowledge we can tentatively formulate an operational or mechanistic definition, in its barest outlines, of an organism or living system. A *living form* is *essentially* a *highly organized*, *self-directing*, *complex system* of *chemically and physically defined structures capable of utilizing the matter and energy of its environment by means of integrated and self-determined chains of physical and chemical reactions for growth and reproduction.* As a necessary part of this definition emphasis must be placed on the realization that the chemical and physical composition of all organisms together with the many molecular reactions constituting their metabolism are predetermined and controlled by a unique class of self-contained substances known as *nucleic acids* (Chapter 7). These acids are not only involved in directing the structure and function of living matter, but by their very nature they are also the means by which this information is transferred from one generation to another (i.e., heredity) in the course of self-duplication or reproduction.

This mechanistic viewpoint or interpretation that living matter is comprehensible in terms of the versatile properties of its many different kinds of molecules (individually and collectively) is held by nearly all biologists. It contrasts sharply with the obsolete notion that life is due to the presence of an indefinable and unique "vital force" which can never really be investigated.

For green plants (and a certain small group of bacteria) energy is provided from the environment in the form of sunlight. For all other organisms it is furnished as chemical energy locked in the chemical bonds of particular nutrient or food substances such as fats, carbohydrates, and proteins. In the green plants the light energy is first converted by means of a series of physical and chemical steps to a form that is ultimately stored in the chemical bonds of certain substances, for example, carbohydrates. Subsequently, as in all other organisms, this chemical-bond energy is released in small bundles by controlled sequences or chains of chemical reactions. Some of the energy thus liberated is utilized for purposes of growth and reproduction. We speak of metabolism as being self-directed or self-determined in the sense that it is controlled, directly or indirectly (as are all other life activities), by a master group of substances already mentioned, the nucleic acids, which are an integral part of the living system.

Certainly the most singular traits of a living system are its capabilities for growth (including self-repair) and reproduction. The additional characteristics associated with living things, such as *movement, responsiveness, metabolism, complexity,* and *adaptation,* are essentially secondary in significance to *growth* and *self-duplication.*

Can we construct models or machines that possess the essential characteristics of life? So far the answer is "no." Man has invented numerous systems that display, to varying degrees, many or all of the foregoing features *except growth and reproduction.* Most of these characteristics (other than the latter two, of course) are embodied, for example, in the modern airplane or automobile which are obviously not alive. Some of these artificial systems exhibit a certain degree of adaptation in being able to adjust by means of particular devices (e.g., temperature and pressure regulating apparatus) to specific changes in their environment. The man-made solar battery and the gasoline engine, as additional examples, are inanimate systems which make available the light energy of the sun and the chemical energy of gasoline, respectively, converting it to a form that can do useful work. The solar battery and gasoline engine, however, are not capable of growth and self-duplication. They obviously cannot reproduce other solar batteries and gasoline engines like themselves; and for this reason they are not considered to be alive. More recently, machines, electron circuits, and model systems are being built or designed which can not only adapt to changing situations but can also evaluate and discriminate, learn from experience, and even duplicate several aspects of human behavior. However, they cannot be considered to be alive by any definition or criteria.

If man should someday be successful in devising a machine that has self-directing and self-sustaining capabilities for growth and for the reproduction of machines with similar characteristics, then on the basis of our operational definition the machine will have to be regarded as a living form. The possession of these unique features by our hypothetical machine necessarily implies a master control apparatus functionally equivalent to the nucleic acids.

Our definition of life, however, is far from complete. There are many large gaps and unexplored areas in our knowledge of living systems. How do these huge and unusual molecules, the nucleic acids, exercise their vast influence in predetermining and directing the pathways of chemical reactions and, therefore, the processes of growth, reproduction, and all other activities of organisms? What are the intricacies of reproduction, cell differentiation and development, and growth and repair? What are the mechanisms of energy transformation, mental processes, hormone action, and a host of other biological phenomena? These are some of the questions that we hope to answer someday.

The Parts versus the Whole

It is not sufficient to examine living things simply in terms of their component parts and mechanisms. The integrated and coordinated action of any living system starts at the molecular level and proceeds to progressively grosser structures and functions to constitute finally a highly intricate and unified entity, the total organism. The total organism in view of its integrated complexity in structure and function has an added dimension, so to speak, by virtue of its wholeness, which would be completely overlooked if we were to study it only in terms of its individual parts. This would be like examining the workings of an airplane by investigating in fine detail the structure and function of each of its individual parts only (e.g., the engine, carburetor, wheels, rudder, and wings), without giving attention to the

Bottle trees of Northern Australia (*courtesy of Australian News and Information Bureau*).

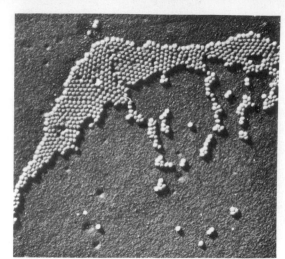

Tomato bushy stunt virus. Magnification, 57,000X (*courtesy of Dr. H. Fraenkel-Conrat*).

Glass model of the protozoan *Gorgonetta mirabilis* (*courtesy of Amer. Mus. Natural History*).

Model of shellworm (*courtesy of Amer. Mus. Natural History*).

VARIETIES OF LIFE

Skunk (*courtesy of Ylla, Rapho Guillumette*).

Dragon fly (*courtesy of Wallace Kirkland, Rapho Guillumette*).

Porcupine fish (*courtesy of Rapho Guillumette*).

overall features, design, and coordinated behavior of the entire system. Each of these parts detached from the airplane is incapable of self-propelled, airborne flight. Together, however, they constitute any entity possessing the unique features of a flying machine.

Similarly, any analysis of a living thing, must rest on an unveiling of fundamental molecular and progressively grosser mechanisms as well as on studies of the intact and whole organism. The ultimate goal of biology is to understand the function and structure of living forms at all levels of organization. The complexity of any living system makes it necessary that we also investigate its component parts to gain an insight into the organism as a whole. Studies of individual parts in isolation or within the intact organism are simply a means to an end, being directed in the final analysis to an understanding of the entire and intact living form.

Relationships among Organisms

The common unity among organisms in terms of structure and function at the molecular level (as well as at higher levels) and their ultimate control by nucleic acids suggests that all living forms are more or less related to each other. From an evolutionary viewpoint it implies that the great variety of contemporary life—plants, animals, and microorganisms—originated from some common ancestral type, now extinct, which existed an estimated two billion years ago.

This basic similarity among all organisms lends itself well to the interpretation that the current structural and functional organization of living systems, with relatively minor variations, is the most effective one yet evolved by nature on our planet earth. Not only has it survived but it has apparently become the predominant, if not the only, living type. In an evolutionary sense the present design of living matter represents the end product of an estimated two billion years of testing by a never-ending process of selection. It is in effect the net result of a relentless natural selection procedure whereby the features that provided an advantage to the organism in its attempts to reproduce and survive in its living and non-living environments were retained and perpetuated. It seems likely that in the course of evolution other less efficient kinds of organized systems may have appeared at one time or another but failed to survive because of the possession of less favorable features. Such organisms were presumably unable to exist in their environment and compete successfully with the more efficient forms, whose descendants are represented by the present-day living systems. They were thus eliminated from the population. In terms of energy utilization living matter is far more efficient than any machine yet devised by man. It is also far more complex in terms of structure and function. By the very nature of their evolution and development contemporary organisms are best suited to survive and thrive in their present natural environments on our planet earth.

Life on Other Planets

It seems reasonable to assume that comparable if not similar forms of life may have evolved on planets in our own solar system, or possibly on the presumed planets of other stellar systems, that possess comparable environmental conditions.

There is strong suggestive evidence based on astronomical observations that living forms may be present on some of the other planets of our solar system. Whether or not life exists on the neighboring planet Mars, for example, may well be determined in the next decade with the advent of space travel. It is plausible that many of the countless billions of stars (of which our star or sun is only one) making up the universe may have their particular collection of revolving planets possibly resembling part of our own solar system. These probably total into innumerable billions. A number of scientists have speculated that the conditions appropriate for the origin and existence of life as we know it on Earth could occur on a small percentage of these planets. Moreover, it is conceivable that on other planets exhibiting radically different environmental conditions, a self-directing and self-reproducing system could have evolved with physical and chemical characteristics markedly different from any of our own organisms but nevertheless fundamentally classified as a form of life on the basis of our modern functional definition.

Subdivisions of Biology

Biology is the study of all living things that inhabit the universe. To date on our own planet a million and a quarter different kinds (or *species*, Chapter 14) of plants and animals have been recognized. They range in an almost infinite variety of sizes and shapes from the smallest microorganisms to the most complex higher forms such as man and the advanced flowering plants. Many other organisms, as yet undiscovered and undescribed, undoubtedly exist, especially in the virtually unexplored seas which cover about 70 per cent of the earth's surface. New species are continually evolving from existing organisms, while others are becoming extinct. Still others remain relatively stable, undergoing little or no evolutionary change during long periods of time.

The field of biology, relatively confined as it is in its present stage to the study of both the identified and unidentified organisms on the planet earth, is almost indescribably large. This profusion of living forms is further compounded by the fact that each species from the relatively simplest to the most intricate is in turn a highly complicated structural and functional entity. Of necessity, therefore, the science of biology, like all other sciences, is divided into several disciplines. These, in turn, are subdivided into still more highly specialized areas of study.

The various disciplines or divisions can be regarded, for purposes of convenience, as falling into two principal groups which are inextricably linked with one another. The first includes the main areas determined by the *organisms* studied; and the second covers those areas delineated by the *approach* taken to the subject matter. As an example of the first, we

Table 1-1
Principal Subdivisions of Biology
According to Organism

1. **ZOOLOGY**: Animals
   (a) *Protozoology:* single-celled animals
   (b) *Entomology:* insects
   (c) *Ichthyology:* fishes
   (d) *Herpetology:* amphibians and reptiles
   (e) *Ornithology:* birds
   (f) *Mammalogy:* mammals
   (g) *Anthropology:* characteristics of man
2. **BOTANY:** Plants
   (a) *Cryptogamic Botany:* plants that produce no seed
       (1) *Algology:* algae
       (2) *Bryology:* mosses
       (3) *Pteridology:* ferns
   (b) *Phanerogamic Botany:* plants that produce seed
3. **MICROBIOLOGY:** Microorganisms
   (a) *Bacteriology:* bacteria
   (b) *Mycology:* fungi
   (c) *Virology:* viruses

Table 1-2
Principal Subdivisions of Biology
According to Approach

1. **GENETICS:** inheritance and variation
2. **PHYSIOLOGY:** function
3. **TAXONOMY:** classification
4. **EVOLUTION:** origin and changes
5. **MORPHOLOGY:** form and structure
   (a) *Anatomy:* gross structure
   (b) *Histology:* tissue structure
   (c) *Cytology:* cell structure
6. **BIOCHEMISTRY AND BIOPHYSICS:** structure and function at the molecular level
7. **EMBRYOLOGY:** embryo formation and development
8. **ECOLOGY:** relationship of organisms to their living and nonliving environments
9. **PALEONTOLOGY:** fossil organisms
10. **PARASITOLOGY:** parasites

have *zoology*, which has to do with the study of animals, whereas *botany* involves the study of plants. Each of these is further subdivided into more specific disciplines. Thus under zoology we have *ornithology* (the study of birds), *mammalogy* (the study of mammals), and so on. As examples of the second major class, we have *physiology* as the study of function, and *morphology* as the study of form and structure of living things. Physiology, in turn, is subdivided, for example, into endocrinology (study of the function of the glands that secrete hormones), neurophysiology, and so on. These can also be even further broken down according to the organism under investigation such as plant physiology, human physiology, plant taxonomy, and so on. The principle disciplines or subdivisions of biology are summarized in Tables 1-1 and 1-2.

IDEAS AND CONCEPTS IN SCIENCE

Unity in Nature

The history of biology in general reflects the history of science. It symbolizes man's progress in fathoming and coping with his physical and chemical environment. Equally important it signifies the tremendous victory of rational thought and careful, critical observation over prejudice, unfounded and preconceived notions, and indiscriminate evaluations of the world around us.

The advances attained by man through the centuries have been a gradual and cumulative process, at times extremely slow and unnoticed, and at other times, such as our present era, exceedingly rapid. The human species in the course of its history has amassed a tremendous array of detailed information about living things. From this welter of discrete facts, the cumulative results of years of research by countless individuals throughout the world, there have already emerged certain fundamental biological principles common to all organisms, which strongly suggests a basic unity in nature. For example, it has become increasingly evident that despite obvious differences in gross appearance, living forms display a remarkable similarity in structure and function at the molecular and microscopic levels. All organisms examined thus far are without exception made up of the same kinds of chemical substances. They carry out essentially similar series of directed chemical reactions which account for the release and utilization of energy for the characteristic activities of living systems.

One of the most important functions of science is to expose and formulate the underlying or fundamental principles implicit in a mass of detailed scientific data and observations. Our most creative scientists are those who have the facility and knowledge to lay bare the basic patterns or principles inherent in a body of detailed data.

The Role of Theory in Science

The foundations of science and therefore of our modern world, are based on concepts or ideas. Science assumes a universal order in nature and attempts to seek out the laws describing this order. Man's first glimmerings of these laws are usually expressed as ideas, concepts, or theories. Frequently these ideas simply represent a fresh way of looking at old observations and facts, and thus lend a new coherence to the observations or expose a unifying principle not previously discerned. Occasionally theories are presented on an almost completely speculative basis, and must await conclusive evidence before they are accepted or rejected. In all cases scientific theories and ideas are distinguished by their innate flexibility. They may be confirmed, changed, revised, or rejected at any time in accordance with the introduction of new and better evidence and concepts. Often one of the important tests of a good idea or theory is its usefulness in predicting correctly the course of future events in the particular area in which it applies.

At times new concepts painfully violate accepted doctrine and even religious beliefs, in turn leading to strong emotional reactions. Often these theories, especially in the physical sciences, are so highly complex, abstract, and mathematical that they have absolutely no meaning except to a few specialists. Nevertheless, they have inevitably led to a more integrated and concise picture of nature in keeping with our observations of the world about us.

A number of examples of such important ideas can be cited. The theory of organic evolution formally presented by Charles Darwin a century ago stated that all living things have a common ancestor and have evolved in a relatively gradual process of change and diversification. The concept was not an entirely original one and had been suggested by a number of his predecessors dating back to the early Greek philosophers. Darwin's important contribution, however, was to substantiate the idea of organic evolution by collecting and organizing an impressive mass of supporting evidence and offering the first satisfactory explanation of how evolution takes place. The concept met with tremendous resistance. It still encounters appreciable opposition among certain segments of the public despite the fact that it has emerged with some modifications as one of the foremost unifying principles of modern biology.

The recognition at the mid-nineteenth century that all living things are made up of an essentially similar complex of substances called protoplasm, organized in the form of cells that can arise only from preexisting cells, was embodied in the notion of the cell theory (Chapter 4). This discovery is regarded as one of the cornerstones of biology.

Another example—early man's concept of himself as the center of the universe—gave way in slow stages to the Copernican view of the sixteenth century when the central reference point was transferred from the earth to the sun. This in turn was followed by a radical revision in the early twentieth century when Harlow Shapley demonstrated that the universe was not centered on the solar system, but that our sun was actually located on the outskirts of a huge congregation of stars, a galaxy known as the Milky Way, one of a vast number of other galaxies composing the universe (Chapter 2).

Newton's theory of universal gravitation presented a unifying concept that accounted for the motion of all matter. Gravitation is the force that guides the planets in their orbits around the sun, holds objects to the earth and ties the moon to it, and determines the speed of a man-made satellite, a planet, or a falling apple.

The interpretation and analysis of the activities and characteristics of living cells in terms of the laws of physics and chemistry, known as the sciences of biophysics and biochemistry, have provided new and sound foundations for modern biology. Biophysics and biochemistry have opened great new vistas of knowledge in the metabolism and energy relationships of cells. They have also made a start in clarifying for the first time the mode of action of genes in development and heredity.

In the overall picture then, new and challenging theories and concepts have led to even broader and more unifying ideas. For example, the theory of organic evolution just cited is a portion of a wider concept stating that the dynamic nature of the nonliving and living components of the universe makes change or evolution inevitable. *Change is a fundamental feature of the universe.*

SUPPLEMENTARY REFERENCES

Bates, M., *The Nature of Natural History*, Scribner, New York, 1950.
Beveridge, W. I. B., *The Art of Scientific Investigation*, Norton, New York, 1957.
Bonner, J. T., *The Ideas of Biology*, Harper and Row, New York, 1962.
Conant, J. B., *On Understanding Science*, Yale University Press, New Haven, Conn., 1947.
Conant, J. B., *Science and Common Sense*, Yale University Press, New Haven, Conn., 1951.
Conant, J. B., *Modern Science and Modern Man*, Columbia University Press, New York, 1952.
Dampier, W. C., *A History of Science*, third edition, Macmillan, New York, 1942.
Parker, J., "Criteria of Life: Some Methods of Measuring Viability," *American Scientist*, October 1953.

Chapter 2   Origin and Evolution of the Universe

**THE EXPANDING UNIVERSE —
A PRESENT-DAY VIEW**

Introduction

The problems of the origin of the universe and the origin of life have occupied human thought since prehistoric times. The ancient concepts were based for the most part on special "acts of creation" and on supernatural phenomena. Most of the older and now discarded theories assumed that the universe was created in very much the same state in which we find it now.

We presently surmise that life originated from the inanimate material of the universe as the result of relatively gradual changes (called a prolonged evolutionary process) occurring during the course of many millions of years. By studying the present-day characteristics of non-living and living things and the probable changes that have taken place, it has been possible to create a picture of their origin and history. This has led to a more integrated and fundamental understanding of life and its connection to the nonliving world. To obtain a more general perspective of the nature of living things, including their relationship to inanimate matter, it is important to have some familiarity with the modern theories regarding the origin and evolution of the universe.

Galaxies

The cosmos or the universe as we view it today is made up of at least a billion aggregations of stars called galaxies. These galaxies, each of which may include hundreds of billions of stars with their accompanying planets and satellites, are far greater and more splendid than the universe was previously imagined to be. They are distributed so far out into the vast reaches of space that the mind can hardly visualize their scope. With the progressive development of more powerful telescopes man has been able to extend his sights farther and farther into the cosmos. The distant objects in the heavens first came into view as fuzzy forms or "nebulae," and as they were brought nearer and nearer by means of better instruments they were identified as collections of stars organized into systems of various shapes and types.

Approximately a billion or so galaxies are now visible with our most advanced telescope, the great Mount Palomar instrument in California. Its 200-inch mirror has permitted man to look at stars more than 3×10^{22} miles (3 followed by 22 zeros) away or five billion light-years[1] into space. This means that it takes five billion

---

[1] A light-year is the distance traveled by light in one year at the rate of 186,000 miles per second (or 670 million miles per hour) and is equal to almost six million million miles.

Two radio telescopes with 90-foot diameter antennas at the Radio Observatory, California Institute of Technology.

Photo of a spiral galaxy (*courtesy of Lick Observatory, University of California*).

years for the light of these distant stars to reach us, traveling at a speed of 186,000 miles per second. The most distant galaxies detected today through this magnificent telescope are actually seen by us in the state in which they were five billion years ago. In this manner it is possible to look not only far into space but also backward into time.

A powerful new tool, the radio telescope which tunes in directly on the powerful radio waves emitted by certain stars and by the great hydrogen clouds in outer space, has enabled astronomers to map the vast cosmic hydrogen clouds and galaxies in the heavens on a scale that was previously impossible.

The galaxies vary widely in shape and texture and are divided into a number of general groups. Our own galaxy, the Milky Way, is classified as a spiral galaxy, a predominant group characterized by spiral-like arms encircling its dense lens-shaped central region. It has been shown to be a collection of some one hundred billion stars with our sun, a relatively average star, and its planets out toward the rim. The Milky Way in turn is a member of a supergalaxy, a cluster of seventeen galaxies of all types, concentrated within a radius of about one million light-years.

Outside this cluster and millions of light-years distant in space are other aggregates of stars tending to gather into groups or *super-galaxies*. It is still not certain whether these stellar clusters are distributed irregularly or scattered uniformly throughout space. No real general pattern has as yet emerged. The evidence thus far favors a random more or less uniform distribution with a tendency to aggregate. Some galaxies may be found alone, in small groups, in large aggregates, or in clusters of aggregates.

Most galaxies are in a state of rotation around their axes as indicated by their elliptical shapes and the spiral arms encircling condensed central bodies. The stars (and the sun) themselves are also in a rapid state of rotation and are made up almost completely of a gaseous mixture of hydrogen and helium. These gases are continuously undergoing so-called *nuclear reactions* (Chapter 6) at very high temperatures liberating nuclear energy in much the same way as the man-made hydrogen bomb. We witness this release of energy as sunlight or starlight.

One of the most unusual properties of the universe is its continuous expansion into space. The galaxies are moving away from each other into space at high rates of speed, a phenomenon discovered some thirty years ago by the eminent astronomer, the late Edwin Hubble, as a result of studies of the light emitted by distant stars.[2] The concept of an expanding universe has played a significant role in speculations about its origin and age.

The Solar System

The solar system consists of the sun, as a medium-sized star with a diameter of about 850,000 miles, its nine known planets, and a variety of smaller bodies ranging from satellites such as our moon to planetary dust. The sun's mass is 330,000 times that of the earth, and its temperature ranges from 6000°C at its surface to energy values equivalent to an estimated 25 million °C at its core. The sun is almost entirely gaseous, the most prevalent gas being hydrogen with traces of 65 other elements. It has been estimated that as a result of the fusion of hydrogen nuclei within its core to form helium the tremendous outpouring of light and heat per second is equal to a billion or so exploding hydrogen bombs (see Figure 2-1).

The planets rotate around their axes and revolve around the sun in elliptical paths determined by the force of gravitation. Included in the solar system are the 31 satellites of the planets (not counting the earth's artificial satellites), thousands of asteroids which are minor planets ranging in diameter from 1 mile to 300 miles, comets (small masses of solid particles held loosely together), and meteors. The planet Mercury is closest to the sun followed by Venus, Earth, Mars, Jupiter, Saturn, Uranus, Neptune, and Pluto in that order, the mean diameter of the solar system being about 7 billion miles (Figure 2-2). The inner planets

[2] The observed shift in light from distant stars and galaxies toward the longer wavelength (or red end of the spectrum) indicates that these bodies are moving rapidly away from us, or, interpreted more broadly, that the universe is expanding into space.

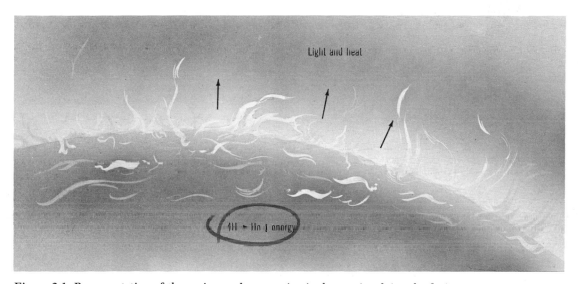

Figure 2-1. Representation of the major nuclear reaction in the sun involving the fusion of hydrogen atoms (H) to form helium (He) with the concomitant tremendous release of energy as light and heat.

are closer together and the outer ones are farther apart. It is possible that our solar system contains still other planets as yet undiscovered. There are certain indications that other planets and smaller bodies of matter are also revolving about other stars in the universe in accordance with the same universal laws of motion and gravitation originally described by the great Sir Isaac Newton.

Matter and Energy

Basic to any modern theory of the origin and evolution of the universe is the important concept that matter and radiant energy (light) make up the universe. Matter has mass and is drawn to other bodies of matter by the force of attraction known as gravity. Until some years ago it was thought that matter could be neither created nor destroyed, but only converted from one form to another. In 1906 Albert Einstein formulated one of the most significant concepts in the history of thought—that mass (or matter) and energy are really equivalent to one another. The mathematical equation

describing this concept is $E = mc^2$ or, energy (E) equals mass (m) multiplied by the velocity of light squared (c^2). Einstein's theory made it possible to show the conversion of matter into energy, and vice versa. The interconversion of matter and energy is illustrated by the hydrogen bomb, the same violent reaction that keeps the sun burning. Einstein's theory that energy also has mass was verified by the observations of astronomers that light rays passing close to the sun were bent toward the sun by its gravitational force.

The material or matter of the universe is composed of essentially 92 different kinds of atoms or elements in various combinations ranging from the smallest, hydrogen, to the largest, uranium.[3] Since the advent of the

[3] The structural units of all matter—solids, liquids, and gases—are discrete particles called *molecules*. Molecules are made up of smaller particles known as *atoms*. Some types of matter may consist of molecules containing only one particular kind of atom, in which case they are spoken of as *elements;* or they may be made up of molecules consisting of a chemical combination of different kinds of atoms and are designated as *compounds* (Chapter 6). The size of atoms is extremely small, ranging from about 2Å to 5Å in diameter.

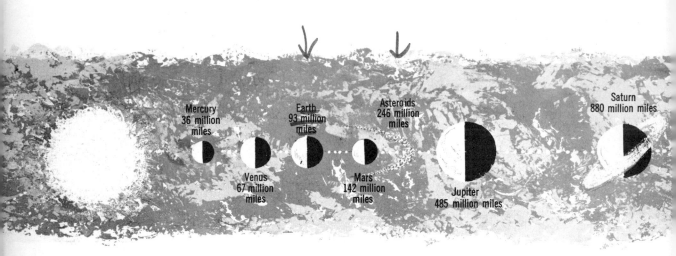

Figure 2-2. Diagram of the planets of the solar system indicating their relative size and their order in relation to the sun.

atomic age in the early 1940's, man has produced about 10 additional elements and he will undoubtedly add more to this list. By studying the relative abundance of the various atoms in the universe it has been possible to construct a picture of their history, evolution, and even their origin. This approach has yielded important concepts concerning the origin and evolution of the galaxies. Hydrogen is the most abundant atom of the cosmos, accounting for 93 per cent of the total number of atoms and 76 per cent of the matter of the universe. Helium is next, making up almost 7 per cent of the number of atoms and 23 per cent of the weight. Remarkably enough, only 1 per cent of the mass of the universe consists of the 90 other naturally occurring types of atoms. With a few exceptions, the abundance of the atoms decreases with increasing mass so that the heaviest atoms constitute only a millionth

by weight of the matter of the universe. Protoplasm, the basic substance of life, is composed of approximately 20 different elements.

Atoms can be considered to be constructed of three types of fundamental subatomic particles known as *electrons, protrons,* and *neutrons.*[4] Although there are other subatomic particles (e.g., positrons and mesons), the properties of atoms can be most simply explained on the basis of electrons, protons, and neutrons. Every atom can be pictured to consist of a dense core or nucleus around which one or more electrons rapidly revolve in elliptical orbits much like the planets around the sun. The nucleus accounts for virtually the entire mass of the atom and is made up of two kinds of building blocks, protrons and neutrons. The electrical charge of the nuclei is positive and that of the revolving electrons is negative.

Under certain circumstances neutrons can

The symbol Å represents an angstrom unit (after the nineteenth century Swedish physicist A. J. Ångstrom) which is 10^{-8} centimeters or about five-trillionths of an inch. Approximately a hundred million atoms arranged in a row would occupy a distance of about one inch (see Chapter 6).

[4] An electron is a form of matter carrying a unit negative electrical charge. It has a certain small mass that is about one two-thousandths of a proton. A proton carries a unit positive charge, whereas a neutron has essentially the same mass as a proton but is electrically neutral (see Chapter 6).

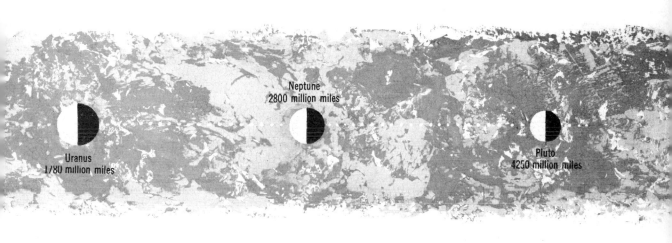

Uranus
1780 million miles

Neptune
2800 million miles

Pluto
4250 million miles

decay into protons and electrons, and conversely a proton may combine with an electron to form a neutron. The structure of the simplest atom, hydrogen, includes a single electron traveling at high speed around a nucleus consisting of only a single proton.)Figure 6-7). The next simplest atom is helium with a nucleus containing two protons and two neutrons surrounded by two electrons revolving at high speed in separate elliptical orbits (Figure 6-7). Progressively heavier atoms contain nuclei composed of correspondingly greater number of protons and neutrons. The nuclei are surrounded by revolving electrons usually in quantities equal to the number of protons in the nucleus. (The properties and reactions of atoms are described in greater detail in Chapter 6).

In short, the universe, composed of inanimate and living components, extends from the infinitesimally small cosmos of subatomic particles to the infinitely vast cosmos of outer space.

THE EXPANDING UNIVERSE — ITS ORIGIN AND EVOLUTION

Origin of the Universe

How old is the universe and how did it begin? The answers are really not known. We can make some educated guesses, however, based for the most part on current observations of physical and chemical phenomena. By studying the properties and the present composition and distribution of matter, we can surmise a good deal about the beginnings of the stars and planets and their subsequent history.

Speculations as to age and origin of the energy and matter that constitute the universe are still highly controversial. They are frequently revised, as new information and new ideas are presented. Usually they represent concepts that are unfamiliar to most of us and are, therefore, difficult to grasp. Is it possible that the universe had no beginning and will have no end? Can we also think of space, as well as time, as being infinite? There are currently two highly favored theories regarding the origin of

the universe, the *evolutionary theory* and the *steady-state theory*.

Evolutionary Theory of the Universe

The evolutionary theory advanced by George Gamow and his colleagues at George Washington University is based on the established expansion of the universe. In its present form the theory contends that about ten billion years ago the universe began as an explosion of a densely concentrated hot core of primordial matter which has continued to expand outward into space ever since. With expansion this matter thinned out, cooled down and presumably reassembled into stars, planets, galaxies, and supergalaxies. One method of arriving at the figure of ten billion years has been to extrapolate backward in time to the hypothetical primordial state (when all the galaxies were compressed together in one place) by using the presently known distances and velocities of the galaxies. The theory implies that at the time the universe began with an explosion from the superdense state, the rate of expansion was greatest; and that it has since been steadily slowing down largely as the result of gravitational attraction.

What was the composition of this hypothetical primordial material which, according to this theory, gave rise to the universe? Gamow theorizes that the primordial matter was made up of densely concentrated subatomic particles, chiefly neutrons. As this primordial mass of compressed neutrons began to expand and cool, some presumably broke down (or decayed) into protons (i.e., nuclei of hydrogen atoms) and electrons. Within a few minutes following the beginning of expansion this mixture of fundamental particles is presumed to have cooled sufficiently to form various relatively stable combinations, thus accounting for the origin of many of the different atoms or elements. Most of the atoms formed were probably hydrogen and helium, as indicated by their present-day abundance mentioned earlier.

The continuously expanding homogeneous

gas mixture that constituted the matter of the universe for an estimated 250 million years was now transformed by a condensation process into isolated clouds or balls of gas. Condensation was presumably initiated by the rapid temperature decrease stemming from the expansion of the gas mixture. The huge masses of gas subsequently gave rise to large aggregations of stars by further condensation as they were drawn away from each other by the continuing expansion of the universe.

It logically follows that the high pressures caused by the rapid contraction of the huge fragments of gas resulted in exceedingly high temperatures in their more dense regions, of the order of a few million degrees centigrade. In turn, the high temperatures were probably responsible for the final stage in the formation of the stars—namely, initiation of the nuclear reactions which released energy. The light emitted from most stars is the result of a continuing nuclear-fusion process whereby hydrogen atoms, in fusing with each other to form helium, release a tremendous store of nuclear energy that results in light and heat. This reaction, the principal source of energy of the sun and stars, involved converting a small fraction of the fusing hydrogen atoms into energy in accordance with Einstein's famous theory of the interconversion of matter and energy indicated earlier, and is essentially similar to the principal of the hydrogen bomb[5] (Figure 2-1).

Gamow's theory, like most theories, has not met with unanimous acceptance. What was the origin of the subatomic particles that constituted the hypothetical dense primordial core? One explanation proposes that the universe experiences an unending cycle of expansion and contraction, extending itself to a certain maximal limit, then contracting to a dense core of subatomic material with successive expansion and contraction, repeating

[5] It basically involves the combination of the nuclei of four hydrogen atoms with a combined mass of 4.032 atomic units to form the nucleus of one helium atom with a mass of 4.002 atomic units. The lost 0.030 atomic unit is converted into light, heat, and other radiation energy (Chapter 6).

the cycle *ad infinitum*. A possible alternative to this cyclic or "pulsating" scheme is the proposition that the universe originally contracted from an infinitely thin state an eternity ago to form the primordial core and is now experiencing an expansion that will go on indefinitely, perhaps forever. Gamow's evolutionary theory argues that our universe corresponds to the latter situation, and that its expansion is steadily slowing down, but will never cease.

Thus the basic question as to the origin of the matter and radiant energy that constitute the universe appears to be unanswered. Can it therefore be inferred that these two, matter and energy, along with time, have always existed and will exist forever?

Steady-State Theory of the Universe

The second major concept of the origin and development of the universe, whose chief spokesman is Fred Hoyle at Cambridge University, is known as the steady-state theory. It views the universe as having existed forever, being infinite in space and time, with neither a beginning nor an end. It contends that the universe is expanding at a steady rate throughout an infinity of time in contrast to the evolutionary theory which conceives of a definite beginning to the formation of matter and a slowing down of the expansion process. Both concepts essentially agree that hydrogen is probably the primary building material from which most of the other elements have been formed by fusion and other nuclear reactions inside the stars.

The radio telescope has provided suggestive evidence that the immense hydrogen clouds in outer space are the raw material from which new stars and galaxies are forever being created.

Here is where all similarity between the two theories ends. Gamow's evolutionary theory postulates the creation of hydrogen and some of the other elements in a primordial explosion of neutrons some billion years ago. Hoyle's steady-state concept holds that hydrogen continually has been and still is being created throughout space by the ultimate conversion of energy to matter during the expansion process.

It is not certain which of these two theories is closer to the true state of affairs of the universe. At our present stage of scientific and technical development there is still some difficulty in deciding which concept is favored by the accumulated evidence.

Origin of the Planets and Their Satellites

The prevailing theory of the origin of planets, known as the *dust-cloud hypothesis*, postulates the formation of planets from relatively smaller masses consisting of clouds of dust particles and gas. According to this theory, clouds of dust and gas, torn away from the edges of the newly forming stars, and held together by the mutual attraction of gravity, proceeded to grow by the gradual accumulation of solid dust particles composed in large part of iron oxides, silicates, and water crystals. Growth occurred through collision and capture of smaller bodies by the larger ones to form still larger bodies called *"protoplanets."* At some point in their evolution these rotating "protoplanets," which revolved about their stars in accordance with the laws of motion and gravitation, condensed to form planets. The heat generated by contraction was probably sufficient to convert the newly formed planets to a molten state, but not to initiate nuclear reactions within their centers, in view of their relatively small size. The varying distances of the planets of our solar system from the sun apparently reflect the distances of their "protoplanets" before condensation occurred. Strong supporting evidence for the dust-cloud theory is the present existence of gigantic clouds of microscopic dust and gas in interstellar space, observed by the manner in which these clouds scatter light from distant stars.

The planet earth has a density of 5.5, which is a convenient way of stating that it is 5.5 times as heavy as an equal volume of water.

On the other hand the average density of some of the larger planets is less; Jupiter and Saturn are approximately 1.0, the same as the density of water. The lower density of the larger planets of our solar system is ascribed to the fact that these planets were larger at the outset. Therefore, with an initially greater gravitational attraction, they were able to attract and hold more of the lighter elements; the smaller planets could do this only to a limited extent. As a result the larger planets are relatively lighter in proportion to their volume than the smaller planets.

The dust-cloud hypothesis explains numerous facts concerning our solar system. It accounts for the characteristic rotation and revolution of the planets, and indicates that the satellites, with the probable exception of our moon, were formed from the "protoplanet" stage. When a "protoplanet" finally condensed to form the initially molten planet, the outer material of the contracting dust cloud could have collected separately and given rise to rotating satellites. The few satellites that revolve in the opposite direction, such as Neptune's moon or certain satellites of Jupiter and Saturn, were probably not part of these original "protoplanets," and were presumably "captured" after the planets had formed.

There is no general agreement about the origin of our moon. One of the most popular concepts, postulated approximately 60 years ago by Charles Darwin's son, George Darwin, considers the moon as having formed from the earth at the time when the planet's surface was just beginning to solidify. According to this view a portion of the earth's surface was flung into space, presumably the result of a mounting gigantic tidal wave of semiliquid matter arising from the centrifugal force of the earth's rotation. This is supposed to have left a scar which is now the floor of the Pacific Ocean. The calculated density of the moon, about 3.3, compares favorably with the density of the earth's surface layers, a fact that has been used as a supporting argument. The theory has experienced alternating periods of acceptance and rejection. Most astronomers since the 1930's have regarded it as an unlikely hypothesis.

The huge collection of approximately 1600 asteroids (minor planets ranging from about 1 mile to 300 miles in diameter) revolving in the region between Mars and Jupiter may be the debris of a smashed planet. Meteorites, which are fragments of interplanetary material described as shooting stars when they fall to earth, are also considered to be fragments of a broken planet.

Another more controversial concept known as the *planetary theory* visualizes that planet formation in our solar system originated from fragments of burning gas torn away from the sun. Some four or five billion years ago, according to this theory, the sun and another great star either came close to each other or actually collided, giving rise to huge tidal waves of burning gas resulting in some masses of the flaming gas being torn away from the sun. Very slowly these balls of intensely hot gas cooled, liquefied into droplets by condensation, and ultimately coalesced into planets. A serious objection to this theory is the physical improbability that a relatively small mass of extremely hot burning gas suddenly released from the great gravitational force of the sun would tend to cool and condense rather than to expand explosively.

It is almost certain that many of the countless billions of stars in the various galaxies have their own systems of planets, probably similar to those in our solar system. As yet we have not been able to observe these planets directly with our most powerful telescopes, although there is other evidence for their presence. It also seems likely that on a small percentage of these planets, perhaps an estimated 100 million planets, proper environmental conditions exist for the origin and existence of life as we know it on earth.

The dust-cloud and planetary theories, like those pertaining to the origin of the universe, are based almost completely on speculation. Nevertheless, the more acceptable ones have in their favor a rational explanation which best conforms to the limited evidence available and to the established laws of physics and chemistry.

Age of the Earth

There are a number of methods for estimating the earth's age. At one time it was not unusual to calculate a precise date for the beginning of the world based on narrations in the Bible. The old theological speculations pointing to four or five thousand years ago as the time of creation were founded on stories in the Old Testament and have been, for the most part, discarded. For example, a high member of the church in the seventeenth century concluded that the world was created in 4004 B.C. Geologic studies in the eighteenth and nineteenth centuries broke away from the long-imposed restrictions of theology and suggested 10 million, 100 million, and even a billion years as the age of the earth. This figure has now been extended to at least a few billion years.

Today scientists are attempting to estimate the earth's age by determining the age of its crust. This is best accomplished by measuring the abundance of certain radioactive materials and their products in the rocks. It is well established, for instance, that the atoms of the radioactive element uranium break down or "decay" to the element lead at a slow and constant rate which is unaffected by all known factors, just as is time itself. If it is assumed that uranium decay is the chief means by which lead originated, then by analyzing the relative concentrations of specific types of uranium and lead in a given sample of rock, its age can be computed,[6] assuming that negligible quantities of lead were present when the rock first solidified. This idea can be illustrated by comparing it with the breakdown of a ruined stone building. If we know that one stone falls from the ruins every year, we can count the

[6] The time necessary for half of any given quantity of uranium to decay into lead is called the "half-life" and is four and a half million years. For example, if a given rock sample showed a content of 0.1 grams of lead and 0.3 grams uranium, the age of this rock is computed to be $(0.1/0.3) \times 4.5$ million years = 1.5 million years (see Chapter 6).

fallen stones and determine the year that the structure began to fall to pieces.

The oldest rocks found thus far have been in Manitoba, Canada. They were shown to be about two and a half billion years old by the radioactive-decay procedure. We add another two billion years or so as the time required for the initial formation of the planet and for the subsequent cooling of the earth's molten surface to form a rocky crust. The latest estimates indicate the earth to be about five billion years old. The beginning of the universe, the time at which the atoms or elements came into being, is presumed to have occurred a few billion years earlier, or approximately ten billion years ago. At most these are rough estimates that are easily subject to change depending on the discovery of new evidence.

Structure of the Earth

The earth, whose mean distance from the sun is 93 million miles, has a diameter of about 8000 miles and is surrounded by an envelope of air called the *atmosphere*.

We know very little about the interior of the earth itself. Man has only penetrated about 4 to 5 miles, or one-thousandth of the distance of 4000 miles to the earth's center. The mass of the earth is 6×10^{21} tons and has a mean density of about 5.5. The density of the rocks at the surface is about 2.8, gradually increasing toward the earth's core whose calculated density is about 10.

We believe that as the molten planet earth cooled over the millions of years, it evolved into a definite structural pattern. The central core came to consist of the heaviest material covered with successively lighter concentric layers of substances, the outermost ultimately became a layer of mixed gases or the atmosphere. The atmosphere is a vast ocean of air that becomes progressively thinner with increasing altitudes, and extends to approximately 8 miles above the surface of the earth. The air is in a constant state of turbulence due to uneven heating which accounts for the optical phenomenon, the twinkling of stars.

As a mixture of gases surrounding our planet the atmosphere is presently made up of 80 per cent nitrogen, 20 per cent oxygen, water vapor, and small concentrations of other gases including 0.04 per cent carbon dioxide. It is the general consensus of opinion that the early atmosphere of the earth contained little or no oxygen gas. The oxygen now present is considered to be the result of the biological process of *photosynthesis* (Chapters 8 and 17) carried out by green plants on land and in the sea. According to current estimates the atmospheric oxygen is completely renewed about every two or three thousand years.

At some early point in the cooling process, the molten material at the earth's surface began to form a rocky crust. This change to the solid state, which is still not completed, has continued during these many years. To date the solidification process has yielded an outer shell, the earth's crust, which is about 20 to 25 miles thick under the continents and about 3 miles thick or less under the oceans. It is composed largely of rock known as basalt. Extruding from the basaltic crust are the isolated continents, chiefly composed of a lighter rock called granite. The protruding continents, like icebergs in an ocean, have more than 90 per cent of their mass embedded in the basaltic material beneath the surface of the earth.

Formation of the earth's crust from molten material was undoubtedly accompanied by wrinkling, cracking, and shifting of the surface layers, phenomena that have never completely ceased as indicated by the present-day occurrence of earthquakes. In the earlier stages of the earth's history, the shifting was evinced by great cracks in the earth's crust, upheavals, and folding of the land masses to form mountains. The most notable cracks in the earth's crust at present are in and around the margins of the Pacific Ocean, and along the crest of the submarine ridge that runs down the middle of the Atlantic Ocean. With the passage of time the oldest mountains were eroded and worn down through the action of ice, wind, rain, sun, and frost (and later by the roots of plants).

The silt that ultimately resulted from this progressive erosion and weathering was incorporated in the formation of soil, and was in part carried away by rivers and streams to be deposited finally on the ocean floors along the edges of the continents. Later periods of mountain building alternating with intervals of weathering and erosion occurred intermittently and irregularly, leaving their mark on the earth's surface and climate. These in turn have exerted a tremendous influence on the biologic history of our planet. The Rocky Mountains, the Himalayas, and the Alps are examples of relatively recent mountain-building periods. The Appalachians, a result of a much older disturbance, display a greater degree of erosion and weathering.

We know from the behavior of earthquake or *seismic* waves that the earth's interior is made up of different materials of increasing density arranged in a series of separate, concentric layers.

The flow of molten lava from active volcanoes located in different parts of the world illustrates the present hot liquid properties of matter underlying the relatively thin crust of the earth. This hot, semifluid molten rock or magma immediately below the earth's crust is called the *mantle*. Denser than the crust, it occurs in two layers, the *upper* and *lower* mantles, with depths of about 600 miles and 1200 miles, respectively. The upper mantle is probably the seat of most of the earth's great earthquakes and volcanoes.

Below the mantle is the earth's core (also composed of two layers—an outer and an inner one) with a radius of approximately 2200 miles. The core is widely believed to be made of molten iron and nickel. Another theory regards the core as a highly compressed gas

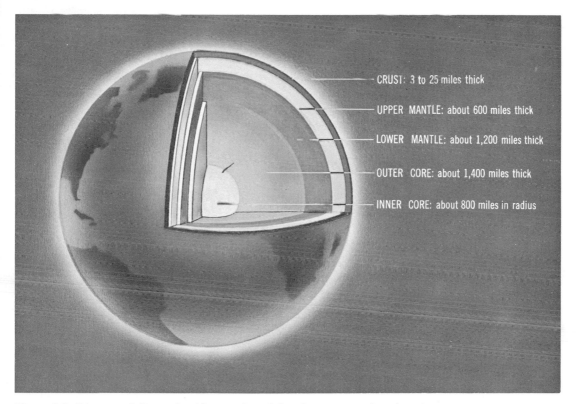

CRUST: 3 to 25 miles thick

UPPER MANTLE: about 600 miles thick

LOWER MANTLE: about 1,200 miles thick

OUTER CORE: about 1,400 miles thick

INNER CORE: about 800 miles in radius

Figure 2-3. Diagram of the earth with a section of the planet removed to show its core and various layers.

at elevated temperatures having the properties of a rigid metal.

The earth's crust is extremely thin in relation to the size of the globe, far thinner than a chicken eggshell compared to the whole egg. The mantle of viscous magma is analogous to the egg white, and the earth's core is comparable to the yolk. A representation of the earth's structure as we visualize it today is shown in Figure 2-3.

Observations record a progressive rise in both temperature and pressure as one bores vertically into the earth. At a depth of about 7000 feet the boiling point of water (100°C) is reached. It is estimated that the temperature at 25 to 30 miles below the earth's surface is about 1000°C, whereas that of the earth's core is probably nearly the same as the temperature existing at the surface of the sun (about 6000°C). The tremendous increase in pressure that goes hand in hand with increasing depth is illustrated by the following values. At 400 miles below the earth's surface the pressure is calculated to be about 8 million pounds per square inch, whereas that at the earth's core is estimated to be about 50 million pounds per square inch. These figures are in marked contrast to the pressure of 15 pounds per square inch which we experience at sea level as a result of the weight of the atmosphere above us.

The Oceans of the Earth

In attempting to picture the earth during its early development, it is logical to assume that until sufficient cooling had occurred, free water could not accumulate, let alone exist, on its surface. A good deal of the planet's water must have taken the form of huge layers of clouds mounting to tremendous altitudes, almost completely blocking out the light of the sun. While gargantuan downpourings of rain and other forms of precipitation surely occurred, they were immediately transformed into vapor and steam upon approaching the hot earth. With further cooling of the earth the falling rains, hail, sleet, and snow began to collect in the crevices, basins, and depressions of the earth's crust to form the oceans, the lakes, the rivers, and the streams. With the passage of centuries and the concomitant accumulation of water on the planet's surface, the thick clouds grew correspondingly thinner, thus permitting more of the sun's light to reach the earth.

Geologists can estimate the age of the oceans by studying the salinity of ocean water. The salts in the oceans were deposited primarily by rivers and streams containing dissolved and suspended minerals washed out from the rocks of the earth's crust through the action of rain and other forms of precipitation. The process started with the first precipitation reaching the earth's surface and has continued since that time. The primeval oceans must have been only slightly salty. Salt concentration in the oceans today is much greater, of course, amounting to about 3 per cent, or enough to cover an area the size of the United States with a layer approximately 2 miles high. In a never-ending cycle the oceans' salinity has gradually increased and continues to increase. The persistent flow of river waters containing dissolved minerals, silt, and larger suspended rock particles into the oceans occurs concomitantly with the evaporation of water from the oceans. Precipitation returns the water to the land and then to the oceans again, maintaining the cycle continuously.

Slowly, but inexorably, the stage was being set for the initial appearance of life, for it was undoubtedly in the primeval ocean with its accumulating salts and its continuously reacting substances of ever-increasing complexity that the first primitive living forms arose.

The Climate of the Earth

The history and evolution of living things has been profoundly influenced by the earth's climate. The surface of the globe has an average temperature of 15° to 20°C with extremes ranging from approximately −15°C to 50°C. The temperature at the earth's surface is primarily determined by the heat and light energy which it receives from the sun. It is only slightly affected by the heat escaping from the earth's hot interior in view of the poor heat-conducting properties of most of the substances comprising the layers that surround the core of the globe. Of some interest are the present indications that the temperatures of the layers of the earth's crust starting downward at several hundred feet below the surface are largely determined by radioactive decay in the crust itself. The phenomenon apparently accounts for the liberation of considerably greater quantities of heat than that gained from either the surface or the interior.

Of the numerous factors (including periodic changes in the earth's orbit and angle of rotation) that determine the different climates occurring on various portions of our planet, winds and ocean currents are among the most significant. The sporadically repeating sequence of geologic upheavals (in terms of mountain building and immense shifts of land and sea) followed by prolonged weathering and erosion has changed the course of winds and ocean currents, and thus, together with other factors, has modified the climate of large and small expanses on the surface of the earth. Periods of great mountain building frequently led to intervals of vast ice formation or glaciation in which large areas of the globe were covered with thick sheets of ice. These periods were characterized by a great loss of life and a general retreat of living forms, terrestrial and marine, toward the equator. The decreased availability of water because of glaciation, and the effect of high mountain ranges in diverting moisture-laden winds and lowering their water content, have in turn contributed significantly to the spread of continental deserts.

In contrast to these climatic features associated with periods of high elevation, the climate accompanying intervals of low elevation has been characterized by the spread of warm ocean currents into the polar regions and warm shallow waters over land areas. In general the intervals of low continental relief resulting from the prolonged erosion and weathering between mountain-building episodes gave rise to conditions of increased moisture and temperature favorable for the growth, development, and wide distribution of living things.

In this manner geologic changes and climate have played an important role in directing and influencing the course of evolution of living things on the surface of the earth.

Overall Features of the Universe

In a broader sense, all the events that preceded and contributed to the formation of life represent the background for a more complete understanding of the nature of living things. The ultimate setting is the universe, and, like all other forms of matter, the fundamental units of living organisms are also atoms or, more basically, the subatomic particles, protons, neutrons, and electrons. Living things are made up of some of the same atoms that constitute our planet. Approximately twenty of these elements make up protoplasm, the basic substance of life.

Earth, like the other planets of our solar system, probably originated from the sun by the accumulation and condensation of dust particles from the sun's periphery, as suggested by the dust-cloud hypothesis discussed earlier. The sun is an average star belonging to a galaxy of about 100 billion stars, the Milky Way. Like most of the stars of the innumerable galaxies expanding into space, the sun is fundamentally an enormous mass of hydrogen atoms undergoing a nuclear reaction by fusion into helium. Other types of nuclear reactions that are directly or indirectly related to hydrogen are also occurring in the sun, leading to the ultimate formation of all the other elements, some of which make up the substance of life—protoplasm.

Hydrogen, then, appears to be the starting material of the other elements. Did hydrogen arise from an explosion of a primordial concentrated core of fundamental particles (*evolutionary theory*), or is it being continuously created from radiant energy and forming new stars in the constantly expanding universe *(steady-state theory)*? We can only speculate about all these processes at our present stage of knowledge. Nevertheless, these are the necessary steps that we now envisage as the logical course of events which prepared the scene for the origin of life on our planet approximately two billion years ago.

SUPPLEMENTARY REFERENCES

Blum, H., *Time's Arrow and Evolution*, Princeton University Press, Princeton, N.J., 1951.
Editors of Scientific American, *The Physics and Chemistry of Life*, Simon and Schuster, New York, 1955.
Gamow, G., "The Origin and Evolution of the Universe," *American Scientist*, **39**:393 (1951).
Hoyle, F., *The Nature of the Universe*, Harper, New York, 1950.
Oparin, A. I., *The Origin of Life on the Earth*, third edition, Academic Press, New York, 1957.
Ross, H. H., *A Synthesis of Evolutionary Theory*, Prentice-Hall, Englewood Cliffs, N.J., 1962.
Schroedinger, E., *What Is Life?*, Macmillan, New York, 1945.

Chapter 3   Origin and Evolution of Life

SPONTANEOUS GENERATION

Ancient Beliefs

Throughout the history of man, it has not been uncommon to find a belief that certain living things could arise suddenly and spontaneously from inanimate substances, a concept known as *spontaneous generation*. In ancient China it was accepted that aphids originated through spontaneous generation on bamboo shoots in warm, moist weather. The Babylonians and Egyptians believed that the mud and silt of the Nile formed worms, toads, snakes, and mice.

In ancient Greece, in India, and in Europe during the Dark Ages and the Renaissance, and, in fact, until very recently, various forms of life were believed to originate directly from the nonliving. It was thought that flies, beetles, and maggots appeared from sweat; mice from refuse and damp earth; intestinal worms from dung and rotting meat; lice from human decaying parts of the human body and excreta; and microorganisms from spoiling broths and infusion.

Belief in the spontaneous generation of life was an integral part of the religious traditions of India, Babylonia, and Egypt. It was viewed as an expression of the gods' (or the demons') will, and fitted in with the mythical accounts of a supernatural creation of life.

In western civilization spontaneous genera-tion was also the accepted dogma of prominent scientists and thinkers. Harvey, the esteemed seventeenth-century physiologist and origi-nator of the theory of blood circulation, Francis Bacon, the outstanding English spokesman of seventeenth-century materialism, and Des-cartes, the great French philosopher of the same era, considered the origin of living forms from inanimate material to be perfectly feasi-ble and beyond dispute.

Our own religious traditions reconciled the principle of the spontaneous generation with the will of a divine being. On the third day of Creation, according to the Book of Genesis, God bade the earth and waters to bring forth living creatures—first, the plants, then fishes, birds, land animals, and finally man. Both St. Basil the Great, a leading authority of the Eastern Church in the fourth century, and St. Augustine of Hippo, a high authority for the Western Church, independently attributed the emergence of living things from inanimate matter to the manifestation of a divine will. St. Thomas Aquinas, in the thirteenth-century classic, *Summa Theologica*, accepted spontan-eous generation as a manifestation of anima-tion by good or evil spiritual principles.

Early Experiments

THE WORK OF VAN HELMONT. The unfounded acceptance of spontaneous generation was essentially based on preconceived and uncritical evaluations of nature. Observations of the origin of insects, rodents, microorganisms, and other living forms from nonliving substances were accepted too readily without critical and careful examination or without adequate control of experimental conditions.

An outstanding example of this indiscriminate approach is seen in the work on spontaneous generation by the famous seventeenth-century Belgian physician J. van Helmont. He concluded, on the basis of his experiment utilizing a sweat-soaked shirt and wheat grains stored in a container, that human sweat was the life-forming principle for creating mice from grain. Surprisingly enough, the "artificially" produced rodents born after 21 days were identical with those "naturally" born from their parents.

And even more surprising, this experiment was conceived by the same van Helmont who performed one of the most significant and elegant experiments in the history of plant nutrition, a classic in its simplicity and clarity of results. In the latter experiment he proved that most of the materials needed for plant growth came from water and air, and not from the soil as was previously believed. Growing a willow seedling in a carefully covered and regularly watered tub of weighed soil, he observed after five years that the tree had gained almost 200 pounds, whereas the soil had lost only a few ounces!

REDI'S CONTRIBUTION. Until the middle of the seventeenth century, the theory of spontaneous generation was widely accepted and held in high regard. There was little or no doubt that it represented a true biological phenomenon. The main controversy centered only about its spiritual implications, whether or not it reflected divine will. Slowly but inexorably, starting with the work of the Italian physician Francesco Redi in the latter half of the seventeenth century the first great rumblings of challenge and uncertainty appeared. They gradually grew in depth and intensity as the study of nature became broader and more precise until the theory of spontaneous genera-

tion finally toppled in complete ruin 200 years later.

In 1668 Redi described his experiments refuting the accepted evidence that maggots arose spontaneously from spoiling meat. He demonstrated that meat placed under a protective covering, so that the eggs of flies could not be deposited on it, never developed maggots. Maggots appeared only when the eggs fell on the decaying meat. Ironically enough, despite his outstanding experiments and correct conclusions, Redi believed that spontaneous generation could occur in other cases.

THE NEEDHAM-SPALLANZANI CONTROVERSY. By the beginning of the nineteenth century, spontaneous generation of the more complex animals such as reptiles, insects, and worms from filth and decaying matter was proven impossible. However, the concept of the origin of life from inanimate matter was not so easily discarded. Instead, the emphasis shifted to the spontaneous generation of simpler living forms, the microorganisms, with the theory receiving widest acceptance in the eighteenth and nineteenth centuries. The use of an optical system of magnification known as the *microscope* by the Dutchman Anthony van Leeuwenhoek (1632–1723) at about the time that Redi was performing his unusual experiments, revealed an entirely new world of the microorganisms. The appearance of these minute organisms in decomposing meat, spoiling broths, sour milk, and other decaying organic matter was almost unanimously attributed to spontaneous generation. Interestingly enough, Leeuwenhoek was not responsible for this belief; he reasoned that the microorganisms dropped into the infusions from the air.

One of the most celebrated scientific controversies in the history of biology revolved about spontaneous generation. In 1745, John T. Needham, an English Jesuit priest and naturalist, published a report describing extensive experiments in which hermetically sealed vessels containing meat extracts and a variety of infusions soon swarmed with microorganisms despite previous exposure to elevated temperatures. Needham ascribed this phenomenon to the presence in each particle of organic matter of a special "vital force," which was responsible for the animation and, therefore, the appearance of living things.

The views and results of Needham were experimentally challenged by an Italian scientist, the Abbé Lazzaro Spallanzani, who in 1765 published evidence opposing Needham's ideas. He found that through prolonged heating in hermetically sealed vessels vegetable broths and other organic substances never developed microorganisms. Spallanzani attributed Needham's positive results instead to inadequate heating, which failed to destroy completely the contaminating microorganisms in the vessels. Needham countered that by too much boiling Spallanzani had "tortured" or destroyed the "vital force" in the broths as well as spoiled the small amount of air that remained in the vessels. Spallanzani responded with new experiments demonstrating that his heated broths could develop microorganisms when the flasks were subsequently opened to unsterilized air. On the other hand, he was unable to prove that his boiling treatment had not altered the air within the vessel. The dispute remained unsettled, and in fact was regarded at that time as a victory for Needham.

FINAL DESTRUCTION OF SPONTANEOUS GENERATION THEORY BY PASTEUR. During the next hundred years, numerous experiments by various scientists yielded inconclusive results. Although on the whole they tended to refute the possibility of spontaneous generation, the recurring incidence of failures was interpreted in favor of the theory. In retrospect we realize, of course, that the instances in which the microorganisms appeared were undoubtedly caused by contamination and not spontaneous generation.

The controversy was finally and decisively resolved by Louis Pasteur in 1862 through a series of rigorous and convincing experiments which are still accepted today as models of scientific acumen and experimental design.

First, he demonstrated the presence of microorganisms in the air, a fact previously doubted by the proponents of spontaneous generation. By drawing air through a tube containing a gun cotton plug, then dissolving the plug in a mixture of alcohol and ether, he showed that the resulting solution contained undissolved particles which under microscopic examination were identified as microorganisms. He also showed that, by heating incoming air to high temperatures before allowing it to enter a flask of boiled broth, no spoilage occurred.

In another experiment Pasteur used a half-filled flask with a long S-shaped neck open to the air. When the nutrient broth in the flask was boiled in the absence of any further precautions and allowed to cool, the broth could keep indefinitely with no development of microorganisms. Air could pass freely in and out of the flask but all accompanying particles of dust, bacteria, molds, and other microorganisms were trapped on the inner curved surfaces of the S-shaped neck and seldom reached the contained liquid. Pasteur's investigations also produced evidence showing that the experimental results obtained by others was due to contamination by microorganisms, and not to mystical life forces.

Pasteur's great contribution in this area was to refute irrevocably by means of careful and critical experiments the concept of spontaneous generation. Thus he succeeded in dislodging a concept that had dominated the minds of men for thousands of years. For this revolutionary work Pasteur was awarded a special prize by the French Academy of Sciences.

MODERN EVOLUTIONARY THEORY OF THE ORIGIN OF LIFE

Emergence of the Theory

The hypothesis of spontaneous generation oddly enough had served in an important theoretical role for the two opposing schools of thought concerning the origin of life. To most scientists of the nineteenth century, spontaneous generation represented the only logical explanation for a mechanistic view of the origin of life. They contended that no fundamental difference existed between living and nonliving matter. Organisms simply represented a more highly complicated and integrated arrangement of energy and matter, consisting of different kinds of inanimate materials collectively endowed with the characteristics of life by virtue of their organization. Spontaneous generation was basically the primary transformation of inanimate matter to the living state. Many had favored this mechanistic view in contrast to the vitalistic or religious belief in the divine creation of life through the power of a mystical "vital force."

The vitalistic school, in large part, had also adopted the idea of spontaneous generation (e.g., the work of Needham and others cited earlier) as an expression of divine creation. It had only a few years earlier (1859) been dealt a stunning blow by Darwin's theory of evolution, which had offered a well-documented explanation of how higher organisms arose from simpler forms. The demise of the concept of spontaneous generation as a result of Pasteur's unequivocal experimental evidence was followed by a resurgence of vitalism. The vitalists stated that it was beyond the human intellect to comprehend the "life force" and that an impenetrable barrier existed between living and inanimate matter. According to their outlook, the origin of life could only be explained on the basis of a special, mysterious "vital force." the result of a divine act of creation.

On the other hand, the great majority of scientists of that era representing the mechanistic approach were now left without any conceivable explanation of the origin of life in view of Pasteur's conclusive work. They were faced with a seemingly insoluble dilemma. Either the creation of life had been effected by some supernatural or mystical force, a belief that they were unwilling to accept, or living things could arise spontaneously on the basis of certain laws of nature, a possibility that had seemingly been eliminated by Pasteur.

Several scientists responded to this situation by attempting to refute Pasteur's data. Numerous experiments were subsequently conducted to demonstrate spontaneous origin of life, but none were successful. A small group of naturalists, however, began to hold the view that the origin of living things involved not a sudden and spontaneous development from organic matter but rather a prolonged evolution of inanimate matter during the course of millions of years, ultimately leading to the emergence of a primitive form of life. Despite a period of disillusionment extending well into the twentieth century regarding a scientific basis for the origin of life, this evolutionary concept persisted and grew, receiving support from an increasing number of facts and deductions.

The modern evolutionary theory of the origin of life stands today as the most likely hypothesis explaining the emergence of the first living forms by a process of evolution from inanimate substances.

Role of the Ancient Seas

The theory assumes that the first primeval organisms arose in gradual stages from nonliving substances in the ancient oceans. We believe that life originated in the sea from a number of reasons. Salts and water, the predominant materials in oceans, are two of the necessary components of living things. Water makes up 70 to 95 per cent of most organisms and is, in a biological sense, the universal solvent. In the primeval oceans it provided the medium for dissolving, suspending, and ceaselessly mixing a wide variety of colliding molecules, thus facilitating the chemical reactions that converted simpler materials to more complex substances. These in turn reacted with each other to form molecules of even greater size and complexity. Presumably, simple organic compounds (Chapter 7) resulted from chemical reactions between inorganic substances, accumulated in the ancient seas and with time evolved by further reactions into larger and more complex molecules.

One unique condition that permitted the

evolution and accumulation of organic from inorganic molecules was, paradoxically enough, the absence of living things. Almost all organic molecules in the natural environment of our present-day world exist for relatively short periods of time since there are innumerable organisms, especially microorganisms, which rapidly break down these molecules, utilizing them for their growth and other life activities.

In this manner the ancient seas began to assume the characteristics of a huge, dilute sterile broth. It was sterile in the sense that it could not be decomposed or broken down by living organisms since none existed. It is further envisaged that many of these molecules became associated with each other in various physical and chemical combinations, forming the complex structures of highly organized, dynamic nonliving systems—the forerunners of the first living forms. It is supposed that, by a gradual series of changes over the centuries, the more stable systems survived at the expense of the others, evolving into more complex systems of a higher and higher order until they were finally endowed with the characteristics that we ascribe to living things.

Evolution of Complex Organic Substances from Simpler Materials

One of the first important steps in the conversion of matter, which ultimately gave rise to living organisms, was the transition of inorganic substances to organic materials. Until 1828 when the German chemist Wöhler synthesized an organic substance, urea, in the laboratory for the first time without the participation of living organisms, it was generally accepted that the formation of organic molecules could occur only in living organisms. Wöhler's work opened up the entirely new area of organic chemistry, and since his time more than a half million different organic substances have been synthesized.

Since the 1930's there has been unequivocal evidence that a class of simple organic compounds known as *hydrocarbons* (Chapter 7) are found everywhere in the universe—in the sun and the stars, in interstellar dust and gas clouds, on the larger planets of the solar system and their satellites, and in comets and meteorites—thus providing support for the origin of organic substances in nature without the mediation of living organisms.

We know that chemical reactions for producing organic substances of increasing complexity are facilitated by a variety of conditions including high temperatures and pressures, electrical discharges, and ultraviolet irradiation. In the laboratory it has been possible to produce some of the naturally occurring amino acids, the building blocks of proteins, by exposing a mixture of simple chemicals to such conditions. The experiments of Miller and Urey, for example, showed that a number of biologically important amino acids could be randomly synthesized by passing electric discharges through a gaseous mixture of ammonia, hydrogen gas, water vapor, and a simple organic substance, the hydrocarbon *methane*. Comparable experiments by other workers demonstrated the formation from simple substances of certain complex organic molecules known as *purine* and *pyrimidine bases*, which serve as important structural units of the nucleic acids (Chapter 7).

Localized regions of high temperatures and pressures must have been common during the shifting of the earth's crust and during the frequent volcanic outpourings of hot lava in the early history of the earth. The energy of the sun in the form of ultraviolet light and heat undoubtedly facilitated the transformation of simple organic compounds to more complex substances, as did electrical discharges in the atmosphere (e.g., lightning), cosmic irradiation, and radioactive breakdown. Some of these organic substances were transferred from the atmosphere and from the land by the rains, finally accumulating in the oceans where they continued to undergo further transformations. It seems reasonable to assume that the salts in the oceans catalyzed or accelerated some of the reactions between these molecules. In addition, the adsorption of a number of different organic substances by the small particles of matter suspended and deposited in the waters facilitated various chemical reactions. It has been estimated that at one point the primeval ocean must have been composed of at least 10 per cent organic matter, prior to the appearance of living things.

The four principal groups of organic constituents of protoplasm are *carbohydrates, fats, proteins,* and *nucleic acids* (Chapter 7). The results of laboratory experiments just mentioned suggest that carbohydrates and fats, which are so important as energy sources and a building material for living things as well as the building blocks of proteins and nucleic acids, could have arisen spontaneously in the oceans by purely chance chemical reactions long before the appearance of the first form of life.

The possibility, however, that proteins and nucleic acids as such could have been produced in a similar chance manner is considered to be highly improbable. It appears more likely that only the formation of amino acids and their combination into long molecular chains known as *polypeptides* (Chapter 7) took place by random chemical reactions between molecules. However, the formation of proteins, perhaps from these polypeptides, might have occurred in a directed fashion much later in highly organized systems, as indicated in the following section. The formation of nucleic acids is attributed to a comparable scheme: first, the chance formation of long chains known as *polynucleotides* (Chapter 7) which later, in the presence of highly organized systems, probably gave rise to nucleic acids. In present-day organisms, nucleic acids and proteins are not regarded as "living molecules" in themselves but instead are essential components of living matter called *protoplasm.*

Transition from Nonliving to Living Systems

Although some work has been done in clarifying the chemical evolution of various molecules of biological significance, the most serious gap in our knowledge is the transition from these mixtures of inorganic and highly complex organic molecules to the first unit of primeval life. The concept of organic chemical evolution has come to be widely accepted, whereas theories concerning the transition of inanimate substances to a living state are still highly speculative and controversial. Some authorities believe that it would be erroneous to picture the origin of the first form of life as having simply occurred by a fortuitous combination of proteins, nucleic acids, carbohydrates, and other substances previously formed by chance chemical reactions.

A number of hypotheses, which were presented as recently as 15 or 20 years ago, proposed the origin of life to be merely the sudden appearance of an aggregate of particles or extremely large and complex molecules endowed with the characteristics of a living entity. Two of the most likely candidates that were postulated at that time for the role of the first organic particles possessing properties of life were *viruses* and *genes*, which we now know to be composed of nucleoproteins. Viruses and genes were regarded as having arisen purely by a chance chemical combination. Presumably they were molecules that had some unidentified and unusual structural features giving them the unique property of self-duplication or reproduction, the key characteristic of life. It was further proposed that the cumulative reaction of these molecules with each other gradually formed more complicated aggregates, finally yielding a mixture of materials possessing properties identical with those of living matter or protoplasm.

Other biologists suggested that the first form of life arose by chance from the organic ancient sea in the form of a simple autocatalytic unit, that is, a simple protein known as an *enzyme* (Chapter 7) which accelerates the rates of specific chemical reactions. Simple enzymes were then presumed to evolve into enzymes capable somehow of reproducing themselves, finally serving as the basis for the subsequent formation of organisms. Most of these theories are now regarded as unlikely explanations of the beginnings of life.

Oparin's Theory of the Origin of Life

1. **EVOLUTION OF COMPLEX INANIMATE SYSTEMS.** One of the most reasonable and well-constructed hypotheses of the origin of life has been presented by the Russian biologist I. A. Oparin. He has attempted to put together a picture of the probable complex organization and evolution of different combinations of inorganic and organic matter, as well as a history of the chemical and physical events that must have preceded the emergence of the first form of life. In addition, he has endeavored to describe the transition from these complex inanimate physical and chemical systems to a living form, based on available evidence.

Oparin contends that the inanimate forerunner of the first living forms must have been an organization of polypeptides, polynucleotides, carbohydrates, and other substances constituting a system with definite boundaries, structures, and spatial configuration. Such complex nonliving systems, which have been created in highly simplified form in the laboratory, tend to remove and concentrate various substances from the surrounding medium. These substances may then undergo a variety of chemical reactions, directed in part by the structural features of the organized system with some of the products of the reactions being eventually released to the external environment. In this respect Oparin considers this type of inanimate system to be analogous to a living thing in that both are essentially dynamic systems which undergo a continuous influx and outflow of matter and energy.

Oparin assumes that by an evolutionary process of selection a progressive improvement occurred in the chain of chemical reactions within the nonliving systems. Those physical and chemical differences that were favorable for the existence of a particular system, such as greater stability or greater ability to compete for chemicals in the surrounding environment, presumably endowed a system with a better chance for longer survival. This is simply an extension of Darwin's fundamental theory that higher living forms evolved from lower forms based on the principle of natural selection. Organisms developing features that favored their ability to cope with their environment therefore had an added advantage in survival as compared to other living things. In this manner they tended to become the dominant living population. Oparin believes that this same evolutionary selection principle could profitably be applied to the inanimate complex multi-molecular systems.

This type of selection could be conceived as having led to a definite direction in the evolution of these increasingly complex inanimate systems. In this fashion systems are posited to have evolved which had a capacity for self-renewal or self-preservation of parts by selected chemical and physical processes. An additional step in this direction would be an increased growth or mass of some of these systems as a result of an increased rate of withdrawal of more substances from the surrounding medium. This could have occurred because of enhanced physical or chemical processes. Greater speeds of reactions within an inanimate system of this type could be advantageous since they would provide for an increased flow of substances through the system.

Catalysts that enhanced the rate of a chemical reaction probably gave marked advantages to those inanimate systems that acquired them. Some of the polypeptides formed at random may have had catalytic activity. Those that were most efficient in favoring the existence of a non-living system must have been indirectly preserved by a selection process, whereas systems having less efficient catalysts were eliminated. Thus the polypeptide catalysts apparently evolved in a definite direction within the increasingly complex systems. They were constantly being sorted out by a process of selection until they finally evolved within the first living systems into the first primitive *enzymes*—extremely efficient protein catalysts with a high degree of specificity for the types of chemical reactions which they accelerate (Chapter 7).

We know that protoplasm contains many different enzymes which are in effect responsible for virtually all the chemical reactions (i.e., metabolism) of the living cell. The chemical reactions occurring in living organisms are governed by the same principles that govern those performed in the test tube in the chemistry laboratory. However, one of the specific characteristics of living things is the organization of these enzyme-catalyzed chemical reactions into sequences or pathways in a predetermined and coordinated manner that is constantly repeated. The various reaction pathways are responsible for the metabolic properties of protoplasm, including the synthesis of proteins and nucleic acids, respiration, and other processes.

2. **TRANSITION FROM NONLIVING TO LIVING SYSTEMS.** At most we can only speculate or guess at the course of events that led from the complex inanimate systems to the first form of life on earth. Oparin regards the evolutionary stage in which the complex nonliving systems gradually acquired these coordinated chains or cycles of replicable chemical reactions as part of the transition from the nonliving state to the first living form. The chance formation of catalysts and their selective evolution into protein-like catalysts of high specificity and activity undoubtedly played an important role in this transition. Oparin believes that the constant repetition of these coordinated and connected chains or cycles of reactions were somehow responsible for the appearance of the most unique characteristic of all, reproduction. How this occurred is not clear. Nevertheless, at this point the system was regarded as being alive. This is estimated to have occurred about two billion years ago.

According to this evolutionary theory, then, the first living forms gradually originated from highly organized inanimate systems in the primeval seas. These nonliving systems must have been able to take up a number of substances, especially organic compounds, from the surrounding medium, All living organisms

TIME, YEARS AGO	EVENTS
20-50 thousand	Modern man, modern plants and animals
1-60 million	Evolution of higher mammals and plants, even greater diversification and distribution of flowering plants
50 million	Some mammals enter the oceans, continuing diversification and distribution of flowering plants
100-150 million	First mammals and first birds, increasing diversification and distribution of flowering plants
125-200 million	Rise and predominance of reptiles, development of extensive gymnosperm forests, rise of flowering plants
250-300 million	First amphibians, insects, mosses, ferns; rise of dense swamp forests which later formed major coal beds of the world
350 million	First successful invasion of land by animals and plants, appearance of first vertebrates as ancient fish in the sea
500 million	Ancestors of all major groups of invertebrates present in the oceans, also alga and ancient seaweed
1 billion	Increasing population of unicellular and simpler multicellular organisms including many invertebrates in the seas, origin of photosynthesis
2-5 billion	Formation of increasingly complex organic molecules in primeval seas, origin of life
5-6 billion	Formation of the earth and other members of solar system
10 billion	Origin of universe?

Summary of Evolution of Life on the Planet Earth.

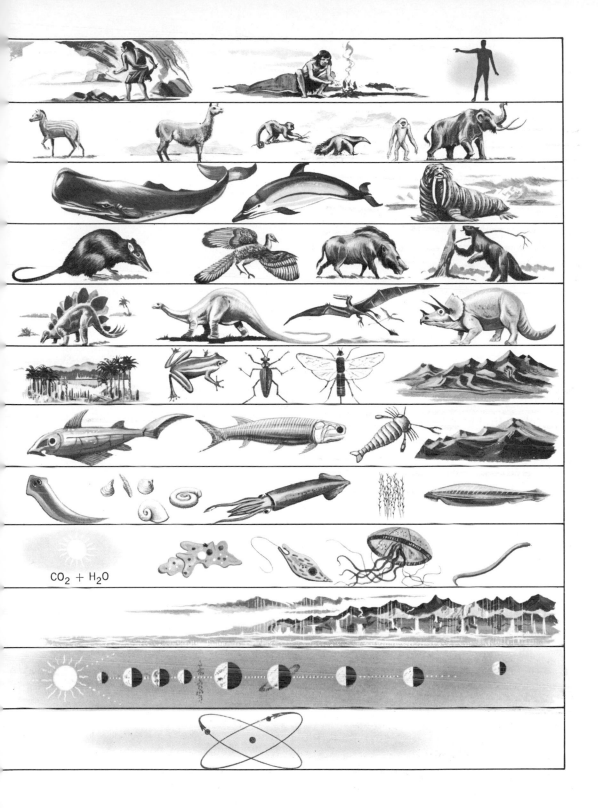

$CO_2 + H_2O$

carry on essentially the same kind of activity—the intake of organic and inorganic substances, which are necessary in metabolism, or as a source of energy and building material for the unique processes of reproduction and the growth and repair of protoplasm. The subsequent evolution of nonliving systems was determined by the natural selection of those relatively stable types that could metabolize these materials most efficiently and rapidly. The transition to a living form presumably occurred when the systems acquired the characteristics of reproduction (and growth, including self-repair) by virtue of their coordinated and catalyzed chains of chemical reactions. In the final analysis living systems represent one of the most complex states of organization that matter and energy have attained in our universe.

SUBSEQUENT EVOLUTION OF ORGANISMS

General Features

The essential biological feature of metabolism is the step-by-step release of the energy stored in the chemical bonds of organic compounds, such as carbohydrates, and its subsequent utilization in the primary life processes of reproduction as well as the repair and growth of protoplasm. This is ultimately accomplished in living cells by coordinated chains of many chemical reactions, each step of which is catalyzed by its own specific enzyme. The detailed mechanisms and control of growth and reproduction are largely still unknown, however, and represent major unanswered problems in biology.

Remarkably enough, it has been established that the first stage in the energy metabolism of nearly all living organisms is essentially made up of the same sequence of chemical reactions catalyzed by similar enzymes. The similarity of the chemical sequences suggests the remains of a primitive metabolism inherited from the early forms of life, and, therefore, common to all present-day living things. The ability of almost all organisms to utilize ready-made organic substances in their metabolism is considered to be an indication of the basic nature of the metabolic process and its antiquity in biological systems.

The primitive forms of life evolved through millions of years into highly efficient organisms, such as those existing today. The complex organization of contemporary living forms is attributed to a combination of interwoven factors, including the networks of different enzyme-catalyzed reactions and their quantitative and spatial relationships to each other, the various physical structures of the cell, and the physical and chemical substances in the cell. It represents the results of an evolutionary process directed by selection over billions of years which still goes on in living organisms today.

Early Forms of Life

It logically follows from the foregoing hypothesis of the origin of life that the first organisms appearing on the earth required the presence of ready-made organic compounds in their environment in order to survive. With the growth and subsequent multiplication of primitive life there ensued a greater consumption of organic materials from the environment. This must have inevitably led to greater competition between organisms for the limited supply of organic substances and for a natural selection in favor of those living things that were most efficient in utilizing the existing energy sources. The organisms that were predisposed to using simpler organic substances as an energy source by virtue of having developed a means of converting them to more complex substances must have had a distinct advantage in the struggle for existence.

Evolution of Photosynthetic Organisms

The early forms of life existed in the absence of free gaseous oxygen, since there was little or no molecular oxygen presumed to be present in the atmosphere at that time. Nearly all the gaseous oxygen now present in the earth's atmosphere is attributed primarily to the unique process of *photosynthesis* carried out by green plants on the land and in the oceans. Photosynthesis is the biological process whereby organic substances are synthesized from carbon dioxide and water by using the energy of light initially absorbed by special green pigments called chlorophylls (Chapter 17). This process, which produces free gaseous oxygen as a by-product, is regarded as a subsequent evolutionary acquisition in the further development of living things. Some of the early organisms by virtue of possessing such special pigments were probably able to absorb a portion of the sunlight and use the light energy for a more efficient metabolism. By progressive evolution these earliest photosynthetic forms gave rise to the contemporary photosynthetic organisms of today—the green plants, including algae and certain bacteria.

Photosynthetic organisms probably began to become prominent about 700 or 800 million years ago. At that time the waters of the seas contained in large part substances that could serve only as a poor energy source for the great majority of organisms which then existed. Many of these substances were presumably the waste products of the predominant types of metabolism of that era, a metabolism that occurred in the absence of free oxygen, since little or none of the gas was present. Only the photosynthetic organisms thrived. With an abundance of substances present in the environment to satisfy their particular metabolic needs, they must have evolved very rapidly, beginning in relatively short order to enrich the atmosphere with one of the waste products of photosynthesis, molecular oxygen. It has been calculated that the present population of green plants, especially in the oceans, would take approximately 3000 years to replace completely the oxygen in our atmosphere.

Influence of Molecular Oxygen on Biological Evolution

The increasing concentration of free oxygen in the atmosphere as a result of its liberation from water by photosynthesis altered the entire course of biological evolution. Molecular oxygen provided a means of obtaining energy from the organic products of metabolism which had heretofore been discarded as waste products. The living organisms that were able to utilize the energy stored in organic metabolic waste products by further breaking them down with the aid of oxygen had a distinct advantage. They began to evolve more rapidly and in time became one of the predominant groups of living things on the surface of the earth. Most contemporary organisms, including man, belong to this group and are characterized by an absolute requirement for gaseous oxygen.

We have learned from extensive biochemical research that in most living things the first stages in the metabolic liberation of energy from organic substances involve the more primitive set of reactions in which free oxygen is not involved, a process known as *anaerobic respiration* (Chapter 8). The organic products of this chain of reactions are then further metabolized by a series of steps ultimately dependent on free oxygen (*aerobic respiration*). It is significant that these oxygen-requiring chains of reactions release far more energy and make a larger percentage of it available for utilization in the life processes than the oxygen-independent steps that preceded it (Chapter 8). These organisms, which had evolved this oxygen-requiring accessory metabolic pathway, were therefore favored in the competition for existence.

The development of photosynthesis resulted in an important change in the subsequent evolution of life. In addition to exerting an important influence, through the release of free oxygen, on the evolution of better and more efficient chains of metabolism, it also provided a means of replenishing the biological environment with organic substances. Virtually all organisms on the planet Earth obtain their energy indirectly from the sun by way of photosynthesis. All animals, plants, and most microorganisms are completely dependent on the energy locked in the chemical bonds of organic compounds. The vast array of organic compounds in our present-day environment are ultimately derived, directly and indirectly, in nearly all cases from the biological process of photosynthesis, which is a conversion of the energy of sunlight into the chemical energy stored in the bonds of particular organic compounds.

Further Evolution of Different Forms of Marine Life

The protoplasm or living matter of virtually all organisms is organized into basic units called *cells* (Chapter 4). The early forms of life were most likely organized as single cells. With the appearance of photosynthetic forms, two main classes of organisms became apparent, those containing chlorophyll and those without this photosensitive pigment. As millions of years passed, the forms of life grew more complex. Simple one-celled organisms probably gave rise to aggregates of cells and these in turn presumably evolved into multicellular forms. Some of the multicellular organisms developed highly specialized groups of cells with specialized functions such as reproduction, digestion, breathing, and excretion. Sponge-like animals appeared on the ocean's bottom and coral animals thrived in the warm waters of the sea. Increasingly advanced forms of ancient animal life, resembling the jelly fish, the worms, and hard-shelled creatures of our present day, evolved in the oceans. Single-celled algae gave rise to multicellular forms such as the ancient seaweeds.

The sterile, rocky continents continued to undergo cracking, shifting, mountain formation, and erosion while the oceans in that early and ancient period continued to serve as the medium for the evolution of life. By 500 million years ago the ancestors of all the main groups of *invertebrate animals* (those without backbones) had already developed in the seas. At about this time the first fossil records were entered in the rocks of the continents. The sea had repeatedly invaded the land as a result of the shifting and upheavals of the earth's crust.

Early Terrestrial Organisms

It is believed that the first successful venture of organisms onto the land was accomplished approximately 350 million years ago by a hard-shelled invertebrate resembling a scorpion, a member of a group of organisms that later gave rise to the lobsters, crabs, and insects. The first *vertebrates* (animals with backbones) were beginning to make their appearance in the sea at about the same time in the form of ancient fish now extinct. At this time the first land plants, derived from the simple aquatic green plants, were also slowly gaining a foothold on the land. They spread and diversified, aiding in crumbling the rock and converting it into soil.

The unstable nature of the earth's crust led to flooding of sizable portions of the continents, frequently followed by subsequent drainage as the land masses continued to shift, and fall and rise. In the process various forms of ocean life were left stranded in the resulting land-locked bodies of water, swamps, and terrestrial surroundings. Although most of the stranded organisms must have perished, a few managed to survive in view of certain adaptable structures which permitted them to withstand their new environmental conditions. Some forms of fish evolved special structures such as swim bladders which served for the storage of air. Another form possessed an air-breathing lung permitting it to live buried in the mud for relatively long periods of time. With the passage of time there evolved on the land, aided by the mechanism of selection, organisms that were best suited for a terrestrial existence. Animals with fins were gradually replaced by organisms with legs. Gills, as the organs for taking in oxygen and giving up carbon dioxide, gave way to the lungs which assumed the major respiratory function. The first amphibians probably appeared about 300 million years ago, and during the next 75 million years or so they developed rapidly and became widespread.

Further Evolution of Terrestrial Organisms

Primitive insects, mosses, ferns, and seed plants also appeared on the land. New forms of life continued to evolve as environmental conditions changed. Other forms, old and new, which were placed at a disadvantage, declined and became extinct. At times gigantic catastrophes (e.g., floods, earthquakes, volcanic action, glacier movements, and rapid mountain formation) wiped out huge segments of the living population. An infinitesimally small portion of these ancient organisms, however, were preserved in the rocks and coal formations of the earth's crust—our only evidence of their past existence. The major coal beds of the world today represent some of the dense, widespread swamp forests of 250-300 million years ago. Primitive reptiles probably developed from some ancient amphibian ancestor approximately 200 million years ago, the period during which the early flowering plants also evolved. Within the next 75 million years or so, they became the predominant form of animal life on the continents. Flowering plants continued to diversify and spread. The first primitive mammal must have had its origin in this period from some ancient reptile now extinct, as did the birds approximately 30 million years later.

Some land animals such as reptiles and mammals returned to the sea. The descendants of huge reptiles, which 150 million years ago reentered the oceans, are now represented by the sea turtles and porpoises. Contemporary ocean mammals (e.g., seals and whales) are descendants of certain mammals who 50 million years ago also returned to the ocean waters.

Evolution of Man

Many of the higher plants and mammals developed during the last 60 million years. It is only during the past million years, however, that the most advanced and unique animal of them all, man, finally evolved.

Man descended from a group of arboreal land mammals, animals that lived among the trees and moved principally by swinging from branch to branch with their hands. Acute stereoscopic vision and unusual manual dexterity must have been of distinct advantage in the survival of these tree-living forms. Later in their evolutionary history these animals descended to a terrestrial existence and eventually gave rise to a form with an exceptionally expanded brain—the forerunner of man.

Modern man evolved in his present form about 20 to 50 thousand years ago, the culmination of a vast biological evolutionary process which began with the origin of the first primitive living form some two billion years earlier. His two most distinct biological attributes—a highly developed brain, which accounts for his amazing ability to reason, and his unusual manual dexterity, which is responsible for his ability to manipulate the environment about him—have made man the most successful terrestrial organism in the entire history of living things on the planet earth.

In a broader sense man represents one of the most advanced and complex states in the incredibly long sequence of the evolutionary organization of energy and matter, a chain of events that started with the beginning of the expanding universe and evolved by steps from nonliving to living systems and thence to contemporary living organisms.

SUPPLEMENTARY REFERENCES

Blum, H., *Time's Arrow and Evolution*, Princeton University Press, Princeton, N.J., 1951.
Editors of Scientific American, *The Physics and Chemistry of Life*, Simon and Schuster, New York, 1955.
Gabriel, M. L., and S. Fogel, *Great Experiments in Biology*, Prentice-Hall, Englewood Cliffs, N.J., 1955.
Miller, S. L., "A Production of Amino Acids under Possible Primitive Earth Conditions," *Science*, May 15, 1953.
Oparin, A. L., *The Origin of Life on the Earth,* third edition, Academic Press, New York, 1957.
Schroedinger, E., *What Is Life?*, Macmillan, New York, 1945.
Wald, G., "The Origin of Life," *Scientific American*, August 1954.

TWO
THE CELL AS THE UNIT OF LIFE

The fundamental unit of life is the cell. It is the lowest common denominator, interms of structure and function, that fulfills the requirements of a living system. For numerous forms of life, especially at the microscopic level, the single cell constitutes the entire organism. For others, many groups of specialized cells working in close harmony with one another compose the whole organism.

The typical activities of the living cell are an expression of the coordinated behavior of its subcellular parts. Strictly speaking, each of these components by itself cannot be regarded as a living system. Yet when integrated structurally and functionally with one another a new dimension is added; they compose a living unit, the cell. To understand the cell we must therefore understand its component parts, as isolated structures ranging from the gross to the molecular, and as whole structures interacting within the integrity of the intact cell.

The basic relationship among all cells in terms of the resemblance of their component parts reflects the basic similarity at the molecular level. Nature exhibits an underlying unity in the molecules and reactions that it uses in carrying out the characteristic life processes in all living things from the simplest unicellular forms to the most advanced many-celled organisms such as man. In general the same molecules have similar roles independent of the cell type in which they occur. This fundamental molecular likeness gives added support to our theory of evolution that all living forms are related ultimately by way of an ancient common ancestor. A logical extension of this view would imply that biological evolution is an expression of the evolution of molecules and their organization with each other at the cell or organism level.

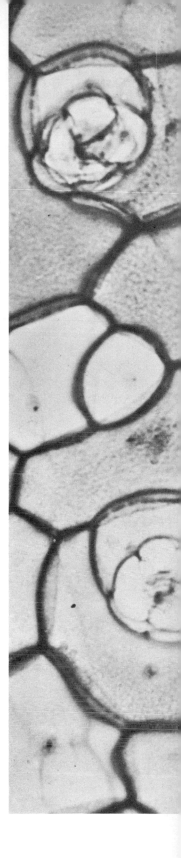

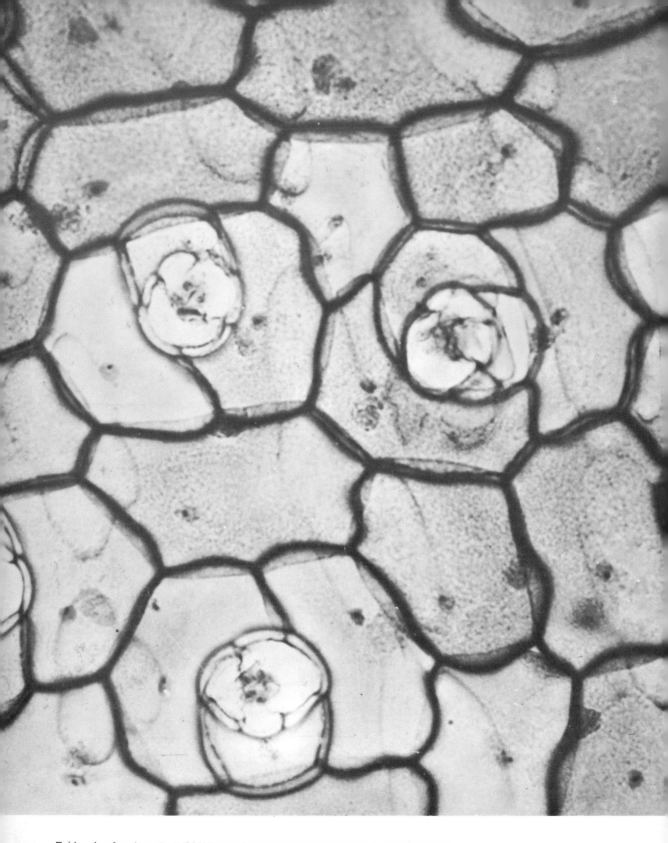

Epidermis of sedum plant (300X) showing guard cells (courtesy of Hugh Spencer).

Chapter 4   Structure of the Cell

GENERAL FEATURES

Unity of Structure and Function

Living things, or organisms, display a remarkable and fundamental similarity in both structure and function. With rare exceptions all living forms are essentially made up of one or more basic units or structural compartments called the cell.

The cell consists of a highly integrated and organized group of components exhibiting specialized structures and performing specialized functions. In those few organisms and tissues that apparently are noncellular, the same basic subcellular components as in ordinary cells are nevertheless present, thus indicating a fundamental similarity among all living forms. (Examples of such noncellular types are described in the next chapter.) In most such cases there is evidence that this seemingly noncellular arrangement of living matter was at one time organized into cells and was subsequently modified in the course of development. In unicellular living forms the activities of the cell constitute the activities of the organism. In multicellular organisms the integrated activities of the various constituent cell types are responsible for the characteristic activities and behavior of the whole organism.

The concept of the cell as the unit of life has been universally accepted since the mid-nineteenth century. As the unit of life the cell can be operationally described by the same definition that we presented for a living system in Chapter 1. The living cell is essentially a dynamic, self-directed, and highly organized complex system of molecules and molecular aggregates which appropriates and utilizes the energy of its surroundings for the purposes of growth and reproduction. The energy of the environment is available to most cells for their life activities either as energy stored in the chemical bonds of such substances as sugars, fats, and proteins; or as light energy, a form used exclusively by green plants and certain bacteria. By predetermined pathways of chemical and physical reactions, the chemical energy or light energy, as the case may be, is transformed and utilized to manifest ultimately the classic characteristics of living things. All activities of the cell at the molecular level and therefore at higher levels are ultimately determined and controlled, directly or indirectly, by a unique class of substances, the deoxyribonucleic acids or DNA. These master molecules by their very nature are also primarily responsible for the transfer of information from one cell generation to another (i.e., heredity).

This common unity of all cells (and noncellular forms) in terms of structure and function, no matter what their source (plant, animal, or microbial), implies that the great variety of current living things ultimately originated from the same primitive ancestral type an estimated two billion years ago.

The present chapter deals with the structure of the cell and to a lesser extent with the principal physiological roles associated with the main subcellular constituents. Consideration of the specialized biochemical activities of the various cellular components are reserved for a section in Chapter 8, following the presentation of of basic physical, chemical, and biochemical phenomena (Chapters 6, 7, and 8).

STUDY OF THE CELL

Techniques of Investigation

With few exceptions almost all cells — animal, plant, and microbial — are too small to be seen with the naked eye. The human eye normally cannot detect an object whose diameter is smaller than $1/250$ of an inch, or 0.1 mm.[1] Most animal and plant cells have dimensions which range in the order of one-hundredth to a few hundredths of a millimeter, or a few ten-thousandths of an inch. Only a very few cells, like birds eggs and certain algae, can be seen without a microscope.

The study of cell structure, or cytology, has been based almost completely on direct observation with the microscope. The light microscope, which is the one most commonly used, extends our range of visibility at best about a thousandfold so that we can just see objects whose diameters are about 1/250,000 of an inch

or $0.1\,\mu$. This is the size of many bacteria which are among the smallest cells known.

The electron microscope, introduced in the mid-1930's, passes a stream of electrons instead of visible light through the object being studied to a fluorescent screen or to a sensitive photographic plate (Figure 4-1). It has extended our vision another hundredfold down to diameters of 1/25,000,000 of an inch (about 10 angstrom units). It has made possible observation of ultracellular structure, some of the very smallest virus particles (such as those responsible for infantile paralysis), and certain large protein and nucleic-acid molecules. Unfortunately a major limitation of the electron microscope (Figure 4-2) has been the fact that the specimen must be exposed to the penetrating electron beam in a vacuum, so that only the dried remains of the specimen are actually examined. New techniques are now being developed for looking at living cells with this instrument.

The phase-contrast microscope developed in 1935 is a light microscope employing an optical system that exaggerates certain optical properties of subcellular structures, highlighting contrasts and thus facilitating visibility. It has proven to be an especially powerful tool for the study of living cells.

The introduction of several procedures led to the rapid accumulation of a great mass of descriptive cellular details in the latter half of the nineteenth century. These included the preservation of cell structure, known as fixation by treating cells with various chemicals (for example, alcohol, formaldehyde, and acetic acid), and the use of more refined sectioning techniques and straining methods.

The relatively recent application of homogenization and centrifugation techniques for isolating the various cell structures in appreciable quantities has been responsible for significant progress during the past decade in the study of cells. The disruption of a large mass of similar cells (for example, liver) by various homogenization techniques (including the use

---

[1] The meter, centimeter, millimeter, micron, and angstrom are units of the metric system of measures used internationally in science in contrast to yards, feet, and inches of the British system of units.

1 meter (m) = 39.37 inches = 3.28 feet.
1 centimeter (cm) = 1/100 m = .39 inches = 1/2.5 inches.
1 millimeter (mm) = 1/1000 m = 1/10 cm = .039 inches = 1/25 inches.
1 micron (μ) = 1/1000 mm = .000039 inches = 10^{-4} cm
  3.9×10^{-5} inches = 1/25,000 inches.
1 millimicron (mμ) = 1/1000 μ = 10^{-7} cm =
  3.9×10^{-8} inches = 1/25,000,000 inches.
1 angstrom unit (Å) = 1/10 mμ = 10^{-8} cm =
  3.9×10^{-9} inches = 1/250,000,000 inches.

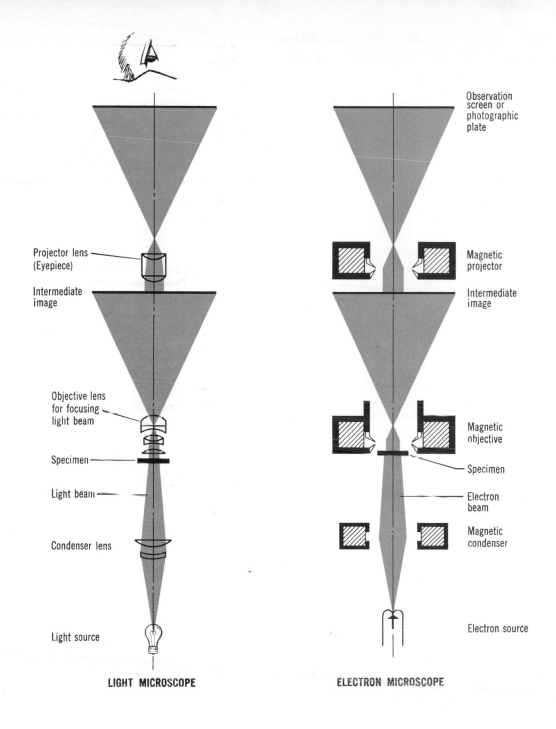

LIGHT MICROSCOPE

Projector lens (Eyepiece)

Intermediate image

Objective lens for focusing light beam

Specimen

Light beam

Condenser lens

Light source

ELECTRON MICROSCOPE

Observation screen or photographic plate

Magnetic projector

Intermediate image

Magnetic objective

Specimen

Electron beam

Magnetic condenser

Electron source

Figure 4-1. Schematic representation comparing the light microscope and electron microscope.

Figure 4-2. An RCA electron microscope. A microscopist is shown changing photographic plates in the instrument's camera located below the fluorescent viewing screen.

of the Waring blendor), followed by centrifugation of the homogenate at different speeds for given time intervals, results in the separation of the various cell components in relatively pure form and high yields. For instance, exposure of the liver homogenate to a low centrifugal force for a short period results in the deposition of the heaviest components, namely the unbroken cells and cell debris. Further centrifugation of the remaining suspension at a higher speed, and therefore at a higher centrifugal force, removes the next heaviest components, the cell nuclei (p. 49) as shown in Figure 4-3. Progressively higher centrifugal forces remove correspondingly lighter and smaller cell components.

This procedure, known as *differential centrifugation,* can furnish relatively large quantities of isolated cell constituents, thus making them available for subsequent analysis in terms of chemical composition and the metabolic re-

actions which they mediate. This approach together with that of electron microscopy of cell components and intact cells is opening up new vistas in our knowledge of the relationship of structure to function. The foregoing methods and others, including X-ray diffraction analysis and additional techniques employed by the physicist and chemist, have also contributed valuable information concerning the composition and structure of proteins and nucleic acids. They are also important procedures for eventually unveiling the means by which the nucleic acids control the various cell characteristics as well as the transmission of traits from one cell generation to another.

Certain physical and chemical agents have also served as powerful tools in the investigation of cells. X-rays, ultraviolet rays, atomic irradiation, and specific chemicals that induce changes in the structure of nucleic acids are used to modify the biochemical and hereditary patterns of cells.

The Modern Cell Theory

The seemingly simple but all-important concept that the cell is the unit of life is the culmination of centuries of study and research by numerous investigators in different parts of the world. It is formally called the *modern cell theory* and explicitly states that all forms of life—plant, animal, and microbial—are composed of cells (and their products) and arise only from preexisting cells. The cell theory is a fundamental cornerstone of biology upon which all the biological sciences are based.

Historical Background

The study of cell structure and function has experienced three distinct periods of progress. The *first period,* extending from the mid-seventeenth to the late nineteenth century, involved the early use of the light microscope. Observations of cells or remains of cells magnified by means of optical instruments (microscopes) were reported for the first time in the mid-seventeenth century. Robert Hooke, an English microscopist, in 1665 introduced the term *cell* in describing the honeycomb-like structure of cork and other plant tissues. A few years earlier (1656) in France Pierre Borel had reported microscopic studies of what probably were human red blood cells; and Marcello Malpighi, the discoverer of capillaries, apparently referred to cells when he spoke of "utricles" and "saccules" in 1661. Anton van Leeuwenhoek, a Dutch lens maker, was the first to observe single-celled organisms (1674).

Reports by numerous other microscopists over the years with progressively improved lenses confirmed and extended these initial observations. By the early nineteenth century a general pattern had emerged, confirmed by such men as Oken in Germany (1805), Lamarck (1809) and later Dutrochet (1824) in France, among others, who independently stated that all plants and animals are composed of cells. This generalization was finally widely accepted and firmly established as the cell theory through the independently published works of the German biologists, Mathias Jakob Schleiden and Theodor Schwann, in 1838-1839. Schleiden, a botanist, regarded the cell as the structural unit of all plants, a theory that Schwann as a zoologist applied to animals.

Meanwhile other important findings bearing on the nature of the cell were being made. A few years earlier (1831) Robert Brown in England had reported the discovery of a round distinct structure in cells, the *nucleus.* In 1839 Johannes Purkinje spoke of the living material of the cell as *protoplasm,* which Max Schultz in Germany some twenty years later called the physical basis of life. Schultz described the cell as a mass of nucleated protoplasm.

A major contribution to the cell theory was the principle advanced by Rudolph Virchow in 1858 that new cells arise by division from pre-existing cells—a conclusion that suggested an unbroken line of cell generations extending back into time to the very beginnings of life. The modern cell theory recognizes the cell as the common structural unit for all living things and which arises only from other living cells. It has inevitably directed our attention to the

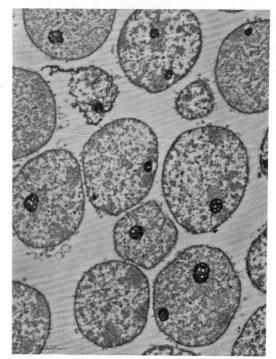

Figure 4-3. Nuclei isolated by differential centrifugation from a liver homogenate. Magnification 3172X. (*Courtesy of Dr. G. E. Palade, J. Cell Biol.*)

evolutionary implication that all cells and therefore all organisms have a common ancestry.

The remarkable achievements attained by biologists at the mid-nineteenth century are even more striking in view of the limited techniques available to them. They were severely handicapped in their microscope studies for lack of adequate slicing and staining techniques. For the most part their investigations were necessarily limited until that time to direct microscopic examination of single-celled organisms, thin membranes and scrapings of thick tissues.

The subsequently rapid development of preservation methods for cell structure (i.e., fixation) and improved tissue slicing and staining techniques resulted in a vast compilation of descriptive cellular details. By the close of the century virtually every feature of the fixed and stained cell that could be resolved by the light microscope had been described. Basic patterns of cell change during growth and multiplication were becoming increasingly clear. The significance at that time of the recently observed details of cell division and fertilization (the union of the nuclei of egg and sperm) in terms of heredity and evolution were also beginning to be recognized.

The second period of progress, which actually started before the end of the nineteenth century, was characterized by an experimental approach and by attempts to interpret cell structure in terms of function. Most of the early work at the experimental level involved studies of the development of fragmented and enucleated egg cells. The founding of the science of genetics in 1900 was rapidly followed by a correlation between the dark-staining chromatin material in the nucleus (which is recognized as the chromosomes during cell division) and genetic behavior. At the experimental level it soon involved investigations of various techniques in modifying chromosome structure and environment and the subsequent effects on inheritance.

The third distinct period of the study of cell structure and function was launched around 1920 and is currently in progress. It is an extension of the previous experimental period but with emphasis on the function of cell components at the molecular level. This biochemical and biophysical approach together with the use of modern instrumentation, such as the electron microscope and high speed precision centrifuges, has led to a remarkable increase in our knowledge of the structure and function of the cells.

CELL STRUCTURE

Protoplasm and Protoplast

The term protoplasm has conveniently served to designate an important concept during an earlier and rapidly developing phase in the history of biology. Its introduction by Purkinje in 1839 to denote the living material of the cell was followed by its wide adoption as the name for the "physical substance of life." For many years the concept of protoplasm implied that the cell was constructed of a complex and fundamental living substance which was essentially similar in all living things. With further investigation it came to be regarded as a mixture of various materials, a dispersion of many substances in many conditions. Detailed studies classically described the physical states that it assumed at various times in different cells and parts of cells as granular (dispersed granules in a semifluid mass), alveolar (bubble-like), and fibrillar (dispersed fibers in a semifluid mass).

The rapid progress of the last twenty-five years in analyzing ultracellular structure in terms of modern biochemistry and biophysics has made the conceptual term protoplasm, as originally introduced, somewhat archaic. The unit of life is the cell, and we can no longer strictly regard it as being made up simply of a living substance protoplasm. Instead, it consists of a highly integrated organization of diverse, complex subcellular structures of intricate chemical composition – including salts, water, proteins, nucleic acids, fats, carbohydrates, and other materials. These substances, by virtue of their involved organization and interrelationships, are collectively responsible for the characteristics of life. By analogy an airplane is obviously not composed of a fundamental aircraft substance; it is an intricate organization of specialized structures composed of a variety of metals, alloys, rubber, plastics, and numerous other materials put together into highly complex and specialized structures which collectively add up to a typical flying machine.

Aside from its historical significance, the term protoplasm today serves as a convenient way of loosely referring to the living contents of the cell. A related word has come into common usage, the protoplast, more or less synonymous with the cell, to designate the collective organization of the intact living cell.

Overall View of the Cell

All cells are generally observed to be in one of two general states. They are either undergoing a regular kind of division to form two daughter cells, and are therefore in the *dividing state*, or alternatively they are not experiencing cellular division and are spoken of as being in the *nondividing or "resting" state*. The latter term is not meant to imply that the cell is metabolically inactive, inert, or dormant; it is simply used to indicate that the cell is not undergoing division.

Cells in the nondividing state have a number of features in common. Although different cells from different sources may vary tremendously in size and general appearance, certain basic subcellular structures performing characteristic functions are almost universally present. During regular cell division, or *mitosis*, described later in the chapter, some of these structures undergo a typical cycle of changes which have revealed important aspects of their make-up and function.

The nondividing cell, whether it exists singly as in unicellular organisms, or in groups as in multicellular organisms, is seen under the microscope to be a definite and delineated three-dimensional mass of protoplasm (Figure 4-4). It is surrounded by a specialized, thin protoplasmic envelope called the *cell membrane* and contains a small spherical structure, the *nucleus*.

The protoplasm of the cell other than the nucleus is conveniently called the *cytoplasm*. The cytoplasm often appears granular, and, upon close microscopic examination in the fixed and stained condition, these granules are seen to be definitive subcellular structures. Recent studies with the electron microscope have revealed a number of important details about their ultrastructure.

The cell and its components are three-dimensional entities having parameters of length, breadth, and depth. Microscopic observations are usually made at one particular focal plane at any one time, tending to give the false impression that cells and subcellular components are essentially flat with dimensions only of length and width. In numerous cases the depth of the cell (and its subcellular structures) actually equals or exceeds its width.

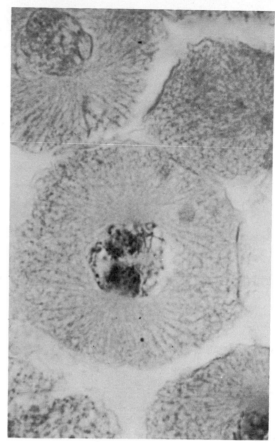

Figure 4-4. A whitefish embryo cell photographed through a light microscope. The nucleus with its dark-staining contents is suspended within the granular cytoplasm. *(Courtesy of Upjohn Co.)*

Detailed View of the Nondividing Cell: Structures Common to all Cells

THE NUCLEUS. The typical nucleus (of a nondividing cell), when seen under the light microscope, without resorting to fixing and staining procedures, appears to be a barely discernible, pale, spherical or oval body with no obvious internal detail suspended in the surrounding cytoplasm. This fact was originally noted in 1831 by Robert Brown, discoverer of the nucleus. In fixed- and stained-cell preparations, however, the nucleus stands out as the most prominent structure of the cell. During cell division the refractivity of the nucleus is modified, making it possible to observe nuclear changes without necessarily resorting to fixing and staining procedures.

The nondividing nucleus is bounded by a delicate but clearly defined membrane, the *nuclear membrane*, which sets it off from the surrounding cytoplasm and possesses many of the properties of the corresponding cell membrane discussed later. Recent electron-microscope studies show that the nuclear membrane is double and porous. In addition to a clear, nonstaining, viscous fluid, the *nuclear sap*, about which little is known, the nucleus possesses one or more refractive spherical bodies, the *nucleoli* (singular: *nucleolus*). Of great importance, the nondividing nucleus is seen to contain an organization of twisted and intermingled fine threads known as the *chromatin material*, without doubt the most significant structure of the cell, for, as we shall soon see, these are the chromosomes that determine the activities and inheritance of the cell.

The chromatin material is deeply stained by a number of standard dyes, a phenomenon that quickly brought it to the attention of earlier investigators. Several dyes show a strong tendency to react with the nucleic acids. The nucleic acids are often found combined to particular proteins in nature and are therefore collectively called *nucleoproteins*. By means of suitable staining procedures, the presence of nucleoproteins in the nuclei of animal cells was already established toward the end of the nineteenth century.

By the mid-1920's the use of a specific staining procedure known as the *Feulgen reaction* (employing the dye fuchsin) demonstrated that the chromatin material in the nucleus of the resting animal cell contained one of the two main types of naturally occurring nucleic acids, namely deoxyribonucleic acid (or DNA). The other nucleic acid, known as ribonucleic acid (or RNA), is also found in the nucleus as well as in the cytoplasm. There are many different kinds of DNA and RNA. The finding that plant cells also contained DNA in their chromatin network was significant because it had previously been believed that plant cells differed from animal cells in having only RNA in their nuclei. It is now established that RNA is present in the nondividing nucleus and the cytoplasm of all cells, whereas DNA is confined largely to the chromatin material (or chromosomes). Recent studies have shown the presence of small quantities of DNA in several cytoplasmic structures such as mitochondria, chloroplasts, and centrioles described in later sections of this chapter.

The nucleus is of prime importance in determining the structure and functioning of the cell. The all-important deoxyribonucleic acids, almost exclusively contained in the nucleus, serve as the ultimate master-control center for all cellular activities, and are also responsible for transmission of the cell characteristics from one generation to another. A cell whose nucleus has been removed (by microsurgical techniques) runs an inevitable downhill course and within a short time deteriorates and perishes.

Current evidence indicates that just prior to the start of cell division, the amount of DNA of the chromatin material is doubled. Cell division or mitosis itself involves the regular reassembling of the chromatin material into pairs of duplicate short rod-like bodies, or *chromosomes*, and their equal and precise distribution in a regular manner between the nuclei of the two daughter cells that subsequently form.

We know virtually nothing about the role of the nucleoli other than that they are somehow involved in cell division. Their staining properties indicate a rich concentration of RNA.

There are certain exceptions to the foregoing description of the nondividing nucleus as a clearly defined cellular component containing the highly complex exclusive deoxyribonucleoproteins. Until recently it was believed that the blue-green algae, a lower form of plant life, as well as bacteria did not display a definite nucleus. Instead the chromatin material appeared to be diffusely distributed through the cytoplasm, presumably reflecting a primitive kind of nucleus. The latest evidence, however,

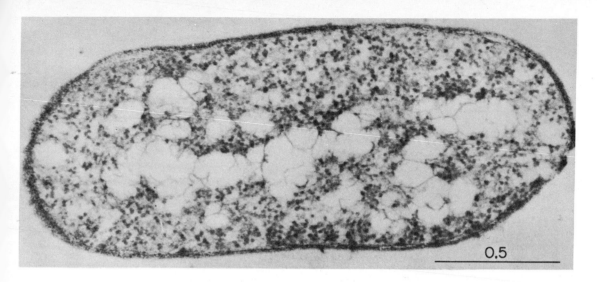

Figure 4-5. Electron micrograph of the bacterium *Escherichia coli* illustrating the relatively clear nuclear regions containing a dispersed network of fibers. The comparatively uniform cytoplasm displays conspicuous particles of variable size, shape, and density. Magnification 18,500X. (*Courtesy of Dr. S. F. Conti, J. Bact.*)

based on newer methods of preparation of cells for microscopic examination, indicates definite nuclear regions (but lacking nuclear membranes) with the properties expected of nuclei in all such cells thus far observed (Figure 4-5).

By contrast the mature red blood cells of humans and certain cells involved in the transport of materials in higher plants (*sieve tube cells*, p. 96) lack a nucleus, although they all contained this important structure during their early development.

There are also exceptions to the generalized picture of each cell containing a single nucleus. Certain algae, a number of fungi and molds, and some lower animals have more than one nucleus associated with their compartments of cytoplasm. While the practice has been to consider these multinucleate compartments of protoplasm as noncellular, the structural and functional characteristics of the cytoplasm and nuclear components and the relationships between them are similar to that of typical cells.

THE CYTOPLASM. The term cytoplasm is conveniently used to designate the protoplasm of the cell other than the nucleus. Until recently

it has also served to cloak our ignorance of this amazingly complex and highly organized ultrastructure which comprises the internal environment and machinery of the cell. At one time cytoplasm was conceived to be comparable to a minute bag of water containing a dispersion of freely interacting molecules and particles of all sizes and shapes. At a later period it was recognized not as a simple material but as a ground substance or matrix consisting principally of proteins in a watery medium plus several kinds of suspended and clearly delineated subcellular structures. = Cytoplasm

Recently, however, primarily as a result of studies with the electron microscope, the cytoplasmic ground substance in plant and animal cells has been shown to be largely organized into a fine ultrastructure of submicroscopic protein fibers arranged in parallel double-membrane structures collectively known as the *endoplasmic reticulum*. Such a picture of an organized cytoplasmic ultrastructure is entirely consistent with the mechanical properties displayed by cytoplasm such as elasticity, contractility, and, on occa-

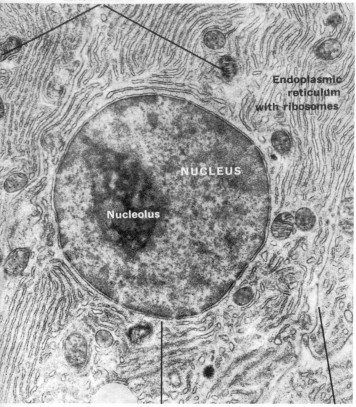

Mitochondria

Endoplasmic reticulum with ribosomes

NUCLEUS

Nucleolus

Nuclear membrane with pores   Cell membrane

Figure 4-6. Electron micrograph of a portion of a bat pancreas cell showing several general cellular structures. Magnification 28,400X. *(Courtesy of D. W. Fawcett, Scient. Amer.)*

sion, rigidity. The term cytoplasm is now usually taken to include not only the ground substance organized into the endoplasmic reticulum system, but also any other cellular structures and inclusions outside the nucleus including the *Golgi apparatus*, *cell membrane*, *mitochondria*, *lysosomes*, the *centrosome*, *plastids*, and certain *other inclusions* described below (Figures 4-6 and 4-7).

The Endoplasmic Reticulum and the Ribosomes. The membranes of the endoplasmic reticulum provide a large internal surface and form a system of interconnected canals. They have a "rough" appearance when their outer surfaces are studded with tiny dense ribonucleic acid-rich particles called *ribosomes*,

which consist of 60 per cent ribonucleic acid (RNA) and 40 per cent protein. In other cells the ribosomes lie free in the cytoplasm and are absent from the endoplasmic reticulum accounting for the "smooth" appearance of this structure. Bacteria apparently do not possess an endoplasmic reticulum. Their ribosomes are entirely free in the cytoplasm.

Suitable disruption of liver cells, for example, produces a homogenate consisting of cell debris, nuclei, smaller definite structures known as *mitochondria*, the still smaller ribosome particles, and an aqueous solution containing a variety of molecules. The various particulate subcellular components can be separated in relatively pure form and in appreciable quantities by the previously mentioned method of differential centrifugation. Ribosomes as relatively tiny particles, ranging from about 0.06 to 0.2 μ in diameter, are collected usually as a pellet from a cell-free homogenate by centrifuging first at 10,000 times the force of gravity (10,000 × g) to remove the heavier structural components (e.g., mitochondria) followed by exposure in a high speed or ultracentrifuge to a centrifugal force of 100,000 × g for approximately an hour or so. Actually the ribosomal pellet collected at the bottom of the centrifuge tube by this high-speed spinning may be somewhat heterogeneous depending upon the cells from which it is prepared. The pellet may consist not only of free ribosomes but of small membranous fragments of the endoplasmic reticulum as well, some with ribosome particles on their surfaces. The term "microsome" (or small particle fraction) is often applied to this pellet, but is used in a strictly operational sense to designate the foregoing preparation of small particles and fragments.

Recent biochemical investigations have demonstrated that the ribosomes (very likely in clusters called *polyribosomes*) play an important role in the synthesis of proteins (Chapter 11). This fits in well with the evidence that the endoplasmic reticulum, which has been observed in nearly all animal cells examined thus far (except in the mature red blood cell), appears to be most highly developed in cells actively synthesizing protein for secretion. The cells of the pancreas, which produce large quantities of digestive enzymes (i.e., proteins), have a rich concentration of the ribonucleoprotein particles on the membrane surfaces of the endoplasmic reticulum. The RNA classically detected in the cytoplasm of such cells by staining procedures can be attributed largely to that of the endoplasmic reticulum. This system of membranes has also been implicated in striated muscle contraction and in the synthesis of the important fatty-like substance, cholesterol, a biologically important compound belonging to the chemical group known as steroids found in most cells (Chapter 7). It is conceivable that the endoplasmic reticulum, by virtue of its large membrane surface, may also provide the basic structure for orientation of numerous physical and chemical systems (e.g., enzymes) within the cytoplasm itself.

The Golgi Apparatus. The Golgi apparatus is a cytoplasmic structure that takes on various shapes and forms. At times it is observed as a distinct collection of lobed, droplet-like bodies in the vicinity of the nucleus, and at other times as a continuous filamentous network (Figure 4-7). Its shape varies from cell to cell and in secretory cells changes with secretory activity. It is seemingly dispersed during cell division and is subsequently reconstituted in the daughter cells. Electron-microscopy studies have revealed the fine structure of the Golgi apparatus to consist of a series of closely spaced smooth-contoured membranes and a variable number of small vacuoles or vesicles. Although the Golgi apparatus appears to be continuous with the endoplasmic reticulum, its precise relationship to the endoplasmic reticulum is still under active investigation. Its chemical composition, determined largely by staining reactions observed under the microscope, includes fats, proteins, and carbohydrates.

The Golgi apparatus was discovered by Camillo Golgi in 1898. Until recently it had been the subject of an intermittent contro-

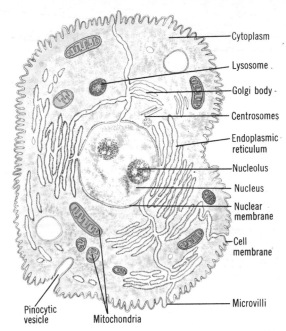

Figure 4-7. Composite representation of a "typical" animal cell illustrating various cellular structures as seen by means of the electron microscope. *(Adapted from Scient. Amer.)*

versy as to whether it is in reality an artifact created by fixation and staining procedures, or a specialized cytoplasmic structure performing specialized functions. The use of the electron microscope and other techniques have clearly established it to be a cell structure. The cyclic physical changes that the Golgi apparatus of glandular cells undergoes during secretion strongly suggest a role in the packaging of certain proteins into the secretory granules. Its role in other cells is not understood—of particular interest would be elucidation of its role in nerve cells where it is extremely highly developed. At one time the Golgi apparatus was regarded as a cellular characteristic of animals and primitive plants only, but it is now known to occur in higher plant cells as well. There is no evidence, however, for its presence in bacteria and blue-green algae. It should be noted that bacteria and blue-green algae fail to show the characteristic nucleus, mitochondria, endoplasmic endothelium, or Golgi apparatus observed in the cells of higher plants and animals.

Cell Membrane. All cells are bounded at their outer surface by a specialized cytoplasmic layer, the *cell membrane*, so exceedingly thin and delicate that it is not visible with even the best light microscope. In fact, at one time its existence was seriously challenged by a number of biologists.

That the cell membrane is a definite, discrete, and essential entity of the cell is indicated by several lines of independent evidence. First, its presence readily accounts for the fact that only certain substances can freely enter or leave the cell from a surrounding solution, a selective ability known as *semipermeability* or *differential permeability*. A semipermeable membrane is permeable to certain substances but relatively less so, or not at all, to others. Semipermeability has been elegantly demonstrated by means of microsurgical experiments. A particular dye in solution, such as phenol red, when introduced directly into the cytoplasm by means of special microinjection instruments, readily distributes itself through the cytoplasm but cannot pass out of the cell because it is presumably held back by the cell membrane. Second, minor tearing or rupturing of the cell surface is quickly and spontaneously repaired by the cell, whereas more drastic injury to the cell membrane may result in the rapid disintegration of the entire cell. Third, the elastic quality of the membrane is demonstrated by the ability to restore its former position after being plucked or indented with a microinstrument. Finally, electron microscopy has directly established that the cell membrane exists as a definite boundary (Figure 4-8) to the cytoplasm of the cell, and that it is possibly continuous with the endoplasmic reticulum.

Studies with the electron microscope also have demonstrated that the cell membrane is frequently convoluted, displaying many small outfoldings (called *microvilli*) and inpocketings or invaginations. The convoluted nature of the cell membrane may be quite important in accounting for the adhesion of cells to each other by a dovetailing effect, and in presenting

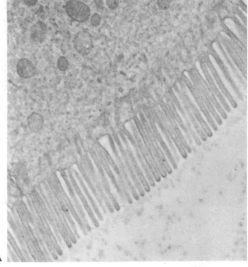

A

B

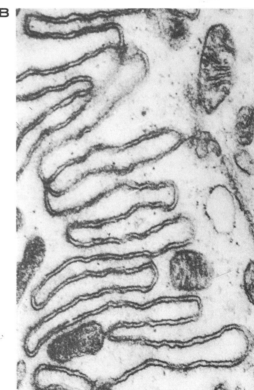

Figure 4-8. Electron micrographs showing (A) microvilli of human intestinal epithelial cells, magnification 18,000X (*courtesy of Dr. A. L. Brown, J. Cell Biol.*); and (B) convolutions of cell membranes of two adjacent columnar epithelial cells, magnification 20,500X (*courtesy of Dr. D. W. Fawcett, Yale Univ. Press.*)

a large surface contact between cells thus facilitating the exchange of materials between them. At times the inpocketings or invaginations which are filled with fluid external to the cell may pinch off internally into the surrounding cytoplasm to form small fluid-containing vacuoles or vesicles (with diameters ranging down to 0.01 μ), a process known as *pinocytosis*. Pinocytic vacuoles as a rule contain no visible particles and may be carried to other regions of the cytoplasm (Figure 4-7). The process of pinocytosis thus serves as a means of ingesting fluid and dissolved substances from the external environment of the cell.

Some biologists view the cell membrane as an altered and uniquely oriented layer of cytoplasm, somewhat denser and less fluid than the main body of cytoplasm in the cell—the result of being at a surface between different phases of matter. They consider it to be analogous, for example, to the decreased fluidity and high surface tension exhibited at the surface of water droplets. The nuclear membrane as well as other protoplasmic membranes associated with subcellular structures (e.g., mitochondrial and plastid membranes) would also be regarded from this viewpoint as similar manifestations of physically modified protoplasmic layers with special properties similar to those seen in the cell membrane.

Despite numerous investigations the intrinsic structure of the cell membrane is still obscure. The presence of fatty substances and proteins as the fundamental building blocks of the cell membrane is suggested by the destruction of the membrane when treated with any substances that dissolve or digest fats and proteins. It seems quite possible that the fat and protein molecules are interspersed with each other. On the basis of various studies the cell membrane is pictured to be about 100 to 200 Å thick and essentially composed of several layers of protein and fat molecules.

Mitochondria Another important component of the cytoplasm of living cells includes the highly specialized and organized bodies, the *mitochondria* (singular: *mitochondrion*).

These cytoplasmic structures carry out a variety of integrated chemical reactions including those that supply most of the useful energy for the cell's vital activities. For this reason the mitochondria have been aptly nicknamed the "powerhouses" of the cell.

Mitochondria were first clearly described at the beginning of the century. Until the 1940's their principal distinguishing feature was the fact that as cytoplasmic granules they were uniquely stained by the dye Janus green. Since that time, largely as the result of electron microscopy and innumerable biochemical studies, we have gained a vast insight into the architecture and workings of mitochondria. Although the appearance and distribution of mitochondria in the cytoplasm may vary in different types of cells and within the same cell under different conditions, they are generally spherical or rod-shaped. Mitochondria are barely visible under the light microscope and at times may be so small that they can only be seen under the electron microscope. They are much larger than ribosomes, their size as spheres ranging from 0.5 to 3 μ in diameter (compared to the ribosomal diameter of 0.06 to 0.2 μ).

Mitochondria change in size and shape depending on the chemical and physical state of their surroundings, cell type, age, their own chemical activity and the activity of the cell. They are present in greater numbers in the cytoplasm of metabolically active cells, being very plentiful, for example, in heart muscle and secretory cells. They are absent in the mature red blood cell, although they are present prior to the cell's maturation. Mitochondria tend to slowly disappear in senescent cells, and during cell division may rearrange and aggregate themselves in particular regions of the cell. At times they appear to fuse with each other; and on other occasions they have also been shown to increase in number by simply pinching in two.

A striking feature of mitochondria in the living cell is their constant and ceaseless motion. The phenomenon is attributed not to the movement of the mitochondria under their own power, but rather to the impacts they receive from the moving molecules and particles of the surrounding cytoplasm (see Brownian movement, Chapter 6), and to the streaming activity of cytoplasm which is often observable in metabolically active cells.

Electron-microscopic examination of isolated mitochondria, or mitochondria within intact animal and plant cells, shows that each is bounded by a double membrane whose inner layer is usually folded into a characteristic system of ridges or *cristae* extending well into the mitochondrion itself. (Figure 4-9). In addition to providing a large surface area the folded membrane allows for expansion or swelling of mitochondria under different metabolic and environmental conditions. The semipermeable properties of the mitochondrial membrane are similar to those of other protoplasmic membranes such as the cell membrane and nuclear membrane in permitting some substances but not others to pass through.

Modern biochemical studies of isolated mitochondria have revealed a fundamental role of these structures in providing most of the energy used by the animal and plant cell. This function as the "powerhouse" of the cell is accomplished by a sequence of self-directed enzymatic steps, collectively called *aerobic respiration*, in which the bulk of the energy of foodstuffs is released in a form useful to the cell (Chapter 8). The fact that isolated mitochondria can still perform these reactions with such a high efficiency suggests that their internal organization has not been radically disturbed.

We know that sequences of other biochemical steps including those concerned with the breakdown of fats also occur in the mitochondria. Physical disruption of mitochondria by various procedures (e.g., bursting them as we do red blood cells by suspending them in water, or subjecting them to intense high-frequency sound waves) has demonstrated that they possess a large array of enzymes. Some are soluble whereas others are intimately bound to the internal membranous mitochondrial structure. Chemical analysis of isolated liver mitochondria reveals that they are rich in fat and protein, accounting for about 25 per cent of that found in the whole cell. In addition they contain appreciable quantities of RNA. More recently they have also been shown to contain small quantities of DNA.

Lysosomes. The mid-1950's witnessed the discovery of a new group of membranous subcellular particles of about the same size as small mitochondria called *lysosomes*. They were first identified in rat liver and have since been shown to occur in many other types of animal cells. Lysosomes are membranous-bounded structures or sacs (with no inter-

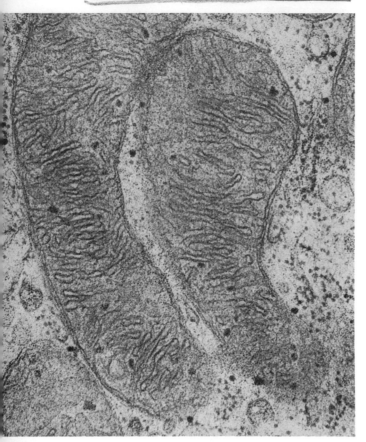

Figure 4-9. Electron micrograph of mitochondria containing numerous cristae in a bullfrog stomach secretory cell. Magnification 62,320X. *(Courtesy of Dr. A. W. Sedar, J. Biophys. Biochem. Cytol.)*

nal cristae) containing a host of hydrolytic enzymes (Chapter 7) that catalyze the digestion of most of the organic constituents of the living cell such as proteins, nucleic acids, certain carbohydrates, and possibly fats. Disruption of the lysosomal membrane and subsequent release of the digestive enzymes lead to a rapid dissolution of the cell. Lysosomes are believed to function normally in various ways including digestion of food materials stored within cells, breakdown of foreign particles by white blood cells, dissolution of the structures surrounding the egg cell in the course of fertilization by sperm, bone-digesting activity of certain cells, and in the death and destruction of aged cells. Although up to the present time there are no clear indications of lysosomes in plants, actually only a little work has been done in the investigation of these structures in plant cells.

Characteristics of Animal Cells, Plant Cells, and Protists

By virtue of their obvious differences in gross organization and function, we can easily distinguish most higher animals from plants. Animals are made up of certain characteristically organized systems (e.g., digestive, circulatory, nervous, and other systems), are usually capable of movement under their own power, and are completely dependent on preformed organic substances for their energy and carbon supply, to name but a few of their more obvious characteristics. Higher plants contain the green pigment chlorophyll, which uniquely permits them to carry on photosynthesis, are usually immobile, and consist of their own characteristically organized systems.

In the long run it is not of major importance whether we classify organisms as plants, animals, or otherwise. The distinction is in reality a concept existing in the minds of biologists. An appreciable number of unicellular organisms exhibit characteristics of both plants and animals. Several biologists classify them as plants whereas others place the very same organisms in the animal kingdom. Still others have been inclined to regard all unicellular organisms as neither plant nor animal but as a separate group called protists. It is important to recognize the natural relationships that exist among all organisms. The realization by biologists that all living things are fundamentally alike, and therefore very probably related to each other is of great significance. That all living things can be classified on the basis of their structural and functional characteristics into two or three broad groups known as plants, animals, and protists implies that they evolved from a common primitive ancestor (perhaps a protist) at some time in the distant past. The evidence suggests that at the lower level in the organization of living things (as represented by certain unicellular organisms), a sharp differentiation between plants and animals has not yet occurred. The two separate lines of organisms that we call plants and animals may well have arisen in the course of evolution from a now extinct ancient protist bearing a resemblance to certain present-day species. Not only does this view support the basic concept of a common unity among all organisms, but it points to the different lines of evolution that life has taken in the course of time.

What are the specialized features at the cellular level that distinguish plants from animals? We know that the cell, as the fundamental biological unit of structure and function consists essentially of a nucleus (or several nuclear regions as in certain lower forms) which controls its activities, cytoplasm (including endoplasmic reticulum, ribosomes, and mitochondria) which contains its complex chemical machinery, and a cell membrane which determines the exchange of materials with the surrounding cells or environment. There are, however, certain cellular features that serve as the basis for classifying organisms in either the plant or animal kingdom. These particular characteristics (described below) at the cellular level are reflected ultimately in the gross differences exhibited by the two groups at the level of the whole organism.

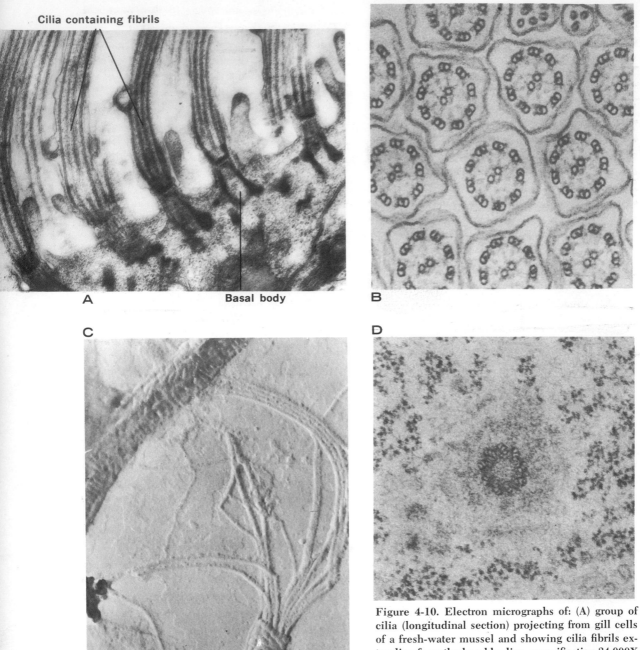

Cilia containing fibrils

A

Basal body

B

C

D

Figure 4-10. Electron micrographs of: (A) group of cilia (longitudinal section) projecting from gill cells of a fresh-water mussel and showing cilia fibrils extending from the basal bodies, magnification 34,000X (*courtesy of Dr. P. Satir, Scient. Amer.*); (B) cross-sectional view of cilia illustrating that each cilium has ten pairs of fibrils, magnification 90,000X (*courtesy of P. Satir, Scient. Amer.*); (C) disrupted tip of human sperm tail showing several fibrils (*courtesy of Upjohn Co.*); and (D) cross-sectional view of centriole of rat liver embryonic cell, magnification 64,000X (*courtesy of Dr. K. R. Porter*).

Unique Features of the Animal Cell

THE CENTROSOME (AND CILIA AND FLAGELLA). Virtually all animal cells and a number of lower or primitive plant cells contain a unique structure in the cytoplasm called the *centrosome*. In the resting cell it usually is present near the nucleus as a small clear region with radiating aster-like fibers and one or two deeply staining granules at its center called the *centrioles* (Figure 4-7). The cells of higher plants have no centrosome but instead display two small clear areas during cell division called the *polar caps* (p. 68) which apparently carry on the same function as the centrosome during cell division.

The centrosome, in addition to its primary role in cell division as described later in the chapter, somehow controls the formation and activity of *cilia* and *flagella*, slender filamentous cytoplasmic structures projecting from the external surface of the cell membrane of certain cells. Cilia are relatively short protoplasmic projections usually present in large quantity, whereas flagella are considerably longer and generally fewer in number. Certain unicellular organisms (e.g., *Paramecium*, described in the next chapter) possess large numbers of rhythmically beating coordinated cilia or flagella ranging into the hundreds which are responsible for the motility of these single-celled forms. Cells such as those lining the inner surface of the human windpipe also have large quantities of active cilia. Their coordinated beating movement gives rise to currents of fluid and air at the outer cell surface and thus propels out any minute foreign bodies that might gain entrance to the windpipe. Flagella are also found among many unicellular organisms (e.g., certain bacteria) and the great majority of sperm cells of plants and animals. Their whip-like action accounts for the motility of these cells.

The extraordinary resolving power of the electron microscope has shown that the cilia and the flagella consist in part of a bundle of ten pairs of fibrils (a circle of nine pairs about a single central pair) extending into a structure within the cytoplasm called the *basal body*, which is strikingly similar if not identical to a centriole (Figure 4-10). For example, the basal body of the flagellum of a sperm cell has actually been identified as one of the two centrioles of the cell.

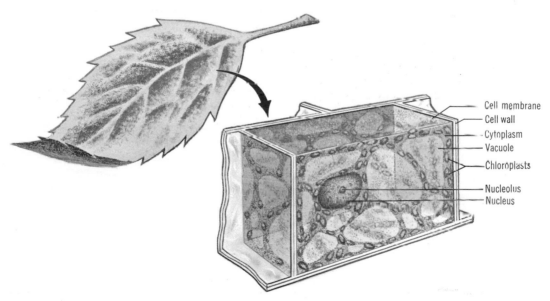

Figure 4-11. Representation of a "typical" plant cell showing various structures.

Cell membrane
Cell wall
Cytoplasm
Vacuole
Chloroplasts
Nucleolus
Nucleus

Unique Features of the Plant Cell

THE CELL WALL. The cell wall is the most distinguishing characteristic of the plant cell. It is a moderately rigid envelope of inanimate material (external to the cell membrane) which entirely surrounds each of the protoplasts (Figure 4-11). Although it is synthesized and secreted by the cytoplasm of the plant cell, strictly speaking the cell wall is not a cellular component but an extracellular deposition. In most green plants it is primarily composed of a complex carbohydrate called *cellulose* (Chapter 7). Depending on the particular plant cells the cell wall contains in addition to cellulose, varying amounts of other substances including salts, lignin (a complex organic material responsible for the characteristic "woody" property of some plants), and certain waterproof fatty-like substances such as *waxes* and *suberin* (Chapter 7).

The cell wall varies considerably in thickness depending on the particular plant tissue and the conditions of growth. In mature plant cells it usually consists of three layers and is always much thicker than the underlying cell membrane. Unlike the cell membrane it is per-

Figure 4-12. Electron micrograph revealing the numerous cellular fibers composing the cell wall of an algal cell. Magnification 17,250X. (Courtesy of Dr. R. D. Preston.)

meable to most molecules and exercises no control in permitting the passage of materials in and out of the cell. In effect the cell wall is a kind of plant skeleton serving to protect, support, and maintain the individual cell as well as the whole plant. It is believed that strands of cytoplasm permeate the cell walls, thus providing a continuous protoplasmic connecting system to adjoining cells and therefore to the different parts of the plant. The presence in bacteria and fungi of a definite cell-wall structure, although of an apparently different composition from that of higher plant cells, has been used by some biologists as a major criterion for designating these organisms as plants. Similarly the appearance of a cell wall in only one stage of the complex life cycle of the slime molds (Chapter 15) has served as a basis for classifying them in the plant kingdom.

Many animal cells also deposit extracellular material around the exterior surfaces of their cell membranes. These deposits, which do not contain cellulose or wax, vary considerably in composition and are referred to as *interstitial substances*. Unlike the plant cell wall they have no definite organization, and they fail to create the effect of a distinctly delineated wall-like structure. In most animal tissues the interstitial substance acts as a cement holding the cells together. It expands with the swelling cell, offering little or no protection against the bursting of the protoplast; and in water loss it conforms to the shape of the shrinking cell. By contrast the cell walls of higher plants, bacteria, and fungi more or less maintain their shape and size, despite changes in volume of the protoplast due to changes in water content, thus preventing bursting of the protoplast.

In bone the interstitial substance, which is made up largely of an amorphous matrix of inorganic calcium salts together with organic materials secreted by the bone cells, represents the bulk of the tissue. In other tissues such as cartilage, insect skin, mammalian skin, and scar tissue the interstitial substance varies widely in composition and properties. In certain single-celled animals the secreted matrix is in the form of protective tough elastic layer called a *pellicle.*

PLASTIDS. These are unique and discrete cytoplasmic structures found in the cells of higher plants and certain unicellular organisms but not in the cells of higher animals. Although their size, shape, and color may show considerable variation depending on the particular tissue, organism, and growing conditions, they most often occur as spherical or disc-like bodies lying free in the cytoplasm.

Plastids are generally grouped into two broad classes: the colorless *leucoplasts* and the pigmented *chromoplasts.* Leucoplasts are often found in plant tissues not exposed to light and are involved in forming and storing starch granules or oil droplets. The most important and most prevalent kind of chromoplasts occurring in plant cells are the so-called *chloroplasts* (Figures 4-11 and 4-13), which contain the green pigment *chlorophyll* that is responsible for the green color of plants. The chloroplasts, like most other plastids, are usually carried along in the flow of streaming cytoplasm within the cell, and range in size from about 3 to 7 μ. Several lower plant forms such as the green algae may have a single large and uniquely shaped chloroplast in each of their cells, whereas the more primitive blue-green algae lack a definite chloroplast structure, their chlorophyll being dispersed throughout the cytoplasm. Other kinds of chromoplasts often found in fruits and flowers contain pigments other than chlorophyll, frequently accounting for the characteristic colors of these tissues.

That the various plastids are related to each other is seen by the transformation that occurs from one type to another. Exposure to sunlight of colorless plant tissue such as roots or potato tuber cells causes them to turn green because of the formation of chlorophyll in their leucoplasts. The latter are thus transformed into functioning chloroplasts. Although chloroplasts and other plastids multiply by simple division, which is not necessarily correlated with cell division, the nature of the origin of plastids from the cytoplasm is still unknown. Some in-

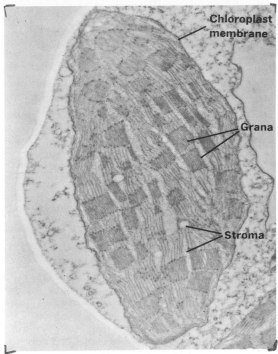

Figure 4-13. Electron micrograph of a chloroplast in a corn plant cell. Magnification 40,000X. *(Courtesy of Dr. A. E. Vatter, Scient. Amer.)*

vestigators consider them to be closely related to mitochondria in view of their relative similarity in chemical composition and enzyme make-up. Chloroplasts resemble mitochondria in their rich protein and fat composition, in their relatively low but definite DNA content, and to a lesser extent in their enzyme constitution. The virtual absence of ribonucleic acid in chloroplasts, however, is in sharp contrast to the rich amounts present in mitochondria (and ribosomes).

Chlorophyll occurs in most higher plants in the form of two green pigments slightly different in chemical structure and designated as chlorophylls *a* and *b* (Chapter 7). They are exclusively located in the chloroplasts (except for the primitive blue-green algae) and are necessary for the all-important process of photosynthesis, whereby the energy of sunlight is transformed into the energy locked in the

Figure 4-14. Electron micrograph of spinach quanto-somes, the highly ordered array of presumed photo-synthetic units in the laminations of grana. Magnification 63,000X. *(Courtesy of Dr. R. B. Park, Science.)*

chemical bonds of organic substances. These substances in turn serve as the ultimate energy source for all plants and animals on our planet earth. The electron microscope has proven to be an indispensable tool for elaborating the finer structure of the chloroplast, as it has for mitochondria and the endoplasmic reticulum. Chloroplasts of higher plants like other plastids are each bound by a separate membrane with semipermeable properties. Each chloroplast is constructed internally of numerous (*a*) non-green granular areas called *stroma* and (*b*) minute disc-like units called *grana*, consisting of parallel chlorophyll-containing laminations or lamellae, embedded in the stroma. Apparently the chlorophyll, proteins, and lipids including *carotenoids* (Chapter 7) are oriented in precise layers to constitute the grana. Electron-microscopy studies have recently revealed that the lamellae contain a repeating unit structure called the *quantosome* (Figure 4-14) which some believe to be the physiological photosynthetic unit.

LARGE VACUOLES. Large vacuoles are characteristically found in the cytoplasm of mature

plant cells and to a lesser extent in certain single-celled animals. Essentially they consist of a thin envelope or bag of cytoplasm, the *vacuolar membrane*, which is filled with a fluid called the *cell sap*. The cell sap is made up largely of free water and a variety of dissolved substances including salts, sugars, organic acids, and pigments. Vacuoles are small or absent in young, metabolically active dividing cells; but in most mature plant cells a single vacuole often occupies most of the volume of the cell, tending to confine the cytoplasm and nucleus of the cell to the peripheral regions close to the cell membrane. At times it appears as if the nucleus of a living plant cell is actually contained within a vacuole. This, of course, is an erroneous impression that is often due to the fact that the nucleus is suspended at the very periphery of the cytoplasm and indents the vacuolar membrane. Many kinds of animal cells, especially in fixed sections, display small vacuoles, or *vesicles*, but these occupy only a small volume of the cell and have a fleeting existence, appearing and disappearing at various times.

Pigments in the cell sap and chromoplasts determine the color of the various gross plant structures. In higher plants the red, blue, and purple color of leaves, flowers, fruits, and stems are due to a genetically determined class of pigments, the *anthocyanins*, which are dissolved in the fluid of the vacuoles. Although plant vacuoles maintain the turgor of the cell and serve to store various materials including water, reserve products, and waste products, it is quite possible that they have other roles which have not yet been elucidated.

In unicellular animals the vacuoles are of a different type from that of higher plant cells, and they perform a number of definite and important roles. In *Amoeba*, for example, there are at least two kinds of functionally specialized vacuoles, the *food vacuole* and the *contractile vacuole*, described in the next chapter.

OTHER CYTOPLASMIC INCLUSIONS. Depending on the metabolic condition, age, and specialization of plant cells, certain deposits, mostly organic in nature, may accumulate in the cytoplasm, especially in plant cells. For example, starch granules made up of concentric layers which frequently become so large as to burst the leucoplasts in which they originated are common to certain plant cells such as those of the potato tuber.

The cytoplasm may also contain dispersed oil droplets, crystals of certain organic and inorganic salts, resins, and other substances including secretion granules observed in secretory cells. The latter are frequently seen in animal gland tissues. The various cytoplasmic inclusions are generally products or by-products of the cell's metabolism. Their accumulation, which may serve as a means of excretion or of storage, is considered to be indicative of senescence in certain cells.

In summary, the two most significant characteristics of the plant cell are the presence of a cell wall and the photosynthetic pigment chlorophyll. Of the two the presence of the cell wall is probably the more basic criterion. Fungi and bacteria, for example, possess a cell wall and in almost all cases no chlorophyll. They are placed by most systems of classification in the plant kingdom, whereas certain unicellular organisms (e.g., *Euglena*, Chapter 18), which have chlorophyll and carry on photosynthesis, are frequently classified in the animal kingdom primarily because they have no cell wall. A structural feature usually associated with the animal cell includes the centrosome, although it is also present in some of the lower plants. The possession of a cell wall and chlorophyll by plant cells, and the centrosome by animal cells, constitutes the principal basis for distinguishing plant from animal cells.

THE DIVIDING CELL

Basic Features

It would be glaringly inadequate to consider the nondividing cell without including a description of regular cell division (also called mitosis), for this is the process that gives rise to new but identical cells. Moreover, changes and rearrangements observed in the nucleus and certain cytoplasmic structures during mitosis have exposed additional basic facts about the cell which could not have been revealed by studies of the nondividing cell alone.

Mitosis or regular cell division involves a self-directed and continuous flow of orderly cellular events whereby the all-important deoxyribonucleic acids (DNA) of the chromatin material of the nondividing cells, which have been previously duplicated, are equally and precisely distributed to form two identical daughter nuclei. The best available evidence indicates that duplication of these master molecules has already occurred in the nondividing nucleus prior to the onset of cell division. The process of mitosis therefore is not one of DNA replication, but is instead a means for the exact and equal distribution of the already duplicated DNA possessing coded information to the two daughter nuclei (and therefore from one cell generation to another) which are formed in the process. In their final stages of formation the daughter nuclei are usually separated from each other by a less precise division of the cytoplasm into two cells. With some minor variations the process of cell division is essentially identical in plant and animal cells.

Despite the fact that cell division was observed and described on various occasions as far back as the early nineteenth century, recognition of its significance as the major means of procuring new cells escaped attention for more than half a century and was not actually realized until about 1880 as a result of a number of independent studies. Yet 22 years earlier in 1858 the German physiologist Rudolph Virchow had already crystallized one of the major generalizations of the modern cell theory, namely that all cells arise from preexisting cells (the only exception to this is, of course, the origin of life some two billion years ago). Virchow's contribution was even more remarkable in view of the fact that this concept was put forth approximately 15 years before the final demise of the theory of spontaneous generation by the experiments of Louis Pasteur.

The Chromosomes

We now know that DNA, the fundamental substance of the diffuse chromatin material (as seen in the nondividing cell), is structurally and functionally organized together with certain proteins and other constituents in the form of rod-like structures called *chromosomes*. The DNA units responsible for the structural and metabolic characteristics of the cell and for the transmission of these characteristics from one cell generation to another are called *genes* and are arranged in a single linear order along the chromosomes. The concept of genes is discussed in detail in Chapter 11.

We were not aware that chromosomes existed until they were first seen as dark-staining rods of nucleic acids and proteins during the process of cell division. In view of the past difficulty in detecting chromosome structures in the resting cell, it was believed for a time that chromosomes formed only during mitosis and lost their identity in the nondividing nucleus. This view has since been discarded because different lines of research indicate that they are also present as distinct structural and functional entities between cell divisions, even though in most cases they appear elongated, twisted, and intermingled with each other to constitute the characteristic chromatin network.

All cells of any particular organism, with the exception of certain reproductive cells, contain a characteristic number of chromosomes. For instance, most cells of the human body (except for the sperm, the egg cell, and certain other cells) contain 46 chromosomes (Figure 13-4). We tend to think of the chromosomes as acting in pairs (i.e., 23 pairs in human cells), each member of a pair resembling its corre-

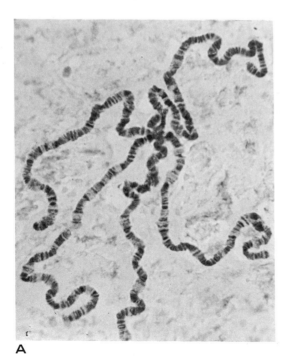

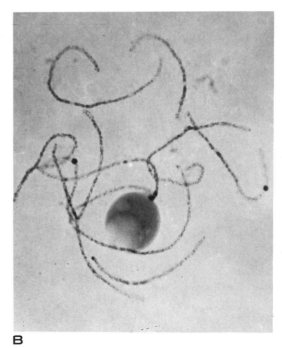

A   B

Figure 4-15. Micrographs of (A) salivary gland chromosomes of the fruit-fly *Drosophilia* (*courtesy of Dr. B. P. Kaufman, J. Hered.*); and (B) corn chromosomes showing the attached nucleolus (*courtesy of Dr. T. Morgan, Jr.*).

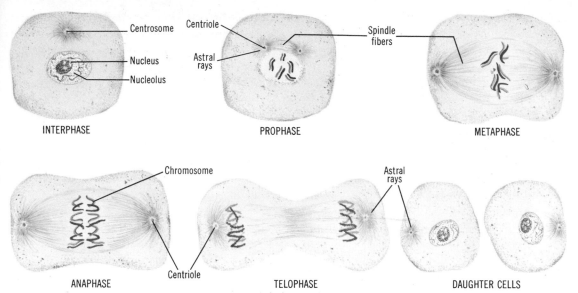

Figure 4-16. Schematic summary of various stages of mitosis in an animal cell.

sponding partner or homologue although not being necessarily identical. The characteristic number of chromosomes in the cells of plants and animals varies widely from species to species. It ranges from at least one chromosome in certain marine worms to well over several hundred in other organisms. A microscopic, single-celled marine animal has been reported to contain approximately 1600 chromosomes, the highest number observed thus far in any organism. The chromosome number for most plants and animals, however, ranges between 10 and 50. The frog, for example, has 26 chromosomes or 13 pairs, and the corn plant 20 chromosomes or 10 pairs in each of its body cells. Since more than a million and a quarter different kinds or *species* (Chapter 14) of plants and animals have already been described (many more exist which have not yet been studied and classified), it follows that many species must have the same number of chromosomes in their cells. The fact that several species possess the same chromosome number does not necessarily mean that they are closely related. In certain cases, however, a similar chromosome number among two or

more species may have a significant bearing on their evolutionary relationship provided other independent lines of evidence also relate them to each other.

The shape and size of chromosomes show many variations depending on the species, the particular chromosome pair under consideration, and certain environmental conditions including temperature and chemical surroundings. Chromosomes may exhibit characteristic knobs, constrictions, and unique staining properties at particular sites along their length. These can serve as important features for identifying and studying particular chromosomes, especially in attempting to relate certain inherited characteristics with certain chromosomes or chromosome regions. The average length of chromosomes in their most contracted state during mitosis is about 5μ in humans, as long as 30μ in some plants, and so small in most fungi as to be barely visible with the light microscope.

Chromosome structures have been definitely shown to exist in bacteria. In the few bacterial species in which these have been extensively investigated, however, the chromosomes have proven to be circular instead of rod-like. The rapidly accumulating evidence resulting from many different kinds of genetic and biochemical experiments with bacteria indicate a DNA organization similar to that of plants and animals.

Overall View of Mitosis

Regular cell division or mitosis first involves the conversion of the chromatin network fibers into short rod-like structures, the chromosomes, each consisting of two helically coiled identical strands lying side by side called *chromatids* (Figure 4-16). This double-stranded nature of the chromosomes during early mitosis is the result of a duplication of the chromatids during the previous nondividing state of the nucleus. The entire complement of chromosomes, each composed of two chromatids at this stage, then rearranges itself on a barrel-shaped spindle apparatus in the cytoplasm. The fibers constituting the spindle are anchored at opposite ends to the now separated centrioles in the animal cell, or to two separate diffuse cytoplasmic regions, the *polar caps*, in the plant cell. The separation or prying apart of the chromatids of each chromosome pair, which are attached to individual spindle fibers, occurs to yield single chromatids called *daughter chromosomes*. These are then moved away from one another to opposite ends of the cell.

Each of the two sets of daughter chromosomes, which have been moved to opposite ends of the cell, is then transformed to a typical resting nucleus. Subsequent cytoplasmic division forms two daughter cells with identical nuclei.

In a strict sense mitosis applies only to the formation of two identical daughter nuclei, although it is also commonly used to include cytoplasmic division. The division of the cytoplasm to form two daughter cells, each containing a daughter nucleus, usually occurs during the later stages of nuclear division or shortly after its completion. The two events, nuclear division and cytoplasmic division, are actually separate and distinct processes which are generally coordinated or synchronized with one another.

Detailed View of Mitosis

For purposes of description the detailed events of mitosis are conveniently divided into four successively distinct stages called *prophase*, *metaphase*, *anaphase*, and *telophase*, although it is a continuous and smoothly functioning process with each stage blending gradually into the next (Figure 4-17). Unfortunately little is known of the nature of the chemical changes and enzymatic reactions associated with mitosis and accompanying cytoplasmic division.

PROPHASE. One of the earliest indications that mitosis has begun is the visible shortening, thickening, and rearrangement of the nuclear threads constituting the chromatin material. This first stage of mitosis, known as *prophase*, primarily involves the transformation of the chromatin material into the recognizable and characteristic rod-like chromosomes accompanied by other typical changes in the nucleus and cytoplasm.

The chromatin threads progressively thicken, shorten, and become more stainable during the early stages of prophase so that each soon comes to be recognizable as a structure consisting essentially of two coiled, intertwined, and twisted strands, the *chromatids*. As the process continues each pair of chromatids untangles and continues to thicken and shorten, presumably by a process of coiling.

Thus by the end of prophase they have formed into typical, deeply staining rods or chromosomes (46 in the case of the human) about $1/10$ to $1/20$ of the original length which they displayed as long delicate threads at the start of mitosis. The individual chromosomes at this stage appear doubled, consisting of two identical and separate highly coiled chromatids lying side by side and attached to one another at some particular point along their length known as the *centromere*.

Until recently it was considered that one

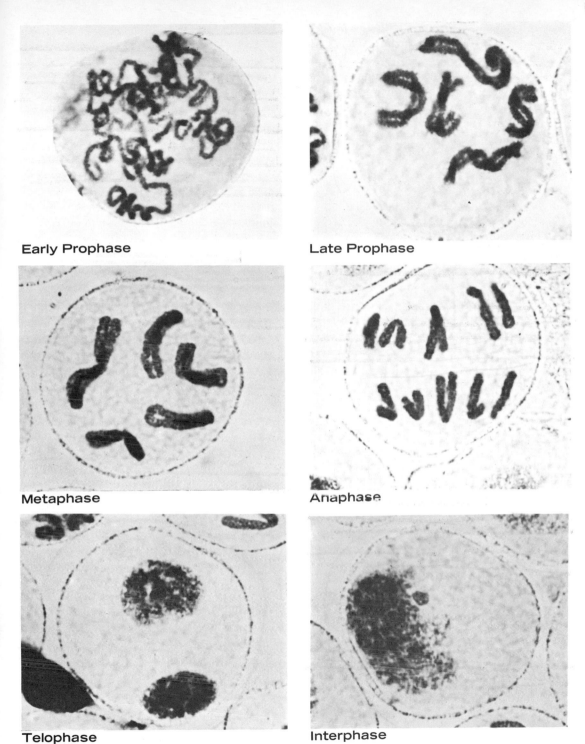

Early Prophase

Late Prophase

Metaphase

Anaphase

Telophase

Interphase

Figure 4-17. Some stages in the mitotic cycle in microspores of the higher plant *Trillium erectum*. The spindle structure is not evident in these micrographs. *(Courtesy of A. H. Sparrow and R. F. Smith, Brookhaven National Laboratory.)*

member of a chromatid pair within each chromosome at prophase arose from the other by an undefined process of splitting. We know now that the presence of the second chromatid in the chromosomes at the prophase stage is primarily the result of DNA synthesis which occurs during the preceding resting state of the nucleus. Each chromatid is essentially composed of proteins and a single linear array of DNA units or genes possessing coded information.

A number of other nuclear and cytoplasmic changes occur during prophase in addition to the conversion of the chromatin network into characteristic chromosomes. In most organisms the nucleoli progressively decrease in size (as the chromatin material rearranges into chromosomes), and finally disappear. During prophase the already divided centrosome of an animal cell separates into two separate centrioles which migrate to opposite sides of the cell. As the two daughter centrioles move away from each other they send out a system of radiating protoplasmic, gel-like fibers or astral rays which form a three-dimensional biconical spindle structure tapering at both ends where they connect to the opposite centrioles. In plant cells lacking a centrosome the spindle structure that forms is somewhat similar except that the fibers radiate from the typical diffuse cytoplasmic areas, namely the *polar caps*. During this time the nuclear membrane has been thinning out and its eventual disappearance marks the end of prophase. For purposes of description the prophase stage is often divided into *early, middle,* and *late* prophase substages.

METAPHASE. The second stage of mitosis is characterized by the rearrangement of the chromosomes on the hypothetical equatorial plane of the spindle structure. If a cross-sectional cut is made during metaphase through the center or equatorial plane of the spindle structure, the chromosomes are observed to be distributed in a more or less single plane. The chromosomes at metaphase, each composed of two coiled but separate chromatids

lying side by side throughout their length, are seen to be attached by means of their centromeres to fibers of the spindle structure.

ANAPHASE. The transformation of metaphase into anaphase occurs when the centromeres divide and the two identical chromatids of each chromosome begin to move apart towards the opposite poles. Anaphase involves the separation and movement of identical chromatids, called *daughter chromosomes*, to two different spindle poles.

Longitudinal separation of the chromatids commences at the doubled centromeres where each is connected to an individual spindle fiber. During their subsequent movement towards the opposite poles, the daughter chromosomes (each consisting now of a single chromatid in contrast to the double-chromatid structure of chromosomes during prophase and metaphase) are usually V-shaped and pointing toward the poles. These observations are tentatively explained by assuming that the daughter chromosomes are being pulled through the viscous protoplasm toward the poles by contraction of the individual spindle fibers, although there is little evidence for or against this proposal. The arms of the chromosomes are apparently dragged along and tend to lag behind, an effect similar to that produced by pulling a limp piece of string at some point along its length through water. This is further substantiated by the finding that the chromosomes lacking a centromere, usually as a result of certain treatments such as X-ray, generally fail to move at all.

A pattern seems to be emerging which suggests a role for the centriole or centrosome in the organized movement of certain cellular components. We have already pointed out that the centriole appears to be acting as the control center for the movement of flagella and cilia. In mitosis of animal cells we see that the centriole is involved too in the movement of chromosomes during anaphase. There is also evidence that the centriole and the centromere (which is also necessary for chromosome movement) are closely related. The ana-

phase stage is usually subdivided into the early, middle, and late substages for descriptive convenience.

TELOPHASE. The final stage of mitosis involves a series of events which are essentially the reverse of those occurring during prophase. Each of the two complements of daughter chromosomes present at the opposite poles is progressivley transformed into a daughter nucleus with its own chromatin material concomitant with the reappearance of nucleoli and a new nuclear membrane. Simultaneously the fibers comprising the spindle structure also begin to disappear. By the end of telophase two new typical resting stage daughter nuclei possessing identical chromosomes and therefore an identical DNA constitution have been formed.

INTERPHASE. In a broader and more modern sense mitosis can be regarded as a portion of a cyclic process known as the *mitotic cycle* (Figure 4-17). The mitotic cycle, in addition to mitosis, includes the nondividing or so-called *interphase* state of the nucleus as one of its stages. We now recognize that just as there are various stages of mitosis or chromosomal separation (prophase, metaphase, and so on), so there are several stages of interphase. We speak of (a) the G_1 *stage of interphase*, which is the nondividing state of the nucleus prior to the occurrence of DNA synthesis; (b) the S *stage of interphase*, when DNA synthesis takes place; and (c) the G_2 *stage of interphase*, which occurs after DNA synthesis but before the onset of prophase. The mitotic cycle therefore consists of the continuous sequence of both interphase and mitosis, and thus includes the duplication of the chromosomes as well as their precise and equal distribution to the two resulting daughter nuclei.

Division of Cytoplasm

Although mitosis or nuclear duplication is a process separate and different from cytoplasmic division, the two are generally synchronized. In most cells division of the cytoplasm begins during or immediately after telophase. It may even start earlier during the later stages of anaphase.

Under some circumstances nuclear division and cytoplasmic division can be uncoupled from one another with nuclear division occurring at a faster rate than division of the cytoplasm. Certain drugs can inhibit cytoplasmic division without affecting the formation of the daughter nuclei. In some algae and in numerous fungi cytoplasmic division is characteristically absent so that nuclear duplication results in the formation of multinucleate cytoplasm. Experiments with cytoplasmic fragments from sea-urchin eggs demonstrate that successive cytoplasmic divisions could still take place despite the absence of the nucleus. In view of the widespread occurrence among plants and animals of nuclear division coupled to cytoplasmic division, it seems reasonable to assume that from an evolutionary standpoint the coordination of these two processes may possibly have been a distinct advantage for more efficient survival

The manner in which cytoplasmic division occurs is markedly different in animal and plant cells. In animal cells it is achieved by a process of *furrowing* which is initiated by the appearance of a shallow groove or furrow in the cell membrane at about the same location as the hypothetical equatorial plane. This peripheral indentation gradually deepens by progressing towards the center of the cell, breaking any spindle fibers that remain until the cytoplasm is cleaved into two cells, very much like constricting a balloon into two compartments by gradually tightening a string around its middle. Each of the two new cells, which are not necessarily equal in size, contains one of the two daughter nuclei.

In the plant cell the cytoplasm is partitioned into two cells by the formation of a special membrane called the *cell plate*. It arises at the equatorial plane from the disappearing spindle deep in the center of the cytoplasm and gradually grows outward toward the surface until the original cell is cut in two (Figure 4-18). The cell plate is not the same as the cell membrane, although it arises in part from the cytoplasm and from the spindle fibers. More recent evidence indicates that the cell plate is formed by the endoplasmic reticulum. The two daughter cells shortly form a new cell membrane on their respective sides of the plate followed soon afterwards by the appearance of the cell wall. The cell plate, which is eventually impregnated with a complex carbohydrate called *pectin* (Chapter 7), becomes sandwiched between the cell walls formed by the cells on either side of it, and is now called the *middle lamella.*

In summary the major differences between plant and animal cells during mitosis and cytoplasmic division are that (*a*) animal cells possess centrioles that serve as the poles for the spindle structure, whereas plant cells develop polar caps instead; and (*b*) the division of the cytoplasm into two cells occurs in animal tissues by a process of furrowing which proceeds from the cell periphery toward the center.

In plants it takes place by the formation of a cell plate that grows from the center of the cell towards the suface to become eventually the middle lamella.

Sequence of Mitotic Events: Flemming's Contribution

What is the basis for claiming that the order of events in mitosis occurs as just described? Most studies of cell division have been performed with fixed, sectioned, and stained cells. In effect such preparations capture only scattered instants in the life of any cell, like a series of candid photographs representing split-second views of a complicated chain of phenomena which may pass almost indistinguishably from one phase to the other. With what degree of certainty can we arrange these snapshots in a correct order? How confident can we be that we are not observing artifacts instead of real cell structures in fixed and stained tissues?

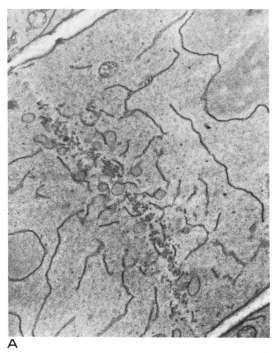
A

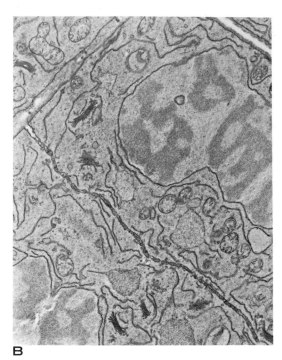
B

Figure 4-18. Electron micrographs of an early (A) and late (B) stage of cell plate formation during telophase in onion root tip cells. (*Courtesy of Dr. K. R. Porter, J. Biophys. Biochem. Cytol.*)

These two questions were satisfactorily answered around 1880 by the outstanding work of the German biologist Walther Flemming. His contribution was all the more remarkable since it established the sequence and events of mitosis essentially as we know it today. Flemming, by using living epidermal cells of salamander in which he was able to observe most of the important transformations of the nucleus during cell division, determined the sequence of events in mitosis. At the same time, by checking his observations in living cells against those in fixed and stained sections, he could distinguish to a certain extent artifacts from real structures in the latter preparations.

Significance of Mitosis

Mitosis is an orderly process for the precise and equal distribution of duplicate chromosomes (i.e., consisting in part of the master molecules, DNA) to form two daughter nuclei with identical numbers and kinds of chromosomes. It accounts for the identical genetic constitution in the daughter cells and, therefore, for the same structural and functional organization as the parent cell from which they originated. Thus it is in part responsible for the inheritance or transmission of characteristics from cell to cell in multicellular organisms, and from generation to generation in the organisms (mostly unicellular) in which mitosis also constitutes reproduction.

The primary significance of mitosis, therefore, resides in its role of maintaining the continuity of the various forms of life by accurately transmitting the essential DNA in the form of duplicated chromosomes from cell generation to cell generation. Occasionally something goes amiss such as the breaking of a chromosome, a modification in the structure of a gene, or an unequal distribution of daughter chromosomes. If this should happen in the cells concerned with reproduction, it could lead on rare occasion to certain hereditary changes that might be significant in future evolutionary development, but it is usually detrimental and leads to death.

In many unicellular organisms mitosis corresponds to true reproduction since two new individuals are produced from the original cell. In multicellular organisms mitosis is in part responsible for growth and development. All multicellular organisms arise from a single cell or the fusion of two reproductive cells. In higher organisms and in many lower forms sexual reproduction involves first the fusion of two specialized cells to form one. The latter subsequently undergoes repeated cell division, accounting for the growth and development of the organism. Thus, for example, the 10^{14} (or 100 trillion) cells that make up the body of an adult human originated by cell division from a single egg cell fertilized by a sperm cell.

Cell division is also necessary for maintenance of the individual. Cells that have a short life span such as those of the lining of the digestive tract, the outer skin layer, the cornea of the eye, and the red blood cells are replaced by new cells produced in mitosis.

Time Span and Frequency of Mitosis

The time necessary for the occurrence of mitosis varies considerably depending on a number of factors including organism, tissue, temperature, and various environmental influences. Many animal cells in tissue culture complete their cell division in about 30 minutes at 37°C. Higher temperatures markedly accelerate the rate of mitosis. With certain plant cells, for example, the time interval of 135 minutes for complete division to occur at 10°C is decreased to 30 minutes by raising the temperature to 45°C.

Although cell division often occurs in higher animals in approximately 30 minutes, the frequency with which it takes place depends on numerous factors, including the needs of the tissues. The relatively rapid wearing out of red blood cells, and cells of the skin and lining of the digestive tract, implies that they are also being rapidly renewed by the process of mitosis. Other cells such as those of the kidney or liver experience a slower rate of replacement, whereas to the best of our knowledge nerve cells, once formed, fail to undergo division and are never replaced when destroyed.

Initiation and Control of Mitosis

What are the mechanisms or factors that initiate and control mitosis? Why should the frequency of mitosis, which is so high in most cells of a developing embryo, progressively decrease until it is restricted to just a few specialized kinds of tissues in the mature organism? The answers are still unknown.

A number of speculations and theories, some bordering on the fantastic and others possessing absolutely no basis in fact, have been proposed to explain initiation and control of cell division. A few have invoked mysterious radiations produced by adjacent living cells, and others have suggested fields of force, magnetic or otherwise, in view of the shape of the spindle and its relationship to the centrioles or polar caps. More reasonable possibilities involving gelation of protoplasm and the influence of unidentified substances have also been indicated, but these must await further proof and confirmation.

A factor that may have a strong bearing on the initiation of mitosis concerns the definite size limit that growing cells can attain. When rapidly growing cells reach a particular size, which varies with the particular cell type, they undergo division. This may be due to an unknown stimulus produced perhaps by the unfavorable relationship between cell membrane surface and cell volume or between nuclear membrane surface and cell volume. There is no evidence for or against such a view. It is conceivable that a rapidly growing cell may reach a limiting size whereby the total membrane *surface* of the cell or the nucleus, which increases at a slower rate (in proportion to the square of its mean linear dimension) than does the cell *volume* (which increases in proportion to the cube of its mean dimension), can no longer adequately accommodate the needs of the large volume of cell protoplasm in terms of an adequate rate of exchange of nutrients and metabolic waste products. Cell division restores a more favorable surface-volume relationship.

Several implications of initiation and control of cell division can be dramatically illustrated by a few examples. Many types of insects in their normal life cycle undergo an early stage known as *diapause* (e.g., the pupa or cocoon stage in the life of the butterfly) in which metabolic activity is at a minimum and mitosis ceases. Cell division can be induced, and therefore diapause broken (thus accelerating the life cycle) by a variety of chemical and physical agents not unlike those that initiate mitosis in the egg cells of certain marine organisms mentioned later. Dormancy in plants and seeds, characterized also by a minimal rate of metabolism and a cessation of mitosis, can likewise be broken or "forced" by somewhat similar treatments. In all cases the mitotic initiation and control are still obscure.

The two broad experimental approaches used in studies of the initiation and control of mitosis have been concerned with (*a*) the induction of cell division or embryo development in egg cells of certain lower animals (for example, sea urchins and starfish) which ordinarily would never divide unless they first fused with an appropriate sperm cell; and (*b*) an examination of the effects of cancer-producing (*carcinogenic*) substances or treatments in inducing mitosis in cells of various organisms. A very practical interest in the question of initiation and control of mitosis stems from its relationship to the cancer problem, for cancerous tissues are an improperly organized mass of cells exhibiting an extremely high rate of mitosis and an unlimited ability to grow and spread at the expense of surrounding cells. The first approach has demonstrated that a wide variety of chemical and physical agents, rather than one specific agent, are effective in initiating mitosis in egg cells. The second approach has shown that the production of cancer is also not limited to the action of any one particular group of compounds but includes a wide range of chemical substances, irradiation treatments, and physical agents.

Meiosis

There is still another type of regular nuclear division, known as *meiosis*, which is highly specialized and restricted to the formation of certain reproductive cells. In meiosis four daughter nuclei (each in a separate cell) are usually produced instead of two as in mitosis. A most significant aspect of meiosis is that each of the resulting four daughter nuclei has only half the number of chromosomes as the parent cell. In addition it is during meiosis that the highly important phenomenon of "crossing-over" occurs. The details and implications of meiosis and "crossing-over" are discussed in Chapter 12.

THE WHOLE CELL

In describing the details of cell make-up we have dwelled on each of the individual structures comprising the cell. Our ultimate interest, however, is in the whole cell as an intact entity. We have had to examine the separate parts before we could gain an insight into the whole.

What can we say about the organization of the intact cell? For one thing the biologist has come to realize that the living cell has a more complex and highly integrated organization than he has ever previously conceived it to be.

The cell as the unit of life is a dynamic and highly integrated structural organization composed of the cytoplasm (representing the major structural and functional machinery) and the nucleus (as the master control apparatus). Through the activity of its cell membrane it selectively takes up certain substances from its external environment and gives off others in an incessant interchange of materials among its component parts and between its external and internal environments. Through the varied but synchronized activity of its cytoplasm, under the direction of the nucleus, the cell subjects the materials to a predetermined multitude of coordinated physical and chemical reactions. In the course of these events energy is released, captured in part by the cytoplasmic organization, and utilized for the different life activities of the cell. Certain products of these reactions are selectively released by the cell membrane as either waste products or useful secretions to be utilized by other cells. Other products are selectively transferred to the nucleus for further transformation and utilization while the nucleus in turn sends out substances controlling the cytoplasm activities. In one way or another the various reactions contribute to the characteristics of the cell and are ultimately directed and controlled by a centralized master apparatus, namely the deoxyribonucleic acids of the nucleus.

The relatively recent discovery of the endoplasmic reticulum (and its intimate relationship to the ribosomes), the unveiling of detailed mitochondrial structure and function, and our newer knowledge of the central directing role exercised by the chromosomal DNA have made us aware that the cytoplasm of the cell is a highly complex and unified structural organization. Biologists can no longer merely describe it as a random and haphazard mass of granular protoplasm which at times becomes more fiber-like (fibrillar) or more bubble-like (alveolar). By the same token the numerous molecular reactions that occur reflect the integrated structural organization of both the nucleus and cytoplasm and are neither random nor chance events but orderly, directed, and synchronized processes serving some role in the functioning of the cell.

The intact cell is in many ways like a great factory. Each of its subdivisions or department ments carries on its own specialized activities which are coordinated with those of the others, contributing to the functioning of the factory as a whole; and each is under the ultimate direction and regulation of a central controlling body or organization. We are still not certain how this central control is exercised by the nucleus in the living cell. Present indications are that some of ribonucleic acids which are made in the nucleus act as messengers for the deoxyribonucleic acids of the chromosomes. The RNA is presumably transferred to the ribosomes where it exerts its effect by directing protein synthesis including enzymes, thus directing the metabolism of the cell. These aspects, are discussed in detail in Chapter 11. During the many events that occur incessantly in the lifetime of the cell, the nucleus may or may not undergo mitosis, depending on several factors previously indicated.

This is our current picture of the living cell. At best our knowledge is rudimentary. How do the chromosomes replicate themselves? How do they exercise their vast control over the cytoplasm of the cell? What are the mechanisms by which cells are differentiated into particular highly specialized units such as nerve cells, blood cells, and so on? These are some of the major biological questions that remain unanswered.

SUPPLEMENTARY REFERENCES

Bloom, W., and D. W. Fawcett, *Textbook of Histology,* Saunders, Philadelphia, 1962.
Brachet, J., and A. E. Mirsky (Editors), *The Cell,* Academic Press, New York, 1959-1961.
De Robertis, E. D. P., W. W. Nowinski, and F. A. Saez, *General Cytology,* third edition, Saunders, Philadelphia, 1960.
Engstrom, A., and J. B. Finean, *Biological Ultrastructure,* Academic Press, New York, 1958.
Giese, A. C., *Cell Physiology,* second edition, Saunders, Philadelphia, 1962.
Loewy, A. G., and P. Siekevitz, *Cell Structure and Function,* Holt, Rinehart, and Winston, New York, 1963.
Robbins, W. W., T. E. Weier, and C. R. Stocking, *Botany,* third edition, Wiley, New York, 1964.
Swanson, C. P., *Cytology and Cytogenetics,* Prentice-Hall, Englewood Cliffs, N.J., 1957.
Swanson, C. P., *The Cell,* second edition, Prentice-Hall, Englewood Cliffs, N.J., 1964.
The Living Cell, special issue of *Scientific American,* September 1961.
Wilson, C. L., and W. E. Loomis, *Botany,* revised edition, Dryden Press, New York, 1957.

Chapter 5   Types of Cells and Tissues

GENERAL CONSIDERATIONS

Unicellular Organisms, Multicellular Organisms, and Other Types

Nearly all living things are made up either of one cell *(unicellular)* or many cells *(multicellular)*. A third group of organisms are considered as intermediate or transitional between the two major groups, being neither truly unicellular nor multicellular. Finally there are also a small number of forms referred to as *noncellular* or *acellular* organisms which seem to contradict the thesis of the modern cell theory that all living things are made up of cells.

In the unicellular organism the size, shape, and unique characteristics of the single cell constituting the whole organism vary with the species. Some types such as bacteria display a relatively simple cellular organization performing the basic activities common to all cells, whereas others have in addition unique or specialized features. Several unicellular organisms in addition possess certain unusual cytoplasmic structures whose roles are similar to those of the complex organs and systems of the more advanced multicellular animals. This is illustrated by the protist *Paramecium* described in a later section of this chapter.

In most multicellular types the cells composing the organism tend to be highly specialized. They consist of different cells or groups of cells which have the ability to perform special functions beyond the fundamental ones common to all cells. Liver cells, for example, in addition to displaying the usual activities attributed to living systems (reproduction, growth, metabolism, and so on) also carry out the special function of secreting bile. Similarly, muscle cells are highly specialized to contract and relax, thus performing mechanical work.

The organisms that are intermediate between the unicellular and multicellur types represent only a small percentage of the total life on our planet. They consist of colonies or aggregates of single cells and exhibit a primitive kind of organization whereby some cells have become specialized for reproduction, others for feeding, others for the mobility of the colony, and so on (see *Volvox*, (p. 82). They differ from the unicellular organisms (e.g., numerous bacteria) that characteristically tend to aggregate to form loose colonies of cells. The latter are still considered to be unicellular because they show no particular specialization with respect to any of the other cells of the colony and simply represent a cluster of independent cells tending to adhere together as a group.

Where do we draw the line between unicellular and multicellular organisms? In most cases we can easily distinguish between the two. By contrast organisms of the intermediate type in one sense belong to both groups, and yet in another sense belong to neither. What are the natural relationships that exist among these various groups? Present indications are that multicellular organisms as unified and coordinated entities of many cells of specialized structure and function, ultimately evolved from unicellular organisms. One theory proposes that the transition occurred by way of intermediate colonial stages consisting of increasingly specialized cells. Another theory suggests that the multicellular condition evolved from single-celled organisms of large size possessing highly specialized structures.

What are the noncellular types? Numerous fungi, for example, are apparently not cellular. During most of their life cycle they consist of a continuous mass of cytoplasm with many nuclei retained within a long, often branching, cylindrical cell wall (Figure 5-1). In some species the cytoplasm is compartmentalized by periodic cross walls but is nevertheless still multinucleate. Other fungi such as the slime molds during a stage of their life cycles form naked shapeless masses of multinucleated protoplasm without a retaining cell wall. We can observe the formation of uninucleate cells

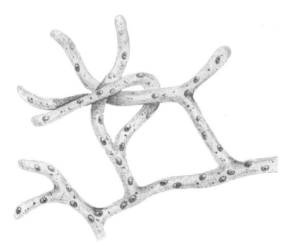

Figure 5-1. Multinucleate filaments, or hyphae, of certain true fungi (e.g., *Rhizopus)* as seen through the light microscope. Each filament is enclosed within a cylindrical cell wall.

during certain stages of the life cycles of these organisms, especially during the period of reproduction.

The multinucleate condition is also found among higher organisms. The subcuticular layer of the body wall of some roundworms is a mass of protoplasm with many nuclei; and in higher animals, such as man, heart muscle and skeletal muscle are also multinucleate. In such cases we know definitely, or have strong evidence for believing, that the multinucleate condition originated from or was preceded by cells that subsequently experienced a normal change to the multinucleate condition through modification or loss of cell membranes. Some biologists believe that highly specialized unicellular organisms such as the *Paramecium*, because of their extremely complex make-up, should probably not be considered as single cells but instead as exceptions to the basic contention of the cell theory that the cell is the unit of life.

The complexities of living systems are further compounded by the fact that an appreciable number of organisms undergo a regular sequence of transformations in the course of their normal existence. The resulting stages, which may differ radically from one another, make up the life cycle of the organism. The frog, for example, is gradually transformed from a fish-like stage via the tadpole phase to that of amphibian adulthood. A description of the amazing changes exhibited by the slime mold (p. 84) in the course of its life cycle, during which it passes through unicellular, multicellular, and noncellular stages, reads like an imaginative account from science fiction.

Can we consider viruses to be alive? There is still no common agreement on this question. Viruses are specific infective agents that invade plant, animal, and bacterial cells. They are essentially highly organized and unique systems of nucleoproteins, perhaps most comparable to naked chromosomes, and in certain cases they can be crystallized in much the same manner as a variety of compounds

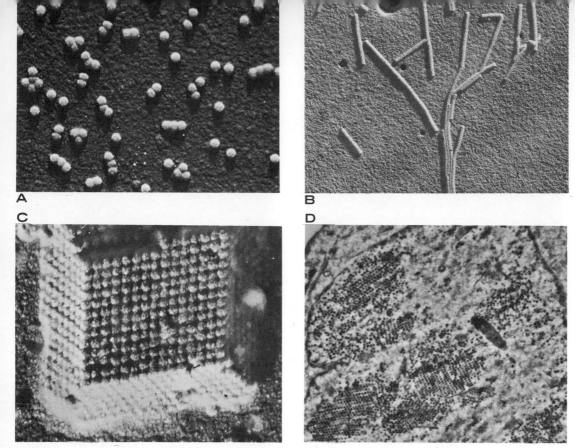

Figure 5-2. Electron micrographs of several viruses. (A) Poliovirus, magnification 74,000X *(courtesy of Dr. R. C. Williams)*. (B) Tobacco mosaic virus *(courtesy of Dr. R. W. G. Wyckoff)*. (C) Crystal of tobacco necrosis virus, magnification 109,200X *(courtesy of Dr. L. W. Labaw, J. Ultrastruct. Res.)*. (D) Human cancer cells infected with adenovirus particles, magnification 9660X *(courtesy of Dr. C. Morgan, J. Biophys. Cytol.)*.

(Figure 5-2). Viruses have never been shown to grow or reproduce other than within a living host cell. Moreover they fail to display the typical metabolism (if any at all) manifested by most cells.

The particular group of viruses that infect bacteria are called *bacteriophages* (or *phages*). We probably know most about phages because they have proved to be the easiest of the viruses to study, especially in view of the convenience of manipulation. Some of the remarkable properties of viruses may be illustrated by referring to several properties of phages. The invasion of a host cell by a single phage particle radically transforms and redirects the entire metabolism of the bacterium within a matter of minutes to the single purpose of reproducing identical phage particles.

In certain cases 30 minutes after infection of a bacterial cell by a single phage unit, approximately 200 virus particles will have been formed by the machinery of the host cell under the explicit direction of the DNA of the invading virus (Figure 5-3). The host cell shortly bursts or disintegrates and the virus particles are released. In other cases a portion of the phage DNA may actually be incorporated into that of the host cell.

In many respects viruses defy nearly all the structural and functional criteria that we have heretofore associated with cellular and noncellular living systems. By applying the classic criteria of typical life activities cited in Chapter I, the answer would be to regard them as inanimate, or at most borderline. Yet on the basis of our more modern concepts we

A

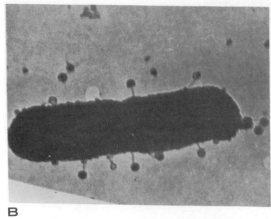

B

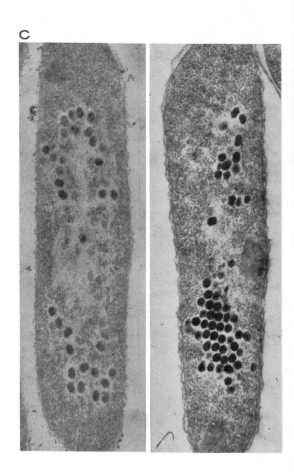

C

Figure 5-3. Electron micrographs of bacteriophages. (A) Bacteriophage particle, magnification *ca* 77,000X. (B) A stage in bacteriophage infection showing several bacteriophage particles adsorbed to a single bacterial (*Escherichia coli*), magnification 41,580X (*courtesy of Dr. T. F. Anderson, Cold Spring Harbor Symposium*). (C) Mature bacteriophage particles produced within the host bacterial cell (*E. coli*) thirty minutes after infection. The two infected bacterial cells shown differ only in the procedures used in preparing the specimens for electron microscopy, thus demonstrating the importance of fixation conditions in increasing the contrast of the phages as well as of the bacterial cytoplasm, magnification 38,500X (*courtesy of Dr. E. Kellenberger, J. Biophys. Biochem. Cytol.*).

might be inclined to classify them as living forms. In effect, viruses are nucleoproteins that appropriate and utilize the energy of their surroundings (by harnessing and redirecting the metabolic machinery of the host cell) for purposes of growth and self-duplication.

As a final alternative, and perhaps the most reasonable one, can we consider viruses as noncellular borderline forms which are intermediate between living and nonliving systems? Several biologists feel that viruses, by virtue of their complex nucleoprotein composition, could not have evolved directly from nonliving systems (Chapter 3). Instead they tend to view them possibly as "cell products," or more likely as transitional types that were transformed in the course of evolution from some primitive *living* ancestor to their present state. However, there is no common agreement on this point.

Cell Shape

Many single cells, whether as unicellular organisms or as isolated cells, produced by multicellular organisms (e.g., the egg cell of higher animals), tend to be spherical. The spherical shape is attributed in part to the phenomenon of *surface tension* in much the same way that this force is responsible for the spherical form of individual soap bubbles. It is the most efficient or economic shape for any given mass including protoplasm. Unicellular organisms may have characteristic forms which are variations of the spherical shape. These are largely determined by inherent properties of the species itself, and are frequently maintained by the particular shape that the cell membrane and cytoplasm themselves assume as well as by the presence of extracellular materials (e.g., the cell wall).

In multicellular organisms the size and shape of the cells are intimately related to their specialized functions and to the packing and arrangement of the cells with each other. Muscle cells or fibers, for example, are elongated and thus well suited for their function of contraction and relaxation in per-

forming mechanical work. Cells that are packed or arranged tightly against one another tend to be many-sided rather than spherical. Cell shape, like any other property of a cell, is primarily effected by its genetic composition. This is simply another way of saying that the manner in which a cell responds in terms of shape and size to any given environment will ultimately be decided by its inherent make-up, namely the DNA of its chromosomes.

UNICELLULAR ORGANISMS AND INTERMEDIATE TYPES

The fundamental similarity as well as the wide diversity in size, shape, and unique features displayed by single-celled organisms and those intermediate between unicellular and multicellular forms can be seen from the following examples. Some are clearly either animal cells or plant cells, whereas others display the characteristics of both types. As mentioned earlier several biologists classify all unicellular organisms as neither animals nor plants, but place them instead in a separate kingdom of their own, the *Protista*.

Bacteria

Bacteria as a group are among the smallest single cells found in nature, ranging from about 0.1 to 1μ in width and depth, and 0.5 to 10μ in length. They have characteristic cell walls which are not made up of cellulose (as they are in cells of higher plants) but of other complex substances. Bacteria are usually placed in the plant kingdom and are generally classified according to shape into three general groups, rod-shaped (*bacillus*), spherical-shaped (*coccus*) and spiral-shaped (*spirillum*) (Figure 5-4). They may occur singly, in groups of two, in long chains, or in irregular clumps depending on the species and environmental conditions. The nature of their major subcellular components, including the nuclear regions and free ribosomes in the cytoplasm as well as the absence of an endoplasmic reticulum, mitochondria, and golgi apparatus, were mentioned in Chapter 4. An appreciable number of bacterial species are motile by virtue of their many flagella (Figure 5-5).

The Amoeba

As one of the simplest unicellular animals the *Amoeba* (Figure 5-6) is composed of an irregular, gelatinous, flowing mass of granular protoplasm of indefinite and constantly changing shape. Movement is accomplished by the formation of streaming extensions of cytoplasm called *pseudopods*. The cell contains a single nucleus and two special kinds of vacuoles, the *food vacuole* and the *contractile vacuole*. The food vacuole is formed as a small, clear, membranous sphere during the normal movement of the amoeba as its cytoplasm flows around food particles in its path. The food particles are subsequently digested by

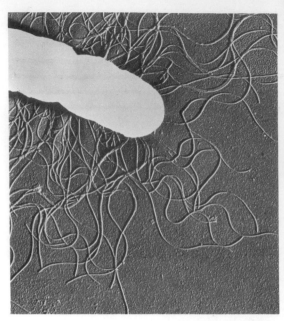

Figure 5-5. Electron micrograph of the bacterium *Caryophanum latum* showing flagella.

enzymes secreted from the cytoplasm into the vacuoles. Undigested remains are simply left behind as the organism continues to move about in its environment. The contractile vacuole also forms as a clear spherical body that grows progressively larger as it fills with water obtained from the surrounding cytoplasm, until it suddenly disappears by emptying its contents through the vacuolar and cell membranes in a rhythmic contraction (Figure 5-7). It therefore serves as a means of balancing the intake of water by the organism from the external environment.

Euglena

As a spindle-shaped organism *Euglena* belongs to the so-called *flagellates* which are unicellular forms characterized by one or a few flagella. *Euglena* (Figure 5-6) is equipped with a single flagellum at its front (anterior) end by which it propels itself through water. It has a large, centrally located nucleus, numerous chloroplasts, and the usual granular cytoplasm making up the main body of the cell. It also possesses at its anterior end a gullet-like

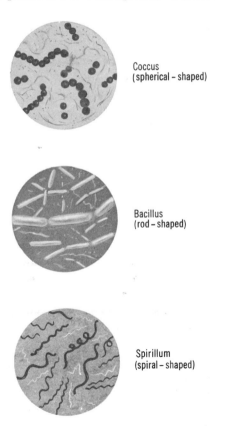

Coccus (spherical – shaped)

Bacillus (rod – shaped)

Spirillum (spiral – shaped)

Figure 5-4. Diagram of the three general types of bacteria—bacillus, coccus, and spirillum.

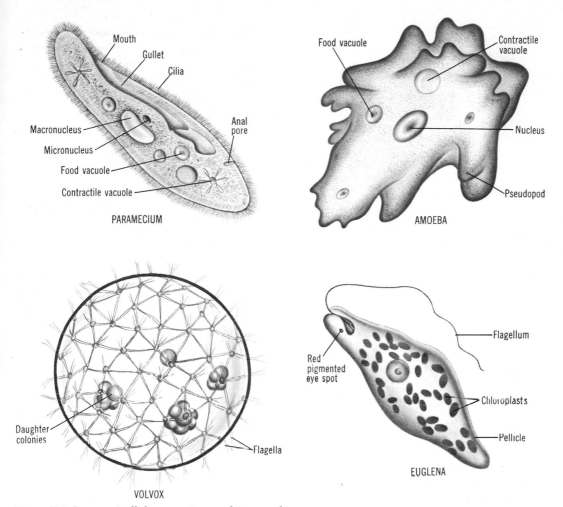

Figure 5-6. Some unicellular organisms and intermediate types.

structure and a red-pigmented *eye-spot* which is sensitive to light.

Many flagellates such as *Euglena* display both plant-like and animal-like characteristics, accounting for the lack of agreement as to their classification. The ability of numerous flagellates to carry on photosynthesis is the basis used by some biologists for designating these organisms as plants. On the other hand the absence of a cell wall (and the presence instead of an external envelope of nonliving material, namely the pellicle) has been sufficient

reason for other biologists to classify them with animals. Still others consider them as a separate transitional group of unicellular organisms, perhaps closely related to some primitive form that presumably gave rise to plants and animals.

Paramecium

The high degree of specialization achieved within a single-celled organism by virtue of unique cytoplasmic structures and organization is well illustrated by the *Paramecium* (Figure 5-6). The *Paramecium* which has the

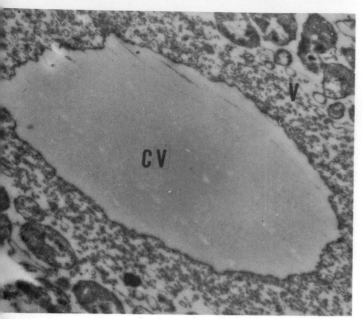

Figure 5-7. Electron micrograph of a section through the contractile (CV) vacuole of an *Amoeba*, magnification 9,000X *(courtesy of Dr. G. D. Pappas, J. Biophys. Biochem. Cytol.).*

characteristics of an animal cell, has a definitely shaped, elongated form surrounded by a pellicle through whose pores extend some 2500 cilia. By their coordinated and rhythmic beating, the cilia propel the animal in any direction. The organism contains two or three nuclei consisting of one or two *micronuclei*, which function in sexual reproduction, and a *macronucleus*, which controls other cellular activities. It has a fixed mouth and gullet for food ingestion, and forms food vacuoles that circulate within the organism while carrying out digestion. Waste products are discharged via the *anal pore*, whereas water is removed by way of two contractile vacuoles each with a set of radiating canals.

Volvox

Volvox as a flagellate displaying both plant-like and animal-like characteristics is considered by some biologists to be intermediate between the unicellular and multicellular forms. It is a colony of cells in which the first primitive signs of specialization have become evident. A *Volvox* colony (Figure 5-6) consists of several hundred to as many as 40,000 cells arranged in a single layer in the form of a hollow sphere held together by a gelatinous secretion. Each cell is connected to adjoining cells by cytoplasmic strands, and the interior hollow cavity of the colony is filled with a watery mucilage. Nearly all the cells are equipped with two flagella at the anterior end together with an eye-spot and contractile vacuoles. The granular cytoplasm of each cell contains a centrally located nucleus and a single cup-shaped chloroplast. A small number of cells located in the rear of posterior end of the colony have the capcaity to reproduce. They give rise within the hollow sphere of the parent colony to daughter colonies which escape through a rupture in the cell layer of the parent. Other cells in the anterior portion of the colony are also specialized by having larger eye-spots which exert a definite effect on the orientation and movement of the colony. The colony itself moves with a rotating motion with the anterior region headed in the direction of movement.

Blue-Green Algae

These are fundamentally unicellular organisms often occurring as filaments or colonies (e.g., *Nostoc* and *Gleocapsa*, Figure 5-8). As indicated in Chapter 4 they resemble bacteria in several of their subcellular structures. Their chlorophyll and other pigments (including the characteristic blue-green pigment *phycocyanin*, Chapter 15) are not present in discrete plastids but are dispersed through the cytoplasm. Several taxonomists group these organisms with the simpler plants, the algae, whereas others place them with the bacteria.

Chlorella

This is a simple unicellular green alga (Chapter 15) consisting of a small spherical cell containing a cup-shaped chloroplast, a central nucleus, and the usual granular cytoplasm surrounded by a cell membrane and cell wall (Figure 5-8).

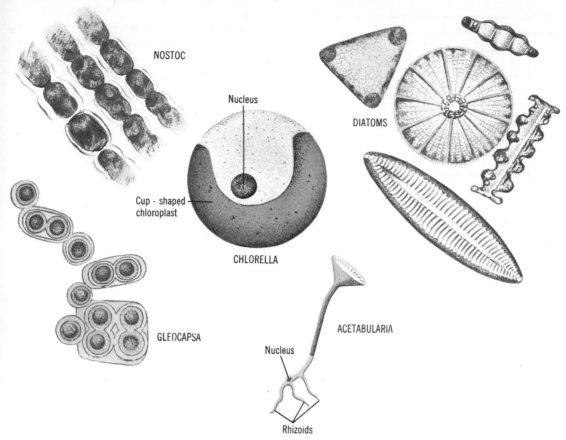

NOSTOC

Nucleus

Cup - shaped
chloroplast

CHLORELLA

DIATOMS

GLEOCAPSA

ACETABULARIA

Nucleus

Rhizoids

Figure 5-8. Some unicellular photosynthetic organisms.

Diatoms

These constitute a unique group of unicellular organisms possessing an unusual skeletal structure made of silica (a glass-like material) which is secreted by their protoplasm. The extremely intricate and delicate designs of these skeletons (Figure 5-8) vary from species to species. Aside from this outstanding characteristic, diatoms are photosynthetic single-celled plants possessing the usual cellular structures of plants.

Acetabularia

This is a single-celled green alga (found in the marine waters of the tropics and sub-tropics) which is remarkable for its immense size and ability to change form radically during the course of its life cycle. In the adult stage the organism as a single cell may attain a height of 8 to 10 cm, consisting of a long stalk (4-6 cm) topped by a large umbrella-like cap with leaf-like members (Figure 5-8). At the opposite end are several root-like structures, the *rhizoids*, one of which usually contains the single nucleus for the entire organism. During its life cycle, which takes approximately three years, *Acetabularia* first converts itself into a resting cyst made up of many cells, each containing a nucleus. The cells are eventually liberated as individual flagellate cells that swim about and soon fuse in pairs with each pair eventually giving rise to the adult form to complete the cycle.

Slime Molds

These are nonchlorophyll-containing organisms which display a remarkable sequence of changes during their life cycle. At one stage they are composed of a slimy, multinucleate mass of naked protoplasm, a *plasmodium*, which forms a worm-like mass that gives rise to a fruiting body containing many cells, or spores, each possessing a cell wall of cellulose. The spores are released and under suitable conditions produce individual flagellate *swarm cells* resembling animal cells. The cells may lose their flagella, becoming amoeboid, and eventually fuse in pairs to form *zygotes*. The zygotes develop into the multinucleate plasmodium to complete the life cycle (Figure 5-9). These varied stages resembling plants, animals, and noncellular life indicate the difficulties of classifying the slime molds (Chapter 15).

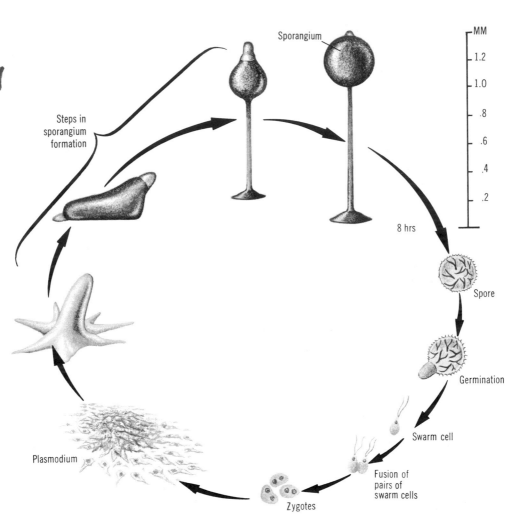

Figure 5-9. Life cycle of a slime mold showing various stages resembling plant, animal, and unicellular life.

True Fungi

This is a moderately large group of non-chlorophyll-containing organisms which display both cellular and multinucleate stages in their life cycles (Chapter 15). The fungal body consists of a mass of *hyphae*, which are multinucleate filaments each surrounded by a cylindrical cell wall. In some species there are regularly placed cross walls whereas in others they are absent (Figure 5-1).

CELLS AND TISSUES OF MULTICELLULAR ORGANISMS

General Features

At first glance the variety of cells that make up higher plants and animals indicates a wide diversity in size, shape, and structure. A more careful examination reveals that these different cells are fundamentally alike in possessing the basic structural and functional subcellular features described in the preceding chapter. Most of these cells are also endowed with unique structural and functional characteristics in addition to the basic features common to all cells. They are highly specialized, with each type performing a particular function leading to a specialization and division of labor among the cells of the plant or animal body.

In multicellular organisms the cells that are similar in structure and function constitute a *tissue*.[1] The cells of a tissue generally do not occur as isolated entities, but are usually bound together with varying amounts of interstitial substance to form an organized, compact group. The blood cells appear to contradict this statement, but the plasma (or cell-free fluid) of blood can also be regarded as interstitial substance or intercellular material.

[1] The term *tissue*, despite the precise definition given above, is also used in a broader sense, especially with reference to multicellular plants. Certain plant tissues (e.g., conductive tissues) may consist of a number of different cell types performing related functions. At other times the term is used to designate a particular anatomical region (e.g., the *phloem* (p. 96) of higher plants), even though it may consist of a number of unrelated cell types performing different functions.

Various tissues are usually bound to one another and coordinated in their activities to form *organs*. Particular organs function together in a highly integrated and organized manner to constitute an *organ system*. Together the various systems (e.g., the digestive and nervous systems in higher animals), in a remarkably integrated, harmoniously interacting organization, collectively constitute the whole organism.

How do these various cells know when, where, and in what quantities to develop and maintain themselves? What accounts for their intricate structural and functional coordination? How do they manage to synchronize their various activities with one another to constitute a normal functioning organism? These are basic questions of biology. From one viewpoint they are part of one and the same problem, namely the means by which cells of a multicellular organism exchange information and interact with one another. Although our knowledge on this point is extremely meager, there is sufficient indication that the coordination is achieved in large part by particular chemical substances or messengers whose production is ultimately controlled by genes. These various chemical messengers are able somehow to initiate, stimulate, and inhibit various cellular reactions, thus regulating metabolic events. They are more fully discussed in the chapters on the nervous system, hormones, and embryonic development.

The advantages of specialization in multicellular organisms, in terms of more efficient function as a result of division of labor, far outweigh the apparent disadvantage of interdependence of body parts. This seems evident from the fact that multicellular animals and plants consisting of various highly specialized cells have proved to be among the most successful of living forms, from an evolutionary point of view.

Animal Cells and Tissues

The various specialized cells or tissues of a complex animal such as man can be classified into five fundamental types: *epithelial, connective, muscle, nervous,* and *blood.*

EPITHELIAL TISSUES. Epithelial tissues consist of cells that are characteristically closely packed with little interstitial material. They occur as one or more layers of cells that line the inner and outer body surfaces protecting against injury, excessive dessication, and invasion by microorganisms. They are also concerned with the absorption of materials (digestive and respiratory tracts) from the external environment and the excretion (lungs, skin, kideny tubules) of waste products. As glands they secrete important specific substances (e.g., hormones and digestive enzymes) which are used in other parts of the body. As components of sense organs such as the eye they are highly specialized and extremely sensitive to certain kinds of stimuli. Epithelial cells, therefore function in protection, absorption, secretion, sensation and excretion.

They may occur either as a single or as multiple (*stratified*) layer of cells and many be conveniently subclassified into six kinds according to shape and specialized structure (Figure 5-10).

1. *Squamous* epithelial cells are thin, flattened, and tile-like, occurring in single or stratified layers. They line such cavities as the mouth, esophagus, vagina, and the inner surface of the eardrum. Stratified squamous epithelium makes up the outer layers or epidermis of the skin.

2. *Cuboidal* epithelial cells, as their name implies, are as high as they are wide. They make up glands including the thyroid, and form the lining of the kidney tubules. They also constitute the *germinal epithelial* tissues

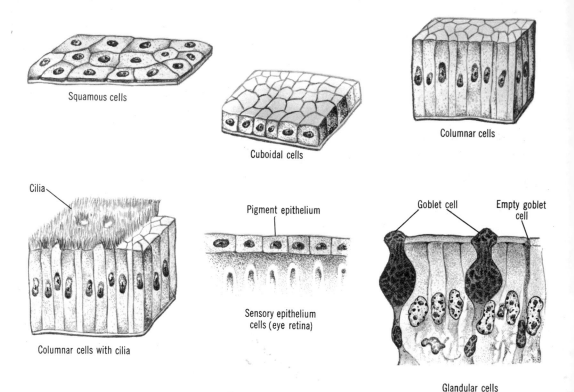

Squamous cells

Cuboidal cells

Columnar cells

Cilia

Columnar cells with cilia

Pigment epithelium

Sensory epithelium cells (eye retina)

Goblet cell

Empty goblet cell

Glandular cells

Figure 5-10. Types of epithelial tissue.

which produce the egg cells and sperm.

3. *Columnar* epithelial cells occur in one or more layers and are column-shaped with their height markedly exceeding their width. They form, for example, the lining of the stomach and intestines.

4. *Ciliated* epithelial cells are also columnar, but in addition possess on their free surface (the part exposed to the cavity which they line) rhythmically beating cilia. They serve as the lining for most of the respiratory passages and for certain structures (oviducts) of the female reproductive tract. By the coordinated beating motion of their cilia they function in the respiratory tract for the removal of dust and other foreign particles; and in the oviducts (Chapter 30) they direct the movement of the liberated egg cell.

5. *Glandular* epithelial cells are usually simple columnar or cuboidal cells capable of synthesizing and secreting certain substances (e.g., hormones, mucus, digestive enzymes, milk, and waxes). Glands may consist of isolated, single epithelial cells, such as the goblet cells of the intestinal lining, or of many cells joined together in complex structural arrangements, such as in the liver or pancreas.

6. *Sensory* epithelial cells, by virtue of their specialized cellular components or structures, are particularly sensitive to certain stimuli. For example, special epithelial cells in the retina of the eye are responsible for night vision. They contain a special pigment which undergoes a chemical reaction even when exposed to a weak light, thus presumably initiating a nerve impulse in the connecting nerve cell (Chapter 22).

CONNECTIVE TISSUE. Connective tissue cells function primarily in supporting the body and in binding or connecting together its parts. They also provide a mechanical framework (the skeleton) for locomotion for numerous higher animals, and furnish a protective coating against dessication or mechanical injury (as in the hard outer coat of many insects). The connective tissues are characterized by relatively huge intercellular deposits of interstitial material or *matrix*. In most cases the matrix represents the bulk of the tissue and is responsible for its characteristic supporting and binding qualities. Connective tissue cells are conveniently grouped into three classes: *fibrous* (including *fat* tissue) *cartilage*, and *bone* (Figure 5-11).

1. *Fibrous connective tissue* is the connecting material of the body which holds or anchors together organs as well as tissues. It also serves as an ensheathing agent of many muscle fibers and nerve cells, binding them together into individual muscles and nerves, respectively. Fibrous connective tissue cells possess an intercellular matrix consisting largely of interlacing protein fibers together with a lesser quantity of a jelly-like ground substance surrounding the cells that produced them. In some cases the matrix fibers extend loosely in all directions as in *scar* tissue and connective tissue binding the skin to the underlying muscle. In the latter instance the industrial chemical process known as *tanning* transforms the fibrous connective tissue into leather. In other cases the fibers are packed together and oriented in one direction to form specialized cord-like tissues know as *tendons* and *ligaments*. Tendons connect muscle to muscle or muscle to bone, whereas ligaments connect one bone to another, permitting some freedom of movement. A predominance of elastic fibers occurs in the connective tissue of the larger arteries.

Certain connective tissue cells develop into *fat* or *adipose* tissue. They have the special ability to accumulate and store fat, often as a huge droplet that occupies most of the cell volume, thus displacing the nucleus and cytoplasm to the periphery against the cell membrane. Fat cells are widely scattered, occurring singly or in groups; and they are usually referred to as adipose tissue when they accumulate in large, closely compressed numbers. They often have other cells packed among them as well as intercellular fibers running in all directions. Unlike most connec-

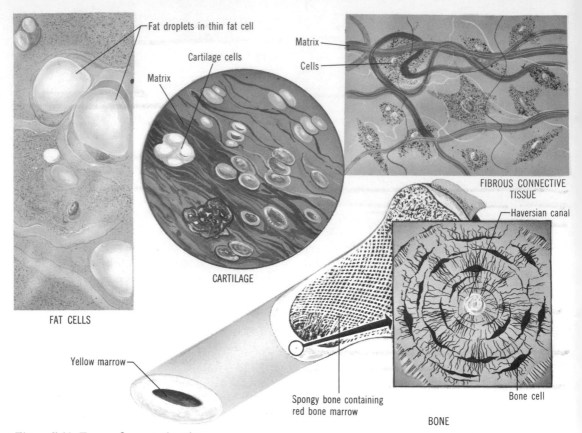

Figure 5-11. Types of connective tissue.

tive tissue types, the bulk of adipose tissue is not *inter*cellular substance but *intra*cellular material, that is, the fat droplets are within the cells.

2. *Cartilage* (or gristle) is primarily a supporting connective tissue typified by an extensive and usually homogenous rubbery matrix which is both elastic and firm. It is also permeated with fibers running in all directions or joined together into oriented bundles furnishing extra strength to the tissue against stresses and strains. Cartilage cells themselves are generally spherical (at times flattened or even angular, depending on their location) and lie singly or in small groups in cavities within the matrix. A number of different types of cartilage can be distinguished because of differences in the chemical and physical properties of their intercellular material.

Cartilage constitutes the temporary skeleton of the embryo of vertebrates (animals with backbone) and serves as the template for the development of most bone. It gradually undergoes conversion into bone during embryo development and the growth period after birth. Some cartilage, however, persists in the adult animal, such as in the joints at the end of long bones, at the end of ribs, in some of the respiratory passages, and in the ears and the nose. In sharks and related fishes it functions as the whole skeleton throughout the life of the animal, never being replaced by bone.

3. *Bone* is a uniquely hard and rigid connective tissue whose characteristically dense matrix is composed in large part of complex inorganic salts of calcium and phosphate and to a lesser extent of organic matter. Although its most obvious role is to serve as the skeletal

support of the body, it also functions as (a) protection for the brain, spinal cord, and chest organs; (b) housing for the vital red bone marrow which is one of the sites of blood-cell formation (Chapter 25); and (c) a reserve source of calcium and phosphate for use by other cells of the body. In its gross structure the shaft of the long bones of the body (arms and legs) displays a long central *marrow* cavity filled with *yellow marrow* (largely fat) surrounded by a tube of hard compact bone. The ends, however, consist mostly of spongy bone containing intercommunicating spaces filled with *red bone marrow* which produces red blood cells and certain white blood cells.

Microscopic examinations of hard compact bone structure reveals the presence of dispersed canals, known as *Haversian canals* (each containing an artery, vein, and nerve), surrounded by concentric layers of bone matrix and concentric rows of small spaces in the matrix containing the bone cells themselves. The bone cells are in communication with one another and with the Haversian canals by a system of minute interconnecting channels which penetrates the matrix in all directions, thus permitting the transfer and exchange of nutrients and metabolic wastes. There are essentially two types of bone cells, those that deposit the bony matrix and those that are responsible for its dissolution and absorption. Their combined action helps determine the characteristic shape and size of the bone. With increasing age the composition of bone matrix tends to become richer in inorganic salts and correspondingly poorer in organic material. The consequent increase in brittleness accounts for the more frequent occurrence of bone fracture in elderly persons.

Among the simpler animal forms, different types of connective tissue matrix, organic and inorganic, may serve as skeletons. For example, the interlaced fibers of the proteinaceous substance *spongin* forms the skeleton in certain sponges (Chapter 18) as do *calcium carbonate* and even *glass* fibers in others. The jelly-like substance in the *mesoglea* of coelen-terates (Chapter 17) and the nitrogen-containing polysaccharide *chitin* in crustaceans (Chapter 19) and insects are other examples of connective tissue matrix skeletons.

MUSCLE TISSUE. Muscle tissue is characterized by its highly developed ability to undergo contraction and therefore to perform mechanical work. It is responsible for the movement of the whole organism as well as its various parts in all but the lowest multicellular animals. It consists of slender, elongated cells usually found grouped into bundles ranging in length from a few microns to as much as four centimeters. The cytoplasm contains long parallel threads called *myofibrils* (Chapter 29) which are believed to be the contractile elements. The human body, like most higher animals, contains three distinct types of muscle—*smooth, skeletal,* and *cardiac* (Figure 5-12).

1. *Smooth muscle* cells occur primarily as constituents of the walls of internal organs (e.g., in the digestive tract, respiratory passages, arteries, and veins). They are spindle-shaped cells with long, tapering, pointed ends and a centrally located nucleus. Unlike skeletal and cardiac muscles, they are slow to contract, are capable of prolonged contraction, and show no cross-striations on their myofibrils. The contraction and relaxation of smooth muscle cells are directly controlled in part by the nervous system and in part by their chemical environment. Unlike skeletal muscle but like cardiac muscle, they are not under voluntary control.

2. *Skeletal muscle,* also called *voluntary muscle* because its action can be consciously controlled, is attached to the bones or tendons and is responsible for the movement of the skeleton and therefore of the body. Our arms move and perform work as we direct them to because their bones are moved by the coordinated contraction and relaxation of the attached voluntary muscle. Skeletal muscle composes 40 per cent by weight of the body and is completely and directly controlled by the nervous system. It contracts and relaxes the most rapidly of the three muscle types. Microscopic examination of a disrupted or teased preparation of fresh

A. Smooth muscle

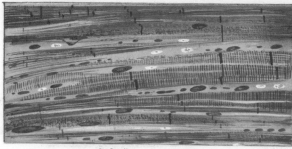

C. Cardiac or heart muscle

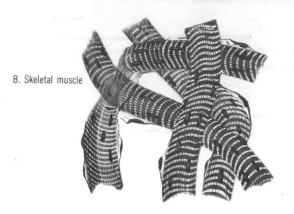

B. Skeletal muscle

Figure 5-12. Types of muscle tissue.

skeletal muscle reveals it to consist of long, cylindrical and tapering multinucleate cells called *fibers* which at an earlier stage in development were uninucleate. Each fiber is surrounded by a thin envelope of fibrous connective tissue binding the muscle cells together. Large numbers of fibers are in turn collectively enveloped in connective tissue sheaths continuous with the tendons in the instance of skeletal muscle, thus attaching muscle to bone. The nuclei are unusually placed in that they are characteristically peripheral, lying just under the delicate cell membrane which ensheaths each fiber or cell. Within the fiber itself are the long, parallel, unbranching units, the *myofibrils*, extending for indefinite lengths separately or in bundles in the cytoplasm. The details of muscle structure and function are given in Chapter 29.

In skeletal and cardiac muscle the myofibrils exhibit characteristically alternating regions of light and dark at regular intervals along their length, thus giving a distinctive cross-banding or cross-striated quality to the fiber. For this reason both skeletal and heart muscle, although different from each other, are referred to as *striated* muscle.

3. *Cardiac* or *heart muscle* is a unique type of muscle tissue found only in the heart. It resembles skeletal muscle in being made up of striated multinucleate fibers. The nuclei of each fiber, however, are not peripheral as in skeletal muscle but are distributed within the cytoplasm. The cardiac fibers are distinctively arranged to form a network or branching effect. Cardiac muscle also resembles smooth muscle in that its action is involuntary. It is distinctive in possessing an inherent and basic rhythmic beat (contraction and relaxation). Although the rate of beat may be regulated directly by nerve impulse, its independence of the nervous system is displayed by the fact that small isolated

pieces of heart muscle continue to contract and relax in regular rhythmic fashion.

NERVOUS TISSUE. The structural and functional unit of the nervous system is the highly differentiated *nerve cell* or *neuron*. Neurons never occur as isolated cells but are organized into an intricate and branching system, like a tree and its branches, extending to all parts of the body and constituting the nervous system. Each neuron consists of a *cell body* made up of a nucleus and surrounding cytoplasm which often extends into two kinds of fibers or processes called *dendrites* and *axons*. Dendrites conduct impulses toward the cell body, and axons conduct them away from the cell body. Most of the axon is usually enveloped in one or more sheaths. The size and shape of the cell body, dendrites, and axon, as well as the number and kinds of branches of the latter two structures, range widely, accounting for an almost infinite variety of neurons. In one type of nerve cell called the *motor neuron* (Chapter 21) the dendrites are frequently short and branched, whereas the axons, which usually arise from the opposite side of the cell body, are generally single, long, and slender extensions or fibers with branches near the terminal portion (Figure 5-13). In another type, the *sensory neuron*, the dendrites and axons are visually indistinguishable. Nerve cells are functionally connected to each other at a junction known as a *synapse*, where the terminal branches of an axon and the dendrites of another neuron lie in close proximity but never come in direct physical contact with one another.

The activities of the nervous system account in large part for the coordinated function of the different organs and systems of the body as well as for the maintenance of the integration and unity of the organism at both the conscious and unconscious levels. In most multicellular animals it represents the principal, if not the only, means of contact with the external environment since the organism receives, transmits, and interprets all stimuli through the nervous system. The nervous system is undoubtedly the most complex, and least under-stood, of the body systems.

BLOOD TISSUE. Blood is made up of a number of distinctive kinds of cells collectively called the *blood cells* and a noncellular, complex, aqueous fluid, the *plasma*, which contains a great variety of dissolved and suspended molecules. The general role of blood, and a related fluid *lymph*, is to maintain the stability of the internal environment of the body. The means by which this is accomplished are described in Chapter 25. Blood cells (Figure 5-14) include (*a*) *red blood cells*, which are enucleated biconcave discs concerned with the transport of oxygen to the various body tissues; (*b*) *white blood cells*, which are irregular-shaped and nucleated motile cells consisting of five different types that function in fighting disease; and

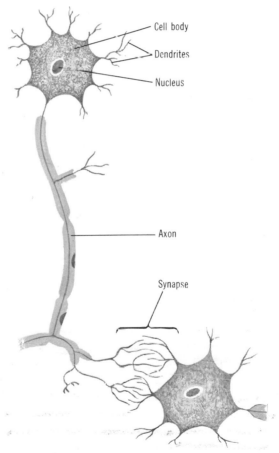

Figure 5-13. Diagram of a motor neuron.

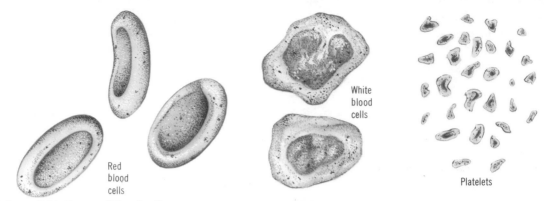

Figure 5-14. Types of blood cells.

(c) blood platelets, which are small fragments of specialized bone marrow cells having an important role in the blood-clotting mechanism. In some tissue classification systems blood is considered to be a form of connective tissue, since it originates in the developing embryo from cells similar to those that give rise to connective tissues.

Plant Cells and Tissues

Plant tissues may be classified in a variety of ways, based not only on structure and function but on other criteria such as stage of development as well as site and method of origin and development. Many botanists classify the cells or tissues of higher plants from the developmental standpoint into two broad types, *meristematic cells* and *mature* or *permanent cells*.

MERISTEMATIC CELLS OR TISSUES. Meristematic cells or tissues are not fully differentiated (or specialized), but they still undergo cell division and give rise to all other plant tissues. The cells are usually small and cubical, contain a single nucleus and a dense metabolically active cytoplasm with few or no vacuoles, and are thin-walled and tightly packed with few if any intercellular spaces (Figure 5-15).

Meristematic tissues account for the growth of the plant. Those that are present at the tips of stems and roots are known as *growing points* or *apical meristems* and are responsible for the increase in length of stems and roots. Growth in

diameter of stems and roots are made possible by a particular type of lateral meristem known as the *cambium*. The cambium often occurs as a cylinder of tissue made up of a single layer of cells located between the two fundamental types of conductive tissue, the *xylem* and *phloem* (p. 95). Depending on the plant, other types of meristems may also be present (including those that produce the cork cells), for example, at the base of leaves and at particular sites along the stem. New cells furnished by the mitotic activity of meristems produce all the other tissues by a process of maturation to form the permanent tissues of the plant body.

PERMANENT TISSUES. Permanent tissues, un-

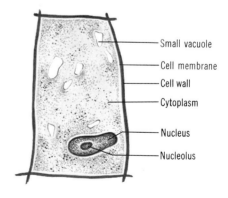

Figure 5-15. Meristematic plant cell.

like meristematic tissues, have become fully specialized and mature, and do not generally divide or change into other kinds of tissues. They usually retain their specialized structural and functional characteristics. In some specific cases, however, they resume activity as meristematic tissues undergoing mitosis and giving rise to other cells and tissues. They may also occasionally be transformed from one type of permanent cell to another. They may consist largely of one kind of cell, or, as in the conducting tissues, of several kinds of cells. Permanent tissues are often subdivided into the following three classes: *fundamental, protective,* and *conductive.*

Fundamental Tissues. Fundamental tissues consist of three types known as *parenchyma, sclerenchyma,* and *collenchyma* (Figure 5-16).

1. *Parenchyma.* This is probably the most common and abundant of the permanent tissues constituting large parts of various organs on higher plants, including a greater portion of the leaf structure and the pulp of fruits. It also makes up various parts of the stem and root and occurs freely in the conducting tissues. In addition it constitutes the body mass of lower plants and is regarded as the primitive tissue of plants, presumably having given rise to the many specialized and elaborate cell types of higher plants in the course of evolution.

Parenchyma cells are usually many-sided and thin-walled, often with numerous intercellular spaces, and possess a large vacuole and a metabolically active cytoplasm. The parenchyma cells of leaves contain chloroplasts and carry on photosynthesis in addition to their function of storage. Exposure of colorless parenchyma tissue such as colorless roots or stems to light often results in the appearance of chloroplasts in their cytoplasm. Parenchyma and meristematic cells are alike in certain characteristics such as their thin-walled and relatively unspecialized nature. This fact, together with the observation that parenchyma has a capability for cell division even as permanent tissue, is possibly suggestive of its primitive status.

2. *Sclerenchyma.* This tissue is composed of cells consisting of heavily and uniformly thickened cell walls of cellulose and lignin secreted by the protoplasts which usually die shortly after the walls reach their maximum thickness. It is primarily a supportive type of tissue providing firmness and mechanical strength to the plant body and, to a lesser extent, protection. Two general types of sclerenchyma cells recognized are *fibers* and *stone* cells. In addition to displaying the usual thickened and lignified cell walls, fibers are typically elongated, tapering cells with pointed ends. They possess little

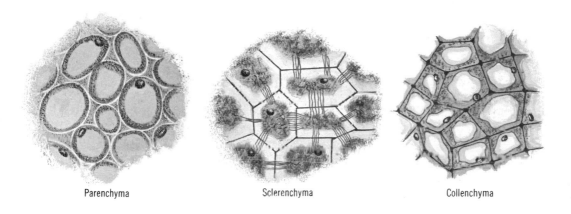

Parenchyma   Sclerenchyma   Collenchyma

Figure 5-16. Fundamental plant tissues: parenchyma, sclerenchyma, and collenchyma.

or no space in the cavities formerly occupied by protoplasts which have since died and disappeared. Fibers occur singly or in small groups, and are most often found among the various cells of root- and stem-forming strands or sheets of tissue extending lengthwise for appreciable distances. Because of their strength and pliability they have been used as a source of rope, twine, and numerous types of textiles such as hemps and linens. Stone cells, in contrast to fibers, are not elongated although they possess the usual thick, tough lignified walls. Although they occur almost anywhere in the plant body, either singly, in small groups, or in large masses, they are most abundant in stems, roots, fruits, and seeds. They form the hard parts of nuts, such as the walnut shell, and the gritty masses in the skin and pulp of certain fruits such as the pear.

3. *Collenchyma.* Collenchyma is a supporting tissue whose protoplasts, unlike those of sclerenchyma, remain alive for long periods of time after maturity. Its cells are not as elongated as fiber cells and are characterized by cell walls that are usually more markedly thickened at the corners. Collenchyma tissue is relatively soft and plastic compared to sclerenchyma. It occurs commonly in the elongating parts of stems and to a lesser extent in petioles and midribs of leaves and soft, mature plant parts.

Protective Tissues. Protective tissues cover the outer surfaces of plants as a single or multiple layer and function primarily to protect, largely against drying out and mechanical injury of the underlying cells. Protective tissues consist of cells characteristically possessing thick or specialized cell walls and interstitial substance. The two main types in this class are *epidermal* and *cork* tissues.

Epidermal Tissues. Epidermal cells usually exist as a layer (the *epidermis*) one cell thick and cover the outer surface of leaves, flower

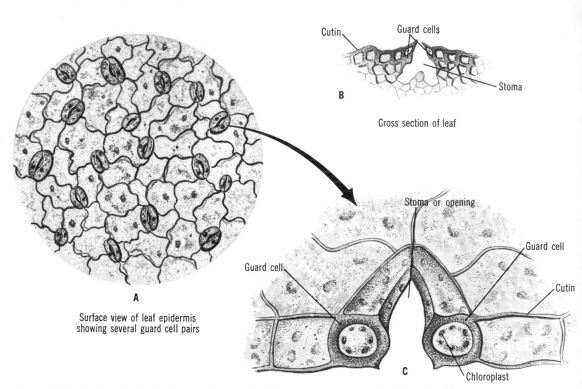

Figure 5-17. Epidermis of a leaf showing guard cells, stomata, and usual epidermal cells.

parts, and younger portions of stems and roots. They form a continuous coat of living cells covering the entire plant except for older parts of roots and stems where the epidermal layer has been ruptured or sloughed off by growth in diameter. Although epidermal cells occur in a variety of shapes—irregular in outline, flattened, brick-shaped, and so on—they fit together snugly like the pieces in a jigsaw puzzle without intervening spaces except for certain specialized types called *guard cells*. The outer walls of epidermal cells covering aerial organs are usually quite thick and have an external layer of a waxy, waterproof material known as *cutin* secreted by the protoplasts (Figure 5-17). The cells are colorless and somewhat transparent, and except for the *guard cells* do not contain chloroplasts. Occasionally blue or purple pigments may be present accounting for the unusual color of an organ (e.g., purple-leafed cabbage). Epidermal cells may also grow out from the surface layer forming single-celled or many-celled hair-like structures which give the plant a wooly or velvety appearance.

Cork Tissue. Cork cells are formed by a special lateral meristematic tissue, the *cork cambium*, and consists of one kind of cell making up the outer portion of the bark of stems and roots of woody plants. Of the daughter cells produced by cork cambium cells, the inner daughter (Figure 5-18) cells remain meristematic, whereas the outer ones soon secrete a waterproof substance, *suberin*, into the cell wall. Shortly afterward the protoplasts of the latter die and disappear, leaving only the suberized cell-wall structure which represents the mature cork tissue. The suberized cell walls were precisely what Robert Hooke observed when he discovered the cell in 1665 (Chapter 4).

Conductive Tissues. These tissues are responsible for transporting various materials, including water, dissolved minerals, carbohydrates, and so on, to different parts of the plant. They consist of two complex tissue types, *xylem* and *phloem*, each of which includes several kinds of cells.

Xylem. Although parenchyma and fibers are

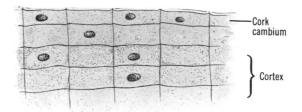

Figure 5-18. Cork cells.

some of the cells included in the xylem, the two chief conducting units are the *tracheids* and *vessels*. Mature tracheids are elongated, tapering cells whose protoplasts have died. The large empty spaces in the tracheid, formerly occupied by the protoplast, make it well suited for water conduction. Their cell walls, which aid in support of the plant, often exhibit thickened spiral rings of lignified cellulose and small thin or pitted areas connecting them to other tracheids and cells (Figure 5-19). Further specialization of the tracheids for water conduction during the evolutionary course of plant development has resulted in the enlargement of these cells with perforations usually in the end walls to form long verticle tube systems, known as *vessels*, at times several yards in length. The individual vessel elements making up the vessel itself were formerly living cells. They contain various kinds of wall thickenings and pits like the tracheids from which they evolved. The vessels function primarily in water conduction and secondarily as a supporting tissue. Tracheids constitute the chief conducting elements of that group of plants known as the *gymnosperms* (for example, the evergreens and firs, (Chapter 16). On the other hand, the more highly evolved water-conducting structure, the vessels, are characteristically present in the more advanced plants known as the *angiosperms* or *flowering plants* (Chapter 16). Angiosperms possess both tracheids and vessels in their xylem whereas gymnosperms have only the former.

Phloem. The fundamental structural and functional cell type in the phloem is the *sieve tube cell* (Figure 5-20), just as the tracheid is the important cell type in the xylem. Parenchyma cells and fibers, which function in structure and support, are also included in the phloem as they are in the xylem. The sieve tube cell is an elongate living cell containing protoplasm which loses its nucleus at maturity. The protoplast is characterized by a central vacuole and peripheral streaming cytoplasm which is continuous with the cytoplasm of vertically adjacent sieve cells by way of sieve-like perforations in the end walls (Figure 5-21). The verticle living sieve tubes thus constitute a continuous vertical cytoplasmic connection which aids in the transport of food to the various parts of the plant. A specialized type of parenchyma cell called the *companion cell* is structurally and functionally associated with the sieve tube cells in the angiosperms (flowering plants) but not in the less advanced plants such as the gymnosperms. Companion cells (Figure 5-20) are elongated nucleated cells somewhat shorter than the sieve tube cells which they laterally adjoin. They are connected by numerous cell wall pits to the sieve cells with which they are associated, and are believed to assist the sieve cell in the transport of food.

The predominant and most successful group of land plants are the angiosperms. From an evolutionary viewpoint they have achieved to date the highest state of development in the plant kingdom. The arrangement of the cells and tissues of the flowering plants into stems (and branches), roots, and leaves of the plant body are discussed in Chapter 16. Their physiology and biochemistry are described in Chapter 17.

Form and Function

The inseparable bond between form and function is aptly reflected in the structure of the various animal and plant tissues. Cells possessing large quantities of interstitial material or thick walls provide strength and support such as bone and cartilaginous tissues in animals, and sclerenchyma and collenchyma tissues in plants. Conductive tissues in plants by virtue of their thin-walled areas and perforations and large cell space are eminently suited for their basic function of transport. Protective cells in

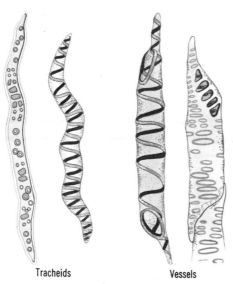

Tracheids   Vessels

Figure 5-19. Chief conducting units of the xylem: tracheids and vessels.

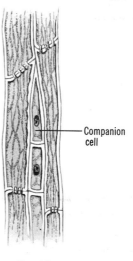

Companion cell

Sieve tube

Figure 5-20. Sieve-tube cells and associated companion cells.

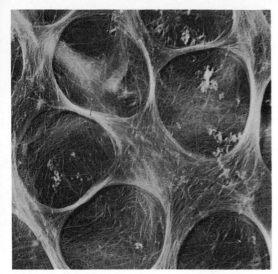

Figure 5-21. Electron micrograph of the sieve-like perforations in a sieve-tube cell, magnification 17,500X *(courtesy of Dr. A. Frey-Wyssling, J. Ultrastruct. Res.).*

plants such as epidermis and cork are waterproofed with cutin and suberin, respectively, thus preventing the loss of moisture from underlying tissues. In animals the epithelial cells, for example, are adapted to perform various specialized functions such as protection, absorption, secretion, and so on as a result of corresponding specialized structures and arrangements of cells. Obviously the study of structure and function must go hand in hand and cannot be considered separately.

ORIGIN AND DIFFERENTIATION OF CELLS AND TISSUES

The Problem of Differentiation

The process by which the cells of a multicellular organism in the course of its development acquires specialized structural and functional characteristics is called *differentiation*. What are the mechanisms by which the cells of a developing embryo undergo specific and predetermined changes in the course of their maturation, gaining new capacities and losing old ones to become differentiated tissues? How can a single microscopic droplet of protoplasm, in the form of a fertilized egg, become a human being with arms, legs, heart, and brain, or a fully developed flowering plant with roots, stems, leaves, and flowers?

Until now we have said nothing about the means by which cells and tissues of multicellular organisms undergo differentiation; nor have we indicated any of the factors that influence this important process. Our reasons are obvious. Despite the intensive and sustained research efforts of many biologists over the years, knowledge in this area is virtually nil.

All organisms basically originate from a single cell. In multicellular plants and animals this single cell is the female reproductive cell (egg) which has fused with the nucleus of the male reproductive cell (sperm) by a process known as *fertilization*. The fertilized egg cell develops into an embryo through repeated cell divisions (mitosis) with the resulting daughter cells taking their place in the various parts of the future adult body. In nearly all multicellular animals (with the exception of certain simpler groups, Chapter 18) there are three fundamental layers of cells which make up the embryo at an early stage of its development. They give rise to all the cells and tissues of the organism. The outer embryonic cell layer is called the *ectoderm*, the inner is the *endoderm*, and the middle layer is the *mesoderm* (Chapter 31). For example, nerve cells originate from the ectoderm, muscle and blood arise from the mesoderm, and the lining of the intestine develops from the endoderm. Although plants are also derived from embryonic undifferentiated tissues, they generally differ from animals in that some of the actively growing embryonic tissues persist through most of the life of the adult plant. We have already described these undifferentiated cells as the *meristematic tissues*. The manner in which they give rise to the specialized cells and tissues of the stems, leaves, and roots of the angiosperm is indicated in Chapter 16.

At first the embryonic cells appear to be identical; but as cell differentiation proceeds they gradually assume particular structural and metabolic features which allow them to carry on certain specialized functions. The specialized functions of differentiated cells are present in addition to the usual basic activities common to all cells (respiration, growth, responsiveness, and so on). In many cases differentiated cells display specialized structural features which are apparently the physical basis for specialized function. This is apparent from some of the foregoing descriptions of the various animal and plant cells and tissues (e.g., the myofibrils of muscle cells, the matrix of cartilage and bone, the suberized walls of cork cells).

To the best of our knowledge all cells of a multicellular organism possess an identical genetic endowment, having arisen from a single embryonic cell by repeated mitotic division. Is it possible that the chromosomal DNA has been somehow altered in different cells during development and that this is reflected by cell differentiation? Such an explanation is not at present regarded as a likely one, although it has by no means been disproven. There is no doubt in the minds of biologists that cellular differentiation is based on changes in the chemical constitution of the cell, undoubtedly due in part to changes in the enzyme pattern within the cell itself. But how is this brought about, especially if the master nucleic acids are unchanged as we believe them to be? We are still unable to answer this question to our satisfaction despite the great advances that have been made in the biological sciences. One of the more favored theories ascribes differentiation to an activation of latent genes in the nucleus according to a predetermined time sequence. This is presumably accomplished by appropriate chemical agents, among which might be hormones, nutritional factors, and other substances of metabolic significance. Elucidation of the process of cell differentiation still remains as one of the major unsolved problems of biology.

Regeneration

All organisms are subjected to varying degrees of wear and tear in the course of their normal existence. Cells are dynamic systems in which innumerable metabolic events are constantly taking place contributing to the degradation and resynthesis of their various components. In many multicellular organisms certain cells and tissues are actually destroyed as part of the normal physiological processes. Occasional injury is also responsible for the destruction of a tissue or body part. In order for most multicellular organisms, especially animals, to survive it is necessary that some of these vital tissues be replaced. The process of replacement of destroyed cells, tissues or body parts is known as *regeneration*. The degree of regenerative powers varies considerably depending on the species and the cell type. In some lower animals, such as earthworms, crustaceans (crabs, lobsters), and starfish, entire parts of the body that have been removed or destroyed can be restored by regeneration. For example, we can remove the claw of a crab and observe that this part can be completely replaced by the process of regeneration. As we go higher in the evolutionary scale we find that some animals, such as the frog, possess the ability for regeneration only during the earlier stages of their life history. In the tadpole stage a missing limb can be replaced, while in the adult frog stage this ability has been lost.

When we proceed still higher in the animal kingdom we observe that other animals including man lack the ability at any stage of development to regrow arms or legs, or fingers or toes once they have been removed. Nevertheless these higher forms still possess a certain degree of regenerative power. The surface of our skin, consisting of numerous layers of epithelial cells, is constantly drying out, dying, and being shed. This is readily seen in the instances of dandruff and "skin peeling" following severe sunburn. The everyday loss of surface layers of the skin is counteracted constantly by the formation of new cells, the result of an actively growing and dividing underlying cell layer. The replacement of hair, fingernails, and feathers is based on a similar regenerative process. The various blood cells in man and other higher animals have definite life spans which are counted in days and are therefore normally replaced through the regenerative powers of certain tissues. When cells have been damaged by injury the ability for self-repair, a form of regeneration, is exhibited by many different types of cells. Skin can repair itself, as can bone, muscle, tendons, ligaments, and certain nerve cells. In man even certain internal organs such as the pancreas and liver, consisting of several tissues, have a striking ability to regenerate when a portion has been removed or damaged.

The general rule appears to be that lower animals have the greatest powers of regeneration, and that these become progressively more limited as we proceed to the correspondingly higher forms. At one extreme we have lower forms such as certain sponges and coelenterates (Chapter 18) which can be cut into small pieces with each piece eventually regenerating into a new organism. At the other we have the highly limited regeneration powers exhibited in man as just indicated. Between these two extremes are graded degrees of regenerative ability.

Regenerating tissues in some respects resemble embryonic cells. The cells are undifferentiated; they multiply rapidly and eventually mature to yield specialized tissues. Whether these regenerating cells originate from undetected embryonic cells or possibly by a reversion of mature specialized cells to the undifferentiated state has not been clarified. However, regenerating tissues differ from embryonic tissues in that they represent undifferentiated cells developing in close association with adult cells.

In plants we have already indicated that at times mature differentiated cells (e.g., parenchyma) may become meristematic and produce new tissues. Regeneration is not a serious consideration in plants since they are unique in possessing meristematic tissue throughout most of their adult life for the growth of the stem and roots (apical meristem and cambium) and the production of leaves.

The Cancer Problem

The term *cancer* is used collectively to include some 300 types of cellular disorders, all of which have the common denominator of unrestrained cellular growth and multiplication. Cancer is a disease centering about the regulation of cell division. For reasons as yet unknown cancer cells arise initially from normal body cells and undergo repeated uncontrolled divisions presumably by the normal process of mitosis. In this manner they give rise to masses of newly formed cells, which frequently invade adjacent healthy tissues and organs. By breaking away as small groups of cells from the primary growth they may spread via the blood and lymphatic systems to other parts of the body. There they may lodge and proliferate, forming secondary cancerous growths or *metasteses*. When vital organs are affected, death of the organism becomes inevitable.

Cancer was recognized as a disease as early as 1500 B.C. by the Egyptians. Although the incidence varies widely with sex, race, age, geography, and socioeconomic group, it is known to occur in all races and ages of mankind and in many other animal species as well. More than two million people throughout the world die from cancer each year.

The ability of cancer cells to multiply freely by repeated and unregulated cell division is accompanied by a certain degree of loss of specialized features or *dedifferentiation*. Cancer cells tend to be less differentiated than the highly specialized normal cells from which they originate. They show a higher frequency of the mitotic figures of cell division and usually an increased number of chromosomal and other structural changes in the nucleus.

The problem of cancer and the process of regeneration are fundamentally related, representing different aspects of the underlying phenomenon of cell differentiation. In regeneration or repair the new cells that are formed soon differentiate into either connective tissue (scar formation) or cells of the type that are being replaced. Moreover, cell division ceases when repair is completed. Growth and multiplication are regulated and restrained. In the case of cancer, the controls are somehow lacking, resulting in a less differentiated, freely dividing, and wildly growing mass of cells which ultimately destroy the organism.

What are the metabolic differences between cancer cells and normal cells? We are still not certain. However, there is presently an emerging pattern of evidence favoring the idea that cancerous growth reflects a disturbance in structure and function of the DNA of the cell.

Tissue Culture

Tissue culture is one of the newer methods of studying the living tissues of plants and animals (including those of man). It consists of placing isolated cells or isolated parts of tissues or organs in a nutrient medium under conditions free of microbial contamination (Figure 5-22). Under these circumstances, with a regular replenishment of nutrients and oxygen, the tissues will continue to grow and proliferate. Depending on the conditions of the medium and the cell type, the tissues may revert to a relatively less differentiated state, or they may retain many of their specialized structural and functional characteristics. For example, embryonic skin grown in tissue culture continued to differentiate as long as certain nutrients were provided. On the other hand kidney cells in

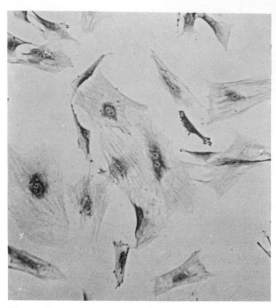

Figure 5-22. Rat muscle cells grown in tissue culture as seen under the light microscope, magnification 50X (courtesy of Dr. C. G. MacKenzie, J. Biophys. Biochem. Cytol.).

tissue culture resembled undifferentiated embryonic tissue until kidney connective tissue was also added; the cells now became characteristically specialized, tending to form kidney tubules (Chapter 28). Thus the technique offers a means of examining the effects of various factors on the process of differentiation of isolated cells.

SUPPLEMENTARY REFERENCES

Easu, K., *Anatomy of Seed Plants,* Wiley, New York, 1960.
Picken, L. E. R., *The Organization of Cells and Other Organisms,* Clarendon Press, Oxford, England, 1960.
Romer, A. S., *The Vertebrate Body,* Saunders, Philadelphia, 1949.
Smith, G. M., E. M. Gilbert, G. S. Bryan, R. I. Evans, and J. T. Stauffer, *A Textbook of General Botany,* fifth edition, Macmillan, New York, 1953.
Sussman, M., *Animal Growth and Development,* second edition, Prentice-Hall, Englewood Cliffs, N.J., 1964.

See also the references cited in Chapter 4.

THREE

THE MOLECULAR BASIS OF BIOLOGY

One of the unifying principles of nature states that the properties of all matter, whether living or nonliving, are governed by the same basic laws of chemistry and physics. It clearly implies that the characteristics and behavior of all organisms will ultimately be explained in terms of their physical and chemical properties. It calls for an analysis of biological form and function at the molecular level as well as of the whole organism and its component parts. During the last three decades man has gained considerable knowledge of the natural world by means of the disciplines of biochemistry and biophysics.

Appreciation of modern concepts in biology therefore presupposes some fundamental knowledge of chemistry and physics, particularly in the study of the biochemical sections contained in subsequent chapters.

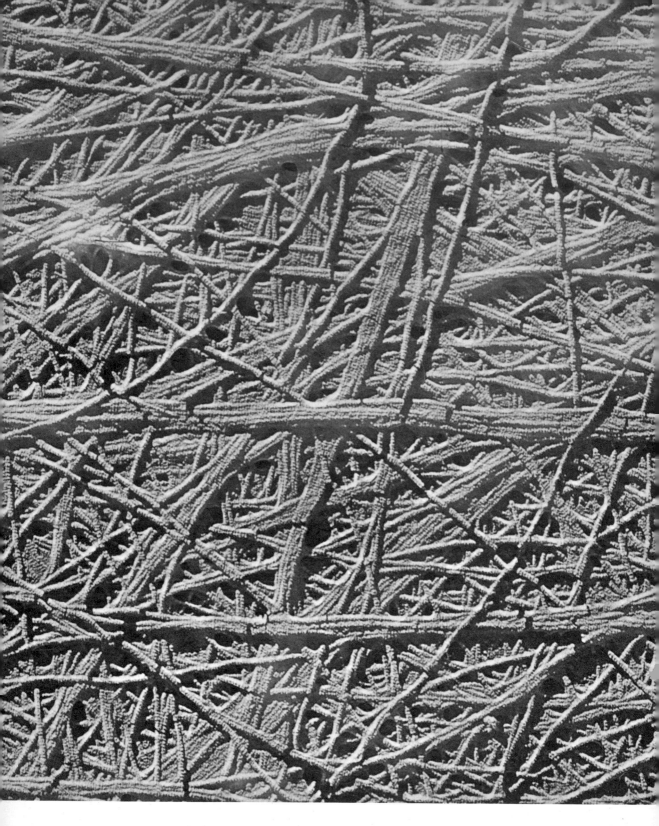

Electron micrograph of collagen fibers, 37,000X (courtesy of Drs. K. R. Porter and G. D. Pappas, J. Biophys. Biochem. Cytol.)

Chapter 6   Chemical and Physical Principles

MATTER AND ENERGY

Mass-Energy

The universe is made up of *matter* and *energy*. Matter has mass and therefore occupies space. It is drawn to any other body of matter by a mutual force of attraction known as *gravity*. *Weight* is a quantitative expression of this attractive force between any object of matter and a standard body, the planet earth. Matter therefore has weight.

Energy is usually defined as the ability to do work. Another way of putting it is that energy is actually the motion of a body of matter, or the ability to produce the motion of a body of matter. The various forms of energy that exist (heat, electricity, light, chemical energy, mechanical movement, and so on) are generally classified into two broad groups, *kinetic* energy and *potential* energy. Kinetic energy (or motion energy) is the form of energy displayed by matter that is in motion. It depends on the mass (m) of the moving object and its rate of speed or velocity (c), and is expressed by the following quantitative equation:

$$\text{Kinetic energy} = \tfrac{1}{2}\,mc^2$$

For example, when two objects possessing the same mass travel at different velocities, the faster moving body has a greater kinetic energy. Similarly, when two different masses move at the same speed, the larger body has a larger kinetic energy.

Potential energy is represented by all other forms of energy which do not involve motion and can ultimately be converted into kinetic energy. For example, the potential energy of a stretched slingshot is released and converted to the kinetic energy of a moving shot or pellet. Chemical energy is a form of potential energy stored in the chemical bonds of various substances. Under suitable conditions substances undergoing chemical change may release and convert this energy to other forms. The potential energy stored in the chemical bonds of rocket fuel, for example, is transformed into both heat and the kinetic energy of a swiftly moving rocket or missile. The potential energy stored in the chemical bonds of food materials such as carbohydrates and fats is converted in a living cell to other forms of energy, as indicated by the different activities of the organism. The burning of a coal is a chemical reaction whereby stored chemical energy is released in the form

---

[1]There are several different units of energy just as there are different units of measure (e.g., inch, centimeter, and so on). The *calorie* is a widely used unit of energy. It is precisely defined as the amount of energy (heat) required to raise the temperature of one gram of water one degree centigrade (from 14.5°C to 15.5°C). At times, especially in nutrition, it is more convenient to use the kilocalorie (or large calorie) which is equal to 1000 calories. The *erg* is a smaller unit of energy as compared to the calorie. There are 2.39×10^8 ergs in a calorie.

of light and heat. The heat energy under suitable conditions transforms water to high-pressure steam. Steam in turn can be converted to the kinetic energy of the moving parts of electrical generators and then to electrical energy which can be changed to other forms of energy such as light, sound, heat, and motion. Thus different forms of energy are interconvertible.

Until some years ago it was believed that energy and matter were different and separate entities and that neither could be created nor destroyed. It had been recognized for some time that energy could be converted from one form to another, and that matter could also be converted from one form to another. In 1906 Einstein formulated the idea that energy and mass are interchangeable. He stated that they were really different forms of the same thing and equivalent to each other as expressed by the equation

$$E = mc^2$$

where E is energy in ergs, m is the mass in grams, and c is the speed of light in centimeters per second (3×10^{10} cm/sec). This fundamental concept has since been confirmed and verified by other investigators.

The changes in energy and mass accompanying the conversion of one element to another, known as nuclear reactions, are given by the foregoing Einstein equation. For example, seemingly unrelated phenomena such as the emission of light by certain stars and the hydrogen bomb reaction result from the same fundamental fusion of four hydrogen atoms (with a combined mass of 4.032 units) to form a single helium atom (with a mass of 4.002 units). The reaction in all cases is accompanied by the disappearance of a small quantity of mass (0.030 units) for each helium atom formed since one helium atom weighs less than the four hydrogen atoms that formed it. The decrease in mass is reflected by the release of vast quantities of energy (light and heat and other radiations) corresponding to the loss in mass as indicated by the Einstein equation. The formerly sepa-

rate scientific laws that energy can be neither created nor destroyed (the Law of Conservation of Energy) and that mass can be neither created nor destroyed (the Law of Conservation of Mass) have therefore been combined into a single general law called the Law of Conservation of Mass-Energy or the First Law of Thermodynamics. It states that although mass and energy are interchangeable, mass-energy can neither be created nor destroyed; a net gain or net loss of mass-energy can never occur.

In brief the entire universe consists of a constant quantity of mass-energy which can neither be destroyed nor created. Mass and energy are interchangeable so that their proportions can change without any net loss or gain in the total mass-energy.

PHYSICAL STRUCTURE AND PROPERTIES OF MATTER

Molecules

The concept devised by the human mind that all matter — solid, liquid, or gas — is composed of discrete, continuously vibrating or moving invisible particles called molecules originated as early as 400 B.C. It provided an explanation of the observed behavior of many ordinary substances and numerous events. The commonly observed facts that such substances as salt or sugar can be dissolved in water, that a crystal or a colored dye can be added to water and thus produce a uniformly colored solution, and that solid crystals of iodine can form a purple vapor in the surrounding air can best be explained by assuming that matter is made up of extremely small, discontinuous but constantly moving particles or molecules with spaces between them permitting intermingling and mixing.

That molecules are in constant motion is further suggested by viewing under the microscope the irregular zigzag motion of small particles of dust suspended in water, or of particles of cigarette smoke suspended in air. This incessant jostling motion, as exemplified by the dust and smoke particles, is known as *Brownian movement*[2] and reflects the impacts they receive from the constantly moving molecules of the water or air medium. It is comparable to the motion of bread fragments in a fishpool produced by the jostling of the nibbling fish.

We now know, of course, that molecules, contrary to ancient belief, are not the smallest indivisible units of matter but are instead constructed of smaller particles known as *atoms*. Before proceeding to a discussion of atomic and subatomic structure it would be well to consider certain physical properties of molecules which have a direct bearing on several important biological phenomena.

Gases

Matter can exist in any of three physical states—gas, liquid, or solid. In the gaseous state it consists of rapidly moving molecules whose average distance from each other is so great that the volume occupied by the molecules themselves is negligible compared to the relatively vast empty spaces between them. This is illustrated by the tremendous decrease in volume that occurs when a gas is compressed to form a liquid. For example, the gaseous form of water, known as *water vapor*, upon being converted to the liquid state occupies about $1/1000$ of its original volume, indicating that under average room conditions at least 99.9 per cent of the volume of water vapor is actually made up of empty space.

Gas molecules experience an extremely weak attraction for one another, which accounts for their great freedom of movement and their completely disordered state. The molecules are constantly undergoing a rapid and random straight-line motion, frequently colliding with one another and the walls of their container. A molecule of oxygen gas, for example, has an average speed of 1000 mph at 0°C and standard atmospheric pressure, traveling about 300 times its own diameter between collisions. A gas, therefore, has neither a fixed volume nor a fixed shape, but distributes itself equally throughout any container or space in which it happens to be.

Like any other molecules, gas molecules by virtue of their mass and motion possess kinetic energy. An increase in the temperature of a gas is reflected by an increase in the average velocity and therefore kinetic energy of the gas molecules themselves. The temperature of a gas can therefore serve as a means of estimating the average motion of its molecules. The frequent collisions of molecules with each other do not generally slow them down but result in a change of direction of the moving molecules. Virtually no net loss of kinetic energy occurs as long as the temperature is maintained, although energy transfers might take place between the colliding molecules. If kinetic energy were progressively lost in these frequent collisions, one would expect the molecules to lose their motion eventually and to settle out. The collision of each molecule with the container wall produces a slight push or force whose sum per unit area is called *pressure*.

Liquids

When a gas is sufficiently cooled and compressed, its molecules, which were originally far apart, are brought considerably closer together. The resulting increase in attractive forces between molecules causes them to move more slowly and may become great enough to allow the molecules to coalesce and settle to the bottom of the container as a liquid. Although the molecules of a liquid still have movement, their freedom of motion is markedly less than in the gaseous state. They are also impeded in their motion by the many more collisions which they experience in view of the considerably higher concentration of molecules in a liquid as compared to a gas. Liquids

---

[2] After the Scotch botanist and discoverer of the cell nucleus, Robert Brown, who first observed this phenomenon in 1827 while examining pollen grains in a drop of water under the microscope.

unlike gases are practically incompressible because the amount of free space between the molecules of a liquid is negligible. Liquids tend to maintain their volume but have no characteristic shape, assuming the form of their container.

Some molecules in a liquid (as in a gas) move faster and others slower than the *average* speed. Those molecules near the surface moving in an upward direction and having kinetic energies sufficient to overcome the attractive forces of neighboring molecules escape into the atmosphere. This conversion from the liquid to the gaseous state is called *evaporation*, illustrated by the gradual disappearance of a street puddle after a rain. Some of the vaporized molecules may also be randomly knocked back to the liquid in a reverse of evaporation called *condensation*.

Solids

On further cooling, the molecules of a liquid arrange themselves into an ordered state whereby they are held closely together in definite spatial relationships to one another by strong attractive forces acting in particular directions to form the *solid* state. Unlike gases and liquids the molecules of a solid lack almost entirely the freedom to move in any direction around each other from one position to another, although they do oscillate or vibrate within a limited space. For these reasons solids exhibit a characteristic incompressibility, hardness, and shape.

Some solids such as iodine, for example, can pass spontaneously and directly to the gaseous state, indicating that at times the oscillation of individual molecules may be large enough to allow them to escape from the attractive forces holding them to their neighboring molecules.

Figure 6-1. Schematic illustration of diffusion using an imaginary model system with basketballs representing molecules. See text for explanation.

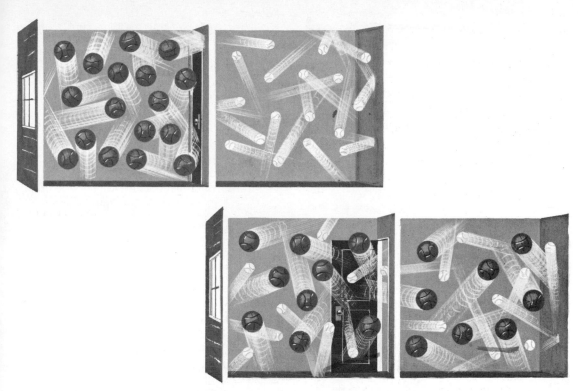

Figure 6-2. Schematic illustration of diffusion of two kinds of molecules using basketballs and baseballs to represent molecules. See text for explanation.

Diffusion

The constant and random motion of gas molecules as well as their great freedom of movement accounts for the dynamically uniform distribution which they rapidly attain upon being introduced into any given space or volume. This spontaneous spreading or migration of molecules or particles (which also applies to liquids, and to a lesser extent to solids) is termed *diffusion*. More precisely diffusion is the net spontaneous movement of molecules or other particles from a region of its higher concentration to that of its lower concentration. It is a dynamic process which is entirely due to the random motion of individual molecules or particles by virtue of their kinetic energies. Diffusion is therefore a probability phenomenon due primarily to the inherent motion or kinetic energy of molecules, and it occurs en-

tirely independently of any drafts or convection currents.

Although movement occurs in all directions the *net* movement of any particular kind of molecules will necessarily be from the region of its higher concentration to that of its lower concentration. At higher concentrations there are a greater number of molecules, and they therefore have by virtue of their random motion a greater probability of moving in any direction as well as towards the region of fewer molecules. An equilibrium or balance is reached when a uniform distribution of molecules has been attained. Equilibrium is a dynamic state in which there is no longer a *net* movement of molecules, since the number of molecules moving in any given direction is essentially the same as those moving in the opposite direction.

Different molecules when introduced into

the same container diffuse essentially independently of each other at rates determined by the mass and speed (and therefore the kinetic energy) of each type of molecule.

The phenomenon of diffusion is best illustrated by analogy to an imaginary model system. Envisage a large room containing a few hundred practically gravity-free basketballs each representing a molecule and traveling through the air along random straight-line pathways at different rates of speed. They frequently collide with each other and the surrounding ceiling and walls and thus are deflected along new linear pathways whose directions are changed again and again by subsequent collisions. If we were to follow the course of any particular ball for a short period it would show a haphazard zigzag path. Although the speed of any ball may change as a result of collisions, the average speed and therefore the kinetic energy of all the balls will remain the same provided that the temperature is kept constant. If a large door is opened to an adjoining room of equal size, some of the balls on a purely chance or probability basis will travel into the second room (Figure 6-1). Several balls that enter the adjoining room may also return to the original room by random movement. There is a greater probability at first that more balls will enter the adjoining room than those that leave it because the concentration or number of balls in the original room is greater. Thus diffusion or a *net* movement of balls from a region of its higher concentration (original room) to a region of its lower concentration (adjoining room) will occur until the concentration of gravity-free basketballs is more or less the same in each of the two rooms. When this takes place equilibrium has been achieved. A dynamic situation has been attained whereby the number of balls moving through the doorway into one room is equal to the number moving in the opposite direction into the other room.

Suppose that in this imaginary model system we were to start with a set of gravity-free basketballs in one room and a set of gravity-free baseballs (representing another kind of molecule) in the other. Upon opening the door, diffusion would occur simultaneously for the basketballs in one direction and the baseballs in the opposite direction. Each of the two sets of balls would experience a net movement toward the room in which its initial concentration was zero. Except for minor interference by collision the rate of diffusion of the basketballs would be independent of that of the baseballs. At equilibrium the concentration of basketballs and baseballs would be the same in both rooms (Figure 6-2).

The random motion of molecules as described for gases also applies to liquids and solids, although to a more limited extent because of the restricted freedom of motion of their molecules as indicated previously. The diffusion of molecules of liquids and solids nevertheless occurs, but at a slower rate. That the diffusion of molecules of a solid also occurs is illustrated by the presence of particles of gold in a silver bar and particles of silver in a gold bar after having placed the two metals in close contact for a period of years. From the biological viewpoint diffusion plays an important role in the movement of nutrients, oxygen, waste products, carbon dioxide, hormones, and other substances within cells and in and out of the cells of all organisms.

Solutions

When molecules, or electrically charged fragments of molecules known as *ions* (p. 122), of two or more substances are uniformly dispersed to form a homogeneous molecular mixture, they constitute a *solution*. The particular kind of molecule present in the greatest numbers is called the *solvent*, whereas the molecules of other substances uniformly dispersed in lesser quantities through the solvent are called the *solutes*. Gases mix freely in all proportions to yield gaseous solutions or mixtures. Liquid solutions are formed by dissolving (i.e., uniformly dispersing the molecules) a gas, a liquid, or a solid in a liquid.

Solutions in which water is the solvent are

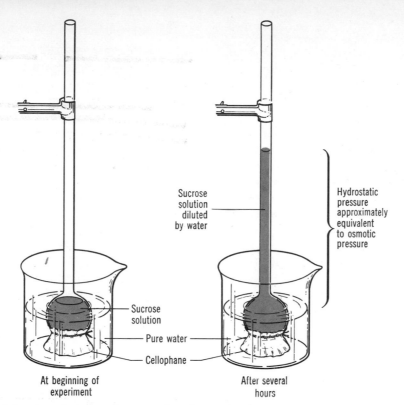

Sucrose
solution
diluted
by water

Hydrostatic
pressure
approximately
equivalent
to osmotic
pressure

Sucrose
solution

Pure water

Cellophane

At beginning of
experiment

After several
hours

Figure 6-3. Model system demonstrating osmosis and osmotic pressure.

by far the most important in living organisms. A unique property of water is its ability to dissolve a great many of the substances occurring in nature, thus forming solutions (called *aqueous solutions*) of numerous gases, liquids, and solids. As the "universal solvent," water is the chief component of living things, constituting 70 to 95 per cent by weight of most organisms. A significant feature of solutions, aside from the obvious biological requirement that most substances must be dispersed at the molecular level in order to pass into or out of the cell, is that they permit chemical reactions between various substances to take place more readily and rapidly. The involvement and action of all matter (gases, liquids, and solids) in biological systems occur in part as aqueous solutions, in which separate molecules of various substances are uniformly distributed in a vastly larger quantity of water molecules.

Osmosis and Osmotic Pressure

An understanding of the water relationships of cells and tissues is based on an understanding of the dynamics of diffusion of water into and out of living cells. The net movement of water in and out of cells is markedly influenced by the *semipermeability* of the cell membrane, namely its ability to permit readily certain molecules to pass in or out of the cell while not permitting, or less readily permitting, other kinds of molecules to do so. This is best illustrated by referring to simple model systems. What would happen if we were to place a volume of water and a 10 per cent aqueous sugar solution on opposite sides of a semipermeable membrane which permits the passage of water but not sugar molecules through it? This experiment is easily performed by covering the end of a thistle tube with a semipermeable membrane (permeable to water molecules but considerably less so to sugar molecules), partially filling it with sucrose solution, and immersing it in a beaker of water (Figure 6-3). Various materials including cellophane, gelatin, collodion (cellulose nitrates), or pig bladder can serve as the semipermeable membrane. Within the next few hours the level of fluid in the thistle tube will rise significantly as a result of the net movement of water from a region of its higher concentration (the beaker) through the membrane to a region of its lower concentration (the thistle tube). Water molecules move across the membrane in both directions except that the quantity traveling from the direction of the sugar solution in the thistle tube is less than that entering from the pure water (where the concentration of water is greater). The sugar molecules of the solution, however, for all practical purposes do not pass out of the thistle tube because the membrane is virtually impermeable to them. The diffusion of water through a semipermeable membrane (as illustrated) is known as osmosis. Although this term could conceivably be applied to any liquid containing dissolved molecules of other substance, in biology osmosis, by definition, is restricted to water.

Osmosis continues to occur until the hydrostatic pressure of the now diluted sugar solution in the thistle tube (the pressure due to the height of the sugar solution) balances the tendency for any further net movement of water from the container. Thus the system finally attains a state of equilibrium in which no further changes occur in the height of the sugar solution in the thistle tube.

The term osmosis is derived from the Greek word "push." The tendency of water to "push" its molecules from its more concentrated state through a semipermeable membrane to its less concentrated state may also be thought of as a force which we call *osmotic pressure*. Since osmotic pressure is directly dependent on the concentration of dissolved and suspended materials, it is simply another way of expressing water concentration, or alternatively the total concentration of materials dissolved and suspended in water. The greater the concentration of solutes and suspended materials the greater is the osmotic pressure. Pure water, of course, has a zero osmotic pressure. Osmotic pressure is often used interchangeably with the term osmotic concentration and implies that the solution has a potential or rating to produce under certain conditions (as in the thistle-tube experiment) a net maximal push of water molecules which can be balanced by the indicated opposite pressure. Osmotic pressure may be expressed in various ways either directly in standard units of pressure (e.g., pounds per square inch) or by some correlated figure such as number of atmospheres.[3]

Osmosis and Living Cells

PERMEABILITY OF PROTOPLASM. It is important to emphasize that osmotic systems in living cells are far more complex than the sugar solution-membrane models described earlier. Permeability of the various membranes of the cell to water and numerous substances in solution differs not only by permitting the passage of specific molecules at different rates, but varies with temperature, age, and physiological condition of the cell. Differential permeability, or semipermeability, is a general property of protoplasm and is most highly developed in the various membranes of the protoplast such as the cell membrane, nuclear membrane, mitochondrial membranes, and vacuolar membrane. It restricts or partially restricts the passage of various substances into and out of the cell, while allowing others to pass freely. The cell walls of plant cells, however, are not semipermeable, but are permeable by virtue of their large pore size which permits the free passage of almost all molecules in solution.

Permeability itself is frequently a relative property. For example, water molecules, gas molecules (such as oxygen, carbon dioxide, nitrogen, and hydrogen), and a number of other substances of metabolic significance penetrate cell membranes quite rapidly, whereas certain sugar molecules pass through very slowly. Cell membranes in many cases are virtually completely impermeable to large molecules such as proteins.

[3]An atmosphere of pressure is equal to the pressure imposed by the weight of the atmosphere and is taken to be equal to the weight of a column of mercury 760 mm high at 0°C.

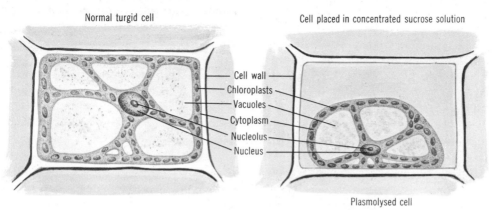

Normal turgid cell

Cell placed in concentrated sucrose solution

Cell wall
Chloroplasts
Vacuoles
Cytoplasm
Nucleolus
Nucleus

Plasmolysed cell

Figure 6-4. Plasmolysis of a plant cell resulting from exposure to a hypertonic solution. A net loss of water has occurred from the cell accompanied by a shrinkage of the protoplast away from the cell wall.

Osmosis in living organisms, as in model systems, can result in a net movement of water from a less concentrated solution (i.e., greater water concentration) to a more concentrated solution. In some situations the less concentrated solution may be a relatively dilute, aqueous solution as in the case of soil water surrounding plant roots. The more concentrated solution in this instance would be represented by the cells of the roots.

If red blood cells are placed in water, they begin to swell as a result of osmosis, changing from characteristic biconcave disc shapes to turgid spheres, and soon burst. The semipermeable membrane of the red blood cell does not permit the passage outward of many of the cell's molecules (including hemoglobin) to which it is impermeable, but it allows water to enter freely. The fact that the osmotic concentration is greater inside than outside the cells results in a net movement of water molecules into the cells. The progressive increase in pressure, as the water content within the cell increases, soon exceeds the structural strength of the cell membrane and causes it to burst. A solution of this type, whose osmotic pressure or concentration is less than that of the cell, is said to be *hypotonic.*

If red blood cells are instead immersed in

an aqueous sucrose solution whose osmotic pressure or concentration exceeds that of the cell (the cell membrane is relatively impermeable to sucrose), then the cells visibly shrink as a result of osmosis or a net movement of water out of the cell into the higher osmotic environment of the surrounding concentrated sucrose solution. A solution whose osmotic pressure exceeds that of the cell is called *hypertonic.* An *isotonic* solution is one whose osmotic pressure is the same as that of the cell. Red blood cells immersed in an isotonic solution therefore undergo no change in shape or size. Thus the osmotic pressure of cells and tissues can be experimentally determined by exposing them to various aqueous solutions of sucrose until a concentration is found (isotonic) in which no change of cell size or shape occurs. Sucrose is ideally suited as a solute for this technique because most cells are relatively impermeable (or slowly permeable) to it.

Plasmolysis

When plant tissues or bacteria are subjected to a hypertonic solution, certain effects occur in view of the relative rigidity and strength of the cell walls. A loss of water from the cell by osmosis takes place, accompanied by a pronounced and readily observable shrinkage of

Figure 6-5. Electron micrograph of a partially plasmolyzed bacterial cell. The protoplast including the cell membrane has been drawn away from the cell wall. Magnification 8,830X. *(Courtesy of Dr. H. A. Bladen, J. Bact.)*

the protoplast away from the relatively rigid and inflexible cell wall (Figures 6-4 and 6-5). The separation of the cytoplasm from the cell wall as a result of immersing plant cells in a hypertonic solution is known as *plasmolysis.* Plasmolyzed cells or tissues can usually be restored by immersing them in a hypotonic solution or water.

Plant cells or bacteria, unlike the red blood cells, will not burst or "lyse" upon exposure to hypotonic conditions in view of the relative inelasticity and high tensile strength of the cell wall, which prevents overexpansion and bursting of the protoplast by excessive water uptake. Under normal conditions of plentiful water supply cells of higher plants become quite turgid. That is, their swelled protoplasts exert a pressure against the enclosing cell wall called *turgor pressure* which may be inordinately high because of the strength of the cell wall. Turgor pressure aids considerably in maintaining the shape of soft plant tissues. If an excessive loss of water occurs from the plant cells due to a high rate of evaporation or exposure to hypertonic solutions, the net loss of water from the plant results in a substantial decrease in turgor, more commonly referred to as *wilting.*

Active Transport

It was formerly believed that the movement of molecules in and out of living cells could be almost entirely ascribed to diffusion and osmosis. We now know that all cells can also accumulate and push out various substances against a concentration gradient, apparently defying the laws of diffusion and osmosis. Certain seaweed, for example, are capable of accumulating iodine in concentrations a million times greater than that of the surrounding sea water from which it is obtained. The evidence in these cases indicates that energy generated by some of the metabolic reactions occurring in living cells is required for the transport of various substances against a concentration gradient, thereby concentrating molecules and keeping them concentrated. This type of concentration of molecules and movement of molecules through cell membranes against a concentration gradient (thereby requiring an expenditure of energy), is known as *active transport*. It is proving to be a far more common phenomenon in the normal passage of substances between cells and their environment than was originally believed. Present indications suggest that the movement of most molecules including water in and out of all cells is effected by active transport as well as diffusion and osmosis. For example, the absorption of digested food materials from the small intestine into the blood stream (Chapter 24) and certain aspects of urine formation (Chapter 28) are largely dependent on the active transport phenomenon.

Colloidal Systems

GENERAL PROPERTIES. Protoplasm is an extremely complex and still poorly understood system. It consists largely of water containing a multiplicity of substances—solid, liquid, and gas—dispersed and organized in various sizes and shapes. The latter range from uniformly distributed small separate molecules (as in true solutions), which are still beyond the visibility of our best microscopes, through an almost continuous and infinite array of sizes to giant protein and nucleic acid molecules and highly organized aggregates of molecules that are finally discernible with the light microscope as the subcellular components. Although aqueous solutions obviously play an important role in contributing to the characteristics of protoplasm, they account for only some of the features of living systems.

Many properties of protoplasm, including viscosity, elasticity, and ability to change from a liquid state, termed a *sol*, to a semisolid, termed a *gel*, can be ascribed to what is known as its *colloidal state*. A colloidal state or colloidal system is characterized by a stable and uniform dispersion of particles of a relatively larger size range in a liquid, gaseous, or solid medium. The suspended particles consist of molecules or aggregates of molecules that are too large to be considered in true solution but not large enough to settle out under the influence of gravity. Colloidal particles range in size from about 1 millimicron (mμ) to 100 mμ, or 10^{-7} to 10^{-5} cm in diameter and can be seen through the phase microscope and the electron microscope but not the light microscope. If the size of the dispersed particles or molecules is smaller than 1 mμ in diameter, they form a true solution. If larger than 100 mμ, they form a *suspension*. Colloidal systems are therefore intermediate between true solutions on the one hand and suspensions (e.g., finely divided sand suspended in water) on the other. The suspended particles of a colloidal system are collectively called the *disperse* or *discontinuous* phase, whereas the suspending medium is termed the *dispersion* or *continuous* phase. An *emulsion* is a particular type of colloidal system in which one liquid is dispersed in another for example, milk or mayonnaise (consisting in part of oil droplets of colloidal size in a continuous phase of water). Protoplasm includes a complex of colloidal systems.

Sols are liquid-like colloidal systems which often appear to be true solutions to the naked eye. Their discontinuous phase usually consists of uniformly distributed solid particles surrounded by a continuous liquid phase which is frequently water. When protoplasm is in the sol state, the water as the continuous phase is usually a solution of many different kinds of dissolved substances. The sol state under given physical and chemical conditions can be converted into the semisolid jelly-like condition called the *gel* state. As a model system Jello powder or custard powder dispersed in hot water first forms a *sol* which upon cooling is transformed to a *gel*; upon heating, the gel is reconverted to a sol. The semisolid or gel state of protoplasm can reversibly transform itself in the course of its normal activity into the sol state. The changes that take place in the transformation of sol to gel in colloidal systems are not entirely clear.

Some of the most important characteristics of the colloidal state are a consequence of the enormous amount of surface area presented by the disperse phase. The smaller the particle size the greater is the total surface area of the disperse phase. For example, a cubic centimeter of a substance in the form of a solid cube one cm along an edge has a total surface area of 6 square cm, or about one square inch. If subdivided into smaller cubes whose average size is within the colloidal range, such as .00001 cm (10^{-5} cm) along an edge, the same mass will now consist of 10^{15} small cubes having a total surface area of 600,000 square cm or about 700 square feet. Thus by subdivision into smaller particles the same total mass of material has experienced a 100,000-fold increase in total surface area.

Colloidal particles are capable of accumulating and concentrating other molecules (gas, liquid, or solid) at their surfaces, a phenomenon known as *adsorption*. Adsorbed molecules still possess kinetic energy or motion, although of a restricted type. Water molecules adsorbed on the surfaces of colloidal proteins are known as *bound water* in contrast to unbound or *free* water. When electrically charged fragments of molecules (called ions) are adsorbed on particles they impart a net electrical charge to the colloid. Thus some types of colloidal particles may become positively charged and others negatively charged.

BIOLOGICAL SIGNIFICANCE. Two prominent types of colloidal systems found in protoplasm and responsible for many of its properties are: (1) those in which the solid disperse phase consists of a vast variety of large, individual, and aggregated protein molecules in an aqueous dispersion phase, and (2) the emulsion type in which aggregates of fat molecules as minute droplets constituting the disperse phase are distributed in an aqueous dispersion phase.

The numerous smaller molecules and ions present in protoplasm are considered to be adsorbed in large part to the vast surface area of the proteinaceous colloids which constitute the basic matrix of living cells. The chemical reactions collectively constituting the metabolism of the cell take place at the surface of

specific proteinaceous colloidal particles called *enzymes* (Chapter 7). Adsorption phenomena are associated with enzyme action and are also responsible for a greater concentration of molecules and therefore a greater probability of more chemical reactions occurring at the colloidal surfaces. The numerous functions or physiological processes carried out by the various cell components therefore have their ultimate basis in the chemical and physical reactions which are mediated by the highly specialized colloidal organization of the cell (i.e., the proteins).

Several other biological implications of colloidal systems are illustrated by a number of examples. The various membranes of the living cell are considered to be colloidal gels. Injury to these membranes may result in the loss of some of the fluid contents unless a portion of the escaping sol is transformed to a gel state, thus sealing the wound. Amoeboid motion whereby certain cells such as amoeba and white blood cells move from one place to another is effected by a flow of protoplasm probably involving reversible sol to gel transformations. The mechanism of blood clotting is essentially the conversion of a particular blood protein (*fibrinogen*) from the sol to the gel state (*fibrin*) to form a clot which normally seals the injury in the blood vessel (Chapter 25).

MOLECULAR AND ATOMIC STRUCTURE

Elements and Compounds

The basic units or building blocks of molecules are called *atoms*. There are 92 naturally occurring, different kinds of atoms in the universe. Since the early 1940's man has produced about 11 additional ones and he will undoubtedly add more to this list. Individual atoms have never been seen. In fact it has been only with the advent of the electron microscope that we have been able to observe single molecules directly, namely those of particularly large proteins and the nucleic acids. Each kind of atom exhibits its own unique properties, retaining its individuality and failing to be decomposed by any form of *chemical treatment.*

The 92 naturally occurring atoms are found in a variety of chemical states. Depending on its particular properties, each atom may occur singly, in chemical combination with atoms identical to itself, or in chemical combination with one or more other kinds of atoms, thus forming molecules that constitute all the material or matter of the universe. Any substance whose molecules are composed of only one kind of atom is spoken of as an *element*. Although the molecules of an element may consist of one or more identical atoms, the element cannot be decomposed by *chemical means* to any other substance or to any simpler material. An element, therefore, is chemically an irreducible primary (or elementary) substance. There are 103 different elements (naturally occurring and man-made), each corresponding to a particular kind of atom. Atoms of any particular element are identical in all their properties but different from atoms of other elements. By international scientific agreement each element has been assigned a particular abbreviation to serve as a form of chemical shorthand for convenient use in chemical formulas and equations. The abbreviations for the 20 or so elements known to be essential for life are shown in Table 6-1.

Those substances whose molecules consist of two or more *different* kinds of atoms in chemical combination with one another are called *compounds*. Their atoms are chemically bound in *fixed and definite proportions* and in a *specific configuration* or structural relationship to constitute the molecule of a compound. Unlike an element, a compound can be broken down by suitable chemical means to simpler substances or to its constituent atoms or elements. The molecules of a compound have their own individual properties which are usually markedly different from those of their constituent atoms. Water (H_2O), for example, which at room temperature is a liquid possessing its own characteristic properties, can be broken down by appropriate chemical manipulation to yield its constituent

TABLE 6-1   Elements Known to Be Essential for Protoplasm

ELEMENT	SYMBOL	ATOMIC NUMBER	ATOMIC WEIGHT
Hydrogen	H	1	1.008
Boron	B	5	10.811
Carbon	C	6	12.000
Nitrogen	N	7	14.007
Oxygen	O	8	15.999
Sodium	Na	11	22.990
Magnesium	Mg	12	24.312
Phosphorus	P	15	30.974
Sulfur	S	16	32.064
Chlorine	Cl	17	35.453
Potassium	K	19	39.102
Calcium	Ca	20	40.08
Manganese	Mn	25	54.938
Iron	Fe	26	55.847
Cobalt	Co	27	58.933
Copper	Cu	29	63.54
Zinc	Zn	30	65.37
Selenium	Se	34	78.96
Molybdenum	Mo	42	95.94
Iodine	I	53	126.904

atoms as hydrogen gas and oxygen gas with each possessing its own particular properties.

The presence of various atoms in different substances can be demonstrated in a number of ways. If wood, sugar, or meat, for example, is burned or charred, it always yields the element carbon or charcoal as one of its original constituent atoms. Various chemical treatments are unsuccessful in the further breakdown of carbon. Although it is true that heating at high temperatures in air will cause it to disappear, the carbon itself has not been destroyed or broken into smaller units. It has simply entered into chemical combination with the oxygen of the air to form molecules of the colorless and odorless gases carbon monoxide (CO) and carbon dioxide (CO_2). By appropriate chemical treatment of these gases, the carbon can be obtained again in its typical elemental form. On the other hand the heating of a substance such as glass under a variety of conditions even to temperatures that cause it to melt fails to show the appearance of charcoal or carbon.

Carbon atoms are obviously not part of the structure of glass.

By employing various chemical and physical means, the kinds and exact numbers of atoms making up the molecules of different substances including those of biological importance can be determined. Thus it has been shown that proteins are composed of highly complex chemical combinations of thousands of carbon, hydrogen, oxygen, and nitrogen atoms. Carbohydrates consist of an entirely different chemical arrangement of carbon, hydrogen, and oxygen atoms. Fats have the same kinds of atoms as carbohydrates but in different proportions and chemical configurations. And nucleic acid molecules consist of carbon, hydrogen, oxygen, nitrogen, and phosphorus chemically combined with each other in such proportions and configurations as to form their own unique molecules (Chapter 7).

Structure of the Atom

How do atoms join with each other in chemical combination to form molecules? What are the structural features of the atom that permit it to form chemical bonds with other atoms?

Atoms can be considered to consist of various combinations of three fundamental subatomic particles—the electron, proton, and neutron. The electron as the fundamental unit of electricity consists of an extremely small particle. It possesses a negative electrical charge of 1 and a mass $\frac{1}{1850}$ of that of the lightest known atom, hydrogen. Numerous experiments have demonstrated that electrons can be obtained from all kinds of matter. Two familiar examples are the frictional contact between various materials (such as dragging our feet on a carpet) creating an electrical charge which is apparently due to a rubbing off of electrons, and the heating of a metallic wire under vacuum giving rise to a stream of electrons (as in the vacuum tubes of television and radio sets).

Since atoms possess negatively charged particles (i.e., electrons), it follows that positively charged particles must also be included in the structure of the atom to account for its electrical neutrality. These particles have been shown to be protons, each possessing a positive charge of 1 and a mass of 1 (i.e., 1850 times the mass of the electron). The finding that the atoms of all the elements (other than hydrogen) have masses which markedly exceed that contributed by their electrons and protons led to the discovery in 1932 of the electrically neutral particle, the neutron, possessing a mass practically equal to that of the proton. Although other types of subatomic particles have been identified (e.g., *mesons*) the properties of atoms and their ability to react chemically with each other can be most simply explained on the basis of electrons, protons, and neutrons.

Each atom contains a positively charged, dense core or nucleus consisting of a characteristic quantity of protons and neutrons which virtually constitute the entire mass of the atom. The atomic nucleus of each of the 103 elements possesses its own typical quantity of protons and, with the sole exception of hydrogen, a number of neutrons which equals or exceeds the number of protons. Surrounding the atomic nucleus is the remainder of the atom—a space with a diameter about 10,000 times larger than that of the nucleus and containing a quantity of rapidly revolving electrons equal to the number of protons in the nucleus, at times rather close to the nucleus and at other times relatively far away. The rapidly revolving electrons are therefore pictured as forming a diffuse, hazy, electron cloud of varying density about the nucleus. Atoms range from 2 to 5 Å (10^{-8} cm) in diameter, but only about one-tenthousandth or less of this distance is occupied by the dense nucleus with the rest of the space being taken up by the electron cloud (Figure 6-6). An atom is therefore electrically neutral, being composed of a cloud of rapidly moving electrons orbiting around a dense nucleus which contains an equal number of protons and (except for the hydro-

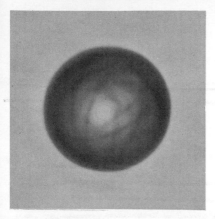

Figure 6-6. Schematic representation of the atom as a cloud of rapidly moving electrons orbiting around a dense nucleus.

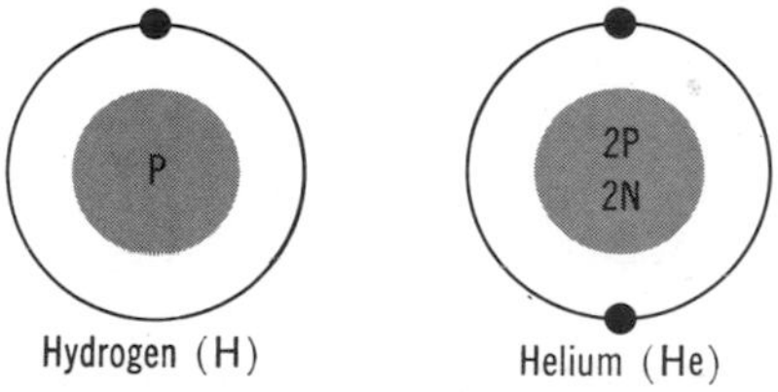

Hydrogen (H)   Helium (He)

Figure 6-7. Representation of the hydrogen and helium atoms.

gen atom) an equal or greater number of neutrons.

The simplest (and lightest) of all atoms is hydrogen, consisting of a positively charged nucleus of one proton around which is a rapidly orbiting electron with an equal but opposite charge (Figure 6-7). Its electron can easily be removed in a variety of ways, leaving the positively charged nucleus or proton which is also called a *hydrogen ion* (designated as H⁺). Hydrogen ions are responsible for the acidity of a solution and exert a marked effect on the activities of biological systems as indicated in a later section.

The helium atom as the next lightest element has two protons which account for the two positive charges in its nucleus. These are balanced by two electrons revolving rapidly around the nucleus to give the typically electrically neutral atom. The mass or weight of a helium nucleus, however, is four units instead of two, indicating that in addition to two protons two neutrons are also present (Figure 6-7). Uranium, one of the heaviest atoms known, possesses a nucleus composed of 92 protons and 146 neutrons to give a weight of 238.

Atomic Weight and Molecular Weight

The atomic weight of an element is equal to the sum of its protons, neutrons, and electrons. In practice, however, it is often computed as the sum of the protons and neutrons because the contribution to the mass of any atom by its electrons (1/1850 of the mass of protons or neutrons) is almost negligible. For example, as indicated, hydrogen has an atomic weight of 1, helium of 4, and uranium of 238.

The values used for designating the atomic weights of the elements are based on the relative weights of the different elements to each other. In any system of relative weights, one reference value or standard must be selected as the basis for comparison. Until recently the oxygen atom was the defined base. In 1961, however, chemists and physicists agreed to use instead the carbon atom (the $_6C^{12}$ isotope) as the arbitrary standard of reference. The relative atomic weight arbitrarily assigned to carbon is 12.000. It results in a value of almost 1 (1.008) for the lightest atom, hydrogen, as well as approximately whole number atomic weights for most of the other elements. Atomic weight is therefore defined as the relative weight of any atom compared with the weight of the carbon atom arbitrarily taken as 12. In other words, the unit of atomic weight, that is, the weight of a proton or neutron, is by definition one-twelfth the mass of the carbon atom.

The *molecular weight* of any substance (element or compound) is equal to the sum of the atomic weights of its constituent atoms. For example, the molecular weight of hydrogen gas consisting of molecules made up of 2 hydrogen atoms chemically bound to each other (designated as H_2) is therefore 2 times the atomic weight of the hydrogen atom (1.008) or 2.016. Water is a compound made up of 2 atoms of hydrogen (of atomic weight 1.008) chemically linked to an atom of oxygen having an atomic weight of 16. Its molecular weight is therefore the sum of its atoms or 18.016. Although many simple compounds such as salts, sugars, and so on have molecular weights that are of the order of a few hundred, substances of great biological significance such as proteins and nucleic acids possess molecular weights that often range from a few thousand to as high as 10 million and more.

If we had some way of counting the atoms in a given weight of an element, we could then determine their actual or absolute weight. For instance, if we could measure the number of atoms in 12 grams of carbon, we could then arrive at the weight of a single carbon atom by dividing the number of atoms into 12 grams. We know from indirect means of estimating the number of atoms (e.g., X-ray diffraction techniques) that 12 grams of carbon, which happens to be the atomic weight of carbon expressed in grams (termed the *gram-atomic weight*), consists of 6.02×10^{23} atoms. This number is known as *Avogadro's number* and is the same for the gram-atomic weight of any element. For example, there are 6.02×10^{23} atoms in a gram-atomic weight of the lightest element hydrogen (1.008 g) or in a gram-atomic weight of the heaviest naturally occurring element uranium (238.07 g). Therefore, by dividing Avogadro's number into the gram-atomic weights of the elements, we obtain the absolute or actual weights of the different atoms. They are almost inconceivably small, too small of course to be weighed directly. For example, a single atom of hydrogen weighs

only 1.7×10^{-24} g, carbon 20.4×10^{-24} g, and uranium 404.7×10^{-24} g.

Atomic Number and Electron Arrangement

The number of protons present in the nucleus of an atom is defined as its *atomic number*. Each of the 103 elements has its own characteristic atomic number which is primarily responsible for the unique chemical properties exhibited by their atoms. The quantity of electrons constituting the electron cloud of an atom is in turn determined by and equal to the atomic number or the number of protons in its nucleus. According to our present concepts the unique chemical behavior of each of the elements reflects the fundamental organization of the electron cloud about the atomic nucleus. Studies of the laws of motion governing the behavior of small particles, a discipline known as *quantum mechanics*, have established certain principles regarding the energy relationships of the revolving electrons. They indicate that electrons orbiting in the cloud around an atomic nucleus can be viewed as being arranged in concentric shells, representing definite energy states or levels, which are progressively increased with increasing distance from the positively charged nucleus. Of all the electrons in an atom, electrons in the outermost energy shell have the greatest energies and are held the least tightly and least closely to the nucleus. The ability of these outer electrons to engage the outermost electrons of other atoms in the formation of chemical bonds is the very basis of the chemical reaction, as we shall see shortly.

The lowest energy level or innermost shell of electrons surrounding the atomic nucleus is referred to as the K shell, with succeeding shells indicated by the successive letters, L, M, N, O, P and Q. Some of the heavier elements have as many as 7 shells of electrons while others have fewer depending on their quantity of electrons. There are certain useful generalizations or rules which indicate the maximum number of electrons that can be represented in

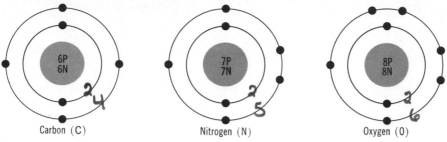

Figure 6-8. Representation of the carbon, nitrogen, and oxygen atoms.

a given shell. For our purposes it will suffice to say that the lowest energy level or K shell can contain 2 electrons at most, whereas all other shells when occupying the outermost energy level may have a maximum number of 8 electrons (in a number of elements the next to outermost level may be as high as 18 electrons). The electron shell structure of the carbon, nitrogen, and oxygen atoms are shown in Figure 6-8.

Chemical Properties of Atoms

The chemical properties of atoms depend on the number of electrons in the outermost energy level or shell. For reasons that are still not clear there seems to be a special chemical stability associated with atoms whose outermost shell contains 8 electrons (a maximal number of 2 electrons results in chemical stability solely in the instances of the two smallest atoms, hydrogen and helium, which have only the K electron energy shell). This is simply another way of saying that atoms possessing 8 electrons in their outermost electron shell (or 2 electrons in their K shell when this is the only electronic energy level present as in hydrogen and helium) rarely undergo chemical reactions because the electrons of their outermost shell are so stable that they rarely interact with the outer electrons of other atoms to form chemical bonds. The hydrogen atom with an atomic number of 1 is a highly reactive element tending either to lose its electron to form a proton (or hydrogen ion), or to gain an electron by sharing one

with another atom. In the latter type of reaction it may combine with another hydrogen atom to form molecular hydrogen or with numerous other atoms such as oxygen, carbon, and nitrogen to yield an almost infinite variety of compounds including many of great biological significance. The next lightest element is helium with an atomic number of 2, and therefore with a stable configuration of 2 electrons in its single shell, the K shell. For this reason it is an almost inert atom, virtually incapable of reacting with any other atoms or molecules.

In addition to helium there are 5 other nearly inert elements which are collectively called the noble gases. They are neon, argon, krypton, xenon, and radon, each containing 8 electrons in its outermost electron cloud shell. All the other elements are chemically reactive to varying degrees depending on their atomic make-up.

As described in the later section on chemical reactions, atoms react with each other to form chemical bonds by tending to surround themselves with an outermost shell of 8 electrons. (In the hydrogen atom it would be 2 electrons.) Elements therefore exhibit a tendency to acquire an electronic environment in their outermost shell resembling that of the noble gases. Accordingly, a certain number of bonds are characteristically associated with each element depending on the number of electrons that it must gain, lose, or share (as the case may be) to attain the stable electron configuration of 8 (or 2 in hydrogen) in their outermost shell. For example, hydrogen forms 1 chemical bond,

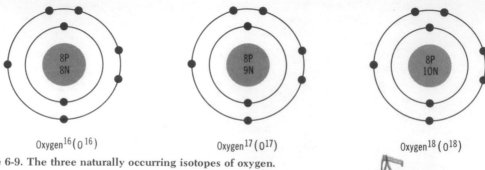

Figure 6-9. The three naturally occurring isotopes of oxygen.

carbon 4 bonds, oxygen 2 bonds, and nitrogen 3 or 4 bonds. It should be pointed out that this is a useful generalization but some exceptions exist.

The atoms of each element, when heated to a high temperature, emit or absorb characteristic bands or wavelengths of light, collectively termed a *light spectrum,* the result of the temporary movement of some of their electrons to and from higher and lower energy level shells. Each element has its own unique spectrum or "fingerprint," which can serve as an important means for detecting its presence, as in the stars by examining the wavelengths of light emitted. In fact, several organic compounds of biological significance also exhibit characteristic light absorption spectra, the result of temporary electron shifts to different energy shells. These unique spectra have proved to be extremely useful tools in the study of these substances in biological systems.

Isotopes

Atoms of an element having the same atomic number (and therefore the same chemical properties) but different atomic weights because of different amounts of neutrons are called *isotopes.* Isotopes of any given element have the same number of protons and therefore the same number of electrons, differing only in the quantity of neutrons.

For example, the oxygen atom (in molecular oxygen or in a variety of compounds including water, carbohydrates, fats, and so on) occurs in nature as three different isotopes. Each has 8 protons in its atomic nucleus and 8 surround-

ing electrons, but differs from the others in its number of neutrons (Figure 6-9). The most abundant oxygen isotope has 8 neutrons (atomic weight 16) and represents 99.76 per cent of the naturally occurring oxygen atoms. The abundance in nature of the second oxygen isotope having 9 neutrons (atomic weight 17) is 0.039 per cent, whereas that of the third isotope with 10 neutrons (atomic weight 18) is 0.20 per cent. The oxygen 18 isotope (designated as O_{18}) has been concentrated and used as an effective "tracer" to elucidate a number of important biochemical processes.

Isotopes are classified into two groups, *radioactive isotopes* and *stable isotopes.* Radioactive isotopes are those whose nuclei undergo disintegration or "decay." The process occurs at a particular rate unique for each isotope by the emission of one or more characteristic kinds of particles and energy waves known as *alpha, beta,* and *gamma* rays, and results in the transformation of radioactive isotopes to other elements. Stable isotopes do not undergo nuclear decay.

Radioactive atoms experience nuclear disintegration whether or not the atom occurs as an element, ion, or constituent atom of a compound molecule. Alpha rays are made up of a stream of helium nuclei (particles consisting of 2 protons and 2 neutrons) which are released at tremendous velocities from certain radioactive atoms. Beta rays consist of streams of electrons moving nearly at the speed of light from radioactive nuclei. Gamma rays are identical with X-rays and represent a portion of the liberated energy accompanying nuclear changes. The emission of alpha or beta rays results in the spontaneous transformation of the nucleus of the radioactive element to that of another element.

What confers stability on an atomic nucleus? Neutrons in some unknown fashion are in part responsible for proton binding and stability of the nucleus. Apparently when the neutron-proton ratio is unfavorable, the atom is unstable, undergoing radioactive or nuclear decay by emmiting some or all of the indicated particles and energy waves until it is transformed to another atom with a more stable neutron-proton relationship.

Several unstable radioactive isotopes exist in nature. Moreover, artificial radioactivity can be induced in stable atomic nuclei by bombarding them with high-speed atomic particles. The bombarding particle at high enough speed may get sufficiently close to the nucleus to be absorbed and thus produce a new nucleus. If the latter proves to be unstable it will undergo radioactive disintegration to form ultimately a new stable nucleus. For example, the naturally occurring radioactive uranium isotope with atomic number 92 and atomic weight 238, written $_{92}U^{238}$, disintegrates first by expelling an alpha particle (helium nucleus), thus becoming transformed into the element thorium, $_{90}Th^{234}$, as follows:

$$_{92}U^{238} \longrightarrow {_{90}Th^{234}} + {_2He^4}$$

The newly formed $_{90}Th^{234}$ is also radioactive and decays into another radioactive element which decays to still other radioactive atoms, in this manner constituting a chain of radioactive disintegrations ultimately leading to the formation of the stable element lead (Pb) with atomic number 82 and atomic weight 206, $_{82}Pb^{206}$.

The relative stability of a radioactive atom is indicated by its rate of radioactive decay, the more stable radioactive isotopes taking a longer time to undergo nuclear disintegration. The rate of radioactive decay is a constant statistical process which is unaffected by temperature, pressure, chemical binding or any other known factors, just as is time itself. Each radioactive isotope decays at its own specific rate, which is usually expressed as the *half-life*—the time required for half of a given quantity of radioactive material initially present to disintegrate. The half-life of uranium 238 is 4-5 billion years, which is the time that must elapse for half the number of uranium atoms present in any sample to undergo radioactive decay. Another 4–5 billion years would be required for disintegration of half the remaining sample. Analyses of rocks containing radioactive elements such as uranium and some of its disintegration products (e.g., lead and trapped helium gas) have proved very useful in estimating the age of the earth. By this means several rocks or ores have been shown to be about two and a half billion years old, representing the oldest rocks found thus far on the planet earth.

A number of artificially produced radioactive isotopes, in particular the isotope carbon 14 (written C^{14}) which has a half-life of 5580 years,[4] have proven to be of tremendous value in elucidating a variety of biological processes. Isotopes, both stable and radioactive, are being increasingly used to clarify numerous biological processes. Because the reactivity of an element is established by its atomic number and not its mass, substances labeled with certain isotopic atoms undergo metabolic transformations identical with those of correspondingly unlabled substances. The analytical methods for isotopes (especially

[4] The most prevalent naturally occurring form of carbon is the stable carbon 12 atom, $_6C^{12}$, possessing 6 protons (i.e., atomic number 6) and 6 neutrons in its nucleus to give an atomic weight of 12. The radioactive C^{14} isotope also possessing 6 protons but 8 neutrons (i.e., atomic weight 14) is produced by irradiating the highly abundant usual nitrogen atom ($_7N^{14}$) with neutrons emitted from an "atomic pile" or nuclear reactor. The $_7N^{14}$ atoms capture a neutron and emit a proton to yield $_6C^{14}$ as follows:

$$_7N^{14} + {_0n'} \longrightarrow {_6C^{14}} + {_1p'}$$

The radioactive C^{14} atom emits beta particles (or electrons) at its own constant rate (half-life, 5580 years) to form $_7N^{14}$ as shown:

$$_6C^{14} \longrightarrow {_7N^{14}} + {_{-1}e^0}$$

radioactive isotopes) are exceedingly sensitive. They have provided the basis for important studies, heretofore not possible, of metabolic transformations of a number of biologically significant compounds appropriately labeled with isotopic atoms in their structure.

Radiations emitted by radioactive atoms also have important physiological effects, in general exerting a destructive action on living cells. Fortunately, with proper handling these radiations exhibit a selective action, more readily inhibiting or destroying young and rapidly growing cancer cells as compared to normal cells. Thus the radioactive emanations of radium and the unstable isotope, cobalt 60, have been put to an important direct medical use in the clinical treatment of cancer or malignant growth.

THE CHEMICAL BOND

Types of Bonds

When two or more atoms are joined to each other as a result of electronic interaction, the force or attraction that holds them together is called a *chemical bond*. The outermost electrons surrounding an atomic nucleus are involved in the interaction with electrons of other atoms to form chemical bonds. On the one extreme the linkage may be so strong that very powerful forces are necessary to pry the atoms apart, whereas in the other the combination may be so weak that no effective bond can be said to exist. All degrees of bond strength exist between these two extremes depending on the particular atoms involved.

The interactions of the outermost electrons of atoms to yield chemical bonds are called *chemical reactions*. They consist fundamentally of two types, those involving (*a*) a loss or gain of electrons in which electrons are transferred from one atom to another to form an *ionic bond*, and (*b*) a sharing of electrons between two atoms to form a *covalent bond*. Chemical reactions occur between atoms of either elements or compounds to yield new ionic and covalent bonds and therefore new

molecules. The underlying principle is that the tendency of atoms to react or form other chemical bonds reflects the tendency of their electron clouds to rearrange themselves in the most stable patterns possible, namely those with an outermost energy shell configuration of 8 electrons (i.e., 4 electron pairs).

IONIC BOND. The transfer of electrons to form an ionic bond is illustrated by the reaction between sodium and chlorine. The element sodium (Na) is a highly reactive, silvery, soft metal with an atomic number of 11. Its outermost energy shell is occupied by a single electron which is the one that is easily removed in ionic bond formation. Chlorine (Cl_2) is a greenish, poisonous gas of atomic number 17 with 7 electrons in its outermost shell. Considerably more energy would be required to withdraw an electron from its outer shell as compared to the energy needed to gain an electron. When these two elements react with each other the single electron in the outermost energy shell of the sodium atoms is transferred to the outer shell of the chlorine atom, thus constituting a chemical reaction. By losing an electron the sodium becomes positively charged (10 electrons, 11 protons) and acquires an outermost energy shell configuration of 4 electron pairs. The chlorine atom which gains the electron has now become negatively charged (18 electrons, 17 protons) and thereby acquires a similar stable electron configuration (Figure 6-10).

Atoms or molecules that acquire a net electric charge are called *ions*. They are also called *electrolytes* because they can conduct an electric current in solution. As a result of the foregoing reaction between sodium and chlorine atoms, the sodium has been converted into a positive ion, Na^+, and chlorine into a negative ion Cl^-. Since these ions are of opposite electrical charge they attract each other to form a substance with an ionic bond called sodium chloride, commonly known as table salt. The reaction is conveniently represented as follows:

$$2Na + Cl_2 \longrightarrow 2Na^+ Cl^-$$

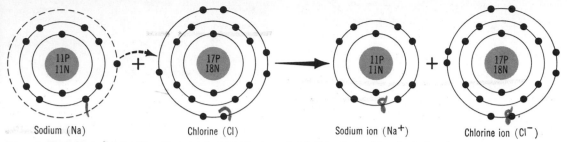

Figure 6-10. Formation of sodium and chloride ions (and therefore of an ionic bond between Na⁺ and Cl⁻) by electron transfer from elemental sodium to elemental chlorine.

COVALENT BOND. Most chemical bonds are not ionic but instead fall in the class of co-valent bonds, in which two atoms are held together as the result of the sharing of electrons. For example, the two atoms of hydrogen in a molecule of hydrogen gas are covalently linked to each by the mutual sharing of a pair of electrons. The one and only electron level, the K shell, of each hydrogen atom is therefore filled with its maximal (and most stable) electron number of two. The picture is similar for the oxygen gas molecule except that the two atoms share two pairs of electrons to give a stable octet of electrons in the outermost energy shell around each of the two oxygen atoms. A water molecule consists of two atoms of hydrogen each covalently linked to an atom of oxygen (Figure 6-11) resulting in a stable arrangement of outer electrons about each of the atoms.

The linkage of carbon to other atoms such as hydrogen, oxygen, and nitrogen (as in proteins, nucleic acids, carbohydrates, and fats) is of a covalent type. The carbon atom has an atomic number 6 and therefore has a total of 6 electrons—2 in its K shell and 4 in its L or outermost shell (Figure 6-8). It most easily attains a stable octet of electrons by sharing electrons with other atoms. For example, methane gas, which is believed to be one of the first carbon compounds formed in the early history of the earth, consists of molecules in which a single carbon atom is covalently bound to each of 4 hydrogen atoms (Figure 6-11). Thus the carbon atom in meth-

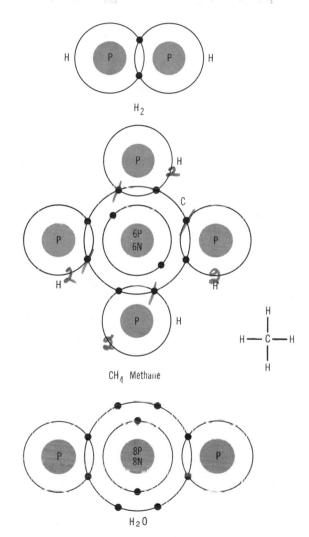

Figure 6-11. Covalent bonds between the hydrogen atoms of molecular hydrogen, the carbon and hydrogens of methane, and the hydrogens and oxygen of water.

ane has acquired a complete octet of electrons in its outer shell while each hydrogen now shares a maximum of 2 electrons.

In a covalent linkage involving a sharing of a single pair of electrons between two atoms, the linkage is called a *single bond*. It is usually designated by a short straight line connecting the two atoms with one another. If two or three pairs of electrons are shared between two atoms then the linkage is called a *double bond* or *triple bond* respectively, and is designated by double or triple straight lines between the atoms:

$$-\overset{|}{\underset{|}{C}}-\overset{|}{\underset{|}{C}}- \qquad \overset{\diagdown}{\diagup}C=C\overset{\diagup}{\diagdown} \qquad -C\equiv C-$$

Single bond   Double bond   Triple bond

In the previously cited example of oxygen gas, each molecule consists of two atoms of oxygen joined to each other by a double bond since they share two pairs of electrons to acquire the outer stable electron octet. In carbon dioxide, written as CO_2 or $O=C=O$, which is an important biochemical reactant as well as a significant respiratory product of all living cells, an atom of carbon shares two pairs of electrons with each of the oxygen atoms. As a result each atom has attained the stable octet of outer electrons.

Before leaving the concept of ionic and covalent bonds it should be emphasized that these two classes in reality represent opposite extremes. Most chemical bonds combine the properties of both to various degrees depending on the particular molecule and the atoms concerned, and are therefore partly ionic and partly covalent.

ACIDS, BASES, AND SALTS

Acids are substances that yield hydrogen ions, H^+, in solution. They have a typically sour taste, react with certain metals to liberate H_2 gas, and effect a change in the color of certain dyes, for example, the vegetable dye called *litmus*, transforming it from blue to pink.

Bases or alkalis are substances that produce hydroxide ions, OH^-, in solution. They are characterized by a bitter taste, a slippery, soapy feel in aqueous solutions, and the ability to restore the blue color of litmus previously made pink by exposure to acid.

Acids and bases are generally classified into two groups, *strong* and *weak*. A strong acid dissociates to a large extent, producing relatively high concentrations of hydrogen ions and negative ions (other than OH^- ions), while a weak acid dissociates to a lesser extent. Hydrochloric acid, HCl, is an example of a strong acid. When dissolved in water a large proportion of the molecules are dissociated into H^+ and Cl^-. Acetic acid, CH_3COOH, is a weak acid, which means that only a relatively small percentage of its molecules in aqueous solution dissociate into hydrogen ions and negative acetate ions ($CH_3COOH \rightleftharpoons CH_3COO^- + H^+$). Phosphoric acid is another example of a weak acid in which a relatively small proportion of its molecules dissociates into hydrogen ions and phosphate ions ($H_3PO_4 \rightleftharpoons 3H^+ + PO_4^{3-}$). Similarly strong bases produce a relatively high concentration of hydroxide ions and positive ions (other than H^+ ions), whereas weak bases dissociate to a lesser extent. Sodium hydroxide, $NaOH$, is an example of a strong base ($NaOH \rightleftharpoons Na^+ + OH^-$), and ammonium hydroxide, NH_4OH, is a typically weak base ($NH_4OH \rightleftharpoons NH_4^+ + OH^-$). It should be noted that there are more generalized and more fundamental definitions of acids and bases. The foregoing version, however, is adequate for our purposes.

When acidic and basic (or *alkaline*) solutions are mixed together, they neutralize each other forming water and ionic compounds known as *salts*. H^+ and OH^- ions have a great affinity for one another, combining very rapidly to produce water ($H^+ + OH^- \rightleftharpoons H_2O$). Salts, as the other principal product of the reaction between an acid and base, consist of the negative ion of the acid and the positive ion of the base. For example, in the reaction of the strong acid HCl and the strong base $NaOH$, the hydrogen ions and hydroxide ions combine to form water while the Na^+ and Cl^- ions remain. If the water molecules are subsequently removed by boiling or evaporation the remaining ions will aggregate to form the salt sodium chloride.

$$H^+ + Cl^- + Na^+ + OH^- \longrightarrow H_2O + Na^+Cl^- \quad (1)$$

or

$$HCl + NaOH \longrightarrow H_2O + NaCl \quad (2)$$

Salts are therefore composed of positive and negative ions, neither of which are H^+ or OH^- ions. They represent (in addition to water) the neutralization products of the reaction of a base with an acid.

pH. Water has many unique properties which account for its role as the "universal solvent" in biological systems. It consists almost completely *but not entirely* of H_2O molecules. The fact that highly purified water prepared by repeated distillation still conducts an electrical current to a slight but measurable degree suggests that in addition to water molecules it also comprises an extremely small but detectable number of H^+ ions and OH^- ions. These ions are in dynamic equilibrium with the water molecules and are present in equal concentrations because each arises from the dissociation or ionization of a H_2O molecule:

$$H_2O \rightleftharpoons H^+ + OH^-$$

Since a liter of water contains approximately 1000 g, and a *gram-molecular weight* of water (the molecular weight of water in grams) is 18.0 g, there are 1000/18 or 55.5 gram-molecular weights (also called *moles*) of H_2O in a liter. Refined measurements have shown that of this number only about .00001 per cent (one in every 10 million molecules) or 10^{-7} moles of water per liter (written as 10^{-7} M) are dissociated into H^+ and OH^- ions. This means that there are only 10^{-7} equivalents of H^+ ions and 10^{-7} equivalents of OH^- ions in each liter of pure water. Yet this seemingly negligible concentration of ions accounts for one of the most significant properties of water affecting biological systems. Small shifts in H^+ ion (or OH^- ion) concentration may strongly influence

numerous enzymatic reactions as well as the physical state of proteins and other protoplasmic components, in this manner affecting metabolic and physiological patterns of the cell.

A convenient designation[5] known as **pH** has been devised for expressing the concentration of H^+ ions. It has proven to be especially useful in quantitatively expressing acidity (or basicity) in biological systems. A solution having an equal concentration of H^+ ions and OH^- ions, such as pure water, is said to be *neutral*, being neither acidic or basic. All neutralized systems have a concentration of 10^{-7} equivalents of H^+ ions or (grams of H^+ ions) per liter of solution and therefore a pH of 7.0. The greater the acidity the smaller the pH value; and the greater the basicity the larger the pH value. In an acidic solution the H^+ ion concentration is greater than at neutrality and the pH is therefore less than 7.0. In a basic solution the H^+ ion concentration is smaller than at neutrality and the pH is therefore greater than 7.0. The pH scale and its relationships are shown in Figure 6-12.

Buffers. The pH of water and various solutions can be markedly changed by the addition of small quantities of acid or base. For instance, the addition of a single drop of a strong acid to a liter of water may decrease its pH as much as 3 or 4 pH units. Yet when certain substances are also present known as *buffers*, which can com-

---

[5] By definition pH is the negative log of the H^+ ion concentration:

$$pH = -\log(H^+)$$

where (H^+) stands for H^+ ion concentration expressed as the number of equivalents or number of ionic weights of H^+ (in grams) per liter of solution. (Since the mass of the H^+ ion is 1, the concentration of H^+ ions would be the same as the number of grams of H^+ ions per liter of solution.) If the H^+ ion concentration of a particular solution were 10^{-5} equivalents or g per liter of solution, then by substituting in the above equation its $pH = -\log 10^{-5} = 5$. If the H^+ ion concentration were 10^{-9}, its $pH = -\log 10^{-9} = 9$. The product of the concentrations of H^+ ions and OH^- ions in *any* aqueous solution is a constant of 10^{-14} as indicated by the equation: $(H^+) \times (OH^-) = 10^{-14}$. If the H^+ ion concentration is increased by adding an acid to water, equal quantities of H^+ and OH^- ions will reassociate to form water molecules, thus maintaining the ionic product at 10^{-14}. Under these circumstances the H^+ ion concentration is greater than 10^{-7} and the OH^- ion concentration is correspondingly less than 10^{-7}. The solution is therefore acidic (pH < 7). In a similar manner, adding a base to water the concentration of H^+ will be correspondingly less than 10^{-7} (pH > 7) to give the ionic product of 10^{-14}.

line with added H^+ ions or OH^- ions, the subsequent addition of relatively large amounts of strong acid or base will cause within limits little or no change in pH. This depends on the buffer, the quantity of H^+ or OH^- ions added, and the particular part of the pH scale under consideration. Buffered solutions therefore resist changes in H^+ ion concentration. All cells and most biological systems are maintained at a particular pH by virtue of their natural buffering capacity. Blood in the human body, for instance, has a constant pH of 7.4, largely as a result of the buffering action of its constituent proteins.

CHEMICAL REACTIONS

Types of Chemical Reactions

Chemical reactions (i.e., the processes of formation of chemical bonds) can be classified into two broad types: (1) those in which there is electron transfer from one atom to another, known as *oxidation-reduction* reactions, and (2) those in which there is no electron transfer, called *recombination* or *substitution* reactions.

OXIDATION-REDUCTION REACTIONS. Numerous biochemical reactions representing important steps in carbohydrate, fat, and energy metabolism are of the oxidation-reduction type. The previously cited example involving the transfer of electrons from the atoms of sodium metal to those of chlorine gas to form sodium chloride is a case of an oxidation-reduction reaction. Sodium provides the electrons, is called the *reducing* agent or *electron donor*, and is said to be *oxidized*. Chlorine gains the electrons, is called the *oxidizing* agent or *electron*

acceptor, and is said to be *reduced*. When any substance loses electrons (is oxidized) some other substance must gain these electrons (is reduced). Similarly, in order for a substance to receive electrons (be reduced) the electrons must come from some source (reducing substance) which becomes oxidized in the process. Therefore an oxidation is always accompanied by a reduction, and vice versa.

The term oxidation was originally used years ago to designate reactions involving the formation of chemical bonds with oxygen. For example, when charcoal (carbon) burns in air it chemically combines with oxygen to form the gas carbon dioxide, liberating energy as light and heat:

$$C + O_2 \rightarrow CO_2 + energy$$

It was subsequently discovered that carbon and various substances could also burn or combine

with certain other elements such as chlorine and sulfur in place of oxygen to form chemical bonds resembling those produced with oxygen. Recognition of the similarity of these reactions eventually led to a more modern generalized concept of oxidation. In almost all of its reactions oxygen forms covalent bonds. For example, hydrogen and oxygen react with each other to form water ($2H_2 + O_2 \rightarrow 2H_2O$) in which each of the hydrogen atoms now shares a pair of electrons with oxygen. However, the pair of electrons is not distributed equally in the covalent bond between hydrogen and oxygen (in contrast to the equal sharing of the electron pair between the two hydrogen atoms of a hydrogen gas molecule, H_2). Instead the

[handwritten margin note: Oxidation - loss of electrons; reduction - gaining elec.]

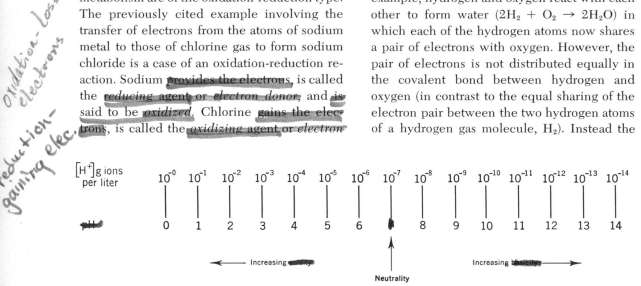

Figure 6-12. The pH scale and hydrogen ion concentration.

oxygen atom, because of certain properties (strong electronegativity), tends to draw the shared pair of electrons more closely to itself. By this unequal sharing of electrons in the covalent bond between the hydrogens and oxygen of the water molecule the two hydrogen atoms have in effect given up their electrons to oxygen. The formation of H_2O from H_2 and O_2 can therefore be regarded as an oxidation-reduction reaction. The strong tendency of oxygen and certain other atoms such as chlorine and sulfur to monopolize the electron pairs in its covalent bonds with most other atoms accounts for the general application of the term "oxidation" to those reactions dealing with the loss or unequal sharing of electrons, even though oxygen may not be involved. The following diagram compares the equal sharing of electrons (designated as dots) between the two nuclei of the hydrogen gas molecule, and the unequal sharing of electrons between the hydrogen and oxygen of water.

H:H   H :O: H

Oxygen-reduction reactions may also involve ions as reactants and products. For example, iron occurs in two common ionic states, the ferrous ion (Fe^{2+}) and the ferric ion (Fe^{3+}). The Fe^{2+} ion differs from elemental iron (Fe) in having already lost 2 electrons, thus accounting for the net positive charge of 2, while Fe^{3+} is the result of a removal of 3 electrons. Fe^{3+} can be reversibly reduced to Fe^{2+} by using hydrogen as the electron (e^-) donor as indicated in the following equations:

$$H_2 \rightleftharpoons 2H^+ + 2e^- \tag{1}$$

$$2Fe^{3+} + 2e^- \rightleftharpoons 2Fe^{2+} \tag{2}$$

The overall reaction therefore is:

$$2Fe^{3+} + H_2 \rightleftharpoons 2Fe^{2+} + 2H^+ \tag{3}$$

In the forward reaction of Equation 3, Fe^{3+} ions are the oxidizing agent (electron acceptor) and hydrogen gas is the reducing agent (elec-

tron donor). In the reverse reaction, Fe^{2+} ions are the reducing agent, becoming oxidized to Fe^{3+} ions as they give up their electrons to the H^+ ions to yield hydrogen gas. When iron is part of a certain larger molecule called *heme* (Chapter 7) bound to a particular protein to constitute an important biological substance, *cytochrome* (Chapter 7), the reversible oxidation of Fe^{2+} to Fe^{3+} plays an important role in the respiration and metabolism of living cells.

RECOMBINATION OR SUBSTITUTION REACTIONS. This second broad group of chemical reactions, in contrast to oxidation-reductions, usually consists of a substitution, transfer, or recombination of atoms or groups of atoms between molecules, resulting in neither a net gain nor loss of electrons. This is illustrated by the reaction between the hypothetical molecules AB and CD to produce AC and BD:

A:B + C:D   ⟶   A:C + B:D

In one sense the reaction constitutes a splitting of molecule AB by the molecule CD which is also split in the process. If CD represents a molecule of water, written as HOH, the reaction would be:

AB + HOH   ⟶   AOH + BH

When water is involved as shown, the reaction is spoken of as a *hydrolysis reaction* — the splitting of compounds by the introduction of water molecules to form other compounds. For instance, the ionic compound ferric chloride, $FeCl_3$, is hydrolyzed when dissolved in water to form a brownish precipitate $Fe(OH)_3$ called ferric hydroxide and HCl or hydrochloric acid. In typical chemical shorthand the reaction is indicated as follows:

$$FeCl_3 + 3H_2O \longrightarrow Fe(OH)_3 + 3HCl$$

Hydrolysis reactions, in addition to oxidation-reductions, are of great significance in biological processes. Digestion, for example, is essentially the result of enzymatic hydrolysis — the splitting of larger molecules such as proteins, starch, and fats into smaller molecules by water.

Certain transfer reactions, whereby particular groups of atoms in chemical combination with each other are transferred from one molecule to another to yield a new compound, are also of primary importance in several fundamental biochemical phenomena (e.g., transamination and transphorphorylation, (Chapter 8)).

Collision Theory of Chemical Reactions

According to the widely accepted *collision theory of chemical reactions,* in order for molecules to react to form new chemical bonds they must first collide with one another so that electronic interaction may occur. The theory applies to all chemical reactions in both living and nonliving systems.

The modern collision theory provides a unified explanation for four observed factors that affect the rates of chemical reactions: (1) the concentrations of reacting substances (or the frequency of collisions between the reacting molecules); (2) the nature of the reacting substances and their suitability from an energy viewpoint to react with each other; (3) temperature; and (4) the presence of catalysts. A consideration of these factors is also of prime importance in interpreting biological phenomena at the molecular level for they are the very same ones that affect the rates of all biochemical reactions and therefore all metabolic processes in the living cell.

CONCENTRATION OF REACTING SUBSTANCES. Higher concentrations mean that more molecules occupy a given volume, thus furthering the chances that they will collide with one another. An increase in the frequency of collisions between molecules *capable of reacting with each other* will therefore cause an increase in the rate of the chemical reaction. For example, the frequency of collision between the molecules of two gases is about 10^{28} times per second in a ml of the mixture at standard conditions of temperature and pressure, and is progressively less for liquids and solids. Since chemical reactions occur between molecules it is desirable to express concentration of reactants

in terms of concentrations of molecules, namely as moles (or gram-molecular weights) per liter of volume. However, not every collision that occurs between molecules will result in a chemical reaction. In many cases only a small fraction of the colliding molecules undergo chemical reaction. A second major requirement must also be fulfilled, namely that the colliding molecules are in an appropriate activated condition or energy state to undergo reaction.

ACTIVATION ENERGY. All of the molecules of any given quantity of matter do not possess the same energy. They have an average energy which means that while most of the molecules have energies in the region of the average figure some have very low and others have very high values. According to the collision theory, only those molecules capable of reacting that possess sufficiently high energies will produce a chemical reaction upon colliding with each other. This extra energy needed by molecules in order to react is called *activation energy.* It is the amount of energy over the average energy of a given quantity of molecules that is necessary for colliding molecules to undergo chemical reaction. Its required magnitude depends on the particular type of reaction and the nature of the reacting substances. Colliding molecules possessing less than the necessary activation energy will not react but will simply bounce apart and go their separate ways. For those chemical reactions that occur rapidly, a relatively large number of the reactant molecules presumably already possess the necessary activation energy. For those reactions that occur slowly, the percentage of molecules possessing the required activation energy is quite small.

One interpretation of activation energy is that it is the energy necessary for colliding molecules to approach sufficiently close to each other in order to overcome electrical repulsion between their electron clouds. Thus it would permit electron rearrangement and therefore chemical bonding to take place. The collision theory postulates that, upon colliding, molecules possessing the necessary activation energy form a transient intermediate called an *acti-*

vated complex. The activated complex then quickly rearranges itself to produce the products of the reaction. For example, in a hypothetical reaction of molecules *a* and *b* to produce *c* and *d*, formation of an intermediary activated complex (*ab*) is therefore postulated.

$$a + b \rightarrow (ab) \rightarrow c + d$$

The relationship of a chemical reaction to the activation energy of the reacting molecules and the formation of an intermediary activated complex can probably be best visualized by comparing it to an energy barrier as shown in Figure 6-13. In order for two colliding molecules *a* and *b* to react with one another they must have sufficient energy to reach the top of the energy barrier. This energy represents the activation energy, and the colliding molecules that possess it are capable of forming the activated complex (*ab*). The activated complex has the most energy in the system, being at the very top of the energy barrier. It then re-

arranges to yield the new molecules *c* and *d*. The situation is analogous to a sled placed on a hillside. In order for it to slide down the opposite side of the hill, energy must first be imparted to the sled by a strong enough push (i.e., activation energy) to get it to the top of the hill (i.e., activated complex). The sled can now readily slide down the opposite side of the hill. Similarly, many chemical reactions can be initiated by providing sufficient energy to get them over the barrier.

The relative average energies of molecules *a* and *b*, the activated complex (*ab*), and the products *c* and *d* are represented in Figure 6-13. The difference between the average relative energy of reactants *a* and *b* and that of the activated complex (*ab*) is the activation energy. If the amount of energy given off in the rearrangement of the activated complex to yield the products *c* and *d* is greater than the activation energy, then energy will be released and the chemical reaction is called *exergonic*

{ If less energy is given off to acquire the activated complex than is given off after activation, energy will be released — reaction called exergonic }

{ If necessary to have more energy for activated complex & then less energy is given off after activation — endergonic }

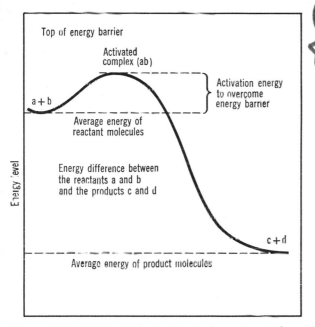

Figure 6-13. Relationship of a chemical reaction to the activation energy of the reacting molecules a and b, formation of an intermediary activated complex (ab), and the energy differences between the reactants (a and b), the activated complex (ab), and the products (c and d). See text for explanation as well as the analogy to pushing a sled over the top of a hill.

(p. 133). On the other hand, should the difference between the average relative energies of the activated complex and the products c and d be less than the activation energy, then the chemical reaction has required a net input of energy and is called *endergonic*.

TEMPERATURE. A rise in temperature speeds up the rate of a chemical reaction in at least two ways. First, by increasing the velocity or kinetic energy of molecules, a higher temperature increases the frequency of collisions. Second, by virtue of their increased velocity a greater proportion of the molecules now possess a sufficiently high energy (i.e., activation energy) to react upon collision with each other. The effect of increased temperature in speeding up a chemical reaction by increasing the frequency of collisions is minor compared to its effect in activating a greater fraction of the reactant molecules. The overall rate of the chemical reaction increases because a greater percentage of the collisions are now more effective. The extent of change in the rate of a chemical reaction as a result of a change in temperature varies from one reaction to another and from one temperature range to another.

CATALYSTS. Many chemical reactions can be remarkably accelerated by the addition of a substance that remains essentially unchanged at the end of the reaction. Such substances, known as *catalysts*, are usually effective in trace amounts. For example, at room temperature hydrogen peroxide, H_2O_2 (a metabolic product formed in many cells), decomposes into water and oxygen at a very slow rate ($2H_2O_2 \rightarrow 2H_2O + O_2$). If a small quantity of finely divided platinum or a specific biochemical catalyst such as the enzyme *catalase* is added, the reaction proceeds at a highly accelerated rate.

According to the collision theory, a catalyst increases the rate of a chemical reaction by participating in the formation of an activated complex of a lower energy state. Thus in the presence of a catalyst the required energy of activation is less, which means that there is now a lower energy barrier for the molecules to overcome in order to undergo chemical reaction. More molecules per unit of time therefore get over the lowered energy hump, resulting in a faster reaction rate under the same conditions of temperature and concentration. A catalyst is used over and over again by the reacting molecules, thus accounting for its effectiveness in small quantities.

The energy relationships for a noncatalyzed and catalyzed chemical reaction, such as the decomposition of hydrogen peroxide in the absence and presence of the finely divided platinum catalyst or the enzyme catalase, are shown in the energy diagram of Figure 6-14. In the noncatalyzed reaction (indicated by the solid line) two molecules of H_2O_2 possessing the required activation energy react with each other to form a presumed H_2O_2-H_2O_2 activated complex which then rearranges to form the products H_2O and O_2. In the catalyzed reaction (dotted line) a different kind of activated complex at a lower energy level involving peroxide and the catalyst must form since the reaction rate is now faster, indicating that more molecules are reacting with each other per unit of time.

Virtually all chemical reactions occurring in living cells, and therefore all metabolic processes, are mediated by the unique and highly specific proteinaceous catalysts, namely enzymes. The mechanism by which enzymes accelerate chemical reactions is essentially the same as just described for catalysts in general. Most chemical reactions that take place in living cells would proceed at a negligibly small rate if enzymes were not present. Enzymes are involved in such biological processes as digestion, respiration, the stepwise breaking down, building up, and interconversion of carbohydrates, fats, proteins, and nucleic acids, and the release and utilization of energy by living cells. A more detailed discussion of their properties is given in the next chapter.

Chemical Equilibrium

Most chemical reactions rarely go to completion. That is, the reacting substances are not

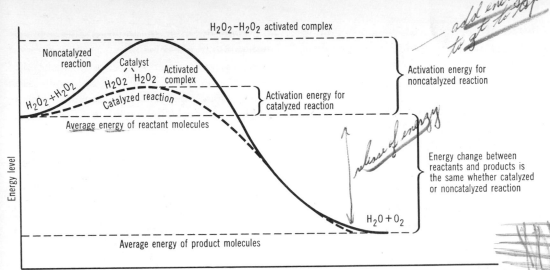

Figure 6-14. Comparison of the energy relationships of the catalyzed and noncatalyzed decomposition of hydrogen peroxide to water and oxygen. The activated energy for the catalyzed reaction is less than that for the noncatalyzed reaction.

completely used up to form the products. In the course of a chemical reaction the concentrations of the reactants progressively decrease and those of the products correspondingly increase until a point is finally reached where no net change occurs. This is known as an equilibrium state and is due to the fact that the reverse reaction is now proceeding at the same rate as the forward reaction, resulting in no apparent net change in the concentration of reactants and products.

In the example of carbon dioxide (CO_2) and water (H_2O) reacting to form carbonic acid, H_2CO_3, the reverse reaction is also occurring as indicated by the arrow pointing in the opposite direction:

$$CO_2 + H_2O \rightleftharpoons H_2CO_3$$

As the concentration of H_2CO_3 increases its rate of breakdown to CO_2 and H_2O also increases until finally an equilibrium is reached in which the rate of formation of CO_2 and H_2O from H_2CO_3 is equal to the rate of the opposite reaction, namely the rate formation of H_2CO_3 from CO_2 and H_2O. A chemical equilibrium therefore does not represent a static state or a system at rest. Instead it is a dynamic state in which chemical reactions are occurring in both the forward and reverse directions at equal rates. For this reason there is no net change in the composition of the reaction mixture.

The effect of a catalyst, biological or otherwise, is to speed up the rate of a chemical reaction. In the case of reversible reactions (and all chemical reactions are considered to be theoretically reversible), it equally accelerates both the forward and backward reactions so that the equilibrium state is reached in a shorter time. If a catalyst is added at the beginning of a reaction, the equilibrium point will be reached sooner. If added to a system already in the equilibrium state, it will have no effect.

CHEMICAL THERMODYNAMICS

General Features

The fundamental energy relationships of chemical reactions (an area of study called chemical thermodynamics) apply equally to all systems whether nonliving or living.

All chemical reactions exhibit two fundamental properties: (1) the total weight of the products is equal to the total weight of the reactants, which is the same as saying that the total number of each of the atoms is unchanged; and (2) energy is either liberated or absorbed. In many cases it appears largely as heat generated or absorbed, whereas in other instances it may manifest itself in other energy states.

Chemical Bond Energy

Chemical energy represents a form of potential energy and is present in substances as a result of the motion of electrons and arrangement of atoms within its molecules. As a good approximation the chemical energy is viewed as being concentrated or stored in the bonds between the atoms composing a molecule. Therefore any change in the chemical linkages between atoms (that is, chemical reaction) results in either a net gain (endergonic chemical reaction) or release (exergonic) of energy. For example, the reaction of hydrogen and oxygen gas to yield water and a net liberation of energy $(H_2 + \frac{1}{2}O_2 \rightleftharpoons H_2O + 68,400$ calories) is exergonic. (The energy is produced almost completely as heat.) This means that the total energy locked in the H—H and O=O bonds of the reactants H_2 and O_2 is considerably greater than the energy contained in the H—O—H bonds of the product H_2O. The energy released represents the difference in energy of the bond combinations before and after the reaction.

To reverse the reaction, namely to decompose water into hydrogen and oxygen gas, the same quantity of energy at the very least would have to be provided. It could be furnished as heat or electricity depending on the conditions of the experiment. Strongly exergonic reactions can be used to produce elevated temperatures by having them occur rapidly and continuously as in the oxygen-hydrogen torch (based on the foregoing reaction) which achieves temperatures as high as 2800°C.

Free Energy and Entropy

In the late nineteenth century an extremely valuable energy concept known as *free energy* was developed to represent the total energy possessed by a chemical substance. Free energy is the sum of a substance's heat content (as measured by the release of heat energy upon complete oxidation of its chemical bonds) plus

the energy it contains by virtue of its organization or inherent probability, known as *entropy*.[6] The liberation of free energy in a chemical reaction represents the difference in total energy states between the reactants and the products and is called *useful energy* because it can perform useful work. It includes not only the change in the heat content of the system but also the change in the additional energy factor, entropy. The concepts of free energy and entropy are somewhat abstract and difficult to visualize. Nevertheless, they represent a fundamental viewpoint in modern chemistry, and in an even broader sense provide a basic

[6]Entropy is a state of probability, or randomness, and is a measure of the disorder of a system. Entropy is not energy but is *related* to the energy possessed by a chemical system by virtue of its orderliness or arrangement. The more random the distribution of molecules in a system, the more disorderly is the arrangement, and the larger is the entropy. The smaller the entropy of a system, the more ordered is its organization, and the higher is its useful or free energy. A change therefore in entropy relates to the change in the degree of order or arrangement.

All systems, if unattended, are inclined toward a state of randomness or higher probability corresponding to an increase in entropy. Any system of greater order and organization represents a more improbable state. It is therefore at a higher energy level, implying that work or energy must have been necessary to bring it to this condition. If such a system is left unattended it will spontaneously do work or dissipate energy, thus tending to a more random or disorganized state (i.e., greater entropy).

A uniform state of disorder and simplicity is considered to be the most probable state for energy and matter. This represents the fundamental principle called the *second law of thermodynamics* which applies to both animate and inanimate systems and states that all systems in the universe tend to arrange or run themselves down towards their lowest useful energy state, a condition characterized by a randomness or disorganization (i.e., greater entropy). It can only be prevented or reversed by utilizing the free or useful energy provided by other systems in order to maintain or restore the condition of order and arrangement. Therefore, unless useful energy is furnished by other organized systems, a given system will ultimately become disorganized and random. Its energy becomes progressively less useful as the completely disordered and random state is approached, generally being dissipated in the form of heat. The basic principle of the second law is that a decrease in the amount of useful energy occurs whenever energy is transformed from one kind to another. In other words all systems, all forms of energy are eventually dissipated into heat and thus tend to approach a state of equilibrium.

Unless useful energy is constantly furnished from other sources (such as chemical energy stored in the molecules of carbohydrates, fats, and proteins) an organism like any other system would tend toward a disordered and random state or death.

understanding of the overall energy changes occurring in the universe for all systems, animate and inanimate.

According to the free-energy concept a chemical reaction can proceed spontaneously if it experiences a release of free energy. This is the modern definition of an *exergonic* reaction. In other words if the free energy of the reactants is greater than that of the products, the reaction can readily take place. In the reverse situation where free energy is required, the process is *endergonic*, and energy must therefore be provided to the system in order for the reaction to take place. This means that a spontaneous chemical reaction cannot take place unless the free energy change proceeds from a higher to a lower value. A greater free energy of the reactants as compared to the products, therefore, constitutes the driving force of a chemical reaction. A spontaneous chemical reaction can be compared to a waterfall. The forward reaction is analogous to the spontaneous descent of water over the falls, thus going from a higher to a lower energy value. The reverse reaction, from a lower to a higher free-energy level of the reacting chemical system, requires an input of energy from some outside source, just as the return of water to the top of the waterfall would require an energy input.

In all reactions, whether exergonic or endergonic, the activation, energy requirement must be fulfilled as indicated above as well as in the section below.

It should be noted that the energy transformations that occur in chemical reactions represent neither creation nor destruction of energy, but are simply conversions of energy from one form to another. In an exergonic reaction the free energy liberated is not a creation of energy but rather a transformation to another form of some of the energy stored in the chemical bonds of the reactants.

Activation Energy and Free Energy

No general relationship appears to exist between the previously discussed activation energy and the free-energy change occurring in a chemical reaction. Activation energy is an important factor in determining the rate of a chemical reaction whereas the free-energy change indicates whether or not the reaction is feasible from an energy point of view. Activation energy is required for all molecules to react, whether or not the chemical reaction which they undergo is exergonic or endergonic. This is best visualized by analogy to the example of a sled on the side of a hill. Before it can slide down the opposite side of the hill, energy must first be extended to get the sled to the top of the hill. This is analogous to activation energy. If the sled slides down the hillside to a lower level than it originally occupied on the opposite side of the hill, it will have experienced a net loss in energy, comparable to the release of free energy in an exergonic chemical reaction. If the sled comes to rest at a level higher than the one it originally occupied on the opposite side of the hill, it will have experienced a net increase in energy, comparable to the free-energy requirement of an endergonic chemical reaction. These relationships are illustrated in Figure 6-13.

Energy Utilization

The net release of free energy (i.e., useful energy) during a chemical reaction means that it can be employed for the performance of useful work, provided a properly organized system is present to utilize the energy. If a system of suitable organization is not present, then the useful energy released will be wasted, usually as heat. For instance, when gasoline is poured on the ground and ignited, it burns and emits energy that is dissipated in the form of heat and light. If it is instead burned in a highly organized system such as a gasoline engine, some of the liberated free energy (useful energy) can be transformed and utilized as mechanical energy, electricity, or possibly some other form depending on the means available for transforming it. Similarly, in living cells the useful energy made available by respiration is captured and stored in part as chemical energy in certain chemical bonds of a unique compound called *adenosine triphosphate* or ATP (Chapter 8). This substance serves as the energy source for all the activities of a living system.

Energy Relationships in the Biological World

What is the source of the free or useful energy made available during respiration in living cells? The answer is that it is liberated principally from the transformation of higher energy carbon-hydrogen bonds such as carbohydrates to lower energy carbon-oxygen bonds by means of self-directed enzymatic chemical reactions, a process known as *respiration* (Chapter 8). Where do these higher energy bonds originate in nature? They arise in all cases (with the exception of the chemosynthetic bacteria, Chapter 9), in the biological process of photosynthesis carried out by green plants. Here the radiant energy of the sun is utilized to convert the low energy carbon-oxygen bond of carbon dioxide to the higher energy carbon-hydrogen bond of compounds such as carbohydrates, fats, and proteins by a series of enzymatic reactions. Animals ingest plants and in turn ultimately serve as a food source for many other organisms.

In all cases respiration results in the liberation of energy, of which some is utilized and some wasted. Therefore, in the chain of biological events in which energy in the form of food is transferred within an organism and from one organism to another, less energy is passed on than is received. Thus the free energy originally obtained by plants from the sun is inexorably whittled down in a biological sequence that ultimately terminates in its complete conversion to a dissipated and useless form as heat.

Here is an example of the operation of the second law of thermodynamics at the biological level—the inevitable running down or degradation of useful energy originally derived from the sun.

Energy transformation in the biological world therefore is not a cyclic process but a pathway running in only one direction—downward toward the value of zero useful energy. Thus the transfer of useful energy within and between living organisms proceeds as on a downhill one-way street. It declines from the high level provided originally by the sun, becoming continuously and unavoidably dissipated as it passes from one metabolic event to another, and from one organism to another. In the inevitable downhill conversion of sunlight to heat, a portion of the available energy serves as the power source for all activities characteristically associated with life. In accordance with the first law of thermodynamics the total amount of energy is unchanged since it can be neither destroyed nor created. In accordance with the second law of thermodynamics the useful energy becomes steadily smaller and smaller as it passes from one organism to another, until it is completely dissipated.

In one sense the pattern of life centers about a competition or struggle for useful energy, energy that can perform work. The ultimate source of this energy for virtually all biological systems is the sun, which like other systems is governed by the laws of thermodynamics. In time the sun will burn itself out and cease to serve as the fountain of free energy for life on our planet. When that occurs some billions of years from now, we can predict on the basis of our present knowledge that life on our planet will cease soon afterward.

SUPPLEMENTARY REFERENCES

Andrews, D. H., and R. J. Kokes, *Fundamental Chemistry*, Wiley, New York, 1962.
Daniels, F., and R. A. Alberty, *Physical Chemistry*, second edition, Wiley, New York, 1961.
Pauling, L., *College Chemistry*, Freeman, San Francisco, 1952.
Selwood, P. W., *General Chemistry*, third edition, Holt, New York, 1959.
Sienko, M. J., and R. A. Plane, *Chemistry*, McGraw-Hill, New York, 1957.

Chapter 7   Organic Constituents of the Living Cell

Chemistry of Protoplasm

Protoplasm is a vastly complex arrangement of ions, molecules, and colloidal particles of many sizes uniquely organized into a multiplicity of structural and functional systems which collectively display the characteristics of a living system. These constituents are organized for the most part into a variety of units which in turn make up successively larger and more intricate units and systems (e.g., mitochondria, ribosomes, and so on) to compose finally the unit of life—the cell.

Chemical analysis of any cells or tissues show that they consist of numerous kinds of atoms. The number of different kinds of atoms varies, depending on the given cells or tissues and the chemical environment to which they are exposed. In some cases as many as 65 or even more of the 92 naturally occurring elements are found, whereas in others as little as 30 different kinds of atoms can be observed.

To date we know that about 20 elements are essential for the normal structure and function of protoplasm. These include carbon, hydrogen, oxygen, nitrogen, phosphorus, sulfur, calcium, magnesium, chlorine, potassium, and sodium, which appear to be needed in relatively large quantities by most of the organisms studied. In addition appreciably smaller amounts of the metals, iron, copper, manganese, zinc, and, for some living things, iodine, boron, molybdenum,

cobalt, and selenium are also required. It seems very likely that with more refined techniques we shall be able to demonstrate that other elements are also essential.

The fact that other elements are present in protoplasm does not constitute evidence that they are required. They must be shown to be irreplaceably essential for the normal structure and functioning of protoplasm, criteria that can prove to be very difficult to fulfill.

Most of the elements making up protoplasm are present as components of a large variety of substances ranging from small molecules to vast colloidal particles. Any fundamental understanding of the chemical and physical nature of living systems makes it imperative that we know the structure and properties of these substances as they occur in the cell.

Principal Chemical Substances of the Cell

The chemical constituents of protoplasm can be conveniently classified into two broad categories, *inorganic substances* and *organic substances*. Inorganic substances are characterized by the lack of carbon-hydrogen bonds in their chemical make-up. They include (*a*) water (in free and bound forms), which is the chief component of living systems, accounting for 60 to 95 per cent of the composition of most organisms; (*b*) dissolved gases (particularly molecular oxygen and carbon dioxide); and (*c*) salts and ionic states of certain metallic and nonmetallic elements such as iron, copper, zinc, manganese, phosphorous, calcium, magnesium, potassium, sodium, and chloride. The different roles of inorganic substances in biological systems are indicated in Chapter 9.

Organic substances characteristically contain carbon-hydrogen bonds. Many organic compounds of biological importance may also contain as part of their chemical make-up other atoms such as oxygen, nitrogen, sulfur, phosphorus, and several metals. The carbon, hydrogen, oxygen, and nitrogen of organic compounds alone account for approximately 99 per cent of the dry weight of living cells.

At present the key to our knowledge of metabolism, growth, repair, and reproduction resides primarily in four important classes of organic compounds that contribute to the make-up and activity of protoplasm. These are the *carbohydrates*, *fats*, *proteins*, and *nucleic acids*. Before dealing with the nature of these substances it is important first to consider certain fundamental aspects of organic chemistry, especially those pertaining to biochemistry.

ORGANIC CHEMISTRY

Properties of Carbon and Its Compounds

An unusual property of the carbon atom is its ability to combine chemically with other carbon atoms to form chains of varying lengths, either unbranched, branched, or cyclic. Organic compounds are therefore made up of a skeleton or backbone of carbon atoms ranging from one to many carbons, chemically linked to each other

and to other atoms such as hydrogen, nitrogen, and sulfur.

The carbon atom has an atomic number of 6 and accordingly has 6 electrons surrounding its nucleus—2 in its K shell and 4 in its L shell (Figure 6-8). As a result of its tendency like most other atoms to acquire the stable configuration of 8 in its outermost electronic-energy shell (Chapter 6), carbon forms a characteristic number of 4 chemical bonds which are almost always of the covalent type. The 4 bonds of carbon are identical and equidistant from each other around the three-dimensional carbon atom and are directed in space towards the four corners of an imaginary tetrahedron with the carbon atom at the center (Figure 7-1). For example, a simple organic compound like methane, CH_4, where the carbon atom is covalently bonded to each of four hydrogen atoms, is a three-dimensional molecule as shown in Figure 7-1. For convenience organic molecules are represented on paper as two-dimensional structures by means of the dot formula or dash formula as shown for methane:

$$
\begin{array}{ccc}
\text{H} & & \text{H} \\
\text{H} : \overset{\displaystyle\cdot\cdot}{\underset{\displaystyle\cdot\cdot}{\text{C}}} : \text{H} & \text{or} & \text{H}-\overset{\displaystyle|}{\underset{\displaystyle|}{\text{C}}}-\text{H} \\
\text{H} & & \text{H}
\end{array}
$$

Although a single bond (sharing of one pair of electrons) between any two carbon atoms is the most prevalent kind in organic compounds, double and triple bonds also occur. Thus two carbon atoms may be chemically bound to each

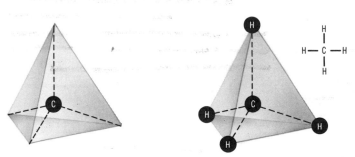

Figure 7-1. Representation of the carbon atom and the simple organic compound methane in three dimensions illustrating that the four chemical bonds of carbon are directed toward the four corners of an imaginary tetrahedron.

other by the sharing of two or three pairs of electrons instead of by one pair of electrons as in a single covalent bond. For example, the organic compound ethane possesses a carbon-carbon single bond, ethylene a carbon-carbon double bond, and acetylene a carbon-carbon triple bond:

$H_3C\!-\!CH_3$ $H_2C\!=\!CH_2$ $HC\!\equiv\!CH$

Ethane   Ethylene   Acetylene

The carbon atoms in proteins, nucleic acids, carbohydrates, and fats are combined mostly by single bonds and to a lesser extent by double bonds. Triple bonds of carbon in biological systems seem to occur far less frequently. Single bonds between carbon atoms are also referred to as *saturated* bonds, whereas double or triple bonds between carbon atoms are called *unsaturated*. The latter are called unsaturated because they can undergo further chemical reaction by addition of other atoms to these bonds. Organic compounds tend to burn rather easily which means that when they are heated to high enough temperatures they are oxidized by molecular oxygen, becoming degraded ultimately to water and carbon dioxide. Energy in the form of light and heat is liberated in the process.

Types of Organic Compounds

HYDROCARBONS. Organic compounds may be classified in various ways. We can regard them as molecules whose carbon atoms are arranged in either unbranched chains, branching chains, or cyclic chain structures. For example, *normal*-hexane is a saturated, straight-chain organic compound consisting of 6 carbon and 14 hydrogen atoms. Isohexane is a saturated branched-chain organic compound consisting also of 6 carbon and 14 hydrogen atoms but obviously possessing a different structural configuration than *normal*-hexane. Although both compounds have the same number of carbons and hydrogens they are different molecules by virtue of the different arrangement of their atoms and therefore exhibit different physical and chemical properties. Such compounds having the same composition but different structures are said to be *isomers* of each other. This is analogous to the construction of two words such as *late* and *tale* which are composed of the same four letters but which are quite different because of the arrangement of the letters. Cyclohexane is a saturated organic molecule made up of 6 carbon atoms attached to each other in the form of a ring or cyclic structure. It can also be thought of as a chain hexane molecule whose end carbons have joined together in a covalent bond by the elimination of two hydrogen atoms (thus still satisfying the four-bond requirement of the carbon atom) to form a cyclic structure. As would be expected, cyclohexane has properties that differ from those of the other hexane isomers:

n-Hexane

Isohexane

Cyclohexane

Organic compounds can also be classified according to other chemical and structural features. For example, the organic compounds containing only carbon and hydrogen are called *hydrocarbons*. They may be either straight-chain, branched-chain, or cyclic molecules.

Hydrocarbons may also be either saturated or unsaturated.

The relationships among certain organic compounds are conveniently indicated by arranging them into so-called *homologous series* in which each member differs from the preceding member by a $-CH_2-$ group as illustrated by the saturated hydrocarbons. The first member of the series is methane, CH_4, followed by ethane, C_2H_6, propane, C_3H_8, butane, C_4H_{10}, and so on. All contain the maximum number of hydrogens compatible with the requirement that carbon always has 4 bonds and hydrogen 1. After the third member of the series, propane, there are a number of possible isomers which include the unbranched chain molecule as well as branched-chain configurations.

Another class of hydrocarbons is the *aromatic* hydrocarbons which include one or more six-membered carbon rings each containing 3 double bonds. The configuration of these particular six-membered cyclic compounds, which are commonly known as *benzene* rings, is often written as a hexagonal-shaped structure with 3 alternating double bonds with the tacit understanding that a carbon atom is covalently linked to one hydrogen at each apex:

Benzene

Hydrocarbon Derivatives and Functional Groups. Nearly all organic compounds composing the living cell are hydrocarbon derivatives, possessing in addition to carbon and hydrogen, the atoms oxygen and nitrogen, and to a lesser extent phosphorous, sulfur, and certain metals. In most cases these additional atoms are chiefly responsible for the chemical reactivity of the organic compound. For this reason they are called *functional groups* (the remainder of the hydrocarbon molecule may also undergo chemical reaction but far less readily).

A number of different kinds of functional groups exist for organic compounds. The molecules that react similarly do so because of the possession of the same functional groups. Therefore, despite their vast number, organic compounds can also be classified into a relatively few types depending on their reactivity which in turn largely depends on the nature of their functional groups. As might be expected these are the very same functional groups that undergo chemical reactions in the living cell, thus constituting the various steps in the metabolism of the cell.

Some of the more common functional groups in organic compounds, especially those directly involved in biochemical reactions, are discussed in the following paragraphs.

ALCOHOLS — THE HYDROXYL GROUP. The $-OH$ functional group is known as an *alcohol* or *hydroxyl* group. When it has taken the place of a hydrogen atom in its covalent linkage to the carbon of an organic compound, the molecule displays the properties of an alcohol. (The alcohol group is different from the negatively charged OH^- or hydroxide ion which is responsible for the alkalinity of solutions.) Substitution of the alcohol group, $-OH$, for a hydrogen atom in the methane molecule, CH_4, gives the compound CH_3OH, called *methyl alcohol* or *methanol*; an $-OH$ in place of a hydrogen atom in the ethane molecule, CH_3CH_3, gives *ethyl alcohol* or *ethanol*, CH_3CH_2OH. A single organic molecule may contain several alcohol groups provided that there is not more than one $-OH$ group per carbon atom if it is to be stable. Glycerol, a product of fat hydrolysis, is an example of this type possessing a total of three alcohol groups, one linked to each of its three carbons, CH_2OH $CHOH$ CH_2OH.

Ethyl alcohol and certain derivatives of glycerol are important intermediates and products in the cellular respiratory process (Chapter 8). Alcohol groups also occur on a number of important hormones known as the *steroid hormones* (p. 151), including those responsible for development of the sexual characteristics of many animals.

ALDEHYDES AND KETONES — THE CARBONYL GROUP. The carbon-oxygen double bond, $>C=O$, is known as the *carbonyl* group. Organic molecules which contain the carbonyl group at the beginning or end of their carbon chains are called *aldehydes*. Formaldehyde (HCHO), for example, is the simplest of the aldehydes, and acetaldehyde (CH_3CHO) is the next simplest. If the carbonyl group is attached to an organic molecule other than at the end, the compound, it is called a *ketone*. The carbonyl group of ketones is covalently linked to each of two carbon atoms in the chain, and unlike that of aldehydes has no hydrogen atom attached to it since the four bonds of its carbon are already satisfied. The simplest ketone is acetone,

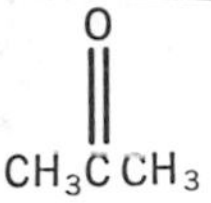

$$CH_3\overset{\overset{\displaystyle O}{\|}}{C}CH_3$$

The same general concept of oxidation-reduction reactions mentioned in the preceding chapter applies to organic compounds. Aldehydes and ketones can readily be formed by the oxidation of corresponding alcohols, namely by the removal of two hydrogen atoms. The oxidation of an alcohol group located at the end of a carbon chain produces the related aldehyde, whereas the oxidation of an alcohol group in a nonterminal position forms the corresponding ketone. For example, the mild oxidation of ethyl alcohol, CH_3CH_2OH, produces acetaldehyde, CH_3CHO, whereas the oxidation of isopropyl alcohol, $CH_3CHOHCH_3$, yields the ketone acetone,

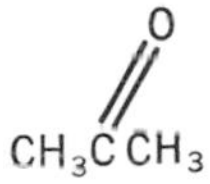

$$CH_3\overset{\overset{\displaystyle O}{\|}}{C}CH_3$$

The reactions form the carbonyl group by removal of two hydrogen atoms and are usually freely reversible. The hydrogens that are removed reduce in turn another substance, namely the oxidizing agent itself (not shown here). Several important oxidation-reduction reactions occurring in living cells involve the reversible transformation of carbonyl-containing compounds to their corresponding

alcohols (e.g., the interconversion of acetaldehyde to ethyl alcohol in the fermentation of glucose by yeast, and pyruvic acid to lactic acid in the glycolysis of mammalian muscle, Chapter 8).

ORGANIC ACIDS — THE CARBOXYLIC ACID GROUP. The

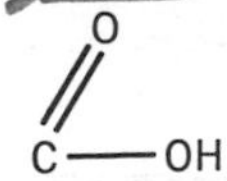

$$\overset{\overset{\displaystyle O}{\|}}{C}-OH$$

group, often written as —COOH, is known as the *carboxylic acid group*. Compounds possessing the carboxylic acid group are called *organic acids* because they ionize to produce H^+ ions (—COOH $\rightleftharpoons$ —COO$^-$ + H$^+$). They are weak acids ionizing to a relatively small extent in aqueous solutions as in the case of acetic acid, CH_3COOH, a small proportion of which dissociates into H^+ ions and so-called acetate (CH_3COO^-) ions.

$$CH_3COOH \rightleftharpoons CH_3COO^- + H^+$$

The carboxylic acid group can readily be formed by the oxidation of an aldehyde group as in the typical conversion of acetaldehyde to acetic acid. In this reaction we postulate a first step involving the chemical addition of water to the aldehyde group to form a hypothetical intermediate,

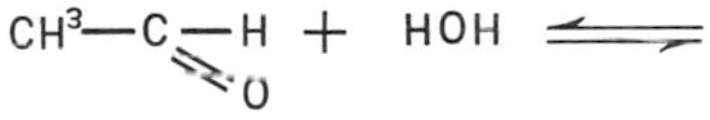

$$CH_3-\overset{\diagdown}{\underset{\diagup}{C}}{\overset{}{O}}-H + HOH \rightleftharpoons$$

Acetaldehyde

$$\left[CH_3-\overset{\overset{\displaystyle OH}{|}}{\underset{\underset{\displaystyle H}{|}}{C}}-OH \right]$$

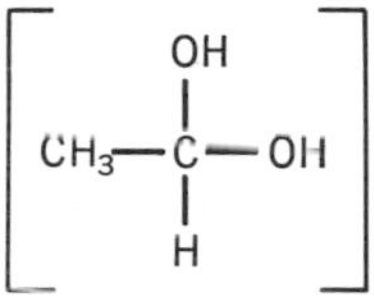

which is then oxidized by the removal of two hydrogens to form the organic acid.

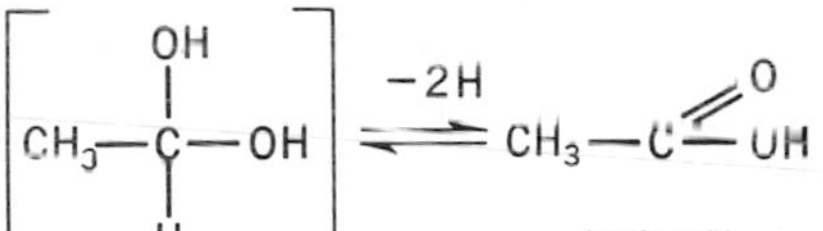

$$\left[CH_3-\overset{\overset{\displaystyle OH}{|}}{\underset{\underset{\displaystyle H}{|}}{C}}-OH \right] \overset{-2H}{\rightleftharpoons} CH_3-C\overset{\diagup O}{\underset{\diagdown}{OH}}$$

Acetic acid

An alcohol such as ethanol can be successively oxidized in a stepwise fashion to acetaldehyde and then to acetic acid:

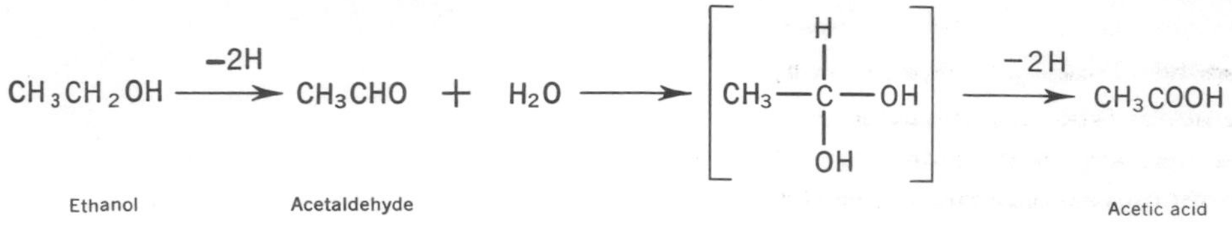

$$CH_3CH_2OH \xrightarrow{-2H} CH_3CHO \ + \ H_2O \longrightarrow \left[CH_3 - \overset{\overset{\displaystyle H}{|}}{\underset{\underset{\displaystyle OH}{|}}{C}} - OH \right] \xrightarrow{-2H} CH_3COOH$$

Ethanol   Acetaldehyde   Acetic acid

Certain organic acids may have two and even three carboxylic acid groups attached to a single molecule and are designated as *dicarboxylic* and *tricarboxylic acids*, respectively. Certain dicarboxylic and tricarboxylic acids happen to be key intermediates in the respiratory process.

Organic molecules which possess a carboxyl acid group and a carbon chain exceeding four carbons in length are relatively insoluble in water and are called *fatty acids*. If the molecule has one or more double or triple covalent bonds between any of its carbon atoms, it is called an *unsaturated* fatty acid; if none is present it is a *saturated* fatty acid. Stearic acid, $C_{17}H_{35}COOH$, is a common saturated fatty acid often found in the tissues of both plants and animals. Its structural formula is shown below.

Linoleic acid, $C_{17}H_{31}COOH$, is an example of a naturally occurring unsaturated fatty acid whose structural formula is shown below.

Fatty acids are present in cells chiefly as part of larger molecules called *fats* (described later in the chapter).

Esters. Under certain conditions an alcohol and an organic acid will react in a characteristic way to form a compound known as an *ester*. More precisely the reaction involves the combination of the $-OH$ group of the alcohol with the $-COOH$ group of the acid to yield water and the ester. For example, ethyl alcohol, C_2H_5OH, reacts with acetic acid, CH_3COOH, to produce water and ester *ethyl acetate*, $CH_3CH_2-O-CO-CH_3$, as shown below.

All living cells contain numerous esters, the most important of which are the fats and oils.

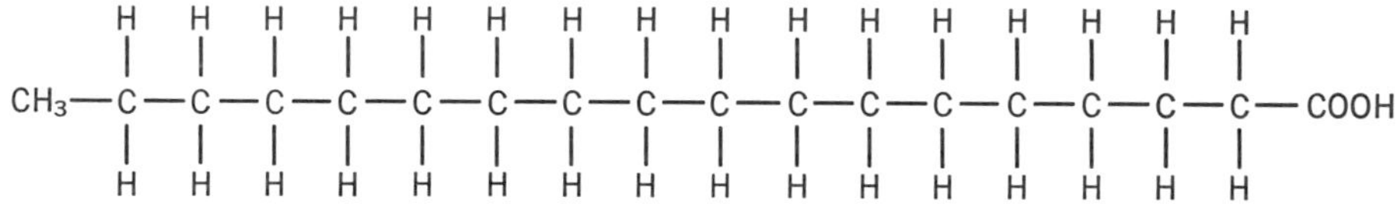

Stearic acid

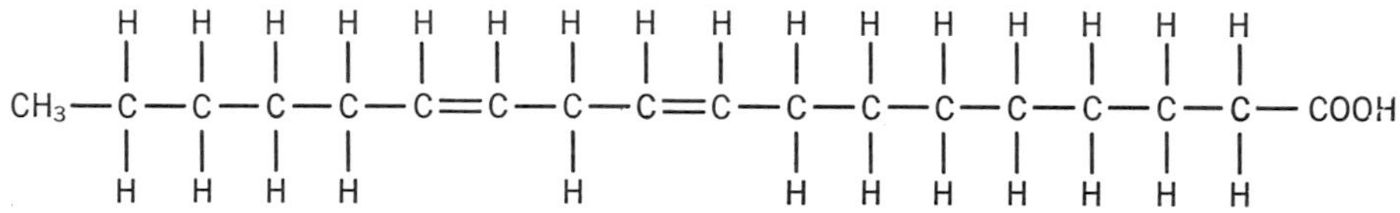

$$CH_3 - \overset{\overset{\displaystyle H}{|}}{\underset{\underset{\displaystyle H}{|}}{C}} - \overset{\overset{\displaystyle H}{|}}{\underset{\underset{\displaystyle H}{|}}{C}} - \overset{\overset{\displaystyle H}{|}}{\underset{\underset{\displaystyle H}{|}}{C}} - \overset{\overset{\displaystyle H}{|}}{\underset{\underset{\displaystyle H}{|}}{C}} - \overset{\overset{\displaystyle H}{|}}{\underset{\underset{\displaystyle H}{|}}{C}} - \overset{\overset{\displaystyle H}{|}}{\underset{\underset{\displaystyle H}{|}}{C}} - \overset{\overset{\displaystyle H}{|}}{\underset{\underset{\displaystyle H}{|}}{C}} - \overset{\overset{\displaystyle H}{|}}{\underset{\underset{\displaystyle H}{|}}{C}} - \overset{\overset{\displaystyle H}{|}}{\underset{\underset{\displaystyle H}{|}}{C}} - \overset{\overset{\displaystyle H}{|}}{\underset{\underset{\displaystyle H}{|}}{C}} - \overset{\overset{\displaystyle H}{|}}{\underset{\underset{\displaystyle H}{|}}{C}} - \overset{\overset{\displaystyle H}{|}}{\underset{\underset{\displaystyle H}{|}}{C}} - \overset{\overset{\displaystyle H}{|}}{\underset{\underset{\displaystyle H}{|}}{C}} - \overset{\overset{\displaystyle H}{|}}{\underset{\underset{\displaystyle H}{|}}{C}} - \overset{\overset{\displaystyle H}{|}}{\underset{\underset{\displaystyle H}{|}}{C}} - \overset{\overset{\displaystyle H}{|}}{\underset{\underset{\displaystyle H}{|}}{C}} - COOH$$

Stearic acid

Linoleic acid

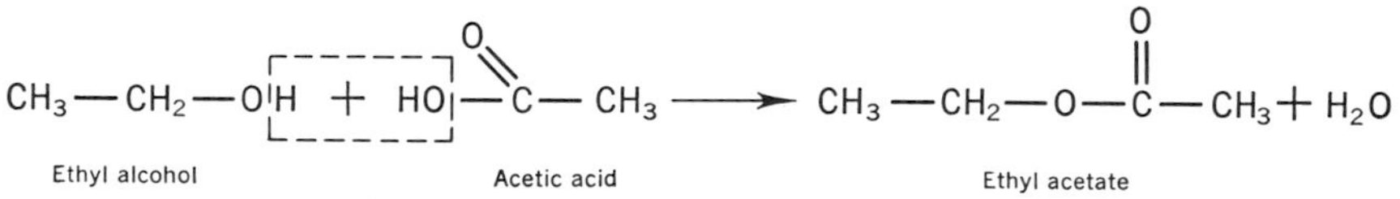

Ethyl alcohol   Acetic acid   Ethyl acetate

These are principally esters of the trihydroxy alcohol, glycerol, and particular fatty acids. Their general structure and properties are indicated in the section dealing with fats. Esters are also the compounds responsible for the fragrance and pleasant flavors of flowers and fruits.

AMINES AND AMINO ACIDS—THE AMINO GROUP. Amines are essentially derivatives of

$$NH_3 \left(or \quad \begin{matrix} H \\ | \\ N-H \\ | \\ H \end{matrix} \right)$$

ammonia, in which one or more covalent linkages of hydrogen has been replaced by a chemical bond to carbon. The substitution of one of the hydrogen atoms of ammonia by a CH_3— group results in the formation of the simple amine compound

$$\begin{matrix} H \\ | \\ H-C-NH_2 \\ | \\ H \end{matrix}$$

known as *methyl amine*. Similarly $CH_3CH_2NH_2$ (ethyl amine) and $CH_3CH_2CH_2NH_2$ (propylamine) are the corresponding amino derivatives of ethane and propane, respectively. Many of the amines have disagreeable odors and account for the unpleasant smell of putrefaction and decay.

Organic compounds that contain both the amino and carboxylic acid groups are called *amino acids*. *Alanine*, whose structure follows, is one of the approximately 20 different naturally occurring amino acids (Table 7-1) that serve as the building blocks of the important biological molecules, the *proteins*, discussed

$$CH_3-\underset{\underset{H}{|}}{\overset{\overset{NH_2}{|}}{C}}\overset{\overset{O}{\parallel}}{-C}-OH$$

Alanine

in a later section of this chapter.

The amino and carboxyl groups of alanine, as in most naturally occurring amino acids, are attached to the carbon adjacent to the carboxyl group designated as the *alpha* (α)-carbon and for this reason the compound is called an alpha-amino acid. Of the two remaining atoms or groups linked to the alpha-carbon, one is nearly always a hydrogen atom whereas the other, represented arbitrarily by the letter R, is a carbon chain of varying length and structure which is characteristic for each of the different amino acids.

$$R-\underset{\underset{H}{|}}{\overset{\overset{NH_2}{|}}{C}}\overset{\alpha}{-}COOH$$

α-Amino acid

Some amino acids contain two carboxyl groups (aspartic and glutamic acids) and others contain more than one amino group (e.g., lysine). At least three have the sulfur atom in their structure (cysteine, cystine, and methionine).

Stereoisomerism

The configuration of atoms in a molecule depends on both their structural and spatial arrangements with one another. Thus not only are there structural isomers (same composition but different structure) for numerous organic compounds (e.g., hexane and isohexane), but certain molecules also exist as spatial isomers called *stereoisomers*.

ASYMMETRIC CARBONS. Of great biological significance is a particular class of stereoisomers which is based on the spatial arrangement of chemical bonds about so-called *asymmetric carbons*. The carbon atom as a three-dimensional structure characteristically forms 4 covalent bonds equidistant from each other and directed in space toward the four corners of a tetrahedron. By definition an *asymmetric carbon* atom is one which has 4 *different* atoms or

Table 7-1. The Naturally Occurring Amino Acids

1 Glycine (Gly)

$$NH_2-CH_2-COOH$$

2 L-Alanine (Ala)

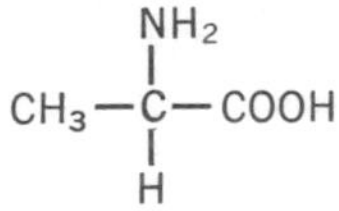

$$CH_3-\underset{\underset{H}{|}}{\overset{\overset{NH_2}{|}}{C}}-COOH$$

3 L-Valine (Val)

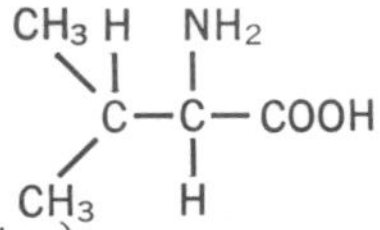

$$\underset{\underset{CH_3}{|}}{\overset{\overset{CH_3}{\diagdown}}{C}}-\underset{\underset{H}{|}}{\overset{\overset{NH_2}{|}}{C}}-COOH$$

4 L-Leucine (Leu)

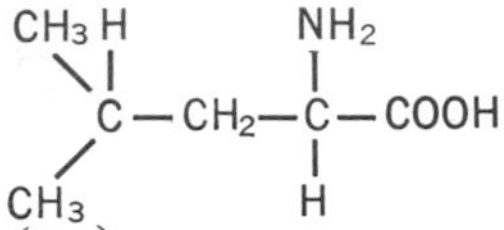

$$\underset{\underset{CH_3}{|}}{\overset{\overset{CH_3}{\diagdown}}{C}}-CH_2-\underset{\underset{H}{|}}{\overset{\overset{NH_2}{|}}{C}}-COOH$$

5 L-Isoleucine (Ileu)

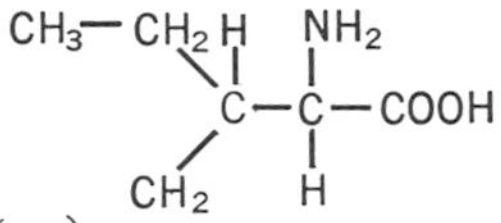

$$CH_3-CH_2-\underset{\underset{CH_2}{|}}{\overset{\overset{H}{|}}{C}}-\underset{\underset{H}{|}}{\overset{\overset{NH_2}{|}}{C}}-COOH$$

6 L-Serine (Ser)

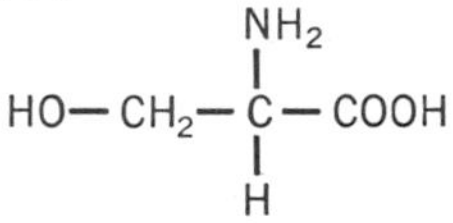

$$HO-CH_2-\underset{\underset{H}{|}}{\overset{\overset{NH_2}{|}}{C}}-COOH$$

7 L-Threonine (Thr)

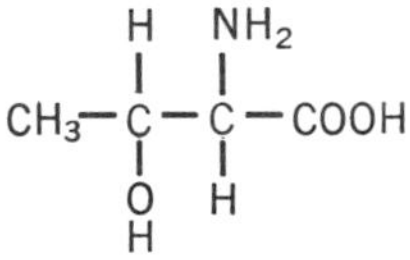

$$CH_3-\underset{\underset{O\,H}{|}}{\overset{\overset{H}{|}}{C}}-\underset{\underset{H}{|}}{\overset{\overset{NH_2}{|}}{C}}-COOH$$

8 L-Cysteine (Cysh)

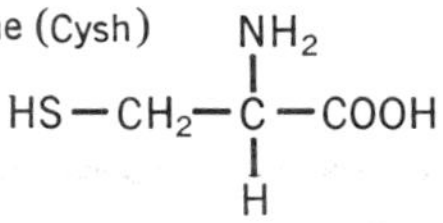

$$HS-CH_2-\underset{\underset{H}{|}}{\overset{\overset{NH_2}{|}}{C}}-COOH$$

9 L-Cystine (Cys)

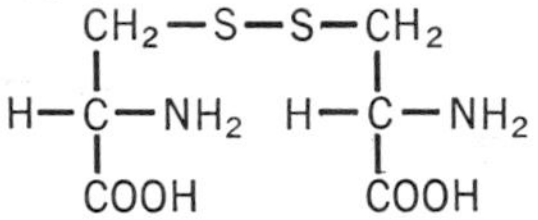

$$CH_2-S-S-CH_2$$
$$H-\underset{\underset{COOH}{|}}{\overset{|}{C}}-NH_2 \quad H-\underset{\underset{COOH}{|}}{\overset{|}{C}}-NH_2$$

10 L-Methionine (Met)

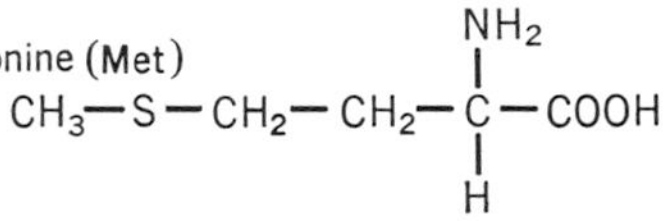

$$CH_3-S-CH_2-CH_2-\underset{\underset{H}{|}}{\overset{\overset{NH_2}{|}}{C}}-COOH$$

11 L-Glutamic acid (Glu)

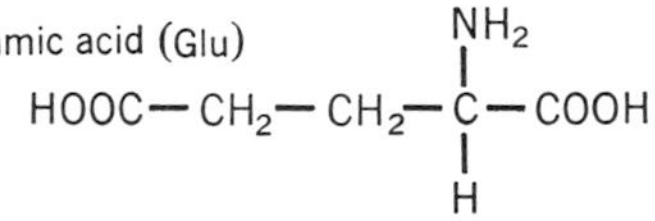

$$HOOC-CH_2-CH_2-\underset{\underset{H}{|}}{\overset{\overset{NH_2}{|}}{C}}-COOH$$

12 L-Aspartic acid (Asp)

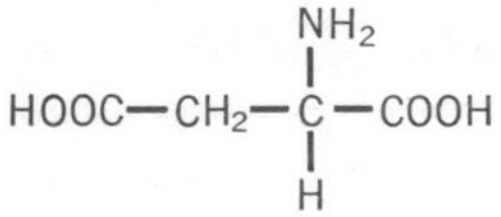

$$HOOC-CH_2-\underset{\underset{H}{|}}{\overset{\overset{NH_2}{|}}{C}}-COOH$$

13 L-Lysine (Lys)

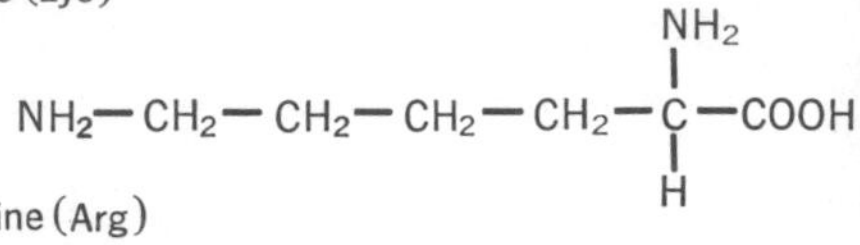

$$NH_2-CH_2-CH_2-CH_2-CH_2-\underset{\underset{H}{|}}{\overset{\overset{NH_2}{|}}{C}}-COOH$$

14 L-Arginine (Arg)

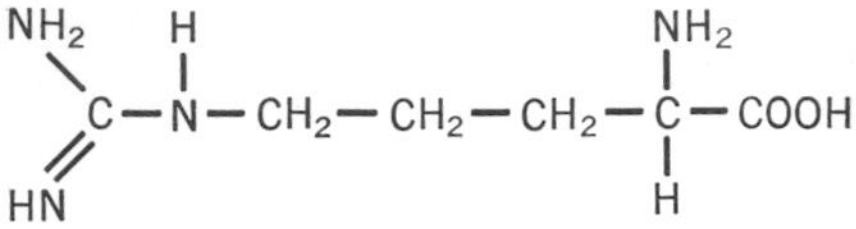

$$\underset{\underset{HN}{\diagup}}{\overset{\overset{NH_2}{|}}{C}}-N-CH_2-CH_2-CH_2-\underset{\underset{H}{|}}{\overset{\overset{NH_2}{|}}{C}}-COOH$$

15 L-Histidine (His)

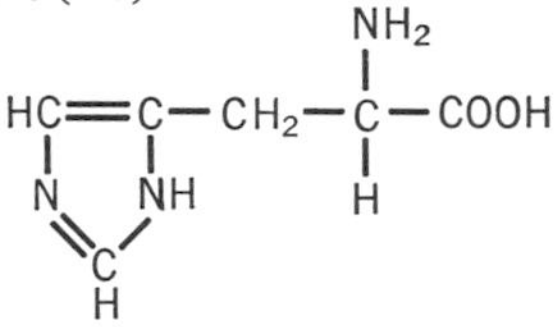

$$HC=C-CH_2-\underset{\underset{H}{|}}{\overset{\overset{NH_2}{|}}{C}}-COOH$$

16 L-Phenylalanine (Phe)

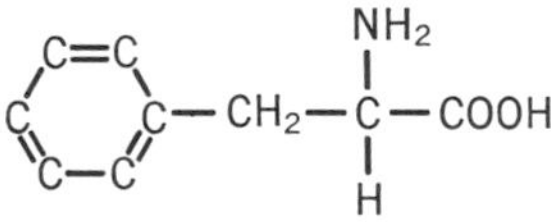

$$C_6H_5-CH_2-\underset{\underset{H}{|}}{\overset{\overset{NH_2}{|}}{C}}-COOH$$

17 L-Tyrosine (Tyr)

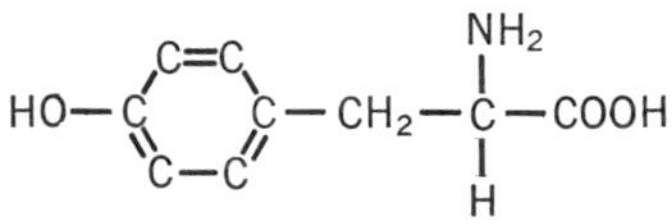

$$HO-C_6H_4-CH_2-\underset{\underset{H}{|}}{\overset{\overset{NH_2}{|}}{C}}-COOH$$

18 L-Tryptophan (Try)

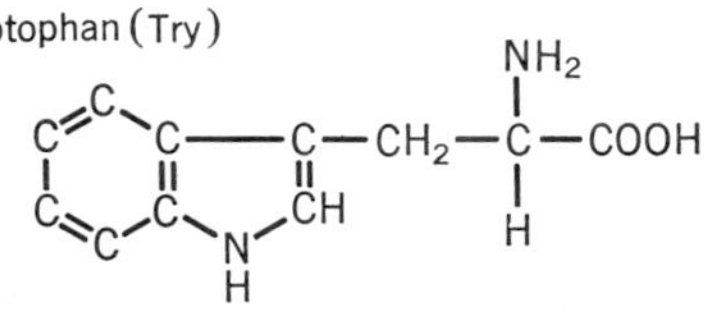

$$\text{(indole)}-CH_2-\underset{\underset{H}{|}}{\overset{\overset{NH_2}{|}}{C}}-COOH$$

19 L-Proline (Pro)

$$\begin{array}{c} CH_2-CH_2 \\ | \qquad | \\ CH_2 \quad CH-COOH \\ \diagdown N \diagup \\ H \end{array}$$

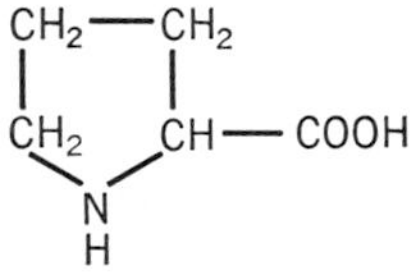

20 L-Hydroxyproline (Hpro)

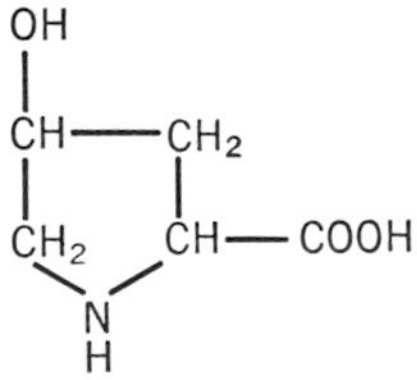

$$\begin{array}{c} OH \\ | \\ CH-CH_2 \\ | \qquad | \\ CH_2 \quad CH-COOH \\ \diagdown N \diagup \\ H \end{array}$$

groupings chemically linked to it. It is asymmetric because under these circumstances no hypothetical plane can be passed through the center of the carbon atom which will divide it into two similar halves (carbon atoms possessing double or triple bonds are not asymmetric). For example, in the amino acid alanine, the alpha or number 2 carbon which is linked to 4 different atoms is asymmetric, whereas the other carbons are not. Similarly in the three-carbon compound glyceraldehyde the number 2 carbon is asymmetric whereas the others are not.

Only two different spatial configurations are possible for each asymmetric carbon so that a molecule possessing a single asymmetric carbon (e.g., alanine or glyceraldehyde) can exist in two stereoisomeric forms.

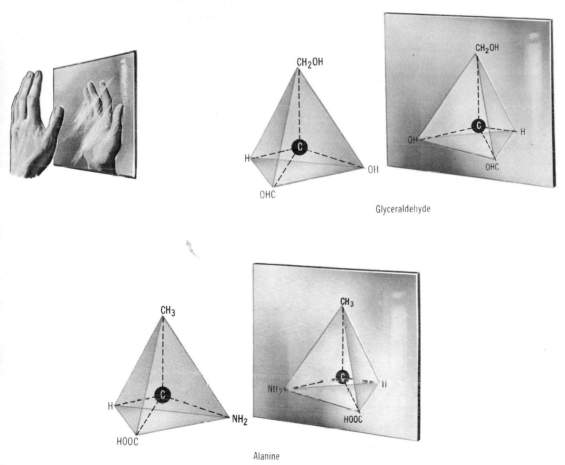

Figure 7-2. The two stereoisomers of glyceraldehyde and of alanine are not identical but mirror images of one another like the relationship between the right hand and left.

These are best visualized by means of three-dimensional atomic models (Figure 7-2). Although the two stereoisomers of alanine at first appear to be the same, careful examination shows they are similar but not identical. They are not superimposable in that one is the mirror image of the other like the relationship between our right hand and left hand. We know that both hands are similar but not identical, one being the mirror image of the other. Stereoisomers are represented two-dimensionally on paper by putting the atoms or groups chemically bonded to the asymmetric carbon on opposite sides. If a particular grouping is on the left in one of the stereoisomers it will be on the right in the other and vice versa.

OPTICAL ACTIVITY AND ABSOLUTE CONFIGURATION. Stereoisomers that are mirror images of each other are indistinguishable in nearly all of their properties. They differ, however, in at least two important respects. First, living cells when presented with organic compounds containing one or more asymmetric carbons (e.g., amino acids and carbohydrates) utilize or metabolize in nearly all cases only one of the stereoisomers to the complete exclusion of the other. This is ascribed to the fact that most enzymes exclusively catalyze reactions of only one of the stereoisomers, leaving the other unchanged. The preferential metabolism of particular stereoisomers is in turn attributed to the asymmetric constituents, namely the amino acids, composing the enzymes themselves. Thus one can use organisms or enzymes to distinguish between stereoisomers of a number of organic compounds.

Second, stereoisomers differ markedly from each other in certain optical properties because of the presence of one or more asymmetric carbons. Many naturally occurring organic compounds display the remarkable property of *optical activity* — an ability to rotate the plane of *polarized light*[1] because of the presence in

these molecules of an asymmetric carbon atom. Of the two possible spatial arrangements of the different atoms or groupings about an asymmetric carbon, one arrangement is somehow responsible for the rotation of polarized light to the right whereas the other stereoisomer is responsible for an equal rotation to the left. Those substances that cause a rotation of the polarized light to the right, as one faces the light source, are said to be *dextrorotatory* (designated by a + sign); those that rotate it to the left are called *levorotatory* (designated by a − sign). Because of their equal and opposite effect in rotating polarized light stereoisomers are also referred to as *optical* isomers. When the two optical isomers of a given compound are mixed in equal proportions they exhibit no apparent optical activity since each will balance out the other. Such mixtures are spoken of as *racemic* mixtures.

Optical activity, however, does not tell us about the *absolute configuration* of the several substituents about an asymmetric carbon. A more meaningful designation of compounds has been devised, based on configurational rather than on optical properties. Roman small

[1] *Optical activity* and *polarized light* are best explained by referring to the wave theory of light. According to the *wave theory* light is made up of electromagnetic vibrations or waves similar to other electromagnetic phenomena such as radio waves, infrared, ultraviolet, and X-rays. They are comparable to the waves in oceans and lakes, except that water waves vibrate vertically, simply moving up and down as the wave goes forward, whereas light waves vibrate in all possible planes, including up and down as well as sideways at every possible angle. When ordinary light consisting of wave vibrations occurring in all planes is passed through a sheet of synthetic material known as polaroid or through a Nicol prism (especially arranged plates of crystals of the calcium carbonate mineral called calcite or Iceland spar), the light which emerges is that which vibrates in only one plane analogous to the single-plane vibration of a water wave. Such light is called *polarized* light. Polarized light will not pass through a second Nicol prism if the latter is set at right angles to the first prism which originally selected the polarized light. If the second prism is now turned so that it is parallel to (or at the same angle as) the first, it will permit the polarized light to pass through. Such an instrument, consisting of two Nicol prisms and a light source, is called a *polarimeter*. Organic molecules possessing one or more asymmetric carbons have the power of quantitatively changing the plane of vibration of the polarized light either to the left or right depending on the particular stereoisomer, a phenomenon that can be measured with the polarimeter. Those substances that thus rotate the plane of polarized light are said to be *optically active*, a property displayed by many naturally occurring organic compounds. Stereoisomers exhibit optical activity no matter what their physical state, since this property resides in the spatial configuration of the atoms or groupings about an asymmetric carbon.

capitals D and L are used as prefixed symbols to designate each of the two possible configurations about the asymmetric carbon atom in a molecule. Glyceraldehyde has been adopted as the standard reference compound with respect to the arrangement of groupings about the asymmetric carbon. In 1951 it was finally determined that the dextrorotatory and levorotatory forms of glyceraldehyde had the D and L configurations, respectively, shown below.

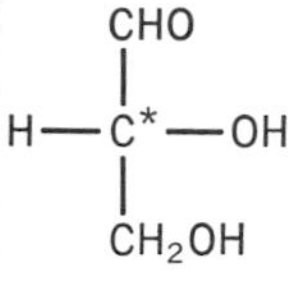

D(+)-glyceraldehyde 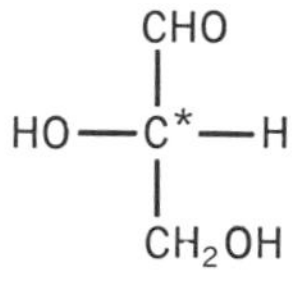   L(−)-glyceraldehyde

The configurations about the asymmetric carbons of several other compounds in relation to glyceraldehyde have been determined over the years by interconversion through chemical reactions which do not disturb the asymmetric carbons. For example, D (+)-glyceraldehyde can be converted to levorotatory (−) lactic acid without breaking the bonds to the asymmetric carbon atom, thus indicating that the configuration about the asymmetric carbon of lactic acid is the same as that of D (+)-glyceraldehyde. Levorotatory (−) lactic acid must therefore have a D configuration.

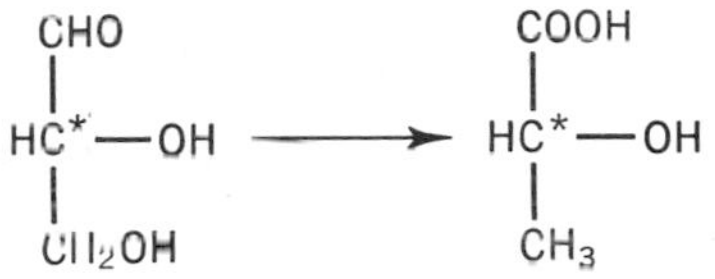

D(+)-glyceraldehyde   D(−)-lactic acid

These examples illustrate that all dextrorotatory compounds do not have the same relative configuration about their asymmetric carbons; and that all levorotatory substances are also not alike in this respect.

Nearly all the naturally occurring amino acids have an asymmetric carbon (the carbon to which both the carboxyl (−COOH) and amino (−NH₂) groups are attached). The amino acids constituting proteins are exclusively in the L configuration, and nearly all living organisms can only utilize the L form. In the simple sugars, (p. 146) most forms of life metabolize only the D form. Actually most sugars have several asymmetric carbons but the D and L rule applies only to the asymmetric carbon most distant from the carbonyl end of the molecule. For example, in the case of the biologically important sugars such as glucose and fructose this would be the number 5 carbon atom.

BIOLOGICAL SIGNIFICANCE OF STEREOISOMERISM. Why can living organisms metabolize only one of the stereoisomers of asymmetric molecules such as the L amino acids and the D sugars, and what is the biological significance of this phenomenon? Although the answers are not clear, several suggestions have been proposed from an evolutionary viewpoint. It seems reasonable to assume that optically active or asymmetric substances had their origin in the early history of the earth before the first appearance of life. There are indications that the synthesis of asymmetric organic substances in a nonliving world can be achieved in several ways, possibly through the action of some asymmetric physical factor or in the presence of another asymmetric substance. Experiments have been reported that circularly polarized ultraviolet light (which can occur under natural conditions) may resolve a racemic mixture into an optically active one by effecting a differential rate of decomposition of the optical isomers making up the racemic mixture. It has also been possible to demonstrate the formation of optically active substances by use of optically active crystals such as quartz which are widely distributed in nature.

The fact that living systems exhibit a highly differential optical asymmetry in their structure and metabolism has made them a major influence in perpetuating and extending the occurrence of optical isomers in nature. It also suggests that these molecular configurations possibly offered some selective advantage (as compared to racemic mixtures or opposite molecular configurations) in the origin and evolution of life. Perhaps the many coordinated series of chemical reactions which ultimately evolved into a living system might have proceeded at a faster rate and exhibited greater stability with particular stereoisomers.

IMPORTANT ORGANIC CONSTITUENTS OF CELLS

The major classes of biologically important organic substances principally responsible for the structural and functional characteristics of protoplasm are the *carbohydrates, fats, proteins,* and *nucleic acids.* In many organisms an additional group of organic compounds, the *porphyrins,* also play an important role in metabolism.

Carbohydrates

GENERAL CHARACTERISTICS. The group of organic compounds known as *carbohydrates* are intimately involved in the life processes of all living things. First, they play a key role in the energy relations of all organisms. On the one hand they are the principal products arising from the capture of solar energy by the process of photosynthesis, whereby the energy of sunlight is utilized to convert the low energy bonds of carbon dioxide and water to the higher energy bonds of carbohydrates. On the other hand all cells are able to obtain their energy for the characteristic life activities from the stepwise breakdown of these carbohydrates by the process of *respiration* (Chapter 8). Second, within the living cell certain carbohydrates are integral structural units of all nucleic acids. Finally, they also serve as important building materials for both the animate and inanimate structures of cells, contributing as well to the biological formation (called *biosynthesis*) of other organic substances such as fats and proteins.

The term carbohydrate literally means *hydrate of carbon.* The name was adopted years ago because it included many compounds (but not all) that contained atoms of hydrogen and oxygen (in addition to carbon) in the same proportions as occur in water. A carbohydrate is chemically defined as an organic compound that contains a carbonyl group (aldehyde or ketone) in addition to two or more alcohol groups, or that yields such compounds upon hydrolysis. In brief, carbohydrates are aldehyde or ketone derivatives of polyhydric alcohols. Carbohydrates occur in a variety of forms ranging in structure from relatively simple molecules called sugars (because they are sweet to the taste) to those of vast and complex size such as starches and cellulose. They may be physically or chemically bound to proteins and to fats, or free and not linked to any other type of molecule. In some tissues carbohydrates constitute less than 0.1 per cent of the dry weight of the cell, while in others (e.g., liver) they range as high as 15 per cent. They are usually classified into three broad categories—*monosaccharides, oligosaccharides,* and *polysaccharides*—on the basis of the complexity of their structure.

MONOSACCHARIDES. Monosaccharides, or simple sugars, cannot undergo hydrolysis to form simpler sugars. They are classified according to the lengths of their carbon chains, which range from 3-carbon compounds (*trioses*) such as glyceraldehyde and dihydroxyacetone through 4-carbon sugars (*tetroses*), 5-carbon sugars (*pentoses*), 6-carbon sugars (*hexoses*) and so on to the 10-carbon sugars. The particular pentoses, *ribose* and *deoxyribose,* are part of the nucleic-acid structure. For most organisms the hexoses, *glucose* and *fructose,* serve as the principal source of energy and building material undergoing a metabolic breakdown to intermediates which include the trioses, glyceraldehyde, and dihydroxyacetone (Chapter 8).

The more significant properties of the monosaccharides, especially as they relate to metabolism, are best illustrated by referring to the structure of two groups of biologically important sugars, the hexoses (e.g., glucose and fructose) and the pentoses (e.g., ribose and deoxyribose). These sugars like many other monosaccharides also occur as ring structures. Glucose, for example, exists in solution largely as a stable ring structure in equilibrium with a small amount (less than .025 per cent) of the corresponding noncyclic or open-chain form. The open-chain compound is a free aldehyde form with the aldehyde group designated as the number 1 carbon of glucose. Each of the remaining 5 carbon atoms is numbered in order as indicated. Although two different ring structures exist for glucose, we shall describe the more stable and therefore the more prevalent type known as the *pyranose* form. This is a 6-membered ring consisting of 5 carbon atoms and 1 oxygen atom in which carbons 1 (aldehyde group) and 5 are linked by the oxygen atom of the alcohol group belonging to the number 5 carbon.

Glucose (straight-chain form)   Glucose (pyranose form)

The simple sugar or monosaccharide fructose with the same atomic composition ($C_6H_{12}O_6$) as glucose has a ketone group (the number 2 carbon) instead of an aldehyde group. Fructose in aqueous solution exists also for the most part as a predominant pyranose ring structure in equilibrium with a small quantity of the open-chain compound. The ketone carbon is linked to the number 6 carbon by means of the oxygen atom of the alcohol group attached to the number 6 carbon.

Fructose (straight-chain form)   Fructose (pyranose form)

The other biologically outstanding monosaccharides are the pentoses, ribose and deoxyribose. Ribose is a constituent of RNA and of several important cofactors (Chapter 8) functioning in enzyme systems. Ribose exists largely as a stable 5-membered ring structure in which carbon 1 (aldehyde group) and carbon 4 are linked by the oxygen atom of the alcohol group belonging to the number 4 carbon.

Ribose (straight-chain form)   Ribose (ring form)

Deoxyribose is a constituent of DNA and is distinguished from ribose by the fact that its number 2 carbon lacks an alcohol group, having a second hydrogen in its place. Deoxyribose also exists predominantly in the form of a 5-membered ring like that of the comparable ribose structure.

Deoxyribose (straight-chain form)   Deoxyribose (ring form)

The natural occurrence of ribose and deoxyribose was not known until they were first isolated from nucleic acids.

OLIGOSACCHARIDES AND POLYSACCHARIDES. These are two classes of carbohydrates whose molecules are composed of simple sugars (monosaccharides) chemically linked to each other. No clear line of distinction exists between these two classes other than that oligosaccharides are molecules made up of only a few monosaccharide units (ranging from 2 to 10), whereas polysaccharides usually consist of a great many more simple sugar units (ranging into the hundreds and thousands) linked together to form a considerably larger molecule.

The Glycosidic Bond. In both oligosaccharides and the polysaccharides the monosaccharide units are chemically linked to one another through so-called *glycosidic* bonds in which a hydroxyl-containing carbon atom of one monosaccharide is attached by way of an oxygen atom to the original carbonyl-containing carbon of another monosaccharide. A glycosidic linkage may be formed by the condensation of a hydroxyl group of one monosaccharide with the carbonyl group of another, with a molecule of water being split out in the process. The reverse reaction would be a hydrolysis (Chapter 6). For example, the oligosaccharide *maltose* is composed of two glucose units linked to each other by a glycosidic bond between the number 1 carbon of one glucose unit and the number 4 carbon of the other.

Oligosaccharides. Oligosaccharides consisting of two simple sugar units linked together by a glycosidic bond are called *disaccharides* (e.g., maltose). A similar arrangement of three monosaccharide units joined by glycosidic linkages is called a *trisaccharide*, and so on. Two other common naturally occurring disaccharides are sucrose and lactose. *Sucrose* (or table sugar) is widely distributed in nature and used extensively as a food. It consists of a glycosidic linkage between the number 2 carbon atom of fructose and the number 1 carbon of glucose. *Lactose* is a disaccharide which occurs in the milk of mammals (including man) and is made up of a glucose unit joined by its number 4 carbon through a glycosidic linkage to the number 1 carbon of the hexose, *galactose* as shown at top of the next page.

Polysaccharides. General Features. The great majority of carbohydrates in nature exist as polysaccharides. In many glucose is the principal if not the only monosaccharide unit, although other monosaccharide units and modified products also occur in polysaccharides. The various kinds of naturally occurring polysaccharides differ not only in their constituent monosaccharide composition, but in molecular weight, type of glycosidic bond, degree and nature of branching, as well as other properties. In terms of biological function the polysaccharides are conveniently classified into two broad groups: (1) those that serve primarily in a structural capacity (i.e., protection and mechanical support), and (2) those that have

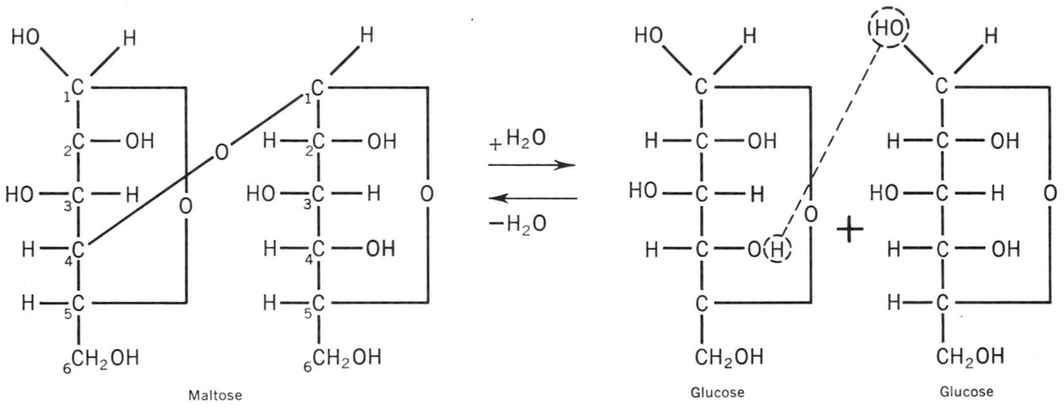

Maltose

Glucose   Glucose

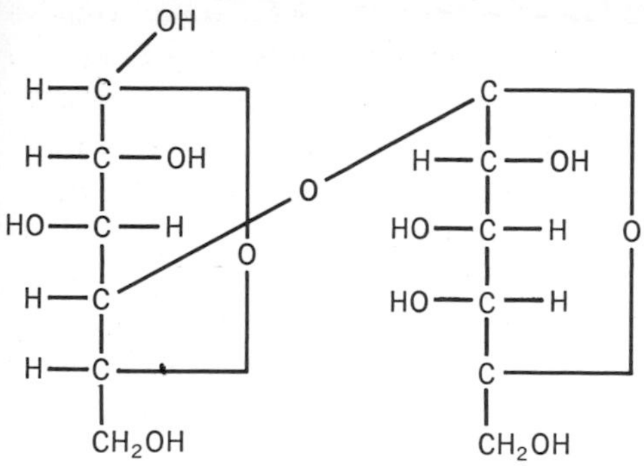

HC
(Glucose)   (Galactose)

LACTOSE

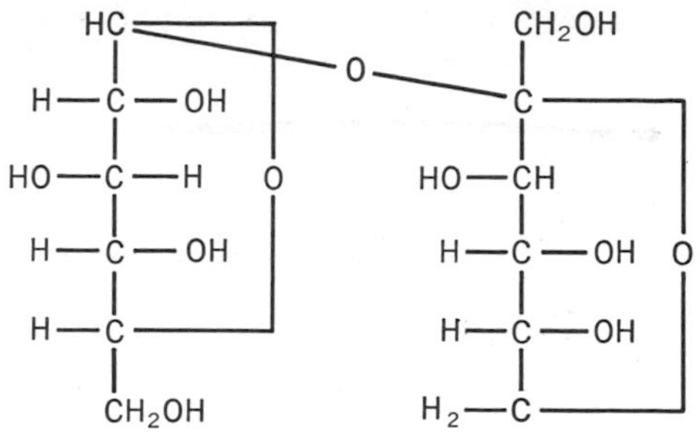

(Glucose)   (Fructose)

SUCROSE

a significant role in nutrition and metabolism.

Structural Polysaccharides. Cellulose as the major polysaccharide occurring in nature is probably the single most abundant organic compound found on our planet, comprising at least 50 per cent of all the carbon in the plant world. Its main function is structural, and it occurs principally as the major component of the plant cell wall. Cotton is one of the purest forms of cellulose and is composed of at least 90 per cent of the polysaccharide. The cellulose molecule is an unbranched chain of 300 to 2500 glucose units linked together by a particular type of glycosidic bond and ranging in molecular weight from about 50,000 to 400,000. In a number of higher plants the cell wall consists of cellulose and a large molecular-weight noncarbohydrate material called *lignin* whose chemical composition is not yet completely known.

Other structural polysaccharides include (1) *xylan*, composed mostly of the 5-carbon monosaccharide, *xylose*, and associated with cellulose in wood; (2) *pectic acids*, apparently composed of long chains of a particular derivative of the hexose, galactose, and occurring especially in fruits; (3) *chitin*, composed of units of a certain amino derivative of glucose and prevalent among certain invertebrates, especially in the shells of lobsters and crabs; and (4) *mucopolysaccharides*, composed of repeating units of highly complex derivatives

of simple sugars including sulfate derivatives, encompassing both structural and metabolic polysaccharides present in a variety of animal tissues (cartilage, bone, skin, tendons, lung, heart valves, liver, and so on). Numerous polysaccharides also occur attached to particular proteins which are collectively called *mucoproteins.* They include the substance responsible for the different blood groups (Chapter 25).

Metabolic Polysaccharides. The most important of the nutrient or metabolic polysaccharides are the *starches.* They are also made up wholly of glucose units, but the units are linked together by glycosidic bonds that differ from those displayed by cellulose. The starches represent a storage form of glucose, and can be enzymatically degraded to the disaccharide maltose and thence to glucose. Many starches are composed of a mixture of two different types called *amylose* and *amylopectin*. Amylose constitutes about 20 per cent of most starches and consists of long unbranched chains of glucose units joined together by a particular type of glycosidic linkage. It is in fact a mixture of straight-chain molecules of varying lengths, ranging in molecular weight from about 5000 to 500,000. Amylopectin, as a more prevalent component of starch, is a branched-chain polysaccharide with branching occurring about every 25 to 30 glucose units by means of another type of glycosidic bond. Molecular

Organic Constituents of the Living Cell   149

weights for this component range into the millions.

The starch found in animal tissues is called glycogen. In mammals it occurs as small particles principally in the cells of liver and to a lesser extent in muscle. Glycogen is a branched-chain polysaccharide, resembling amylopectin rather than amylose. It occurs in a mixture of molecular weights ranging from about 300,000 to possibly as high as 100 million. Like any other starch it yields only D-glucose upon complete hydrolysis.

Lipids

Lipids are a heterogenous group of organic substances originating in the living cell which are insoluble or sparingly soluble in water, but more or less soluble in nonpolar or organic solvents (e.g., in ether, benzene, and chloroform). They are classified into several subdivisions on the basis of their chemical and physical properties, and they include the so-called neutral fats and fatty acids, the phospholipids, the steroids, and the fat-soluble vitamins—A, D, E, and K.

NEUTRAL FATS. These are the most abundant class of lipids in nature and are usually subdivided into three groups—fats, oils, and waxes. They contain only carbon, hydrogen, and oxygen atoms and upon hydrolysis yield fatty acids and an alcohol. Fats and oils are esters of fatty acids and the trihydroxyl alcohol glycerol, and are also called triglycerides.

$$R\text{—COO—CH}_2$$
$$R'\text{—COO—CH}$$
$$R''\text{—COO—CH}_2$$

Fat

in which R–, R′–, and R″– represent the long carbon chains of either the same or different fatty acids. The two most prevalent saturated fatty acids found in neutral animal fats are first palmitic acid, $CH_3(CH_2)_{14}COOH$, and second stearic acid, $CH_3(CH_2)_{16}COOH$. Saturated fatty acids also occur in fats and oils of

molds, bacteria, plants, and animals. The most abundant unsaturated fatty acid in nature is oleic acid, $CH_3(CH_2)_7CH=CH(CH_2)_7COOH$. Several unsaturated fatty acids which apparently are not synthesized in sufficient quantities by the body, must be provided by the diet and are therefore termed "essential fatty acids." Neutral lipids which are solids at room temperatures are referred to as fats, whereas those in the liquid state are called oils. Most animal and vegetable fats and oils are composed of esters of several fatty acids with glycerol. In general animal fats are in a solid or semisolid state at room temperature, whereas vegetable fats or oils are in a liquid state largely because their fatty-acid components have a greater number of unsaturated bonds.

Waxes (e.g., beeswax and the cuticle waxes of fruits, leaves, and flower petals) are principally esters of a fatty acid with a long-chain alcohol rather than with glycerol.

PHOSPHOLIPIDS. The term phospholipid is applied to a large variety of natural lipids which contain not only carbon, hydrogen, and oxygen but phosphorus and in many cases nitrogen as well. The best known of the phospholipids are the lecithins and the cephalins. The lecithins are widely distributed in a great variety of tissues including egg yolk, brain, yeast, liver, and wheat germ, and have the same general chemical structure in which two fatty acids are esterified to two alcohol groups of glycerol with the third alcohol group being attached by means of an ester linkage to phosphoric acid. The latter is in turn esterified to a particular nitrogen-containing alcohol called choline.

Lecithin

The cephalins resemble the lecithins except that they have an ethyl alcohol residue or a particular amino-acid residue (L-serine) in place of choline. Early interest in these compounds stemmed from the fact that they were found in the nerve tissue of animals. They are now known to constitute an appreciable portion of the phospholipids of brain and muscle. Other phospholipides called *plasmalogens* have also been characterized from mammalian tissues.

STEROIDS. The name steroid is used for a group of fat-soluble compounds which possess a particular fundamental structure related to the naturally occurring compound *cholesterol*. They are constructed essentially of four fused rings of carbon atoms to which is usually attached a carbon chain of varying length as typified by cholesterol below.

Proteins

GENERAL ROLE. The term *protein* is appropriately derived from the Greek word *proteios*, meaning "of the first rank," for proteins occupy a central position in the structural and functional characteristics of living things. Not only do they constitute a significant portion of the protoplasm but they have a key role in its vital processes, being intimately linked to all aspects of the chemical and physical activities that make up the life of the cell. They are found in every essential component of the cell itself —in the nucleus as part of the chromosomes, nucleoplasm, and nuclear membrane; and in the cytoplasmic organization (e.g., mitochondria, endoplasmic reticulum, ribosomes, cell membrane, centrosomes, spindle fibers which appear during cell division, and flagella and

Cholesterol

The steroids usually exert profound biological effects at very small concentrations, displaying a great diversity of physiological activity in the intact animal. Not only do they regulate sexual development and function, but they also have an important influence on numerous aspects of metabolism. Vitamin D, the bile acids, steroid hormones secreted by the cortex of the adrenal glands, the male and female sex hormones, and certain heart-stimulant drugs derived from particular plants are all derivatives or modified versions of steroid structure.

FAT-SOLUBLE VITAMINS. The structure and metabolism of the fat-soluble vitamins are considered in Chapter 9.

cilia) where they contribute to its structural features as well as compose a vast array of enzymes.

In addition to their primary action as specific enzymes or biochemical catalysts which mediate virtually all the chemical reactions that constitute cell activities, proteins have other specialized functions. Certain proteins (e.g., *keratin* of skin, fingernails, wool, and hair, and *collagen* of connective tissue and bone) serve in a structural capacity. Other proteins function in muscular contraction, such as the protein *myosin*, which appears to be the fundamental contractile element in muscular action. Several act as hormones or regulators of metabolic processes. Still other proteins are *antibodies* (Chapter 25), which are formed by the body as an immunological defense against invasion by bacteria and viruses. Particular proteins are associated with DNA, the primary material of the genes responsible for heredity and directed control of all cell activities, and others occur in conjunction with RNA.

PROTEIN STRUCTURE. Proteins are molecules of gigantic size, tremendous complexity, and unparalleled diversity. Elementary chemical analyses show that they consist of thousands of atoms, mostly hydrogen, carbon, oxygen, and nitrogen. Historically the nitrogen content has been taken to be the most characteristic chemical feature associated with proteins, averaging about 16 per cent of the protein composition on a dry-weight basis. In some proteins sulfur, phosphorus, and exceedingly small quantities of several heavy metals are also part of the molecular structure. In addition many proteins are linked by chemical and physical means to other organic molecules such as carbohydrates, nucleic acids, lipids, and so on.

Proteins range in molecular weight from about 5000 (insulin) to as high as 40 million (tobacco mosaic virus protein), existing for the most part in the size class of colloidal particles—a feature which also contributes to their diverse properties. The vastness of their dimensions is seen by comparing their mass to that of the water molecule (molecular weight 18), the major constituent of protoplasm, or to that of sugars and fats (molecular weights of about 200 in the hexoses to about 700 in the fats). Although our knowledge of the physical and chemical make-up of proteins is still very incomplete, we know that the complex and diverse properties of these giant molecules can be attributed to at least three facets of their intricate structure, known as *primary, secondary,* and *tertiary* structure.

Primary Structure. Proteins consist primarily of many amino-acid units chemically linked to one another by so-called *peptide bonds.* Under suitable conditions the carboxyl group of one amino acid may react with the amino group

of another to form a linkage between the amino acids with the elimination of water.

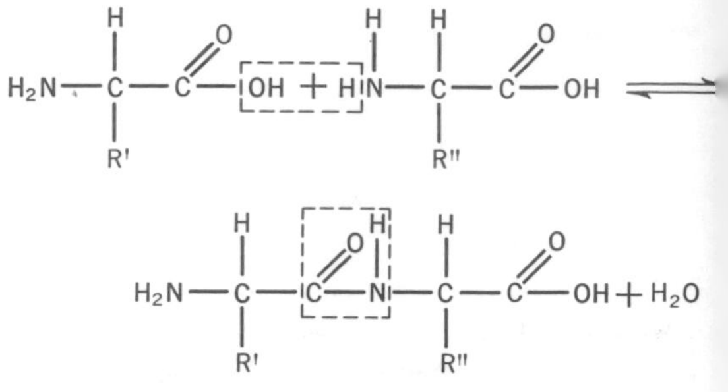

Peptide

R', R'', and so on, are used to designate the different carbon chains of the different amino acids. The resulting bond between the carboxyl group of one amino acid with the amino group of another is designated as a peptide or amide linkage. The new compound which has been formed is accordingly classified as a *peptide.* The simplest peptides consist of only two amino-acid residues as shown above and are called *dipeptides* even though they contain only one peptide bond. Those containing three or more amino-acid residues as illustrated below are called *polypeptides.*

When is a polypeptide called a protein? The dividing line between the two is not entirely clear cut. In general a naturally occurring peptide of about 50 or more amino-acid residues is often referred to as a protein, which may also include several polypeptides.

Many proteins are made up of long polypeptide chains consisting of hundreds upon hundreds of amino-acids units connected to one another by peptide bonds. Since there are 20 or so different naturally occurring amino acids it follows that some of the amino-acid residues in proteins and the longer polypeptide chains must be repeated over and over again. The possible number of different combinations in which they can be linearly arranged in peptide linkages is enormous. Thus it is possible to conceive of an immense number of polypeptide chains, differing in their size and proportions of amino acids as well as in the sequence

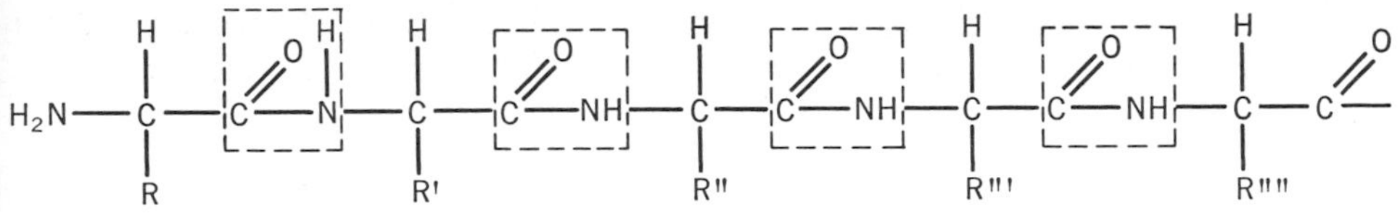

Peptide bonds

of their linear arrangement. The thousands of different specific proteins found in organisms are in part ascribed to this almost countless variety of possible combinations.

It should be noted that the peptide bonds of proteins as far as we know are not synthesized by a simple condensation reaction between the carboxyl group of one amino acid and the amino group of another. Instead they are formed by the cell in an energy-requiring, stepwise series of complex enzymatic steps described in Chapter 11. Peptides can be split into their component amino acids in a reversal of the above reaction by the introduction of water, that is, hydrolysis, a process which is markedly catalyzed by high concentrations of acids, alkalis, or appropriate enzymes. The digestion of proteins in the stomach and intestine essentially involves hydrolysis of the peptide bonds of proteins catalyzed by specific enzymes contained in the digestive juices.

The primary structure of a protein is determined by its composition and sequence of the amino-acid residues as well as by its polypeptide chains attached to each other. The polypeptide chains of proteins are often attached together in parallel fashion by a number of chemical and physical linkages including bridges of two sulfur atoms chemically bound to one another (as illustrated for insulin, Figure 7-5), hydrogen bonding, ionic bonding (attraction of oppositely charged groups), and general attractive forces between molecules. Hydrogen bonding, as one of the most important, involves the sharing of hydrogen atoms between two different atoms such as oxygen or nitrogen of the same or different molecules (Figure 7-3). In proteins it generally occurs between the carbonyl oxygen of

one peptide group and the amino nitrogen of a neighboring group. The forces of hydrogen bonding are relatively weak compared to most covalent bonds. Collectively, however, they are sufficiently strong to hold polypeptide strands in certain spatial configurations as well as in association with neighboring chains. Nevertheless, they are weak enough to allow the chains to separate and unfold on occasion. Hydrogen bonding within groups of the same polypeptide chain also accounts in large part for the folded and helical nature as well as several other features of most proteins.

Secondary and Tertiary Structure. Proteins in addition possess definite spatial arrangements which contribute significantly to their chemical and biological properties. We

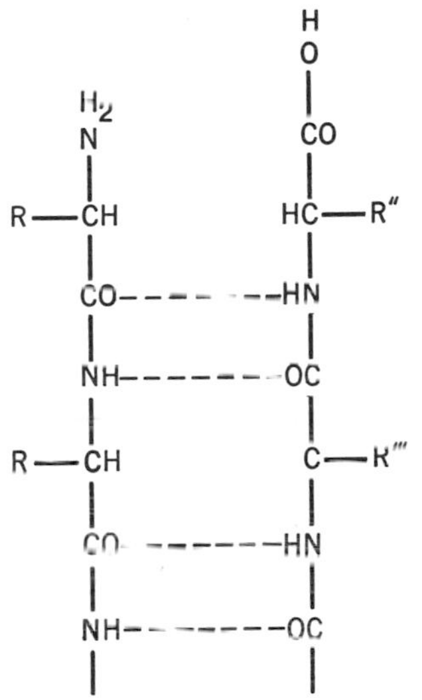

Figure 7-3. Representation of hydrogen bonding illustrating the sharing of hydrogens between the carbonyl oxygen of some peptide groups and the amino nitrogen of others.

have good evidence from the application of various methods including X-ray techniques that the long polypeptide chains making up proteins are not perfectly straight chains but instead exist as spirals or helices of varying degrees which are maintained or stabilized by hydrogen bonding. An example of one very important type of spatial configuration is the *alpha*-helix which appears to be a fundamental structure in many proteins. In this configuration the chain takes up a helical or spiral pattern (in a clockwise direction) which is stabilized by hydrogen bonds along the axis of the helix (Figure 7-4). This spiral nature of polypeptide chains of proteins is spoken of as its *secondary* structure.

Many proteins also have a third or *tertiary* structural feature. Not only are their polypeptide chains arranged in typical spirals, but in addition these chains are frequently folded forward and backward on each other to form a globular rather than a long-fibered molecule. The folded physical state of most proteins is not a chance arrangement but a definite type of spatial configuration specific for each particular protein and held together in part by hydrogen bonding.

Finally, it should be noted that proteins, huge molecules in the size range of colloidal particles, have electrical charges distributed over their surfaces. These charges contribute to several chemical, physical, and biological properties of protein molecules and are in part responsible for the buffering capacity of proteins as well as for their ability to combine with various other molecules and ions.

STRUCTURE OF INSULIN AND MYOGLOBIN. The independent contributions of Sanger, Perutz, and Kendrew in England illustrate the remarkable advances that have been made recently in our knowledge of proteins. Sanger established for the first time the exact chemical structure of a protein, namely *insulin*. Insulin, a proteinaceous hormone formed by special cells of the pancreas gland, is necessary for the proper utilization of sugar by the body (Chapter 23). When secreted in insufficient amounts the dis-

ease, *diabetes mellitus* results. As a protein insulin is usually small, having a molecular weight of about 5000. Sanger, by his painstaking efforts, determined the exact order of the 51 amino-acid residues, consisting of 15 different amino acids, which make up the insulin molecule. He showed that the amino-acid units are arranged in two distinct chains, one con-

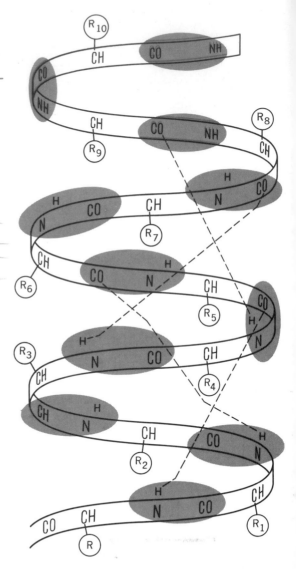

Figure 7-4. The *alpha*-helical or spiral pattern (in a clockwise direction) of a polypeptide chain stabilized by hydrogen bonding. The shaded areas represent peptide bonds.

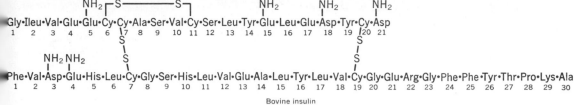

$$Gly·Ileu·Val·Glu·Glu·Cy·Cy·Ala·Ser·Val·Cy·Ser·Leu·Tyr·Glu·Leu·Glu·Asp·Tyr·Cy·Asp$$

Bovine insulin

Figure 7-5. Amino-acid composition and sequence of beef insulin showing the two distinct parallel chains of amino-acid residues.

taining 30 amino-acid units and the other 21. The two chains are parallel to each other and held together by connecting bridges involving two sulfur atoms (Figure 7-5). Sanger also demonstrated that slight modifications in the structure of insulin such as removal of one of its amino acids could markedly decrease its biological activity as a hormone. A comparison of the amino-acid composition of insulin from various species such as oxen, pigs, and sheep indicated a striking similarity except for a difference in a particular section of the molecule of only three amino acids for each species. For these epic-making discoveries, Sanger was awarded the Nobel Prize in 1957.

The outstanding X-ray analysis work of the British chemists Perutz and Kendrew on the oxygen-carrying muscle protein *myoglobin* (Chapter 29), which is closely related to hemoglobin of the red blood cells, has permitted us for the first time to construct a three-dimensional model of a protein molecule. Their contribution earned the Nobel Prize for Perutz and Kendrew in 1962. Myoglobin possesses a nonprotein group, called a *heme* (p. 169) and is a folded, long polypeptide chain of 153 amino-acid residues with a molecular weight of 17,000. Its spatial configuration, which looks like a tangled rope (Figure 7-6), including the three-dimensional folding of the long polypeptide chain, is apparently precisely defined.

PROTEIN CLASSIFICATION. Protein molecules may be classified in a number of ways. On the basis of the shape we can consider them to be either rod-like (*fibrous*) or spherical (*globular*).

Most are globular, the result of being folded over at numerous places along their length. A comparison of the size and shape of various proteins are shown in Figure 7-7.

A widely used system of protein classification divides all proteins, no matter what their biological source, into two broad groups: *simple proteins* and *conjugated proteins*. *Simple proteins* yield only amino acids on hydrolysis. This

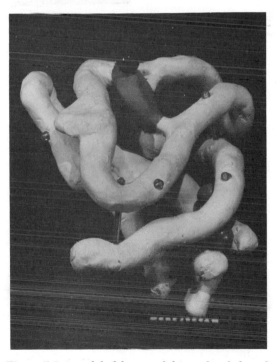

Figure 7-6. A model of the myoglobin molecule based on X-ray crystallographic data. The gray structure represents the heme. *(Courtesy of Dr. C. B. Anfinsen, Molecular Basis of Evolution, Wiley.)*

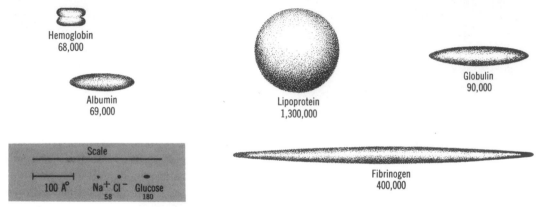

Figure 7-7. Comparative size (including molecular weights) of some proteins *(adapted from J. L. Oncley, Conference on the Preservation of the Cellular and Protein Components of Blood, American National Red Cross, Washington, 1949).*

does not mean that they are simple in structure, for like any other protein their chemical composition and physical configurations are highly complex and intricate. *Conjugated proteins upon hydrolysis yield nonamino-acid components as well as amino acids.* They are usually classified according to the type of nonproteinaceous substance with which they are combined and reflect the important property of proteins to combine specifically with other substances. The stability of the linkages between a protein and its nonproteinaceous group varies considerably from one conjugated protein to another, depending on chemical structure of the compounds, pH, and other factors. The properties of various classes of simple and conjugated proteins are summarized in Table 7-2.

PURIFICATION OF PROTEINS. One of the important factors responsible for our increased knowledge of protein structure and function has been the development of better purification techniques. In disrupting or extracting any tissues or cells thousands of different proteins, mostly in colloidal solution, are liberated. The problem of separating and purifying individual proteins has been a formidable one, especially because protein structure may easily be modified by relatively mild treatment. Nevertheless, a number of techniques have been successfully used including selective precipitation of proteins by exposing to carefully controlled conditions of salt concentration, pH, temperature, or alcohol concentration; and selective adsorption of proteins to various types of surfaces such as those of starches, charcoal, and synthetic resins followed by selective elution. Various chromatographic procedures, including paper chromatography have also proved to be powerful tools in this respect. The fact that some proteins can be induced to crystallize, an indication that nearly all the molecules are usually similar or identical, suggests a relatively high degree of purity. The state of purity of an isolated protein can be estimated by various physical measurements including analysis of its rate of settling under an imposed field of high centrifugal force.

ENZYMATIC ROLE OF PROTEINS. The most significant function of proteins in the living cell is its enzymatic role. Enzymes are specific biological catalysts consisting wholly or in large part of globular proteins ranging in molecular weight from approximately 10,000 up into the millions. The smallest enzymes are composed of approximately 100 amino-acid residues, and the largest ones of many more. Enzymes are made by living cells and are responsible for the catalysis of virtually all biochemical reactions occurring in protoplasm. A cell is not simply a bag of thousands of enzymes catalyzing chemical reactions at random. Instead it is a highly integrated group of specific structural components with a definite orientation of enzymes constituting in large part the protein composition of the cell. By their very organization and orientation relative to each other, the enzymes of a cell account for the operation of the integrated and interlocking pathways of carbohydrate metabolism, protein metabolism, fat metabolism, and so on.

The term enzyme is derived from the Greek and means literally "in yeast." It was originally coined in 1878 when it was generally but erroneously accepted that the enzymes responsible for the metabolic breakdown of carbohydrates (for example by yeast cells) in the absence of oxygen (called *anaerobic respiration* or *fermentation*, described in the next chapter) could function only within living cells. All attempts to extract the enzymes responsible for fermentation by yeast cells had failed. Louis Pasteur, the leading biochemical authority of that era, was the outstanding proponent of the idea that fermentation was an expression of life itself and could occur only within living cells. It was one of the few instances in which the brilliant Pasteur proved to be wrong, for in 1897 the

Table 7-2 Types of Proteins

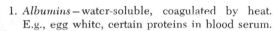

SIMPLE PROTEINS

1. *Albumins*—water-soluble, coagulated by heat. E.g., egg white, certain proteins in blood serum.

2. *Globulins*—poorly soluble in water but soluble in solutions of neutral salts (e.g., sodium chloride), coagulated by heat. E.g., certain proteins in blood plasma, muscle, and seeds.

3. *Glutelins*—soluble in dilute acids and alkalis, but insoluble in water or solutions of neutral salts. E.g., certain proteins of cereal grains such as wheat, barley, and rice.

4. *Prolamines*—insoluble in water but soluble in 70-80% alcohol solutions, especially rich in the amino acid proline. E.g., the proteins *gliadin* from wheat, and *zein* from corn.

5. *Histones* and *Protamines*—also called *basic* proteins because they are rich in basic amino acids (those having more than one amino group, e.g., lysine, arginine, histidine). Usually combined with the nucleic acids in the cell nucleus.

6. *Scleroproteins*—heterogenous group of fibrous, insoluble, structural animal proteins
   (a) *Collagens*—rich in the amino acid hydroxyproline. Represent more than 50% of total protein of the mammalian body, e.g., connective tissue, bone.
   (b) *Elastins*—possess many of the properties of collagen. Present in several elastic tissues of the body (e.g., tendons, arteries).
   (c) *Keratins*—rich in the sulfur-containing amino and cysteine, e.g., hair, wool, nails, horns, silk.

CONJUGATED PROTEINS

1. *Nucleoproteins*—proteins (e.g., prolamines and histones) combined to the nucleic acids DNA and RNA.

2. *Mucoproteins* and *Glycoproteins*—proteins combined with carbohydrates, usually a polysaccharide. Mucoproteins and glycoproteins containing only small amounts of carbohydrate. Several albumins and globulins are in reality mucoproteins (e.g., the blood group substances A, B, and AB, Chapter 25).

3. *Phosphoproteins*—proteins combined with phosphate (e.g., pepsin, casein).

4. *Lipoproteins*—proteins combined to fat or liquid substances (e.g., in cell membrane, mitochondrial membrane and cristae, nerve tissue).

5. *Metalloproteins*—proteins combined to metal ions such as magnesium, iron, manganese, cobalt, copper, zinc, molybdenum. E.g., several enzymes are metalloproteins.

6. *Chromoproteins*—proteins combined with other molecules to give a colored substance. E.g., red hemoglobin (particular globulin joined to a heme), red cytochromes (heme-protein complexes), green chlorophyll-protein complex.

Buchner brothers in Germany demonstrated for the first time that cell-free extracts prepared by macerating yeast cells with sand were capable of fermenting sugar to ethanol and carbon dioxide. The epic-making work of the Buchner brothers stands as a landmark in the history of biology. Not only did it demolish an erroneous concept but it also ushered in a new and modern era of biology—the era of biochemistry or molecular biology.

Mechanism of Enzyme Action. According to the modern collision theory of chemical reactions, a catalyst increases the rate of a chemical reaction by decreasing the required energy of activation for the reaction as discussed in the preceding chapter. The enzyme as a catalyst accomplishes this by itself entering with the reacting molecules into the freely reversible formation of a transient, intermediate activated complex called an *enzyme-substrate complex*. The highly unstable activated complex rapidly rearranges itself to give the products of the reaction and the free unaltered enzyme, thus making the latter available for recombination with more substrate. This process is repeated many times. These relationships may be formulated as follows:

$$E + S \rightleftharpoons ES \longrightarrow E + \text{products}$$

where E represents the enzyme, S the substrate or reacting molecules, and ES the enzyme-substrate complex.

Like most catalysts enzymes are extremely efficient in the sense that a single enzyme molecule can be used over and over again in speeding up the rate of a chemical reaction between molecules to water and oxygen (p. 130) within purified enzyme catalase can catalyze the breakdown of five million hydrogen peroxide molecules to water and oxygen (p. 130) within a period of one minute.

Enzymes as biological catalysts act in fundamentally the same fashion as any other catalyst except for two important differences. First, enzymes are highly specific, with each enzyme usually catalyzing one particular kind of reaction. In contrast a nonbiological catalyst such as finely divided platinum catalyzes a wide variety of reactions. Second, all enzymes consist entirely or in part of specific proteins accounting for their unique specificity as catalysts. In general they are extremely sensitive to heat because of the denaturation of their protein by high temperatures. Exposure to a temperature of 100°C for 2 minutes almost always results in a complete and irreversible loss of enzyme activity. Enzymes are also markedly influenced by pH or H^+ ion concentration. In most instances they exhibit their maximal catalytic activity within a characteristically narrow pH range. At pH's appreciably below or above this optimal level, enzymatic activity is considerably smaller or even absent. Different enzymes display different pH optima, a phenomenon attributed largely to the specific nature of their proteins.

Enzyme Specificity. Different enzymes display varying degrees of specificity with respect to the types of substrates and chemical reactions which they catalyze. Some enzymes are so highly specific as to catalyze only one chemical reaction involving a particular reactant or substrate, whereas others may have a broader specificity, catalyzing a number of related reactions and a wider range of reactants.

Most enzymes also display a high degree of stereochemical specificity which permits them to select between stereoisomers (p. 145). Virtually all enzymes involved in carbohydrate metabolism act only on the appropriate D-sugar or its derivative. Similarly the preponderance of L-amino acids in nature is correlated with the fact that nearly all the enzymes involved in amino-acid (and protein) metabolism act only on the L-forms, failing to attack the D-isomers.

What accounts for the unique specificity of enzymes as compared to nonbiological catalysts? The specific combination that occurs between enzyme and substrate to form the enzyme-substrate complex is believed to reflect a particularly suitable spatial relationship between the substrate and certain active sites on

substrate - thing acted upon
= base

the enzyme analogous to a lock and key or jigsaw arrangement (Figure 7-8). It implies that the structural configuration of the enzyme sites can only accommodate a particular type of substrate. The vast differences in size in most instances between an enzyme molecule and its relatively minute substrate molecules supports the notion that the enzyme-substrate complex must form between specific active sites (usually one or at most a few) on the huge surface of the protein molecule and essential groups of the substrate molecule. For example, catalase, one of the largest enzyme molecules with a molecular weight of 250,000, has as its substrate hydrogen peroxide (H_2O_2) with a molecular weight of 34. For those enzymes exhibiting a relatively broader specificity, the structural configuration of the active enzyme sites is pictured as being less specialized, thus allowing for the proper union with a number of substrates. Recent evidence suggests that some enzymes may have "flexible" active sites in the sense that the substrate induces a change in conformation of the enzyme molecule as a hand changes the shape of a glove, thus allowing for a proper fitting between the enzyme and its substrate.

Apoenzymes, Coenzymes, and Metal Com- *ponents.* Many enzymes, but not all, contain in addition to their protein moiety, called the *apoenzyme,* a nonproteinaceous organic component of relatively smaller molecular weight, called the *cofactor* or *coenzyme,* which is essential for enzymatic activity. Dissociation of an enzyme into its apoenzyme and coenzyme causes a loss in enzymatic activity which is restored in most cases by adding both components together. The discovery and characterization of coenzymes have revealed the metabolic role of many of the vitamins, for we have found that coenzymes are made up in part of individual vitamins (Chapter 9). For example, *vitamin* B_1 or *thiamine,* is part of a coenzyme necessary for certain enzymatic reactions involving carbon dioxide. The vitamin *niacin* or *nicotinic acid* is a component of two large coenzyme molecules called *diphosphopyridine nucleotide* and *triphosphopiridine nucleotide* known as *DPN* and *TPN,* respectively. DPN and TPN serve as coenzymes for several enzymes catalyzing oxidation-reduction reactions (Chapter 8) in the cell and undergo reversible oxidation-reduction changes in the process. Other vitamins such as riboflavin, pyridoxine, and pantothenic acid are also components of other coenzymes.

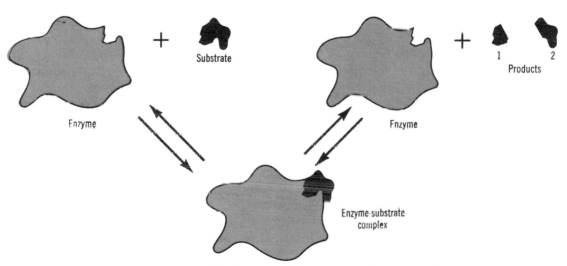

Figure 7-8. Schematic representation of the formation of an enzyme-substrate complex illustrating the "lock and key" relationship between the substrate and active sites on the enzyme.

Numerous enzymes contain small quantities of a particular *metal ion* in their make-up and are accordingly called *metalloenzymes*. The presence of the metal is usually necessary for enzymatic activity, and its removal causes a loss in the catalytic action of the protein. For example, copper, zinc, molybdenum, and iron have been shown to be specific metal components of particular enzymes. In some enzymes the metal ion may be tightly bound to the protein while in others it may be quite easily dissociated. Some enzymes are composed not only of a specific protein moiety but of a coenzyme and a metal component or activator as well.

In summary all enzymes are made up of specific proteins. Several possess in addition an organic moiety or coenzyme combined to the protein portion or apoenzyme. An appreciable number are metalloproteins having a specific metal ion in their composition. Some enzymes consist of both a coenzyme and metal component or activator in addition to the apoenzyme.

Experimental Enzymology. How have we arrived at the above information regarding the nature of enzymes? The following experiments illustrate the approach used in studying the properties of enzymes. Assume that we have just discovered and purified a new enzyme that catalyzes a particular chemical reaction between A and B to form C (A + B → C). We have devised a convenient means for measuring enzyme activity (e.g., by determining the rate at which the product C is formed), and we know that for all practical purposes A and B do not react to form C unless the enzyme is present. We learn that the enzyme is destroyed by heat (and is therefore heat-labile) because immersion in a boiling water bath for two minutes resulted in a complete irreversible loss of activity.

We now transfer a sample of active enzyme solution to a differentially permeable membranous bag made of collodion or cellophane which permits the passage of water and other relatively small molecules but not larger molecules such as proteins. Within a few hours after immersing the bag into a large, suitably buffered bathing solution, most small coenzyme molecules or metal ions associated with the enzyme will probably have dissociated (as is the case for some enzymes) and diffused through the membrane into the water bath, a process called *dialysis*, accounting for the observed loss in activity of the dialyzed enzyme. This can be tested by adding some of the used dialysis bathing solution to the dialyzed enzyme to determine if it will restore activity. Reactivation of enzyme activity by this procedure would strongly implicate a cofactor or metal component. Preliminary evidence can be obtained to distinguish between the two. A sample of the bath is ashed, dissolved, and added to the dialyzed enzyme. If enzymatic activity is restored, then the dissociable component is a metal because an ash contains only metals and their oxides. Organic compounds (e.g., coenzymes) would have been destroyed by the ashing process. Alternatively, if the solution of the ash failed to reactivate, then it could be *tentatively* inferred that the necessary component was a coenzyme.

Two alternative explanations that we have not considered are the instances in which (a) the enzyme maintains its activity despite dialysis, and (b) most or all enzyme activity is lost but not reactivated under any of the foregoing circumstances. In the first instance the enzyme is either a simple protein or it contains a coenzyme or metal ion which is not easily dissociable by dialysis. In the second instance the enzyme is either too sensitive to the dialysis procedure, becoming irreversibly inactivated (or denatured) in the process, or the removal of its cofactor or metal component results for several possible reasons in an irreversible loss of enzyme activity.

Enzyme Classification. Enzymes can be conveniently classified into several major groups according to the chemical reactions which they catalyze. These in turn can be subdivided into smaller groups depending on the more specific aspects of their catalytic properties.

(1) *Hydrolases* are enzymes that catalyze the splitting of numerous substances into smaller

molecules by the introduction of water. They include enzymes that accelerate the hydrolysis of (1) oligosaccharides and polysaccharides into smaller units; (2) peptide bonds of proteins, polypeptides, and dipeptides to yield amino acids; and (3) fats to their component fatty acids and glycerol. Numerous hydrolases occur in living cells and are also secreted in the process of digestion, for example, in the digestive tract of animals. Digestion consists primarily of the hydrolysis of carbohydrates, proteins, and fats to their simpler structural units by specific hydrolases.

The present practice is to name an enzyme by adding the suffix *ase* to the name of the substrate. For example, the specific enzyme responsible for the hydrolysis of the disaccharide sucrose to fructose and glucose, is called *sucrase*. Not all enzymes, however, have been named according to this logical system of nomenclature. Some of the older enzymes (for example, *diastase*, which catalyzes the hydrolysis of starch to maltose) still retain their original names. The *proteases* or proteolytic enzymes catalyze the hydrolysis of peptide bonds or proteins and other peptide-containing structures. The hydrolases also cover the subdivision *esterases* which effect the hydrolysis of esters to their alcohol and acid components. Esterases in turn include the subdivision *lipases* which catalyze the hydrolysis of lipids (or fats) to their constituent fatty acids and glycerol. *Nucleases* are also esterases since they catalyze the hydrolysis of particular ester linkages of nucleic acids to yield the component nucleotides. *Ribonuclease* and *deoxyribonuclease* act on the ribonucleic acids and deoxyribonucleic acids, respectively.

Phosphatases are hydrolases that catalyze the hydrolysis of esters of phosphoric acid as shown by the following generalized reaction.

$$R-O-\overset{\overset{\displaystyle O}{\|}}{\underset{\underset{\displaystyle OH}{|}}{P}}-OH + H_2O \longrightarrow ROH + HO-\overset{\overset{\displaystyle O}{\|}}{\underset{\underset{\displaystyle OH}{|}}{P}}-OH$$

They display varying degrees of substrate specificity depending on each particular phosphatase.

Phosphorylases are enzymes which split certain large molecules into smaller ones by the introduction of phosphoric acid instead of water. They are comparable to hydrolases except that cleavage is accomplished by phosphoric acid in place of water, thus forming esters of phosphoric acid as illustrated by the phosphorylation of starch.

Starch + phosphoric acid $\rightleftharpoons$

many glucose—phosphate molecules

This particular enzymatic reaction, as we shall see in the next chapter, constitutes an important first step in the carbohydrate metabolism of muscle.

(2) *Enzymes catalyzing oxidation-reduction reactions* consist of two subdivisions, the *dehydrogenases* (or *reductases*) and the *oxidases*. A *dehydrogenase* is an enzyme that catalyzes the dehydrogenation or removal of hydrogen atoms (or electrons) from one substrate A, transferring them to another substrate B (other than to molecular oxygen).

$$AH_2 + B \longrightarrow A + BH_2$$

If molecular oxygen were to receive the hydrogens, the enzyme is called an *oxidase*. The enzyme alcohol dehydrogenase, for example, catalyzes the removal of two hydrogens from ethanol to DPN to form acetaldehyde and reduced DPN (written as DPNH):

$$CH_3CH_2OH + DPN^+ \longrightarrow CH_3\overset{\overset{\displaystyle H}{|}}{C}=O + DPNH + H^+$$

Ethanol   Acetaldehyde

The term reductase is synonymous with dehydrogenase except that the emphasis in nomenclature is put on the substrate which is reduced rather than the one which is oxidized. Alcohol dehydrogenase might also be called acetaldehyde reductase, although the custom has been to use the former name.

An *oxidase* is an enzyme that catalyzes the transfer of hydrogen atoms (or electrons) from a substrate to molecular oxygen specifically. The latter is usually reduced to form water although in certain reactions hydrogen peroxide, H_2O_2, instead of H_2O is formed.

$$AH_2 + \tfrac{1}{2}O_2 \longrightarrow A + H_2O$$

Ascorbic-acid oxidase, a typical enzyme of this class, is a copper-containing protein which catalyzes the oxidation of ascorbic acid (vitamin C) by O_2 to form dehydroascorbic acid and water (Figure 7-9).

(3) *Transferases* are enzymes that catalyze the transfer of chemical groups from one substrate to another. Typical of this group are the so-called *transaminases* which mediate the transfer of the amino group of an amino acid to an acid containing a ketone group:

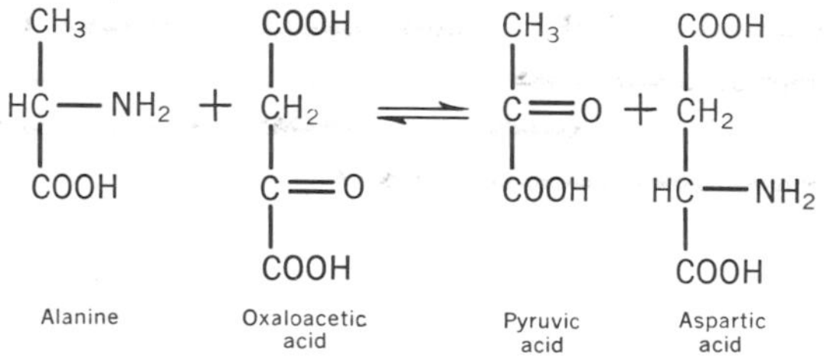

| Alanine | Oxaloacetic acid | Pyruvic acid | Aspartic acid |

Another subdivision of the transferring enzymes are the *kinases* which mediate the transfer of a phosphate group specifically from the biologically important high-energy compound *adenosine triphosphate* (ATP) to particular substrates. The latter are thus converted to the corresponding phosphate esters whereas ATP is changed to a smaller molecule, *adenosine diphosphate* (ADP). For example, the metabolism of glucose by most cells involves first its conversion to an appropriate phosphate ester by the transfer of a phosphate group from ATP, a reaction which cannot occur unless the particular enzyme *hexokinase* is present (Chapter 8).

(4) *Decarboxylases* are enzymes that mediate the removal of carbon dioxide from carboxylic acids. For example, pyruvic acid decarboxylase accelerates the following reaction:

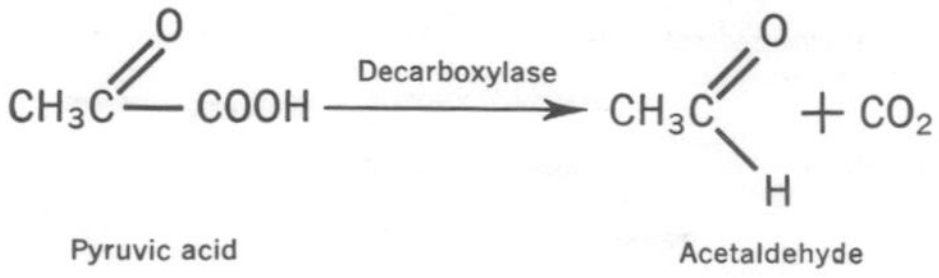

Pyruvic acid   Acetaldehyde

(5) *Isomerases* catalyze the interconversion of a compound to one of its isomers. For example, in one of the early steps of glucose metabolism, the enzyme phosphotriose isomerase catalyzes the conversion of glyceraldehyde-3-phosphate to its isomer dihydroxyacetone-phosphate (Chapter 8).

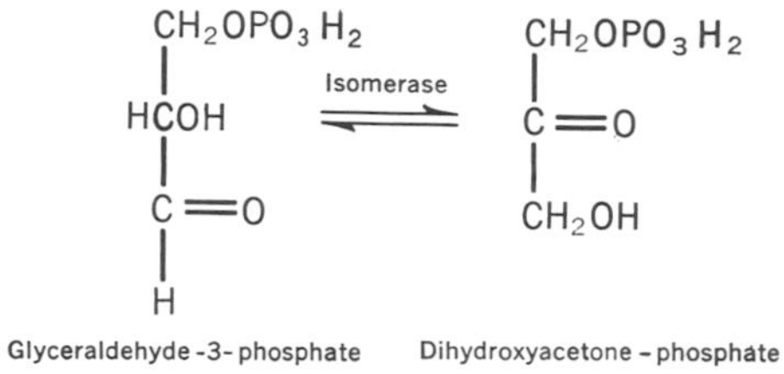

Glyceraldehyde-3-phosphate   Dihydroxyacetone–phosphate

Enzyme Inhibitors. The ability of certain substances to inhibit enzyme activity has yielded important clues about the properties and mechanism of action of enzymes. It has also provided information about the mode and site of action of these particular poisons in the cells themselves.

Metal-Binding Agents. Several enzymes are inhibited by such metal-binding reagents as cyanide, azide, carbon monoxide, and particular organic compounds known as chelating agents. Their inhibitory action depends on their ability to combine with and therefore inactivate the necessary metal components of most metalloenzymes. The deadly gas carbon monoxide (CO), for example, binds very strongly to ferrous iron (Fe^{2+}) and to ionic copper. The involvement of iron in one of the important oxidases known as *cytochrome oxidase* (Chapter 8), which is necessary in the final step of aerobic respiration, was first indicated by use of carbon monoxide.

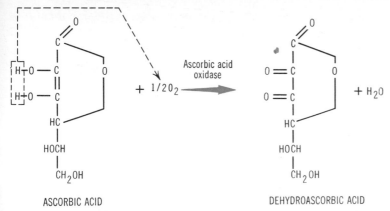

Figure 7-9. Oxidation of ascorbic acid by molecular oxygen, a reaction catalyzed by the copper-containing enzyme ascorbic-acid oxidase.

Competitive Inhibitors. Numerous enzymes are also inhibited by compounds that bear a structural similarity to their substrates. Inhibition by these structural analogues (called *antimetabolites*), which is reversed by simply adding more substrate to the reaction mixture, is known as *competitive inhibition.* The extent of inhibition is entirely dependent on the relative concentrations of substrate and inhibitor.

Competitive inhibition is best interpreted by assuming that the inhibitor combines with the same active enzyme sites as the substrate. The enzyme-inhibitor complex in contrast to the enzyme-substrate complex apparently fails to rearrange itself to yield reaction products, thus making the active sites of the enzyme unavailable for catalysis. According to this view a competitive inhibitor by virtue of its similarity in structure to the substrate therefore competes for the active sites on the enzyme, decreasing enzyme activity to an extent dependent on the ratio of inhibitor and substrate.

The concept of competitive inhibition of enzymes explains the widely observed competitive effects of various substances which are structurally related to biologically active compounds. Often minor alterations in the chemical structure of a natural compound may result in a structural analogue that competes with the biologically active material itself. Some chemical analogues, by selectively inhibiting certain key enzymes in disease-producing bacteria or cancer cells, can seriously disturb their metabolism, thereby inhibiting their growth and function without seriously affecting the normal host cells. For example, the inhibition of bacterial growth by the antibacterial agent sulfanilamide is competitively reversed by the vitamin *p*-amino benzoic acid. The similarity in structure of sulfanilamide and *p*-amino benzoic acid is apparent.

$$NH_2 \qquad\qquad NH_2$$

P-Amino benzoic acid   Sulfanilamide

This phenomenon has served as a basis for the treatment of a number of diseases, an approach known as *chemotherapy.* Such a mechanism is believed to operate in the treatment of certain bacterial infections by sulfa drugs (which chemically resemble the vitamin *p*-amino benzoic acid as just indicated) and in the treatment of certain types of cancer by chemicals resembling the base components of DNA.

All other types of inhibition induced by various substances are classified as noncompetitive. Their modes of action may be quite different depending on the particular inhibitor. Some may poison or denature a protein by reacting with some necessary chemical grouping. Others may bind a necessary metal component as already indicated, and so on.

Control of Enzymes. The kinds and proportions of enzymes within cells are determined primarily by genetic composition (i.e., DNA). The role of the genes as the blueprints for determining the enzyme constitution and therefore the metabolic patterns of the cell, as well as the roles played by such phenomena as *enzyme induction, feedback,* and *repression* in the coordination and regulation of metabolism are discussed in detail in Chapter 11 on genetics.

Nucleic Acids

GENERALIZED STRUCTURE. Nucleic acids are found in all living cells, and are combined in nearly all instances with particular proteins. Chemically, nucleic acids (so-called because they give an acid reaction when suspended in water) are huge, thread-like compounds of very great length with a molecular weight in the tens and hundreds of millions in which a similar but not necessarily identical chemical pattern repeats itself at regular intervals, representing the links or units of the chain. Each of the hundreds upon hundreds of units composing a nucleic acid is called a *nucleotide* and is made up of a phosphate group and a pentose (a five-carbon simple sugar) to which is attached one of several kinds of a particular cyclic organic structure called a *base*, belonging to the compounds known as *purines* and *pyrimidines*. A single nucleic acid strand made up of several or many nucleotides is called a *polynucleotide*. This would be comparable to the amino-acid units constituting the polypeptide chain of a protein.

Hydrolysis of nucleic acids by acid or by certain enzymes yields a mixture of various nucleotides, just as hydrolysis of a protein yields a mixture of amino acids. The sugar and phosphate groups can be regarded as the chemical backbone of the nucleic acid whereas the various bases can be viewed as the important side branches.

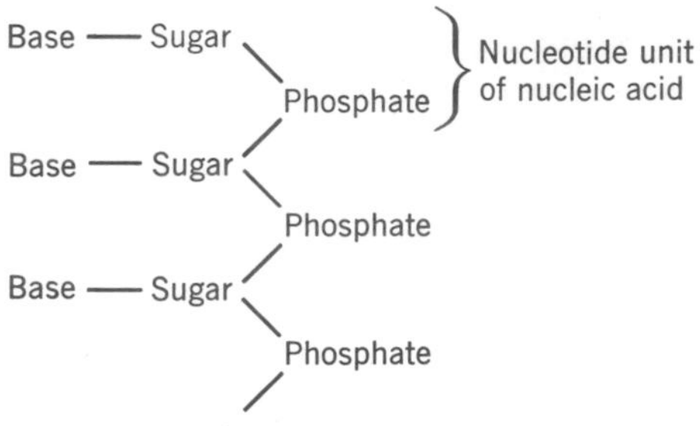

Single nucleic acid strand or polynucleotide structure (generalized scheme)

In any one nucleic acid the sugars consist wholly of one of two possible kinds of pentose sugars. If the sugar is ribose, the nucleic acid is called *ribonucleic acid* or *RNA*; if the sugar is deoxyribose, the nucleic acid is called *deoxyribonucleic acid* or *DNA*. Within both types of nucleic acids the nucleotides are linked to one another through phosphate groups attached (by ester linkages) to the number 5 carbon of one sugar and the number 3 carbon of the next. The bases are connected to the number 1 carbon of the pentoses.

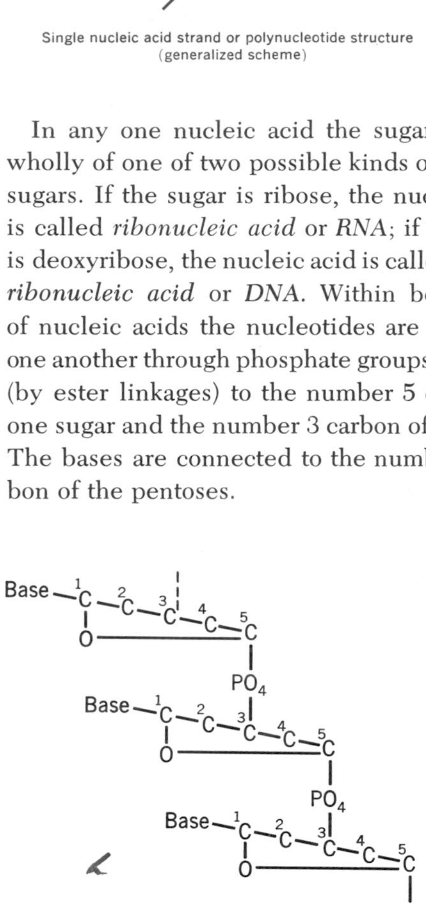

Figure 7-10. Generalized schematic structure of nucleic acids showing the chemical linkage pattern of the base, pentose, and phosphate moieties.

PYRIMIDINES AND PURINES. The nucleic acid bases, so called because they give an alkaline or basic reaction in aqueous solution, are cyclic organic molecules of varying complexity which include nitrogen atoms as part of their ring structure. Two particular classes of these compounds, known as *pyrimidines* and *purines*, are essential components of the nucleic acids. Several of these same compounds are also components of a number of coenzymes.

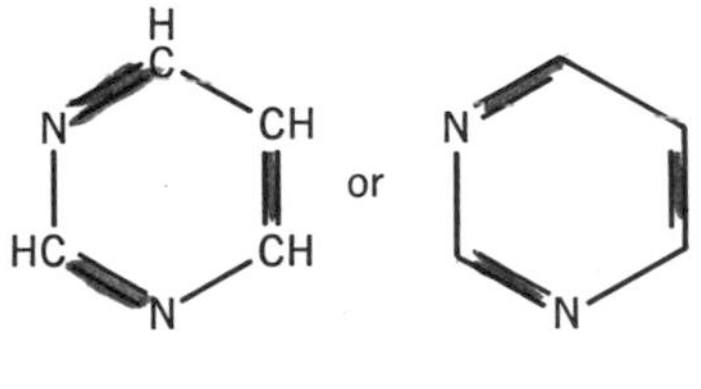

Pyrimidine

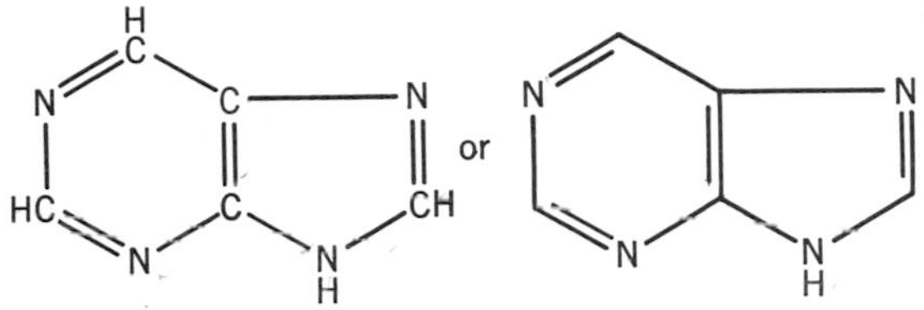

Purine

Purines and pyrimidines occur in nature in a number of different chemical forms. The principal pyrimidine structures in biological systems are *cytosine*, *uracil*, and *thymine*.

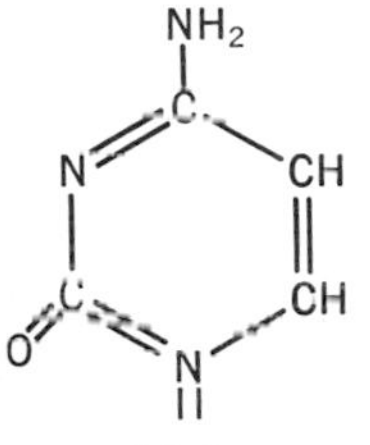

Cytosine

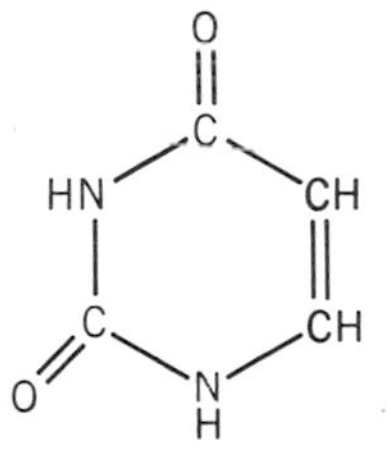

Uracil

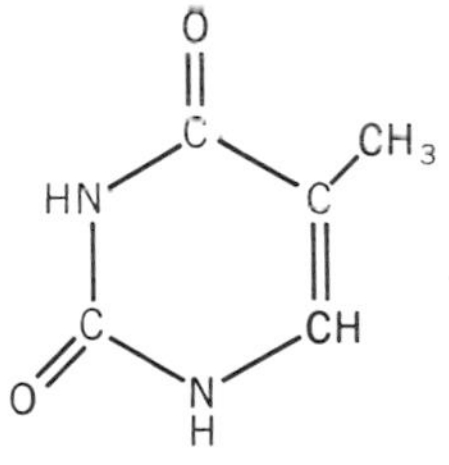

Thymine

The principal purine structures are *adenine* and *guanine*.

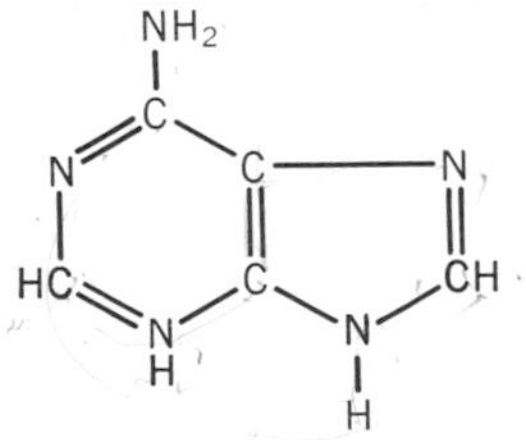

Adenine

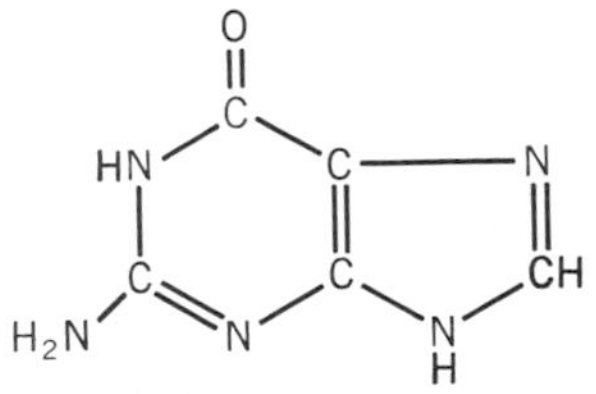

Guanine

DEOXYRIBONUCLEIC ACID (DNA). The deoxyribonucleic acids are found largely in the nucleus of the cell as part of the chromosome structure. As such they are always combined with certain basic proteins such as histones (and in the case of sperm cells, protamines) and are therefore components of conjugated proteins called deoxynucleoproteins. In the isolation and purification of DNA for investigation of its various properties, the protein portion of the nucleoprotein is usually denatured and separated from the nucleic acid in an early purification step.

All indications are that DNA, which together with particular proteins make up the chromosomes, is the primary carrier of genetic information. It is becoming increasingly evident that the order of arrangement of the different bases of the polynucleotide DNA strand may well be the means by which information is coded and transmitted to constitute the process of heredity (Chapter 11). DNA is also regarded as the central control cellular substance which ultimately directs and regulates all activities of the cell primarily by directing the synthesis of proteins (Chapter 11).

DNA from nearly all sources characteristically contains four different kinds of bases consisting of two purines and two pyrimidines. These are in most cases the two purines adenine (A) and guanine (G) and the pyrimidines thymine (T) and cytosine (C). The total number of purines in any given DNA are always roughly equal to the total number of pyrimidines $(A + G = T + C)$. Of even greater significance as we shall see is the relationship that the number of adenines is equal to the number of thymines (A = T) and the number of guanines is equal to the number of cytosines (G = C). The proportions of these bases (A + T/G + C) in DNA appear to be typical and constant for each particular species of organism. In some DNA molecules the content of A + T is greater than that of G + C while in others the reverse is true. Both the *proportions* and the *sequence* of the different nucleotides in a polynucleotide strand vary according to the given DNA so that no two nucleic acids need be alike, just as no two proteins are alike because of differences in the composition and order of arrangement of their amino acid units.

This important information together with certain physical data derived largely from X-ray diffraction studies led Watson and Crick in 1953 to propose a three-dimensional structure for DNA. They deduced that the DNA molecule consists of two long, adjacently attached polynucleotide chains aligned and coiled about each other to form a double helix about a hypothetical central post, much like two adjacently connected banisters of a spiral staircase (Figure 7-11). The two polynucleotide strands of the DNA molecule, as the banisters, are presumably so arranged that they are laterally connected to each other by hydrogen bonding

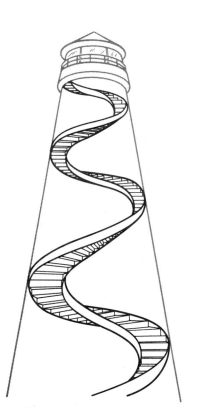
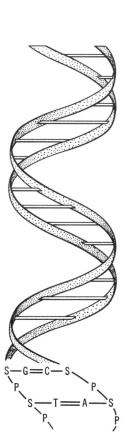

Figure 7-11. Diagrammatic representation of the Watson-Crick model of DNA showing the two adjacently attached polynucleotide chains forming a double helix like the bannisters of a spiral staircase. The two polynucleotide strands are connected by hydrogen bonding between the adenines (A) of one strand and the thymines (T) of the other, and the guanines (G) of one to the cytosines (C) of the other. (S = deoxynbase, P = phosphate.)

(p. 153) between the amino ($-NH_2$) and keto

($\diagdown$C=O) group of specific pairs of complimentary bases on opposite strands, namely the purines of one strand to the pyrimidines of the other to form the steps of the DNA spiral staircase. More precisely, it is conceived that the adenines of one strand are linked by hydrogen bonds to the thymines of the other, and that the guanines are similarly paired to the cytosines of the opposite polynucleotide. These seem to be the only pairing possibilities between the DNA bases in view of (1) the observations that the number of adenines equals the number of thymines and the number of guanines equals the number of cytosines; and (2) considerations of hydrogen bonding and space requirements. The two pyrimidines (cytosine and thymine) as the smaller bases could not be paired with one another in the proposed double-stranded structure because they would be too far apart to be linked securely by hydrogen bonding. Nor could the two purines (adenine and guanine) as the larger bases be paired with each other

because there would now be insufficient space between them as constituents of the opposite polynucleotide strands.

Thus the arrangement proposed by the Watson-Crick model not only accounts for the observation just indicated that the number of purines in DNA equals the number of pyrimidines but that the quantity of adenines equals the quantity of thymines, and the quantity of guanines equals the quantity of cytosines.

The pairing in Figure 7-12 also accounts in part for the equal distance between the two strands and the observed symmetry of the helix. Obviously the two polynucleotide strands of the DNA double helix cannot be identical. Instead they are reciprocally related as complimentary copies of one another, since a base on one polynucleotide chain can only be paired with a specific base on the other (i.e., adenine with thymine, and cytosine with guanine). Thus if the sequence of bases in one strand is TGTCA, that of the adjoining strand would be ACAGT (Figure 7-13).

A vast quantity of data has since been obtained by numerous research workers in genet-

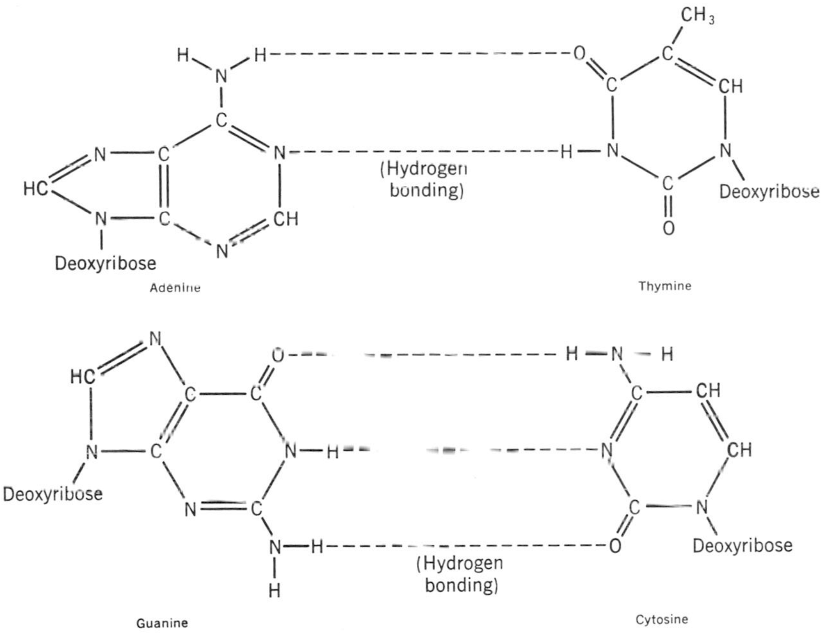

Figure 7-12. Hydrogen bonding of purine and pyrimidine bases, adenine with thymine, and guanine with cytosine.

ics, biochemistry, and biophysics confirming the foregoing molecular structure of DNA. For this epic contribution Watson, Crick, and Wilkens were honored with the Nobel Prize in 1962.

RNA. Our knowledge of the three-dimensional structure of RNA is considerably less than that of DNA. Ribonucleic acids are also universally present in living cells in combination with proteins as ribonucleoproteins. They occur largely in the cytoplasm of cells and to a lesser extent in the nuclei. Three types of RNA are recognized in the cytoplasm; *ribosomal RNA* (representing about 80 per cent of the total cellular RNA), *transfer RNA*, and *messenger RNA*. RNA strands are also polynucleotides somewhat similar to DNA, as already indicated, but with a number of important exceptions. RNA in addition to having ribose in place of deoxyribose has a slightly different base composition, thymine being replaced by the pyrimidine uracil. Finally, the RNA molecule is generally believed to be a single-stranded structure, although there is evidence that some of the regions of the RNA strand may be paired with portions of a complimentary RNA polynucleotide chain to form a helix. This does not occur throughout the length of the RNA strand, unlike the situation for DNA.

It seems likely that RNA is first made in the nucleus under the direct influence of DNA; and that it subsequently moves into the cytoplasm where it is directly involved in protein synthesis by the ribosomes (Chapter 11). Thus in this role RNA serves as a messenger of DNA, representing the means through which the latter regulates cytoplasmic metabolism by controlling protein (i.e., enzyme) synthesis.

The roles of DNA and RNA are discussed in detail in Chapter 11.

Porphyrins

GENERAL FEATURES. *Porphyrins* are a particular group of complex organic substances of great biological significance for they have a central role as components of such important substances as hemoglobin and chlorophyll. They are widely distributed in nature, occurring in almost all living things in one form or another. They are most often found as components of conjugated proteins being bound to specific proteins from which they are dissociable to varying degrees depending on the bonding between the two.

A porphyrin consists of four smaller ring units combined with one another to form a larger ring compound. The smaller rings, known

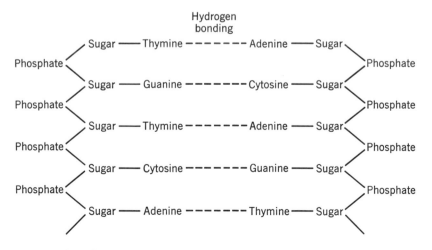

Figure 7-13. Schematic representation of the pairing of two DNA polynucleotide strands by hydrogen bonding between adenine and thymine, and guanine and cytosine.

as a *pyrroles* or *pyrrole-like* structures, are made up of four carbons and one nitrogen

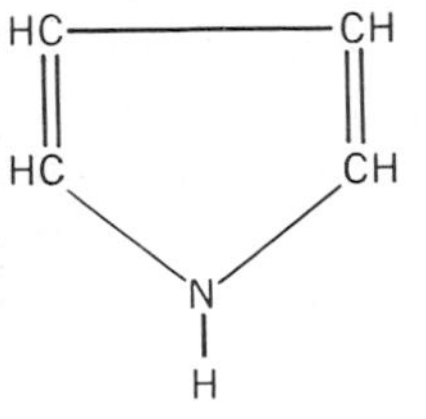

Pyrrole

and are linked by =CH− groups, to constitute the larger ring system, the *porphyrin* itself. In addition to their attachment to specific proteins, most naturally occurring porphyrins contain a metal component. They are accordingly called *metal porphyrins* (Figure 7-14). The two most biologically important types of metal porphyrins are the *hemes* (Chapters 8 and 25) which contain iron and the *chlorophylls* (Chapter 17) which contain magnesium. In both groups the metal (designated as Me in Figure 7-14) is linked to each of the four nitrogen atoms of the pyrrole-like rings at the center of the porphyrin structure like the hub of a wheel. The fundamental structures of all porphyrins found in living things are essentially alike. They differ from each other largely in the type and arrangement of the side chain groups attached to each of the constituent pyrrole-like rings.

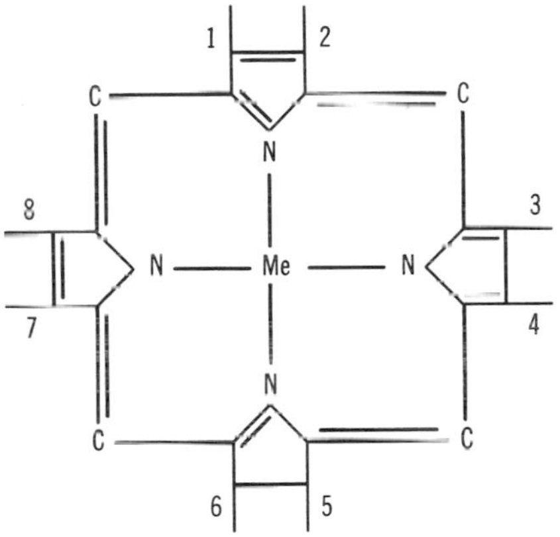

HEMES. The principal hemes and their protein combinations in living systems include *hemoglobin* (Chapter 25), the oxygen-transporting pigment of blood (of numerous animals) which is a red-colored conjugated protein consisting of a heme combined to a specific globular protein; the *cytochromes* (Chapter 8) which are red heme proteins concerned in the final stages of respiration or electron transfer; and two oxidizing enzymes, *catalase* and *peroxidase*, which are also heme proteins.

The heme iron of hemoglobin occurs exclusively in the divalent or ferrous (Fe^{2+}) form. a state which is absolutely essential for hemoglobin to function as the oxygen-carrying component of blood because oxygen combines reversibly with the Fe^{2+} of the heme (Chapter 25). In other heme proteins such as the enzymes catalase and peroxidase, the iron is in the trivalent ferric (Fe^{3+}) state. On the other hand the heme iron of the cytochromes experiences a reversible change from the ferrous to the ferric state during its metabolic function as an electron carrier in respiration. A number

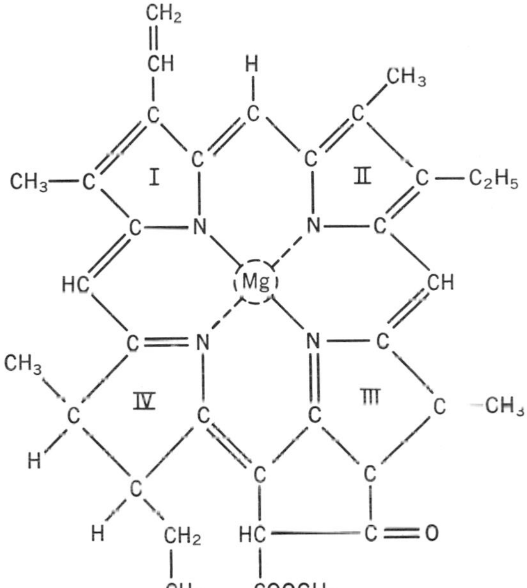

Figure 7-14. Generalized chemical structure of metal porphyrin. For hemes the metal (Me) is iron, and for chlorophylls it is magnesium.

Figure 7-15. Chemical structure of chlorophyll *a*.

of different cytochromes are concerned in respiration involving molecular oxygen (aerobic respiration). These have been partially characterized and designated as cytochromes a, a_3, b, b_1, b_5, c, c_1, and so on (Chapter 8).

CHLOROPHYLLS. Four principal chlorophylls occur in the plant kingdom, and two others are present in the photosynthetic bacteria. The magnesium of the chlorophylls is in the divalent state and apparently does not undergo any change during photosynthesis. The most predominant of the chlorophylls is chlorophyll a which is almost universally distributed in all green plants except for some of the photosynthetic bacteria. Chlorophyll b is the second most widely distributed, being found in all higher plants and some of the algae. In several lower plant forms (except for the green algae) chlorophyll b is absent. In the brown algae and the diatoms, for example, chlorophyll c, but not chlorophyll b, is present. In the red algae, there is still another chlorophyll pigment in addition to chlorophyll a, namely chlorophyll d, but not chlorophyll b. In the photosynthetic bacteria, there are yet other kinds of chlorophyll called *bacteriochlorophyll* and *bacteriovirdin*, depending on the bacterial species. All the chlorophylls as magnesium-containing porphyrins are essentially alike in their chemical structure. They differ mostly in the chemical make-up of their side chains connected to the pyrrole rings of the porphyrin structure.

ORIGIN AND EVOLUTION OF THE PORPHYRINS. From an evolutionary viewpoint, one can speculate that porphyrins appeared as a result of chance chemical reactions in the primeval seas during the early history of the planet earth prior to the appearance of life. Several of the primitive porphyrins might have provided a distinct advantage in the competition for chemical substrates among various living systems at a relatively early stage following the origin of life. We can only guess that when the organic material of the primeval sea became limiting for the support of life some billion or so years ago those organisms that could utilize the energy of sunlight (i.e., carry on photosynthesis) by virtue of possessing, in addition to certain other characteristics, a substance resembling present-day chlorophyll had an added advantage for survival. It also seems reasonable to assume that the increasing concentration of molecular oxygen in the atmosphere resulting from the newly evolved process of photosynthesis markedly influenced the subsequent course of evolution of living things. Organisms that could utilize the gas for the more complete and more efficient liberation of useful energy from organic materials, presumably because they possessed suitable iron-porphyrin-protein systems functionally resembling the present-day cytochromes as well as certain additional systems must have had a better chance for survival.

SUPPLEMENTARY REFERENCES

Conn, E. E., and P. K. Stumpf, *Outlines of Biochemistry*, Wiley, New York, 1963.

English, James, Jr., *Principles of Organic Chemistry*, McGraw-Hill, New York, 1956.

Fruton, J. S., and S. Simmonds, *General Biochemistry*, second edition, Wiley, New York, 1958.

Gerard, R. W., *Unresting Cells*, Harper, New York, 1949.

Lucas, Howard J., *Organic Chemistry*, American Book Co., New York, 1953.

Neilands, J. B., and P. K. Stumpf, *Outlines of Enzyme Chemistry*, second edition, Wiley, New York, 1958.

White, A., P. Handler, and E. L. Smith, *Principles of Biochemistry*, third edition, McGraw-Hill, New York, 1964.

Chapter 8   Cell Metabolism

GENERAL CONSIDERATIONS

Introduction

For many organisms, including ourselves, energy (stored in chemical bonds) and matter are provided by certain organic substances such as carbohydrates, proteins, and fats which undergo various enzymatic reactions. The final chemical products released to the environment are generally of a smaller size and a lower energy content. For green plants the source of energy is sunlight and the sources of matter are carbon dioxide, water, and minerals. The energy of sunlight in the presence of water and carbon dioxide is converted in green leaves to the energy-rich chemical bonds of carbohydrates and their intermediates by the process of photosynthesis.

Metabolism and Respiration

The many chemical reactions and concomitant energy changes that occur in living cells are collectively called *metabolism*. The different areas of metabolism may be classified in several ways. Although it is usual for the sake of convenience to describe separately the metabolism of carbohydrates, proteins, lipids, and nucleic acids, these areas, strictly speaking, cannot be divorced from one another. There is an essential interdependence and interrelationship among them. From one point of view, metabolism may be divided into two broad subdivisions: *catabolism* dealing with the breakdown or degradation of larger molecules to smaller ones (often accompanied by the release of energy), and *anabolism* involving the buildup or synthesis of larger molecules from smaller ones (frequently requiring an input of energy). The degradation, for example, of carbohydrates to carbon dioxide and water by living cells is a catabolic process, whereas the synthesis of proteins from amino acids is anabolic.

The term *respiration* is applied to one particular phase of metabolism. It refers to the integrated series of chemical reactions by which the living cell obtains energy for its various life functions from particular foods or nutrients. In many organisms including man, the respiratory process consist of the oxidative breakdown of carbohydrates and fats as the principal energy sources for the many activities of the cell. Respiration is easily distinguished from digestion (another particular phase of metabolism), although both involve the degradation of larger molecules to smaller ones. In digestion, larger molecules are split into smaller molecules by enzymatic hydrolysis. Any energy released in the rupturing of chemical bonds by hydrolysis during the course of digestion is wasted as heat. In respiration, larger molecules are split into smaller molecules, in part as a result of oxidation-reduction reactions (Chapter 6) which constitute several of the key steps in the process. *Its most significant aspect is that an appreciable portion of the chemical energy released during respiration is trapped as useful energy to be utilized ultimately for the various activities of the cell.*

From one viewpoint, respiration can be regarded as the flow of hydrogens or electrons from a higher chemical energy level (e.g., from carbohydrates) to a lower energy level (e.g., carbon dioxide and water) like the flowing of a river downstream over a series of rapids. Energy is released in the process and a portion of it is captured depending on the organization of the surroundings. In the cell the intricate subcellular chemical and physical structures (and in the case of the rapids, the presence of a paddle wheel with suitable attachments) serve to trap and make available some of the energy which has been liberated in the downstream flow.

Overall *Features of Respiration*

The basic aspects of respiration common to all living systems are the following.

1. *Among the key chemical steps in respiration are oxidation-reduction reactions.* This can be illustrated by comparing the following reactions. In the nonbiological, chemical reaction between hydrogen gas and oxygen gas, water is formed with an explosive release of energy.

(a) $2H_2 + O_2 \longrightarrow 2H_2O + Energy$

(Incidently, the eventual oxidation of H_2 by O_2 is also carried out by certain chemosynthetic bacteria; see p. 208).
If in place of the H—H bond of H_2 we were to substitute the $-\overset{|}{\underset{|}{C}}-H$ bonds of glucose, then energy would also be liberated.

(b) $C_6H_{12}O_6 + 6O_2 \longrightarrow 6CO_2 + 6H_2O + Energy$
Glucose

The complete oxidation of glucose to CO_2 and H_2O is easily accomplished by placing glucose in a hot furnace (at about 500°C) for a few hours.

The same net effect is attained by the respiration of living cells at about 20°C. The reaction of molecular hydrogen with molecular oxygen and the burning of glucose with molecular oxygen (whether they occur in inanimate systems or living cells) essentially involve oxidation-reductions. They are attained by the transfer of hydrogen atoms from relatively higher energy bonds to produce lower energy bonds such as those of water and carbon dioxide with a concomitant net release of energy.

2. *Respiration occurs in a series of many successive and coordinated enzymatic reactions and not in a single chemical step.* Thus the release of energy by the respiratory process is assured to occur in small quantities rather than in one large, wasteful burst as might be expected if a single chemical reaction were involved.

Although the same total quantity of energy is released by both the cell and the furnace per given weight of glucose oxidized, it is liberated in small discrete packages in the cell. This feature in conjunction with the unique organization of the cell as indicated later makes available a significant portion of the liberated energy in a form that can be used for the life activities. It is in sharp contrast to the large waste of energy as heat occurring during sugar combustion in the furnace.

3. *Each of the many steps constituting respiration is catalyzed by a specific enzyme.* In fact most of these reactions in the absence of the appropriate enzyme do not occur at a discernible rate under the normal condition of temperature, pressure, and concentration of substrates found in living cells.

4. *The highly unique physical and chemical organization of the cell makes possible the relatively efficient capture and utilization of the useful energy released in respiration.* The energy liberated in a chemical reaction may be totally dissipated and wasted as heat unless it occurs in an organized environment suitable for the capture of energy in a useful form. For example, the energy liberated from gasoline burning on the ground is lost largely as heat.

The combustion of the same quantity of gasoline, however, in a highly organized system such as a gasoline engine results in the conversion of a portion of the energy to a useful form such as mechanical energy or electricity depending on the organization of the system.

The cell, by virtue of its highly specialized and integrated chemical and physical organization, obtains a significant portion of the useful energy liberated in respiration. It transforms and utilizes it in various ways, as we shall soon see.

CARBOHYDRATE METABOLISM

Respiration and Energy Release

OVERALL ASPECTS. In most organisms energy is obtained primarily from respiration of carbohydrates and fats. As the representative substrate of respiration, glucose is metabolized by several pathways. Our discussion of carbohydrate respiration will be confined to two well-established biochemical routes which at present appear to be the major respiratory pathways in plants, animals, and numerous microorganisms. They are the respiratory chains commonly known as *(a) anaerobic respiration* followed by *aerobic respiration*, and *(b) the pentose oxidative pathway.*

The Anaerobic and Aerobic Respiratory Pathways. The *early sequence* of steps in the respiration of most organisms including man is completely independent of oxygen and is called *anaerobic respiration.* For a small proportion of living things (e.g., several kinds of bacteria), this constitutes the principal if not the only form of respiration. Such organisms thrive in an environment totally lacking in molecular oxygen, obtaining sufficient energy to meet their needs from the series of enzymatic reactions in anaerobic respiration. For this reason they are classified as *anaerobic organisms.*

However, many living systems including man possess *in addition* to anaerobic respiration a subsequent sequence of enzymatic reactions collectively called *aerobic respiration*, which depends on molecular oxygen. In nearly all instances, oxygen is absolutely essential for the life of these organisms despite the fact that their early stages of respiration are anaerobic. They are accordingly called *aerobic organisms.* In such organisms, the principal products of anaerobic metabolism are further broken down to carbon dioxide and water by the subsequent sequence of biochemical reactions namely aerobic respiration. Aerobic respiration is, therefore, a continuation of anaerobic respiration and is always preceded by the latter process. Together in succession they total two dozen or so highly integrated specific enzymatic reactions to constitute a principal pathway of carbohydrate metabolism for most organisms (including man) that require oxygen. Oxygen is directly involved in only the final step of the aerobic respiratory sequence. Nevertheless, all the previous steps of the aerobic respiratory sequence indirectly depend on oxygen, because they would only proceed for a short time if oxygen were not present to participate in the terminal reaction.

The ability of certain microorganisms, such as yeast cells, to carry on a completely normal existence in the presence or absence of molecular oxygen helps to illustrate the relationship between anaerobic and aerobic respiration. When grown in the absence of oxygen, yeast derives its energy solely from the anaerobic respiration of a sugar such as glucose, degrading it to ethyl alcohol and carbon dioxide. If oxygen is provided, the ethyl alcohol is further metabolized by way of the enzymatic steps of the aerobic respiratory sequence to carbon dioxide and water with the release of a considerably more useful energy.

The fact that the anaerobic respiratory scheme is so widely distributed among living systems which range from the most primitive to the most advanced type suggests that it is a more ancient type of respiration from an evolutionary point of view. Similarly, the relatively limited distribution of the aerobic respiratory pathway in what we consider to be more primitive organisms and its widespread occurrence in the more advanced forms of life point to aerobic respiration as a relatively more recent evolutionary acquisition. This is also supported by the fact that the aerobic respiratory sequence utilizes the chemical products formed by the preceding anaerobic respiratory pathway.

The Pentose Oxidative Pathway. The pentose oxidative pathway represents an alternate pathway for carbohydrate oxidation and, therefore, energy release. It is often present in the same tissues that possess the metabolic systems of anaerobic and aerobic respiration. In many tissues, carbohydrates are often metabolized simultaneously by the above respiratory pathways. The broad relationships of anaerobic respiration, aerobic respiration, and the pentose oxidative pathway are diagrammed in Figure 8-1. The extent to which each of these pathways contributes to the total glucose respiration of the living cell varies depending on a number of factors including type of tissue, metabolic state of the cell, and so on.

ANAEROBIC RESPIRATION. *The Fundamental Steps in the Pathway.* The term anaerobic respiration is often used interchangeably with the terms *glycolysis*, *fermentation*, or *Embden-Meyerhof pathway*. The latter term is adopted

from the names of two prominent biochemists, Embden and Meyerhof, who made important contributions in the early elucidation of the sequence. The process of anaerobic respiration with minor modifications is essentially the same in many widely divergent tissues and organisms. The fundamental biochemical steps in the anaerobic respiratory pathway can be summarized in the following simplified version (Figure 8-2).

1. The 6-carbon sugar glucose is split between carbons 3 and 4 into essentially two equal 3-carbon molecules, glyceraldehyde.

2. The glyceraldehyde molecules are then oxidized by the removal of two hydrogen atoms to form *glyceric acid*. This is pictured as taking place first by the prior addition of water to the aldehyde group of the glyceraldehyde molecule, followed by an oxidation step involving removal of two hydrogen atoms to form glyceric acid.

3. Each of the two glyceric acid molecules then undergoes the removal of an H and OH to form *pyruvic acid* and *water*.

4. In most higher animal tissues, pyruvic acid is normally the major end product of anaerobic respiration. It is usually further metabolized by the aerobic respiratory pathway (i.e., in the presence of molecular oxygen) to carbon dioxide and water. If the oxygen supply is limiting, some of the pyruvic acid undergoes enzymatic reduction by the addition of two hydrogen atoms to form *lactic acid*. Under experimental conditions, animal tissues in the complete absence of molecular oxygen quantitatively convert glucose to lactate—two molecules of lactate forming for every molecule of glucose respired.

5. In most higher plant cells and microorganisms pyruvic acid is formed by the same sequence of enzymatic steps that produce pyruvic acid in animal tissues. Subsequently, however, two different enzymatic steps are involved if oxygen is lacking. For example, under anaerobic conditions in yeast, the pyruvic acid formed first experiences a removal of carbon dioxide, a reaction known as a *decarbox-*

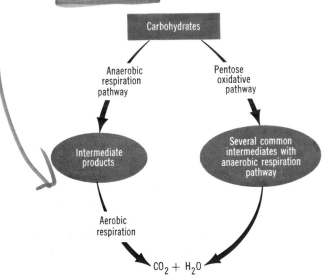

Figure 8-1. Interrelationship of anaerobic respiration, aerobic respiration, and the pentose oxidative pathway.

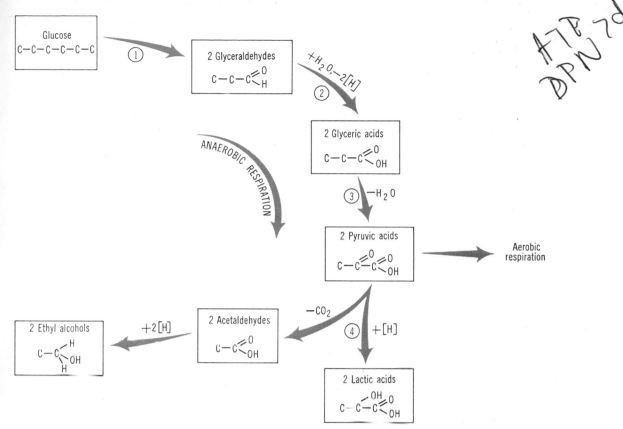

Figure 8-2. Simplified summary of the anerobic respiratory pathway (often called *glycolysis* in animal and higher plant tissues, and *fermentation* in microorganisms).

ylation, to form *acetaldehyde;* second, the acetaldehyde is then enzymatically reduced by accepting two hydrogens to yield *ethyl alcohol.* Thus ethyl alcohol and carbon dioxide instead of lactic acid are the end products of respiration in yeast cells grown in the absence of molecular oxygen. For this reason anaerobic respiration in such organisms is frequently called *alcoholic fermentation.*

Before proceeding to a more detailed discussion of the steps and enzymes involved in the process, a few additional features must be emphasized.

Participating Coenzymes. The intensive research efforts of numerous biochemists over the years following the major discovery of cell-free fermentation by the Buchner brothers, soon revealed several common, underlying patterns.

Not only does anaerobic respiration of sugar proceed by essentially the same pathway in nearly all organisms, but identical coenzymes and metal components also are involved. At least three different classes of coenzymes participate in anaerobic respiration. They are the *pyridine nucleotides* consisting of *diphosphopyridine nucleotide (DPN)* and *triphosphopyridine nucleotide (TPN)*[1] the *adenosine phosphate system* consisting of *adenosine diphosphate (ADP)* and *adenosine triphosphate (ATP),* also known as the *phosphorylating coenzymes,* and *cocarboxylase.*

[1] In 1961 the Commission on Enzymes of the International Union of Biochemistry proposed that DPN+ and TPN+ be renamed *nicotinamide adenine dinucleotide (NAD+)* and *nicotinamide adenine dinucleotide phosphate (NADP+),* respectively.

Pyridine Nucleotides. In step 2 above, what happens to the two hydrogens after they are removed from the donor substance, glyceraldehyde? We now know that in most animal tissues, the coenzyme DPN enzymatically accepts the two hydrogens, becoming reduced to a form which we conveniently designate as DPNH. The structure of DPN consists of *nicotinamide* (a derivative of the vitamin *niacin* which is necessary for most higher animals including man in preventing the nutritional disease *pellagra*, Chapter 9), *two riboses, two phosphates* and *adenine* chemically linked to one another as shown in Figure 8-3. TPN differs from DPN by having another phosphate attached to the ribose adjacent to adenine. In the reduction of DPN and TPN to DPNH and TPNH, respectively, the nicotinamide portion of the pyridine nucleotides becomes reduced.

In other cells and tissues, TPN may serve in place of DPN to form TPNH. The DPNH or TPNH subsequently donates the hydrogens for the enzymatic reduction of (*a*) pyruvic acid to lactic acid (step 4) in animal tissues such as muscle under conditions of limited oxygen supply and (*b*) acetaldehyde to ethyl alcohol (step 5) in yeast fermentation.

No molecular oxygen is consumed in anaerobic respiration, although two of the individual steps are oxidation-reduction reactions. The process is cyclic in the sense that DPN (or TPN) undergoes an alternate reduction and oxidation as indicated in the foregoing section. Thus the pyridine nucleotides are used over and over again, alternately undergoing enzymatic reduction (by glyceraldehyde) and oxidation (by pyruvate or acetaldehyde, as the case may be) during the course of anaerobic respiration. In this manner, DPN and TPN account for the oxidation-reduction reactions of a large number of substrate molecules (i.e., glyceraldehyde, pyruvate, and acetaldehyde) even though they are present in the cell in extremely small quantities.

Phosphorylating Coenzymes. Anaerobic respiration is in reality a process of breakdown, not of free glucose as such, but of a phosphorylated derivative of glucose. The first step in anaerobic metabolism therefore involves the conversion of glucose to its appropriate phosphate ester form. The phosphorylating coenzyme ATP, consisting of the chemical linkage of adenosine (adenine and ribose) and three phosphates, serves in the transformation of glucose to its suitable phosphate ester, a reaction accomplished by the specific enzymatic transfer of the terminal phosphate grouping of ATP to glucose to form ADP and glucose-phosphate.[2]

[2] The symbol $\textcircled{P}$ will be used to designate the esterfied phosphate group $(-\overset{\overset{\text{O}}{\|}}{\underset{\underset{\text{H}}{|}}{\text{P}}}-\text{O})$ in the appropriate chemical reactions.

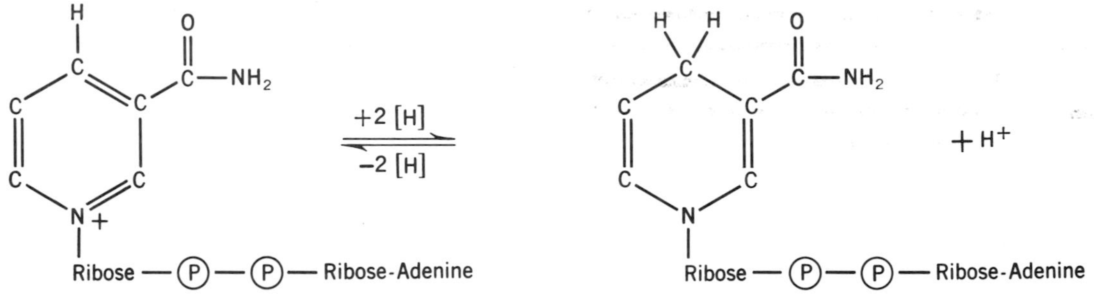

Figure 8-3. Chemical structure of the pyridine nucleotide DPN (in the oxidized and reduced states).

(a) Adenosine $-$ (P) $\sim$ (P) $\sim$ (P) $+$ Glucose $\longrightarrow$

ATP

Adenosine $-$ (P) $\sim$ (P) $+$ Glucose $-$ (P)

(ADP)   Glucose · phosphate

Glucose-phosphate is then enzymatically transformed to fructose-phosphate which is enzymatically phosphorylated by ATP to form fructose diphosphate:

(b) ATP $+$ Fructose (P) $\longrightarrow$ ADP $+$ (P) $-$ Fructose $-$ (P)

(Fructose diphosphate)

All subsequent steps in anaerobic respiration until the formation of pyruvic acid involve phosphorylated intermediates, as we shall soon see.

The ATP-ADP system also performs another major function, namely in capturing useful energy released during respiration. ATP itself is exceptionally rich in chemical energy, because it contains two "high-energy" chemical bonds (between the terminal and second, and between the second and third phosphate groups) as part of its chemical structure. These bonds, conveniently designated by a wavy line ($\sim$), are ester linkages (p. 140) but are different in possessing an inordinately high level of chemical energy. Each of these two bonds contains about 10,000 calories per gram-molecular weight at ATP in contrast to the 2000 to 3000 calories of the ordinary phosphate ester bond. For purposes of our discussion, we shall be primarily interested in the terminal high energy phosphate bond of ATP. It is formed from ADP, inorganic phosphate (designated as Pi), and an adequate energy supply in the presence of a suitable enzyme system:

Adenosine $-$ (P) $\sim$ (P) $+$ Pi $+$ 10,000 calories $\rightleftharpoons$

ADP

Adenosine $-$ (P) $\sim$ (P) $\sim$ (P)

ATP

Of the dozen or so reactions making up anaerobic respiration, only two provide useful energy

trapped in the form of ATP by the cell. ATP formation occurs at step 2 above, following the oxidation of glyceraldehyde, and at step 3, where a molecule of water is removed to produce pyruvic acid. Considerably more ATP is generated during aerobic respiration as described later in the chapter. ATP is the immediate and direct source of energy for all the energy-requiring activities of living cells to yield ADP and Pi (reversal of the above equation). Its use is analogous to the withdrawal of energy from a storage battery that is constantly being charged by the respiration of the cell.

COCARBOXYLASE. Associated with the enzyme called carboxylase, which is responsible for the decarboxylation of pyruvic acid to acetaldehyde (step 5 above), is a coenzyme called thiamine pyrophosphate or cocarboxylase; the latter is the diphosphate derivative of vitamin B_1 or thiamine (Chapter 9) as shown at bottom of the page.

Cocarboxylase also participates in two of the key steps of aerobic respiration, namely in the enzymatic oxidation of pyruvic acid (p. 185) and ketoglutaric acid (p. 186). A dietary deficiency of thiamine in most higher animals results in the characteristic nutritional nerve disease known as beriberi (Chapter 9).

ANAEROBIC RESPIRATION — Detailed Enzymatic Steps. Starting with glucose as the typical substrate, the following successive detailed enzymatic events make up the anaerobic respiratory pathway.

1. Phosphorylation of glucose. This step is catalyzed by the enzyme known as hexokinase and involves the transfer of the terminal phos-

Cocarboxylase or Thiamine pyrophosphate

phate group of ATP to the number 6 carbon of glucose to form glucose-6-phosphate and ADP.

$$\text{ATP} + \text{Glucose} \xrightarrow{\text{Hexokinase}} \text{Glucose-6-} \textcircled{P} + \text{ADP}$$

In several animal and plant tissues *glycogen* or *starch* instead of glucose serves as the initial substrate for glycolysis. It is first cleaved by inorganic phosphate through the action of the enzyme *phosphorylase* to yield many molecules of glucose-1-phosphate.

$$\text{Glycogen} + \text{Pi} \underset{\text{Phosphorylase}}{\rightleftarrows} \left(\text{Glucose-1-} \textcircled{P}\right)_n$$

The glucose-1-phosphate is in turn transformed to glucose-6-phosphate by the enzyme *phosphoglucomutase*.

$$\text{Glucose-1-} \textcircled{P} \underset{\text{Phosphoglucomutase}}{\rightleftarrows} \text{Glucose-6-} \textcircled{P}$$

The glucose-6-phosphate (whether it is derived from glycogen, or directly from glucose as above) is then metabolized by the successive enzymatic steps described below.

2. *Glucose-6-phosphate conversion to fructose-6-phosphate.* The glucose-6-phosphate formed undergoes an *isomerization* to fructose-6-phosphate catalyzed by an enzyme appropriately called *phosphohexoisomerase*.

$$\text{Glucose-6-} \textcircled{P} \underset{\text{isomerase}}{\overset{\text{Phosphohexo}}{\rightleftarrows}} \text{Fructose-6-} \textcircled{P}$$

3. *Phosphorylation of fructose-6-phosphate to fructose-1,6-phosphate.* Fructose-6-phosphate is converted in this step to the disphosphate derivative by the transfer of the terminal phosphate group of another ATP to the number 1 carbon of fructose-6-phosphate to form fructose-1,6-diphosphate, a reaction catalyzed by the enzyme called *phosphofructokinase*.

$$\text{Fructose-6-phosphate} + \text{ATP} \xrightarrow{\overset{\text{Phospho-}}{\text{fructokinase}}}$$
$$\text{Fructose-1, 6-diphosphate} + \text{ADP}$$

Thus far the foregoing three enzymatic steps in anaerobic metabolism have served solely to transform the original glucose molecule into a particular phosphorylated and isomerized derivative, namely fructose-1,6-disphosphate. (Note that enzymes which catalyze the transfer of the terminal phosphate group from ATP to another substance are called *kinases*. In the nomenclature of specific kinases the name of the major substrate phosphorylated is conveniently used. For example, phosphofructokinase catalyzes the phosphorylation of fructose phosphate by ATP.)

4. *Cleavage of fructose-1,6 diphosphate to triose phosphate. Fructose-1-6, disphosphate* is split between carbons 3 and 4 into two essentially similar molecules, a reaction which is mediated by the enzyme *aldolase*.

Fructose-1, 6-diphosphate

Dihydroxyacetone phosphate

+

Glyceraldehyde-3-phosphate

The reaction corresponds to step 1 of the simplified version of anaerobic metabolism (p. 174). The two resulting triose phosphates, namely *glyceraldehyde-3-phosphate* and *dihydroxyacetone phosphate*, are not identical but are isomers of one another. They are interconvertible by means of an isomerizing reaction catalyzed by the enzyme *phosphotriose isomerase.*

Glyceraldehyde-3-phosphate is oxidized in the next reaction step of the pathway, and with its progressive utilization more and more of the dihydroxyacetone phosphate is converted to glyceraldehyde-3-phosphate through the action of the phosphotriose isomerase. Thus the triose phosphates formed by the aldolase reaction are metabolized by way of the glyceraldehyde-3-phosphate along the main pathway of anaerobic respiration as shown below.

5. *Oxidation of glyceraldehyde-3-phosphate and formation of ATP.* First, *glyceraldehyde-3-phosphate* under the influence of the specific enzyme *phosphoglyceraldehyde dehydrogenase* is oxidized to *phosphoglyceric acid* by donating two of its hydrogen atoms to DPN and at the same time reacts with *inorganic phosphate* (Pi) to form DPNH and *1,3-diphosphoglyceric acid.* This corresponds to step 2 in the previously presented simplified version of anaerobic respiration.

(a)

Glyceraldehyde-3-phosphate

1, 3-Diphosphoglyceric acid

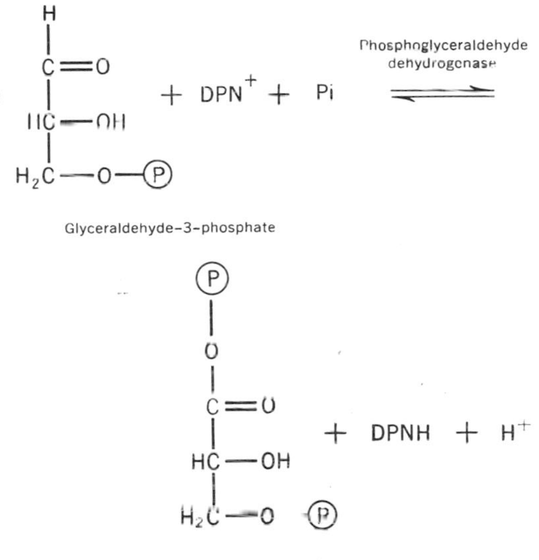

The newly formed phosphate bond in the glyceric acid derivative is a high-energy type similar to that of ATP. In the presence of the proper transferring enzyme (called the *ATP-phosphoglyceric transphosphorylase*) the high

energy-phosphate is transferred from the *diphosphoglyceric acid* to ADP to form *3-phosphoglyceric acid* and *ATP.*

(b) 1, 3-Diphosphoglyceric acid + ADP $\underset{\text{Transphosphorylase}}{\rightleftharpoons}$

3-Phosphoglyceric acid + ATP

Note that the reverse of the above reaction is of the kinase type (p. 178). For this reason, the name *3-phosphoglyceric kinase* is also assigned to the enzyme. The above two reactions (*a*) and (*b*) can conveniently be written as a single collective equation:

(c) Glyceraldehyde 3-(P) + Pi + DPN$^+$ + ADP $\rightleftharpoons$

3-Phosphoglyceric acid + DPNH + ATP + H$^+$

6. *Conversion of 3-phosphoglyceric acid to phosphopyruvic acid.* This transformation involves the successive action of two enzymes. The first enzyme *phosphoglyceromutase,* which catalyzes the conversion of *3-phosphoglyceric acid* to *2-phosphoglyceric acid* effects a shift of the phosphate group from the number 3 carbon to the number 2 carbon.

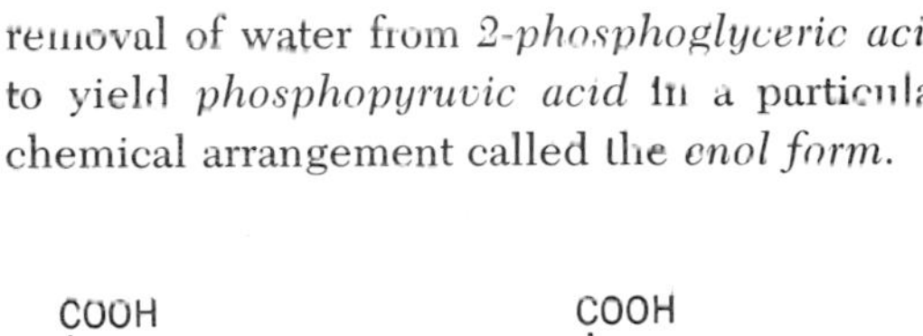

3-Phosphoglyceric acid   2-Phosphoglyceric acid

The second enzyme *enolase* catalyzes the removal of water from *2-phosphoglyceric acid* to yield *phosphopyruvic acid* in a particular chemical arrangement called the *enol form.*

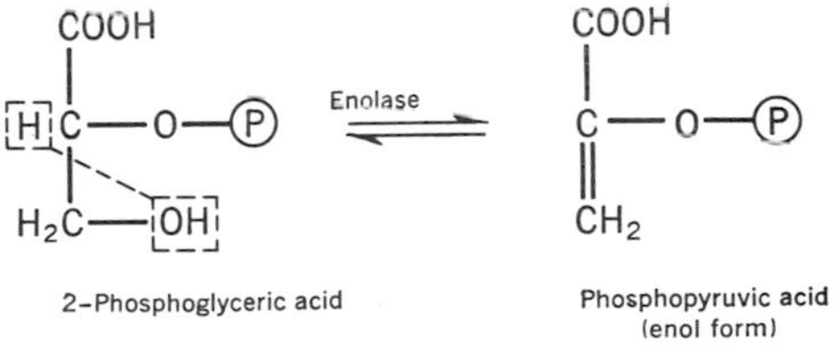

2-Phosphoglyceric acid   Phosphopyruvic acid (enol form)

7. *ATP formation from phosphopyruvic acid.* In the presence of ADP and the appropriate transferring enzyme, namely *ATP-phosphopyruvic transphosphorylase* or *pyruvate kinase*, the enol form of phosphopyruvic acid gives up its phosphate group to ADP to form pyruvic acid and ATP.

$$
\begin{array}{c}
\text{COOH} \\
| \\
\text{C}-\text{O}-\text{\textcircled{P}} + \text{ADP} \\
|| \\
\text{CH}_2
\end{array}
\quad \xrightleftharpoons[\text{kinase}]{\text{Pyruvic}} \quad
\begin{array}{c}
\text{COOH} \\
| \\
\text{C}=\text{O} + \text{ATP} \\
| \\
\text{CH}_3
\end{array}
$$

Phosphopyruvic acid   Pyruvic acid

Note that the reverse reaction is also of the kinase type accounting for the enzyme name *pyruvate kinase.* Steps 6 and 7 above were collectively represented in the previous simplified version as step 3 (p. 174).

8. *Pyruvic acid to lactic acid.* Under normal circumstances the pyruvic acid formed by the above anaerobic respiratory process in many cells and tissues would be further metabolized by way of the aerobic respiratory pathway to carbon dioxide and water. In situations, however, in which molecular oxygen is at times limiting as in skeletal muscle, pyruvic acid is converted to lactic acid by an oxidation-reduction in which *DPNH* reduces *pyruvate* to *lactate* in the presence of the specific enzyme *lactic dehydrogenase.*

$$
\begin{array}{c}
\text{COOH} \\
| \\
\text{C}=\text{O} + \text{DPNH} + \text{H}^+ \\
| \\
\text{CH}_3
\end{array}
\quad \xrightleftharpoons[\text{dehydrogenase}]{\text{Lactic}} \quad
\begin{array}{c}
\text{COOH} \\
| \\
\text{HCOH} + \text{DPN}^+ \\
| \\
\text{CH}_3
\end{array}
$$

Pyruvic acid   Lactic acid

The DPNH utilized in the above reduction of pyruvate to lactate was formed in the earlier oxidation reaction of glyceraldehyde-3-phosphate (reaction 5). Thus the coenzyme DPN, by accepting hydrogens or electrons from glyceraldehyde and then donating them to pyruvic acid, undergoes an alternate reduction and oxidation in the anaerobic respiratory process.

In many plant cells and microorganisms under conditions of a limited oxygen supply, the pyruvic acid is principally converted to ethyl alcohol and carbon dioxide instead of lactic acid by means of the following two reactions.

8a. *Pyruvic acid to acetaldehyde.* This reaction which is catalyzed by the enzyme *carboxylase* is essentially a splitting off of *carbon dioxide (decarboxylation)* from *pyruvic acid* to form *acetaldehyde.*

$$
\begin{array}{c}
\overline{\text{COO}}\,\text{H} \\
| \\
\text{C}=\text{O} \\
| \\
\text{CH}_3
\end{array}
\quad \xrightleftharpoons{\text{Carboxylase}} \quad
\text{CO}_2 +
\begin{array}{c}
\text{H} \\
| \\
\text{C}=\text{O} \\
| \\
\text{CH}_3
\end{array}
$$

Pyruvic acid   Acetaldehyde

The enzyme is a conjugated protein consisting of a specific protein moiety (apoenzyme) and the coenzyme *cocarboxylase* (p. 177).

8b. *Acetaldehyde to ethyl alcohol.* Acetaldehyde is then reduced by *DPNH* in the presence of the enzyme *alcohol dehydrogenase* to *ethyl alcohol*

$$
\begin{array}{c}
\text{H} \\
| \\
\text{C}=\text{O} + \text{DPNH} + \text{H}^+ \\
| \\
\text{CH}_3
\end{array}
\quad \xrightleftharpoons[\text{dehydrogenase}]{\text{Alcohol}} \quad
\begin{array}{c}
\text{H} \\
| \\
\text{H}\text{C}-\text{OH} + \text{DPN}^+ \\
| \\
\text{CH}_3
\end{array}
$$

Acetaldehyde   Ethyl alcohol

The overall results of anaerobic respiration in animal cells such as muscle when oxygen is limiting is the splitting of glucose into two molecules of lactic acid with the release of energy.

Glucose $\longrightarrow$ 2 Lactic acid + Energy

In plant cells and microorganisms under anaerobic conditions, glucose is split to form two molecules of ethyl alcohol and two molecules of carbon dioxide with the release of energy.

Glucose $\longrightarrow$ 2 Ethyl alcohol + 2CO$_2$ + Energy

In both instances, the energy released is captured in part as ATP in only two of the dozen steps constituting anaerobic respiration. The remainder of the energy liberated appears as heat.

The detailed route of anaerobic respiration in animals and plants is summarized in Figure 8-4. A metabolic pathway is comparable to a factory mass production line. Each enzymatic

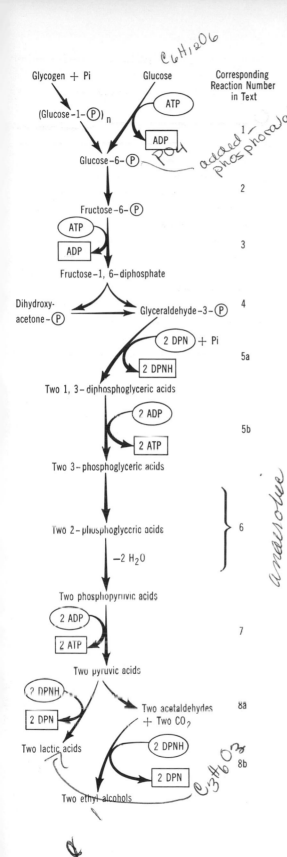

	Corresponding Reaction Number in Text
Glycogen + Pi Glucose	
(Glucose-1-P)$_n$ ATP → ADP	1
Glucose-6-P	
Fructose-6-P	2
ATP → ADP	3
Fructose-1, 6-diphosphate	
Dihydroxy-acetone-P Glyceraldehyde-3-P	4
2 DPN + Pi → 2 DPNH	5a
Two 1, 3-diphosphoglyceric acids	
? ADP → 2 ATP	5b
Two 3-phosphoglyceric acids	
Two 2-phosphoglyceric acids	6
−2 H_2O	
Two phosphopyruvic acids	
2 ADP → 2 ATP	7
Two pyruvic acids	
? DPNH → 2 DPN Two acetaldehydes + Two CO_2	8a
Two lactic acids 2 DPNH → 2 DPN	8b
Two ethyl alcohols	

Handwritten annotations: $C_6H_{12}O_6$; added 1-phosphorylation; PO_4; anaerobic; $C_3H_6O_3$

reaction in a metabolic pathway (like each step in a factory production line) performs a specific operation on the substrate. In both the cell and the factory the sequence of events must be unbroken in order to complete the process. If one of the enzymes is poisoned or missing (or if one of the machines in the factory breaks down), the entire production line may be brought to a standstill with serious effects.

It should be noted that the product of any one of the enzymatic reactions is not as a rule exclusively used for the succeeding reaction only. Usually several different reactions compete for the same intermediate, thus constituting the different branches and connecting links between various metabolic pathways. For example, as we shall soon see, glucose-6-phosphate which is the first intermediate in our sequence of glucose respiration is also a key intermediate in glucose metabolism by way of the pentose oxidative pathway.

Another aspect that bears emphasizing is the fact that at least nine of the dozen or so enzymes which participate in the pathway are metalloproteins in that they require a specific metal constituent for enzyme activity. The metal ions include magnesium, zinc, manganese, potassium, and iron.

AEROBIC RESPIRATION – FUNDAMENTAL FEATURES. The aerobic respiratory pathway consists of a succession of enzymatic reactions in which the principal products of anaerobic respiration are ultimately oxidized to yield energy, water, and carbon dioxide. Although oxygen is a reactant in only the final step of the aerobic respiratory pathway, it is an indispensable reaction and the pathway would soon cease to function if oxygen were withheld.

For convenience of description, aerobic respiration can be subdivided into two main sequences of reactions known as (1) the *citric-acid* or *Krebs cycle* and (2) the *terminal respiratory* or *cytochrome pathway*. The first consists

Figure 8-4. Summary of anaerobic respiration (the number assigned to each reaction is the same as in the text).

of a cyclic series of enzymatic reactions in which citric acid is one of several key intermediates. The British biochemist and Nobel Prize winner Hans Krebs, whose name is frequently associated with the cycle, was responsible for a number of the major contributions to our knowledge of the process. The *terminal* respiratory pathway in which several cytochromes (p. 188), participate involves the stepwise transfer of hydrogens or electrons to oxygen from certain specific products of the citric-acid cycle, namely, DPNH (and TPNH) and succinic acid, to form water. The formation of carbon dioxide in aerobic respiration occurs during the citric-acid cycle sequence of events, whereas the formation of most of the ATP produced in respiration takes place in the terminal respiratory sequence. Starting with glucose as the substrate the overall respiratory pathway consisting of anaerobic respiration and aerobic respiration is diagrammed in Figure 8-5.

The fundamental biochemical changes oc-

curing in the citric-acid cycle using pyruvic acid as the starting material can be summarized in the somewhat simplified version which follows:

1. *Pyruvic acid is oxidized* (removal of two hydrogens) and decarboxylated (removal of carbon dioxide) to form an *"active"* two-carbon *acetic-acid derivative* (acetyl-coenzyme A).

2. The above *two-carbon derivative* is enzymatically combined with a particular four-carbon organic acid called *oxaloacetic acid* to form a larger and more complex organic molecule *citric acid*. The latter is then rearranged (via *aconitic acid*) to its isomer, *isocitric acid*.

3. *Isocitric acid* (and its intermediate breakdown products) subsequently undergo a series of enzymatic reactions in which the coenzymes *DPN* and *TPN* receive the hydrogens or electrons removed and *carbon dioxide* is liberated. The other organic acids which appear as direct intermediates during the course of oxidation and decarboxylation in the citric-acid cycle are *ketoglutaric acid, succinic acid, fumaric acid,*

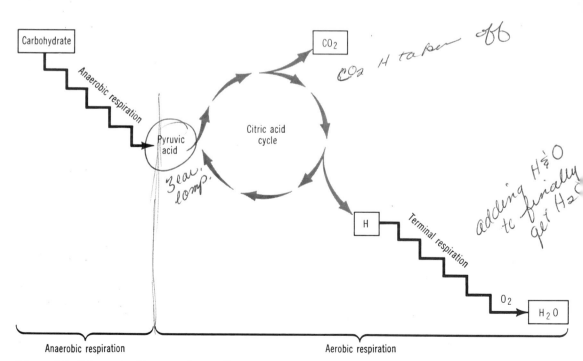

Figure 8-5. Schematic diagram of overall respiratory pathway consisting of anaerobic respiration and aerobic respiration.

malic acid, and *oxaloacetic acid* in that order.

4. The resulting *oxaloacetic acid* can now be used to condense again with another *"active" acetic-acid derivative,* thus repeating the cycle.

The citric-acid cycle, therefore, by virtue of its cyclic chain of enzymatic reactions, effects the breakdown of pyruvic acid to carbon dioxide and hydrogens or electrons. The hydrogens or electrons which have been made available through the action of the citric acid cycle first appear in the form of DPNH, TPNH, and succinic acid, and are eventually transferred to molecular oxygen by the enzymatic steps of the terminal respiratory pathway. It is during the course of electron transfer through the terminal respiratory scheme that the major release of the energy of respiration and its maximal capture in the form of ATP take place. The terminal respiratory scheme also acts to make DPN and TPN available from DPNH and TPNH by oxidizing them from the reduced state so that they can be used over and over again to accept electrons.

Studies of aerobic respiration, especially with isolated enzymes, have also led to the discovery of a number of new coenzymes. These include the so-called *flavin nucleotides, coenzyme A, lipoic acid* and *coenzyme Q.* The flavin nucleotides consist of two related coenzymes *flavin adenine mononucleotide* (abbreviated as *FMN*) and *flavin adenine dinucleotide* (*FAD*) as shown in Figure 8-6. Both contain the vitamin *riboflavin* as part of their structures (Chapter 9). The flavin nucleotides not only

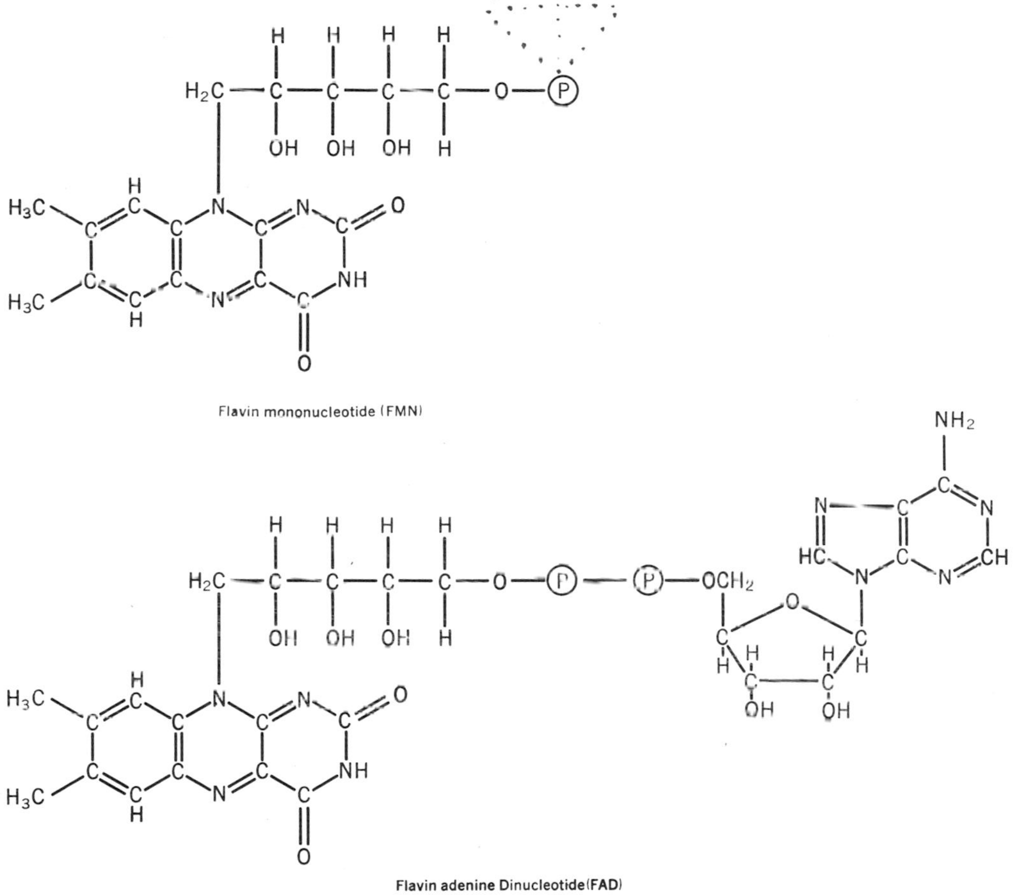

Figure 8-6. Flavin mononucleotide (FMN) and flavin adenine dinucleotide (FAD).

function in the terminal respiratory scheme but also act as coenzymes of certain other enzyme systems. As in DPN and TPN they serve as electron or hydrogen carriers undergoing alternate oxidation and reduction reactions in the course of receiving and donating electrons.

Coenzyme A (or *CoA*), which includes the vitamin *pantothenic acid* (Chapter 9) as part of its structure, plays an essential role in the activation of numerous substrates in preparation for certain subsequent enzymatic reactions of various metabolic pathways. The discovery of coenzyme A (shown in Figure 8-7) by the American biochemist Dr. Fritz Lipmann earned him the Nobel Prize in 1955.

Lipoic acid and coenzyme Q (shown below), like DPN, TPN, and the flavin nucleotides, are also electron carriers that become chemically reduced and oxidized as they receive and donate electrons in particular enzymatic reactions. DPN, TPN, and cocarboxylase or thiamine pyrophosphate, already discussed as coenzymes in anaerobic respiration, also

function in certain enzymatic steps of aerobic respiration.

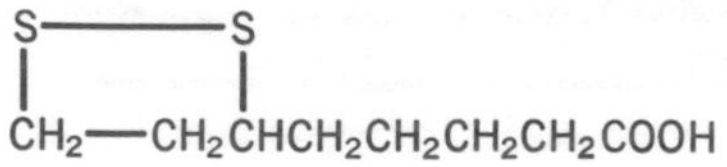

$$S\text{------}S$$
$$CH_2\text{---}CH_2CHCH_2CH_2CH_2CH_2COOH$$

Lipoic acid

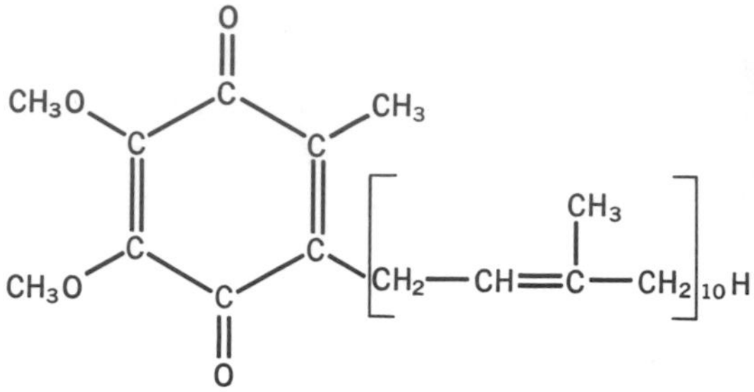

Coenzyme Q

AEROBIC RESPIRATION – DETAILED ENZYMATIC STEPS. *The Citric-Acid Cycle.* Pyruvic acid as an immediate and direct product of anerobic respiration is the initial substrate for the citric-acid cycle. The following detailed

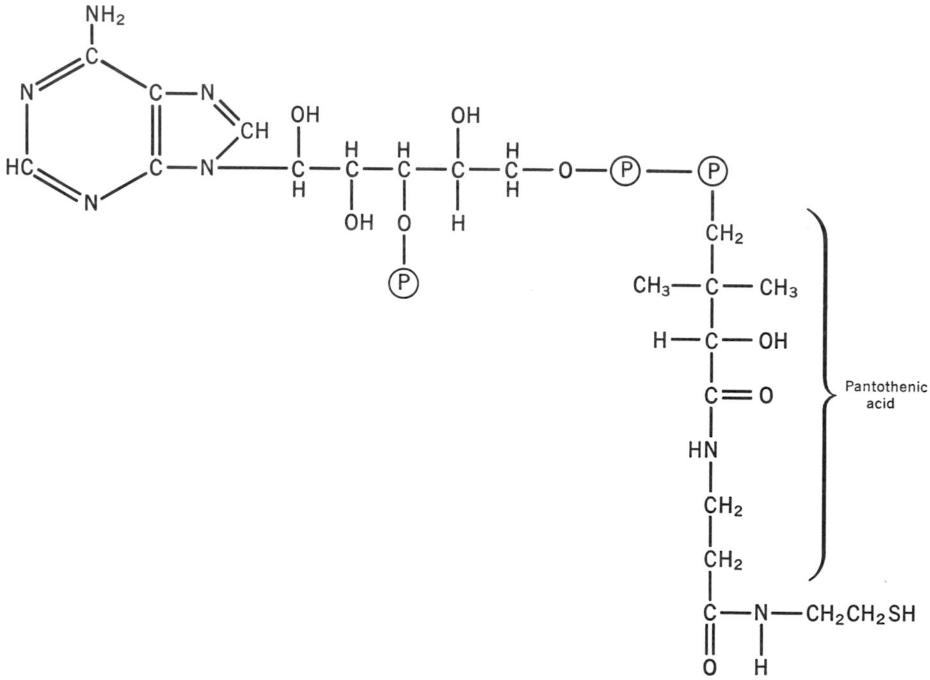

Figure 8-7. Coenzyme A.

enzymatic events constitute the cycle.

1. *Oxidative decarboxylation of pyruvic acid.* This is a series of several reactions involving the removal of carbon dioxide and two hydrogens from the pyruvic acid molecule to yield finally an "activated" form of acetic acid called *acetyl-coenzyme A* (or *acetyl-CoA*). At least two different enzymes and four different coenzymes (cocarboxylase, lipoic acid, coenzyme A, and DPN) participate. The reaction mechanisms are quite complex and not yet clearly established. The net effect of these reactions are summarized by the following overall equation:

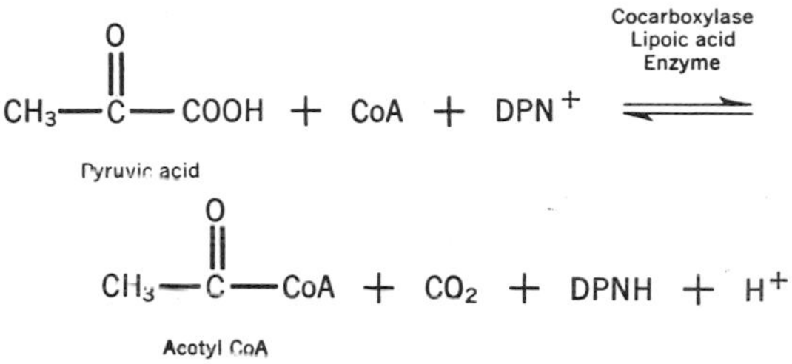

$$CH_3-\overset{\overset{\displaystyle O}{\|}}{C}-COOH + CoA + DPN^+ \underset{}{\overset{\text{Cocarboxylase Lipoic acid Enzyme}}{\rightleftharpoons}}$$

Pyruvic acid

$$CH_3-\overset{\overset{\displaystyle O}{\|}}{C}-CoA + CO_2 + DPNH + H^+$$

Acetyl CoA

Although both cocarboxylase and lipoic acid undergo chemical changes during the course of the reactions, they end up in their original states. For this reason they are not included in the above equation. The important products of the above reactions are *acetyl-CoA* and *DPNH*. Acetyl CoA will now be used in the next step of the citric-acid cycle, whereas the DPNH will eventually be oxidized to DPN largely by way of the terminal respiratory scheme to yield DPN, water, and ATP (see below).

Although pyruvic acid participates in several other biochemical reactions (e.g., reduction to lactic acid and conversion to glucose), in the presence of a suitable supply of oxygen in cells that normally carry on aerobic respiration it principally undergoes the above overall oxidative decarboxylation to form acetyl CoA, DPNH, and carbon dioxide.

2. *Condensation of acetyl-CoA and oxaloacetic acid.* The *acetyl-CoA* formed by the previous oxiative decarboxylation of pyruvate is now enzymatically condensed with *oxaloacetic acid* to form *citric acid* and *CoA*. The

reaction which is catalyzed by the so-called *condensing enzyme* involves attachment of the number 2 carbon of acetyl-CoA to the carbonyl group of the oxaloacetic acid as shown:

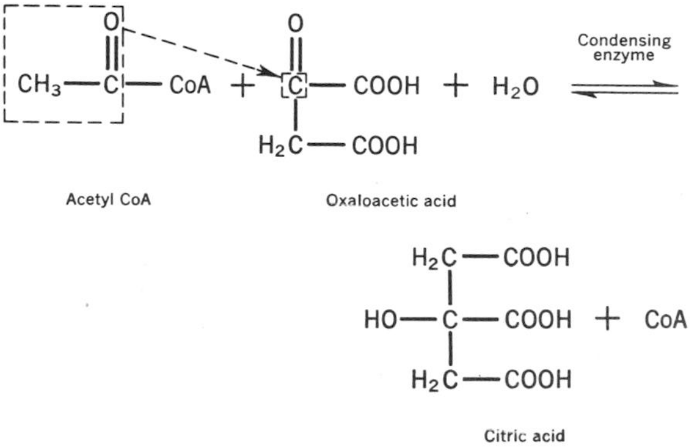

$$CH_3-\overset{\overset{\displaystyle O}{\|}}{C}-CoA + \overset{\overset{\displaystyle O}{\|}}{\underset{H_2C-COOH}{C}}-COOH + H_2O \underset{}{\overset{\text{Condensing enzyme}}{\rightleftharpoons}}$$

Acetyl CoA   Oxaloacetic acid

$$\begin{array}{c} H_2C-COOH \\ | \\ HO-C-COOH \\ | \\ H_2C-COOH \end{array} + CoA$$

Citric acid

3. *Conversion of citric acid to isocitric acid.* Citric acid is enzymatically transformed by way of *cis-aconitic acid* to isocitric acid. The reactions are reversible and center about the successive removal and addition of water from the original citric acid molecule to form first *cis*-aconitic acid and then isocitric acid. A single enzyme called *aconitase* is responsible for the interconversions as shown:

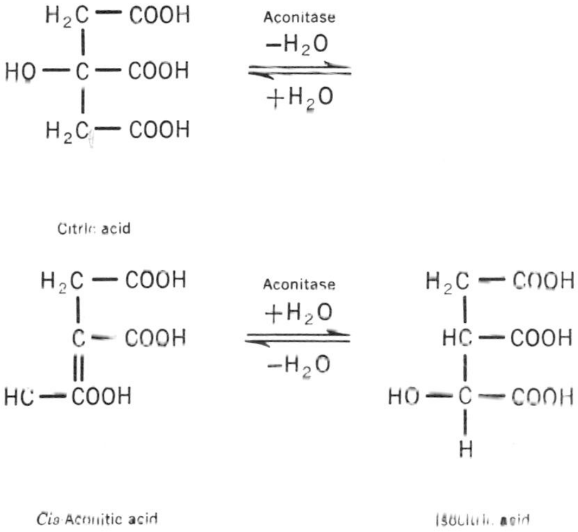

$$\begin{array}{c} H_2C-COOH \\ | \\ HO-C-COOH \\ | \\ H_2C-COOH \end{array} \underset{+H_2O}{\overset{\text{Aconitase} \\ -H_2O}{\rightleftharpoons}}$$

Citric acid

$$\begin{array}{c} H_2C-COOH \\ | \\ C-COOH \\ \| \\ HC-COOH \end{array} \underset{-H_2O}{\overset{\text{Aconitase} \\ +H_2O}{\rightleftharpoons}} \begin{array}{c} H_2C-COOH \\ | \\ HC-COOH \\ | \\ HO-C-COOH \\ | \\ H \end{array}$$

Cis Aconitic acid   Isocitric acid

4. *Oxidative decarboxylation of isocitric acid.* The *isocitric acid* now undergoes a two-step reaction involving the removal of two hydrogens followed by a decarboxylation or loss of carbon dioxide to form the biologically im-

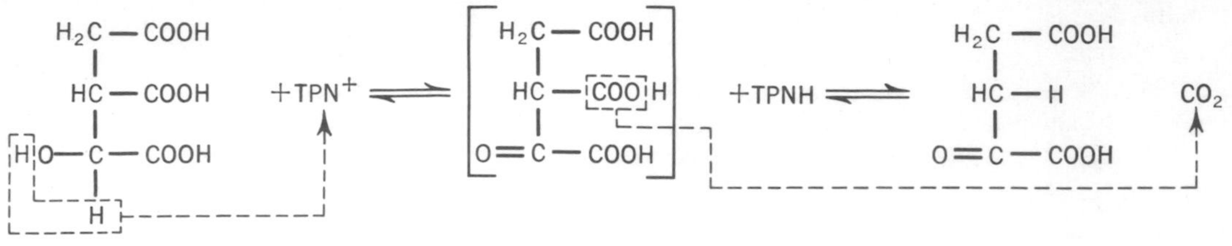

$$H_2C - COOH \quad\quad\quad\quad\quad [H_2C - COOH] \quad\quad\quad\quad\quad H_2C - COOH$$

Isocitric acid · Oxalosuccinic acid · α-Ketoglutaric acid

portant organic compound *alpha-ketoglutaric acid*. Both reactions are catalyzed by the same enzyme called the *isocitric enzyme*. In the first step two hydrogens are donated by isocitric acid to TPN which thus becomes reduced to *TPNH*. The intermediate product formed is believed to be *oxalosuccinic acid*, which is then decarboxylated to yield the important substance *alpha-ketoglutaric acid*. The overall steps are summarized in the equation above. Alpha-ketoglutaric acid is also a key intermediate in amino acid metabolism, since it is directly involved in the enzymatic formation of several amino acids (p. 199). Therefore, it represents a connecting point of carbohydrate metabolism with protein metabolism.

5. *Oxidative decarboxylation of alpha-ketoglutaric acid to succinic acid.* The conversion of *alpha-ketoglutaric acid* to *succinic acid* is catalyzed by two enzymes in a series of reactions that are analogous to those which mediate the oxidative decarboxylation of pyruvic acid already described (p. 185). The coenzymes cocarboxylase, lipoic acid, coenzyme A, and DPN are similarly involved. The net effect of these reactions are summarized by the following overall equation:

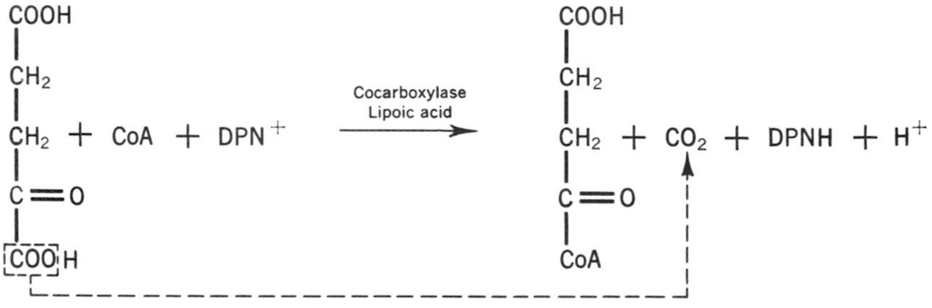

The *succinyl-CoA* which is formed above possesses sufficient energy in the chemical bond between the succinate and coenzyme A to form the high energy compound ATP from ADP and inorganic phosphate (Pi). This is accomplished by means of two additional enzymatic reactions. The overall reaction is:

$$\text{Succinyl-CoA} + \text{ADP} + \text{Pi} \xrightarrow{\text{2 enzymes}}$$
$$\text{Succinic acid} + \text{ATP} + \text{CoA}$$

6. *Oxidation of succinic acid to fumaric acid.* This step of the citric-acid cycle is concerned with the oxidation of *succinic acid* by the removal of two hydrogens to form *fumaric acid*. The reaction that is catalyzed by an enzyme called *succinic acid dehydrogenase* is shown:

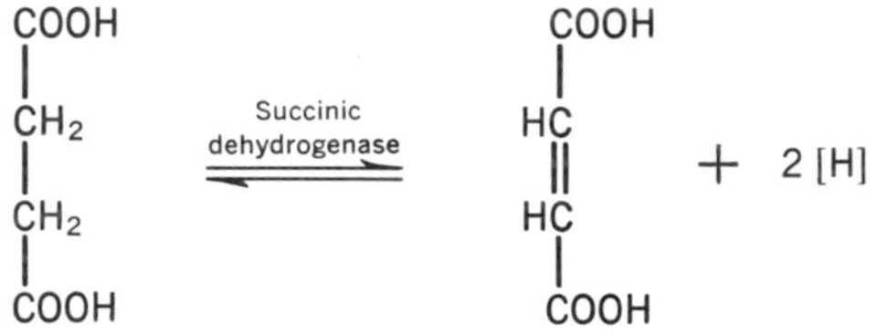

$$\text{COOH} \quad\quad \xrightarrow[\text{dehydrogenase}]{\text{Succinic}} \quad\quad \text{COOH} \quad + \quad 2[H]$$

Succinic acid · Fumaric acid

The hydrogens removed (indicated as 2[H]

$$\text{COOH} \quad\quad \xrightarrow[\text{Lipoic acid}]{\text{Cocarboxylase}} \quad\quad \text{COOH}$$
$$CH_2 + CoA + DPN^+ \longrightarrow CH_2 + CO_2 + DPNH + H^+$$

alpha–Ketoglutaric acid · Succinyl · CoA

in the above equation) are transferred, as we shall soon see, along the *terminal respiratory pathway* to unite finally with *oxygen* to form water and chemical energy in the form of *ATP*.

7. *Hydration of fumaric acid to malic acid.* The *fumaric acid* formed by the previous step in the citric-acid cycle now undergoes an enzymatic addition of *water* to form *malic acid* as shown. The specific enzyme concerned is called *fumarase*.

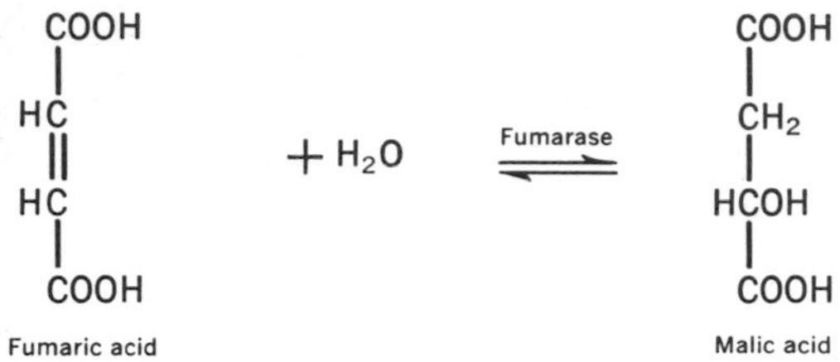

$$
\begin{array}{c}
\text{COOH} \\
|\\
\text{HC} \\
\|\\
\text{HC} \\
|\\
\text{COOH} \\
\text{Fumaric acid}
\end{array}
\quad + H_2O \quad \underset{}{\overset{\text{Fumarase}}{\rightleftarrows}} \quad
\begin{array}{c}
\text{COOH} \\
|\\
\text{CH}_2 \\
|\\
\text{HCOH} \\
|\\
\text{COOH} \\
\text{Malic acid}
\end{array}
$$

8. *Oxidation of malic acid to oxaloacetic acid.* This is the final step by which oxaloacetate is regenerated thus completing the citric-acid or Krebs cycle. It involves the transfer of two hydrogens from *malic acid* to *DPN* to produce *oxaloacetic acid* and *DPNH*, a reaction that is catalyzed by the enzyme *malic dehydrogenase*.

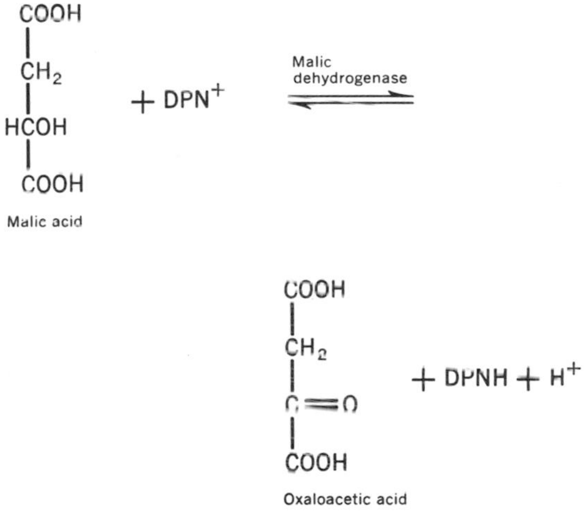

$$
\begin{array}{c}
\text{COOH} \\
|\\
\text{CH}_2 \\
|\\
\text{HCOH} \\
|\\
\text{COOH} \\
\text{Malic acid}
\end{array}
\quad + DPN^+ \quad \underset{}{\overset{\text{Malic dehydrogenase}}{\longrightarrow}}
$$

$$
\begin{array}{c}
\text{COOH} \\
|\\
\text{CH}_2 \\
|\\
\text{C}=O \\
|\\
\text{COOH} \\
\text{Oxaloacetic acid}
\end{array}
\quad + DPNH + H^+
$$

The citric-acid or Krebs cycle consisting of the above reactions and their intermediates is outlined in Figure 8-8.

The citric-acid cycle can be pictured as operating in a continuous manner. For each complete turn of the cycle, commencing with the oxidative decarboxylation of pyruvate to an "active" acetate and its condensation with oxaloacetate, only oxalocetate remains. The starting acetate molecule is thus broken down completely into carbon dioxide and hydrogens with each circuit of the cyclic pathway, whereas the oxaloacetate in effect is regenerated to be used over and over again for the subsequent degradation of other acetate molecules. A small amount of oxaloacetic acid, therefore, functions in the respiration of large quantities of pyruvic acid.

The Terminal Respiratory Pathway. The final stages of aerobic respiration deal with the enzymatic stepwise transfer to molecular oxygen of the electrons or hydrogens produced in the previous stages of respiration. These hydrogens or electrons are present as part of the structure of DPNH, TPNH, and succinic acid. In the anaerobic respiratory pathway, DPNH is formed in the oxidation of the 3-phosphate-glyceraldehyde (p. 179). In the aerobic respiratory scheme, it is produced during the oxidative decarboxylation of pyruvic and α-ketoglutaric acids (p. 186) and in the oxidation of malic acid. TPNH is formed in the oxidation of isocitric acid, whereas succinic acid makes available two hydrogens per molecule during its oxidation to fumaric acid.

The passage of electrons from DPNH, succinate, and probably TPNH to molecular oxygen proceeds by several enzymatic reactions of the terminal respiratory pathway through a regular sequence of different cofactors. The electrons are transferred first from DPNH to the flavin coenzyme FAD (p. 183), reducing it to $FADH_2$, then to coenzyme Q converting it to the reduced form, and finally on to a sequence of several different cytochromes (p. 189). More specifically, from reduced coenzyme Q the electrons pass successively to cytochrome b, cytochrome c_1, cytochrome c, cytochrome a, and cytochrome a_3 in that order before finally combining with molecular oxygen to form water. Each of the cytochromes, in accepting electrons that pass through the terminal respiratory chain, experiences a reduction of its heme iron from the ferric (Fe^{3+}) to the ferrous (Fe^{2+}) state, and a subsequent reoxidation back to the ferric (Fe^{3+}) state as the electrons move on to the next component. The transfer of electrons from the final cytochrome component, namely cytochrome a_3, to molecular oxygen represents the last step in the terminal respiratory chain and results in the formation of water. The sequence of components of the terminal respiratory chain from DPNH to molecular oxygen is shown in Figure 8-9.

The portion of the respiratory chain that extends from DPNH or succinate to cytochrome *c* is designated as *cytochrome c reductase*. The remainder of the chain extending from cytochrome *c* to molecular oxygen is called *cytochrome oxidase* and contains the metal copper. New evidence is beginning to accumulate sug-

gesting that there are very likely still other components in the terminal respiratory chain, including possibly the fat soluble vitamins E and K.

The electrons or hydrogens removed from succinic acid by its oxidation to fumaric acid in the citric acid cycle are transported to oxygen along a separate but similar respiratory chain. The means by which the electrons of TPNH are ultimately transferred to molecular oxygen probably occurs by way of DPNH (and the terminal respiratory pathway) although this is still not entirely clear.

THE TERMINAL RESPIRATORY PATHWAY AND ATP FORMATION. An important feature of the terminal respiratory chain is its intimate association in mitochondria with a system for making ATP from ADP and inorganic phosphate. The process by which ATP is formed using the en-

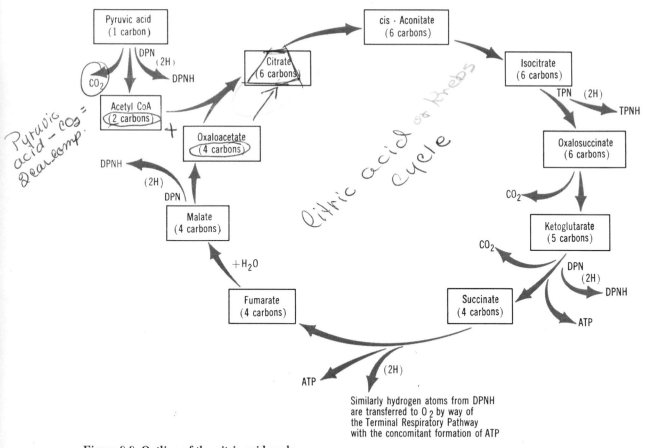

Figure 8-8. Outline of the citric-acid cycle.

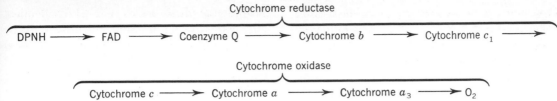

Figure 8-9. Sequence of components of the terminal respiratory chain extending from DPNH to O_2.

ergy liberated during the passage of electrons through the terminal respiratory chain is known as *oxidative phosphorylation*. It is the principal means for capturing an appreciable portion of the energy liberated during respiration. For every molecule of DPNH which is oxidized by oxygen via the terminal respiratory chain, three molecules of ATP will be formed from ADP and Pi. Two of the ATP molecules are produced during the passage of electrons from DPNH to cytochrome c, whereas the third is formed during the transport of electrons from cytochrome c to molecular oxygen as shown:

aerobic pathways compare with each other in this respect? If glucose as the typical substrate of respiration is completely burned or oxidized in a furnace to carbon dioxide and water $(C_6H_{12}O_6 + O_2 \rightarrow 6\ CO_2 + 6H_2O)$, 686,000 calories per mole (180g glucose) are liberated almost entirely in the form of heat. Within the living cell the successive combination of the anaerobic and aerobic respiratory pathways accomplishes the same complete combustion of glucose to carbon dioxide and water with the identical liberation of total energy, except that a major portion of the energy released is

$$DPNH \longrightarrow FAD \longrightarrow Co\ Q \longrightarrow b \longrightarrow c_1 \longrightarrow c \longrightarrow a \longrightarrow a_3 \longrightarrow O_2$$
$$\underbrace{\qquad\qquad\qquad\qquad\qquad\qquad}_{2\ ATP} \qquad \underbrace{\qquad\qquad\qquad\qquad\qquad}_{ATP}$$

The same relationships are presumed to apply in the terminal respiration of TPNH.

In the terminal oxidation of succinic acid, two molecules of ATP instead of three are formed per molecule of succinic acid oxidized, one during the passage of electrons between succinate and cytochrome c and the other between cytochrome c and oxygen.

captured in an available chemical form as the bond energy of ATP, specifically in the chemical bond between the second and third phosphates.

Energetics of Anaerobic Respiration. The oxidation of glucose by anaerobic respiration results in the release of less than 10 per cent of the total chemical energy stored in the sugar

$$Succinic\ acid \longrightarrow FAD \longrightarrow Co\ Q \longrightarrow b \longrightarrow c_1 \longrightarrow c \longrightarrow a \longrightarrow a_3 \longrightarrow O_2$$
$$\underbrace{\qquad\qquad\qquad\qquad\qquad\qquad}_{1\ ATP} \qquad \underbrace{\qquad\qquad\qquad\qquad\qquad}_{1\ ATP}$$

ENERGETICS OF RESPIRATION. The primary role of respiration is to provide available energy for the various functions and activities of the cell. What is the efficiency of the respiratory process in effectively capturing the energy that is released? And how do the anaerobic and

molecule. Of the 686,000 calories per mole only 60,000 calories are liberated by the anaerobic respiratory pathway. What has happened to the 60,000 calories that were released in anaerobic respiration? We know that during the anaerobic respiration of a mole of glucose, four moles of ATP are produced from ADP and inorganic phosphate—a mole of ATP following the oxidation of each of the two moles of 3-phosphoglyceraldehyde (reaction 5*b*, p. 179) and another during the transphosphorylation of each of two moles of phosphophenolpyruvic acids (reaction 7, p. 180). Since the production of each mole of ATP from ADP and inorganic phosphate represents the incorporation of about 10,000 calories, a total of 40,000 of the 60,000 calories liberated by anaerobic respiration has been captured in a form useful to the cell. The remainder is lost as heat. Actually the *net yield of energy* in yeast is two ATP's instead of four (with a resultant efficiency of 33 per cent), since two ATP molecules are used to phosphorylate the sugar (glucose $\xrightarrow{\text{ATP}}$ glucose-6-℗ and fructose 1-℗ $\xrightarrow{\text{ATP}}$ fructose-1,6-di℗, reactions 1 and 3, pp. 177 and 178) in the early stages of anaerobic respiration.

The anaerobic respiration of muscle tissue is more efficient than that of yeast cells, because only one ATP instead of two is used for phosphorylation since glycogen is the substrate instead of glucose. You will recall that glycogen is first enzymatically split by phosphoric acid to yield glucose-1-phosphate and then enzymatically converted to glucose-6-phosphate without consuming any ATP. Thus the anaerobic respiration of muscle cells results in the net formation of three ATP's (i.e., $(30,000/60,000) \times 100 = 50$ per cent efficiency).

Energetics of Aerobic Respiration. Under aerobic conditions the main products of the anaerobic pathway, namely pyruvic acid and DPNH, are further metabolized by the aerobic respiratory pathway. The DPNH formed in the oxidation of 3-phosphoglyceraldehyde (reaction 5*a*, p. 179) of the anaerobic pathway will pass in its electrons or hydrogens to oxygen via the terminal respiratory chain to yield three more ATP's per mole of pyruvic acid formed. It is actually in the stepwise oxidation of the two moles of pyruvic acid (containing a total of 626,000 calories) by way of the citric-acid cycle and terminal respiratory chain that

the release of the major portion of chemical energy originally present in the glucose occurs.

In the citric-acid cycle itself, ATP is formed directly in only one of the steps—in the oxidative decarboxylation of α-ketoglutaric acid (reaction 5, p. 186). In several of the citric-acid steps, however, DPNH, TPNH, and succinic acid are also formed. The subsequent transport of electrons from these substances via the terminal respiratory chain to molecular oxygen concomitant with the release of energy coupled to phosphorylation gives rise to ATP. For each mole of DPNH or TPNH oxidized via the terminal respiratory chain, three moles of ATP are formed, whereas the corresponding oxidation of succinic acid results in two moles of ATP. Table 8-1 lists the ATP-yielding reactions of the aerobic respiratory sequence.

Thus in the aerobic respiratory pathway starting with the oxidation of pyruvic acid and proceeding successively through the citric-acid cycle and the terminal respiratory chain, a total of 36 moles of ATP are produced (15 for each of the two moles of pyruvic acid oxidized and 3 for each of the two moles of DPNH arising in the triose phosphate dehydrogenase reaction of the anaerobic pathway). This represents about 360,000 calories ($36 \times 10,000$ calories per mole of ATP) of the 626,000 calories originally present in the two moles of pyruvic acid and DPNH which arose from the anaerobic breakdown of a single mole of glucose. The efficiency of energy captured in the aerobic respiratory scheme is therefore nearly 60 per cent ($360,000/626,000 \times 100 = 58$ per cent). The overall capture of useful energy in the total process of yeast respiration (anaerobic and aerobic), for example, would be represented by the formation of 38 moles of ATP (a net of 2 moles of ATP contributed by the anaerobic respiratory pathway and 36 moles of ATP from the aerobic portion) corresponding to about 380,000 calories or an overall efficiency of about 55 per cent ($380,000/686,000 \times 100 = 55$ per cent). This is another way of saying that the cell is able to capture in useful form (as ATP) about 55 per cent of the total chemical energy stored in the glucose molecule.

It can be seen from the above values that in a yeast cell, for example, the aerobic pathway yields about 20 times more available energy (38 moles of ATP per mole of glucose) than the anaerobic pathway (2 moles of ATP). A yeast cell, therefore, must metabolize 20 times more glucose in the absence of oxygen to obtain the same amount of energy as provided by respiration in the presence of air. Since aerobic organisms by virtue of the aerobic respiratory process can extract considerably more useful energy from the same substrate for their life activities as compared to anaerobic organisms, they would appear to have a distinct survival advantage in the utilization of energy sources.

ROLE OF RESPIRATION. Respiration performs two important functions in the living cell. First, it converts organic compounds such as carbohydrates to intermediate products which can now be used as building blocks in the synthesis of other biologically important components of the cell such as lipids, proteins, nucleic acids, and other kinds of molecules.

Second, respiration also carries out the all-important role of liberating and making available the energy stored in the carbon-hydrogen bonds of carbohydrates and lipids (and even amino acids) for the life activities of the cell. This is accomplished by the formation and utilization of high-phosphate bond energy in the form of the ATP molecule.

It should be noted that ATP itself is present in relatively small concentrations in the cell at any given time. It is, therefore, not really a means for storing energy but rather a means for making energy immediately available for cell function. It is the immediate and direct energy source for the entire array of activities manifested by all living systems. The major energy storage substances in cells, however, are fats and carbohydrates; but in vertebrate muscle there is an additional energy storage compound called *creatine phosphate* which is discussed in Chapter 29.

UTILIZATION OF ATP. We are still uncertain as to the actual mechanisms by which the chemical energy of the terminal phosphate bond of

Table 8-1   ATP-Yielding Reactions of the Aerobic Respiratory Pathway

(1) Pyruvic acid $+$ DPN$^+$ $\longrightarrow$ acetyl-CoA $+$ DPNH $+$ H$^+$

$\qquad$ DPNH $+$ H$^+ + \frac{1}{2}O_2 \xrightarrow[\text{chain}]{\text{Terminal respiratory}}$ DPN$^+ +$ H$_2$O $+$ 3ATP

(2) Isocitric acid $+$ TPN$^+$ $\longrightarrow$ α-ketoglutaric acid $+$ CO$_2$ $+$ TPNH $+$ H$^+$

$\qquad$ TPNH $+$ H$^+ + \frac{1}{2}O_2 \xrightarrow[\text{chain}]{\text{Terminal respiratory}}$ TPN$^+ +$ H$_2$O $+$ 3ATP

(3) α-ketoglutarate $+$ DPN$^+$ $+$ ADP $+$ Pi $\longrightarrow$ succinic acid $+$ CO$_2$ $+$ DPNH $+$ H$^+$ $+$ 1ATP

$\qquad$ DPNH $+$ H$^+ + \frac{1}{2}O_2 \xrightarrow[\text{chain}]{\text{Terminal respiratory}}$ DPN$^+ +$ H$_2$O $+$ 3ATP

(4) Succinic acid $+ \frac{1}{2}O_2 \xrightarrow[\text{chain}]{\text{Terminal respiratory}}$ fumaric acid $+$ H$_2$O $+$ 2ATP

(5) Malic acid $+$ DPN$^+ \xrightarrow[\text{chain}]{\text{Terminal respiratory}}$ oxaloacetic acid $+$ DPNH $+$ H$^+$

$\qquad$ DPNH $+$ H$^+ + \frac{1}{2}O_2 \xrightarrow[\text{chain}]{\text{Terminal respiratory}}$ DPN$^+ +$ H$_2$O $+$ 3ATP

$\qquad\qquad\qquad$ Total $\qquad\qquad$ 15 ATP/ mole of pyruvic acid oxidized

ATP is transformed to mechanical (muscular contraction), light (bioluminescence of fireflies), osmotic (diffusion against a gradient as in kidney function) chemical (synthesis of proteins, nucleic acids, etc.), and other forms of energy manifested by living organisms.

The phenomenon of *bioluminescence*, for example, which is the emission of light by certain organisms such as the firefly, glow-worm, luminescent bacteria, sponges, crustaceans, and others is the result of an enzyme-catalyzed release of free energy. The general terms *luciferin* and *luciferase* are used to designate the substrate and enzyme respectively in bioluminescent systems, although these constituents as well as the reaction itself may differ considerably in different bioluminescent organisms. In the firefly where many of the biochemical details of the bioluminescent reaction have been worked out, the natural organic substance luciferin (in reduced state) reacts with ATP in the presence of the enzyme luciferase to form first a complex intermediate. Upon oxidation of the latter in presence of oxygen, light is emitted while oxidized luciferin, water, and two degraded products of ATP are produced.

By contrast, the biochemistry of bacterial luminescence is different resembling more the terminal respiratory chain described earlier. In some bioluminescent organisms, such as the firefly and certain marine organisms, the ability to emit light appears to attract the sexes in the mating process. In most other bioluminescent organisms its significance is not known. The overall relationships of respiration, ATP, and energy transformation in living systems are diagrammed in Figure 8-10.

EVOLUTION OF RESPIRATION. From the evolutionary viewpoint, anaerobic respiration is considered to be more ancient than aerobic respiration. This is supported by the fact that the anaerobic respiratory scheme in one form or another is present in virtually all organisms, whereas the aerobic pathway is less ubiquitous. The aerobic pathway is regarded as a relatively recent evolutionary acquisition that was established after the accumulation of appreciable quantities of molecular oxygen in the atmosphere as a result of photosynthesis.

With the gradual depletion of complex organic energy and carbon sources from the primeval seas by living systems during the early history of the earth, those organisms which evolved more efficient respiratory pathways for obtaining energy were probably more successful in the competitive survival for existence. The evolution of environmental conditions and biological mechanisms (e.g., the accumulation of molecular oxygen in the environment by photosynthesis, and the develop-

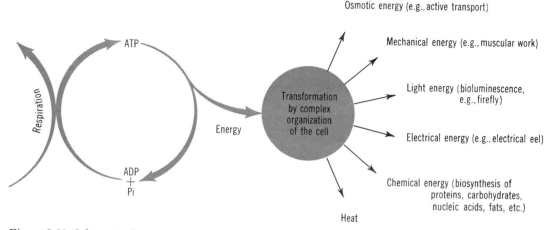

Figure 8-10. Schematic diagram of energy transformations in biological systems.

ment of the greater energy-yielding process of aerobic respiration) which permitted a more effective and complete liberation of energy from the remaining organic substances must have provided an added advantage in the competition for existence.

THE PENTOSE OXIDATIVE PATHWAY AND OTHER ALTERNATE ROUTES OF CARBOHYDRATE METABOLISM. The *pentose oxidative pathway* is also of major importance in carbohydrate metabolism and has only been elucidated in recent years. It is well distributed in nature, occurring in various tissues of animals and plants and in numerous microorganisms. Like the anaerobic pathway, the enzymes of the pentose oxidative pathway are also localized in the cytoplasm of the cell. The pathway itself is cyclic and consists of about a dozen enzymatic reactions, a few of which are shared with the anaerobic scheme.

The first reaction of the pentose oxidative pathway involves the phosphorylation of glucose by ATP in the presence of the enzyme hexokinase to form glucose-6-phosphate, a reaction that is identical with the first step in the anaerobic respiration of glucose (reaction 1, p. 177). The resulting glucose-6-phosphate undergoes an enzymatic dehydrogenation (glucose-6-phosphate dehydrogenase) to form 6-phosphogluconic acid.

fragments to form a number of different phosphorylated intermediates. These include the phosphate esters of seven-carbon (sedoheptulose-7-phosphate), four-carbon (erythrose-4-phosphate), three-carbon (glyceraldehyde-3-phosphate), and six-carbon (fructose-6-phosphate) sugar molecules.

The cyclic nature of the pentose oxidative pathway is best summarized by stating that for each complete turn of the wheel one carbon dioxide, two TPNH molecules, and several smaller sugar derivative molecules are produced starting with a single molecule of glucose. Thus for six rotations of the cycle, starting with six molecules of glucose, we end up in effect with five molecules of glucose or its equivalent, six molecules of carbon dioxide, and twelve molecules of TPNH. In essence, a complete breakdown of glucose to carbon dioxide and hydrogens (the latter in the form of TPNH) has occurred without the participation of the citric-acid cycle. A schematic presentation of the pentose oxidative pathway is shown in Figure 8-11.

In terms of energy yield, if we assume that TPNH is ultimately oxidized like DPNH by the terminal respiratory chain, then we should expect a yield of three ATP molecules for each TPNH molecule. This would make, therefore, a total of thirty-six ATP molecules formed in

$$\text{Glucose-6-} \textcircled{P} + \text{TPN}^+ \xrightleftharpoons[\hspace{1cm}]{\text{Glucose-6-} \textcircled{P} \text{ dehydrogenase}} \text{6-Phosphogluconic acid} + \text{TPNH} + \text{H}^+$$

This is followed by an oxidative decarboxylation to yield a pentose phosphate derivative, ribose-5-phosphate.

$$\text{6-Phosphogluconic acid} + \text{TPN}^+ \xrightleftharpoons[\hspace{1cm}]{}$$

$$\text{Ribose-5-} \textcircled{P} + \text{TPNH} + CO_2 + H^+$$

In both reactions, TPN acts as the electron or hydrogen acceptor becoming reduced to TPNH. The ribose-5-phosphate then experiences a successive series of other enzymatic steps involving isomerization, cleavage, and the transfer and rejoining of the resulting active

the total respiration of a glucose molecule by the pentose oxidative pathway, a value almost equal to that produced during aerobic respiration. Most of the evidence suggests that the TPNH formed in the pentose oxidative pathway is not necessarily consumed in the terminal respiratory chain but is actually used for the synthesis of fats and steroids. Of major importance also is the role of the pentose oxidative pathway in providing a source of pentose for nucleic-acid synthesis.

The anaerobic and aerobic respiratory pathways and the pentose oxidative route are apparently the principal pathways for glucose breakdown in most living systems. It should be noted, however, that a number of microorganisms display still other routes of carbohydrate metabolism involving certain unique enzymatic reactions and intermediates in addition to the above established principle pathways.

PHOTOSYNTHESIS

General Features

What is the source of the energy stored in the complex molecules of carbohydrates, fats, and proteins from which all animal cells and most organisms derive their energy to perform their biological work? The answer is *sunlight*. By possessing unique biochemical machinery in addition to the basic metabolic pathways contained by most other living forms, green plants are able to harness the energy of sunlight to convert carbon dioxide and water into carbohydrates (e.g., glucose) and certain other organic molecules. The process, called *photosynthesis*, consists of a series of physical and biochemical events which in green plants is ultimately accompanied by the release of molecular oxygen into the atmosphere.

Thus by the process of photosynthesis they are able in effect to push hydrogens or electrons in the opposite direction of the energy gradient, like pushing the water of the rapids upstream.

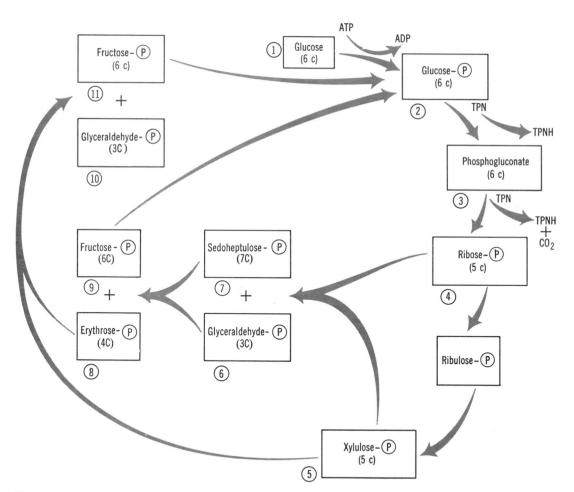

Figure 8-11. Schematic representation of pentose oxidative pathway.

Green plants trap the energy of sunlight and transform it into the stored chemical energy of the carbon-hydrogen bonds of carbohydrates starting with the lower energy-containing substances CO_2 and H_2O. A glucose molecule, for example, in a sense possesses solar energy—now in the form of chemical energy—within its structure. Photosynthesis therefore ultimately provides the necessary higher-energy carbon-hydrogen bonds for the respiration of all forms of plants and animals and nearly every kind of microorganism.

In its overall aspects, the conversion by the process of photosynthesis of carbon dioxide, the energy of sunlight, and water to the level of carbohydrates (e.g., glucose) is fundamentally the reverse of respiration, and is often written essentially as a reverse of the net process of aerobic respiration:

$$6CO_2 + 6H_2O + \text{Light energy} \xrightarrow{\text{Photosynthesis}} C_6H_{12}O_6 + 6O_2$$

The mechanisms and pathways by which this is attained in photosynthesis, however, are not a simple reversal of the respiratory processes but are routes and reactions that are in part unique to the photosynthetic process.

The important accomplishment during the last decade of demonstrating photosynthesis in a cell-free system of isolated chloroplasts has constituted a major breakthrough in this area. This together with studies of some of the individual enzymatic steps in the process as well as the use of radioactive tracer techniques have provided us with significant information of this all-important process.

From the preceding overall equation for photosynthesis, it is evident that two basic requirements must be met. First, there must be a source of energy. This is provided by sunlight which as we shall soon see is converted in part to ATP. Second, there must be a source of hydrogens or electrons which we speak of as *reducing power*. This is also provided by sunlight (and water molecules) to form TPNH, molecular oxygen being released as an end product. Photosynthesis is therefore essentially a process involving the net cleavage of water by the energy of sunlight and the stepwise utilization of its electrons or hydrogens (now raised to a higher energy level) for the transformation of carbon dioxide to organic compounds such as carbohydrates.

The Light and Dark Phases

The physiological evidence originally obtained in the early 1900's that photosynthesis consists of two successive series of events called the *light phase* followed by the non-light-requiring *dark phase* has been confirmed and extended by modern biochemical investigations. The absorption of light by chlorophyll in the chloroplasts is considered to be the primary photochemical act of photosynthesis. It has been shown to lead to the production of chemical energy in the form of ATP and reducing power as TPNH to constitute collectively the *light phase* of photosynthesis. In fact ATP and TPNH, which together drive the conversion by chloroplasts of carbon dioxide to carbohydrates, are known to be the first chemically identified products of photosynthesis in green plants. They cannot accumulate to any appreciable extent in the cell, being present only in catalytic quantities. They are promptly used by a series of enzymatic reactions taking place entirely in the dark for the assimilation of carbon dioxide to carbohydrates and its intermediates (and to fats, proteins, and other cellular constitutents) to constitute the *dark phase* of photosynthesis.

Actually the assimilation of carbon dioxide (or the dark phase) in both green plants and photosynthetic bacteria consists of enzymatic reactions that are not peculiar to photosynthesis. All the enzymes now known to participate in the conversion of carbon dioxide to carbohydrates have been found in a wide variety of organisms many of which are not photosynthetic. In its most fundamental aspects, therefore, photosynthesis can be regarded as the unique biological process for converting sunlight into the energy of ATP and the reducing power of TPNH for the synthesis of cellular substances. In effect the fundamental distinction between photosynthetic and nonphotosynthetic cells resides in the way in which they form ATP and reduced pyridine nucleotides. Photosynthetic cells can synthesize these compounds at the expense of light energy (and also by the usual metabolic reactions that occur in the dark such as in respiration), whereas nonphotosynthetic cells including animal tissues and most microorganisms cannot utilize light in this manner.

The detailed biochemical and physiological features of photosynthesis are described in Chapter 17.

LIPID METABOLISM

Fats and Fatty Acids

Our knowledge of lipid function and metabolism centers mostly about the fatty acids and the steroids. Fatty acids are present in the mammalian body largely in the form of triglycerides or fats (p. 150). The triglycerides themselves represent about 10 per cent of the body weight and are distributed in different amounts in all tissues. Within the cell itself, fats usually take the form of droplets in the cytoplasm.

The main role of fats is to serve as a reservoir or store of chemical energy. They are in a considerably more reduced chemical state than either carbohydrates or proteins, possessing significantly more carbon-hydrogen bonds and, therefore, more chemical energy than either of these two classes of biological substances. Fats also function in higher animals as a structural component of the living tissues. They serve as insulation against excessive loss of heat to the environment, as protection against mechanical injury, and apparently in certain metabolic roles (e.g., as components of enzyme systems) which are only now beginning to be elucidated.

Most of our biochemical information to date centers about the breakdown and synthesis of the fatty-acid components.

Fatty-Acid Breakdown

Fatty acids are metabolically degraded by way of a characteristic pathway of enzymatic reactions which result in the removal of two-carbon fragments in the form of acetyl-CoA units. The latter include the carbon in the carboxyl or acid group of the fatty acid. In the process, a new carboxyl group is formed at the cut end of the fatty-acid chain, which in turn, as a CoA derivative, undergoes the same kind of two-carbon cleavage.

The detailed enzymatic steps involve first the conversion of the fatty acid to an activated form, namely as the derivative of coenzyme A. The energy necessary for this conversion is provided by ATP in the following enzymatic reaction:

$$\text{Fatty acid} + \text{CoA} + \text{ATP} \rightleftharpoons$$
$$\text{Fatty acid-CoA} + \text{ADP} + \text{Pi}$$

Subsequent steps include the enzymatic transfer of two hydrogens from the fatty acid-CoA derivative to the flavin coenzyme FAD to form an unsaturated fatty acid-CoA and $FADH_2$ (fatty acid-CoA + FAD $\rightleftharpoons$ Unsaturated fatty acid-CoA + $FADH_2$) followed by three successive enzymatic reactions involving (1) hydration of the unsaturated or double bond of the fatty acid-CoA, (2) a dehydrogenation or removal of two hydrogens to DPN, and (3) a cleavage by another CoA molecule of acetyl-CoA from the CoA derivative which thus becomes shorter by two carbon atoms. The preceding reactions are repeated until the original fatty-acid molecule is completely broken down to individual molecules of acetyl-CoA.

The acetyl-CoA molecules obtained from fatty-acid oxidation and from carbohydrate respiration (p. 185) are identical and are, therefore, an important intermediate common to both processes. Acetyl-CoA is also a product of amino-acid breakdown and is thus a link joining carbohydrate metabolism, fat metabolism, and protein metabolism to one another. Fats, by being metabolized to acetyl-CoA, may enter the respiratory pathways and thus act as an important energy source. This involves first an enzymatic hydrolysis to its component fatty acids and glycerol, a subsequent conversion of the fatty acids to acetyl-CoA units as just outlined, and finally the degradation of the acetyl-CoA by way of the citric-acid cycle and the terminal respiratory scheme. In turn, carbohydrates (e.g., glucose) may ultimately be converted to fatty acids by first undergoing degradation via the respiratory pathway to acetyl-CoA, and then fatty-acid synthesis as described below.

Fatty-Acid Synthesis

Most organisms including higher animals such as man are capable of synthesizing nearly all their fatty acids from nonlipid substances. The building unit or precursor material of fatty acid is acetyl-CoA. Since carbohydrates and amino acids can be metabolically degraded to acetyl-CoA, they may clearly provide the precursors for the formation of fatty acids.

Fatty-acid degradation occurs largely in the mitochondria whereas fatty-acid biosynthesis takes place principally in the endoplasmic reticulum. Although fatty-acid synthesis essentially involves the joining together of acetyl-CoA units to form longer carbon-chain molecules with the liberation of coenzyme A, it does not proceed by a reverse of the reactions outlined for the metabolic breakdown of fatty acids. A number of different enzymes as well as ATP, TPNH, coenzyme A, the vitamin biotin, and vitamin B_{12} are necessary in the biosynthesis of fatty acids from acetyl-CoA. The requirement for TPNH, which in numerous tissues is provided primarily by the pentose oxidative pathway (p. 193) suggests a relationship of this pathway to fatty-acid synthesis.

Steroid Metabolism

The steroids and steroid-like substances include vitamin D, the sex hormones, the hormones secreted by the cortex of the adrenal glands (Chapter 23), and the substance cholesterol (p. 151). Cholesterol, which is contained in all animal tissues and in many plants is intimately involved in numerous aspects of lipid metabolism. Acetyl-CoA is the basic building block in the biosynthesis of cholesterol. Many of the enzymatic steps in the synthesis of cholesterol from acetyl-CoA have been studied and most if not all reside in the cytoplasm, notably in the endoplasmic reticulum. Cholesterol serves as a precursor of the steroid hormones and various acids found in the bile secretions of the liver. In certain pathological situations, cholesterol contributes significantly to the formation of gallstones in the gall bladder and related liver ducts and to arterial plaques in the walls of the arteries, a condition known as *hardening of the arteries* or *atherosclerosis* (Chapter 26).

Central Metabolic Role of Acetyl-CoA

In summary, the central role of acetyl-CoA is indicated by the fact that it is an important intermediate in several fundamental metabolic processes. As a product of carbohydrate metabolism, fat metabolism, and amino-acid metabolism, it can be utilized in a number of different ways. Acetyl-CoA may be completely broken down to carbon dioxide and water by means of the citric-acid cycle and terminal respiratory chain thus serving as an energy source. It is also a building unit in fatty-acid synthesis, carbohydrate synthesis, and sterol synthesis. The important function of acetyl-CoA in linking carbohydrate, lipid, and protein metabolism is diagrammed in Figure 8-12.

PROTEIN METABOLISM

Aside from fundamental considerations of unraveling the complexities of protein structure (Chapter 7), one of the most exciting and difficult problems in biology has been that of elucidating protein synthesis. Over the years, a good deal of knowledge has accumulated concerning the metabolism of the individual amino acids, in terms of breakdown, synthesis, interconversions, and relationships to carbohydrate and lipid metabolism at both the enzymatic and intact-organism levels. We have also acquired extensive information about the enzymatic breakdown of proteins. But it is only recently that a major breakthrough has been achieved in the area of protein synthesis at the level of cell-free enzyme systems. The long-sought goal of protein synthesis by cell-free extracts has finally been attained. It has already yielded important information with regard to some of the steps and mechanisms of the process (Chapter 11).

Amino-Acid Metabolism

Nearly all plants and many microorganisms are capable of synthesizing all the twenty or so naturally occurring amino acids (Table 7-1) starting with inorganic nitrogen (generally as nitrate or ammonia) and particular organic acids which arise as intermediates in carbohydrate and fat metabolism. The transformation of nitrate to the amino level of amino acids as well as the cyclic nature of interconversions of various forms of nitrogen in the biological world are discussed under the heading "Nitrogen Cycle" in the next chapter.

Many higher animals including man, however, can synthesize only some of the amino acids. Those amino acids which they are unable to synthesize in sufficient quantities and

which are needed for the normal functioning of the animal must, therefore, be provided in the diet. For this reason they are known as *essential amino acids*. Man, for example, requires ten of the twenty or so naturally occurring amino acids in his diet, because he is unable to synthesize them in sufficient quantities to meet his needs. Some of the more important enzymes concerned with the metabolism of amino acids are:

1. *Glutamic dehydrogenase.* This enzyme catalyzes the reversible incorporation of ammonia (as the ammonium ion, NH_4^+) into *α-ketoglutaric acid* to form the important amino acid called *glutamic acid*. The reaction in which DPNH or TPNH participates, depending on the particular enzyme, is as follows:

$$NH_4^+ + \alpha\text{-ketoglutaric acid} + DPNH \text{ (or TPNH)}$$

$$+ H^+ \underset{}{\overset{\text{Glutamic}}{\underset{\text{dehythogenase}}{\rightleftharpoons}}} \text{Glutamic acid} + DPN^+ \text{ (or } TPN^+)$$

In plants this enzymatic reaction is the principal means by which inorganic nitrogen in the form of ammonia is converted to the organic state as the amino acid glutamic acid. This system also seems to serve in the same capacity in animals but only to a very limited extent.

Of great importance to many higher animals

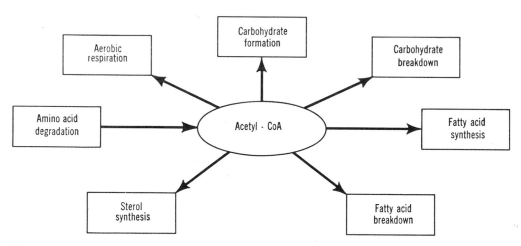

Figure 8-12. Central role of acetyl-coenzyme A in linking carbohydrate, lipid, and protein metabolism.

is the fact that glutamic dehydrogenase also functions in part in the removal of the highly toxic ammonia. The latter is released in the course of amino-acid breakdown and is for the most part rapidly converted by a series of enzymatic steps to urea (Chapter 28) in which form it is usually excreted by many higher animals. The action of glutamic dehydrogenase is also an important link between carbohydrate and protein metabolism, since it converts α-ketoglutaric acid, an intermediate of the citric-acid cycle, to the key amino acid glutamic acid. The latter is not only incorporated as an amino-acid component of many proteins but also plays a major role in the formation of other amino acids as indicated below.

2. *Transaminases.* These enzymes catalyze the reversible transfer of an amino group from amino acids to certain organic acids (called *keto acids*) possessing a keto or carbonyl group. In this manner, it accounts for the interconversion of an amino acid to the corresponding keto acid and a keto acid to its corresponding amino acid as shown in the following generalized equation:

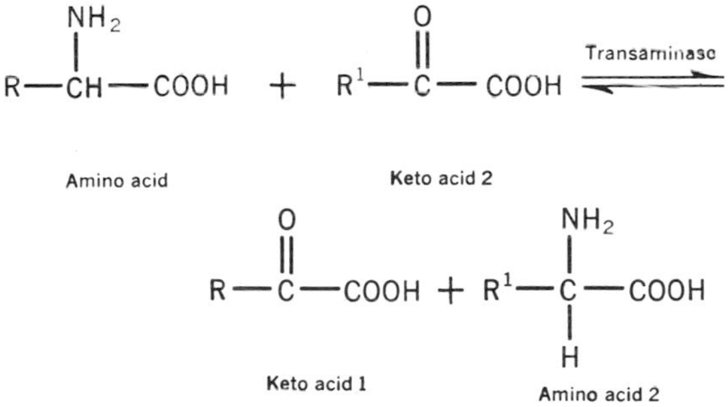

$$\underset{\text{Amino acid}}{R-\underset{\underset{NH_2}{|}}{CH}-COOH} + \underset{\text{Keto acid 2}}{R^1-\underset{\underset{O}{\parallel}}{C}-COOH} \underset{\text{Transaminase}}{\rightleftharpoons}$$

$$\underset{\text{Keto acid 1}}{R-\underset{\underset{O}{\parallel}}{C}-COOH} + \underset{\text{Amino acid 2}}{R^1-\underset{\underset{H}{|}}{\overset{\overset{NH_2}{|}}{C}}-COOH}$$

Nearly all of the naturally occurring amino acids except two have been shown to participate in the transaminase reaction. Numerous transaminases are found in animals, plants, and microorganisms. Glutamic acid or its corresponding keto acid form, α-ketoglutaric acid (an intermediate in the Krebs cycle, p. 186), is usually one of the specific reactants that donates or accepts amino groups respectively. For example, the specific enzyme, glutamic acid-pyruvic acid transaminase, reversibly catalyzes the following reaction:

l- Glutamic acid $+$ Pyruvate $\rightleftharpoons$
α- Ketoglutaric acid $+$ Alanine

Oxaloacetic acid, another of the intermediates of carbohydrate metabolism in the Krebs cycle, is also an important reactant for a number of the transaminases becoming reversibly transformed to its corresponding amino acid called *aspartic acid.* Thus by means of transaminase reactions pyruvic acid and oxaloacetic acid also serve as links between carbohydrate and protein metabolism.

Each of the transaminases requires the specific coenzyme *pyridoxal phosphate* which is a phosphorylated derivative of one of the water-soluble vitamins, pyridoxine or vitamin B_6 (Chapter 9). The coenzyme functions as carrier,

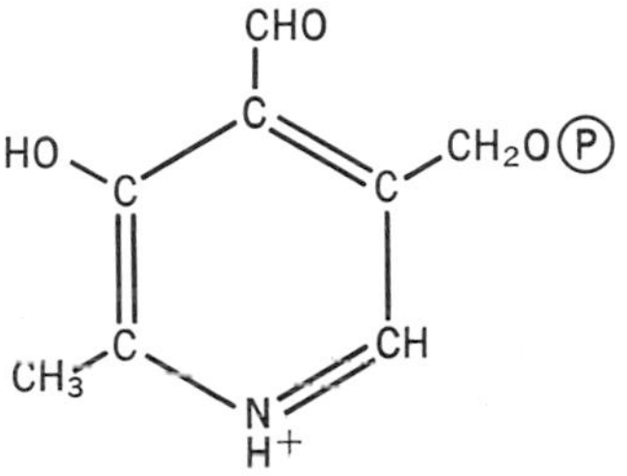

Pyridoxal phosphate

accepting the amino group from amino acid and donating it to keto acid.

3. *Amino acid oxidases, deaminases, and decarboxylases.* These are specific enzymes which catalyze the oxidation, deamination (removal of the amino group), and decarboxylation respectively of different amino acids. Specific amino-acid *oxidases* mediate the oxidation of particular amino acids to produce the corresponding keto acid and free ammonia:

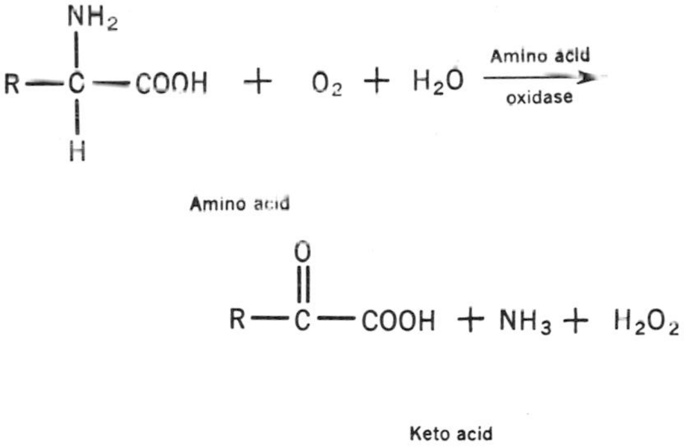

$$\underset{\text{Amino acid}}{R-\underset{\underset{H}{|}}{\overset{\overset{NH_2}{|}}{C}}-COOH} + O_2 + H_2O \underset{\text{oxidase}}{\overset{\text{Amino acid}}{\longrightarrow}}$$

$$\underset{\text{Keto acid}}{R-\underset{\underset{O}{\parallel}}{C}-COOH} + NH_3 + H_2O_2$$

Deaminases catalyze the deamination or removal of the amino group from specific amino acids converting them to the corresponding hydroxy acids as shown:

$$R - \underset{\underset{H}{|}}{\overset{\overset{NH_2}{|}}{C}} - COOH + H_2O \; \underset{\longleftarrow}{\overset{Deaminase}{\longrightarrow}}$$

Amino
acid

$$R - \underset{\underset{H}{|}}{\overset{\overset{OH}{|}}{C}} - COOH + NH_3$$

Hydroxy
acid

Decarboxylases catalyze the decarboxylation of amino acids to the corresponding amines:

$$R - \underset{\underset{H}{|}}{\overset{\overset{NH_2}{|}}{C}} - COOH \; \underset{\longleftarrow}{\overset{Decarboxylases}{\longrightarrow}} \; R - \underset{\underset{H}{|}}{\overset{\overset{NH_2}{|}}{C}} - H + CO_2$$

Pyridoxal phosphate is also a coenzyme for this reaction. The foul odors of putrefaction are largely due to the accumulation of amines as a result of the action of bacterial decarboxylases on amino acids.

In higher animals such as mammals, excess quantities of amino acids are rapidly metabolized—for the most part, by the various enzymatic reactions already indicated. Most of the excess nitrogen is ultimately converted into urea and excreted as such.

In summary, amino acids experience the following major metabolic fates:
1. Synthesis to protein, which is discussed in Chapter 11.
2. Transamination, oxidation, deamination, and decarboxylation reactions, whereby they are metabolized via characteristic but often interrelated biochemical pathways specific for each amino acid.
3. Conversion to other nitrogen-containing compounds, such as certain vitamins.

Protein Synthesis

Our recent success in obtaining cell-free preparations from animals, plants, and microorganisms capable of synthesizing proteins from amino acids has revealed the intricate involvement of nucleic acids and, therefore, the genetic relationships in this process. For this reason, the details and significance of protein synthesis are more appropriately discussed in Chapter 11 on genetics.

Protein Degradation

The enzymatic breakdown of proteins to their component amino acids consists essentially of hydrolysis reactions. The various enzymes responsible are collectively called *peptidases* and they are discussed more fully in Chapter 24 on digestion.

NUCLEIC-ACID METABOLISM

The nucleic acids in recent years have become the focus of attention for many experimental biologists. We have grown increasingly aware of the central role of nucleic acids as the carriers of genetic information and the master control substances of the cell which predetermine the composition, activity, and internal destiny of protoplasm.

Although the genetic and metabolic functions of nucleic acids in a sense are inseparable, it seems appropriate in a general chapter on cell metabolism to point out the salient features of our knowledge of the biosynthesis and breakdown of the nucleic acids. The fundamental chemistry of these substances was presented earlier (Chapter 7), and their central role in heredity and protein synthesis is described in Chapter 11 on genetics.

Biosynthesis of Nucleic Acids

The purine and pyrimidine bases of the nucleic acids for both RNA and DNA are synthesized by most animals, plants, and microorganisms from simpler molecules. They are not required, therefore in the diet or nutrient media of these organisms. By means of the radioactive tracer technique, the origin of the different carbon and nitrogen atoms composing the purine structure has been established. Thus we know that particular carbon and nitrogen atoms of the purine structure are derived from the carbon and nitrogen atoms, respectively, of carbon dioxide and other compounds including certain amino acids such as glycine, aspartic acid, and so forth. Enzymatic studies have elucidated many of the intermediates and reaction steps involved.

The early stages of pyrimidine biosynthesis involve the enzymatic formation of a particular addition product of aspartic acid and its stepwise conversion to a ring structure. This is followed by its transformation to a ribose nucleotide stage and subsequent reactions to form the different purine nucleotides.

Our current knowledge of nucleic-acid synthesis, like many other areas of biochemistry, has experienced great advances in the last few years. The outstanding accomplishment of the American Nobel Prize winner Dr. Arthur Kornberg and his colleagues in synthesizing a DNA-like material by means of a highly purified enzyme system constitutes a major breakdown in our understanding of DNA formation. Kornberg and his colleagues demonstrated that DNA can be enzymatically synthesized from the deoxyribonucleotide triphosphates of the four purine and pyrimidine bases—adenine, guanine, cytosine, and thymine (Figure 8-13).

Added DNA is required as a primer in this enzymatic synthesis and apparently serves as an anchoring point and template for the synthesis of new DNA.

RNA-like substances also have been synthesized by means of another specific enzyme system in somewhat analogous reactions. A central feature of the RNA-synthesizing system is the requirement of the reaction mixture for DNA indicative of the role of DNA as a template in the formation of RNA. The important genetic implications of the DNA- and RNA-synthesizing systems, especially in protein synthesis, are discussed in Chapter 11.

Breakdown of Nucleic Acids

Nucleic acids can be broken down to their component parts through the action of several enzymes known as nucleases. This is probably best illustrated by their digestive breakdown in the intestinal tract described in Chapter 24 on digestion. *Ribonuclease* specifically hydrolyzes ribonucleic acids, whereas *deoxyribonuclease* hydrolyzes only deoxyribonucleic acids. The liberated polynucleotides and nucleotides may then be further hydrolyzed to yield inorganic phosphate and the base-sugar residue called a *nucleoside*. The latter is probably subsequently hydrolyzed to form the free base and sugar. The sugar may eventually be completely metabolized to carbon dioxide and water by way of one or more carbohydrate respiratory pathways indicated previously in this chapter.

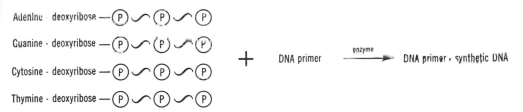

Figure 8-13. Chemical formulation of the enzymatic synthesis of DNA starting with the deoxyribonucleotide triphosphates of the four purine and pyrimidine bases and primer DNA as an anchoring point and template for the new DNA.

The purine and pyrimidine bases undergo different fates. In higher animals we know that purines are not completely broken down but are excreted largely as ring structures, with only small amounts appearing as urea or ammonia. In the lower forms, however, the purines may be degraded mostly to urea, ammonia, and carbon dioxide. Pyrimidines in higher animals on the other hand are converted mainly to certain amino acids which may be excreted as such or used in other metabolic pathways.

FUNDAMENTAL ASPECTS OF METABOLISM

Although the vast welter of detailed biochemical reactions and mechanisms which constitute the various pathways and routes of metabolism appears to be overwhelming, a number of basic patterns become self-evident.

First, the respiratory processes are primarily a means of liberating chemical energy in a form that will be useful to the cell. This necessitates that energy be released in small parcels, a phenomenon that is attained in nature by numerous enzymatic reactions instead of a single large energy-yielding reaction. The organization of protoplasm is such that an appreciable fraction of the energy released can be captured in a form useful to the cell.

Second, cells capture useful energy in the form of ATP, which serves as the direct source of energy for all the life activities. ATP is the universal biological substance which is intimately involved in the energetics of all major routes of metabolism of carbohydrate, fat, protein, and nucleic acids, as well as other energy-requiring activities.

Third, certain substances, especially coenzymes, are widely distributed in biological systems participating in the numerous pathways of metabolism. The coenzymes TPN and DPN, for example, serve as hydrogen or electron carriers in anaerobic respiration, aerobic respiration, the pentose oxidative pathway, fat metabolism (synthesis and degradation), and amino-acid metabolism.

Fourth, in a number of biochemical reactions the substrates or reactants must be in a so-called "activated" state. This is frequently achieved by forming a derivative with coenzyme A in a reaction that requires an energy input, which is usually provided by ATP. In the citric-acid cycle, for instance, in order for the condensation of oxaloacetic acid to occur with acetic acid, the acetic acid must be in the form of the coenzyme A derivative. Similarly, in fatty-acid synthesis and fatty-acid breakdown, the coenzyme A derivatives of most of the substrates are essential for the reactions to take place. In the oxidation of α-ketoglutaric acid in the citric-acid cycle, succinyl-CoA is a product.

Fifth, the various pathways of metabolism within the living cell are in one or more ways interlinked to each other. For convenience of description we have discussed them separately, but always with a view that they are inevitably related to one another. For example, acetyl-CoA is a key intermediate in carbohydrate, fat, and protein metabolism, whereas oxaloacetic acid, pyruvic acid, and α-ketoglutaric acid are important links between protein and carbohydrate metabolism.

Finally, the entire complement of enzymatic reactions making up the metabolism of the cell is under the basic direction and control of DNA in the nucleus. The vast quantity of information encoded in the molecular structure of DNA is ultimately expressed in the proteins (i.e., enzymes), the fundamental machinery of all living cells.

ASSOCIATION OF METABOLIC PATHWAYS WITH CELL STRUCTURE

The elucidation of the various routes of metabolism has been inevitably correlated with the distribution and localization of these pathways among the subcellular components themselves. These can be briefly summarized as follows.

In many tissues and cells, the enzymes of anaerobic respiration are located in the cytoplasmic matrix other than in the mitochondria and endoplasmic reticulum. The ready isolation of these enzymes in "soluble" form, together with cytochemical studies, provide strong evidence for this point. The aerobic respiratory route, however, appears to reside almost completely in the mitochondria. The enzymes of the citric-acid cycle are relatively tightly bonded and organized within the mitochondria. The terminal respiratory chain is even more insoluble and highly organized. In fact, the data indicate that the terminal respiratory chain is part of the membranous structures (cristae and membranes) of the mitochondria.

The enzymes responsible for the degradation of fatty acids are found in the mitochondria, and fatty-acid synthesis occurs principally in the endoplasmic reticulum.

Protein synthesis, as we understand it at present, takes place largely on the ribosomes. There is also evidence, however, that it may occur perhaps by different mechanisms in the mitochondria.

With respect to nucleic-acid metabolism, DNA is synthesized in the nucleus and RNA is synthesized in both the nucleus and the cytoplasm. Degradation probably occurs at similar localities.

SUPPLEMENTARY REFERENCES

Arnon, D. I., "The Role of Light in Photosynthesis," *Scientific American*, November 1960.

Baldwin, E., *Dynamic Aspects of Biochemistry*, fourth edition, Cambridge University Press, New York, 1963.

Calvin, M., *The Path of Carbon in Photosynthesis*, Prentice-Hall, Englewood Cliffs, N.J., 1957.

Conn, E. E., and P. K. Stumpf, *Outlines of Biochemistry*, Wiley, New York, 1963.

Franck, J., and W. E. Loomis (Editors), *Polysynthesis in Plants*, Iowa State College Press, Ames, Ia., 1949.

Fruton, J. S., and S. Simmonds, *General Biochemistry*, second edition, Wiley, New York, 1958.

Giese, A. C., *Cell Physiology*, second edition, Saunders, Philadelphia, 1962.

Karlson, P., *Introduction to Modern Biochemistry*, Academic Press, New York, 1963.

Loewy, A. G., and P. Siekevitz, *Cell Structures and Function*, Holt, Rinehart, and Winston, New York, 1963.

McElroy, W. D., *Cellular Physiology and Biochemistry*, second edition, Prentice-Hall, Englewood Cliffs, N.J., 1964.

Neilands, J. B., and P. K. Stumpf, *Outlines of Enzyme Chemistry*, second edition, Wiley, New York, 1958.

Stein, W. H., and S. Moore, "The Chemical Structure of Proteins," *Scientific American*, February, 1961.

White A., P. Handler, and E. L. Smith, *Principles of Biochemistry*, third edition, McGraw-Hill, New York, 1964.

Chapter 9

Nutrition and Metabolism:

Basic Relationships

GENERAL CONSIDERATIONS

From prehistoric times man has been aware that the amount and kind of food he eats affects his well-being. During his early history he focused largely on the quantity of available food which was attained only through his skill as a hunter. Cannibalism was not an unusual occurrence and, in fact, is still practiced by certain present-day primitive tribes.

With the development of agriculture and the art of cookery, the pleasure of eating became more self-evident. The great advances in science—particularly in chemistry, physiology, biochemistry—and medicine during the nineteenth and early twentieth centuries further stimulated the ever-present interest of man in the problems of food. The concept that disease could be caused not only by infectious agents such as microorganisms but also by the lack or absence of an essential nutrient in the diet marked the opening of the era of discovery of vitamins, essential amino acids, and other nutritional factors. This was soon followed by the great advances in biochemistry which revealed the exact role of many of these nutrients.

Nutrition and Metabolism

The science of *nutrition* is concerned primarily with the study of the composition and the quantities of the nutrients required by or-

ganisms and the physiologic role and fate of these substances once they enter the living system. One phase of nutrition centers about the chemical changes (i.e., metabolism) that a nutrient experiences within an organism or cell. Biochemistry, as the study of the chemistry of living systems, was originally one aspect of nutrition. It has advanced so rapidly and extensively as to have become a biological discipline in its own right. A knowledge of the food requirements of living organisms, therefore, has provided the necessary basis for the study of metabolism. We have had to know first which substances could serve as foods or nutrients before we could study their chemical conversions and functions in the living cell.

Types of Food

All organisms require food or nutrients for their life activities. Foods or nutrients are those substances that serve as: (*a*) energy sources for the various life activities of cells, (*b*) constituents in the building and repair of protoplasm, or (*c*) regulators of metabolic processes. Nutrients can be classified into the following groups:

1. *Energy source.* In many animals, for example, this is provided by the energy-rich carbon-hydrogen bonds of carbohydrates, fats, and proteins.

2. *Carbon source.* The carbon atom is the backbone of all organic substances including the organic constituents of protoplasm. Carbohydrates, fats, and proteins serve as the carbon source for all animals and most microorganisms, whereas carbon dioxide is the primary carbon source for photosynthetic organisms such as green plants.

3. *Nitrogen source.* Nitrogen atoms are part of the structure of amino acids, proteins, nucleic acids, and numerous coenzymes and cofactors. All green plants and many microorganisms can utilize inorganic nitrogen (e.g., nitrates and ammonia) as their nitrogen source, whereas most animals require it in the form of organic compounds.

4. *Growth factors.* These are essential organic compounds which are not synthesized in sufficient quantities by the organism to meet its needs. They include the vitamins, essential amino acids, and certain fatty acids in the case of man. The requirements vary with the species of organism.

5. *Mineral salts or inorganic nutrients.* These include ions of a dozen or so mineral elements such as potassium, calcium, magnesium, sulfur, phosphorus, and several heavy metals. The inorganic nutrients are divided into two classes—the *macronutrient* or *major elements* which are needed in relatively large amounts by living organisms, and the *micronutrient* or *minor elements ("trace" elements)* which are required in only very small or trace amounts (p. 226).

6. *Water.* As the unique universal solvent of all life on our planet, water may constitute as much as 95 per cent of the bulk of protoplasm.

Significance of Nutritional Requirements

The quantitative requirements for certain nutrients have provided us with important clues as to their possible function long before their metabolic role was established. For example, the fact that vitamins and trace elements are needed in extremely small amounts strongly implicated these nutrients in a catalytic role, probably as components of certain enzymes. This has proved to be precisely the case. Conversely, in several instances metabolic studies have also led to the finding of hitherto undiscovered nutrients.

The nutritional requirements of an organism can also provide us with certain fundamental information about its metabolism. For example, in order to grow yeast cells the following nutrients must be present in the aqueous growth medium: (1) an energy and carbon source such as sucrose and (2) several inorganic salts including nitrogen and various minerals. Man's diet, on the other hand, requires not only an energy and carbon source such as sucrose and certain inorganic ions but in addition must include: (1) ten different amino acids, (2) at least three different fatty acids, and (3) approximately a dozen different organic substances in extremely small quantities which are called *vitamins*.

Nevertheless, despite these differences in nutritional requirements, yeast cells and human cells show a striking similarity in their composition and metabolism. Yeast cells contain more or less the same amino acids, vitamins, and fatty acids, which are required by man in his diet, even though these were not provided to the nutrient medium. The pathways of respiration—anaerobic and aerobic as well as the pentose oxidative route—and various other metabolic aspects in both yeast cells and human cells are essentially alike. Their enzymatic reactions and the participation of identical coenzymes and intermediates such as DPN, TPN, ATP, coenzyme A, flavins, and citric-acid cycle substrates, to name but a few, are the same. Here is an illustration of the fundamental metabolic unity that exists among living things, lending support to the evolutionary theory that all forms of life are related.

But if their composition and metabolism are more or less alike, how is it that yeast cells and human cells show such striking nutritional differences? The answer is that yeast is obviously capable of synthesizing from simpler materials the same amino acids, vitamins, and fatty acids nutritionally required by man. Man, on the other hand, is incapable of deriving these molecules in sufficient quantities from other substances and therefore must obtain them preformed in his diet. This is not to say that the yeast cells have no need for these organic substances in their metabolism. On the contrary, they serve in the same important metabolic roles in yeast as they do in human beings. The main difference is that yeast cells, by virtue of their genetic make-up, have greater biosynthetic abilities than man for manufacturing certain molecules such as amino acids, fatty acids, and vitamins. It means that yeast cells have additional enzyme systems, not possessed by human cells, which mediate the synthesis of these substances. This can be summarized by the statement: *simplicity of nutritional requirements reflects complexity of biochemical synthetic abilities.*

Nutritional Basis for Classifying Organisms

All forms of life — animals, plants, and microorganisms — on the basis of their nutritional requirement for carbon can be conveniently classified into two broad groups, *heterotrophs* and *autotrophs*.

HETEROTROPHS. Organisms that require their carbon primarily in the form of carbon-hydrogen bonds of organic substances (such as carbohydrates, fats, and amino acids) for normal growth and development are called *heterotrophs*. They include all animal life (as well as man) and many microorganisms. Heterotrophs derive their carbon and energy from the respiration (Chapter 8) of the preformed external supply of complex organ molecules such as carbohydrates, fats, and proteins, usually giving up carbon dioxide to the atmosphere as one of the end products.

AUTOTROPHS. Living things, however, that utilize inorganic carbon, usually in the form of carbon dioxide, as their sole source of carbon are called *autotrophs*. They consist of two main subdivisions. The first and largest are the *photosynthetic* organisms (or *photoautotrophs*) represented almost entirely by green plants and, to a very small extent, by certain photosynthetic bacteria. The second subdivision of autotrophs is made up of a small exclusive group of bacteria known as the *chemosynthetic organisms* (or the *chemoautotrophs*).

Photosynthetic Organisms (or Photoautotrophs). Green plants and photosynthetic bacteria are capable of utilizing the energy of light to assimilate or convert the low energy carbon-oxygen bonds of carbon dioxide to the higher energy carbon-hydrogen bonds of carbohydrates and their intermediates by the process of photosynthesis. The fact that their energy and carbon requirements are not normally provided by organic substances suggests that they manufacture these substances in sufficient quantities by using sunlight and the simpler molecules carbon dioxide, water, and inorganic nutrients. Photosynthesis represents the operation of a complex series of synthetic biochemical pathways consisting of enzymes, intermediates, and cofactors which are possessed by green plants in addition to the usual metabolic machinery contained in most other organisms (Chapters 8 and 17).

Photoautotrophs are therefore among the most biochemically complex organisms. By virtue of their photosynthetic machinery they are the primary means for providing directly and indirectly the necessary energy and carbon source (largely in the form of carbon-hydrogen bonds of carbohydrates, fats, and proteins) for nearly all other living things, including all animals and the great majority of microorganisms. In the overall economy of nature, therefore, green plants are indispensable for the existence of almost all other forms of life on earth. The single known exception is the small group of chemosynthetic bacteria (discussed below) which are exempt from this primary dependence on photosynthetic organisms for their energy and carbon source.

Photosynthesis also has been responsible for

our fossil fuels—coal, oil, and natural gas—which are in large part ancient petrified plants containing, in the form of chemical energy of organic compounds, the stored energy of sunlight that fell on the earth some two hundred million years ago, long before man's appearance. It is this transformed ancient sunlight that is released when fuel is burned supplying the energy for the wheels of our industrial civilization.

Strictly speaking, sunlight could be regarded as a nutrient for green plants according to our earlier definition of a nutrient. Sunlight is the primary energy source for green plants (and ultimately for all other forms of life with the exception of the chemoautotrophs), although it is not regarded as a substance in the usual sense of the word. In a broader and more modern meaning, however, matter and energy are interchangeable, and light is in fact considered to have mass (Chapter 6).

Chemosynthetic Organisms (or Chemoautotrophs). The chemoautotrophs also utilize carbon dioxide as their source of carbon for normal growth and development, but unlike the photoautotrophs they cannot use sunlight as their source of energy. Their energy is furnished instead by the biological oxidation of particular inorganic substrates, usually by molecular oxygen.

Specific chemoautotrophs oxidize specific inorganic substrates (e.g., ammonia, nitrite, hydrogen sulfide, and molecular hydrogen) as a means of obtaining energy. For example, the ammonia-oxidizing soil bacteria known as *Nitrosomonas* exclusively oxidize ammonia to nitrite by molecular oxygen:

$$2NH_4^+ + 3O_2 \longrightarrow 2NO_2^- + 4H^+ + 2H_2O + \text{Energy}$$

The nitrite that is formed is in turn usually oxidized in the soil to nitrate by the nitrite-oxidizing chemoautotrophic bacteria known as *Nitrobacter.*

$$2N_2^- + O_2 \longrightarrow 2NO_3^- + \text{Energy}$$

Nitrosomonas and *Nitrobacter* are collectively called the *nitrifying bacteria.* In these nitrifying bacteria (as in all chemoautotrophs), a portion of the energy released in the oxidation of inorganic substrates is captured and used to transform carbon dioxide to the higher energy-containing carbon-hydrogen bonds of organic substances. Experiments with cell-free extracts of *Nitrobacter* have now demonstrated that a portion of the energy released in the oxidation of nitrite is captured in the form of ATP. Moreover, the reactions in the assimilation of carbon dioxide by chemosynthetic organisms are similar to those which account for carbon dioxide conversion to the carbohydrate level in the *dark phase* of photosynthesis (Chapter 17).

The major subdivisions of the chemoautotrophic bacteria include (a) the *iron bacteria which oxidize ferrous ion (Fe^{2+})* to ferric ion (Fe^{3+}), (b) the *nitrifying bacteria* already indicated, (c) the *sulfur-oxidizing bacteria* which oxidize various inorganic forms of sulfur such as hydrogen sulfide, H_2S, elemental sulfur, and so on, and (d) those bacteria that oxidize molecular hydrogen. The nutritional requirements of these bacteria are fulfilled by a simple nutrient medium consisting of the appropriate oxidizable inorganic substrate, inorganic salts, water, and carbon dioxide.

The presence of organic material in the growth medium is often inhibitory to the chemoautotrophs. Many green plants, however, can utilize organic compounds such as sugars for their carbon source instead of carbon dioxide as demonstrated by experiments in which plants have been grown in the dark on nutrient media containing certain carbohydrates as the carbon and energy source.

The significance of the chemosynthetic organisms in the economy of nature seems to be insignificantly small. They probably represent less than 0.001 of 1 per cent of the protoplasm present on our planet earth. The chemoautotrophs are, nevertheless, a highly interesting group in view of their utilization of inorganic substances as their primary energy source.

In summary, a classification of all living systems on the basis of their carbon requirement can be made as follows:

1. Heterotrophs
2. Autotrophs
   (a) Photoautotrophs or photosynthetic organisms
   (b) Chemoautotrophs or chemosynthetic organisms

ENERGY REQUIREMENTS OF MAN

Basal Metabolic Rate

The minimal amount of energy required by the human body during the course of a single day is called the *basal metabolic rate (BMR)*. By definition it is equal to the minimal energy expended per unit of time by the individual under conditions where he is performing only the fundamental functions of metabolism and breathing. It represents the overall rate of metabolism of the body when physical and digestive activities are maintained at a minimum, and it is therefore a measure of the amount of energy just necessary to keep an individual alive. Determination of the basal metabolic rate can serve at times as a useful tool in diagnosing certain abnormal metabolic conditions. It can be conducted directly by recording the heat production of the body, for under the defined conditions for determining the basal metabolic rate (i.e., a minimum of muscular and digestive activities) heat production is the principal means of energy dissipation. However, the basal metabolic rate is far more conveniently determined by the indirect method of measuring oxygen consumption and carbon dioxide production. The ratio of these two values ($CO_2 : O_2$) is called the *respiratory quotient* (RQ) and is characteristically different for each of the three energy food stuffs. It can therefore frequently indicate the major respiratory substrate being utilized. In the aerobic respiration of carbohydrates (e.g., glucose) for each molecule of glucose oxidized six molecules of oxygen are taken

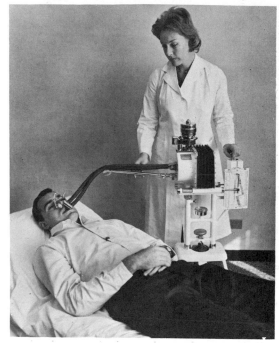

Figure 9-1. Equipment for determination of basal metabolic rate (*courtesy of Picker International Corp.*).

up and six molecules of carbon dioxide are produced.

$$C_6H_{12}O_6 + 6O_2 \longrightarrow 6CO_2 + 6H_2O + 686,000 \text{ calories}$$
Glucose

The RQ is therefore 1.0 in the carbohydrates.

Fats have more carbon-hydrogen bonds per carbon atom than carbohydrates and are therefore in a more chemically reduced state. Accordingly more oxygen is consumed in the course of fat oxidation than carbon dioxide produced. The RQ for fats is significantly less than one, averaging close to 0.7. Proteins or amino acids are also in a more reduced chemical state than carbohydrates. Their respiratory quotient averages about 0.8.

The fact that brain tissues and heart muscle to a lesser extent exhibit a respiratory quotient of 1.0 implies that they depend almost exclusively upon carbohydrates as their respiratory substrate. The RQ for most other tissues of the human body, however, is about 0.82 which together with other evidence suggests that all three energy substrates are used in respiration.

In practice oxygen consumption and carbon dioxide production are conveniently measured through inhalation and exhalation tubes (Figure 9-1) for 10 to 15 minutes while the individual is resting in a prone position at least 12 to 14 hours after the last ingestion of food. From these measurements and from the known values of heat produced by the complete combustion of carbohydrate, fat, and protein, the basal metabolic rate can be calculated. This is conveniently obtained from standard reference tables devised for this purpose.

The basal metabolic rate shows wide variation from individual to individual depending on such factors as age, hormonal balance, sex, diet, inheritance, climate, weight, and so on. It is smaller under conditions of sleep and controlled lowering of body temperature. The average basal metabolic rate for the young American adult male ranges between 1500 and 1800 kilocalories[1] per day (24 hours), and is about 5 per cent less for the female. The daily energy requirement for a normal active existence is about 3000 kilocalories, whereas a vigorous physical life requires about double that quantity. Actually the present practice is to express the basal metabolic rate in terms of calories per hour per square meter of body surface. The average basal metabolic rate for the young American adult expressed on this basis ranges between 38 to 45 kilocalories per hour per square meter of body surface.

Energy Storage. It is of interest to note that energy storage in living systems is attained by means of the carbon-hydrogen bonds of lipids and carbohydrates. Most but not all animals store their energy largely as fats. For plants, however, the chief energy reservoirs are carbohydrates. The energy stored in fats is more than twice that contained by an equal weight of carbohydrate. This could be a distinct ad-

[1]See footnote on page 103 for definition of calories and kilocalories.

vantage for organisms that depend on self-movement for survival. Some of the exceptions to this generalization are the molluscs (e.g., clams and oysters) which show a rich glycogen and poor lipid store. These animals, however, seem to be more or less independent of movement for their survival. Also, several kinds of seeds show a high level of lipids in their storage tissues, a fact which is possibly correlated with the fact that they are in part dependent on movement (e.g., by winds and animals) for adequate dissemination. Finally, it should be noted that in muscle tissue some energy-storage is also attained by means of the energy-rich phosphate bonds of the so-called *phosphagens* such as *creatine phosphate* (Chapter 29).

ROLE OF THE NUTRIENTS
Carbohydrates

CARBOHYDRATES AS A FOOD SOURCE. For most heterotrophic organisms, carbohydrates serve as a major source of both energy and carbon. Similarly, autotrophic organisms such as green plants respire carbohydrates, which they have produced by photosynthesis, in essentially the same manner as indicated for heterotrophs. This is also presumed to be the case for the chemosynthetic organisms.

In higher animals including man as much as 50 per cent and even more of the total food ingested may be carbohydrates. Most of it is usually in the form of large polysaccharide molecules chiefly as starches. For the majority of animals with the exception of the ruminants or "cud chewers" (e.g., cows and sheep), the plant polysaccharide cellulose is of little nutritional value since it is not digested. Simple sugars such as glucose and fructose are generally present in small quantities in the human diet, usually to a lesser extent than the disaccharide sucrose. The latter is used in variable quantities in the preparation and seasoning of foods.

In the course of carbohydrate digestion the starches and disaccharides are enzymatically hydrolyzed to simple sugars as a result of the action of specific enzymes in the digestive juices (Chapter 24). The simple sugars can now be transported across the epithelial lining of the digestive tract into the blood stream.

ROLE OF THE LIVER IN CARBOHYDRATE METABOLISM. Any examination of the interrelationships of nutrition and metabolism in vertebrates soon reveals the all-important functions performed by the liver. As the largest organ of the body it exercises a central role together with the kidneys and the endocrine glands in maintaining the internal chemical environment of the organism by regulating the concentrations of numerous substances in the blood. The latter in turn directly influences the immediate environment of each and every cell of the organism. In mammals the liver is the organ normally richest in carbohydrate stores which occur principally in the form of animal starch called *glycogen*. Skeletal muscle is the second major site of glycogen storage as indicated below. The storage of small-sized molecules in cells would be an unusual occurrence in nature because it would drastically disturb the osmotic relationships of cells. Glycogen constitutes about 2 to 8 per cent of the fresh weight of the liver in various mammalian species and is usually entirely depleted by fasting the animal for twenty-four hours.

The glycogen of liver is in a dynamic state in the sense that it is constantly experiencing degradation and breakdown. The quantity of glycogen stored in the liver depends upon:

(a) *Composition of the diet as well as the quantity of food consumed.* The greater the intake of calories, especially as carbohydrates, the greater the level of glycogen in the liver. Other energy-rich nutrients affect the glycogen content of the liver since fats, proteins, and carbohydrates can be interconverted to one other especially by liver cells. As the maximal glycogen level in liver is approached, fat formation chiefly by the liver also occurs with its subsequent transport by the blood stream to the adipose tissue.

(b) *Exercise.* Exercise represents the utilization of energy largely by the skeletal musculature of the body. It ultimately results in the withdrawal of glycogen in the form of simple sugars from the liver. As the glucose concentration of the blood is utilized by the many cells of the body, it is constantly replenished by conversion of the glycogen stores of the liver.

(c) *Hormonal control.* Carbohydrate utilization by the cells of the body as well as glycogen storage in the liver are markedly influenced by a number of hormones including *adrenalin* secreted by the adrenal medulla, *insulin* and *glucagon* by specialized cells located in the pancreas, the *thyroid hormones,* and certain *steroid hormones* of the adrenal cortex (Chapter 23).

ROLE OF MUSCLE, BLOOD, AND OTHER TISSUES IN CARBOHYDRATE METABOLISM. The second principal site of storage of glycogen in mammals is skeletal muscle. Although the 0.5 to 1 per cent concentration of muscle glycogen is less than in liver, it is nevertheless appreciable in terms of absolute amounts because of the large quantities of muscle (about 40 per cent) constituting the body weight. Muscle glycogen is more or less influenced by the same factors which affect liver glycogen levels with the principal exception that it is not as readily depleted by fasting. It is apparently the immediate substrate for muscle respiration: it is enzymatically split by phosphoric acid to many glucose-1-phosphate molecules which are then converted to glucose-6-phosphate before undergoing the usual steps of the anaerobic and aerobic pathways.

The normal glucose level of blood in human beings is about 100 mg per 100 ml of blood. The main sources of blood glucose are the sugar absorbed from the digestive tract and the glycogen stored in the liver. Interestingly enough, muscle glycogen makes no significant contribution to the blood glucose level. The increased level of glucose in the blood after ingestion of food is soon lowered by absorption of the sugar by the liver and subsequent conversion to glycogen. Under conditions where glucose is being rapidly removed from the blood by actively metabolizing cells, such as by those performing muscular work, the blood glucose concentration is maintained by the reverse process, namely by conversion of liver glycogen to glucose.

Under normal circumstances blood glucose enters the various cells of the body where it is generally phosphorylated to glucose-6-phosphate by ATP via the enzyme hexokinase (p. 177). It may then experience a number of alternative metabolic changes including (a) transformation to glycogen in liver and skeletal muscle, (b) degradation by way of the anaerobic and aerobic respiratory pathways or by the pentose oxidative pathways, (c) ultimate synthesis to fat via acetyl-CoA, and (d) conversion to amino acids and proteins via the intermediate of the Krebs cycle (Chapter 8). The requirement for glucose by the different tissues of the body varies considerably. The nerve cells of the brain and spinal cord, for example, show the highest requirement. They are most sensitive to a decrease in sugars, a lowering of the blood glucose level resulting in a lapse into the unconscious state.

Fats

FATS AS A FOOD SOURCE. Fats, like carbohydrates, serve as both an energy and carbon source, and are furnished chiefly in the human diet as the triglycerides (p. 150) of both animal and vegetable origin. Following ingestion, fats are enzymatically hydrolyzed in the small intestine by certain digestive juices to yield glycerol, fatty acids, and partially hydrolyzed fragments of the original fats, called *diglycerides,* and *monoglycerides.*

Glycerol is absorbed directly by the bloodstream as in the case of the simple sugars, while the fatty acids and very probably the diglycerides and monoglycerides pass through the intestinal epithelial lining directly into the lymphatic system, appearing as resynthesized triglycerides (Chapter 24).

STORAGE AND DISTRIBUTION OF FATS. In mammals the fats (largely as triglycerides) represent 10 per cent or more of the body weight and serve as a principal reservoir of potential energy. They are present in varying quantities in all tissues as liquid droplets in the cytoplasm and are particularly concentrated under the skin as droplets occupying a large proportion of the cell volume in certain *depots* of specialized connective tissue (p. 87). The amount, distribution, and storage of fat are determined in part by the basal metabolic rate, hormonal pattern, type of exercise, genetic make-up of an individual, and diet. Since most mammalian fat is localized in the cells (adipose tissue) immediately below the skin, it also functions in a secondary role as an insulation and protective layer against excessive heat loss and mechanical injury. This is of particular significance in the maintenance of a constant body temperature by mammals living in the

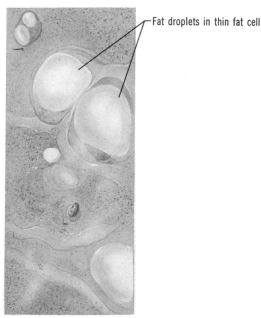

Fat droplets in thin fat cell

FAT CELLS

Figure 9-2. Liquid fat droplet in cytoplasm of cell.

sea (e.g., the whale) where the water is generally colder than body temperature and a better conductor of heat than air. The lipid content of human blood is about 500 mg per 100 ml. Almost one-third (about 180 mg) is cholesterol, one-quarter (125 mg) is triglycerides, with the remainder distributed equally between phosphatides and fatty acids (Chapter 7).

GENERAL METABOLISM OF FATS. The biochemical steps in the metabolism of fats including pathways of breakdown and synthesis of fatty acids and interrelationships to carbohydrates and proteins have been discussed previously in Chapter 8. Most of the fatty-acids of the body can be synthesized in man and other mammals in sufficient quantity from simpler molecules. However, at least three known unsaturated fatty acids must be provided in the diet of experimental animals such as rats and chickens to maintain them in a healthy state, and accordingly these are called the "essential" fatty acids. The same unsaturated fatty acids may also be necessary for man.

The major site in the body of fat metabolism — synthesis and breakdown of the fatty-acid components — is in the liver although various tissues and organs also metabolize fats but to a far lesser extent. The mode of transfer of fats by the blood stream between the liver and other organs and tissues is not entirely clear. The present evidence indicates that the fats are transported by the blood stream as triglycerides and as dissolved glycerin and liberated fatty acids bound to the albumin protein fraction of the blood.

When the caloric intake is less than the energy expenditure of the organism, there is a net decrease in the lipid content of the body. Under these circumstances the glycogen reservoirs of the body, namely those of liver and skeletal muscle, are first depleted, during which time the fats are increasingly utilized to meet the organism's energy needs. The stores of glycogen in the liver are completely consumed within 12 to 24 hours following the absence of an energy source in the diet. Thereafter the principal energy source is the depot fat. The high rate of fat degradation under these conditions especially in the absence of adequate carbohydrates and proteins in the diet results in the accumulation of ketone compounds (Chapter 7) which, if left unchecked, is a major cause of death by starvation. In diabetes (Chapter 23) ketone bodies also accumulate from fat degradation because of an impaired carbohydrate metabolism. In the terminal stages of starvation where the fat depots have been depleted, the protein of the body as the final energy and carbon source commences to be broken down at a faster rate than it is synthesized. Death follows shortly.

When the caloric intake of mammals exceeds their immediate needs, the extra energy is stored as the fat molecules largely deposited in the subcutaneous fat depots. When the caloric intake is the same as the energy expenditure of an organism, the quantity of body fats remains constant. By use of the isotope tracer technique it has been revealed that under these conditions of caloric balance the constant level of body lipid in reality represents a dynamic balance between a constant rate of deposition of fats and an equal and opposite rate of breakdown or removal. This seems to be true for most of the other components of the body with the notable exception of the nucleic acids and certain structural proteins.

Proteins

PROTEINS AS A FOOD SOURCE. Animals, unlike most plants and microorganisms, are unable to utilize the inorganic forms of nitrogen such as nitrate, nitrite, or ammonia as their source of nitrogen for synthesizing proteins, nucleic acids, and certain other organic compounds. Although they can utilize ammonia to a limited extent largely by way of the glutamic dehydrogenase reaction (p. 199), nearly all animals and some microorganisms require the amino group or its derivatives, principally in the form of protein or amino acids, to fulfill their nitrogen requirement. Therefore the primary source of amino nitrogen is plants and numerous microorganisms. The unique and essential roles of proteins (and amino acids) in the diet are twofold: (a) to furnish the "essential" amino acids which cannot be synthesized in sufficient quantities by the biochemical machinery of the animal itself, and (b) to restore the steady loss of nitrogen which is excreted in the course of metabolism. Like carbohydrates and fats, proteins also act as both an energy and carbon source for most animals including man.

"ESSENTIAL" AND "NONESSENTIAL" AMINO ACIDS. Of the twenty or so different amino acids that constitute the proteins of all organisms, ten specific ones must be provided in the diet of most mammals, either as free amino acids or as constituents of dietary proteins for the normal functioning of the organism. They are accordingly called "essential." This means that these animals do not have the capacity to form these amino acids in adequate quantities from other molecules furnished in the diet or from the various intermediates of metabolism. The amino-acid requirements of growing rats, about which we have the most complete information, are shown in Table 9-1. Present indications are that the same "essential" amino acids are also required in the diets of human beings.

Table 9-1 Essential Amino Acids for the Growing Rat

Arginine	Methionine
Histidine	Phenylalanine
Isoleucine	Threonine
Leucine	Tryptophan
Lysine	Valine

GENERAL METABOLISM OF PROTEINS AND AMINO ACIDS. Dietary protein is hydrolyzed in the digestive tract into its component amino acids through the action of a number of digestive enzymes (Chapter 24). The resultant amino acids, like the simple sugars, are transported through the epithelial lining of the digestive tract directly into the blood stream by an energy-requiring process of absorption. They are soon removed from the blood stream principally by the liver and kidney and to a lesser extent by other tissues of the body. Amino acids undergo a variety of metabolic fates as previously described (Chapter 8).

The synthesis and composition of proteins are clearly under genetic control (Chapter 11), and to the best of our knowledge the composition of the various body proteins is essentially unaffected by the proportions and kinds of amino acids that are furnished by our diets. In the living cell, proteins, like fats and carbohydrates, are in many instances in a dynamic state, being constantly synthesized and degraded. Under certain conditions, however, one process may exceed the other, reflecting itself in a net gain or loss of total protein. When no net change of proteins appears to take place, the isotope technique has indicated that the rate of protein breakdown is often balanced by the equal and opposite rate of synthesis. This turnover of proteins varies widely from tissue to tissue, taking place at different rates in some and not at all in others. For example, there is a rapid rate of protein turnover in the liver but apparently none at all in the structural protein *collagen* (p. 157) of the adult animal.

Unlike carbohydrates and lipids which can be converted to glycogen and fat deposits respectively, excessive quantities of amino acids or proteins in the mammal cannot be stored. Whether they arise from the diet or from an unusually rapid metabolic breakdown of body proteins, excessive amino acids within the body are rapidly broken down. The excess amino groups are ultimately converted to several forms which are excreted, whereas the remaining carbon chains usually enter in the pathways of carbohydrate and lipid metabolism as indicated in Chapter 8.

WASTE PRODUCTS OF NITROGEN METABOLISM. The principal waste product of nitrogen metabolism in mammals and certain other animals is *urea*. It is the final product of a series of biochemical reactions collectively called the *urea cycle* (Chapter 28) occurring largely in the liver, thus minimizing the accumulation of the highly toxic ammonia as a breakdown product of nitrogen metabolism. Urea is subsequently excreted by the kidneys as a component of *urine*. In invertebrate aquatic and marine animals and in most fishes, nitrogenous wastes are excreted largely as ammonia itself. In terrestrial animals (other than mammals—e.g., reptiles and birds) which have evolved in a habitat of a more limited water supply, the chief nitrogenous excretion product is the highly insoluble compound called *uric acid* (Chapter 28).

Central Role of the Liver

It becomes evident from the foregoing discussions that the liver has a strategic role in the metabolism of carbohydrates, fats, and proteins. In addition it performs several other key functions. As we shall see in other sections of the book, the liver is primarily responsible for the breakdown of old red blood cells and for the production of bile salts so necessary for the digestion of fats and for the subsequent absorption from the intestine of the fat-soluble vitamins and other lipid materials. It also serves in the detoxification (conversion to a less harmful state) not only of ammonia but also of several foreign substances, which it achieves by various types of chemical reactions, and in the storage or accumulation of certain other nutrients including vitamin A (and vitamin D in fish livers), iron as *ferritin* (p. 227) and some of the water-soluble vitamins and trace elements.

The importance of the liver in the metabolism of the body is dramatically illustrated by surgical removal of the organ in experimental animals. The marked lowering of the blood glucose level within a few hours is followed by convulsions and death, principally as a re-

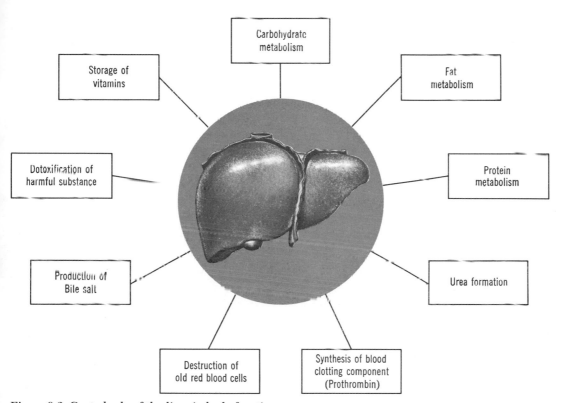

Figure 9-3. Central role of the liver in body function.

sult of the failure to provide sufficient glucose to the brain tissue, which has a very high requirement in this respect. If glucose is administered, the animal may survive a few days at most, but death will occur primarily because of the highly toxic effects of blood ammonia on the brain.

Vitamins

GENERAL CONSIDERATIONS. Vitamins are specific organic compounds which are needed in extremely small quantities in the diet or nutrient media for the well-being and normal functioning of an organism. They are not confined to any particular class of organic substances and may be organic acids, amines, amino acids, esters, alcohols, steroids, and so on. The fact that vitamins are required in extremely small quantities serves as a practical basis for distinguishing them from the essential amino acids and fatty acids which are required in relatively larger amounts.

Vitamin requirements, as in the instances of essential amino acids and essential fatty acids, reflect an inability to synthesize this compound from other dietary and metabolic substances. This has been shown to be due in several cases to the absence of one or more enzymes which are necessary for the formation of the vitamin. Modification of genetic composition by exposing reproductive cells to particular types of irradiation (e.g., X-rays and ultraviolet light) and certain chemicals has created requirements for organic nutrients, heretofore not needed, by adversely affecting the formation of one or more of the enzymes necessary for the synthesis of these substances.

In designating an organic substance as a vitamin, it is important to specify the organism to which this applies. For example, vitamin B_1 (or thiamine) is a vitamin for nearly all animals but not for higher green plants or many microorganisms. Nevertheless, vitamin B_1 like the other vitamins is metabolically important in all organisms, whether it is required in the diet or synthesized in the cell.

In animals prolonged dietary deficiencies of each of the vitamins result in characteristic diseases and eventual death. In microorganisms vitamin deficiencies are manifested by retarded growth and ultimate destruction of cells.

It seems likely that additional growth factors or vitamins as yet undiscovered are required by higher animals. The provision of vitamins by other than dietary means, perhaps by the biosynthetic activity of intestinal bacteria or by transfer from the maternal tissue to the developing embryo, may be in part responsible for the failure to demonstrate their essentiality. The large bacterial population which normally inhabits our intestinal tract makes an important nutritional contribution by furnishing either completely or in part many of the required vitamins and growth factors. The destruction or inhibition of these organisms by the prolonged administration of sulfa drugs and antibiotics can lead to a multiple vitamin deficiency condition unless vitamins are supplemented in the diet.

The fact that the vitamins must be regularly supplied to the diet implies that they are continually being broken down and excreted in the course of metabolism. This has been verified by studies employing the isotope technique.

Thus far most of the vitamins have been shown to serve as components of specific coenzymes (p. 159). Of fundamental significance is the pattern which has emerged from the vast welter of details concerning the action of vitamins, namely that these substances function in identical fashion in all living cells, be it microbe or man. It has provided us with further evidence for the fundamental likeness and unity of all forms of life, thus further supporting the evolutionary theory that all living things are related.

HISTORICAL NOTE. Clues for the existence of vitamins have been in the records of human history since ancient times. The remedial effect of dietary liver on night blindness (now known to be due to a deficiency of vitamin A) was recognized by the early Egyptians and noted by Hippocrates (fourth century B.C.) in Greece. The occurrence of scurvy among the crusaders in the thirteenth century and the realization in 1520 by the Austrian physician Kramer that it could be cured by citrus fruits was finally followed in 1795 by the introduction of lime and lemon juices in the English navy as a preventive of the disease. The Japanese admiral Takaki in the 1880's obtained a striking decrease of the painful nerve disease *beriberi* among sailors of the Japanese navy by raising the vegetable, meat, and milk content or their diet.

The first well-defined experimental work on the relationship of vitamins to disease, however, was made in 1896 by Eijkman, a military physician in the Dutch Indies. He observed that a polished rice diet (rice from which the hulls had been removed) caused a paralytic nerve disease in chickens similar to beriberi in man, whereas unpolished rice resulted in their recovery. It took five years, however, before the conclusion was finally made by another researcher, Grijns, that beriberi is due to an insufficiency of an unknown essential nutrient which is concentrated largely in the discarded grain hulls. The significance of these results escaped the attention of most nutritionists until the famous British biochemist Hopkins and later Funk entered the scene. In 1906 Hopkins recorded his views that animals could not live on a diet of pure protein, fat, and carbohydrate alone and suggested that deficiencies of other unknown natural dietary factors were responsible for such diseases as scurvy and rickets.

In 1912 Funk introduced the term "vitamine" to designate these special unknown organic nutrients and proposed that the diseases beriberi, scurvy, pellagra, and possibly rickets were caused by a deficiency or lack in the diet of "vitamines." The era of vitamins had begun. It started with animal nutrition and in short order involved what at first appeared to be un-

related fields and phenomena—microbial nutrition, competitive inhibition (p. 163), enzymes and coenzymes, and so on. In the years that followed, many vitamins in animal nutrition were chemically identified and synthesized and their mode of action elucidated as functional compenents of coenzymes. A few vitamins, however, still refuse to give up the secrets of their biological roles.

FUNCTION OF THE VITAMINS. The vitamins are generally subdivided into two broad groups based on their solubility properties. The majority dissolve relatively easily in water and are called *water-soluble vitamins*. Those that are insoluble in water can be dissolved in fats, or in solvents that dissolve fats, and are accordingly called *fat-soluble vitamins*. Nearly all our information to date on the mechanism of action of vitamins in biological systems centers about the water-soluble vitamins.

THE WATER-SOLUBLE VITAMINS. L-*Ascorbic Acid or Vitamin C*. This vitamin was first recognized as the dietary factor necessary for the prevention of the painful disease of the joints and gums called *scurvy*.

L-Ascorbic acid

Fresh vegetables and fruits, particularly tomatoes and citrus fruits, are excellent dietary sources of ascorbic acid. Vitamin C is easily destroyed by oxidation in air, especially at higher temperatures, such as cooking and canning procedures. It is required by the primates (man, apes, monkeys, and so on) and, oddly enough, by the guinea pig. All other vertebrate animal species as well as plants and most microorganisms are apparently able to synthesize ascorbic acid from carbohydrates, and therefore display no nutritional requirement for it.

Most of the enzyme steps responsible for the enzymatic conversion of glucose to L-ascorbic acid have been worked out in recent years. One of the enzymes in the biochemical pathway has been shown to be lacking in humans and guinea pigs, thus breaking the chain of synthesis and accounting for the dietary requirement displayed by these animals. Despite our knowledge of the precise chemical structure of vitamin C, the detailed steps of its biological formation from glucose, and the symptoms induced by its deficiency, we have been unable to establish its actual metabolic role. No enzyme system has yet been found in which the vitamin acts as a specific coenzyme or part of a coenzyme. The normal daily dietary ascorbic acid requirement for the human adult is about 75 mg.

The Vitamin B Group. The vitamin B group consists of a dozen known vitamins, each performing its own characteristic biological role. They are collectively called the B vitamins not only because of the history of their discovery but also because they are often found together in the same food sources such as liver, yeast, and unpolished rice.

Thiamine or Vitamin B_1. This vitamin was among the first members of the vitamin B group to be identified.

Thiamine

A deficiency of vitamin B_1 in the diet of many animals results in the characteristic nutritional disease *beriberi*. The advanced stages of the disease are typified by a painful inflammation of the nerves and muscular weakness and wasting, resulting in paralysis. Ruminants (p. 210), like many other animals, are unable to synthesize thiamine. They possess intestinal bacteria, however, which can synthesize the vitamin from other substances and thus provide the host animal with sufficient amounts to satisfy its nutritional requirements. Thiamine is not a vitamin for plants and most microorganisms since they appear to synthesize sufficient amounts for their metabolic needs.

The vitamin functions as part of the coenzyme cocarboxylase (p. 177), which is the coenzyme for pyruvic decarboxylase and for several other enzymes including those responsible for the enzymatic oxidation of pyruvic acid to acetyl-CoA (p. 185) and α-ketoglutaric acid to succinyl-CoA (p. 186). Many animal tissues and the outer layers of seeds are dietary sources of thiamine. The normal daily dietary allowance in human beings is about 1-2 mg.

Riboflavin or Vitamin B_2. This vitamin is a widely distributed yellow fluorescent compound which occurs almost entirely in the form of its coenzymes *FMN* and *FAD* in biological materials.

Riboflavin

FMN is the phosphate ester of riboflavin, whereas FAD consists of the purine adenine, ribose, and phosphate chemically linked to FMN (p. 183). Riboflavin deficiency in human beings is characterized by symptoms such as fissures at the corners of the mouth, dermatitis, and the appearance of blood vessels in the cornea of the eye.

Riboflavin appears to be a vitamin for all animals, whereas green plants and most microorganisms synthesize their own riboflavin.

Since the rate of growth of riboflavin-requiring bacteria is dependent on the quantity of riboflavin provided in their nutrient media, these microorganisms have been employed as a specific and sensitive means of assaying for the vitamin in various materials. All other factors being equal, the bacterial growth produced in a riboflavin-free nutrient media by the addition of any other substance can be used as an accurate measure of the latter's riboflavin content. This is obtained by comparing the growth induced by the unknown level of the vitamin with that induced by known quantities of added riboflavin under identical conditions. This principle also serves as the basis of the *microbiological assay* for various growth factors. By using an appropriate microorganism that displays a nutritional need for a particular substance, we can now assay for this substance in various materials in much the same manner as described for the microbiological determination of riboflavin.

The coenzymes FMN and FAD are separately associated with several different enzymes in carbohydrate, fat, and protein metabolism as hydrogen or electron carriers in oxidation-reduction reactions (Chapter 8).

Although no minimal dietary riboflavin requirement for man has been definitely established, the recommended daily intake is about 1-2 mg. Liver, yeast, wheat germ, milk, eggs, and green leafy vegetables are good sources of the vitamin.

Nicotinic Acid or Niacin. Although this compound was first recognized in 1867 as a chemical breakdown product of nicotine, it was finally identified in 1937 as the dietary factor responsible for the prevention of the nutritional deficiency disease *pellagra* in man and

Nicotinic acid or niacin

black tongue in dogs.

Pellagra is characterized by dermatitis, diarrhea, and disturbances of the nervous system leading to dementia. The disease, recognized as far back as the early 1700's, occurs in populations subsisting for the most part on diets rich in corn. This has been attributed largely to the fact that most varieties of corn were strikingly low in nicotinic acid and in the essential amino acid tryptophan. The latter is converted to the vitamin by a known series of biochemical reactions. The supplementation of nicotinic acid and its precursor tryptophan to the diet together with the development of strains of corn containing a higher level of both substances have literally wiped out pellagra in the United States. In man and undoubtedly in other animals this is further supplemented with niacin synthesized by intestinal bacteria.

Niacin functions primarily as a component of the pyridine nucleotides DPN and TPN (p. 175), which are the coenzymes of several important enzymes catalyzing oxidation reductions in carbohydrate, fat, protein, and nucleic-acid metabolism. (Chapter 8). It is actually the niacin portion of pyridine nucleotides that undergoes reduction and oxidation in the course of their metabolic action. The daily recommended dietary amounts of niacin for human beings is about 10-20 mg. Meats, especially liver, are excellent nutritional sources of the vitamin.

Vitamin B$_6$ This vitamin occurs in essentially three forms called *pyridoxal, pyridoxine,* and *pyridoxamine,* shown at the top of the next page. A deficiency of vitamin B$_6$ in laboratory animals is accompanied by characteristic symptoms such as dermatitis, nervous lesions, and anemia. Like most vitamins, B$_6$ is synthesized by green plants and numerous microorganisms and is therefore not nutritionally required by these organisms. In ruminants the vitamin B$_6$ requirement is fulfilled by the biosynthetic activity of their intestinal bacteria.

Vitamin B$_6$ is a major portion of the coenzyme *pyridoxal phosphate* which functions as a cofactor in the enzymatic transamination

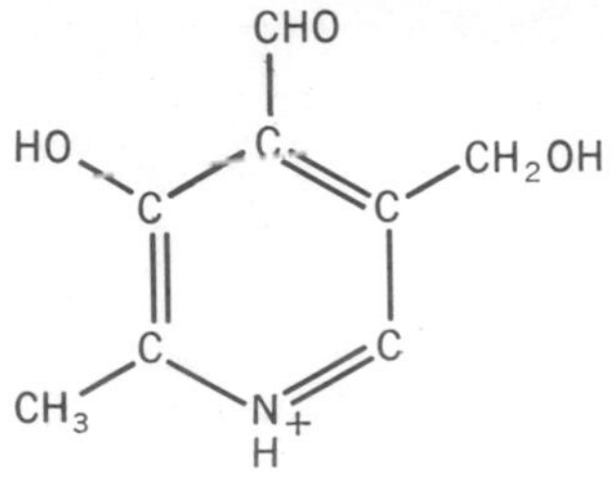

Pyridoxal

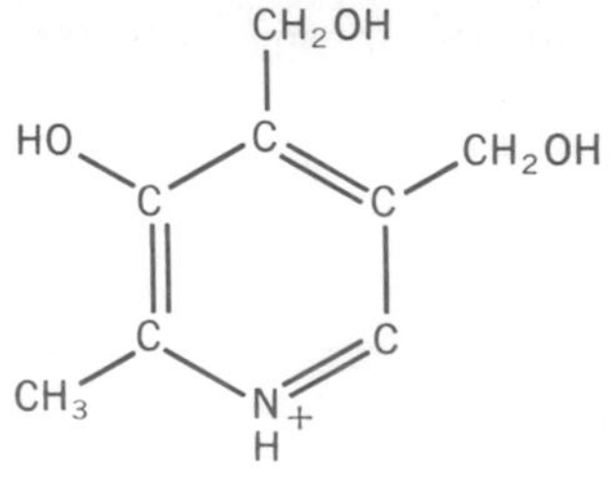

Pyridoxine

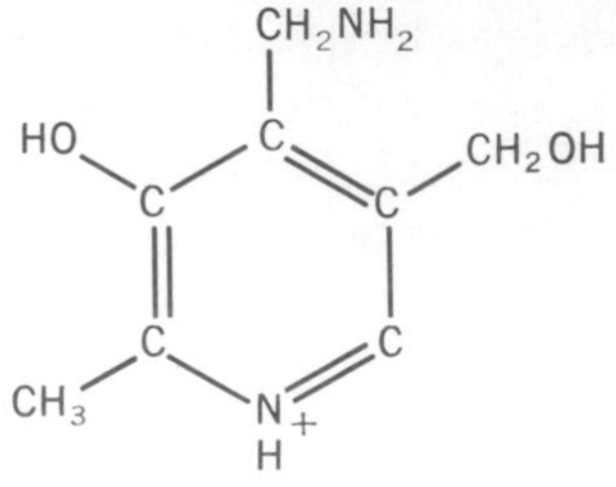

Pyridoxamine

(p. 199) and decarboxylation (p. 200) of nearly all the naturally occurring amino acids. Pyridoxal phosphate is also involved in the synthesis and breakdown of the amino acid tryptophan as well as in the metabolism of certain sulfur-containing amino acids. The human dietary need for vitamin B_6 has not yet been clearly established. The vitamin is found in many foods, particularly in liver, kidney, yeast, egg yolk, grains, and various seeds.

Pantothenic Acid. This vitamin is an essential nutrient for a variety of animals but its nutritional requirement in man has not yet been determined.

In rats a lack of the vitamin causes retardation of growth, impaired reproduction, a graying of the black hair, and lesions in the cortex of the adrenal glands. The vitamin is synthesized by green plants and by most microorganisms. Pantothenic acid occurs in tissues principally as a portion of the coenzyme A molecule (p. 184). CoA has a key role in the "activation" of particular intermediates in the metabolism of carbohydrates, fats, and amino acids. The central role of acetyl-CoA as an important metabolic intermediate and connecting link in the interconversion of carbohydrates, fats, and amino acids has already been indicated (p. 197). Liver, yeast, eggs, and particularly royal jelly are rich sources of the vitamin.

Biotin. This vitamin was first isolated in 1936 from egg yolk as a crystalline substance necessary for the growth of yeast.

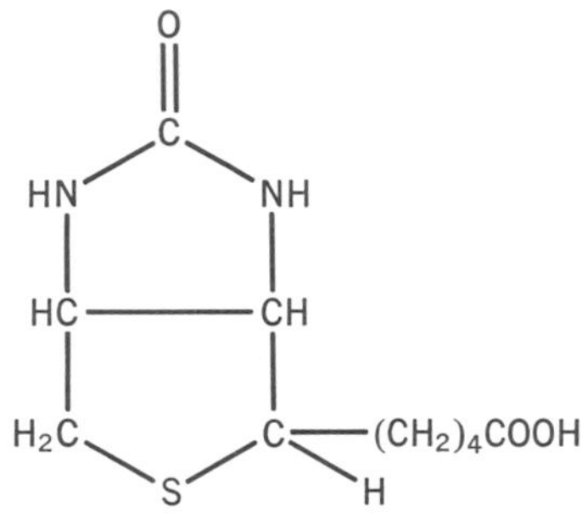

Biotin

Within a few years it was shown to be necessary for the growth and respiration of a particular bacterial species, and for the protection of rats and other animals against the toxicity induced by the inclusions of large amounts of raw egg white in the diet. The toxicity of raw egg white was subsequently demonstrated to be due to the presence of a particular protein called *avidin*. The latter combines with biotin to form a nondigestible complex and prevents its absorption from the intestine. The biotin-binding capacity of avidin, however, is irreversibly destroyed by heating (e.g., boiling an egg).

The symptoms of a biotin deficiency in animals induced by feeding excessive amounts

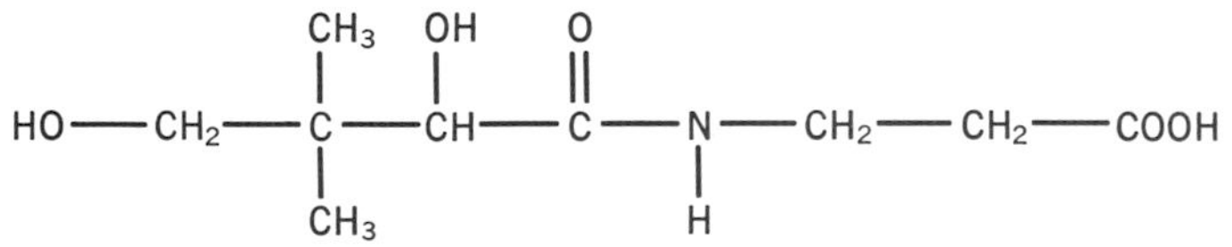

Pantothenic acid

of raw egg white include dermatitis, loss of hair, and nervous disorders. Most animals obtain sufficient biotin to meet their needs from the biosynthetic activity of their intestinal bacteria. The inhibition of intestinal bacteria by antibiotics or other antibacterial drugs, the use of synthetic diets from which biotin is absent, and the addition to the diet of certain analogues or antimetabolites (p. 163), which are chemically similar but not identical to biotin, have also been effective in creating a biotin deficiency.

Biotin has only recently been shown to be necessary for a particular enzymatic reaction in fatty acid synthesis involving the incorporation of carbon dioxide into a larger organic molecule. Liver and yeast are rich sources of biotin, as they are of all other vitamins of the B complex. The daily human nutritional requirement is considered to be about $10\mu g$.

Folic Acid. The general term folic acid designates a group of chemically and biologically related compounds which serve in a vitamin capacity for a number of organisms including various birds, mammals, several insects, and certain microorganisms. Several different forms of folic acid are known depending on the biological source. Perhaps the simplest of these is the *folic-acid molecule*, also called *pteroyl-glutamic acid*, isolated from liver and consisting of a glutamic acid, *para*-aminobenzoic acid, and a double-ring structure called *pterin*.

Folic-acid compounds from other sources generally contain more than one glutamic-acid portion. Another form of folic acid originally observed as a growth factor for a particular bacterial species is called *citrovorum factor*. Present indications are that the *citrovorum factor* may well be the coenzyme form of folic acid. Aside from green plants a number of microorganisms (including certain intestinal bacteria) and to a limited extent animal tissues appear capable of synthesizing folic acid, although apparently not in sufficient quantities to meet the needs of the organism. In mammals the most prominent symptom of a folic-acid deficiency is a characteristic anemia.

The role and metabolism of folic acid are extremely complex. The vitamin has an important metabolic function in the enzymatic synthesis of the amino acid *serine* from the amino acid *glycine* (one of the key intermediates in the biosynthesis of the purine and pyrimidine bases of nucleic acids). Folic acid is also somehow related to the metabolism of the amino acid tyrosine and to other vitamins such as vitamin B_{12}, ascorbic acid, and biotin. Certain analogues or antimetabolites of folic acid, notably *aminopterin* and its derivatives, which competitively inhibit the growth of organisms requiring folic acid, have proved to be partially effective in temporarily offsetting *leukemia*, cancer of the blood (Chapter 25). The dietary requirement for folic acid

Pterin moiety   p–Aminobenzoic–acid moiety   Glutamic–acid moiety

Folic acid (pteroyl – glutamic acid)

by human beings has still not been determined, but it is undoutedly being fulfilled in part by the biosynthetic activities of intestinal bacteria.

Vitamin B$_{12}$ or the Antipernicious Anemia Factor. This vitamin occurs in nature in a number of different chemical forms. In its most biologically active and abundant state, vitamin B$_{12}$ is a highly complex and unusual porphyrin (p. 168) containing the metal cobalt, cyanide, the simple five-carbon sugar ribose, and other structures. Vitamin B$_{12}$ has been shown to be a growth factor or vitamin for numerous animals, including man and several microorganisms, but not for higher plants.

A deficiency of vitamin B$_{12}$ in the tissues of higher animals is responsible for the fatal blood disease *pernicious anemia* (Chapter 25). The discovery of the vitamin in fact stems from the early work of two Boston physicians, Minot and Murphy, who in 1926 showed that the disease symptoms were markedly alleviated by large quantities of liver in the diet. The occurrence of pernicious anemia however, is primarily the result of insufficient absorption of the vitamin from the digestive tract. Unless an enormous excess of vitamin B$_{12}$ is furnished in the diet, the pernici-anemia patient does not respond. Injection of tiny quantities into the blood stream however, is highly effective.

The defect in pernicious anemia has been shown to reside in the secretions of the stomach. Normal individuals contain in their gastric juice an as yet unidentified material called *intrinsic factor* which is essential for the successful absorption of ingested vitamin B$_{12}$. When vitamin B$_{12}$ is taken by mouth together with a source of intrinsic factor, normal absorption takes place. Vitamin B$_{12}$ has recently been shown to function as a portion of a newly discovered coenzyme in the interconversion of certain organic acids. Its interrelationship with folic acid is still obscure. Estimates of its daily requirement in the human diet are about 1μg.

Other B vitamins — Inositol, Choline, Lipoic Acid, Carnitine. A deficiency of *inositol* in the diets of several different laboratory animals results in characteristic symptoms including retardation of growth. It is also a growth factor for several yeasts and fungi.

Inositol

Inositol has been established as an essential nutrient for the growth of human cells in tissue culture but not for the intact organism, where it is apparently formed from glucose. Inositol is widely distributed in plants, animals, and microorganisms; it is found in especially large quantities in sharks where it possibly functions as an energy reserve material much like glycogen in other animals.

A dietary deficiency of *choline* (p. 150) produces symptoms (hemorrhaging of the kidneys and deposition of excess fat in the liver) similar to those induced by a nutritional deficiency of the amino acid methionine. Choline and methionine serve as a source of certain simple chemical groupings called methyl groups (CH_3-) in cell metabolism. Choline is also a portion of *lecithin* (p. 150), one of the cell *phospholipids*.

Lipoic acid as an eight-carbon, straight-chain organic acid containing two sulfur atoms (p. 184) was originally discovered as a growth factor for certain microorganisms. Although it has not been shown to be required in the diets of animals, it functions in animal, plant, and microbial cells as a hydrogen or electron carrier undergoing alternate oxidation and reduction in the metabolism of pyruvic acid and α-ketoglutaric acid (Chapter 8).

The compound *carnitine* is nutritionally necessary for the successful completion of the life cycle of a number of insects. This same substance has been known for some time to be a constituent of skeletal muscle, although its function is still not known.

$$(CH_3)_3\overset{+}{N}\text{---}CH_2\text{---}CH\text{---}CH_2\text{---}COO^-$$
$$|$$
$$OH$$

Carnitine

THE FAT-SOLUBLE VITAMINS. Four distinct fat-soluble vitamins designated as A, D, E, and K are known. Unlike most of the water-soluble vitamins their actual metabolic role at the enzymatic level is not yet elucidated. This has been in part due to the difficulty of working with these fat-soluble substances in aqueous systems.

Vitamin A. Vitamin A exists in several different chemical forms. It was discovered in 1913 by McCollum and Davis who recognized it as a fat-soluble nutritional factor necessary for the growth of rats. The carotenes of plants (e.g., the pigments responsible for the orange color of carrots) are closely related chemically to vitamin A and upon ingestion are transformed by the body to the vitamin. Since the carotenes, which are present in all green plants, are precursors of vitamin A and can replace it in the animal diet, they are collectively called *provitamin* A.

illustrated by the transformation of chick epidermal cells in tissue culture to mucous-like epithelial cells as a result of providing vitamin A to the nutrient medium.

One of the earliest indications of a vitamin A deficiency in man is *night blindness*, an inability to see objects in dim light or in the dark. The condition is independent of xerophthalmia and is due to a direct effect of a vitamin A deficiency on a particular pigment called *rhodopsin* (Chapter 22) in the cells of the retina of the eye responsible for night vision. Rhodopsin is a conjugated protein which can be dissociated into a protein called *opsin* and a form of vitamin A.

In adult mammals and fishes the main reserves of vitamin A, mostly in the form of fatty-acid esters, are in the liver in sufficient quantities to meet the needs of the organism for several years. In new-born infants there is no reserve of vitamin A so that the occurrence of xerophathalmia is far more frequent in children than in adults.

Fish livers are a rich source of the vitamin, depending on the species and time of year.

Vitamin A

A deficiency of the vitamin in the growing animal is characterized by a retardation in growth and a change in the epithelial cells. The cells become dried out, horny, and more susceptible to infection as a result of increased deposition of the albuminoid protein keratin (Table 7-2). This is particularly manifested in the cornea of the eye and is responsible for encrustation of the eyes, leading to a condition of blindness called *xerophthalmia*. The effect of the vitamin on epithelial cells is also

The liver oils of shark and halibut are particularly high in vitamin A. About 1-2 mg of vitamin A per day is considered to be the normal dietary allowance.

Vitamin D. Vitamin D is the nutrient in cod-liver oil which prevents or cures rickets was discovered by McCollum and his associates in 1922. *Rickets* is primarily a disease of growing bone in which the normal deposition of inorganic minerals in the final stages of bone growth is markedly impaired. The main disease symptoms are deformities of the skeleton (usually seen in children as a bowing of the legs), defective teeth development, a beaded appearance of the ribs, and knock-knees.

Vitamin D exists in several different chemical states, one of which is a particular sterol compound related to cholesterol called *calciferol* or vitamin D_2.

Vitamin D_2 (calciferol)

The unique action of ultraviolet light in exerting a curative effect on rickets and in converting a diet which produced the disease to one that could cure or prevent the condition was finally clarified after considerable investigation. It was found that upon exposure to ultraviolet light a naturally occurring cholesterol derivative called *ergosterol* is transformed by a series of chemical reactions to calciferol. Ergosterol itself is inactive in preventing or curing rickets, unless, of course, it is exposed to ultraviolet light and thus changed to calciferol.

Another cholesterol compound called *7-dehydrocholesterol* is also transformed by ultraviolet irradiation to an active rickets-preventing or rickets-curing substance called vitamin D_3 which is closely related in structure to vitamin D_2. Actually the effect of sunlight or ultraviolet irradiation in preventing or curing rickets has been attributed largely to the conversion of this inactive 7-dehydrocholesterol in the skin to the effective vitamin D_3 form. An unsolved riddle is how heavily furred animals and deep-sea fishes, which are seldom exposed to sufficiently strong ultraviolet irradiation, form vitamin D, especially since their diets are considered to be an inadequate source of the vitamin.

Although the vitamin somehow stimulates the absorption of calcium ions from the intestinal tract, its metabolic role has yet to be clarified. It also functions in the metabolism of other tissues of the body in a manner which has still not been elucidated.

As in the case of vitamin A, there are no reserves of vitamin D in the new-born infant. Although mammals and fish have large excesses of vitamin A in their livers, the ability to store vitamin D in the liver is displayed only by fishes. The large reserve of vitamin D in fish livers still has no suitable explanation, especially since their diet of microscopic plant and animal life fails to show the presence of the vitamin or any of its known precursors. Sunlight and milk are the chief means of providing vitamin D to children. In milk vitamin D augmentation is accomplished by irradiation with ultraviolet light, addition of vitamin D, and supplementation of cow diets with irradiated yeast. The recommended daily intake of vitamin D is about 0.02 mg.

Vitamin E or Tocopherol. This vitamin, frequently called the "anti-sterility" vitamin, was originally discovered in the 1920's as a fat-soluble factor necessary for normal reproduction in the rat. A deficiency of the vitamin in rats and other laboratory animals results in a tendency of the female to abort during pregnancy and an irreparable destruction of the sperm-producing tissue in the male.

Vitamin E deficiency in a variety of laboratory animals leads to several other characteristic effects including dystrophy of muscle, necrosis of liver, deterioration of brain tissue, and abnormal functional and structural changes in lung, kidney, blood, teeth, and adipose tissue. None of these deficiency effects, however, have ever been definitely established for human beings. Tocopherol is not yet considered to be a vitamin for man.

Vitamin E exists in several different chemical states, of which *α-tocopherol* is the predominant form found in animal tissues.

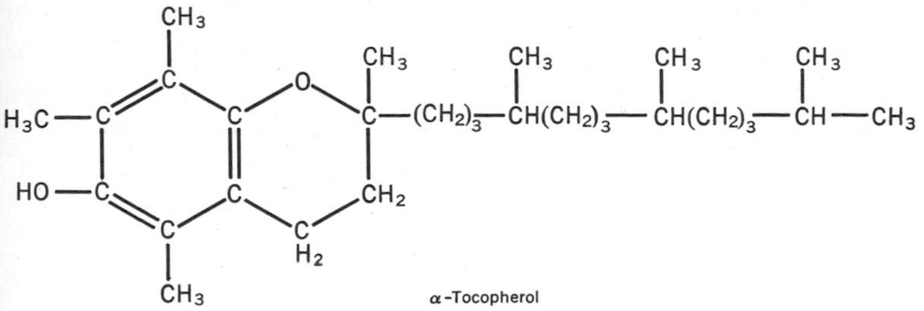

Several other compounds, both natural and synthetic, of related chemical structure also

α-Tocopherol

The vitamin is obviously synthesized by higher plants (and probably by a number of microorganisms) which presumably serve as the principal if not the only source of the vitamin for animals.

Although the main metabolic role of vitamin E has not been conclusively established, recent experimental evidence points to at least three important functions of the vitamin in the tissues of higher animals. First, it protects against or spares the oxidative destruction of certain labile cellular substances such as unsaturated fatty acids (p. 140), vitamin A, and ascorbic acid by tending to undergo oxidation itself. For this reason the vitamin is called an *antioxidant*. Second, it is a constituent of the cytochrome *c* reductase portion of the terminal respiratory pathway (p. 188). Its exact role in this system, however, has not yet been established. Finally, vitamin E is also somehow involved in nucleic-acid metabolism of higher animals.

One of the richest sources of tocopherol is plant oil such as wheat germ oil and the oils of cotton seed and rice grain. Fish-liver oils lack tocopherol although they are high in vitamins A and D.

Vitamin K. This vitamin was discovered in the early 1930's as a factor essential in the diet of chicks for the prevention of prolonged blood-clotting time and fatal hemorrhaging. It was accordingly designated as vitamin K or the coagulation (*Koagulations*) vitamin. It occurs principally in green plants as the so-called vitamin K_1 (see column at right).

possess vitamin K activity.

Impaired blood clotting is the principal symptom of a vitamin K deficiency condition and may be made sufficiently extreme to result in profuse bleeding from relatively small injuries followed by shock and death. A dietary deficiency of vitamin K in mammals is a relatively rare occurrence because of intestinal bacteria which synthesize the vitamin in sufficient amounts to meet the needs of the host. However, inhibition of intestinal bacteria by antibiotics and sulfa drugs, the use of *dicumarol* and *warfarin* (Chapter 25), which are analogues or antimetabolites (p. 163) of vitamin K, and impaired secretion of the bile and the pancreatic juices which leads to diminished absorption of fatty substances (e.g., vitamin K_1) from the intestine can also induce a vitamin K deficiency.

Vitamin K is essential for the biosynthesis by the liver of the protein *prothrombin* (Chapter 25), one of several blood-clotting constituents. There are also indications that vitamin K serves as an active component of the terminal respiratory pathway, possibly in

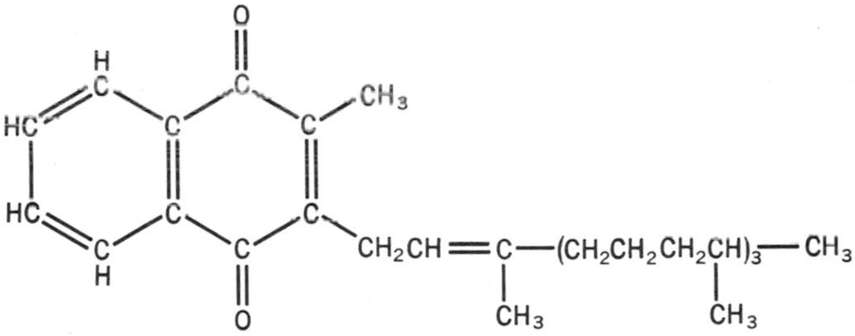

Vitamin K_1

oxidative phosphorylation. The major contribution of the intestinal bacteria in furnishing vitamin K makes it difficult to estimate the nutritional requirement for this vitamin by human beings.

INORGANIC NUTRIENTS

General Aspects

Approximately 95 per cent of the dry weight of protoplasm is composed of four elements—carbon, hydrogen, oxygen, and nitrogen—occurring principally as carbohydrates, proteins, fats, and nucleic acids. Minerals account for only 5 per cent of the body weight. Most of the elements of the periodic table have been found in living cells, but their presence in cells and tissues does not necessarily mean that they are essential. In fact, about fifteen mineral elements have thus far been shown to be necessary for normal growth and development, their individual omission from the diet or nutrient media resulting in physiological disease or death.

The inorganic nutrients or mineral salts required by living things are divided into two broad classes, the *macronutrient* or *major elements* needed in relatively large amounts, and the *micronutrient* or *trace elements* required in only very small quantities (Table 9-2). About 4 per cent of the dry weight of protoplasm is made up of the *major elements*, whereas less than 1 per cent is accounted for by the *trace elements*.

Table 9-2 Essential Minerals

MACRONUTRIENT OR MAJOR ELEMENTS	MICRONUTRIENT OR TRACE ELEMENTS
Potassium (K)	Iron (Fe)
Sodium (Na)	Copper (Cu)
Chlorine (Cl)	Zinc (Zn)
Phosphorus (P)	Manganese (Mn)
Calcium (Ca)	Cobalt (Co) ⎫
Magnesium (Mg)	Iodine (I) ⎬ for higher animals only
Sulfur (S)	Selenium (Se) ⎭
	Vanadium (V) ⎫ for higher plants only
	Boron (B) ⎬
	Molybdenum (Mo) (for higher plants only?)

The fact that the trace elements are needed in only extremely small quantities does not necessarily mean that they are less important than the macronutrient elements.

Both groups are essential. Although it has been relatively easy to establish the essentiality of the major elements, that of the trace elements has been demonstrated through the use of painstaking purification techniques and long-term experiments often over a number of generations in order to induce deficiency states.

The fact that the major elements are needed in relatively large amounts suggests that they are functioning in a structural capacity. In addition it has been found that several have highly important metabolic roles aside from structural considerations. The trace elements, like the vitamins, are needed in only extremely small quantities, and in most instances have been shown to be specific components or activators (p. 159) of enzyme systems.

Macronutrient Elements

POTASSIUM, SODIUM, AND CHLORINE. These elements function principally in maintaining suitable osmotic relationships in the cellular and tissue fluids and in furthering an appropriate physical state of protoplasm, especially of the cell membranes. Potassium and sodium ions are also essential activators for a number of specific enzyme systems in carbohydrate metabolism. In green plants sodium has been implicated in the early steps of photosynthesis. Potassium functions in muscular contraction and is an important activator of the enzyme *enolase* (p. 179), which catalyzes one of the important steps in anaerobic respiration.

In animals sodium occurs mainly in the body fluids (e.g., blood) external to the cells in combination with protein, chloride, and bicarbonate, whereas potassium is found chiefly within the cell.

CALCIUM AND MAGNESIUM. In higher animals calcium is an important structural component (together with phosphate) of the skeleton and a necessary constituent of the blood-clotting mechanism (Chapter 25). Magnesium is also associated with phosphate as an ingredient of bone structure. Virtually all the calcium (99 per cent) and most of the magnesium (70 per cent) of the body are found in the bones. In the blood, calcium is present largely in the plasma, whereas magnesium occurs chiefly in the red-blood cells.

At the enzymatic level magnesium ions function as activators of numerous enzyme systems in animals, plants, and microorgansims, particularly of enzymes that mediate the transfer of phosphate groups. Calcium ions activate only a few enzymes. Calcium and magnesium ions also exercise a significant influence on the physical state of protoplasm (as do potassium and sodium), especially on membranes, as indicated by their marked effect on permeability. In the plant kingdom magnesium occupies a unique position as the highly specific metal component of the chlorophylls. The unusually high level of magnesium in muscle tissue is associated with its function in the activation of specific enzymes and the maintenance of the physical state of protoplasm.

PHOSPHORUS. This element in the form of phosphate plays a key role in energy metabolism (as part of the ATP system), in the intermediary metabolism of carbohydrates by way of the anaerobic pathway and the pentose oxidative pathway (Chapter 8), and as a component of nucleic acids, phosphoproteins, and phospholipids (Chapter 7). In higher animals phosphorus is also an important structural constituent of the bone structure and is influenced by many of the factors that affect calcium metabolism. These include vitamin D and the parathyroid hormone (Chapter 23) controlling the deposition and mobilization of calcium and phosphate in the bony tissues as well as excretion from the body.

SULFUR. In higher animals such as man dietary sulfur is provided principally in the form of the sulfur-containing amino acids cystine, cysteine, and methionine. In plants and in many microorganisms sulfur is furnished in the inorganic state, mainly as sulfate, and is subsequently converted by a series of enzymatic steps to the three amino acids just mentioned. The sulfur atoms of several of these amino-acid units in proteins are known to act as bridges or linkages helping to bind polypeptide chains to one another. Sulfur as the sulf-hydryl group (—SH) of the amino acid cysteine is also necessary for the activity of several enzymes.

NITROGEN. The central role of the nitrogen atom and the forms in which it is utilized by organisms is described in Chapters 7 and 10.

MICRONUTRIENT OR TRACE ELEMENTS. The trace elements, like the vitamins, function primarily in enzyme systems, for the most part as metal components. In many cases the catalytic activity of metallo-enzymes is already present in primitive form in the free metal ions and is remarkably enhanced when bound to specific proteins. Inorganic iron salts, for example, can catalyze the decomposition of hydrogen peroxide to form free oxygen and water. The iron enzyme *catalase,* which accelerates the same reaction, does it a billion times more rapidly and thus represents an effective means of ridding the cell of any highly toxic hydrogen peroxide produced by the metabolic machinery of the cell.

Iron. All living organisms probably have a nutritional requirement for iron. It is an essential component of the iron porphyrin complexes called *hemes* constituting the oxygen-transporting *hemoglobin* of red-blood cells, the myoglobin of muscle, the *cytochrome* constituents of the terminal respiratory pathway, and the enzymes *catalase* and *peroxidase* (Chapter 7). At the enzymatic level, aside from its role as a component of heme-proteins (e.g., cytochromes, peroxidase, and catalase), iron is also a component of the cytochrome *c* reductase portion of the terminal respiratory pathway. In addition it is necessary for the biosynthesis of chlorophyll by green plants.

In higher animals iron is stored principally in the liver, the spleen, and to a lesser extent in the bone marrow as a conjugated protein called *ferritin* which contains almost 25 per cent iron by weight. Iron is transported in the blood largely in a form bound to a specific globulin protein in the plasma. About 70 per cent of the total iron of the body is present in hemoglobin, about 3 per cent in myoglobin, about 1 per cent or so in cytochromes, and the the remaining 25 per cent in the form of ferritin.

Iodine. This element is essential for higher animals but not for plants and microorganisms. Approximately one-quarter of the total body iodine is present in the thyroid gland, where it is uniquely accumulated and converted to the organic form as a component of the thyroid hormones (Chapter 23). The continuing need for dietary iodine is illustrated by the relative ease with which an iodine deficiency can be induced when the element is omitted from the diet. Sea water and therefore sea foods are abundant sources of iodine.

Manganese. As an essential element for plants, animals, and microorganisms, manganese is known to function as a component of several enzymes including several in the citric-acid cycle of respiration and nitrogen metabolism. Typical nutritional deficiencies symptoms (necrosis or breakdown of leaf tissue and decreased chlorophyll content in plants, and sterility and degeneration of reproductive tissues and bone structure in animals) are specifically cured by administering the metal.

Manganese is stored largely in the liver and kidneys and excreted into the large intestine and the bile. In plants it is involved not only in chlorophyll synthesis but in the photosynthetic process as well. It has also been implicated in the metabolism of one of the plant hormones, *auxin* (Chapter 17).

Copper. Copper is an essential trace element for numerous organisms. It functions in the absorption of iron from the digestive tract and in the formation of hemoglobin and cytochromes. It is a component of the *cytochrome oxidase* portion of the terminal respiratory pathway. Virtually all the copper of the blood is bound to a specific plasma protein and transported as such. In plants copper is necessary

for chlorophyll synthesis and is the metal constituent of the plant enzyme *ascorbic-acid oxidase* and of the oxidase responsible for the browning of injured tissues.

Zinc. As an essential element for plants, animals, and microorganisms, zinc is a metal component of a number of enzymes, including carbonic anhydrase (Chapter 27), alcohol dehydrogenase (p. 180), and several other DPN- and TPN-linked enzymes. In plants zinc in addition has been implicated in chlorophyll metabolism, in the biosynthesis of one of the plant hormones, and in flower setting and seed production.

Cobalt. Cobalt is an essential element for ruminants whose intestinal bacteria are capable of synthesizing the cobalt-containing vitamin B_{12}. The main function of cobalt appears to be as a component of vitamin B_{12}, in which form it is required by numerous higher animals including man. The element has not yet been shown to be necessary for higher plants.

Molybdenum. Molybdenum is an essential nutrient for higher plants and for microoganisms, but its status in animal nutrition is unsettled. It is a metal component of two or three animal enzymes and of one of the enzymes responsible for the stepwise conversion of nitrate to the amino form in higher plants and certain fungi. The metal is also essential for *nitrogen fixation* (p. 235).

Selenium. Selenium has recently been implicated as a trace element in the nutrition of animals. A nutritional deficiency of the element in rats contributes to a characteristic necrosis of the liver, a condition which can be readily remedied by the addition of trace quantities of selenium to the diet. At higher concentrations the metal is extremely toxic to animals, possibly by substituting for the sulfur in the sulfur-containing amino acids cystine and methionine. The metabolic role of selenium is unknown and is somehow interrelated with that of vitamin E.

Boron and Vanadium. These two metals have thus far been shown to be essential only for plants. Their metabolic roles have not yet been elucidated.

Fluorine. The occurrence of cavities in teeth is markedly decreased by the presence of fluoride ions in drinking water. Fluoride acts at concentrations which do not inhibit bacterial growth, and is ineffective once the teeth are fully formed. This appears to be the only biological function of the element. Whether or not flourine can be considered to be a trace element is an unsettled question.

WATER AS A NUTRIENT. Water is the major chemical component and universal solvent of living systems. It makes up about 70 per cent of the human body and is the principal medium for the occurrence of the metabolic processes. The water content of organisms ranges widely from as high as 96 per cent in some jelly fish to extremely low levels in seeds and certain lower invertebrate animals.

All fluids of the body, including blood and lymph, are essentially water solutions and suspensions of a great variety of substances ranging from simple hydrogen ions to giant protein and nucleic-acid molecules. Water also serves as the vehicle for the transport of foods, metabolic wastes, intermediary metabolic products, hormones, and any other substances to and from cells. It participates chemically in numerous reactions (e.g., hydrolysis of carboyhdrates, proteins, and fats) and physically in stabilizing and distributing the body heat. Most animals obtain water directly from the environment, whereas others such as those that live in the desert obtain their water supply from plants. Some animals (e.g., certain marine forms and certain birds) can consume sea water but they are also capable of excreting large amounts of salt (Chapter 28).

THE PROBLEM OF DIET

The problems of human nutrition in our Western culture have shifted from undernutrition and deficiency diseases to "overnutrition" and obesity. *Obesity* is a condition of excess fat caused by ingesting more calories than the body uses. The extra calories not expended by the numerous activities of the body are stored in the form of fat. Approximately thirty million persons in the United States are overweight. Obesity or overnutrition carries with it a more frequent occurrence of diabetes, degenerative diseases of the heart, blood vessels, and kidneys, atherosclerosis (Chapter 26), and greater risks during surgery and pregnancy. What are the factors that cause an individual to take in more calories than he can use? The answer is not simple. In addition to genetic constitution, emotional problems apparently have an important bearing on excessive calorie intake as does a disturbance in the appetite-regulating mechanism.

Despite the growing problem of obesity or overnutrition in our particular society, ironically enough, one-half of the approximate 2.3 billion people who inhabit the earth today go hungry. In some areas of the globe large segments of the human race are currently experiencing famine and starvation. It has been estimated that only a third of the world's people get enough of the proper nutrients, consuming three-fourths of the world's available food supply in the process. One of the goals of the Food Agricultural Organization and the World Health Organization is to make available suitable quantities of the proper food for the undernourished and overpopulated areas of the world.

SUPPLEMENTARY REFERENCES

Fruton, J. S., and S. Simmonds, *General Biochemistry*, second edition, Wiley, New York, 1958.
Heilbrunn, L. V., *An Outline of General Physiology*, Saunders, Philadelphia, 1952.
Henderson, L. J., *The Fitness of the Environment*, Beacon Press, Boston, 1958.
McCollum, E. V., *The History of Nutrition*, Houghton-Mifflin, Boston, 1959.
Nasset, E. S., *Food and You*, second edition, Barnes and Noble, New York, 1958.
White, A., P. Handler, and E. L. Smith, *Principles of Biochemistry*, third edition, McGraw-Hill, New York, 1964.

Chapter 10   Nutrition and Metabolism:
The Organism and Its Environment

THE ENVIRONMENT

General Considerations

No living system is an isolated and independent entity unto itself. The characteristics of all forms of life at every level of organization in terms of past evolutionary development and present existence represent the result of a vast and complicated interplay with their living and nonliving environment. The most seemingly independent living forms, the autotrophs (Chapter 9), like the heterotrophs, are inextricably tied to their inanimate environment and to other living systems for the adequate provision of nutrients. They also depend on a suitable temperature and, especially in the instance of photosynthetic organisms, on a suitable range of electromagnetic irradiation (i.e., light).

The environment itself consists of (1) *internal environment*—made up of the chemical and physical components of the cell ranging from the molecular to the gross subcellular structures, and (2) *external environment*—consisting of living organisms, on the one hand, and nonliving chemical and physical factors (e.g., water, carbon dioxide, oxygen, salts, various other nutrients and substances, temperature, light, pressure, and gravity) on the other. The internal environment of living systems in terms of molecular and gross make-up as well as metabolic reactions and pathways has already been discussed in previous chapters. The genetic features of this internal environment are considered in Chapters 11, 12, and 13.

The present chapter describes the broad relationships of organisms to their living and nonliving external environment at both the molecular and gross levels, an aspect of biology called *ecology*.

THE CYCLIC UTILIZATION OF MATTER BY LIVING SYSTEMS

General Features

All organisms are in a dynamic state. They are continuously taking in a variety of substances from their environment, subjecting them to a multiplicity of chemical and physical reactions, and excreting various products to the environment. At the same time, many of their own organic constituents are continually being broken down and resynthesized at different rates as indicated previously (Chapter 8) for proteins, fats, and carbohydrates. The dietary need for vitamins implies that these nutrients during the course of normal cell function are being metabolized and excreted so that more must be provided to the organism from the environment. Similarly, inorganic nutrients taken up by the organism are utilized and eventually excreted to the external environment, or in part made unavailable within the living system itself. What are the sources of nutrients and what are the fates of their metabolic products upon being returned to the external environment?

Animals ultimately derive their carbon and energy supply from photosynthetic organisms, notably the green plants. Although many animals consume other animals for their immediate carbon and energy supply, the primary source of energy is sunlight, which is incorporated into living things as chemical energy by the process of photosynthesis. Photosynthetic organisms in turn depend in large part on the metabolic activities of other organisms, including animals and microorganisms, for their necessary supply of carbon dioxide. The decomposition or degradation of dead tissues as well as minerals also provides a source of the essential inorganic elements.

An overall look at the biological transformations experienced by the chemical elements making up protoplasm indicates a sequence of chemical changes by various organisms to form a cyclic pattern. The metabolic products of certain organisms are utilized by other organisms, resulting eventually in the cyclic reconversion of substances to their original state.

The Carbon Cycle

Carbon dioxide and water are the end products of respiration of carbohydrates in most organisms. Death is usually followed by rapid decay or degradation of cells and tissues ultimately to carbon dioxide and water by numerous microorganisms, mostly bacteria and fungi. These very same products are the initial reactants in the process of photosynthesis (Chapters 8 and 17) which results in the reappearance of molecular oxygen and carbohydrates and other organic substances, thus completing the so-called *carbon cycle* (Figure 10-1). Green plants, and to a far lesser extent chemosynthetic bacteria, produce carbohydrates, fats, proteins, and nucleic acids from carbon dioxide and water. Plants are eaten by animals who in turn are eaten by other animals.

In the operation of the carbon cycle in nature, an overall dynamic balance has been es-
tablished in which the concentrations of each of the principal substances remain more or less constant. Carbon dioxide undergoes a continuing cyclic change to the organic state as carbohydrates and its intermediates (as well as proteins, fats, nucleic acids, and other organic constituents by various biochemical interconversions, Chapter 8) and then back again to carbon dioxide. Thus the carbon atom is used over and over again, the result of the varied metabolic activities of different organisms. If it were not so, then our supply of carbon dioxide would soon be exhausted. The magnitude of the biological process of photosynthesis on the earth today could completely deplete the carbon dioxide supply within fifty years. Nevertheless, the carbon dioxide concentration in the earth's atmosphere remains more or less constant at 0.04 per cent. The withdrawal of carbon dioxide by photosynthesis is balanced by other processes in nature, principally respiration of living cells and decay of dead tissues, which restore the gas to the atmosphere. Thus photosynthetic organisms depend on the metabolic activity of other organisms (including themselves) for their necessary supply of carbon dioxide.

Under certain climatological and geological conditions, dead tissues may undergo only partial decomposition to yield finally coal (in the case of plants) and natural gas and petroleum, which presumably are the products of incomplete decay of marine and other organisms. Limestone deposits are composed largely of calcium carbonate ($CaCO_3$) and magnesium carbonate ($MgCO_3$) and have originated in part from the accumulation of shell-forming, marine animals. A break or block in the carbon cycle could result in a limited carbon supply for one of the necessary steps in the cycle. A hypothetical failure in activity of decay microorganisms, for example, could cause an accumulation or piling up of carbon as organic substances with a subsequent decrease of the carbon dioxide in the atmosphere followed by a decrease in the rate of photosynthesis. The removal of carbon in the form of coal, natural

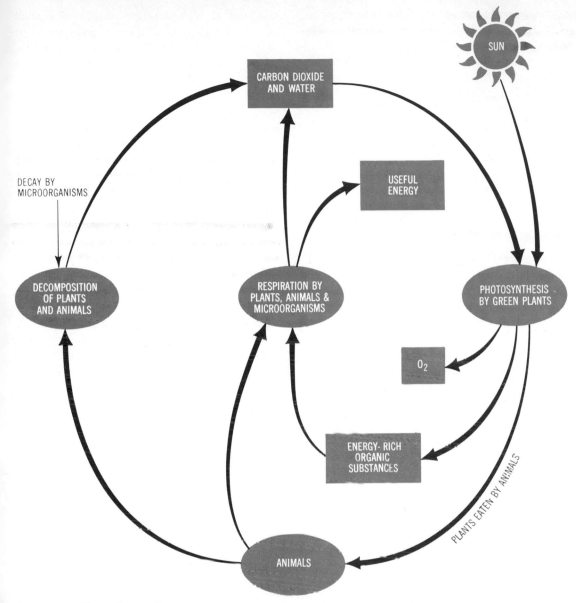

Figure 10-1. The carbon cycle.

gas, petroleum, and limestone from the biological cycle is only a temporary state of affairs. The carbon temporarily locked in these substances is continuously being returned by the action of living cells and by combustion in furnaces, gasoline engines, and other machines. The carbon of limestone is also slowly converted to carbon dioxide by the acid produced

and excreted as a result of the metabolic processes of soil microorganisms and plant roots.

The Oxygen Cycle and Hydrogen Cycle

The oxygen of the atmosphere is also in a state of dynamic equilibrium. Its 20 per cent concentration is essentially the result of an equal rate of removal by oxidative processes of biological systems (largely respiration) which is balanced by an equal rate of replenishment by photosynthesis. Therefore, our diagram for the carbon cycle (Figure 10-1), with attention focused on the oxygen atom instead of carbon, also represents the *oxygen cycle* in nature. Similarly, it can be used to indicate the *hydrogen cycle* in nature. It is estimated that if the atmospheric oxygen were suddenly depleted, it would only take about three thousand years to restore the oxygen concentration to its original level by the process of photosynthesis, all other factors being equal.

The Nitrogen Cycle

A nitrogen cycle similar in principle to the carbon, oxygen, and hydrogen cycles also exists in which the metabolic nitrogenous waste

products of certain organisms serve as food or nutrients for others. Thus the nitrogen atom is used over and over again in different chemical forms by different living systems. The latter metabolically transform it into various chemical states until it has been reconverted to the initial state with which we started to complete the cycle.

The nitrogen atom occurs in several chemical states and constitutes about 2.5 per cent of all living systems. The principal processes in nature responsible for the various chemical transformations of nitrogen are as follows.

NITRATE ASSIMILATION. Nitrates and to a lesser extent ammonia are the principal sources of nitrogen for green plants and many microorganisms. By virtue of their enzymatic make-up, green plants convert nitrates via a stepwise

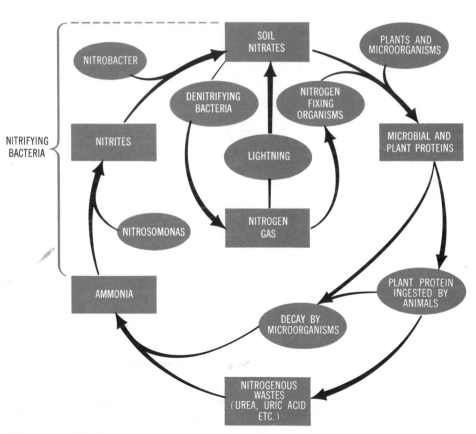

Figure 10-2. The nitrogen cycle.

series of biochemical reactions to the level of amino acids, a process called *nitrate assimilation*.

Plant proteins serve as a source of essential amino acids for numerous animals who utilize the amino acids to synthesize their own cellular proteins. Animals are preyed upon by other animals, thus serving as a nitrogen source for the predators. Many animals excrete their nitrogenous wastes largely as urea in the case of mammals (or ammonia or uric acid, depending on the animal, Chapter 28). It is subsequently decomposed in the soil and water to ammonia and carbon dioxide. Decay and putrefaction of dead organisms eventually transform the nitrogenous substances of dead cells to ammonia, carbon dioxide, and water.

NITRIFICATION. Ammonia is subject to a number of biological fates. It may be absorbed as such directly by the roots of higher plants and used for the synthesis of amino acids and proteins. It may also be oxidized to nitrate by the process called *nitrification*, principally as a result of the successive action of two groups of chemosynthetic soil bacteria collectively called the *nitrifying bacteria* (p. 208). The first group, *Nitrosomonas*, aerobically oxidizes ammonia to nitrite (NO_2^-), which is then further aerobically oxidized to nitrate (NO_3^-) by the second bacterial group, the *Nitrobacter*. The production by *Nitrobacter* of nitrate and its utilization by green plants and numerous microorganisms as a nitrogen source thus "closes the ring" to complete the nitrogen cycle (Figure 10-2).

DENITRIFICATION. The nitrogen cycle, however, is more complex and possesses several important ramifications. Another group of soil bacteria called the *denitrifying bacteria* converts nitrate and nitrite to molecular nitrogen (N_2) which is lost to the atmosphere. Denitrification, therefore, is a drain on the nitrogen cycle.

NITROGEN FIXATION. We might expect an eventual depletion of nitrogen unless there were a means for making available the nitrogen gas of the atmosphere to living organisms. Nature has provided for precisely such a process. Nitrogen gas is a relatively stable substance which does not readily undergo chemical reaction. It is present in great abundance, constituting 80 per cent of the earth's atmosphere, and resents a practically untapped and unlimited source of nitrogen. In nature nitrogen gas is transformed to other chemical forms by essentially two processes. The first is by electrical discharges arising from electrical storms in the atmosphere resulting in the formation of small amounts of nitrogen oxides from molecular nitrogen. The second, and by far the most important, is the biological process called *nitrogen fixation* which is restricted to a small percentage of living systems capable of transforming molecular N_2 to the amino form of amino acids (and proteins). It is one of the most critical links in the nitrogen cycle.

The two groups of microorganisms chiefly responsible for nitrogen fixation in the soil are the strongly aerobic bacteria *Azotobacter*, found in alkaline soils, and the anaerobic bacteria *Clostridium pasteuranium*, residing in acid soils.

Certain higher plants, namely the *legumes* (e.g., peas and beans), living in conjunction with the bacteria known as *Rhizobium*, are also important nitrogen-fixing organisms. Neither of these organisms in the absence of the other can carry on nitrogen fixation. The *Rhizobium* bacteria specifically invade the roots of particular species of leguminous plants resulting in the formation of root swellings called *nodules* (Figure 10-3). It is within these root nodules containing the *Rhizobium* bacteria that nitrogen fixation takes place. *Rhizobium* bacteria in the soil (or in pure culture) or leguminous plants by themselves fail to fix nitrogen. Apparently *Rhizobium* furnishes the leguminous plant with some unknown factor or factors which make possible the fixation of nitrogen by the root nodule tissue, while the green plant in turn provides the bacteria with an energy source—water and other nutrients. This relationship of mutual gain whereby two or more different organisms living together provide nutritional benefits to one another is

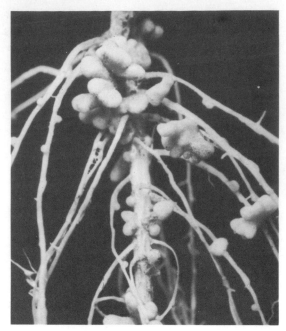

Figure 10-3. Nitrogen-fixing nodules of pea roots.

known as *mutualism* (p. 250).

The trace element molybdenum (p. 228) is necessary for nitrogen fixation and nitrate assimilation. Of great interest was the discovery made some years ago that nitrogen-fixing root nodules of legumes contain a red organic pigment identified as hemoglobin. It is similar to the hemoglobin of mammalian blood and is essential for the nitrogen-fixation process in root nodules, although its role has not yet been elucidated. The nitrogen-fixing system has only recently been attained as a cell-free enzyme system from the anaerobic bacteria *Clostridium pasteuranium*, after innumerable unsuccessful attempts in the past. Several other organisms including blue-green algae (Chapter 15) also carry on nitrogen fixation. A detailed diagram of the nitrogen cycle is shown in Figure 10-2.

The nitrogen-fixation step of the cycle is of prime importance, for it ultimately controls the quantities of nitrogen available for all the other processes of nitrogen metabolism. In the United States, agricultural soils undergo a steady depletion of nitrogen and of other mineral elements. The removal of nitrogen by crops far exceeds the restoration of nitrogen by the combined action of fertilizer treatments, electrical storms, and nitrogen fixation. The latter makes the largest contribution by far toward the replenishment of nitrogen in the soil. In a broad sense, the processes of nitrate assimilation and nitrogen fixation by transforming inorganic nitrogen to the level of the amino group represent the primary means by which all animals (including man) and many microorganisms ultimately obtain their nitrogen.

Other Nutrient Element Cycles in Nature.

Cycles for other nutrients comparable to those described for carbon, oxygen, hydrogen, and nitrogen also exist in nature. Cycles for the various mineral elements, in terms of their ingestion, utilization, and excretion by numerous organisms, can be demonstrated. The availability of mineral nutrients is aided by the release of mineral elements from dead organisms and tissues by the action of the putrefying microorganisms and from rocks by weathering and biological processes. For example, organic acids released by metabolizing roots to the surrounding soil dissolve some of the minerals contained in the soil particles, thus making them more available to living systems.

In contrast, the deposition and sedimentation of minerals render them temporarily unavailable. Unfortunately, the mineral cycles are unbalanced as far as land organisms are concerned because a net movement of inorganic nutrients from the land to the sea is constantly occurring. Erosion of land minerals and their final accumulation in the seas as well as the uptake of minerals by terrestrial plants, ingestion of plant products by animals, and the ultimate disposal of animal wastes into the oceans via rivers and streams are important contributing factors.

The "Downhill" Pathway of Energy Transfer

The outstanding exception to the broad cyclic nature of biological interrelationships just illustrated for nutrients is found in the interconversion and transfer of energy among various living systems. There is really no such phenomenon as an energy cycle in the biological world. Instead, the energy relationships among organisms are best described as a "downhill pathway." The ultimate source of energy for all life (with the exception of the chemosynthetic organisms, p. 208) is sunlight. A portion of energy from sunlight is trapped by the biological process of photosynthesis (p. 194) and stored in the form of chemical energy contained largely in the carbon-hydrogen bonds of carbohydrates, fats, proteins, and other organic substances. Plants are eaten by animals, thus furnishing energy which is subsequently released in the course of respiration. Of the total amount of energy ingested by the animal, only a small fraction is stored in the chemical bonds of its organic constituents, most of the energy being used to carry on its other life activities. When the animal is in turn eaten by other animals or decomposed by microorganisms, again only a small fraction of the total energy taken in will actually be stored in the chemical bonds of its carbohydrates, fats, proteins, and nucleic acids. Thus there is a decrease in useful energy as it is converted first from its primary source, the sunlight, to the chemical energy of carbon-hydrogen bonds by photosynthesis, followed by a progressive decrease in the energy stored as it is transferred successively from organism to organism. The energy is finally and completely dissipated to a nonutilizable form, generally as heat. The physicochemical aspects of the "downhill" pathway of energy utilization were described in Chapter 6.

The Biochemical Cycles of the Sea

The cyclic utilization of the separate elements in the biological world has been described individually for purposes of simplicity. In reality the different cycles are frequently interwined and interlinked in nature. Although environment has a marked influence on the existence of living systems, the cycles illustrate that organisms in turn exercise some effects on their environment. These phenomena are well exemplified in the oceans which house by far the greatest proportion of living things existing on our planet.

The presence and continued formation of organic matter in the sea is due to the photosynthetic activity of vast amounts of floating plants of microscopic size collectively called *phytoplankton*. These plants are necessarily limited to the upper water layers, called the *autotrophic or photic zone,* where sufficient light for photosynthesis is available. The photic zone extends to a maximum depth of about 100 meters or about one-twentieth of a mile and represents less than 5 per cent of the volume of the oceans. In order for photosynthesis to occur in this zone the essential nutrients must also be available, most of which are obtained directly from the water. Carbon dioxide, for example, present in the water as bicarbonate and dissolved carbon dioxide, is contributed by the carbon dioxide of the air as well as by the decomposition of marine organisms. Nitrogen and phosphorus are usually present as nitrate and phosphate, respectively. Many of the other essential elements (e.g., calcium, magnesium, potassium, sulfur, and the trace elements) are present as ions or as simple compounds.

The essential nutrients are constantly being replenished in the photic zone in several ways. The death of plants and their subsequent destruction by animals and microorganisms contribute to the availability of these elements. There is, however, a small but steady depletion of the essential elements from the autotrophic zone. The sinking of organisms and the vertical migrations of animals in the vast underlying reservoir of water (beneath the photic zone) called the *heterotrophic* or *aphotic zone* contribute to the characteristic accumulation and decay of organic matter in the deep water. The vast *net* synthesis of organic matter in the seas by photosynthesis is confined to the photic zone, whereas there is a net degradation of organic material in the aphotic zone. Here is a situation in nature in which the synthetic and degradative aspects of the biochemical cycles are more or less separated from each other in space. Degradation of organic matter also occurs in the autotrophic zone, but on the average it is far exceeded by synthesis.

The three most studied elements of the sea, namely carbon, nitrogen, and phosphorus, vary markedly in their concentrations in different parts of the oceans largely as the result of the biological synthesis or decomposition of organic matter. Phosphate and nitrate, for example, are considerably more abundant in the deep waters of the Pacific and Indian Oceans than in the Atlantic or in the Mediterranean. The concentration of phosphorus in the waters of the North Pacific is six times as great as that in the Mediterranean. The differences in distribution of these elements in sea water are undoubtedly determined by the biochemical cycles in the sea.

The oxygen content of sea and atmosphere is also largely determined by the activity of the photosynthetic organisms in the autotrophic zone of the oceans. Approximately 80 per cent of the total photosynthetic activity on our planet takes place in the sea. The temporary increase in oxygen of the sea water as a result of photosynthesis by marine plants is soon equilibrated with that of the atmosphere. Although it is true that the oxygen content of the atmosphere primarily determines the oxygen content of the seas, ultimately it is the photosynthetic activity in the oceans that determines the oxygen content of the atmosphere. Of the macronutrient elements in the sea, phosphorus and nitrogen are usually present in such small concentrations as to limit plant growth and, therefore, the production of organic matter by the photosynthetic organisms in the photic zone. Some of the trace elements, quite possibly iron, are also probably present in only limited amounts. The resulting limited yield of organic matter will in turn affect all other life in both the photic and aphotic zones, because it represents the primary food source for all other organisms in the sea.

Since the photic zone continues to produce organic matter, the necessary elements for plant growth and photosynthesis are obviously being replenished. The steady withdrawal of nutrients to the ocean depths has been found to be reversed chiefly by the vertical mixing of water, as a result of turbulence and upwelling, thus restoring the inorganic nutrients to the upper surfaces. In summary, the production of organic matter in the sea is directly influenced by light intensity, temperature, and the rate of return of nutrient substances to the photic zone by the vertical motion of the water.

In temperate and northern latitudes, there is a definite climatic sequence to the workings of the biochemical cycle in the sea. During the winter season, because of lower light intensities in the photic zone, the photosynthetic organisms experience a minimum of photosynthesis and growth. Vertical mixing of the water is greatest at this time, thus producing a nearly uniform distribution of inorganic nutrients. In the spring the warmer temperatures of the upper ocean waters permit a greater rate of photosynthetic activity and growth, resulting in a rapid depletion of the inorganic nutrients followed in time by a decreased rate of photosynthesis in the summer. The relatively poor mixing of water in the tropics and in temperate climates during the summer further accentuates this depletion in the surface waters. The level of inorganic nutrients is eventually restored during the winter months primarily by the vertical mixing of water, and secondarily by the greater rate of decomposition and degradation of organic matter as compared to photosynthetic production.

THE COMMUNITY OF LIVING THINGS
The Biotic Community

There are several ways of looking at the biological world. Our preceding discussion of the nutrient cycles and the "downhill energy pathway" has examined only one viewpoint of the interrelationships that exist among organisms. If we now shift our sights from the biochemical level (as represented by the cycles of the nutrient elements) and examine communities of different organisms, other relationships become evident which are inevitably dependent on the fundamental nutrient cycles and energy pathway in nature. The term *biotic community* is used to designate collectively a group of various organisms more or less associated together in a given area or habitat. Each species of organism—plant, animal, or microorganism—making up the community is obviously influenced in its existence and activities not only by the inanimate physical and chemical external environment but by the other species of the community as well. This interdependence among different species extends through varying degrees of intimacy from an extremely loose association (such as man's ultimate dependence for energy and carbon upon green plants) to a very close relationship (such as the highly specific host-parasite alliance illustrated by the life cycle of the liver fluke, p. 252).

Food Chains

In any community of organisms, the ultimate source of carbon and energy are green plants which convert the energy of sunlight and the carbon of the gas carbon dioxide to chemical energy and organic carbon by the process of photosynthesis. Plants are eaten by animals and these in turn may be eaten or degraded by a succession of other animals and microorganisms until the original energy and organic matter stored by the plant has been completely expended. This sequence of different organisms through which energy and materials pass is spoken of as a *food chain*. Food chains may have various degrees of complexity. The simplest would be that involving essentially two links consisting of green plants that carry on photosynthesis and microorganisms that obtain their nutrients from these plants by degrading

or decaying them after their death:

Photosynthetic organisms ⟶ Microorganisms

At the other extreme are food chains consisting of many links. For example, in the oceans the microscopic plants of the photic zone are primarily responsible for the production of organic matter by the photosynthetic process. The plants and their products may be consumed by certain unicellular and multicellular animals (called herbivorous zooplankton) which are present in both the autotrophic and heterotrophic zones. The herbivorous zooplankton are then ingested by other multicellular animals (called carnivorous zooplankton), such as those belonging to the Coelenterata (Chapter 18), which in turn may be eaten by certain worms and some of the hard-shelled *crustaceans* represented by shrimps, lobsters, and crabs. The smaller crustaceans may be devoured by small fish which are then eaten by larger fish. The latter in turn could serve as food for various mammals and birds whose eventual death and subsequent decomposition by microorganisms of decay terminates the food chain.

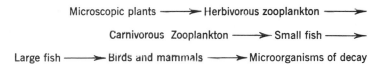

For purposes of simplicity and illustration, we have indicated food chains to be straight pathways of events. They are in fact far more complex and are often accompanied by various branching and parallel sequences. In the preceding food chain protozoa may also be eaten directly by fishes which eventually perish and decay, thus constituting another short, branching food chain connected to the larger one indicated.

On land, food chains extending from higher green plants by way of several animal links and ending with the microorganisms of decay are readily observed. In our own agricultural economy grasses are eaten by cattle which are in turn eaten by man. The final link in the sequence is decomposition by microorganisms following death.

The usual fundamental sequence in food chains, whether it occurs on land or in water is: Photosynthetic plants → Plant-eating animals (*herbivores*) → Animal-eating animals (*carnivores*) → Microorganisms of decay. Some of the links can be extended into a number of components. In the foregoing marine food chain, for example, the animal-eating animal link is in reality made up of several links extending from the unicellular animals or protozoa to the birds and animals. This does not necessarily mean that the larger and more advanced animals feed only on the lower animals. The situation may be reversed and in fact is quite complicated. It should also be noted that in reality food "webs" with all sorts of short circuits and connections occur in the system.

The Natural Community or Pyramid

BASIC RELATIONSHIPS. Two fundamental relationships emerge from the study of food chains. First, food chains are always initiated by photosynthetic organisms and terminated by the microorganisms of decay. The flow of nutrients in any community of organisms begins with photosynthesis and ends with decay. Second, in any natural community the distribution of organisms in terms of their total mass and their contribution to the food chain can be compared to the structure of a pyramid.

The broad base of the pyramid represents plants which are the primary food source for virtually all life on earth. The next higher layer or *trophic level* in the pyramid is composed of small animals that feed on the many plants of the lowermost pyramid layer. The smaller animals in turn serve as a food source for the larger ones which make up the next higher trophic layer in the food pyramid. The successively higher trophic levels in the pyramid are typically constituted of progressively larger but fewer animals. In general for terrestrial pyramids the total mass of protoplasm of any trophic level is always less

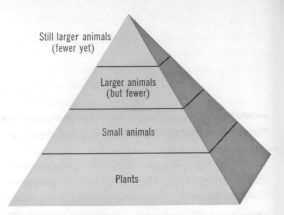

Figure 10-4. The food pyramid as a representation of several features of a natural community of organisms. It indicates the distribution of organisms with regard to their total mass and contribution to the food chain. The broad base is always composed of photosynthetic plants, with successively higher trophic levels usually consisting of progressively larger but fewer animals.

than the layer below it as indicated by the pyramid structure (Figure 10-4). The peak is usually but not always occupied by the fewest but largest animals. By contrast in marine pyramids the microscopic plants (or phytoplankton) usually consist of a smaller total protoplasmic mass than the higher trophic levels because they are unicellular and rapidly consumed. However, their rate of turnover is high. In all cases whether on land or in the sea the amount of organic matter produced *per unit of time* is always greater at the basic trophic level than at the higher trophic strata.

The food pyramid as a graphic device sums up the significant features of an ecological group. It makes evident that larger animals (carnivores) in any natural community feed on smaller animals, and that smaller ones in turn sustain themselves by devouring still smaller ones. The greater body size and, therefore, the greater nutritional needs of larger animals means that they must consume many smaller animals to fulfill these requirements. Consequently, a natural community has many more smaller animals than larger ones, the latter progressively decreasing in number with increasing body size.

The pyramid may also represent the distribution of the protoplasmic mass in an ecological group. The total mass of protoplasm, on the land is greatest at the base which is represented by the many photosynthetic organisms. A substantial portion of the protoplasmic mass taken in by each succeeding higher trophic stratum of animals in the pyramid is expended as an energy source for a variety of activities and thus never appears in the weight of the larger animal. The total mass of protoplasm is, therefore, always less than that of the layer below it. As we continue to ascend the pyramid, the total protoplasmic mass for each layer representing larger and larger animals, which are in turn nutritionally dependent on the smaller animals of the underlying layer, becomes smaller and smaller. This is indicated by the tapering of the pyramid as we proceed to the top towards the animals of greater and greater size.

We can also regard the pyramid organization as representing the inevitable "downhill pathway of energy" in a natural community. The base of the pyramid can be considered as the total biological input of energy furnished to the natural community by the photosynthetic organisms. The total energy present in each succeeding trophic layer of the pyramid is necessarily less than the energy made available to it by the preceding trophic stratum upon which it is dependent. Only a small fraction of the energy taken in during the lifetime of an organism is actually stored in the tissues as chemical bonds of carbohydrates, proteins, fats, and other organic substances, for a good part of the energy has been used for the various life activities of the animal, other than synthesis of various substances. In effect, a progressively smaller proportion of the chemical energy originally provided by the photosynthetic organisms is made available to each successive layer in the pyramid.

TYPES OF PYRAMIDS. Several different pyramids (or natural communities of living things) often exist within a distinct geographical area. For example, a separate pyramid may occur in a pond consisting of the usual fundamental layer of aquatic photosynthetic microorganisms followed by successive ascending layers of bacteria and protozoa → semimicroscopic multicellular animals → small fish → and progressively larger fish until the peak of the pyramid is reached (Figure 10-5a).

On the land surrounding this pond there may be another natural community represented by photosynthetic plants → small herbivores → small carnivores → and larger and larger carnivores and omnivores (devour both plants and animals) culminating, for example, in a pyramid peak (Figure 10-5b) consisting of bears (who actually obtain much of their food from fruits) and lions. Simultaneously, on the very same land another natural community of organisms may exist which is represented by a pyramid comprised in ascending order of photosynthetic organisms → bacteria and unicellular animals → semimicroscopic multicellular animals → small visible multicellular animals such as earthworms and various insects → small birds → and larger and larger birds. The peak of this pyramid (Figure 10-5c) would be occupied by large predator birds such as vultures and eagles. This should not be interpreted to mean that pyramids necessarily reflect in all cases an evolutionary scale.

Pyramids of varying degrees of complexity exist. Some actually interlock, sharing the same lower layers but separating into individual peaks. In fact the preceding two examples of individual land pyramids occupying the same geographical locale can also be diagrammed as a double-peaked pyramid sharing a number of common lower population layers (Figure 10-6).

STABILITY OF NATURAL COMMUNITIES OR PYRAMIDS. *General Features.* A pyramid or natural community of living things is a self-contained and dynamic relationship among living organisms. The degree of stability of pyramids ranges widely from those that exist for only short periods to those that may go on for centuries recreating or maintaining the same conditions that fostered the pyramid originally. By their very nature pyramids tend to maintain

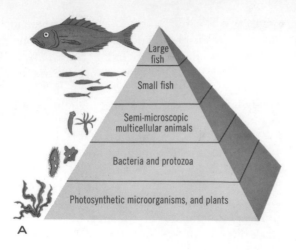

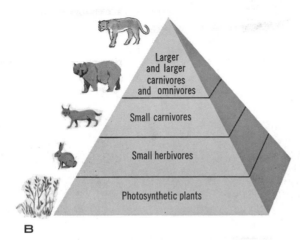

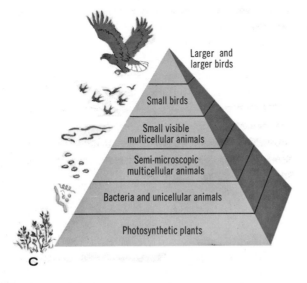

dynamically constant populations within their organization. For example, an increase in the number or production of photosynthetic organisms will lead to an increase in the next population layer, namely the bacteria and unicellular animals, followed by corresponding increases in each of the higher layers since more food is available for each group. In due time, however, the populations will be restored to their original numbers. The increased population of bacteria and unicellular animals resulting from the increased photosynthetic population will soon cause a decrease in the number of plants because of increased feeding by the former group. This in turn will lead to a decreased population of the bacteria and unicellular animals because of the now limited food supply (i.e., photosynthetic organisms). The decrease will reflect itself in a corresponding reduction of the populations of each of the upper population layers of the pyramid. Thus internal population fluctuations within a natural community of organisms tend to be restored or minimized by the very dynamic relationships that exist among living things linked together in a food chain.

The Deer on the Kaibab Plateau. The interesting history of an imposed shift in the equilibrium between prey and predator in a natural community and the subsequent self-restoration to its original dynamic balance is seen in the now-classic example of the deer on the Kaibab Plateau in Arizona. In 1907 the area exhibited a healthy and stable deer population of 4000, the net effect of a dynamic equilibrium of numerous factors. One important factor was the ability of the deer to thrive and survive on the ample local vegetation (which could have adequately sustained about 30,000) as a counterbalance to the high death rate imposed by the heavy predation of wolves, mountain lions, and coyotes. Man's intrusion into this scene by waging a campaign of extermination to protect

Figure 10-5. Food pyramids illustrating: (A) a natural community of organisms in a pond; (B) and (C) two different natural land communities occupying the same geographical locale.

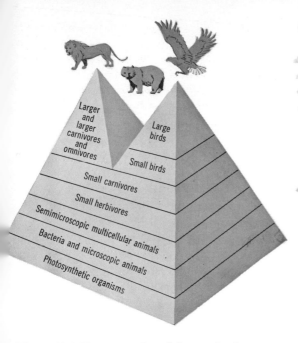

Figure 10-6. Representation of the two land communities of Figure 10-5 as a double-peaked pyramid sharing several common lower population layers.

the deer against their natural predators led to highly dramatic results. Within the next fifteen years or so, following the destruction of some 9000 predators, the deer population on the Kaibab Plateau had increased to twenty-five times as many—a population of about 100,000. The tragic effects of this situation soon became evident. The vegetation of the plateau was now no longer ample to maintain the increased deer population, and within the next two winters about 60,000 deer perished from starvation. The plateau vegetation also suffered heavy damage by over-depletion as a result of the last desperate attempts of the starving deer to obtain food. The remaining deer declined more gradually during the subsequent years reaching a population of 10,000 by 1939 with man acting as the principal predator in place of wolves, mountain lions, and coyotes.

Factors Affecting Stability of a Natural Community. *General Features.* Several factors determine how long a natural community of organisms will exist. The more stable pyramids as indicated by their ability to exist for longer durations are those whose activities cause a minimum of change in their environment. If the nutritional environment is more or less maintained in its original condition by the activities of the community, all other factors being equal, we can expect the natural community to go on indefinitely. Examples of such communities are found in the oceans, large lakes, deserts, and prairies. Net changes in the nutrient environment as a result of the metabolic activities of the organisms constituting a natural community may eventually be so marked as to support no longer the original populations of the pyramid. Under the changed environmental conditions created by the activities of a pyramid, a new natural community of organisms better suited to the modified environment may now arise.

If a drastic environment change should occur (e.g., fires, flood, invasion by a disease-causing organism or by a predatory animal) which eventually eliminates one or more of the populations within a natural community, the original pyramid could be destroyed and possibly replaced by another community. The activities of man in making extinct several species such as the "buffalo" or bison, various birds, and other animals have resulted in a replacement of pyramids. Radical climatological and geological changes and other physical alterations in the environment (e.g., the dust storms in the southwest prairie states during the 1930's) have also been responsible for the toppling of existing pyramids and their replacement by others.

Successive Replacement of Communities. Any particular area tends to experience an orderly sequence of changes in biotic communities, with one community gradually replacing the other, an ecological phenomenon known as *community succession.* The process which is accompanied by physical, chemical, and biological environmental changes ultimately culminates in the establishment of a relatively stable mature community termed a *climax community.* The initial community in the area, which is replaced in time by a sequence of succeeding communities until the climax is reached, is called the *pioneer stage.* The characteristics of community succession are so surprisingly orderly and regular that identification of any of the intermediary stages by a trained ecologist permits a fairly accurate prognostication of future sequential changes. The presence of various plant species is one of the most useful criteria for recognizing a stage in community succession.

One of the best examples of community succession is illustrated by the gradual transformation of a lake to a marsh to culminate ultimately in a climax community which is usually comprised of a basswood-maple forest with its accompanying variety of animal and

plant life (Figure 10-7). The transformations during community succession of a lake area are often observed in telescoped form as one proceeds from the center of the lake toward its periphery. If we consider a relatively young lake formed by the flooding or damming-up of an area, the pioneer community which it encompasses is relatively simple. The plant and animal life in its waters are at first comparatively few. In due course more plants and animals begin to appear and thrive as they are introduced by the brooks and streams draining into the lake as well as by the activities of the wind, man, and other animals.

With the passage of time, sediment gradually accumulates on the lake bottom, the result of deposition of plant and animal remains and fine soil particles transported by brooks and

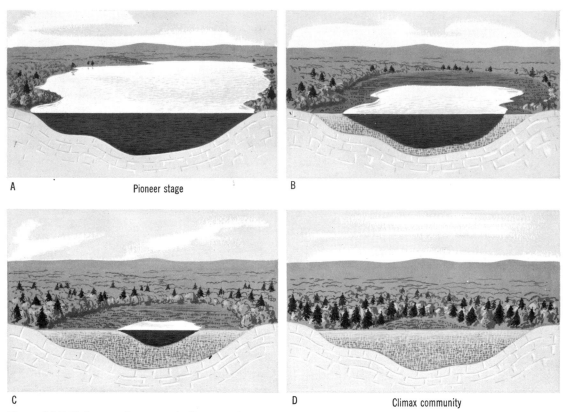

A   Pioneer stage   B

C   D   Climax community

Figure 10-7. Telescoped panoramic diagram of community succession as illustrated by the gradual transformation of a lake through various intermediate stages (proceeding from the lake edges to the dry land) to a climax hardwood forest with its accompanying variety of animal and plant life. See text for details.

streams. The numbers and kinds of plants and animals gradually increase, some becoming extinct and others becoming dominant. Older populations are gradually replaced by a sequence of new populations and thus a succession of communities occurs. The changing communities are significant forces in modifying the physical and chemical environment. As the vegetation at edges of the water becomes thicker with grasses, water lilies, cattails, and the like, the dead remains of these plants, which we call *humus*, accumulates. Thus in a matter of years the lake edges become marshes and swamps, encroaching upon the lake itself.

As we proceed away from the lake edges toward the dry land, we see a telescoped panorama of the changes that will take place as the lake is progressively transformed to a smaller pond and finally to land. The swampy margins of the lake support the growth of grasses, cattails, pickerel weed, water lilies, and related plants. Farther inland the bogs have been invaded by mosses, herbs, sedges, and shrubs including blueberry and wintergreen. Willows take root followed by evergreens such as tamaracks, spruce, and cedar. The climax community is reached with the establishment of such hardwoods as maple and basswood trees. During this entire process of change which takes place over the course of many years the net effect has been a gradual transformation of a water environment with its attendant plant and animal life through successive stages to yield a relatively stable climax community in the form of a hardwood forest. One of the important factors contributing to the conversion of an aqueous to a terrestrial environment has been the accumulation of plant remains (or humus).

The main emphasis in the foregoing example of community succession has been put on the plant population, because it often serves as the major controlling factor in community sustenance and community change. Plants are also the best criteria for identifying a particular stage in the sequence of community succession. It should be stressed that the succession of plant populations is often accompanied by changes in the animal populations. A "young" lake may at first contain a predominantly invertebrate population. Subsequent community succession usually proceeds from predominant populations of invertebrates to those also containing fishes, amphibia, reptiles, and birds, small land animals and larger land animals. Any community, therefore, may consist of plants and animals often representing hundreds and even thousands of different species. At all stages in the succession the invertebrates will be numerically the most abundant group although the kinds or species composition will change.

Frequently, there is a vertical stratification of both plant and animal populations in a given community. The vertical stratification of plants in a forest community, for example, consists of a lower level of mosses and herbs overshadowed by shrubs and bushes with progressively taller and taller trees composing the upper strata. Characteristic animal populations are frequently associated with each of these strata. Vertical stratification is determined in large part by physical, chemical, and biological features of the environment including availability of light, water, and oxygen, and soil composition and food-chain relationships. In many of these situations, however, only a few species are the dominant ones exercising a principal controlling influence on the physical, chemical, and biological environment and thus directing in effect the order of events leading to the next succeeding community.

It should be pointed out that a climax community, although relatively stable compared to the communities preceding it, is really the result of an equilibrium of numerous factors. Any upheaval or significant change in these factors can lead to an imbalance that may manifest itself by a replacement of the climax community by still another community or sequence of communities. Natural or artificial catastrophies such as fires and flood, or the invasion by highly destructive disease-causing organisms can cause sufficiently radical changes in the physical, chemical, or biological environment of a climax community so as to shift the equilibrium and swing the balance in favor of further community succession. Without doubt, one of the most inexorable and important forces in nature inevitably leading to replacement of communities is that of biological evolution. Not only does it contribute significantly to the extinction of species but also to the change and appearance of new and different forms of life.

In the overall picture, therefore, a climax community is relatively stable compared to the succession of communities that preceded it. Inevitably so-called climax communities are replaced as new evolutionary adaptations appear among organisms leading in time to the extinction of some species and the development of others.

EFFECT OF PHYSICAL ENVIRONMENT ON ORGANISMS AND NATURAL COMMUNITIES. The chemical and physical features of any given locale are important in influencing the kinds of organisms and natural communities that will exist in that area. The inanimate chemical and physical environment will in turn also be affected by the activities of the populations constituting the communities as indicated earlier. The significant physical factors of the environment are temperature, light, moisture, pressure, and gravity.

Temperature. On our own planet, organisms can carry on their life activities over a relatively narrow environment temperature range extending from 0°C to 50°C. This viable range is in reality a pinpoint in the vast extremes of temperature that exist in our solar system, ranging from close to absolute zero (−273°C) in the far reaches of space to 10,000,000°C and more in the sun. The internal temperature range for any given organism is considerably more narrow than the external range of 0° to 50°C. In human beings, for example, a change in body temperature below 30°C or above 40°C results in death.

Various means have been evolved by living forms to withstand the extremes of environmental temperature. Birds and mammals possess internal mechanisms for maintaining the body temperature within a relatively narrow range, despite great changes in the external environmental temperature; they are referred to as *warm-blooded* animals. The internally regulated temperature varies with the species, tending to be lower in those animals which have evolved in colder climates. Other evolutionary adaptations, in addition to internal temperature regulating mechanisms, are also possessed by birds and mammals. Those species that inhabit the cold climates, such as the polar bear and the seal, are characterized by specialized protective and insulative coverings of fur and thickened layers of subcutaneous fat as a guard against excessive loss of heat from the body to the external environment.

Some organisms, such as bears, rodents, and bats, during the cold season experience a period of inactivity or dormancy, called *hibernation,* resembling a deep long sleep which continues unbroken for months at a time. The fat depot or stored fat is used during this period to provide the energy for the life activities of the hibernating animal. The body temperature decreases to almost that of the environment and the rates of heart beat, breathing, and general metabolism are considerably lowered. Although the mechanism of initiation of hibernation with the onset of cold weather and its termination in the spring are incompletely understood, it is evident that environmental temperatures as well as internal factors are intimately involved in these changes. Animals such as birds cope with the seasonal changes by migrating to the higher latitudes in the spring and returning to the warmer climates in the fall and winter.

Most animals (other than the birds and mammals) have no internal temperature controlling devices. Their body temperatures fluctuate directly with changes in environmental temperature. They are called *cold-blooded* animals and are less adaptable than birds and mammals to extreme changes in temperature. Warm-environment organisms, especially those lacking internal temperature regulating mechanisms, generally cannot survive in colder climates.

Similarly cold-adapted living things are unable to withstand for any length of time relatively warm temperatures. Since the temperature of cold-blooded animals varies with the temperature of the external environment, we can expect the activities of these organisms to fluctuate directly with changes in temperature. In colder weather, cold-blooded animals may become sluggish to the point of almost complete inactivity. In warm temperatures they become extremely active.

In coping with seasonal temperature changes, other organisms (e.g., insects and certain plants) have evolved life cycles in which they complete their lifetime (from embryo to the adult stage) within a single season or two. They perish with the onset of colder weather, but their progeny survive the winter season in a dormant state as quiescent eggs, embryos, or seeds. The relatively decreased metabolic activity or *dormancy* of protoplasm is seen in seeds, spores of microorganisms and higher plants, hibernating mammals, perennial plants (e.g., trees), and in certain stages of insect development (e.g., pupa or diapause stage, (Chapter 19). With the beginning of favorable weather dormant states are usually terminated and the development of the organism proceeds rapidly.

The dormancy of protoplasm and the mechanisms that initiate and terminate it have not yet been elucidated. In general dormant cells are better able to endure exposure to poisons, extreme temperatures and conditions which are otherwise highly damaging to active protoplasm. One fact seems to be established, namely that dormant protoplasm is in a partially dehydrated state. The return to the active state involves the uptake of water.

The general inability of protoplasm to endure high temperatures can be ascribed in large part to the sensitivity of its protein constituents (i.e., enzymes) to heat. Catalytic proteins (or enzymes) are in nearly all cases irreversibly inactivated by exposure to higher temperatures (usually greater than 50°C) for any length of time. They are, however, far better able to withstand lower temperatures extending even below the freezing point of water. The ability of cells to endure subfreezing temperatures seems to depend principally upon the avoidance of ice formation. The appearance of ice crystals in cells exposed to subfreezing temperatures is almost always associated with the death of these cells, due in part to the mechanical damage inflicted on the subcellular structures by the ice crystals themselves. It may also be due to the removal of water from the protoplasm by ice formation resulting in the disintegration of the dehydrated protoplasm.

Light. Light has a central role as the prime energy source for all life (except for the chemosynthetic organisms) by way of the photosynthetic process. Less than 1 per cent of the radiant energy of the sun which reaches the earth is actually trapped as chemical energy by photosynthesis. A substantial portion of the light striking our planet is absorbed by the earth's surface and converted to heat. During the diurnal rotation of the earth, the portion of the planet that receives no light (i.e., at night) experiences a marked heat loss by heat radiation to outer space. The water vapor or moisture of the atmosphere acts as an insulating envelope preventing in part the loss of heat acquired during the exposure to sunlight. As a result, in more humid climates (i.e., the tropics) the extremes in temperature during a twenty-four-hour period are relatively small. By contrast, in a drier climate (i.e., the desert) the temperature differences between night and day are much more extreme, ranging from as high as 120° at midday to near-freezing temperatures at night.

Effect on Plants. Plants in the course of evolution have adapted themselves to different intensities of light. Some species are unfavorably affected by high light intensities, experiencing an actual inhibition of photosynthesis and an excessive loss of moisture, whereas others thrive under these same conditions. Plants also display striking responses (in direction of growth, for example) to light which are independent of photosynthesis. The response of an organism to a light stimulus is known as *phototropism* and is attributed to the effects of light on the metabolism of one of the plant hormones called *auxin* (p. 414). The duration of light and dark periods also regulates the flowering and reproduction of plants, an effect known as *photoperiodism* (p. 418). Inherited variations and differences in tolerances and requirements for light have influenced strongly the distribution and succession of plants in a natural community by affecting photosynthesis, growth, water relations, and the periodicity of the reproductive cycle. Shade plants, for example, growing in the shadows of trees often display a considerably lower light requirement than large green plants, such as trees, for photosynthesis and probably for other physiological processes affected by light. Other smaller plants in the forest develop their foliage in the early spring before the leaves of the trees appear thus obtaining sufficient light to meet their physiological needs. Several small plants are shade-intolerant and therefore are confined to open areas of sunlight such as fields.

Effect on Animals. In animals light has played a selective evolutionary role in the development of special organs, the eyes, for receiving light stimuli. Animals that live in the light enjoy a definite advantage in survival and have specialized photosensitive organs which offer them an advantage in acquiring food and seeking protection. Such specialized organs are apparently of no significant benefit to animals that live in a completely dark environment (e.g., the depths of the sea and deep caves and burrows) since many sightless animals thrive under such environmental conditions. Light also has a photoperiodic effect on the reproductive cycle of some animals as it does on many higher plants. Several higher animals tend to initiate their breeding activities in the spring at a time when the length of day is increasing. The maturation of eggs and sperm are known to be definitely stimulated by increased exposure of the animal to light. It is common practice to prolong the light period in modern chick hatcheries by using artificial light after dusk in order to stimulate the production of eggs. Day length also plays a role in the migration of birds by mechanisms which are still obscure.

Moisture. The importance of water in living systems as the chief component of protoplasm and as an essential nutrient for all organisms has already been emphasized (p. 229). For organisms living in the seas and fresh waters of our planet, a limitation in the supply of water is rarely a problem. The limited availability of water on land, however, has been a powerful evolutionary force in natural selection for terrestrial plants and animals. Those best adapted for efficiently acquiring and conserving their water supply were favored for existence and perpetuation of the species on the relatively dry land.

Effect on Animals. Certain single-celled animals (e.g., the *Amoeba*) develop a water-proof envelope or cyst which permits them to endure long periods of dessication (several bacterial species under similar conditions form a highly resistant spore stage, p. 358). Adaptations to terrestrial conditions of limited water supply are also seen in several multicellular animals. The thick protective coats surrounding the egg cells of insects and of many parasitic round worms, for example, are highly resistant to dehydration. In vertebrates one of the transition stages illustrating adaptation from an aqueous to a terrestrial environment is seen in the lungfish found in some of the rivers of Africa, Australia, and South America (Figure 10-8). During the hot, dry season the lungfish goes into a dormant stage, burrowing itself in the mud and secreting a protective covering which is impervious to water. With the approach of the cooler wet months, the animal resumes its active state.

Land animals possess several basic structural devices for conserving their body water. First, they exhibit a variety of body surface coverings depending upon the animal group. For example, land-dwelling arthropods such as insects and arachnids (spider family) display an outer chitinous integument (Chapter 19) that minimizes the loss of water from the body fluids and tissues. In terrestrial vertebrates the skin (with or without the aid of hair, feathers, and scales) also serves to prevent excessive loss of moisture from the body. Second, the breathing or respiratory organs, such as the lungs in vertebrates and trachea in insects (Chapter 19), are located deep within the body tending for a minimal loss of water as water vapor from the organism.

Of great evolutionary interest is the fact that the principal kinds of nitrogenous wastes (ammonia, urea, and uric acid) excreted by animals have apparently evolved according to the availability of water. (See Chapter 28 for detailed discussion.)

Effect on Plants. The evolutionary adaptation of plants to their environment, especially to the available water supply, is reflected in several anatomical characteristics. Plants which have evolved under extremely dry conditions (e.g., in the desert) possess deep widespread roots with a large absorbing surface and are classified as *xerophytes* (e.g., cactus plants). The surface area of their stem and leaf structure is considerably reduced and highly cutinized, an evolutionary adaptation to minimize the loss of water from the plant by evaporation (or *transpiration*, p. 412). In addition, the fewer and deeply recessed stomata, the ability of some of these plants to store reserves of water in their tissues, and the relatively high osmotic concentrations of their cells all contribute to a more efficient conservation of water.

At the opposite extreme are the water-dwelling plants, collectively called the *hydrophytes* (e.g., water lilies) which live in an environment of great water abundance. Many are either completely or partially submerged in water. Such plants usually exhibit relatively simple root systems which function largely to anchor the plant body. The submerged organs show little or no cutinized coverings thus permitting direct absorption of water by the surface cells. Frequently, the tissues possess numerous connecting air spaces, an evolutionary adaptation which favors the storage, distribution, and ex-

Figure 10-8. A living lungfish, *Protopterus annecteus.* *(Courtesy of the American Museum of Natural History.)*

change of the metabolically important gases carbon dioxide and oxygen.

Between the extremes of the xerophytes and hydrophytes are the plants classified as *mesophytes* (e.g., oak trees) which have adapted to environment conditions of moderate moisture. Their structural adaptations are, in general, midway between those displayed by the xerophytes on the one hand and the hydrophytes on the other. The mesophytes represent the greater proportion of the terrestrial plants in the temperate regions.

Pressure and Gravity. Although most land animals and plants do not experience great changes in pressure (except perhaps for man by virtue of his ventures into high altitudes and great ocean depths), there is a tremendous range in the pressure of the physical environment in which life exists, extending from the tops of mountains to the depths of the sea. At sea level the pressure of our atmosphere (the weight of a column of air above us) is 15 lb per square inch and is spoken of as a pressure of 1 atm. Atmospheric pressure decreases with increasing altitude, about one-half an atmosphere being the lowest pressure at which a natural community of living things can exist.

Descent into the oceans is accompanied by great increases in pressure because of the weight of the overlying water (in addition to that of the atmosphere itself). Many kinds of marine organisms live at ocean depths of 3 miles or greater where the pressures are approximately 500 atm (and more) equivalent to about 7500 lb per square inch. When deep-sea fishes with swim bladders are brought to the surface, they often fail to survive at the considerably reduced external pressure. Some actually burst because their internal pressure greatly exceeds their new external pressure. By the same token, organisms adapted to atmospheric pressure are unable to withstand the extremely high pressures of the great ocean depths.

The full force of gravity is considerably offset by the buoyancy of water, a phenomenon which is reflected in part by certain structural adaptations in aquatic organisms. For example, large ocean plants such as the gigantic sea weeds may grow upwards hundreds of feet from the ocean floor to which they are attached, and have little or no supporting or strengthening tissues. This is in marked contrast to the predominance of supporting woody tissues in terrestrial plants such as trees which achieve only a fraction of the height of the immense sea weeds. Similarly, the vertebrate skeleton as the principal supporting and strengthening tissue is considerably weaker in fishes (e.g., in the *chondrichthyans*, Chapter 20, the skeleton consists completely of cartilage) as compared to land animals.

OTHER TYPES OF RELATIONSHIPS AMONG ORGANISMS OF A NATURAL COMMUNITY. The relationships that exist among organisms of a natural community vary far and wide, ranging from close and intimate associations to loose and haphazard ones. They may be extremely complex or decidedly simple. They may be designated as described below.

Symbiosis. The general term *symbiosis* is used to designate the relationship of two or more *different* species in a natural community of living things in which at least one of the species benefits from the relationship. The other species may or may not be harmed or placed at a distinct disadvantage. The three general subdivisions of symbiosis are *commensalism, mutualism,* and *parasitism.*

Commensalism. Commensalism is a loose relationship in which one of the species is benefited by the association, whereas the other is neither benefited nor harmed by it. Suckerfish for example by attaching themselves to the underside of a shark (Figure 10-9) manage to obtain protection and bits of food dispersed into the sea water as the shark ingests its prey. The shark, for all practical purposes, is unaffected—deriving neither a disadvantage nor an advantage from this association.

Mutualism. Mutualism is a relationship in which each of the different species mutually

Figure 10-9. Suckerfish attached to a sand tiger shark. (*Courtesy of the New York Zoological Society.*)

benefit by the presence of the other. Until recently the term symbiosis had been applied only to this particular association before it was used more generally and replaced by the term mutualism. An example of mutualism is seen in the previously mentioned symbiotic relationship between the bacterium *Rhizobium* and leguminous plants in nitrogen fixation (p. 235). In mutualism the dependency of the participating organisms may range from an obligatory association which is necessary for the existence of one or more of the participating organisms to the opposite extreme, where the relationship is a loose one that can easily be dissociated without any ill effect on either species. An example of mutualism in which neither symbiont can live without the other is the case of the wood-eating termite and the population of single-celled flagellates which is known to inhabit its digestive tract. Termites utilize the cellulose of the wood that they ingest as their energy and carbon source, because digestion to glucose is carried on by the flagellates within the digestive tract of the termite. The termite in turn provides food and protection to the flagellates. Lichens

Parasitism. Parasitism is a one-sided symbiotic relationship in which one species lives on another, deriving its food from the host during an appreciable portion of its life cycle and giving nothing beneficial in return. Parasitism is an extremely widespread phenomenon in nature and is not necessarily detrimental to the host, although in several instances the parasite has a definitely unfavorable effect. The parasite-host relationship has of necessity achieved a certain balance in nature. Those obligatory parasites that proved to be too detrimental ultimately caused extinction of their hosts and thus must have eventually eliminated themselves by destroying their source of support.

Evolutionary aspects of parasitism. The widespread prevalence of parasitism implies that in the evolutionary testing ground of natural selection it has proven to be a successful means of existence. The general pattern is one in which larger organisms are parasitized by smaller organisms who are in turn hosts for still smaller living forms. The end of the chain is apparently reached in the case of the smallest organisms, the bacteria which are hosts for the bacterial parasites, the viruses known as *bacteriophages* (p. 271).

External parasites live on the surface of their hosts and are usually not specialized in their adaptation to parasitism. Several parasites can actually survive for short periods as free-living independent organisms (e.g., fleas and ticks). Many cling to the outer surface of their hosts and are more or less exposed to the same environmental conditions as are free and independent living forms. The chief structural characteristic of external parasites has been the development of a sucker or hold-fast organ. It is quite plausible, although not proved, that the first parasites may have been external ones that arose from an association of commensalism.

Internal parasites probably evolved from external parasites and were apparently accompanied by specialized structural changes. In the presumed evolutionary transition from external parasitism to internal parasitism, there was probably first an invasion of the soft surface tissues and easily accessible body cavities, such as the young buds of plants and the mouth and rectum of higher animals. Subsequent penetration of the deeper recesses and tissues of the body (e.g., intestines, liver, and blood stream) presented further modifications in the parasite's environment which must have acted as an evolutionary selection device. It favored the survival of those parasites with structural and metabolic features that were advantageous for existence in the new internal environment of the host, and handicapped those parasites whose characteristics were unfavorable in this respect. Several parasites evolved increasingly complex relationships, adapting themselves to live in a fixed succession of different hosts in order to complete their life cycles.

At the biochemical level, most parasites are known to be dependent on their host for various complex organic growth factors, the result of a loss in ability to form adequately these compounds from other substances.

Perhaps one of the most important adaptations made by internal parasites has been their unusual ability for successful reproduction. This has been attained by: (1) *asexual reproduction* (cell division or fission in unicellular parasites, and "budding" or the breaking off in multicellular and unicellular organisms of certain segments, or "buds," each giving rise to a new parasite); and (2) *sexual reproduction* including not only extensive reproductive systems and separate sexes in particular species but also the presence in other species of both male and female sex organs on the same organism, a condition known as *hermaphroditism.* Parasites usually have a potential for producing large numbers of offspring by producing huge numbers of reproductive cells. This is an especially significant evolutionary feature for those parasites which have adapted themselves to live in a definite sequence of specific hosts in order to complete their life cycles. For example, the life cycle of the Chinese liver fluke (described below) involves three different host organisms—man, snail, and fish—in a particular sequence. In complex parasites that use mammals as one of several specific hosts, the chances for sexual reproduction are exceedingly slight. Under such circumstances asexual reproduction (e.g., "budding") has been an important evolutionary adaptation in contributing to the total reproductive potential of the parasite. In the Chinese liver fluke, "budding" as one of the means of reproduction occurs during the passage of the parasite through the snail, one of its hosts. The use of several specific hosts limits the distribution of the parasite and further complicates fulfillment of its life cycle by decreasing the probability of successful transfer of the parasite to its next specific host.

Life Cycle of the Chinese Liver Fluke. Many of the preceding points relating to internal parasites can be illustrated by describing the life cycle of the Chinese liver fluke (*Opisthorchis sinensis*) which infects a large majority of the human population in particular parts of Japan, China, and Korea. In the adult stage, the parasite resides in the liver of man whereas the nonadult or larval stages of the parasite's life cycle are harbored in two other intermediate hosts, the snail and the fish.

The liver fluke belongs to a classification group in the animal kingdom known as the *Platyhelminthes* or *flatworms* (Chapter 18). Compared to that of the corresponding free-living independent forms, the adult liver fluke no longer possesses cilia or any apparent sense organs and displays a more simplified digestive tract. On the other hand, its reproductive and excretory systems are more highly developed. The parasite exhibits an additional structural adaptation in the form of suckers or hold-fast organs for attaching itself to the host. The adult fluke which is almost an inch long lives in the smaller bile ducts that ramify through the human liver.

Fertilized eggs released by the adult liver fluke eventually drain via the main bile duct into the small intestine of the human host and pass out of the body by way of the feces. The common practice in the Orient of using human excrement as a fertilizer, especially in rice paddies, enhances the dispersal of the fertilized parasite eggs in ponds and other freshwater bodies where they can be eaten by certain species of snails. The egg develops within the snail, which thus serves as an intermediate host for the parasite, to yield an immature, free-living, small, worm-like form called a *larva.* This particular larval stage, known as the *miracidium*, under-goes asexual reproduction in the body of the snail to produce numerous other smaller larvae known as *sporocysts.* Each sporocyst in turn gives rise by asexual reproduction to a large number of another type of larvae called *rediae.* Finally each of the rediae yields many larvae of still another type called *cercariae* which find their way out of the snail into the surrounding water as free-swimming forms with large tails.

The cercariae may now attach themselves to their next host, one of several different kinds of fish, and eventually penetrate the muscular tissue in which they become encapsulated. If man eats the fish in the raw state, as is usually done in the Far East, the parasite is released in the human intestine during digestion. The liberated young worm eventually works its way into the main bile duct finally completing its cycle by reaching the smaller bile ducts where it grows to the adult liver fluke stage. Any means of interfering in the life cycle of the liver fluke (Figure 10-10)—for example, by destroying the snails or cooking the fish before eating—can obviously serve to control the disease.

Parasitism versus Predation. Man, like most other animals, preys upon other organisms—plant and animal—for his supply of energy, carbon, and other essential elements. How is this phenomenon of *predation* different from *parasitism* as defined and described earlier? The answer is that there is a very thin and arbitrary line, conceived in the mind of man, which distinguishes between the two. The predatory animal as a rule kills its prey in short order and proceeds to feed on part or all of its body. The parasite, on the other hand, for at least a portion of its life cycle lives on or within its living host from which it derives nutrition. Although it may harm the host and eventually cause death, the parasite nevertheless obtains some or all of its energy and essential nutrients from the living host over a period of time.

OTHER BASIC FEATURES OF A NATURAL COMMUNITY OF LIVING THINGS. *Populations and Their Characteristics.* A biotic community can also be regarded as being made up of units or groups of more intimately associated organisms, usually belonging to the same or similar species, which are called *populations*. There is no sharp line of demarcation, however, between a *community* and a *population*, and at times the two terms are used interchangeably. Populations are not static but are instead dynamic entities which are always in a state of flux. Certain populations may appear to be unchanged in terms of species and number,

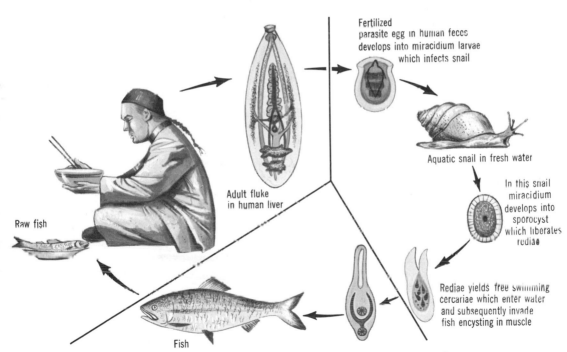

Figure 10-10. Life cycle of the Chinese liver fluke, *Opisthorchis sinensis.* See text for details.

Labels in figure:
Fertilized parasite egg in human feces develops into miracidium larvae which infects snail

Aquatic snail in fresh water

In this snail miracidium develops into sporocyst which liberates rediae

Rediae yields free swimming cercariae which enter water and subsequently invade fish encysting in muscle

Adult fluke in human liver

Raw fish

Fish

but this is merely a reflection of the fact that their birth rate is the same as their death rate. Other populations show rhythmical changes, some according to the season (e.g., the disappearance of annual plants and insects during the colder and shorter-day seasons and their reappearance in the spring and summer) and others over a period of years. Some species may be undergoing extinction while others may be on the ascent towards dominancy.

Population Densities. One indication of the successful existence of a population is its *density*—the number of organisms per unit of area or volume. This may be expressed, for example, as plants per acre of land, number of bacteria per liter of water, or number of people per square mile. The density for any given population of organisms may be decreasing, increasing, or experiencing no net change. If it is decreasing, then obviously the number of individuals in the population who are perishing per unit time exceeds the *birth rate*— the number of new individuals produced per unit time. If the population density is increasing, this must mean that the birth rate is greater than the death rate. When both rates are equal the population density will appear to be unchanged.

Estimates of population densities are determined by several methods and often involve random sampling techniques. For example, counts of the number of birds seen per hour or the number of animals caught in traps over a known period of time are useful in this respect. One of the more widely used methods is to capture a number of animals, tag them in one fashion or another (e.g., by clipping their tails, piercing their ears, or attaching some marker), release them, and then at a subsequent time obtain another sampling of animals. The proportion of the originally tagged animals in the second sampling within the same area provides the basis for estimating the population density. For example, suppose we find that 25 of the 100 animals trapped in the second sampling are tagged. From this we can assume that 25 per cent of the population is represented

by the tagged animals; and since 100 animals were originally tagged, then it follows that the population of the given area is approximately 400.

Population Growth Curve. By measuring the size or density of any given population after successive intervals of time we can obtain not only important information as to its rate of growth, but we can also predict with some degree of accuracy future changes in its size. This holds for nearly all populations of organisms ranging from that of bacteria to that of man, because as populations they all show basically similar growth characteristics.

Suppose we measure the growth of a population of a particular species of bacteria in the laboratory. First we transfer a relatively small number of the given bacteria to a flask of appropriate nutrient solution and then proceed to measure the time course of population increase over a period of one or two days. At first there is a slow increase in the bacterial numbers which is successively followed by an increasingly rapid rate of population growth, a gradual slowing down, and finally a stabilization of population size.

If we plot a graph of the number of bacteria against time, we come up with a typical S-shaped curve called the *population growth curve* (Figure 10-11). The characteristic population growth curve is usually divided into four phases. The first phase initially shows a slow rate of increase in population, often called the *lag period,* followed by a rapidly accelerating stage of multiplication. These collectively constitute the first phase of the population growth curve which is called the *phase of accelerating multiplication.* It is followed by a phase of extremely rapid population rise known as the *logarithmic phase* in which the number of individual organisms increase at an exponential or logarithmic rate. During the logarithmic phase which represents the period of maximal population increase, the number of organisms are increasing in a geometric fashion (2, 4, 8, 16, 32, and so on) instead of an arithmetic manner (2, 4, 6, 8, 10, and so on). The loga-

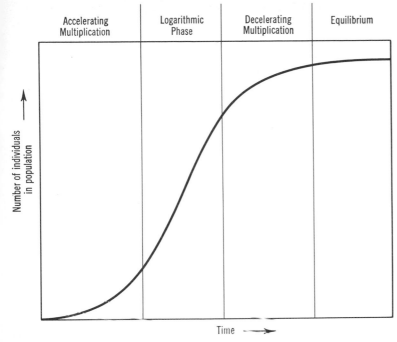

| Accelerating Multiplication | Logarithmic Phase | Decelerating Multiplication | Equilibrium |

Number of individuals in population →

Time →

Figure 10-11. Typical S-shaped population growth curve occurring under optimal conditions with almost every type of living population starting with relatively few individuals.

rithmic phase is succeeded by a period during which the rate of population increase begins to slow down, the *phase of decelerating multiplication*. The final phase termed the *equilibrium phase* is one in which there is essentially no net change in the population, since the death rate is more or less balanced by the birth rate.

Although the total number of individuals and the time intervals are considerably different for different organisms, the S-shaped curve is typical under optimal conditions of the growth of all populations of living things—including civilizations of man—starting with relatively few individuals. For a typical bacterial species growing under optimal conditions, the population growth curve usually manifests itself in a matter of twenty-four to forty-eight hours, whereas that for the fruit fly grown under experimental conditions in the laboratory is observed only after six or seven weeks. The typical population growth curve can be repeated over and over again

by transferring a few of the organisms (e.g., bacteria or fruit flies) from the equilibrium phase to a fresh nutrient medium or environment.

Why is it that the population growth curves for all organisms fall off from the logarithmic phase to become ultimately the equilibrium phase instead of continuing on unchecked? The answer is that the chemical, physical, and biological factors of the environment are incapable of supporting a maximal rate of reproduction for any organism over an extended period of time. For example, under optimal growth conditions in the laboratory certain bacteria can reproduce every twenty minutes, a single bacterial cell giving rise to a bacterial population of about two millions cells at the end of seven hours. It has been calculated that if this rate of growth and reproduction were maintained for twenty-four hours, the resulting bacterial mass would weigh about five million pounds and within a matter of days would exceed the mass of the earth itself—the outcome of growth and reproduction initiated by a single bacterium less than a week earlier! Quite obviously this rapid rate of bacterial reproduction could not be maintained for more than a few hours because of the limited environment and other factors. Such limitations as the restricted supply of nutrients, the inhibitory effects of accumulated metabolic waste products, and the hindrances imposed under natural circumstances by predation, parasitism, and competition of other organisms would markedly increase the death rate as well as restrain the rate of reproduction. The environment, therefore, is capable of supporting only a certain number of organisms of any given species, thus accounting for the inability of any population to maintain itself in the logarithmic phase for other than a relatively short period of time. This applies to all organisms including man as well as bacteria.

The Human Population: Malthusian Theory.
As far back as 1798, the English economist Thomas R. Malthus, in assessing the future of mankind, concluded that the size of the human population on our planet was restricted in large part by the limited food supply. He felt that disease and wars were also means which acted to hinder the increase in size of the human race. Although Malthus was correct in principle in stating that there are definite factors acting to offset the growth of the human population, he was unduly pessimistic—a result of the limited knowledge at his disposal—in feeling that man's economic hardships would become greater as the population increased. Malthus was unable to foresee that vast and extensive improvements in agriculture and technology would increase production of food and power more rapidly than the growth of the human population. During the one hundred and fifty years following the introduction of the Malthusian theory, the economic status of the human population in numerous countries, especially in the Western nations, was vastly improved despite the marked increase in the population. The standard of living, instead of falling as predicted by Malthus, rose considerably.

Nevertheless, Malthus was correct in his basic theory that the rate of increase of any population of living organisms, including human beings, will be inevitably restricted by the limitations imposed by the environment. No matter how efficiently we improve our means of production, food supply, and medical care, there are definite limitations to the earth's capacity to support a large number of persons. When these environmental limitations are finally reached in terms of a large population, the birth rate and death rate will tend to approach each other. This will be reflected by the successive appearance of the *phase of decelerating multiplication* and the *equilibrium phase* in the growth curve of the human population.

The Increasing Size of the Human Population.
Studies of the size of the total human population of the world indicate that we are presently in the logarithmic phase of the growth curve as shown in Figure 10-12. The latest estimates indicate that the world population is now in excess of 3 billion persons. The number of human beings inhabiting the earth has increased with tremendous rapidity during the last century and is now increasing at an even faster rate. In 1650 there were less than one-half billion people on earth representing a doubling of the human population in about 1700 years from the time of Christ until the middle of the seventeenth century. By 1850 the number of human beings had reached one billion, corresponding to a doubling of the population in two centuries. The further rapid growth of world society between 1850 and 1900 proceeded at an even faster rate equivalent to a doubling of the population every century. Between 1900 and 1950 the rate of increase of the human population continued to rise, resulting in a doubling in 75 years. The latest reports indicate that the present world population is increasing at about 2 per cent per year (faster than at any other period in man's history) which is equivalent to a doubling of

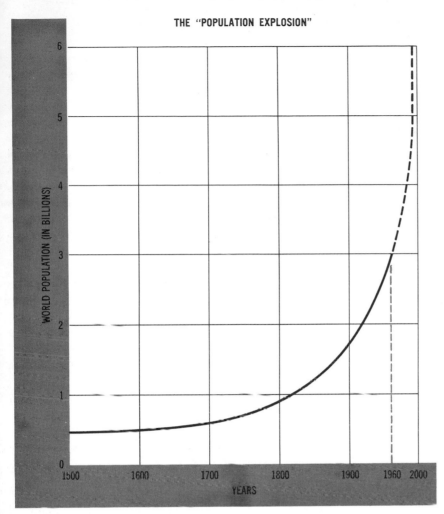

THE "POPULATION EXPLOSION"

Figure 10-12. The human population growth curve.

the world population every 35 years! If the same rate of growth continues, it is predicted that there will be a world population of six billion by the year 2000, over 25 billion by the year 2070 and more than 150 billion persons within two centuries.

The rate at which a population grows is a reflection of the difference between the birth rate and death rate. The development of our scientific-technological-industrial society which began to emerge with the onset of the industrial revolution in the seventeenth century was the fundamental cause of lowered death rates. This is ascribed to the increasing mastery by man of his environment in terms of higher agricultural production, improved systems of transportation, communication, and distribution and increased knowledge in the fields of medicine and public health. The present rapid rate of population increase in the United States is reflected by a birth rate of more than 25 per 1000 persons and a death rate of only 9 per 1000. It is predicted that the present population of 185 million people in the United States will probably exceed 300 million by the end of the century.

Survival and Death Rate. Information about the distribution of deaths among the various age groups of a given population, or how long individuals survive, is important in (1) determining the size and composition of a population of organisms; (2) predicting the future development of population size and make-up; and (3) indicating means of population control. The death rate is usually more strongly influenced by environmental factors than is the birth rate. It can, therefore, serve as an important means for controlling the growth and size of a given population. If we know, for instance, that the death rate for a population of a given species is high during a particular stage of the organism's life cycle, then one of the effective means of increasing the population sizes would be to eliminate if possible those environmental factors that contribute to the high mortality rate at the particular time.

In most populations the death rate is high among the youngest organisms and the oldest organisms. Under theoretically ideal condi-

tions, we can envisage a minimum death rate which would occur only among the oldest individuals as a result of the downhill physiological changes of old age. In actuality, however, the death rate is distributed among the different age groups of a given population depending on the size and composition of the population as well as on environmental factors. The death rate distribution among the various age groups of any given population may be illustrated by plotting the number of survivors (per thousand individuals born) against the maximum life-span. The resulting *survival curve* in effect shows the fraction or percentage of the population still alive at any time during the total life span of the species. The survival curves for a number of different organisms can be directly compared if the life span is expressed on a percentage basis as shown in Figure 10-13. Under theoretically ideal conditions where the minimum death rate prevails as the primary result of the ravages of old age, we would expect for virtually the entire life-span a horizontal line which then drops almost vertically to zero at the very end of the maximal life span. At the other extreme, there are populations (e.g., oysters) in which most members perish early in the life-span, whereas nearly all of the remaining individuals survive for a normal lifetime. In the majority of natural populations the survival curves are found to be in between the above two extremes.

As a general rule the proportions of various age groups in any given population can serve as a useful guide for predicting the future growth of the population. Populations possessing a greater percentage of younger individuals would be expected to expand, whereas those with a greater proportion of older members tend to decline. A more or less equal distribution of age groups reflects the potential of the population to remain unchanged in terms of its size.

Population Cycles. The number of individuals within any given population of a community may experience considerable variations over the years. In some cases it may occur on a

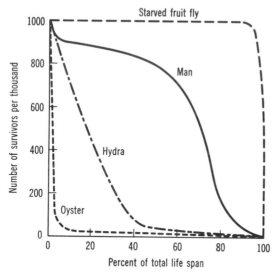

Figure 10-13. Survival curves for man, *Hydra*, and oysters showing the percentage of the population still alive at any time during the total life span of the species. A constant rate of death occurs among hydras, whereas oysters experience their greatest loss in population in the larval stage. Among humans an appreciable number of deaths occur in the first few years of life and considerably more in later life.

year-to-year basis, whereas in others the fluctuations from one extreme to another may take place over a number of years. Most of these variations in population seem to be quite irregular and apparently follow no set pattern. Others, however, display a regular cyclic rhythm occurring in a more or less set manner and are therefore quite predictable. Some of the variations in population size, especially of the noncyclic type, can be attributed to climatic and other environmental changes. The cyclic fluctuations in particular populations, however, are difficult to explain. The alternating abundance and scarcity every ten years or so of the hare and lynx in Canada and Labrador is one of the better known examples of population cycles. Although the hare, like any other organism, experiences population changes as a result of changes in environment, it nevertheless exhibits a cyclic population change over and above that induced by climatic or other environmental factors. The hare population regularly displays a peak population every nine or ten years which is then followed by a period of scarcity. The lynx also has a somewhat similar cycle which reaches its peak of abundance about a year after that achieved by the hare. The two cycles, that of the hare and that of the lynx, are apparently interrelated, since the lynx is a predator of the hare.

SUPPLEMENTARY REFERENCES

Borradaile, L. A., *The Animal and Its Environment*, Oxford University Press, London, 1923.
Chandler, A. C., *Introduction to Parasitology*, Wiley, New York, 1955.
Clarke, G. L., *Elements of Ecology*, Wiley, New York, 1954.
Clements, F. E., and V. E. Shelford, *Bio-ecology*, Wiley, New York, 1939.
Coker, R. C., *This Great and Wide Sea*, second edition, University of North Carolina Press, Chapel Hill, 1949.
Daubenmire, R. F., *Plants and Environment*, Wiley, New York, 1947.
Elton, C., *Animal Ecology*, Macmillan, New York, 1939.
Hesse, R., W. C. Allee, and V. P. Schmidt, *Ecological Animal Geography*, second edition, Wiley, New York, 1951.
Odum, E. P., *Fundamentals of Ecology*, second edition, Saunders, Philadelphia, 1959.
Odum, E. P., *Ecology*, Holt, Rinehart, and Winston, New York, 1963.
Ommanney, F. D., *The Ocean*, Oxford University Press, London, New York, 1949.
Ousting, H. T., *The Study of Plant Communities*, Freeman, San Francisco, 1948.
The Growth of World Population, Publication No. 1091, National Academy of Sciences, National Research Council, Washington, D.C., 1963.
Vevers, H. G., "Animals of the Bottom," *Scientific American*, July 1952.
Weaver, J. E., and F. E. Clements, *Plant Ecology*, McGraw-Hill, New York, 1938.

FOUR

HEREDITY AND GENE ACTION

Heredity is the phenomenon whereby the characteristics of parents are transmitted to their offspring. The study of heredity and its variations is called *genetics*. The current great strides in unraveling the unique process by which living things are able to reproduce organisms like themselves with almost unvarying faithfulness from generation to generation have made genetics one of the most exciting areas of modern biology, perhaps of all science today.

Until the early 1940's genetics was a discipline largely devoted to the study of the distribution of inherited traits among offspring and determination of these traits by particular sites on the chromosome. It has since expanded in an unparalleled series of advances, which continue at an ever-increasing pace. Modern genetics is principally concerned with the mechanisms of heredity at the molecular level, an area known as *biochemical genetics*. It has extended its scope and shifted its emphasis to the chemistry and physics of the hereditary determinants and the molecular basis for their duplication, variation, and coding of information. Genetics now includes the study of the molecular means by which the carriers of genetic information exert their control over all cellular processes, predetermining the course of development and behavior of all living systems. It is a fundamental biological discipline for it provides the very foundation for a basic understanding of the other biological sciences.

At the base of this attack on the secrets of heredity is a remarkable biological substance, deoxyribonucleic acid or DNA, almost exclusively located in the cell nucleus. Various lines of research have led to the conclusion that it is DNA which carries the pattern of the code of life, permitting living cells to be duplicated from generation to generation. This is the same DNA that serves as the master blueprint determining the form and function of the cell. The realization that DNA is the carrier of genetic information and the determinant of cell structure and metabolism, together with our newer knowledge of the chemistry and mode of action of the nucleic acids, has been sufficient reason to reverse the usual order of presentation of genetics found in most textbooks. Instead of employing a strictly chronological approach we shall discuss first the modern-day picture of the hereditary determinants and their mechanisms of action. A second chapter and third chapter are devoted to the transmission and distribution of the hereditary substance and the various phenomena associated with these processes, which we have chosen to call the "mechanics of heredity."

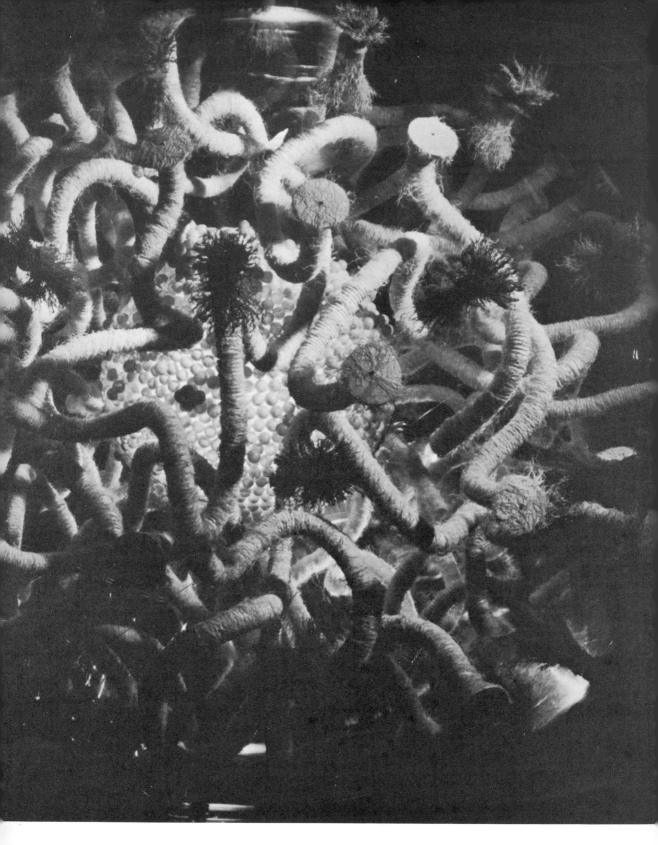

Model of cell nucleus (courtesy of The Upjohn Company).

Chapter 11   The Hereditary Substance and
Its Mechanism of Action

THE CONCEPT OF THE GENE

Historical Note

We were not aware that chromosomes (Chapter 4) existed until they were first seen as dark-staining rods of nucleic acids and proteins during the process of cell division. They had been observed and described as far back as the early nineteenth century but recognition of their significance as the carriers of genetic information went unrealized for more than a century. The past difficulty in detecting chromosomes in the nondividing cell was the basis for the belief that chromosomes formed only during mitosis. This viewpoint has since been discarded because various lines of research have demonstrated that chromosomes are present as distinct structural and functional entities in the nondividing as well as the dividing cell.

The term *chromosomes* came into use in the late 1880's. At about the same time the first evidence was presented by several German biologists that the physical basis of inheritance must lie in these structures. This viewpoint received substantial experimental support in 1902 from the studies of Boveri and Sutton who worked independently on different organisms. Sutton proposed that in the living cell the hereditary factors or units, which were named *genes* some ten years later by Johannsen, were carried by the chromosomes.

As described in the next chapter the epic-making work of the American geneticist Thomas Hunt Morgan and his students A. H. Sturtevant, C. B. Bridges, and H. J. Muller within the decade starting in 1910 firmly established and systemized a number of fundamental concepts in genetics. Morgan and his collaborators at Columbia University, by means of breeding experiments using the fruit fly (*Drosophila*, Figure 11-1) as a new experimental animal, provided a strong foundation for the concept that the genes or units of heredity were carried by the chromosomes. The fruit fly has proved to be a valuable experimental organism in genetic research for several reasons including its rapid rate of multiplication, short life cycle, genetic apparatus possessing only four pairs of chromosomes, and extremely large chromosomes in the cells of its salivary glands.

On the basis of his experimental results Morgan claimed that chromosomes were composed of units or genes (subject at times to change or mutation) which were the carriers of heredity. It followed that the genes were to be held responsible for the entire character of every living thing; and that the course of evolution from the beginning had been determined by changes in these chromosomes. Morgan's proposals became the subject of a great dispute in the 1920's. However, with the passage of time and the accumulation of numerous lines of supporting evidence by geneticists throughout the world, Morgan's views were finally and fully accepted by the late 1930's as the basic tenets of the science of genetics. It was now possible to think of genes as inherited physical entities which express themselves by controlling or determining the process of development of the cell and therefore of the whole organism.

Definitions of the Gene

CLASSIC VIEW. According to the fundamental concepts of classical genetics genes as the physical elements of heredity are responsible for the structural and metabolic characteristics of the cell and for the transmission of these characteristics from one cell generation to another. Inheritance is therefore the transmission of genes from parents to offspring. Each chromosome has many genes arranged in a single and unique linear order along the length of the chromosome, analogous to beads on a string, with each gene occupying a particular

place or *locus* on a chromosome. The size of the smallest hereditary unit or gene is estimated to correspond to a distance on a chromosome of about a millionth of a millimeter. This linear arrangement of genes has since been shown to hold for all organisms examined ranging from bacteriophages to man. In the course of mitosis or regular cell division (Chapter 4) duplicate genes synthesized during the prior *nondividing* stage are separated and distributed as components of separate chromosomes to compose the identical daughter nuclei of the two newly formed daughter cells.

Genes may exist in several different forms called *alleles*, which control the same trait but give contrasting effects, and are reflected by the different expressions of a particular trait. For example, in human beings blue eyes are due to a particular kind of gene whereas brown eyes are determined by another form or allele of the gene.

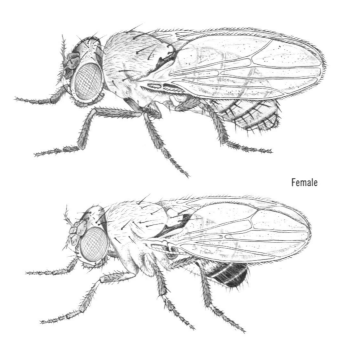

Female

Male

Figure 11-1. The fruitfly *Drosophila melanogaster*, a valuable experimental organism in genetic research.

It should be stressed that the term gene from the time of its introduction by Johannsen in 1911 until recently has been used in an operational sense to define an indivisible and unidentified conceptual unit of heredity. It was commonly conceived as the smallest portion of a chromosome responsible for a single structural or functional trait. In this respect the gene is regarded as a *unit of function*. Implicit in this definition was the reservation that a gene might later be found to be made up of even smaller units. Any variation or modification in the gene was recognized by an observable inherited change or *mutation* (p. 266). The gene therefore was also referred to as the smallest chromosome segment in which a mutation could occur, and in this sense the gene has been considered to be the *unit of mutation*. In fact the ability to mutate has proved to be a major tool for the identification of genes. The gene has also been defined in a third operational sense as the smallest chromosome unit (of transmission) capable of *recombination by "crossing-over"* (p. 309). According to this definition the gene is the *unit of transmission*. Until recently it was believed that the above three definitions of a gene were interchangeable with one another, simply being three different ways of looking at a similar if not the same phenomenon. However, modern genetic studies, together with the other evidence which has identified DNA as the substance of heredity, have changed our concept of the gene.

MODERN VIEW OF THE GENE. We know now that the preceding three definitions of a gene (as a unit of *function, mutation,* and *transmission*) are not one and the same and are in reality not equivalent with one another. A presentation of the highly convincing evidence for this new point of view is beyond the scope of the present book. Suffice it to say that according to our most modern genetic concepts the gene must no longer be regarded as an indivisible unit but rather as a *functional unit* composing a segment of the chromosome and possessing a finer structure of many smaller hereditary units or subunits arranged in a linear fashion. Dr. Seymour Benzer of Purdue University who is largely responsible for this view was able to distinguish by means of several genetic techniques more than one hundred different functional sites arranged in a single linear order along the length of a single "gene" of a bacterial virus. Any of the numerous smaller units (according to our new definition of the gene) can undergo mutation which in turn would interfere with the function of the entire segment which we call the gene. Benzer has introduced the term *cistron* as the genetic *unit of function* and the term *muton* as the smallest subunit (of the gene or cistron) which can be changed or modified to give rise to a mutant form. *A gene or cistron therefore consists of many mutons.* Benzer has also proposed the term *recon* to define the smallest gene subunit that is interchangeable by genetic recombination.

Since DNA is the substance of heredity that makes up the genes, how can we equate gene structure in terms of the nucleotide units constituting the double-helix strands of DNA (Chapter 7)? Estimates based on various types of evidence and several reasonable assumptions indicate that a *muton* consists of one pair of nucleotides. A similar analysis suggests that the *recon* is a measurement of recombination between adjacent nucleotide pairs or mutons. The molecular dimension of the recon therefore is equal to the distance between adjacent mutons. As the unit of function the gene or cistron therefore must be made up of a sequence of one hundred to fifteen hundred nucleotide pairs which constitute a segment of a considerably longer DNA molecule.

In summary our up-to-date definition describes the gene or *cistron* as the functional unit segment of DNA consisting of a sequence of many nucleotide pairs or subunits called *mutons* and *recons*.

In general genes differ in the order in which the four kinds of bases or nucleotides occur along the length of the gene. A definite sequence of hundreds to thousands of these nucleotides repeating within a length of DNA constitutes the classical gene, or the modern cistron.

Mutations

GENERAL FEATURES. We have already emphasized in Chapter 8 that DNA as the genetic substance is the most stable of the active organic constituents of the cell. It remains essentially intact from cell generation to cell generation undergoing no metabolic breakdown under normal conditions. Even during its duplication in the nondividing nucleus prior to cell division DNA is faithfully reproduced and transmitted from cell generation to cell generation with *almost* unfailing invariability. It is also *relatively* stable to many but not all physical and chemical agents in the external environment. It is this unusual overall stability which endows DNA with one of its unique properties to serve in a genetic capacity allowing for the continuity of life from generation to generation, like producing like.

Very infrequently, however, there spontaneously occurs a change in an inherited characteristic which is subsequently transmitted from generation to generation. Any inherited change in a trait of an organism is called a *mutation*. The very fact that the trait is inheritable (i.e., transmitted from generation to generation) indicates that the mutation is due to some modification in the structure of the hereditary substance (DNA) itself. A mutation can also be regarded as an inherited deviation from a defined "normal" standard of reference. The latter is often referred to as the "wild type" and is taken as the predominant form found in nature depending on the organism and trait selected. Major variations, however, do occur in nature and the selection of one as a standard for subsequent mutations is frequently an arbitrary choice. Genes mutate at different rates, causing a wide variety of effects that may be on the one extreme very slight to the other extreme of causing death. A mutant gene of the latter type is called a *lethal gene* (p. 318). On

the average genes may undergo at least a million duplications (in the course of a million successive cell generations) before undergoing a change, but this is sufficient to account for the variations and modifications observed in nature. The genes of all organisms from virus to man mutate from time to time. This ability of the hereditary substance to undergo change or mutation is in fact of the same importance as the property of DNA stability, for mutation is the basic source of all heritable natural variation. It supplies the "raw material" which allows living systems to evolve into new genetic types.

Although spontaneous mutations in nature occur rarely as indicated above, certain physical and chemical agents in the external environment, called *mutagenic agents* or *mutagens*, can markedly raise the frequency of gene mutation. H. J. Muller was the first to demonstrate that the frequency of mutation can be considerably increased by exposure of cells to X-rays. Other factors including ultraviolet rays, higher temperatures, several kinds of ionizing radiation, and different types of chemicals have since been shown to be mutagenic. All undoubtedly act by effecting a change in the structure or content of DNA. Some "spontaneous" mutations are probably caused by natural radiation and chemical accidents in untreated cells.

TYPES OF MUTATIONS. Several types of mutations are recognized. The most commonly detected type is the so-called *"point mutation"* caused by a change within the gene at the molecular level in contrast to mutations which result from a loss or *deletion* of a portion of a chromosome. Most spontaneous mutations are probably point mutations. Point mutations are often reversible in the sense that the gene can mutate back again to its original condition whereas mutations resulting from deletions characteristically fail to undergo reverse mutation. Mutations may also arise from the transfer and reattachment of a chromosome segment to another chromosome, a phenomenon known as *chromosomal translocation*. The particular

deletion - loss of a part of a chromoso
translocaton - from 1 to another
inversion - different order

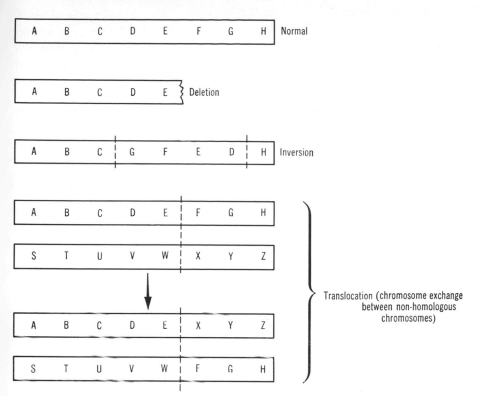

Figure 11-2. Diagrammatic representation of chromosomal deletion, translocation, and inversion. See text for details.

situation in which a chromosome has been broken into two or more segments that reform but in a different order or arrangement is called an *inversion*, and may also account for mutations. The frequency of chromosome deletions, translocations, and inversions (Figure 11-2) is considerably increased by ionizing radiations such as X-rays.

In terms of our modern molecular knowledge of the gene, a mutation consists of (*a*) chemical modification of one or more units of its DNA, (*b*) a loss or gain of one or more units of its DNA, (*c*) a change in the sequence of one or more units such as an adenine-thymine (A-T) into a T-A, or (*d*) an inversion of a portion (one or more units) of the DNA. Thus far approximately four hundred mutational sites (or mutons) have been found in the most fully studied gene or cistron.

Certain chemical analogues or antimetabolites (Chapter 7) of the purines and pyrimidines when incorporated into the DNA structure in place of a normal base have proved to be highly mutagenic. There is in fact strong evidence suggesting that the substitution of a single base in DNA by a chemical analogue can cause a mutation (see definition of a muton, above). According to our definition this would be a point mutation. The interesting phenomenon in certain bacteria of *"mutator genes"* — genes that enhance the mutation rates of other genes in the organism — has been attributed to the genetically controlled production of a purine analogue as a metabolite. The latter acting as a mutagenic agent may then be incorporated into the DNA of the organism thus accounting for an increased frequency of mutations of other genes.

Two final points should be noted. First, the great majority of mutations in general are harmful, giving rise to some defect in structure or function of the organism. And second, although we can increase the frequency of mutations by exposure to mutagenic agents, they are still random events beyond our control in the sense that we cannot direct the formation of a specific or desired inherited change. All we can do at this time is to select for and isolate the particular mutant in which we happen to be interested, once it has appeared.

DNA AS THE GENETIC MATERIAL

Chemical Composition of the Chromosome

Most of the evidence clearly points to DNA as the unique chemical material of the gene or hereditary unit. The chromosome itself, however, as the carrier of genes, is composed of at least two additional substances, RNA and proteins. RNA is present in only small amounts in the chromosomes but in high concentrations in the nucleolus. Chromosomes contain two broad classes of proteins: (1) the basic proteins consisting of the histones and protamines (Chapter 7) which are found in close association with DNA, and (2) nonbasic protein whose concentration varies depending on the tissue in question.

Evidence for DNA as the Substance of Heredity

DNA was first discovered as a constituent of the nucleus of living cells by the Swiss biochemist Frederich Miescher in 1869, but not until relatively recently was its true nature as the unique substance of heredity identified. The important lines of evidence in support of its basic biological role are as follows:

LOCALIZATION OF DNA IN CHROMOSOMES. A wealth of information collected over the years, based on cytochemical studies, indicates that DNA is nearly exclusively located in the chromosomes. The significance of nuclear DNA first became apparent as a result of the important work of Feulgen and Rossenbeck in 1924. These investigators showed by means of a specific staining reaction, now called the *Feulgen reaction*, using the so-called Schiff's reagent (consisting of the dye fuchsin and sulphurous acid) that the chromatin material of

nondividing cells contained DNA. Their discovery that the nuclei of plant cells also contained DNA rectified a hitherto incorrect belief that plant cells differed from animal cells in possessing RNA as the only nucleic acid in their nuclei.

Both DNA and RNA strongly absorb ultraviolet light at a wavelength of 260 mμ which is characteristic of their purine and pyrimidine constituents. Ultraviolet photomicroscopy therefore can determine the intracellular distribution of nucleic acids as well as certain other cell constituents. Although the technique has the disadvantage of not distinguishing between DNA and RNA, this limitation is overcome by the fact that the two types of nucleic acid can be differentiated by various staining reactions. For example, ultraviolet absorption at 260 mμ by the chromosomes together with a positive Feulgen reaction demonstrates DNA to be a nucleic-acid constituent of the chromosomes. We now know that small quantities of DNA also occur in certain other cell structures such as mitochondria and chloroplasts. As an additional example the presence of RNA in the nucleolus was inferred from the observations that this gave a negative Feulgen reaction and yet exhibited absorption of ultraviolet light at 260 mμ characteristic of nucleic acid.

Of particular interest was the discovery in 1934 by Painter that the chromosomes in the salivary glands of *Drosophila* were of enormous size (about 100 times longer and 1000-2000 times thicker than those of other body cells), and that they possessed dark-staining crossbands rich in DNA (Figure 4-15A). Subsequent studies by various investigators showed that genes were located only in the crossbands of these chromosomes, no genes having been found in areas without bands.

Quantitative cytochemical measurements of DNA distribution also give added support that DNA is the active genetic material of the cell. In general the total DNA per cell is constant for each species irrespective of the tissue examined. The sole exceptions are the reproductive cells, the egg and sperm, which have half

Bacterial strain 1   Bacterial strain 2

Figure 11-3. Summary of bacterial transformation. Donor-cell DNA enters recipient cells where it is incorporated into the hereditary material. It functions as part of the genetic apparatus being duplicated and transmitted from cell generation to cell generation.

the number of chromosomes and half of the DNA content of the other cells of the body. Moreover certain cells or tissues with twofold or threefold the usual chromosome count display a corresponding increase in DNA content.

EFFECT OF CERTAIN CHEMICAL AND PHYSICAL FACTORS (*Mutagenic Agents*). Further evidence that DNA is the hereditary substance is seen by the action of certain physical and chemical agents (i.e., mutagenic agents) in increasing the frequency of mutation as well as affecting the structure of nucleic acids. For example, X-rays which have disruptive effects on DNA also increase the mutation rate. Similarly irradiation of reproductive cells with ultraviolet light proved to be the most efficient in producing mutations at wavelengths which experienced the greatest absorption by DNA. The class of chemical compounds called the *nitrogen-* and *sulfur-mustards* which induce mutations are known to react chemically with nucleic acids. It is true, however, that some of these treatments also affect proteins.

More recent evidence relating changes in DNA structure with an increased mutation rate is illustrated by experiments with chemical analogues of nucleic-acid bases and by experiments with DNA that has been modified by chemical treatments which affect the bases. For example, when the thymine analogue, 5-bromouracil, is incorporated by cells into the structure of DNA the frequency of mutation is greatly increased.

BACTERIAL TRANSFORMATION. One of the strongest lines of evidence that DNA is the genetic material stems from the work of the British bacteriologist F. Griffith in 1928 with pneu-

monia-causing bacteria. The virulence or ability of these bacteria to cause pneumonia in a host animal depends on the presence of a polysaccharide capsule around the bacterial cell. Virulent bacterial strains possess a capsule whereas avirulent strains are noncapsulated. Inoculation of mice with either the heat-killed virulent bacterial strain or with the live avirulent bacteria alone proved to be harmless. Griffith observed, however, that animals inoculated with a mixture of a heat-killed culture of pneumonia-causing bacteria and a live but avirulent strain of related bacteria contracted the disease. Obviously the heat-killed virulent bacteria could not have been brought back to life by the live strain. The most likely explanation was that something in the dead virulent bacteria was somehow able to transform the *avirulent* noncapsulated strain into a virulent capsulated one. This interpretation was strengthened by Griffith's isolation from the pneumonia-ridden mice (whose disease was induced by inoculation of a mixture of both the live harmless bacteria plus the dead virulent strain) of virulent *capsulated* bacteria which retained their virulence over numerous successive generations.

Subsequent experiments by other investigators demonstrated that this same phenomenon known as *bacterial transformation* could be accomplished outside the host organism by mixing live bacterial cells with extracts from killed cells. A major breakthrough was attained in 1944 at the Rockefeller Institute by Avery, McCarty, and MacLeod who isolated and identified the active substance or *transforming principle* (responsible for the transformation

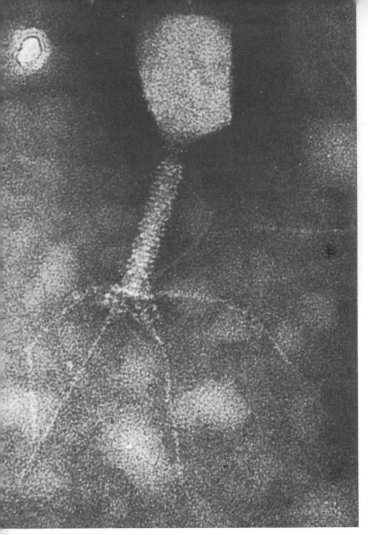

Figure 11-4. Electron micrograph of a T₂ bacterio-phage particle showing some details of its tail structure. Magnification, 500,000X. *(Courtesy of Dr. T. F. Anderson, Viruses, Nucleic Acids and Cancer, 1963.)*

of the pneumonia bacteria) as DNA. Their investigations, which were later corroborated and extended by the other workers, revealed that DNA from the dead virulent bacteria was transferred to the living noncapsulated harmless species transforming it into a virulent capsulated strain. The trait of virulence was now passed on as a truly inheritable characteristic from generation to generation.

Largely through the work of Hotchkiss at the Rockefeller Institute, transformation by DNA has since been demonstrated in other bacterial species for several different traits

including formation of particular enzymes and resistance to certain antibiotics. Neither RNA nor protein can take the place of DNA as the transforming principle. In summary the phenomenon of bacterial transformation involves (*a*) the entry into the recipient cells of donor-cell DNA, and (*b*) its incorporation into the hereditary material of the recipient cell where it now functions as true genetic material directing a portion of the recipient cell's activities (Figure 11-3). It is duplicated and transmitted along with all the rest of the genetic apparatus from cell generation to cell generation.

BACTERIA AS EXPERIMENTAL ORGANISMS FOR GENETIC INVESTIGATIONS. Bacteria have become an important genetic tool within the last fifteen years. Their mechanisms of inheritance and their genetic apparatus, formerly believed to be in a relatively simple state, parallel those of higher organisms. Moreover, they carry on sexual reproduction which is essentially an important means of forming new combinations of genes and therefore greater variability among organisms.

The principal advantages of using bacteria as experimental organisms for genetic investigations are (*a*) their rapid rate of multiplication, which in some instances produces a new generation every twenty minutes, and (*b*) the ease in manipulating and controlling the growth of huge populations of these organisms. Moreover, bacterial geneticists have devised ingeniously simple techniques for detecting and isolating mutants or rare individuals of newly arising types which may only appear in one out of every ten million cells of a bacterial population. For instance, if a bacterial strain which is inhibited by the antibiotic streptomycin is cultured upon agar plates containing streptomycin, only the mutants having resistance to the drug will grow to produce aggregates or colonies of these cells. Thus from a uniform population of a billion bacterial cells fifty to one hundred such mutant colonies may be detected and isolated as just indicated and subjected to further study. Finally, bacteria are the indispensable host organisms for the growth of bacterial viruses called bacteriophages as described below.

BACTERIOPHAGES *(Bacterial Viruses).* Further evidence for the identification of DNA as the ultimate substance of heredity has been obtained from the study of bacterial viruses also called *bacteriophages* (or just *phages*). The particular phage strain designated as T_2, which infects the common bacterial species *Escherichia coli,* has been especially useful in this respect. The T_2 bacteriophage strain is essentially composed of a central core of DNA (40 per cent by weight) surrounded by an outer protein layer or membrane (60 per cent by weight) with traces of lipids. In external appearance the T_2 phage particle is a tadpole-like figure about seven-millionths of an inch long with a hexagonal head and a tail-like structure of approximately equal length (Figure 11-4). The DNA and protein components of phage may be separated from one another by a process called "osmotic shock," a sudden and rapid lowering of osmotic concentration by diluting the medium containing the suspended phage particles with distilled water (Figure 11-5).

In the course of infection the phage particle attaches itself by its tail to the surface of the bacterial cell, and then injects or empties its core of DNA into the bacterial cell. The classic experiments of Hershey and Chase using phage particles containing DNA labeled with radioactive phosphorus and protein tagged with radioactive sulfur demonstrated that only phage DNA enters the infected cell while the protein component remains outside. The protein of the infecting phage is no longer required to carry forward the process of infection once the DNA has entered the host bacterial cell. Within a matter of minutes the entire metabolism of the infected bacterial cell is redirected under the singular influence of injected phage DNA to the synthesis of new phage particles (consisting of protein and DNA) identical with that of the infecting bacterial virus. Approximately thirty minutes after the start of infection the host bacterial cell bursts, releasing about two hundred phages

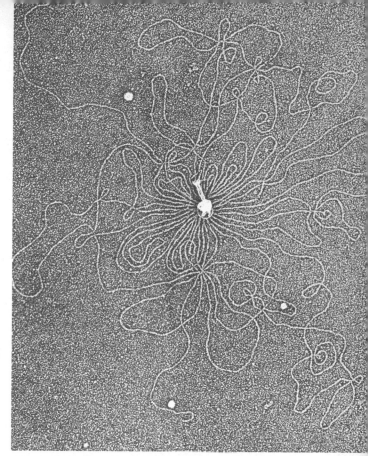

Figure 11-5. DNA content as a single thread released by osmotic shock from a T_2 bacteriophage particle. The resulting phage "ghost" is seen near the center of the electron micrograph. Magnification 80,000X. *(Courtesy of Dr. A. K. Kleinschmidt, Biochim. Biophys. Acta.)*

representing the new generation of bacterial viruses (Figure 11-6). The new replicas of virus DNA and protein synthesized within the host cell are constructed from both the constituents of the bacterial cell as well as nutrients absorbed by the bacteria from its external nutrient medium. Present indications are that the newly formed phage DNA and protein constituents are synthesized separately within the host bacterial cell and are not united until the last moment to yield infective phage particles.

All the evidence indicates that phage DNA, once it has been introduced into the host cell, possesses whatever information is necessary for directing production of a new generation of intact phage particles composed of protein and DNA. The protective protein coat is apparently necessary for attachment of the virus to the bacterial cell prior to injection of the phage DNA into the host. There is little doubt that the DNA of an infecting phage controls the nucleic-acid and protein metabolism of the host cell much as if it were a genetic entity dominating the host genes. For this reason some geneticists refer to viruses as "naked genes." Sexual reproduction or mating (i.e., gene recombination) also occurs among the viruses as it does among bacteria and higher forms of life.

PLANT AND ANIMAL VIRUSES. Although most bacterial viruses contain DNA, certain animal viruses contain DNA, others contain only RNA, whereas still others contain both DNA and RNA. Plant viruses, however, possess RNA ex-

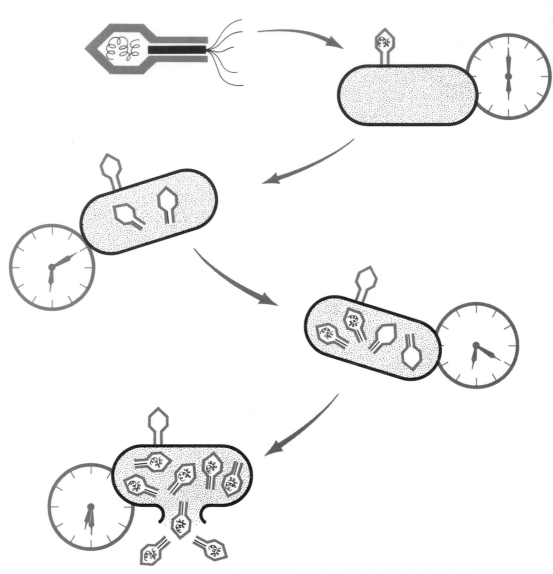

Figure 11-6. Schematic representation of the course of infection of a host bacterial cell by bacteriophage.

clusively. *Influenza virus* and *polio virus* which attack animal cells, and *tobacco mosaic virus* and *turnip yellow mosaic virus* which attack plant cells represent examples of RNA viruses. The fact that the RNA of these viruses apparently acts like the DNA of phages (by transmitting genetic information and apparently directing the production of new virus particles within the host cells) suggests that RNA is the functional equivalent of DNA in these forms.

The RNA content of plant viruses ranges from 6 per cent in tobacco mosaic virus to 35 per cent in turnip yellow mosaic virus with the remainder of the virus particles consisting of protein. Tobacco mosaic virus (called TMV for short) is a rod-shaped particle about ten-millionths of an inch (or 250 mμ) long consisting of a thick-walled cylinder of protein enclosing a rod-like core of RNA within its hollow center (Figure 11-7). The independent experiments of Schramm in Germany and Fraenkel-Conrat in the United States, working largely with crystalline tobacco mosaic virus, clearly demonstrated that the RNA alone of plant viruses and not the protein was responsible for transmitting inherited characters. They separated the protein and nucleic acid components of TMV from each other by chemical extraction procedures and showed that the RNA alone was infectious whereas the separated protein coat was not. They were also able to reconstitute a "hybrid" virus by combining the RNA from one strain of virus with the protein portion from a related but distinguishable virus. The "hybrid" virus particles produced an infection whose characteristics were always the same as those of the strain from which the RNA had been obtained (Figure 11-8).

TRANSDUCTION. The phenomenon called *transduction* discovered by the American geneticists Zinder and Lederberg in 1952 is one in which bacteriophages serve as a vehicle for the transmission of genetic information in bacterial chromosomes from a donor bacterium to a recipient bacterium. Transduction may be initiated in certain bacteria by infection with a class of bacteriophages (called *temperate*

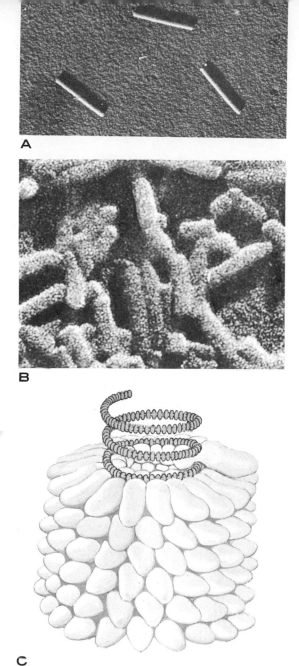

Figure 11-7. Electron micrographs of tobacco mosaic virus. (A) Magnification, 75,000X *(courtesy of Dr. R. C. Williams, Virus Laboratory, Univ. of Calif., Berkeley)*; (B) magnification, 350,000X. Some of the rods exhibit surface detail indicative of their helical structure *(courtesy of Dr. R. G. Hart, J. Mol. Biology)*; (C) conceptual structure of tobacco mosaic virus showing the globular protein units of the protein cylinder enclosing the RNA core *(adapted from H. Fraenkel-Conrat, The Viruses, Academic Press).*

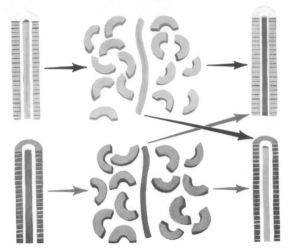

Figure 11-8. Schematic representation of "hybrid" experiments with tobacco mosaic virus in which RNA from one strain of virus was combined with the protein of another (*adapted from H. Fraenkel-Conrat, The Viruses, Academic Press*).

phages) which do not necessarily kill the bacteria they inhabit.

On the rare occasions that the bacterial cell is disrupted or lysed, among the released phage particles consisting as usual of an outer protein coat surrounding an inner DNA core, a few may carry a segment of a bacterial chromosome or DNA. The liberated phage particles now possessing a portion of DNA from their original host cells (donor bacteria) may subsequently infect other bacteria (recipient bacteria) which may then incorporate the transported host DNA into their own genetic apparatus (Figure 11-9). For example, the phages released from strepto-

mycin-resistant bacteria (donor bacteria) can be used to infect streptomycin-sensitive bacteria (recipient bacteria). About one in a million of the streptomycin-sensitive cells which survive this infection by phages can be shown to be resistant to the inhibiting effects of the antibiotic, apparently because a portion of the original host DNA responsible for streptomycin resistance has been carried by the phage particle and incorporated into the DNA of a small number of the streptomycin-sensitive bacteria. The latter have thus been conferred by transduction with resistance to streptomycin, a property which will be inherited by the progeny of the transduced bacteria. In several instances there is evidence that the bacterial DNA which is being carried by the transducing phage has actually been incorporated into the phage DNA, replacing a portion of the viral DNA by recombination.

The phenomena of transduction and transformation resemble each other in at least one significant respect. In both cases the genetic transfer of information is dependent upon the physical transfer of DNA. In transformation DNA is presumably transported in a free form from donor cell to recipient cell, whereas in transduction the DNA is packaged and transported within the protein coat of a temperate phage.

In bacteria, transduction, like transformation, considerably enhances genetic variation. Both phenomena provide additional evidence for the identity of DNA as substance of heredity.

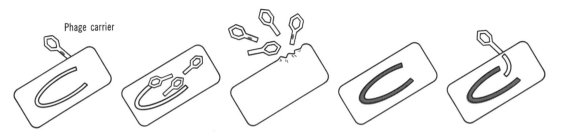

Figure 11-9. Summary of transduction whereby bacteriophage serves as the vehicle for transmission of a portion of DNA from a donor bacterium to a recipient bacterium.

DNA Function at the Molecular Level

Any attempt to analyze the facts of heredity in terms of molecular structure must necessarily explain several important features of the substance alleged to act in a genetic capacity. At the molecular level such a theory must account first for self-duplication, the ability to direct the formation of an identical copy of itself. Second, it must account for specificity. The fact is that the hereditary molecules must exist in many different forms possessing a wealth of coded information, since each organism contains thousands of different genes, and every organism is different from the other. Third, as a suitable genetic material, its molecular structure must be unusually stable to both metabolic action and external agents, but nevertheless possess a sufficiently slight instability to account for modification and variation. Finally, its chemical and physical properties must fit in with its ability to control and regulate cell activities by directing the formation of enzymes. Most of these properties appear to be associated with DNA. The detailed chemical and physical structure of DNA has already been described in Chapter 7.

REPLICATION OF DNA. One of the attributes of the proposed Watson-Crick model for DNA structure, already described in Chapter 7, is its implicit prediction of a reasonable mechanism for gene replication. The Watson-Crick double-helix structure for DNA (Figure 11-10) is consistent with the idea that each DNA strand of the helix serves as a *template* on which a new but complementary strand is formed to constitute DNA replication. According to this so-called *template hypothesis* the new DNA strand that forms must necessarily be complementary to the template strand, comparable to the fitting of a glove to a hand, because of the specificity of base pairing (p. 167). It proposes that in DNA synthesis the nucleotide units align themselves along each of the original DNA strands in a particular order which is determined by specific base pairing. A base on one polynucleotide strand can only be paired with

a specific base on the other, namely adenine with thymine and guanine with cytosine. In all probability the two strands of the original DNA unwind or somehow separate in intact form during the course of replication.

According to the hypothesis, once the nucleotides are linearly arrayed along the template represented by a single DNA strand they are enzymatically "zippered" together in some undetermined manner to form the new strand. The newly formed complementary DNA strand should therefore be identical with the original partner of the template strand. At the same time it would be expected that the second origi-

Figure 11-10 Diagrammatic representation of the Watson-Crick model of DNA showing the two adjacently attached polynucleotide chains forming a double helix like the bannisters of a spiral staircase. The two polynucleotide strands are connected by hydrogen bonding between the adenines of one strain and the thymines of the other, and the guanines of one to the cytosines of the other.

nal strand of the double-helix DNA molecule would also be undergoing replication by this template procedure with the net result that two identical double-stranded DNA molecules are formed (Figure 11-11). The template hypothesis and the Watson-Crick DNA model upon which it is based could account for accurate and specific gene duplication as well as occasional modification of the hereditary material. It can be imagined that on rare occasions a nucleotide containing the wrong base is somehow incorporated into the newly forming complementary polynucleotide strand thus resulting in a mutation.

Several types of evidence are consistent with the proposals of the template hypothesis. Experiments with isotope-labeled DNA within cells have clearly demonstrated that during replication preexisting DNA molecules do not undergo breakdown into smaller pieces with subse-

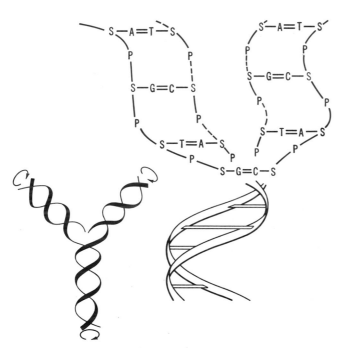

Figure 11-11. The template hypothesis for the replication of DNA. Each polynucleotide strand of the double-helix DNA structure is presumed to unwind and serve as a template for the formation of a new but complementary strand, with nucleotide units aligning in an order determined by specific base pairing.

quent reutilization of these pieces for the synthesis of new DNA molecules. Instead once the DNA has been formed it remains intact through innumerable cell generations, whereas newly synthesized DNA is made from nucleotide building blocks.

The outstanding accomplishment of Nobel Prize winner Dr. Arthur Kornberg and his colleagues in synthesizing a DNA-like substance by means of a purified bacterial enzyme provides major support for the Watson-Crick DNA model. Kornberg and his associates demonstrated that DNA can be synthesized from the deoxyribonucleotide triphosphates of the four different purine and pyrimidine bases in the presence of the enzyme and preformed DNA (Chapter 8). The added DNA is required as a "primer" in the enzymatic synthesis apparently serving as a template for the formation of new DNA. Of great interest is the fact that the newly synthesized DNA (although it lacks biological activity) exhibits the same sequence of bases as that of the primer. The latter results in particular give added weight to the template hypothesis that the DNA which is already present determines the sequence of nucleotide arrangement during DNA replication.

GENE ACTION. How can we explain the action of genes (i.e., DNA) with respect to: (1) their role in determining the form and function of cells and organisms, and (2) their unique characteristics of coding and transmitting information from generation to generation?

A good analogy is to regard the genes or chromosomes as carrying the instructions for the construction and operation of a large factory. The entire set of genes can be likened to a book of blueprints and printed instructions for the building and running of the factory, or the cell.

As we shall see in the next chapter, one of the unique features of these instructions is the fact that for many organisms including man they are supplied in pairs. In animals which reproduce by sexual means one complete set of chromosomes or instructions is provided by the mother (egg cell) and the other set by the father (sperm cell). Each blueprint or instruction corresponds to a gene and any corresponding blueprint or instruction may be identical or may differ from one another. An individual with an identical pair of blueprints or genes for a particular characteristic is said to be *homozygous* for that trait whereas one with an unlike pair of genes is *heterozygous* (p. 297). In the latter instance where the two genes of a pair or set of instructions are alleles of each other which one will be obeyed or followed? The gene whose instructions are obeyed is *dominant* and the other is *recessive* (p. 296). In the more prevalent situation where both genes or instructions are "obeyed," as shown in the trait that develops, then we have the phenomenon of *incomplete dominance* (p. 317). As the master control system of the cell the DNA of the nucleus must send outward into the cytoplasm instructions (in the form of so-called *messenger RNA*, p. 282) which determine the course of metabolism by determining the type of proteins (i.e., enzymes) synthesized. At the same time information from the environment is presumably transmitted through the cytoplasm to the nucleus, ultimately influencing the instructions sent out by the DNA control system. The environmental information with rare exceptions (mutagenic agents) does not basically change the properties of the control system itself. The latter always functions as the primary determinant of the characteristics of all cells.

"One Gene, One Enzyme." The pioneering experiments of Beadle and Tatum at Stanford University in the 1940's with the now famous pink break mold *Neurospora crassa* opened an entirely new area known as *biochemical genetics*. They were among the first to indicate that genes exercise their influence in metabolism by regulating chemical reactions in cells, presumably by controlling the synthesis of enzyme proteins. Beadle and Tatum were primarily responsible for the introduction of a concept and biochemical technique that provided some of the earliest evidence in support of the hypothesis that genes are concerned with the elaboration of protein molecules. For their

important contributions they were awarded the Nobel Prize in 1957.

Beadle and Tatum were able to demonstrate that natural and artificially induced mutations in *Neurospora* abolished the ability of these organisms to synthesize an essential biological substance, for example, a vitamin or amino acid. The resulting inadequacy of the mutant organism in making a necessary metabolic compound could be attributed in most cases to a block in one of a sequence of reactions required to form the essential substance. The fact that the metabolic block was transmitted to subsequent generations as an inherited trait under the control of a single gene suggested that a gene mutation was primarily responsible for the defective reaction. The contention by Beadle and Tatum that the reaction is blocked because of a defect in the particular enzyme as a result of a gene mutation has since been firmly established by several experimental approaches.

The conclusions of Beadle and Tatum on the genetic control of metabolism were formulated in their so-called "one gene–one enzyme" theory which proposed that each enzyme or other specific cellular protein is controlled by a specific gene. Several basic concepts were made apparent from their work. First, that biochemical processes in all organisms are under genetic control. Second, that in those biochemical processes which are resolvable into a series of individual enzymatic reactions, the production, specificity, and function of each enzyme is controlled in a primary fashion by a single gene. Their hypothesis implied that biochemical reactions in all organisms ranging from bacteria to man are alterable by gene mutations. Accordingly each mutant strain differs in only one primary way from a non-mutant parental strain. Subsequent progress in genetics has necessarily modified certain aspects of the hypothesis, but the theory remains essentially sound. For example, the structure of an enzyme in certain instances is determined by more than one gene. We know that some proteins consist of two different polypeptide chains each chain being determined by a separate gene. Therefore the the Beadle-Tatum concept of "one gene-one enzyme" is presently more precisely stated as the "one gene-one polypeptide chain."

The Neurospora Technique. Microorganisms have proved to be ideally suited for studies of biochemical genetics. The fungus *Neurospora*, for example, first used by Beadle and Tatum as a major experimental organism in this area, can be grown in pure culture on a chemically defined medium containing only essential inorganic salts, sugar (as an energy and carbon source) and biotin. The latter as one of the vitamins of the B group (Chapter 9) cannot be synthesized by the fungus and must therefore be provided to the nutrient medium. The mold is able to produce from these relatively simple nutrients the entire complement of its complex protoplasmic components including the twenty amino-acid building blocks of proteins, approximately a dozen water-soluble vitamins, and numerous other organic molecules of biological importance.

Neurospora consists for the most part of a mass of many hyphae or cylindrical strands of cytoplasm each surrounded by a cell wall containing numerous nuclei in a common cytoplasm partitioned by incomplete crosswalls or partial *septae*. The fungus has several characteristics which are especially suited for genetic investigations such as a short life cycle (approximately ten days) consisting of an asexual stage and a sexual stage (Figure 11-12). During the asexual stage it multiplies profusely, as much as one millionfold, by asexual reproduction (asexual spores or *condia* and growth accompanied by nuclear division). During the sexual stage a union of sexual cells occurs comparable to that between egg and sperm in man. The resulting eight *ascospores* which arise in linear array in each of the many spore sacs called *asci* (singular, *ascus*) are the result of meiosis (p. 303) followed by mitosis. Each of the spores can be isolated and grown separately in order to study the transmission of particular inherited characteristics.

If there is a single gene difference for any given trait between the two parents, then four spores of each sexual spore sac have one form of the gene and the remaining four have the other. The mechanism underlying this distribution will be made evident in the description of meiosis or reduction division presented in the next chapter.

We already know that heritable changes in genes (i.e., mutations) take place spontaneously, and can be considerably increased in frequency by exposing the reproductive cells to so-called mutagenic agents such as ultraviolet rays, X-rays, atomic irradiation, and certain chemicals. In the great majority of cases the gene which is "hit" mutates to a defective form, presumably because the chemical or physical structure of that portion of the DNA of the gene or more precisely the muton has been somehow altered. If the one gene-one enzyme theory is correct, a defective gene by giving rise to a defective enzyme should be reflected by an impairment of the specific phase of metabolism in which the enzyme participates. The occurrence of specific mutations either spontaneously or artificially by mutagenic agents is a purely chance phenomenon, and we cannot predict which genes will undergo a change. It is true, however, that certain genes are more unstable (more mutable) than others.

The geneticist by means of various techniques selects or isolates particular mutants after they have appeared. For example, a given *Neurospora* mutant may be unable to grow unless a specific organic compound is added to the minimal nutrient medium indicated. The mutant has apparently lost the ability to synthesize this essential substance. By a routine testing procedure involving the measurement of growth with and without various compounds added to the minimal nutrient medium, numerous mutants have been detected and subsequently isolated which are unable to synthesize one or another compound necessary for growth. That these particular nutritional requirements of *Neurospora* mutants involve gene defects is amply established by the fact that each of these

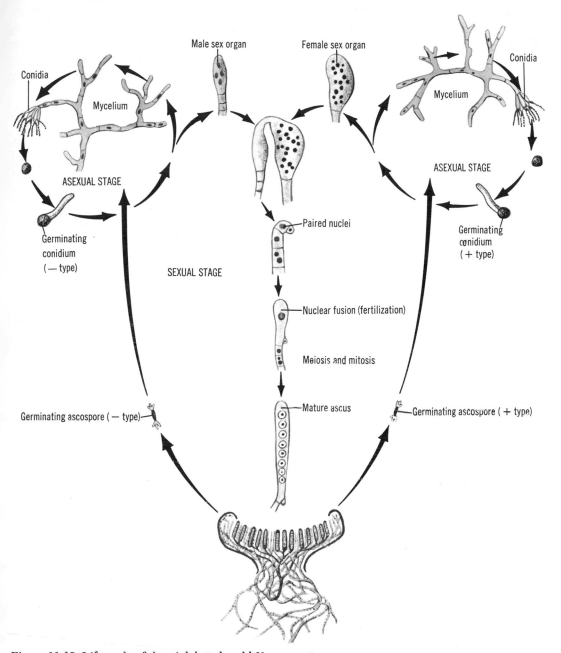

Figure 11-12. Life cycle of the pink bread mold *Neurospora crassa*.

The following labels appear in the figure:

Conidia

Mycelium

Male sex organ

Female sex organ

Conidia

Mycelium

ASEXUAL STAGE

ASEXUAL STAGE

Germinating conidium (— type)

Paired nuclei

Germinating conidium (+ type)

SEXUAL STAGE

Nuclear fusion (fertilization)

Meiosis and mitosis

Germinating ascospore (— type)

Mature ascus

Germinating ascospore (+ type)

traits, involving an inability to synthesize a particular compound, behaves in its transmission from generation to generation as if controlled by a single gene or unit of inheritance. *The Tryptophan-Niacin Relationship.* The usefulness of the *Neurospora* mutant technique in relating the enzymatic constitution and metabolism of an organism to its heredity can be illustrated by the tryptophan-niacin relationship. Several different *Neurospora* mutants have been isolated and studied which fail to grow unless the vitamin niacin, a component of the coenzymes DPN and TPN (p. 176), is supplied to the nutrient medium. By way of illustration some niacin-dependent strains can utilize only niacin (mutant C), others can utilize the compound 3-hydroxyanthranilic acid or niacin (mutant B), and still others can utilize the amino acid tryptophan, 3-hydroxyanthranilic acid, or niacin (mutant A). These observations suggest that niacin may be produced from the amino acid tryptophan by the following sequence of reactions:

sequence. Suppose the machinery responsible for cutting the long girders to an indicated size (prior to their final formation to a given shape) should become impaired because of a defect. Then the production of the specified steel rails as the final product would cease, and the intermediary steel girders would accumulate at the impaired site on the production line until the machinery was repaired or the process halted. Normal production could also be resumed if suitably cut girders were provided from another source much like providing 3-hydroxyanthranilic acid in the above biochemical sequence

$$\longrightarrow \text{Tryptophan} \longrightarrow \text{3-Hydroxyanthranilic acid} \longrightarrow \text{Niacin}$$

(Gene 1,   (Gene 2,   (Gene 3,
mutant A)   mutant B)   mutant C)

If gene 3 is altered in the foregoing sequence as in the case of mutant C, the conversion of 3-hydroxyanthranilic acid to niacin is blocked, and only the addition of niacin to the minimal nutrient medium will permit growth of this mutant. Since mutant B can utilize 3-hydroxyanthranilic acid or niacin but not tryptophan, it is obviously unable to convert tryptophan to 3-hydroxyanthranilic acid, the result of mutated gene 2. Similarly mutant A which can utilize any of the 3 compounds for growth is blocked by a mutation of gene 1 at some unidentified enzymatic step which is involved in the synthesis of tryptophan from other compounds. Additional evidence for this sequence is provided by the observed accumulation of these intermediates by the particular mutants in which further conversion is genetically blocked. In the preceding instance mutant C accumulates 3-hydroxyanthranilic acid which finally spills into the nutrient medium where it can be easily detected. Similarly the used nutrient medium of mutant B will contain a relatively high concentration of tryptophan.

The foregoing type of reaction sequence can be compared to the industrial, automated production line of a modern steel plant where each step in the manufacturing process, for example, of specified steel rails from crude iron ore is analogous to a reaction step in a biochemical

when the conversion from tryptophan is blocked by mutated gene 2 (mutant B).

The foregoing description of the conversion of tryptophan to niacin by *Neurospora*, a process known to occur in animals has been somewhat simplified for purposes of illustration. At least five enzymatic steps in sequence instead of the two indicated are known to participate in the conversion of tryptophan to niacin. All have been established as gene-controlled reactions by the *Neurospora* mutant technique. Note that man like most higher animals can make sufficient niacin from tryptophan to meet his nutritional needs. He is unable, however, to make adequate quantities of tryptophan which is therefore called an "essential amino acid" (p. 214). In effect man is a tryptophan-dependent organism because of a genetic block comparable to the tryptophan-dependent mutant of *Neurospora* (mutant A above). In man the genetic block in tryptophan synthesis is presumably the result of a spontaneous mutation while in the case of the *Neurospora* mutant the genetic block was induced under controlled conditions by certain mutagenic agents.

The original *Neurospora* mutant technique has since been improved and applied to other microorganisms and to higher living forms. The mutant microorganism in particular has proven to be a powerful tool for demonstrating that genes are concerned with specific bio-chemical reactions. It has also provided a highly useful technique for the study of metabolic processes, especially since the pathways of metabolism in most organisms ranging from microbe to man are essentially similar. In addition microorganisms and their various mutant strains have been valuable in studying certain metabolic sequences which higher plants and animals are unable to carry out.

Gene Action and Enzyme Formation. What is the basis for the claim that genes control metabolic reactions by primarily directing and determining the formation of the enzymes themselves?

First, it has been possible to demonstrate in an increasing number of instances that different strains or mutants of microorganisms as well as higher forms are unable to perform particular metabolic reactions because of a genetic loss in the enzyme activity involved. The absence of enzyme activity as a result of gene mutation has been shown in several cases to be due to a genetic failure to synthesize the enzyme protein itself. In other instances, however, where a specific enzymatic activity is apparently absent because of a mutated gene, a protein with most of the physical and chemical characteristics of the enzyme, but lacking enzyme activity could be demonstrated. In these cases the mutant produces a modified and enzymatically inert protein instead of an active one. It is feasible that a change in one of the several hundred amino-acid residues of enzyme protein, particularly at the *active enzyme site* (p. 158), as a result of a mutated gene could readily account for a loss of enzyme activity.

The unusual situation in which the guinea pig and the primates (including man) in contrast to all other mammals are unable to form ascorbic acid (and therefore require it as a dietary vitamin) is attributed to the effect of a gene mutation on enzyme formation. Guinea pigs and primates as a result of genetic block lack one of the several enzymes which participate in the known series of reactions responsible for the conversion of glucose to ascorbic acid thus accounting for the failure of these animals to make ascorbic acid. Other mammals which have no dietary requirements for the vitamin possess the full complement of enzymes for the formation of ascorbic acid. In a broader sense this is merely an example of the relationship of dietary requirements for organic growth factors (vitamins, essential amino acids, essential fatty acids) to a genetic impairment in one or more of the enzymes necessary for the formation of these compounds by the organism.

Second, hereditary diseases in humans and other animals (p. 289), also called "inborn errors of metabolism," can be attributed to inherited defects in metabolism, the result of a genetic impairment in the mechanism for the synthesis of specific enzymes. Finally, the latest findings on the cell-free biosynthesis of proteins, summarized in the following section, further testify to the role of the nucleic acids in controlling protein synthesis.

Mechanism of Protein Synthesis and Its Genetic Control. *General Features.* Amino acids as the building blocks of proteins are put together into peptide linkages (p. 152) to form the vast variety of highly specific proteins. We know that peptide bond formation is an energy-requiring process, a fact which has implicated the participation of ATP. In view of the vast number of biologically specific proteins (e.g., different enzymes) found within a single cell, we also know that certain genetic mechanisms must be operating in protein synthesis to account for this specificity. Such mechanisms must be responsible for the specific order of arrangement of the amino acids in the polypeptide chains comprising the protein, the binding of the polypeptide chains to each other, and their specific spatial relationships.

What is the means by which the code that is locked within the chemical and physical structure of DNA is deciphered and expressed in the structure of proteins? Tremendous progress has been attained in this area within recent years. The indications strongly point to RNA (whose synthesis in the nucleus is apparently directed by DNA) as the "messenger" that carries information from the cell nucleus to the cytoplasm where it participates directly in protein synthesis.

Enzymatic Basis for Protein Synthesis. It is only within the last few years that we have finally been able to obtain cell-free extracts capable of synthesizing proteins from amino acids. These cell-free preparations exhibit a requirement for ATP and have been shown to consist of several different enzymes and ribonucleic acids including ribosomes. They collectively account for the energy requirement in peptide bone formation and the structural specificity of the proteins synthesized. Our present-day views of the mechanism of protein synthesis are based in large part on experimental evidence and in part on hypothesis. The essential features of the most generally accepted mode of protein synthesis starting with amino acids consists of the following sequence of reactions. A good deal more research is necessary to elucidate the process further.

Step 1. The first stage in protein synthesis results in the formation from ATP and an amino acid of an *AMP-amino acid compound* known as an *"activated" amino acid.* The reaction is catalyzed by a ribosomal enzyme which is specific for each different amino acid.

$$\text{Amino acid} + \text{ATP} \underset{\text{Enzyme}}{\rightleftharpoons}$$
$$\text{Enzyme–AMP} \sim \text{Amino acid} + \text{P–Pi}$$

Pyrophosphate (designated as P-Pi) is also produced and represents the two phosphate groups which were originally part of the ATP molecule. The linkage between the acid or carboxyl group of the activated amino acid and the phosphate group of AMP is considered to possess the high energy ($\sim$) originally present in the chemical bond, between the first and second phosphate groups of ATP (adenine-ribose $\underset{1}{\textcircled{P}} \sim \underset{2}{\textcircled{P}} \sim \underset{3}{\textcircled{P}}$). In effect the amino acid activating enzymes serve to select their specific amino acids from the mixture of many substances in the cytoplasm as well as to activate them.

Step 2. The next stage in protein synthesis involves an enzymatic reaction of the enzyme-bound AMP-amino acid with a small molecular-weight *soluble RNA,* usually designated as sRNA, (also called *transfer or adaptor RNA*) located in the cytoplasm, to form an *amino acid~sRNA compound.* The latter presumably retains the high energy bond ($\sim$) originally conferred by ATP in step 1.

$$\text{Enzyme–AMP} \sim \text{Amino acid} + \text{sRNA} \rightleftharpoons$$
$$\text{Amino acid} \sim \text{sRNA} + \text{AMP} + \text{Enzyme}$$

There is a specific sRNA for each particular amino acid. It is now known that sRNA consists of a single chain of some 70 nucleotides that is folded back upon itself.

Step 3. Each *amino acid ~ sRNA* compound is then transferred to a specific site on another RNA called *messenger RNA (mRNA)* attached to the ribosomes.

$$\text{Messenger (on Ribosomes) RNA} + \text{Amino acid} \sim$$
$$\text{sRNA} \rightleftharpoons \text{Messenger (on Ribosomes) RNA} -$$
$$\text{Amino acid} \sim \text{sRNA}$$

You will recall that the ribosomes themselves have a high content of RNA (60 per cent RNA and 40 per cent protein) representing about 80 per cent of the total RNA of the cell. There are, therefore, three types of cytoplasmic RNA: *transfer RNA, messenger RNA,* and *ribosomal RNA.*

Step 4. The various amino acid ~ sRNA compounds then somehow react with other amino acid ~ sRNA compounds properly aligned on the messenger RNA attached to the ribosomes to form a specific polypeptide chain or protein which appears first on the ribosomes. At the same time the transfer RNA molecules are liberated to pick up other activated amino acids.

$$\text{Messenger (on Ribosomes) RNA} - \text{Amino acid} \sim$$
$$\text{sRNA} \rightleftharpoons \text{Protein or Polypeptide chain} +$$
$$\text{Messenger RNA} + \text{Ribosomes} + \text{sNRA}$$

Various lines of evidence indicate that messenger RNA is the specific template for the synthesis of specific proteins. Messenger RNA is in turn apparently enzymatically synthesized in the nucleus using DNA as its template and thus reflects the genetic information contained in the structure of DNA. Very recent evidence also indicates that the ribosomes do not function as isolated units, but appear to be held together in clusters called *polyribosomes* by messenger RNA (Figure 11-13).

In brief protein synthesis consists of (1) amino-acid activation, (2) formation of an amino acid-soluble RNA compound, (3) attachment of the amino acid-soluble RNA compound to a specific site determined by messenger RNA on the ribosomes, and (4) linkage together of the amino acids—each attached to its own specific soluble RNA at a particular site on the ribosomes—in a specific sequence determined by messenger RNA to form a specific polypeptide chain or protein.

Several interesting points emerge from this scheme for protein synthesis. First, the high energy originally obtained from ATP in step 1 above has presumably been preserved during the succeeding steps to be finally utilized in the formation of the peptide bonds of the protein. Second, it can be inferred that the messenger RNA attached to the ribosomes or polyribosomes serves as a template apparatus on which amino acids are assembled in a particular order before they are linked or "zippered" together in an as yet unknown manner to form the polypeptide chain of a protein.

In addition to the partial characterization of some of the enzymatic steps indicated, other important experiments support the foregoing view of protein synthesis. The administration of radioactively labeled amino acids to intact mice results in an initial appearance of the amino acids in the insoluble RNA-protein fraction of liver ribosomes. At the enzymatic level treatment of ribosomes with an enzyme that specifically hydrolyzes RNA destroys their ability to incorporate amino acids into the protein structure. We also know from studies with intact cells that RNA is required for protein synthesis, and that RNA is present in greatest concentrations in the cytoplasm of actively

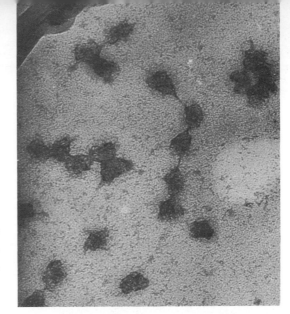

Figure 11-13. Electron micrograph of polyribosomes from rabbit reticuloycytes (cells that make hemoglobin). Note the connecting threads between some of the ribosomes. Magnification, 400,000X *(courtesy of Drs. H. S. Slayter and A. Rich, Scient. Amer.).*

growing cells (e.g., embryonic and tumor tissue) and in cells which are continually synthesizing and releasing proteins (e.g., certain glandular tissue such as the pancreas).

Genetic Basis for Protein Synthesis. Many different lines of evidence have clearly established that the amino-acid composition and structure of proteins are determined by the genetic make-up of the cell, namely by the DNA located in the nucleus. How is this genetic information conveyed from the DNA of the nucleus to the ribosomes in the cytoplasm where the proteins are actually made?

According to the latest experiments the coded instructions for protein synthesis residing in the compositional structure of DNA are reflected in the structure of messenger RNA. The latter is considered to be synthesized in the nucleus under the explicit direction of DNA. More precisely an enzyme, RNA polymerase, catalyzes the synthesis of messenger RNA in a reaction that requires DNA as a primer. Thus information coded in the structure of DNA is transmitted into the ordered arrangement of bases of the messenger RNA which has been synthesized. The messenger RNA with a base composition resembling that of DNA is eventually deposited on the ribosomes where it serves as a template or mold for protein formation as indicated in steps 3 and 4. A diagram summarizing our present views of the chain of events in protein synthesis and its ultimate dependence on DNA in the cell nucleus is shown in Figure 11-14.

The Genetic Code. In a broader sense protein synthesis is a reflection of the genetic messages encoded in DNA. Proteins, primarily in the form of enzymes, are the fundamental machinery of all living cells, and are therefore the means by which genetic information is expressed and put to work.

How can we account for the coding of information within the chemical and physical structure of DNA? Proteins and nucleic acids share a common structural feature in that both consist essentially of a specific linear sequence of amino acid units and nucleotide units respectively. A major difference is that proteins may contain as many as twenty or so different amino acids whereas nucleic acids contain only four different kinds of purine and pyrimidine bases.

What is the nature of the code in the structure of DNA and therefore in the messenger RNA (whose synthesis and composition DNA directs) which permits it to chose specifically any of the twenty or so amino acids and determine its order of arrangement in a protein molecule? It is undoubtedly the sequence of the bases in DNA and therefore of that in the messenger RNA which determines specificity. If we regard messenger RNA (on the surface of the ribosomes) as the template or form to which the activated amino acids are attached in the proper order prior to forming a polypeptide chain, then the sequence of the four bases along the nucleic-acid chain presumably serves as a code in determining the sequence of amino acids in the protein chain.

The DNA molecule can exist in billions of similar but unique forms depending on the exact sequence and proportions of the four different bases in the polynucleotide strands. This varying sequence is a kind of code that contains the genetic information of the individual and the species. The proportions of these bases (A + T/G + C) appear to be constant and typical for each particular species of organism.

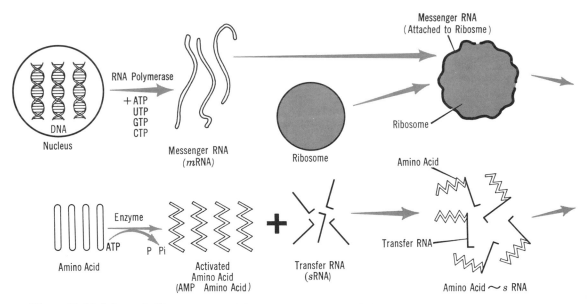

Figure 11-14. Schematic diagram summarizing our present views of the sequence of events in protein synthesis and its dependence on RNA. See text for details.

In some DNA molecules the content of A + T is greater than that of G + C while in others the reverse is true. Each species must therefore have its own specific DNA base sequences which determine whether its reproductive cells will give rise to a mouse, a man, an oak tree, or a fly. Within any given species each individual has a specific pattern of DNA (received from its ancestors) which makes him different from any other individual in the species.

Can a wealth of information such as that which is believed to be carried in DNA be stored in a four-unit code represented by the four different nucleotides? Our own twenty-six-letter alphabet in various combinations of words and sentences is used to represent an almost infinite volume of information. If necessary this information can be recoded in terms of the ten number digits extending from zero to nine as is often done in storing information on punch cards. And in fact at the other extreme we occasionally employ in some of our practices a two-unit code, namely the dot and dash of the Morse code which is also capable of representing a vast volume of information. The idea then that a four-digit code or four-letter alphabet such as that represented by the four nucleotide units of DNA could be the repository of a tremendous store of information seems highly reasonable. Crick, as one of the originators of the Watson-Crick DNA model, has speculated that if we were to consider that the base pairs correspond to the dots and dashes of the Morse code, the DNA contained within a single human cell is sufficient to encode about 1000 large textbooks. The average number of nucleotide units making up a DNA molecule is approximately 10,000 and therefore the number of possible arrangements is tremendous.

How could this information be coded within the DNA molecules? Several possibilities exist. For one thing we know that the proportions and presumably the sequence of the different nucleotides in any given polynucleotide strand varies according to the given DNA so that no two nucleic acids need be alike, just as no two proteins are alike because of differences in the composition and order of arrangement of their amino-acid units. Although little is yet known about the exact sequence of the nucleotides in DNA, it is well established that wide varia-

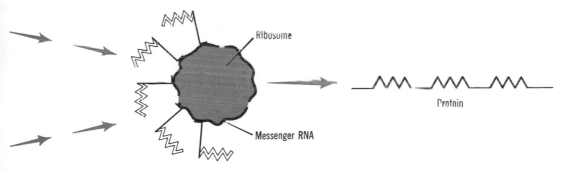

Ribosome

Messenger RNA

Protein

tions in gross composition of individual nucleic acids occur. A reasonable assumption is that the specificity of the nucleic acids depends not only on gross composition but on the different sequences of nucleotides as well. The possible number of different combinations of nucleotides within any DNA molecule made up of an average of 10,000 nucleotides is therefore astronomical.

Nucleotide sequence seems to be the important possible basis for the specificity of DNA molecules. This must manifest itself eventually in specific proteins, for proteins as giant molecules consisting largely of hundreds of amino acid units arranged end-to-end in a particular and unique order obviously requires a master plan or set of instructions of some kind. The sequence of bases in each DNA molecule determines in what particular order amino acids will be assembled in the polypeptide chains that make up the protein. The question is: "How can the sequence of twenty different amino acids be directed by only four kinds of bases? Apparently more than one base pair must be used for each amino acid. Of the several codes that have been proposed those which have attracted the most attention are the ones employing a *triplet system* whereby bases are taken three at a time for a coding unit. From theoretical considerations alone it seems very likely that a particular sequence of three bases as the basic code unit in messenger RNA is specific for each amino acid. Very recent experimental data have in fact strongly indicated this to be the case.

The triplet system would be analogous to making as many different possible three-letter words given four letters to work with. The maximal number of words under the above conditions would actually be sixty-four. Based on certain valid assumptions all but twenty can be eliminated since some of the combinations would be nonsense. For example, given the four letters T, N, E, and P some of the possible three-letter words that could be constructed are PEN, TEN, NET, and PET. Other possible combinations such as PTE, NPE, and

Table 11-1 A Genetic Code for Messenger RNA and the Amino Acids

AMINO ACID	TRIPLET CODE BASES° (SEQUENCE OF BASES NOT ESTABLISHED)
Alanine	CCG
Arginine	CGC
Asparagine	ACA
Aspartic acid	GUA
Cysteine	UUG
Glutamic acid	GAA
Glutamine	ACA
Glycine	UGG
Histidine	ACC
Isoleucine	UAU
Leucine	UUG
Lysine	AAA
Methionine	UGA
Phenylalanine	UUU
Proline	CCC
Serine	UCU
Threonine	CAC
Tryptophan	GGC
Tyrosine	AUU
Valine	UGU

°A=Adenine C=Cytidine G=Guanine U=Uracil

TPE, however, would be eliminated since they obviously make no sense. Similarly, a situation in which all possible arrangements of the letters of our alphabet into words would not be acceptable since many of the so-called "words" would also make nonsense. Presumably each of these twenty combinations of three bases or "three-letter words" would represent the specific code for each of the amino acids.

The ultimate hope is that the vast welter of specific information contained within the chemical and physical structure of the DNA molecule will be understood, and the code will be broken. The attack on this code is being conducted in many laboratories and the latest progress has already brought forth a tentative triplet type of code for the twenty or so naturally occurring amino acids (Table 11-1). It is generally assumed on the basis of certain evidence that all living systems use the same code, although some variations in the code occur.

In summary the present status of our knowledge and theory of the mode of protein synthesis and its genetic control can be described as follows.

1. The linear sequence of nucleotides (i.e., bases) in DNA contains all the information for determining specific proteins.

2. The information is in the form of a triplet code which is based upon specific groups of three nucleotides to specify each of the twenty naturally occurring amino acids.

3. The information thus stored in the nucleotide sequence of DNA is transmitted from the cell nucleus to the ribosomes in the cytoplasm by messenger RNA. The latter (with the base uracil substituting for the base thymine) is a preferential copy of the nucleotide sequence in DNA.

4. The messenger RNA which attaches itself to the ribosomes directs the exact sequence of amino acids that subsequently form the polypeptide chain of proteins.

5. However, before the amino acids can be joined into a specific polypeptide chain by the ribosomes with its attached messenger RNA, the amino acids must have been (a) first previously activated by ATP, and (b) then in chemical association with a specific molecule of soluble RNA transferred to particular locations on the messenger RNA.

In this manner the polypeptide chains or proteins synthesized in the cytoplasm reflect via messenger RNA the nucleotide sequences of the DNA in the nucleus.

Control of Cellular Metabolism

CENERAL FEATURES. From what has already been said it is evident that the metabolism of each and every cell is controlled primarily by the nature and organization of its enzymes. The genetic composition (i.e., DNA) in turn largely establishes the kinds and proportions of all enzymes and other proteins within a cell. In effect the genes that are carried in the chromosomes of the cell nucleus are the blueprints for directing the enzyme constitution (by the previously described process of protein synthesis) and are thus principally responsible for the metabolic patterns of the cell.

However, the regulation of cellular metabolism is determined not only by the types of enzymes present but also by such factors as their quantities, spatial orientation, and distribution within the architecture of the cell. In addition such environmental influences as pH, the concentration of substrate and reaction product molecules, and possibly hormones have an important bearing on the rate and direction of enzymatic reactions (Chapter 7) and therefore on the regulation of cellular metabolism. The role of the genes and environmental factors in the control of cellular metabolism are discussed below.

REGULATION OF ENZYME SYNTHESIS: INDUCTION AND REPRESSION. It has been shown with microorganisms principally, and in some instances with the tissues of plants and animals, that cells have the ability to form certain enzymes, previously undetectable or present in only small amounts, when presented with certain substrates. The phenomenon is known as enzyme induction or adaptation and is under genetic control. Such enzymes are called inducible or adaptive in contrast to constitutive enzymes that are usually present in cells under normal conditions of growth. In bacteria, for example, the concentration of several enzymes are dependent upon particular compounds present in the growth media. In these instances the substrates induce the protein-synthesizing machinery of the cell to produce enzymes metabolizing the particular substrates.

Enzyme induction represents a means by which the cell responds to changes in its chemical environment, a response which is directed by the genetic make-up of the cell. Recent experimental evidence indicates that specific messenger RNA is formed during the process of enzyme induction. The present working hypothesis is that the inducer substrate acts at the genetic site responsible for the synthesis of that particular enzyme, namely with a portion of the DNA in the cell nucleus. It presumably combines with a regulatory portion of the gene (or with the repressor substance that it produces) that normally represses synthesis of the enzyme. In this manner the inducer substrate is believed to offset the effects of the repressor thus allowing for the formation of specific messenger RNA and for the synthesis of the enzyme. According to this biochemical genetic viewpoint the major difference between inducible and constitutive enzymes is that the latter are not associated with a repressor effect. In support of this interpretation is the observation that an inducible enzyme can be converted by genetic changes to a constituitive one.

A related but opposite phenomenon is the situation in which the products of an enzyme reaction inhibit or repress the synthesis of one or more enzymes of the metabolic pathway responsible for their formation. The phenomenon is called *enzyme repression* and is probably the result of a combination of the reaction products (which act as repressor molecules) with the genetic site responsible for the formation of the specific enzyme. As an example of enzyme repression, excessive quantities of the amino acid arginine will repress the synthesis of one of the known enzymes (namely ornithine transcarbamylase) in the metabolic pathway which forms this amino acid. Repression and *negative feedback*, described below, appear to be important mechanisms for regulating metabolic balance by preventing the accumulation of excessive quantities of metabolic products and controlling the wasteful synthesis of unnecessary proteins.

EFFECTS OF SUBSTRATES AND OTHER FACTORS ON CONTROL OF ENZYME ACTIVITY. It is also known in several instances that the products of an enzyme reaction may inhibit the activity (but not the biosynthesis) of one or more of the enzymes of a metabolic pathway responsible for their formation. The phenomenon is called *negative molecular feedback,* a name adopted from the engineering term "negative feedback" for describing self-governing mechanisms which decrease the action of a machine or electronics system. For example, in the biosynthesis of the amino

acid histidine by certain bacteria the addition of the amino acid to the culture medium results in the inhibition of the enzyme which catalyzes the first step in the ten or so reactions constituting the biosynthetic pathway.

Other types of regulatory mechanisms for the control of enzyme activity are evident from our knowledge of the properties of enzymes discussed in Chapter 7. We can expect, for example, changes in pH within the cell to affect enzyme activity. We might also predict that within limits an increase of substrate concentration will increase the enzymatic rate. At the same time, however, the resulting increase in product concentration may cause the reaction to approach equilibrium, thus tending to slow down the forward rate.

Other factors such as limiting quantities of reacting molecules, some of which may be used in several reactions (e.g., ADP and ATP, acetyl CoA, the coenzymes DPN, TPN, and FAD), will also influence the course or direction of metabolism as well as the rate. For instance, if two or more metabolic pathways intersect at a common point in the sense that they share a common metabolic intermediate (e.g., acetyl-CoA as shown in Figure 8-12, Chapter 8), the extent to which the intermediate will be used by one or more of the metabolic pathways will depend among other factors upon its concentration and the enzymes for which it has its largest affinity. As other examples we know that the rates of respiration and oxidative phosphorylation are increased when provided under certain conditions with ADP and inorganic phosphate.

In addition it has been clearly shown, especially in bacterial cells and to some extent in plant and animal cells, that the concentration of cellular substrates are in part determined by the phenomena of cellular permeability and active transport (p.112). It is now believed that the cell membrane possesses active catalytic transport systems called *permeases* which are under genetic control and are capable of utilizing cellular energy for the accumulation of substrates within cells. The permeases are distinct from metabolic enzymes found in the cell and are affected by environmental factors as well as the genetic material. The permeases by influencing cellular substrate concentrations may therefore serve in a regulatory metabolic capacity through its effects on enzyme induction or repression, and on the rates and course of enzyme activity.

Mention should also be made of the fact that the internal organization of the cell has a determining influence on the regulation of metabolic activity. We know that such metabolic pathways as the Krebs cycle and terminal respiratory system (Chapter 8) are bound to the mitochondria in a definite spatial organization which undoubtedly affects the individual as well as overall enzymatic activities of these systems.

Finally, there is preliminary evidence that steroid hormones may possibly exercise their effects on metabolism by influencing the state of organization of particular enzymes. For example, the enzyme glutamic dehydrogenase is known to be made up of four associated polypeptide chains or *monomers* which can be dissociated from one another by certain substances including several steroid hormones. The resulting monomers no longer display glutamic dehydrogenase activity but instead now show appreciable alanine dehydrogenase activity. Therefore it is speculated that these hormones perhaps function through their effects on the state of aggregation of enzyme subunits or monomers (and thus on the types as well as the rates of enzyme activities) in the regulation of cell metabolism.

Heredity and Disease

GENERAL FEATURES. In 1908 the English Physician Sir Archibald E. Garrod, in attributing several human diseases to so-called "inborn errors of metabolism," first formulated the concept of hereditary control of the individual steps in metabolism. He suggested that the hereditary substance exercised its effect by controlling biochemical reactions of the body, an idea that proved to be a forerunner of the "one gene-one enzyme" theory of Beadle and Tatum. To date at least fifty human diseases have been described as metabolic and heritable, the result of aberrations arising from gene mutations. In essence a so-called inherited disease develops as a result of an inherited molecular abnormality. In an appreciable number of inherited diseases a protein has been shown to be modified or lacking whereas in others the biochemical defect or lesion has not yet been demonstrated.

Several examples of human disease which have been traced to a genetic lack or change in a particular protein of the body are as follows.

(a) *Alcaptonuria* is a disease of relatively rare occurrence which is characterized by a darkening of the urine when left standing. The blackening of the urine is caused by a particular substance called *alcapton* (later identified as 2,5-dihydroxyphenylacetic acid or homogentisic acid) which is present because of a genetic metabolic defect. Alcapton is excreted as a result of the body's inability to break it down metabolically by oxidation. Persons manifesting the disease (alcaptonurics) unlike normal individuals lack an enzyme (homogentisic oxidase) which makes possible the further oxidation of the compound to carbon dioxide and water. The gene defect responsible for alcaptonuria is inherited as a simple recessive gene (p. 296).

(b) *Phenylketonuria,* another rare hereditary disease which bears certain biochemical resemblances to alcaptonuria, is characterized by the presence of phenylpyruvic acid in the urine. The substance cannot be oxidized because of the absence of an active oxidizing enzyme, the result of a gene defect which is inherited as a recessive trait. The primary effect of the gene which causes phenylketonuria is the failure to produce the necessary active enzyme. For unknown reasons the accumulation of phenylpyruvic acid in the body is inevitably associated with the development of mental deficiency. As a result most individuals suffering from the disease are also mentally retarded, a condition which could conceivably be due to the poisoning of the nervous system by the accumulation of abnormal substances in the tissues.

(c) *Galactosemia* is a genetic disease of young children in which the hexose galactose as a component of lactose (the sugar of milk) accumulates in the blood as galactose-1-phosphate. Although the latter is in part excreted into the urine it nevertheless somehow causes damage to the brain, liver, and the eye. The disease is due to a recessive defective gene which is responsible for the absence or deficiency of an enzyme (phosphogalactose uridyl transferase). The latter is necessary in the conversion of galactose-phosphate to glucose-phosphate in the red blood cells and the liver. Upon reaching adulthood a galactosemic individual can now usually cope with significant quantities of galactose because of the development of alternate enzymatic means of metabolizing the sugar.

(d) *Sickle-cell anemia*, which is discussed in detail in Chapter 25, is due to the formation of so-called *sickle-cell hemoglobin*. The latter as a result of a mutated gene differs from normal hemoglobin only in the substitution of a valine amino-acid residue for a glutamic-acid residue.

The increasing recognition of the important role of heredity in normal body function and disease will undoubtedly lead to new approaches in the control and cure of disease. The problems of two such diseases, namely galactosemia and phenylketonuria, have thus far been handled in practice by dietary control (exclusion from the diet of galactose and phenylalanine, respectively) to compensate for genetic enzyme defects. There is at present considerable speculation whether certain diseases of rather high incidence such as diabetes, coronary heart disease, and schizophrenia are hereditary. Certain evidence although not conclusive indicates that these may well be related to genetic phenomena.

CYTOPLASMIC INHERITANCE

In addition to the genes carried in the chromosomes, units which reproduce themselves also exist in the cytoplasm of many cells. The chloroplasts of green plants, for example, are self-reproducing units located in the cytoplasm. They arise in the cytoplasm of green plants in an unknown manner and their inheritance depends in part on the transmission of the chloroplasts themselves during the formation of daughter cells and gametes. Chloroplasts like other plant plastids multiply by simple division which is not necessarily correlated with cell division. They experience mutations giving rise to chloroplasts which are altered and whose descendants are altered. Chloroplasts, despite the fact that they display characteristics of extranuclear inheritance, are nevertheless controlled in part at least by genes within the nucleus. A somewhat similar relationship may also apply to mitochondria. The recent findings of DNA in chloroplasts and mitochondria may well prove to have a significant bearing on extranuclear inheritance.

The outstanding demonstration in certain *Paramecium* strains by Sonneborn at Indiana University of a specific cytoplasmic element which is responsible for their ability to kill sensitive *Paramecium* strains is another example of cytoplasmic inheritance. This "killer trait" which is due to the presence in the cytoplasm of a specific factor called "Kappa" can be transmitted to the sensitive *Paramecium* strain converting it into a killer strain. Ability to maintain cytoplasmic element "Kappa" is determined by a specific gene in the nucleus.

The general pattern which appears to be emerging is that cell elements displaying cytoplasmic inheritance are transmitted as such from cell to cell although their replication and activity is under the regulation of genes in the cell nucleus.

Genes, Environment, Growth, and Development

HEREDITY, ENVIRONMENT, AND DEVELOPMENT. The growth and differentiation of all organisms proceeds under the constant control of genetic factors. The resemblance of the embryos of higher animals in their early stages of development to the embryos of lower forms, a phenomenon called *recapitulation* (Chapter 31), has been attributed to the action of certain "primitive" genes which regulate the developmental processes at these stages. Presumably gene mutations, acquired in the later phases of evolution of the species, take over subsequent phases of embryological development as indicated by the successive changes experienced by the embryo (see Chapter 31).

Living things undergo a process of orderly change or typical pattern of development during their lifetimes as a result of an interplay between heredity and environment. More precisely, the course or pattern of development that an organism may take in any given environment is primarily determined by its hereditary make-up. Genes thus establish the types of developmental patterns that an organism will experience in different environments. From one viewpoint therefore the study of inheritance describes the mechanism of inheritance of developmental patterns in different environments.

Some living systems by virtue of their genetic composition are able to survive a relatively wide range of different environments, whereas others by the same token are less adaptable and therefore more limited in this respect. For example, the continued use of galactose (in the form of the milk sugar lactose) in the diet of a galactosemic infant may prove fatal whereas the same sugar is of value in a normal child's diet. Similarly those individuals who as a result of their genetic composition possess little or no potential to develop skin pigmentation will fail to develop a protective suntan, thus suffering dangerous sunburns in strong sunlight.

In essence all organisms by virtue of their hereditary make-up are endowed with a particular potential for adjusting to new environments whenever this becomes necessary. The mental and physical characteristics of an individual (e.g., intelligence and body weight) are effected by his genetic make-up in the course of his many environmental exposures. The limitations of his characteristics (e.g., how intelligent he can possibly be; how heavy he will become) are primarily determined by his heredity. The actual state of these characteristics at any given time is a reflection of the interplay between genes and environment.

In light of the foregoing discussion the question "What is more important in the development of an individual—environment or heredity?" makes little sense. The question is better put by asking "What is the genetic capability of an organism to respond to different environments?"

ACQUIRED CHARACTERISTICS. The roles of heredity and environment in influencing the form and function of living systems has been the subject of heated discussion and controversy over the years. The great evolutionist Lamarck (1744–1829) erroneously believed that changes in traits acquired during the lifetime of an organism as a result of extensive use or disuse would be transmitted to the offspring. For example, the long-continued exposure to the strong African sun over many generations was incorrectly believed to be directly responsible for the Negro's highly pigmented skin, an acquired trait which was somehow incorporated into the heredity of the individual. Similarly the disuse of the eyes over many generations by many subterranean animals living in the dark was erroneously held to be the cause for the absence of eyes in these organisms, an inherited characteristic.

The famous experiments of the German biologist August Weismann in the late nineteenth century were among the first to refute the Lamarckian theory that acquired traits are inherited. Weismann removed the tails of newborn mice for twenty-two successive generations but observed that the tails of the final generation nevertheless grew to normal length. Innumerable experiments have since been performed by scientists in all parts of the world with many kinds of organisms ranging from microbes to mammals. The results have overwhelmingly contradicted the concept that environment is responsible for specific and directed genetic changes. The recent Lamarckian claims by the Russian agriculturist Lysenko that hereditary changes can be produced in plants by grafting, and that a plant strain or species may be transformed into another by environmental influences have also failed to receive confirmation. In keeping with our modern knowledge of genetics, the discarded Lamarckian theory would have to presuppose that an acquired or modified body characteristic must produce some effect on the gene in the sex cells. Moreover this effect would necessarily have to result in a specific mutation of only those genes which determine the same trait in the offspring. There are absolutely no data of any kind that support even the probability that such genetic phenomena occur.

Nevertheless we do know that genes can most assuredly be changed by the environment. The use of mutagenic chemical agents such as the mustard gases, base analogues, X-rays, and certain other types of radiation as well as the phenomena of transformation (p. 269) and transduction (p. 273) definitely result in a change of inherited traits. How can we reconcile this with our refutation of the theory that acquired traits are inherited? In these situations, however, the evidence strongly points to either a modification in the hereditary substance DNA as in the case of mutagenic agents, or to an actual incorporation of DNA into the hereditary apparatus of the cell as in the instances of transformation and transduction. No such evidence exists, however, to support the theory that acquired traits are hereditarily transmitted.

According to our modern theory of evolution (Chapter 33) the seemingly direct relationship between environmental factors and inherited traits can instead be accounted for on the basis of a natural selection from the living population of already existing mutants. Those mutants that are best adapted by virtue of their heredity to cope with their present environment tend to survive and become a dominant species. The dark skin of Negroes is probably the result of a mutation which gave these individuals an advantage over those having only slight pigmentation in surviving in an environment of strong sunlight. Dinosaurs became extinct presumably because there were no mutants present in their population with a genetic composition that could enable them to adapt to the changing environment of the earth some three hundred million years ago. In summary a random inherited change followed by an environmental selection appears to be responsible for the general occurrence of better-adapted species in any given environment.

THE FREQUENCY OF GENES IN POPULATIONS. To some of the early geneticists who had accepted the gene theory it seemed quite puzzling that dominant characteristics did not continue to increase in the population and eventually replace the recessive ones. This problem was independently solved around 1908 by the mathematician G. H. Hardy in England and the geneticist W. Weinberg in Germany. They both arrived at the same conclusion, namely that proportions of dominant and recessive characters in a sexually reproducing population do not change provided there is random mating. In the human population as in most natural populations matings between individuals are not determined or influenced by an awareness of the two partners' genetic makeup. Matings are therefore essentially of a random nature in this respect. In effect Hardy and Weinberg stated that the gene frequencies or the genetic constitution of a sexual population is in an equilibrium state which can be formulated by a definite mathematical equation Actually there are several agents, such as mutation, selection, and other factors which may alter gene frequencies in populations. This aspect as well as the Hardy-Weinberg law are discussed in detail in Chapter 33 on evolution.

SUPPLEMENTARY REFERENCES

Allen, J. M. (Editor), *The Molecular Control of Cellular Activity*, McGraw-Hill, New York, 1962.

Anfinsen, C. B., *The Molecular Basis of Evolution*, Wiley, New York, 1959.

Beadle, J. W., "The Genes of Men and Molds," *Scientific American*, May 1951.

Crick, F. H. C., "The Structure of the Hereditary Material," *Scientific American*, October 1954.

Crick, F. H. C., "The Genetic Code," *Scientific American*, October 1962.

Davidson, J. N., *The Biochemistry of Nucleic Acids*, fourth edition, Wiley, New York, 1960.

Dobzhansky, T., *Evolution, Genetics, and Man*, Wiley, New York, 1955.

Fraenkel-Conrat, H., *Design and Function at the Threshold of Life: The Viruses*, Academic Press, New York, 1962.

Gardner, E. J., *Principles of Genetics*, Wiley, New York, 1960.

Hoagland, M. B., "Nucleic Acids and Proteins," *Scientific American*, December 1959.

Horowitz, N. H., "The Gene," *Scientific American*, October 1956.

Hotchkiss, R. D., and E. Weiss, "Transformed Bacteria," *Scientific American*, November 1956.

Hurwitz, J., and J. J. Furth, "Messenger RNA," *Scientific American*, February 1962.

Kornberg, A., *Enzymatic Synthesis of DNA*, Wiley, New York, 1962.

Nirenberg, M. N., "The Genetic Code: II," *Scientific American*, March 1963.

Sager, R., and F. J. Ryan, *Cell Heredity*, Wiley, New York, 1961.

Sutton, E. H., *Genes, Enzymes and Inherited Diseases*, Holt, Rinehart and Winston, New York, 1961.

Wagner, R. P., and H. K. Mitchell, *Genetics and Metabolism*, second edition, Wiley, New York, 1964.

Zinder, N. D., "Transduction in Bacteria," *Scientific American*, November 1958.

Chapter 12   Mechanics of Heredity:

Early Principles

MENDEL'S CONTRIBUTION

The Genius of Gregor Mendel

According to our latest estimates modern man evolved to his present form about twenty to fifty thousand years ago, the product of an incredibly long sequence of evolutionary events in the gradual organization of energy and matter that dates back at least to the origin of life. His earliest written records reveal not only an awareness of the phenomenon of heredity but also his futile attempts to explain the processes involved. Yet man's first major success in striving to understand the problems of heredity after thousands of years marked by failure was finally attained in 1866, less than one hundred years ago, through the genius of an obscure Austrian monk, Gregor Mendel.

Before Mendel's time it was commonly acknowledged that heredity in sexually reproducing organisms was transmitted by the mixing of parental "bloods" in the progeny, an incorrect belief that was accepted even by so unusual a mind as Charles Darwin's. Implicit in this view was the erroneous idea that parental traits lost their individuality by being blended in the offspring as the result of the mixing of bloods, the presumed carriers of heredity, comparable to the mixing of paints. Ironically enough Mendel's great contribution to genetics postulating the existence of discrete hereditary units (later called genes) went unrecognized for approximately thirty-five years. In 1900 (sixteen years after his death) his remarkable findings were rediscovered through the independent experiments of three scientists— DeVries in Holland, Correns in Germany, and Von Tschermak in Austria.

Why is it that Mendel's work went unnoticed for so many years? In retrospect it seems quite likely that Mendel's experimental data and resultant concepts were so far ahead of the state of knowledge of his times that only a few biologists at most could appreciate their significance. Undoubtedly other contributing factors were that Mendel published his experiments in a journal that was not widely distributed and that Darwin's theory of evolution occupied the center of attention for most biologists of that era.

For several reasons the year 1900 is taken as the birthdate of the science of genetics. First, it marks the date of rediscovery of the fundamental principles of the modern theory of heredity laid down earlier by Gregor Mendel. Second, it represents the beginning of a period extending to our present day which has been notable for the tremendous progress achieved in our understanding of heredity. Virtually all we know of heredity with the notable exception of Mendel's work has been discovered in the past sixty years. Even more exciting is the ever-increasing rate at which new and fundamental genetic findings are being made, especially at the molecular level as indicated in the previous chapter. The biochemical and biophysical approach to genetics holds great promise of unveiling the basic mechanisms not only of heredity but of life itself.

Mendel's Experiments

Mendel's famous plant-breeding experiments consisted simply of mating or "crossing" different varieties of garden peas and systematically recording the distribution of parental traits among the offspring. Why did Mendel succeed where others had failed? His success can be ascribed in part to his experimental approach (and to sheer good luck in his choice of characteristics for study). Mendel concentrated on a few specific traits in contrast to his predecessors who tried to consider the inheritance of many if not all characteristics of an organism at one time. By observing and recording the distribution of a few separate traits in generation after generation of offspring derived from selected crosses of pea plants, Mendel finally discerned an underlying pattern in his data. In devising an explanation or theory to fit his data, he was inevitably led to certain conclusions which today are the foundations of the modern theory of inheritance.

Mendel found that in reality there is no blending or dilution of individual traits in the progeny. Instead he concluded that hereditary traits or characters are transmitted and distributed according to the laws of chance from parents to offspring as separate units which maintain their identity generation after generation. Although particular characteristics may fail to appear in certain offspring, their genes as "recessive" units would eventually express themselves in future generations. As with most great scientific discoveries certain modifications have been necessary in the light of subsequent findings. Nevertheless Mendel's postulates are fundamentally correct.

In all, Mendel studied the inheritance of seven different traits in the garden pea. He usually crossed varieties of peas differing in single contrasting characteristics such as a va-

riety with yellow seeds and one with green seeds, one having a long stem with another having a short stem, and so on. Before carrying out these experiments, however, he made certain that he was dealing with "pure, inbred lines" of plants with respect to each of the traits in which he was interested. This he could determine by mating the plants within a single variety for several generations to see if they would breed true. For example, mating yellow-seeded plants with one another only yielded yellow-seeded progeny whereas green-seeded plants gave only green-seeded offspring. Thus, having established the purity of his lines, Mendel then made numerous crosses involving contrasting pairs of characteristics. He observed that when plants of inbred lines differing in a particular trait were crossed with each other (parental or P_1 generation) the first generation of offspring or hybrids (known as the first filial or F_1 generation) were never intermediate but always posessed only one of the parental traits which Mendel called the dominant trait. The alternative trait of the other parent did not appear in the F_1 generation and was called recessive. Thus the cross of yellow-seeded plants with green-seeded ones gave only yellow-seeded plants in the F_1 generation. Yellow is therefore dominant to green (which is recessive) with respect to seed color in the garden pea.

Of the seven pairs of contrasting traits examined, Mendel found that in all cases one of the contrasting traits was dominant whereas the other was recessive. When he crossed the F_1 hybrids Mendel observed that the recessive characteristic appeared in some of the resulting progeny (the second filial or F_2 generation) in contrast to the majority which possessed the dominant characteristic. He actually counted the number of offspring in the F_2 generation possessing contrasting traits and observed that for each of the seven contrasting pairs examined in the F_2 generation about 75 per cent of the plants possessed the dominant characteristic and 25 per cent the recessive characteristic, approximating a ratio of 3:1. For example, in the F_2 generation of numerous crossings between yellow-seeded and green-seeded plants, Mendel counted 6022 yellow-seeded plants and 2001 green-seeded plants representing an almost perfect 3:1 ratio. The same general results obtained by Mendel in the F_2 generation for the other traits which he studied are shown in Table 12-1.

Table 12-1 Mendel's Results in the F_2 Generation of Garden Peas

TRAIT	DOMINANT	RECESSIVE	RATIO OF DOMINANT TO RECESSIVE
Seed color	6022 yellow	2001 green	3.01:1
Stem length	787 long	277 short	2.84:1
Seed shape	5474 round	1850 wrinkled	2.96:1
Flower color	705 red	224 white	3.15:1
Pod shape	882 inflated	299 wrinkled	2.95:1
Pod color	428 green	152 yellow	2.82:1
Flower location	651 axial°	207 terminal°	3.14:1

°*Axial flowers* are distributed along length of stem whereas *terminal flowers* are located at the end of stems.

Mendel's Theory of Segregation

In order to explain his results Mendel postulated the existence in plants of discrete hereditary units or factors (called *genes* by Johanssen in 1911) as being responsible for the transmission of inherited traits from parents to offspring. These hereditary factors presumably maintained their identity—neither contaminating nor blending with other genes—even though at times they failed to express a given trait as in the recessive factors in hybrid plants.

The important features of Mendel's remarkably accurate hypothesis, now known as Mendel's *First Law* or the *Law of Segregation* (based entirely on the results of the foregoing experiments), and its relationship to modern terminology and concepts of genetics are summarized as follows:

1. *Mendel postulated that each particular trait is controlled or determined by a* pair of *hereditary units* which we now call genes. According to our modern terminology alternative or contrasting forms of the same gene are called *alleles*. For example, the genes for a yellow-seeded pea plant and for green-seeded pea plants are *alleles* of one another. Two or more alleles may exist for any given trait. When both genes are exactly alike for a given trait, the organism is said to be *homozygous* or pure for that characteristic. When the two genes are different, the plant or animal is called *heterozygous* or *hybrid*. In the P_1 generation the yellow-seeded or green-seeded pea plants are homozygous for seed color whereas all the offspring of the F_1 generation are *heterozygous* or hybrid for the same characteristic.

2. *He hypothesized that in the formation of gametes or reproductive cells the two units (i.e., genes) constituting each pair of hereditary factors are separated or segregated from one another with each gamete receiving only one gene of a given pair.* Therefore each gamete has only one of each kind of gene for any particular trait. Thus in the next generation the two factors for any trait are provided by the parents, one member of a pair from each parent.

3. He also concluded that *when the two members of any given pair of hereditary units are different from each other only the trait determined by the dominant factor will be expressed.* Although the recessive factor is present in a heterozygous individual, it will not manifest itself. For example, in the F_1 generation of a cross between homozygous yellow-seeded pea plants and homozygous green-seeded ones all plants will show only yellow seeds even though they are heterozygous (contain a dominant gene for yellow color and a recessive one for green-seed color). In *appearance* these F_1 plants do not differ from their yellow-seeded parents. In *hereditary make-up* for this particular trait, however, they are quite different, as indicated by the recurrence in the F_2 generation of the recessive characteristic.

We speak of the one or more observable traits under consideration as the *phenotype*, whereas the organism's hereditary make-up determining the trait is called its *genotype*. In other words, the visible trait is the phenotype, whereas the genetic composition determining the phenotype is the genotype. In the preceding example the yellow color of the seeds in the parental and F_1 generations is the phenotype. The genotypes for the two generations are different, however, for the yellow-seeded parent is homozygous in this respect whereas the F_2 plants are heterozygous. Very often the central problem of the geneticist who studies the transmission of hereditary traits from parents to progeny is to determine genotype, based on observations of the phenotype. Not only did Mendel's postulates offer a reasonable explanation of his experimental data but also they provided a high degree of accuracy in predicting the results of future breeding experiments.

It should be noted at this time that although many alleles are related in terms of definite recessiveness and dominance, a significant number of characteristics are incompletely dominant (or incompletely recessive). In these instances heterozygous progeny have a phenotype intermediate between the two parents. Nevertheless the same fundamental postulates put forth by Mendel of discrete hereditary factors apply to these traits.

Mendel's postulates can be illustrated by a convenient system of shorthand now widely used by geneticists. In the P_1 cross of yellow-seeded and green-seeded pea plants a common practice is to use the capital letter Y to designate the dominant gene for yellow and the small letter y for the recessive gene for green. The crossings and resultant progeny are accordingly represented as shown in Figure 12-1.

It should be emphasized at this point that the expected distribution of inherited traits, as illustrated by the predicted results of seed-color inheritance in Figure 12-1, is based on statistical or probability phenomena. The expected occurrence in the F_2 generation, for example, of three yellow-seeded plants and one green-seeded plant (3:1) is called a *probability ratio*. It means that when sufficient progeny are produced three-fourths approximately will be yellow-seeded and the remaining one-fourth will be green-seeded. It does not necessarily mean, however, that when there are four offspring in the F_2 generation exactly three will be yellow-seeded and one green-

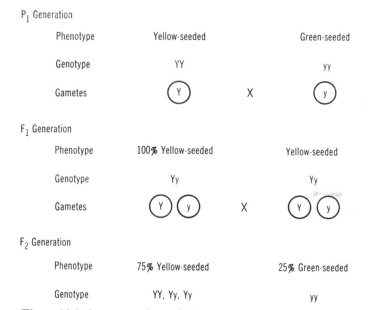

Figure 12-1. Summary of Mendel's results from the mating of yellow-seeded and green-seeded varieties of garden peas.

seeded. All four might be yellow-seeded, or less probably all four might be green-seeded. With a limited number of offspring various other ratios could also appear between these two extremes. If many progeny are produced, however, then the expected ratios will be more closely approached. In other words the preceding probability ratio of 3:1 states that in the F_2 generation arising from the crossing of two identical heterozygous individuals (e.g., Yy) there are three chances out of four that the dominant trait (yellow) will appear in any particular offspring. Similarly there is only one chance out of four that the recessive trait (green) will manifest itself in any of the offspring.

It can be seen from Mendel's original data in Table 12-1 that he recorded the distribution of traits in hundreds and even thousands of offspring. His data in the F_2 generation showed a good approximation towards a 3:1 ratio of the dominant trait to the recessive one. Had Mendel only recorded these traits in ten or fifteen progeny instead of in several hundred he may not have been able to discern the true distribution ratios in the offspring and therefore might have been led to the wrong conclusions.

The phenomenon of probability ratios can be illustrated by the tossing of a coin. There is a 50-50 chance (one chance out of two) that *for each toss of the coin* either heads or tails will appear. This does not necessarily mean that with a few tosses of the coin 50 per cent will be heads and 50 per cent will be tails. Four tosses, for example, may show all heads, but 100 tosses will now show a distribution (e.g., 42 heads and 58 tails) that approaches the expected probability ratio of 1:1. Incidentally this quantitative experimental approach by Mendel was an important factor contributing to his success in revealing basic genetic phenomena where others before him had failed.

Mendel's Theory of Independent Assortment

Having provided a reasonable set of postulates that could adequately explain as well as predict results of matings involving a single pair of characteristics, Mendel then studied the simultaneous inheritance in peas of two or more conspicuous trait differences. For example he examined the distribution in the F_1 and F_2 generation of two seed traits — color and shape — starting with a P_1 cross of a variety of peas having yellow (YY) and round seeds (RR) with one having green (yy) and wrinkled seeds (rr). He had already shown that the hereditary factor for yellow-seed color was dominant to that for green, and round-seed shape was dominant to wrinkled. As expected all the F_1 generation plants displayed only yellow and round seeds.

What was the distribution of seed traits in the F_2 generation? Would the hereditary factors responsible for these two traits assort independently of each other on a purely chance basis during gamete formation? Or would the two different genes be linked to one another in a particular way, say yellow to round and green to wrinkled? Mendel's results showing the appearance of all four possible types of plants with respect to these traits indicated that the hereditary units or genes for different independent traits assorted independently as seen by the phenotype ratio of 9 yellow round: 3 green round: 3 yellow wrinkled: 1 green wrinkled.

The results of such a cross, as illustrated in Figure 12-2, involving the simultaneous inheritance of two different sets of genes (known as a *dihybrid cross* in contrast to *monohybrid cross* where only one pair of genes is considered) reflect the random and equal distribution during gamete formation of the genes under consideration. The F_2 generation of a dihybrid cross involving traits determined by independently assorting genes shows the typical phenotype trait distribution of 9:3:3:1 (9 double dominants: 3 with dominant and one recessive: 3 with the other dominant and the other recessive: 1 double recessive). In a monohybrid cross as illustrated earlier for seed color the typical phenotype ratio in the F_2 generation is 3 dominants: 1 recessive.

For convenience the "checkerboard" or Punnett square (after the English geneticist

Punnett) as shown in Figure 12-2 is highly useful for working out random combinations of gametes in order to determine all possible types of offspring that could be produced by the crossing. From the different possible kinds of progeny shown in the Punnett square it is a simple matter to determine the ratio of the phenotypes. In setting up the Punnett square arrange all possible types of gametes (with respect to the characteristics under study) from one parent on one side of the square and all possible types of gametes from the other parent on the adjacent side of the square. The combination of these gametes as indicated in Figure 12-2 represents the random union of all possible gamete types to yield all possible offspring types. The Punnett square can be applied to monohybrid, dihybrid, and trihybrid (three or more different types of inherited characteristics crosses) and so on.

From the results of these experiments with two or more independent pairs of conspicuously different traits Mendel postulated that *each pair of hereditary factors or genes is assorted at random and is inherited independently* of the other pair, a principle known as the *Law of Independent Assortment or Mendel's Second Law.* Subsequent findings by numerous investigators over the years have confirmed Mendel's Second Law in some instances but repudiated it in others. Such exceptions have eventually led to a deeper understanding of genetics.

We now know that the law of independent assortment applies to independent pairs of genes provided each pair is located on a different pair of chromosomes. On the other hand, if the two different pairs of genes under con-

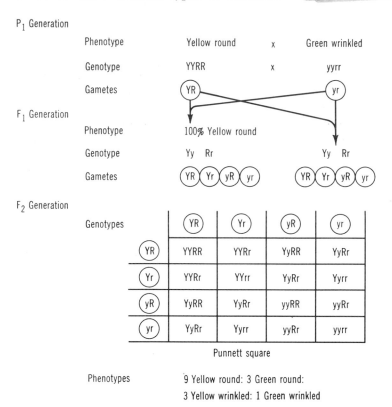

Figure 12-2. Representation of a dihybrid cross (inheritance of two separate traits) between a pea plant having yellow, round seeds (**YYRR**) and one having green, wrinkled seeds (**yyrr**) as the parental generation.

sideration are on the same pair of chromosomes (i.e., *linked*), they do not assort independently but are distributed in a combined fashion. Mendel was extremely fortunate in his selection of pea-plant characteristics for genetic study. Apparently in all his dihybrid crosses he happened to select conspicuously different traits that were controlled by genes located on different pairs of chromosomes.

The Material Basis of Heredity

THE EARLY FINDINGS. Mendel's experiments and the accurate conclusions which he drew from them are all the more remarkable when we consider the backward state of man's biological knowledge in 1866. We know now that in higher sexually reproducing animals and in most higher plants gametes represent the only or major means for transmitting the hereditary substance from generation to generation. Some knowledge of gametes and their union would therefore seem necessary for any understanding of heredity. Yet it was not until 1876, ten years after the report of Mendel's work, that the first clear demonstration was made (in the sea urchin) of the most significant event in the process of fertilization, namely the fusion of the nucleus of the sperm with that of the egg. It was realized shortly afterwards that the union of gamete nuclei during fertilization accounts for the equal contribution of both parents in the transmission of inherited factors to the offspring. The real beginnings in our basic knowledge of chromosomes and mitosis were not made until the 1880's. The process of *meiosis* as a means of distributing half the number of chromosomes in each of the newly forming gametes (p. 303) was discovered about the same time. But it was not until the completion of the first two decades of the twentieth century that the evidence finally accumulated to indicate conclusively that the hereditary substance of cells is located on the chromosomes.

The material basis of heredity had finally been established: the substance of heredity resided in the chromosomes. And as we shall

see in Chapter 33 the physical basis of heredity is also the physical basis of evolution, for changes in the hereditary substance (i.e., mutations) are in part responsible for variations that account for biological evolution. Knowledge of chromosome structure, mitosis, and meiosis provided a firm material foundation for Mendel's postulates and now represents the physical basis for our understanding of genetics. The brilliance of Mendel's experimentation and analysis are all the more apparent for implicit in them was a prediction of the progress to be made. Mendel's hypothesis that the hereditary factors existed in pairs and segregated independently in gamete formation fitted in perfectly with the subsequent findings by others that chromosomes in many organisms also exist in pairs and are separated in meiosis with every gamete receiving only one chromosome of each pair. Numerous additional correlations already indicated in Chapter 11 have since been demonstrated between genetic phenomena and the properties and behavior of DNA, leaving no doubt that the chromosomes are the physical basis of heredity.

Mitosis

Mitosis, described in detail in Chapter 4, is an orderly process for the precise and equal distribution of duplicate chromosomes to form two daughter nuclei with identical numbers and kinds of chromosomes. It accounts for the identical genetic constitution in the daughter cells and therefore for the same structural and functional organization as the parent cell from which they originated. Mitosis is therefore ultimately responsible for the inheritance or transmission of characteristics from cell to cell in multicellular organisms, and from generation to generation in those organisms (mostly unicellular) where it also constitutes asexual reproduction.

Meiosis and Gamete Formation

INTRODUCTION. With the realization in the late nineteenth century that fertilization in plants and animals consisted of the fusion of a

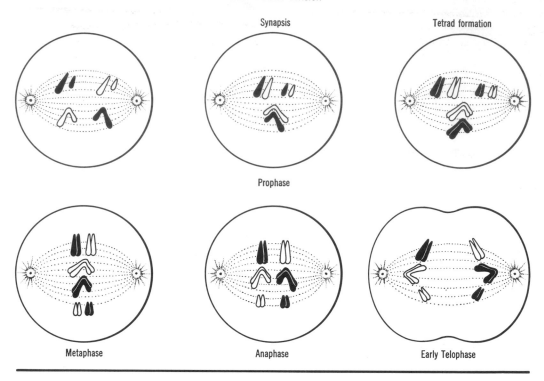

FIRST MEIOTIC DIVISION

Synapsis

Tetrad formation

Prophase

Metaphase

Anaphase

Early Telophase

SECOND MEIOTIC DIVISION

Prophase

Metaphase

Anaphase

Telophase

Figure 12-3. See facing page.

sperm nucleus with an egg-cell nucleus from which a new individual eventually developed, it became evident that some process must exist for reducing the chromosome number in gametes.

It had already been established in the early 1880's that in the union of egg and sperm an equal number of chromosomes was contributed by each parent to the progeny. In a fertilized egg and therefore in all the cells of the body that arise from it by mitotic division, the chromosome number is doubled or *diploid*. It follows that each gamete must possess a single or *haploid* set of chromosomes. The designation 1n is used to symbolize a single or haploid set of chromosomes as in the gametes, while 2n designates a double or diploid set of chromosomes as in the body cells (also called *somatic* cells). It was soon observed by several workers that two unusual cell divisions occur during the formation of gametes resulting in a halving of the diploid chromosome number to give the haploid condition. These two successive divisions collectively constitute the process of *meiosis*.

MEIOSIS. Meiosis as a special type of regular cell division, which is highly specialized and restricted to the reproductive tissue, is essentially a modification of mitosis. Meiosis gives rise to the cells that ultimately become the male and female gametes, each with a chromosome number half that found in all the other cells of the organism. Four daughter nuclei, each in a separate cell, are ultimately produced instead of two as in mitosis. The most significant fact is that maternal and paternal chromosomes are randomly separated from one another and distributed in the resulting four daughter nuclei which now have only half the number of chromosomes as that of the mother cell.

Meiosis actually occurs by two successive divisions called the *first meiotic division* and *second meiotic division*. The first meiotic division consists essentially of the unique process whereby members of each pair of *chromosomes* (the maternal and paternal chromosomes) are first separated from one another. The subsequent separation of *chromatids* in each of these two haploid nuclei to give four resulting daughter nuclei makes up the second meiotic division (a process which in part resembles mitosis). Both meiotic divisions consist of a sequence of events that are conveniently described by the same terms used in mitosis, namely prophase, metaphase, anaphase, and telophase. Although there are strong similarities between the stages in mitosis and those of the two meiotic divisions, certain important differences exist. The process of meiosis is summarized in Figure 12-3.

First Meiotic Prophase. The prophase stage of the first meiotic division resembles the prophase of mitosis in the usual thickening and rearrangement of the threads of the chromatin network into the rod-like chromosomes. It is accompanied finally by formation of a typical spindle apparatus and disappearance of nucleoli and nuclear membrane. The critical difference is that in the prophase of the first meiotic division, unlike that of mitosis, the chromosomes pair together in intimate association but do not fuse, a process known as *synapsis*. One member or *homologous* chromosome of each pair is of paternal origin whereas the other is of maternal origin. Synapsis or pairing eventually occurs along the entire length of the chromosomes, the homologous chromosomes of each pair being intimately coiled and entwined about one another.

At about the time of synapsis, it can be observed that each chromosome consists of two chromatids so that each pair of chromosomes is actually made up of four chromatids called a

Figure 12-3. Diagrammatic summary of meiosis in animal reproductive tissue showing the first and second meiotic divisions each consisting in turn of prophase, metaphase, anaphase, and telophase stages. Note that synapsis and tetrad formation occur only in the first meiotic division, and that each mother cell ultimately yields four daughter cells having only half the number of chromosomes.

tetrad. The characteristic presence of tetrads in the prophase and metaphase of the first meiotic division is a simple means of distinguishing these stages from the prophase and metaphase of mitosis.

First Meiotic Metaphase, Anaphase, and Telophase. In the metaphase stage, which typically possesses a spindle apparatus and lacks a nuclear membrane, the entire complement of chromosomes orients itself on the equator of the spindle.

Anaphase of the first meiotic division is characterized by the movement away from one another of each member or homologous chromosome (consisting of two chromatids connected by a single centromere) of a pair toward opposite poles of the cell. Thus the homologous chromosomes of each pair *but not the daughter chromatids are separated.* It differs from the anaphase of regular mitosis where the centromeres double and the daughter chromatids are separated from each other.

The *telophase* stage like that of mitosis is typified by a retransformation of the two sets of chromosomes into two haploid daughter nuclei. It should be noted that in the resulting interphase between the first and second meiotic divisions no DNA synthesis occurs.

Second Meiotic Division. The two daughter nuclei then undergo the second meiotic division which is essentially similar to mitosis resulting in the separation of daughter chromatids from each other to yield four haploid nuclei. Like mitosis the stages of the second meiotic division consist of *prophase* (chromosomes contract, thicken, and become more distinct; spindle appears and nuclear membrane disappears), *metaphase,* (arrangement of chromosomes on the equator of the spindle apparatus), *anaphase* (doubling of the centromeres and separation of daughter chromatids now called daughter chromosomes to opposite poles), and *telophase* (reconversion of daughter chromosomes to give a total of four nuclei, each containing the haploid number of chromosomes) followed by cytoplasmic division to form four daughter cells.

The second meiotic division differs from mitosis in at least two important respects. First, the chromosome number of the two daughter cells undergoing the second meiotic division is already haploid instead of diploid in the sense that the homologous chromosomes of each pair are in the separate daughter cells. Second, depending on the extent of crossing-over (p. 309) in the prophase of the first meiotic division, the two chromatids of each chromosome that separate as daughter chromosomes in the anaphase of the second meiotic division are not identical but differ in those segments that have been exchanged by crossing-over.

In mitosis there is one nuclear division accounting for the equal distribution of already duplicated chromosomes, whereas in meiosis there are two nuclear divisions for the distribution of duplicated chromosomes thus resulting in four daughter nuclei each containing a haploid number of chromosomes. Meiosis therefore decreases the number of chromosomes by half, segregating the members of homologous pairs into separate cells in contrast to mitosis which preserves the original chromosome number in succeeding generations of cells.

Meiosis occurs in certain reproductive cells of every organism which carries on sexual reproduction. As the mechanism for the segregation of homologous chromosomes it assures that each daughter cell will receive one of each pair of parental factors, either the paternal or the maternal one. It is the mechanism for halving the chromosome number and thus serves to balance the doubling that is attained at the time of the fusion of two gametes. In one sense meiosis is the opposite of fertilization, since it reduces the chromosome number by one-half in contrast to the doubling effected by sexual reproduction.

GAMETOGENESIS. The process of gamete formation is called *gametogenesis* and includes the process of meiosis. In males it results in the formation of the sperm and has the more specialized name of *spermatogenesis.* In fe-

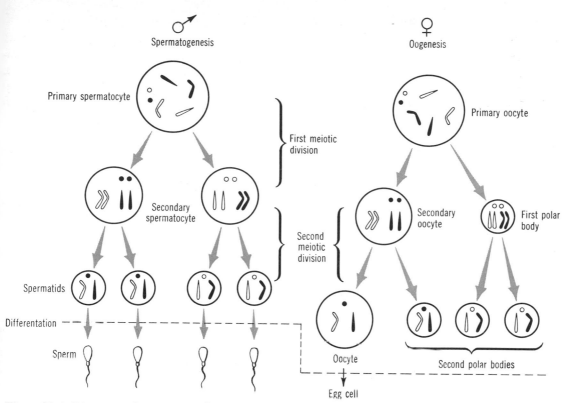

Figure 12-4. Diagrammatic summary of spermatogenesis and oogenesis in mammalian reproductive tissue.

males gametogenesis is the process of egg-cell or *ovum formation* and is called *oögenesis*. The steps in spermatogenesis and oögenesis are summarized in Figure 12-4.

Spermatogenesis. In mammals the primitive unspecialized cells called *spermatogonia* which line the inside walls of the thousands of cylindrical sperm tubules (called *seminiferous tubules*) in the testis (Chapter 30) ultimately give rise to the sperm. During embryonic development and childhood the spermatogonia divide only by mitosis to produce more cells like themselves. However, with the onset of sexual maturity and throughout most of the subsequent life of the mature male, some spermatogonia undergo spermatogenesis whereas others continue to divide mitotically to produce new spermatogonia. In the process of spermatogenesis the spermatogonia first enlarge into cells called *primary*

spermatocytes which then experience the two typical successive meiotic divisions of meiosis to yield four haploid spherical cells or *spermatids*. Each spermatid is eventually transformed by differentiation into a functional sperm. The head of the sperm, consisting largely of the nucleus and some golgi material, is joined to the long flexible cytoplasmic tail by means of a small *middlepiece*. The latter contains a rich concentration of mitochondria which is believed to release energy responsible for the beating of the tail.

Oögenesis. In mammalian females the corresponding primitive unspecialized sex cells, called *oögonia*, located in the surface layers of the ovaries ultimately give rise to the egg cells or *ova*. Like the spermatogonia, the oögonia experience many mitotic divisions during the early life of the female. With the beginnings of sexual maturation and throughout the fertile lifetime of the female one (or more) oögonium periodically undergoes oögenesis.

The oögonium first ceases its mitotic activity and embarks upon an extended period of growth and enlargement to form the large *primary oöcyte*. The first meiotic division experienced by the primary oöcyte results in a strikingly unequal distribution of the cytoplasm and its stored food material or *yolk*. Thus it forms a large cell called the *secondary oöcyte*, containing nearly all the cytoplasm and yolk, and a small attached cell called the first *polar body*. The secondary oöcyte then undergoes the second meiotic division to produce a large *oötid* and a *second polar body* both of which are haploid. During this time the first polar body may have either degenerated or divided to form two polar bodies. An any rate all the polar bodies, which often cluster together on the surface of the maturing egg, eventually disintegrate and disappear. With time the oötid differentiates into a mature ovum.

Thus only one mature egg cell is produced by each primary oöcyte in contrast to the four sperm which arise from each primary spermatocyte in the process of spermatogenesis. From an evolutionary viewpoint the obvious advantage in terms of survival value afforded by the formation from the primary oöcyte of a single functional egg cell instead of four is the assurance of a greater food and cytoplasm supply for the nutrition of the developing embryo should fertilization occur.

In higher plants as we shall see in Chapter 16 the microspores and macrospores which arise from meiosis produce respectively the germinating *pollen grains* with its sperm nuclei and the *embryo sacs* with its egg cells.

FERTILIZATION AND SUBSEQUENT DEVELOPMENT. Fertilization is accomplished by the penetration of the sperm into the egg followed by the union of their haploid nuclei. The fertilized egg or zygote now possesses the diploid number of chromosomes, a haploid set from the mother and haploid set from the father. It subsequently undergoes successive mitotic divisions to form ultimately all the body cells (Chapter 31) each with the identical number and kind of chromosomes. Once the maternal and paternal chromosomes constitute the nucleus of the newly fertilized cell and of all other body cells which arise from it by mitosis the chromosomes do not preserve their identity as maternal and paternal chromosomes as such. In subsequent gamete formation by the new generation the manner in which any given pair of chromosomes segregate will be entirely unaffected by the way the members of any other pair separate.

As a general rule nearly all animals and many higher plants during most of their life cycle are in a diploid state with regard to their chromosome number. By contrast some microorganisms and algae exist only in the haploid condition. Actually in nearly all multicellular plants and numerous microorganisms there is a distinct and regular alternation of the diploid and haploid generations (Chapter 15 and 16) during the life cycle. In most higher plants the diploid generation is the predominant one, whereas in microorganisms (e.g., the fungus *Neurospora*) it usually exists for only a relatively short time.

RELATIONSHIP OF CHROMOSOME BEHAVIOR TO GENETIC PHENOMENA

General Features

Let us now examine several basic genetic phenomena in the light of the established theory that the chromosomes are the physical basis of inheritance. An hereditary trait in diploid organisms is essentially determined and controlled by a pair of genes, originally referred to as hereditary factors by Mendel. Each member of a gene pair is located on a separate chromosome of a particular pair of chromosomes, the other gene being situated at a corresponding position on the homologous chromosome. Any trait determined by a dominant gene will express itself no matter whether the dominant gene is present singly or in duplicate. Both genes for the corresponding recessive trait, however, must be present in order for the trait to manifest itself. As we proceed it will become evident that certain traits are regulated by several sets of genes, that there are exceptions to the phenomena of dominance and recessiveness, and that the inheritance of particular traits are far more complex than originally conceived by Mendel.

Simple Crosses

The example we selected earlier of Mendel's monohybrid cross (Figure 12-1) can be reexamined in the light of the chromosome theory. The heredity units of Mendel can now be designated as specific pairs of genes on a particular pair of chromosomes (Figure 12-5).

If gene pairs for different traits in dihybrid crosses, trihybrid crosses, and so on are located on different pairs of chromosomes then they are so indicated as in the instances of seed color and seed shape in garden peas.

The heterozygous F_1 generation of Figure 12-2 would be symbolized as

When three pairs of genes A, B, and C each situated on a different pair of chromosomes are involved, the F_1 generation of a cross between two pure lines different in each of these genes would give the genotype Aa Bb Cc. The F_2 generation would be represented by different phenotypes in the ratio of 27:9:9:9:3:3:3:1, comparable to the 9:3:3:1 ratio of a dihybrid cross or the 3:1 ratio of a monohybrid cross. This can be easily worked out employing the Punnett or checkerboard-square method and making all possible combinations of the various F_1 gametes—ABC, ABc, AbC, aBC, abC, abc, aBc, Abc.

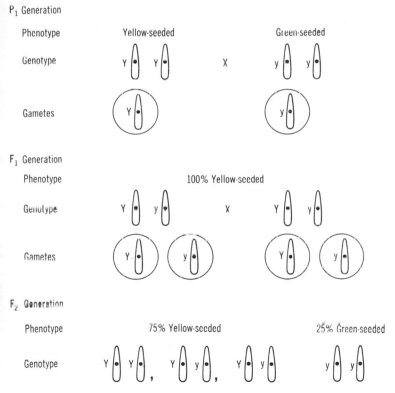

P_1 Generation

Phenotype — Yellow-seeded — Green-seeded

Genotype

Gametes

F_1 Generation

Phenotype — 100% Yellow-seeded

Genotype

Gametes

F_2 Generation

Phenotype — 75% Yellow-seeded — 25% Green-seeded

Genotype

Figure 12-5. Representation of Mendel's monohybrid cross showing the specific pair of genes on a particular pair of chromosomes. Compare with Figure 12-1.

The Backcross or Testcross

The geneticist is frequently confronted with the problem of determining the genotype of an individual from its phenotype with respect to one or more particular traits. In the case of a recessive characteristic the problem is simple enough. The genotype for any recessive trait which appears must obviously be homozygous.

But how can we distinguish whether the phenotype for a dominant trait is due to a homozygous or heterozygous genotypic condition? The answer can be obtained by a simple experimental cross known as the *backcross* or *testcross*. It involves mating the organism in question with an organism exhibiting the corresponding recessive trait. For example, in the inheritance of coat texture by guinea pigs *rough* coat (S) characterized by the growth of the fur in whorls to give the animal a roughened appearance is dominant over *smooth* coat (s). In order to determine whether a rough-coated guinea pig is homozygous or heterozygous with regard to coat texture, it is crossed with a smooth-coated animal and the occurrence of coat texture in the resulting progeny is examined. As illustrated in Figure 12-6, if the guinea pig in question were homozygous for the given trait, it would be expected that all the offspring would display only rough coats. Alternatively, if the guinea pig were

heterozygous, then 50 per cent of the progeny should have rough coats and 50 per cent smooth coats.

In effect, the testcross serves as a standard genetic technique for analyzing the percentages of different gametes produced by an organism with respect to one or more given traits. It is simply accomplished by crossing the organism to be tested with one that is a pure recessive in this respect and observing the progeny. The backcross or testcross has been a useful tool for determining genotypes not only for a single pair of genes but for several pairs of genes in the practical problems of establishing pure breeds of plants and animals with desirable traits as well as in the area of basic genetic research.

Linkage and Crossing-over

LINKAGE OF GENES. The growing realization in the early 1900's that chromosomes were the material basis of heredity was based on the striking parallel between the cytological behavior of chromosomes and the genetic studies of segregation and recombination of genes. Moreover, the chromosomes seemed to remain physically intact, retaining their identity throughout the various cell divisions.

If the chromosomes are the physical basis for heredity as the evidence strongly indicated, then the inheritance of genes must be identical

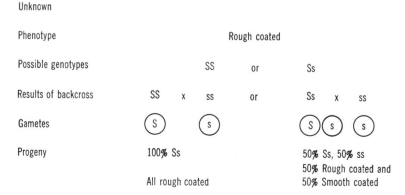

Figure 12-6. Representation of the backcross or testcross for determining genotypes of one or more pairs of genes.

with the inheritance of chromosomes. It becomes evident, however, that Mendel's law of independent assortment could apply only to genes on separate or different pairs of chromosomes, not to genes on the same pair. In the latter situation the genes would be expected to assort not independently of one another but together as if they were connected or linked, since they are located on the same chromosome. The first report of a cross involving two pairs of genes that did not show independent assortment was made in 1906 by Bateson and Punnett in England. They spoke of this *dependent assortment* as *linkage*. Different hereditary units or genes on the same chromosome are said to be *linked*. Genes are arranged in linear order, and since it is known that there are many more genes than there are chromosomes for any organism, it follows that many different genes may occur on the same chromosome and are therefore linked. In *Drosophila*, for example, several thousand genes have been shown to be present on each chromosome.

What kind of genetic results can we expect in the inheritance of two linked genes compared to two genes on different pairs of chromosomes? Suppose we examine some of the classic results of Morgan and his group who used the fruit fly *Drosophila* as an experimental organism for genetic studies. In *Drosophila* the inherited trait *gray body color* (B) is dominant to *black body color* (b), and long wing (V) is dominant to vestigial wing (v). If the two pairs of genes responsible for these traits were located on different pairs of chromosomes, then in the F_2 generation of a parental cross between a homozygous gray-bodied, long-winged (BBVV) fly and a black-bodied, vestigial-winged (bbvv) one, we should expect the typical 9:3:3:1 ratio of a dihybrid cross based on the Mendelian principle of random assortment as shown in Figure 12-7.

If on the other hand these two pairs of genes are linked (i.e., located on the same pair of homologous chromosomes), then in the F_2 generation of the same parental cross as above we should obtain, as indicated in Figure 12-8,

a ratio of phenotypes for these two inherited traits which is different from that predicted by the Mendelian principle of independent assortment.

The transmission of linked genes via gametes from generation to generation in sexually reproducing plants and animals would be expected to behave as if the linked genes were one. We know now as a result of the work of T. H. Morgan in the decade extending from 1910 to 1920 that the genes for the above two traits in *Drosophila* are linked.

CROSSING-OVER. Morgan's data for the F_2 generation for these as well as other linked genes tended to approximate the results expected for a linked-gene relationship. In most cases, however, there were significant deviations. This had first been indicated in 1906 by Bateson and Punnett in their report on a cross with sweet peas involving two pairs of genes that did not show independent assortment. Their observations of small but significant deviations could only be explained by assuming that under certain circumstances genes could be transferred from one chromosome to another. The work of Morgan and his colleagues with *Drosophila* in eventually solving the problem of these deviations laid bare the important and widespread genetic phenomenon of "crossing-over," discussed later. It also provided a new and powerful tool, as we shall soon see, for mapping or locating the sites of genes relative to one another on the chromosomes. The nature and possible meaning of these deviations are best examined by applying the backcross or testcross, a procedure that proved to be highly useful in helping to shed light on this perplexing problem.

If we apply the testcross to the F_1 generation in the above situation, as was actually done by geneticists in successfully analyzing the cause for these variations, we are in effect examining the distribution of these traits in the F_1 gametes. We would have expected that the F_1 generation would produce only two types of gametes for a double pair of linked genes as indicated by the theoretically expected results

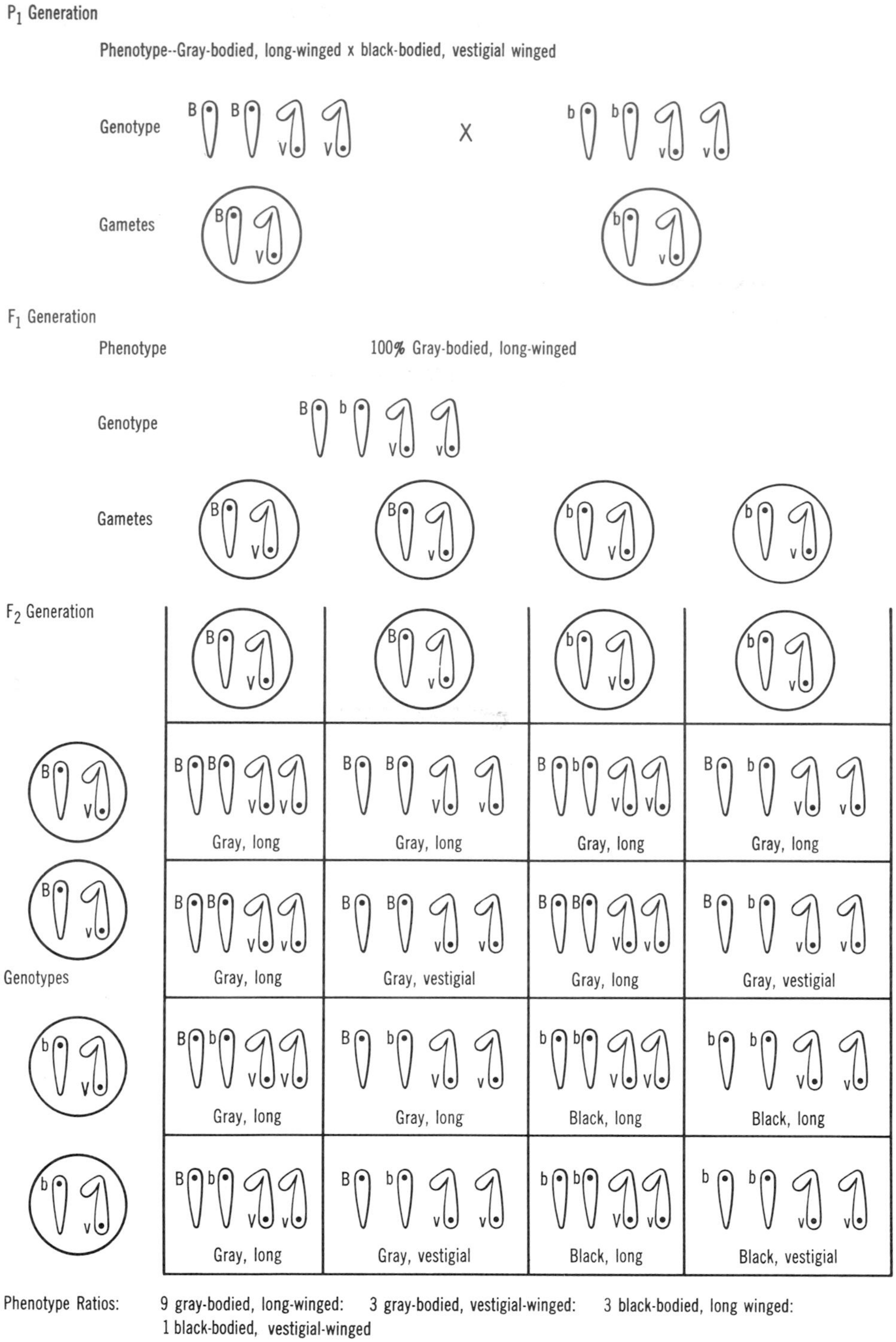

Figure 12-7. Representation of a dihybrid cross involving two pairs of genes on different pairs of chromosomes (i.e., unlinked genes).

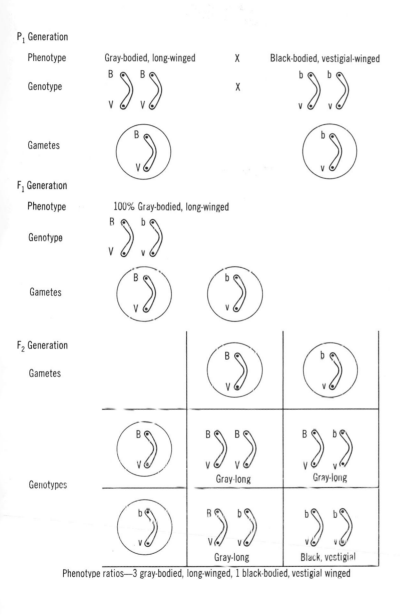

P₁ Generation

Phenotype   Gray-bodied, long-winged   X   Black-bodied, vestigial-winged

Genotype

Gametes

F₁ Generation

Phenotype   100% Gray-bodied, long-winged

Genotype

Gametes

F₂ Generation

Gametes

Genotypes

Gray-long   Gray-long

Gray-long   Black, vestigial

Phenotype ratios—3 gray-bodied, long-winged, 1 black-bodied, vestigial winged

Figure 12-8. Representation of the same dihybrid cross as in Figure 12-7 except that both pairs of genes are located on the same pair of homologous chromosomes (i.e., linked genes).

of the testcross shown in Figure 12-9.

Instead of the 1:1 ratio of expected offspring for this testcross, it was consistently observed that the following percentages of offspring appeared in its place.

Gray bodied, long winged	41.5%
Black bodied, vestigial winged	41.5%
Gray bodied, vestigial winged	8.5%
Black bodied, long winged	8.5%

The simplest interpretation is that the organism being tested produces four different gametes as shown in Figure 12-10 in unequal frequency instead of the theoretically expected two-gamete types. In effect in a small but definite percentage of gametes some recombination or exchange of genes between homologous chromosomes had occurred.

How could these exceptions be explained? The genetic studies of Morgan and his associates with hundreds of *Drosophila* mutants had provided strong evidence for the concept of linked genes. Their observation by 1915 that in *Drosphila* there are four groups of linked genes corresponding to the four chromosome pairs in this organism furnished another striking parallel between genetics and cytology. Morgan postulated that the exceptions or recombinations among genes of the same linkage group as illustrated above could only be explained on the basis of some exchange of genes between homologous chromosomes, representing a transfer of genes from one chromosome to another.

How was this exchange of genes accomplished? If the chromosomes are the physical substance of heredity, there must be a chromosomal basis for the recombination of genes between homologous chromosomes. A possible cytological explanation for the interchange of genes between chromosomes was furnished at about that time by Janssens. He observed that, in some cases during the prophase of the first meiotic division when there is a considerable coiling of the chromatids of the tetrads around

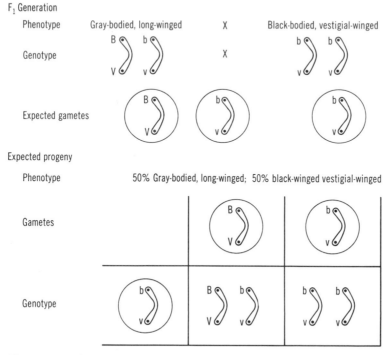

Figure 12-9. Theoretically expected results of a dihybrid cross involving linked genes.

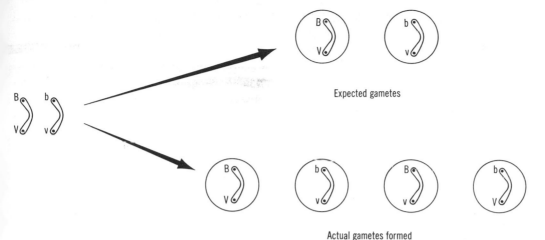

Expected gametes

Actual gametes formed

Figure 12-10. Occurrence of expected gametes and unexpected gametes.

one another, two of the chromatids might possibly break at a corresponding place along their length and rejoin in such a way that a portion of one chromatid is now joined with a portion of the other. This phenomenon of the coiling, breaking, and rejoining of the chromatids of homologous chromosomes is the cytological basis of *crossing-over*. Until recently it was believed that crossing-over occurred during the tetrad stage of meiosis. We now know that it probably takes place during the very early prophase stage of the first meiotic division before the chromosomes condense and the tetrad is actually discerned cytologically. Crossing-over provides a cytological basis for the interchange of genes between homologous

chromosomes already suggested by the genetic data.

The results of the above example of the inheritance of body color and wing structure in *Drosophila* can now be reexamined in the light of the crossing-over phenomenon. We can represent the chromatids of the homologous chromosomes bearing the above two linked genes in a simplified diagram (Figure 12-11). In reality the chromatids are intimately coiled around one another which we can represent simply by showing the bending of two nonhomologous chromatids across one another (Figure 12-11). The breaking of the two crossed-over nonhomologous chromatids and the reunion of the different segments with each

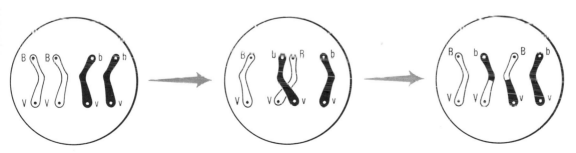

Figure 12-11. Simplified schematic representation of the crossing-over phenomenon between nonhomologous chromatids.

other (Figure 12-11) would constitute *crossing-over*. Thus we can now account by the *theory of crossing-over* for the appearance of the unexpected gametes in addition to the usual gametes as shown in Figure 12-12.

The percentages of distribution of phenotypes for the two genes being studied in the testcross in Figure 12-12 show, according to the crossing-over phenomenon, that 17 per cent (8.5 per cent gray bodied, vestigial winged, and 8.5 per cent black bodied, long winged) of the progeny are derived from gametes whose chromosomes underwent a crossing-over between the two genes being investigated. The remaining 83 per cent of the offspring arose from gametes that did not experience an exchange of nonhomologous chromosome segments for these two genes.

The first direct and conclusive demonstration for the correlation of genetic data with cytological evidence for crossing-over was finally presented by Stern in 1931. By mating a *Drosophila* mutant that had a pair of homologous chromosomes whose members were both structurally and genetically different from one another, Stern showed that the cytological chromosomal changes in the offspring corresponded to the genetic results in terms of interchange of chromosomal material between homologous chromosomes.

It should be emphasized that crossing-over is a normal and widespread biological phenomenon and is not to be considered as an aberrant or abnormal process. It occurs in virtually all higher plants and animals and has also been observed in fungi and yeasts. There are strong indications that it also takes place in bacteria and viruses. In one respect crossing-over can be considered to be part of the sexual process since it occurs during meiosis which is an essential aspect of gamete formation. At any rate it represents still another mode for increasing genetic combination. From an evolutionary viewpoint it is therefore another one of nature's ways of obtaining a greater variety and mixing of genes in offspring.

CHROMOSOME MAPPING. Morgan and his associates also showed that the chance of a crossover occurring between any two genes on a chromosome is directly proportional to the distance between them. The farther apart they are the greater the chance of crossing over. The proportion of "crossovers" between any two given genes, however, was always the same. These facts led to the concept that crossing-over data reflected the relative positions of

Phenotype - Gray-bodied, long-winged   ✕   Black-bodied, vestigial-winged

Genotype

Actual kinds of gametes formed

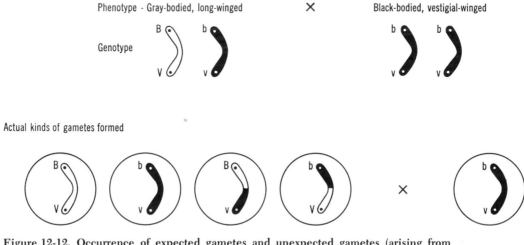

Figure 12-12. Occurrence of expected gametes and unexpected gametes (arising from crossing-over).

the genes on the chromosome and could be used as an index to map the position of the genes with reference to one another. The major assumption is that the distance between two genes determines the chance of recombination between them.

For example, let us suppose that the percentage of crossovers between two genes A and B on the same chromosome is observed to be 30 per cent and between B and gene C 15 per cent. According to the preceding hypothesis we can say that the distance of gene A from gene B is twice as great as the distance of C from B. From the given data at least two possibilities exist for the relative positions of the three genes on the chromosome. The genes A, B, and C are situated either in the sequence

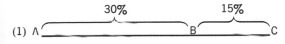

(1) A _____ B ____ C

or in the sequence

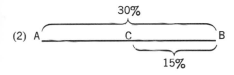

(2) A _____ C _____ B

since both arrangements fit the data. Data on the proportion of crossovers between genes A and C should clearly settle the question. If the percentage of crossovers between A and C were 45 per cent, then only sequence 1 could fit the data; if it were 15 per cent then sequence 2 would be correct.

A third possibility that these three genes are arranged in a triangle or some other type of nonlinear order has been definitely eliminated by an overwhelming volume of evidence of chromosome mapping with various types of organisms. First, the distances between genes have been found to be additive. Second, the use of the crossing-over technique for constructing chromosome maps by locating hereditary units or genes relative to one another on the chromosome has proven highly successful

in predicting the results of crosses not yet tried. Perhaps the most important contribution made by the application of the crossing-over phenomenon as a means of chromosome mapping has been the concept that the hereditary units or genes are located in a linear and specific order along the chromosome like beads on a string. This conclusion and the subsequent findings that DNA as the hereditary substance of the chromosome is a linear molecule chemically differentiated along its length are in keeping with one another. Together they have provided us with a much clearer picture of the material basis of heredity.

By means of several experimental approaches it has been possible to check and confirm cytologically the genetic mapping of chromosomes. This has largely involved correlation studies of genetic behavior with chromosome breakage and rearrangements (e.g., translocations, inversions, and deletions, p. 266) which have occurred naturally or have been induced by exposure to X-rays and other types of radiation. The discovery by Painter in 1934 that the chromosomes in the salivary glands of Drosophila larvae were of enormous size and possessed a distinctive pattern of deeply staining crossbands has made it possible to correlate the cytological maps of the chromosome with genetic maps of the chromosome derived from crossing-over and recombination data (Figure 4-15A).

The Drosophila salivary chromosomes are about one hundred times as long as those of ordinary body cells and their crossbands differ from one another in shape, size, and distinctness. They made it possible for the first time to recognize the various regions of the chromosome. Thus they represented a powerful cytological means for checking inferences that were being drawn solely from genetic data such as a reversal of some of the gene loci (chromosome inversion, Figure 11-2) or a change in the linkage between particular groups of genes (chromosome translocation, Figure 11-2). By means of this approach it was invariably found that where the genetic data clearly indicated that chromosome inversions, translocations, and other gross physical structural chromosome changes had occurred there was also direct cytological evidence for a change in the order of crossbands or structure of one or more regions of the chromosome. Similar results with corn whose chromosomes show typical structural characteristics have also been obtained. Thus the role of the chromosomes as the physical basis of heredity has received further confirmation. Both the genetic and cytological evidence to date with the *Drosophila* salivary chromosomes indicate that the hereditary units or genes are located in the dark staining cross-

bands and not in the areas without bands. It has been estimated that the tentative number of genes contained by a haploid set of chromosomes in *Drosophila* ranges from approximately 5000 to 15,000. In humans the number of genes per haploid set of chromosomes is believed to be between 10,000 and 100,000.

Genetic studies of recombination in several bacteria and bacteriophages have demonstrated that genes are linked in much the same manner as indicated for plants and animals. In bacteria and phages, however, the linear order of genes is arranged in a ring or circular linkage map.

SUPPLEMENTARY REFERENCES

Gardner, E. J., *Principles of Genetics*, Wiley, New York, 1960.
Herskowitz, I. H., *Genetics*, Little, Brown, Boston, 1962.
Sinnot, E. W., L. C. Dunn, and T. Dobzhansky, *Principles of Genetics*, fifth edition, McGraw-Hill, New York, 1958.
Swanson, C. P., *Cytology and Cytogenetics*, Prentice-Hall, Englewood Cliffs, N. J., 1957.
Taylor, H. J., "The Duplication of Chromosomes," *Scientific American*, June 1958.

2\

Chapter 13   Mechanics of Heredity:

Other Relationships among Genes;

Genetics of Sex; Human Genetics

Although the basic principles laid down by Mendel represent the very foundation of genetics, subsequent experiments by numerous other investigators have extended and modified Mendel's conclusions. They have revealed that the relationships among genes and their influence in determining phenotypes may be different and far more complex in many instances than had previously been supposed.

Incomplete Dominance

In actuality, relatively few genes display the relationship of dominance or recessiveness to their allele originally observed by Mendel. Usually the heterozygous phenotype is intermediate between the two parents, displaying a mixture of the traits determined by both alleles. This phenomenon is called *incomplete dominance* (or blended inheritance). In fact some geneticists believe that complete dominance (or complete recessiveness) does not exist and that in all heterozygotes both alleles show their effects to one degree or another in the phenotype. Incomplete dominance is illustrated classically by the cross between red-flowered and white-flowered four-o'clock plants. The resulting F_1 generation is made up neither of red-flowered nor of white-flowered but entirely of pink-flowered plants. The F_2 generation resulting from a cross between two F_1 plants having pink flowers is made up of plants

with white flowers, pink flowers, and red flowers in the ratio of $1:2:1$. These data are in complete agreement with Mendel's first law of segregation and with Mendel's genetic studies, except that contrary to Mendel's experience the condition of incomplete dominance prevails (as it does for numerous other traits) instead of dominance and recessiveness.

In incomplete dominance, although the effects of genes blend, the genes themselves do not blend but remain and segregate as discrete entities in accordance with the Mendelian laws.

Multiple Factors or Multiple Genes

Most traits are affected by several genes. Very often a particular characteristic is determined in an additive fashion by several or many pairs of independent genes each of which when taken separately produces only a small effect. Such genes are spoken of as *multiple factors* or *multiple genes*. It can therefore be expected that traits determined by multiple genes will frequently display many degrees of variation between two extremes depending upon the genetic make-up of the individual. This holds for such human characteristics as height, weight, intelligence, skin color, and special abilities.

One of the classic examples of *multiple gene* inheritance was elucidated by Davenport in 1913. His work suggested that the difference in skin color between whites and Negroes was due to the presence on different chromosomes of two pairs of genes displaying incomplete dominance. One allele of each pair was responsible for the production in the skin of a certain amount of pigment in an additive manner. Each gene causes the appearance of a certain quantity of pigment regardless of the presence or absence of the other independent genes for pigmentation. The two different genes designated as A and B are responsible for the production in the skin of a certain quantity of pigment in a cumulative fashion, whereas the corresponding alleles a and b cause no skin pigmentation. A full Negro therefore with the genotype AABB possesses four pigmentation genes, whereas a white having genotype aabb has no pigment under the control of these four genes. In the mating of a full Negro (AABB) with a white (aabb), all members of the resulting F₁ generation will have an intermediate skin color (mulatto) indicative of the genotype AaBb.

The offspring, however, of a mating between the two mulattoes will exhibit various degrees of skin color ranging from a white to a full Negro. A mulatto produces four different kinds of gametes with respect to the foregoing two pairs of genes determining skin pigmentation, namely AB, Ab, aB, ab. As shown in the checkerboard square (Figure 13-1), the random union of four different gametes will give several different genotypes to yield five different possible phenotypes.

It can be seen that there is a statistical possibility that one-sixteenth of the progeny will

be as dark (AABB) as the Negro grandparent, whereas one-sixteenth will be as light as the white grandparent. Six of the 16 possible offspring could be of the same mulatto phenotype (4 AaBb, 1 AAbb, 1 aaBB), since they will possess two pigmentation genes, either AA, BB, or AB, with each producing in an additive fashion the same degree of skin darkening. There is a statistical chance that one-fourth (2 Aabb, 2 aaBb) of the F₂ generation will possess one pigmentation gene, whereas the remaining fourth (2 AABb, 2 AaBB) will have three and thus will display correspondingly lighter or darker skins respectively than the average mulatto. More recent evidence indicates that four pairs of multiple genes are involved in Negro pigmentation instead of the 2 pairs originally suggested by Davenport.

Multiple Alleles

Our discussions of genetics thus far have emphasized the inheritance of genes existing in only two possible states or allelic forms. In some cases we indicated that one allele was dominant to the other, whereas in others we pointed out that phenomenon of incomplete dominance occurred. Actually an appreciable number of genes can exist in three or more allelic states, a phenomenon known as *multiple allelism*. The relationship of multiple alleles to one another with respect to dominance of the phenotype may differ depending on the allele under consideration. At any one time in diploid organisms, two different alleles at most can occupy any pair of gene loci, one at each of the corresponding positions of a homologous pair of chromosomes.

Genetic studies with *Drosophila* have demonstrated that there are a dozen different alleles for eye color alone. In man the inheritance of blood types designated as A, B, AB, and O is a well-established case of multiple alleles, in this instance three alleles (Chapter 25).

Lethal Genes

Genes responsible for the development of traits that are sufficiently defective under cer-

	AB	Ab	aB	ab
AB	AABB	AABb	AaBB	AaBb
Ab	AABb	AAbb	AaBb	Aabb
aB	AaBB	AaBb	aaBB	aaBb
ab	AaBb	Aabb	aaBb	aabb

Figure 13-1. Multiple gene inheritance as illustrated by the inheritance of skin color in humans based on the research of Davenport.

tain environmental conditions to produce effects severe enough to cause an organism's death are called *lethal genes*. The effect of a lethal gene like any other mutant gene is examined by comparison with the effect of its normal allele. Lethal genes occur in a wide variety of organisms including mice, guinea pigs, *Drosophila*, primroses, and man. They are largely recessive and therefore exercise their fatal effect in the homozygous condition. Some lethal genes, however, are dominant, causing death even in the heterozygous condition. Depending on the lethal genes, death may occur at any stage of development from the fertilized egg to the adult form.

The genetic cause of lethal effects may vary widely, from alterations in the number of chromosomes to changes in chromosome structure and to gene mutations. They may arise as spontaneous mutations or they may be produced by mutagenic agents. Lethal genes are known to produce a great variety of biochemical, physiological, and morphological disturbances which may lead to the death of the organism.

The definitions of deleterious and lethal genes are relative. Such genes are distinguished from one another and from other gene mutations only by the severity of their effects. Lethal genes therefore are not different in principle from any other mutations. The effect of the lethal gene is to cause a disturbance in the normal course of development or functioning of the organism at some period in its life (depending on the mutation and the environment), thus causing death. A less extreme mutant gene instead of causing death will lead to the development of an abnormal phenotype.

Many gene mutations tend to be deleterious, ranging from mildly debilitating effects to the extreme of lethality. Sickle-cell anemia (p. 290) as a genetic disease, for example, is fatal to individuals homozygous for this trait, provided they are exposed to an environment deficient in oxygen. In the heterozygous condition the gene is of distinct survival value in malaria-infested regions of the world.

Gene Interaction and Manifold Effects of Genes

For simplicity and convenience, we have referred to separate genes regulating seed color, stem length, wing structure, animal pigmentation, and so on, as if genes were exclusively representatives of particular body parts or of certain traits. This oversimplified approach in the early days of genetics proved to be helpful in exposing the basic principles of heredity. It also serves to illustrate the fundamentals of genetics to the beginning student.

In actuality a trait may be determined and controlled not by a single pair of genes but by several or many genes as is often the case. For example, many different genes influence eye color in *Drosophila*. By 1915 Morgan and his associates had already shown that at least 13 different normal or so-called "wild-type" genes act together to produce normal red eye color in the fruit fly. Similarly a gene may effect numerous observable traits instead of one. This is probably the case for most genes. After all, the so-called structural and functional characteristics of living systems to a certain extent are arbitrary designations conceived in the mind of man for purposes of convenient description and classification. In short what we may have decided to be separate traits of an organism (e.g., different body parts) may not have been the same decision reached by the genes. Most important is that the development of the organism is ultimately under the control of all genes acting together in response to any given environment. Genes ultimately exercise their effects through biochemical processes in the cells, tissues, and organs of the living system by controlling protein synthesis.

Complementary Genes

One of the commonest types of gene interactions involves two or more independent pairs of genes called *complementary genes*; these genes are so related that in order for the single given dominant trait to be expressed all complementary genes must be represented by at least one of their dominant alleles. The alternate phenotypic character is produced by the homozygous recessive condition of any or all of the complementary genes. In the carnation and sweet pea, for example, two complementary genes (C and R) must be present together in the dominant condition for pigment formation in the flowers to occur. In these instances a mating of two lines of white-flowered plants, the recessive phenotype, may produce 100 per cent purple flowered plants in the F_1 generation. The F_2 generation arising from a cross between two F_1 purple-flowered plants will display the phenotypic ratio of 9 purple- to 7 white-flowered plants typical of two complementary genes segregating independently. The results are shown in Figure 13-2.

In an increasing number of instances the biochemical approach is shedding considerable light on genetic problems by offering simple and rational explanations for what formerly appeared to be complex interrelationships among genes. For example, the action of complementary genes can be readily explained in terms of their control of enzymatic steps in a simple reaction sequence. If genes C and R are each necessary for the formation of two separate enzymes involved in the biosynthesis of the flower pigment, both dominant genes are required to obtain purple flowers. Presumably gene C controls the production of enzyme 1 which catalyzes the formation of a particular colorless intermediate. The latter is converted to the flower pigment through the action of enzyme 2 under the control of gene R. The presence of either

(or both) pairs of homozygous recessive genes will result in a lack of one (or both) of the active enzymes and therefore a failure on the part of the plant to form the pigment. As long as one step is blocked in a reaction sequence no final product can be formed.

Modifier Genes—Suppressors and Enhancers

Those genes which are known to modify the expression of other genes, usually by suppressing or enhancing their visible effects, are called *modifier genes*. For example, in *Neurospora* a particular suppressor gene has been investigated which inhibits the effects of three or more nonallelic genes. In *Drosophila* a particular modifier gene is known which enhances or intensifies a specific dominant gene for a certain eye characteristic known as "star-eye."

Position Effect

It has become increasingly clear that the structure of the chromosome like the structure

P_1 Generation

Phenotype	White - flowered	White - flowered
Genotype	ccRR	CCrr
Gametes	cR	Cr

F_1 Generation

Phenotype	Purple - flowered
Genotype	CcRr
Gametes	CR Cr cR cr

F_2 Generation

Genotype and Phenotype	CR	Cr	cR	cr
CR	CCRR Purple	CCRr Purple	CcRR Purple	CcRr Purple
Cr	CCRr Purple	CCrr White	CrRr Purple	Ccrr White
cR	CcRR Purple	CcRr Purple	ccRR White	ccRr White
cr	CcRr Purple	Ccrr White	ccRr White	ccrr White

Phenotype Ratio 9 Purple : 7 White

Figure 13-2. The effect of complementary genes in the formation of flower pigment as illustrated by a cross in the carnation or sweet pea.

of any organ or subcellular component is a product of a long evolution. The chromosome can no longer be assumed to be an aggregate of completely independent genes arranged in a chance linear order. The harmonious interaction of genes in a chromosome depends in part on the spatial order and relationships of genes to one another on the chromosomes. In numerous instances it has been demonstrated that a rearrangement of the linear order of genes, which can be accomplished by means of X-ray-induced translocations and inversions may result in a change of expression and stability of certain genes, a phenomenon known as *position effect*. In some cases the rearrangement of genes produces an unpredictable instability in function of certain genes during the organism's development as if the particular genes were being "shut on and off." In still other cases a change in the linear order of genes by translocation or inversion may give rise to sterility and lethal effects.

The possibility that the position effect phenomenon resulting from linear rearrangement of genes is due to a modification of gene structure is highly unlikely since reversal of the position effect has been attained in several cases by restoring the linear order of genes to its original normal position.

Polyploidy

Occasionally new species of organisms possessing more than two haploid sets of chromosomes appear, a condition spoken of as *polyploidy*. The occurrence of three haploid sets of chromosomes ($3n$ or *triploid*), four sets ($4n$ or *tetraploid*), and more are known. Polyploidy is far more common among plants than animals, and is considered to be a significant mechanism in the evolution of plants. Polyploids often behave as full-fledged new species. Different polyploid species of numerous plants are known. For example, chrysanthemum species possessing $2n$, $4n$, $6n$, $8n$, and $10n$ have been identified. Polyploid plants frequently have larger leaves and stems and usually exhibit differences in their flowers and

fruits. Polyploidy can be induced artificially by subjecting cells to certain chemicals which permit chromosome duplication but not cell division to occur.

THE GENETICS OF SEX AND RELATED PHENOMENA

The Sex Chromosomes

Cytological observations of chromosome structure and behavior during the late nineteenth and early twentieth centuries revealed that in many organisms the body cells or somatic cells of the male possessed in their chromosome set a single unpaired chromosome called the X-*chromosome*. In the female, however, the X-chromosome was paired to a similar X-chromosome. In other species, instead of a single unpaired chromosome, the male exhibited within its chromosome complement an unusual pair of chromosomes in which the two homologous members were distinctly unlike in size and shape. The normal, rod-shaped member of the pair is the X-chromosome whereas its unusual-appearing smaller homologue is designated as the Y-chromosome. In the *Drosophila* male, for example, the rod-shaped X-chromosome with its spindle fiber attachment near one end is readily distinguished from the Y-chromosome which is hook shaped, possessing a long and a short arm (Figure 13-3). In contrast the female somatic cells contain two X-chromosomes instead of the XY pair. The fact that a consistent relationship was observed between the sex of an organism and the presence or absence of the X- and Y-chromosomes implicated these chromosomes specifically in sex determination. The X- and Y-chromosomes were therefore called the *sex chromosomes* in contrast to the other members of the chromosome complement which are known as the *autosomes*.

In man where the chromosomes are quite small it was erroneously believed until quite recently that the normal diploid chromosome number was 48 consisting of 23 pairs of autosomes and a pair of sex chromosomes. As a result of improved cytological techniques, it has now been established that the diploid number of chromosomes in man is 46 (Figure 13-4), consisting of 22 pairs of autosomes plus a pair of sex chromosomes (XX in the female and XY in the male). In the male the Y-chromosome is only a fraction of the size of its X-homologue. A similar situation holds for *Drosophila* as it does for many flies and beetles. In *Drosophila* there are three pairs of autosomes and a single pair of sex chromosomes (XX and XY).

In species in which the sex chromosomes of the male are of the XY type (e.g., man and *Drosophila*) two kinds of sperm are produced with respect to the sex chromosomes: half the number of sperm contain the X-chromosome and half contain the Y-chromosome. All egg cells, however, carry the X-chromosomes as part of their haploid set. The union of

a sperm bearing a Y-chromosome with an egg cell (X) gives rise to a male (XY), whereas fertilization by an X-carrying sperm produces a female (XX). The Y-chromosome of the male is transmitted only to the sons and X-chromosome only to the daughters. Both sexes always receive an X-chromosome from the mother (Figure 13-5).

In species in which the male lacks a Y-chromosome, 50 per cent of the sperm will carry the unpaired X-chromosome, whereas the other 50 per cent will lack it. The union of a sperm possessing an X-chromosome with an egg cell gives rise to an individual containing two X-chromosomes, a female. On the other hand the fertilization of an egg cell by a sperm without an X-chromosome results in an individual with a single X-chromosome, a male.

The biological sign ♂ representing a sword

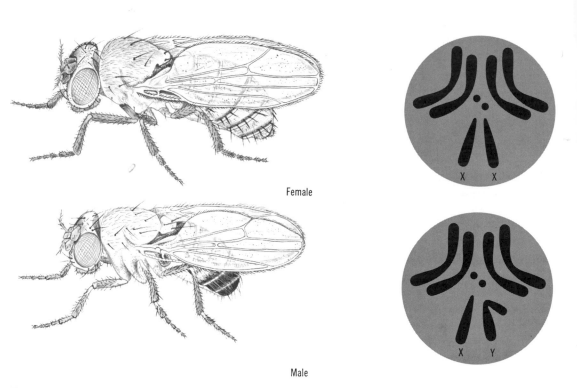

Female

Male

Figure 13-3. The chromosome complement of the *Drosophila* male and female. The female has in addition to its autosomes two X-chromosomes, whereas the male has an X and Y.

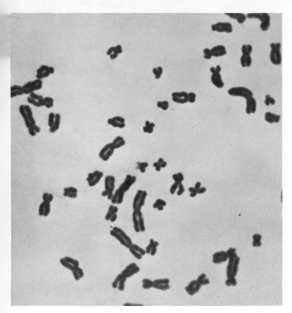

Figure 13-4. Chromosome constitution of a normal human female cell. Cell was in mitotic metaphase which accounts for the double appearance of the chromosomes. *(Courtesy of T. T. Puck.)*

and shield (symbolic of the planet Mars) is used to designate males, whereas the sign ♀ (representing a handmirror—the symbol for the planet Venus) is used to indicate females.

Although the two classes of sex chromosome distribution (X for the male and XX for the female; and XY for the male and XX for the female) are the most prevalent types in the animal kingdom, it should be noted that additional kinds occur. Oddly enough in butterflies, moths, birds, and some fish (and perhaps in certain amphibians and reptiles) the reverse situation exists. In those instances it is the female who is XY, producing two classes of gametes (X and Y) in equal numbers, whereas it is the male who has two X-chromosomes, forming only sperm of the X-type.

Sex Determination

From what has already been said it would appear that the sex of an individual is determined exclusively by the sex chromosomes. In many animals including man and *Drosophila* this viewpoint was consistent with the correlation that males possessed the X and Y chromosomes whereas females had the XX chromosome combination. Actually by the end of the first decade of the twentieth century it was commonly accepted that the sex of an individual was primarily determined by the number of X-chromosomes in its cells. One X-chromosome resulted in a male and two X-chromosomes resulted in a female. The Y-chromosome, because it had been shown to contain so few genes, was regarded as of little or no importance in sex determination, a hypothesis that was further supported by the finding that in numerous animal species (as already indicated) the males had only a single sex chromosome, namely the X-chromosome.

The outstanding investigations, however, of the American geneticist Calvin Bridges with *Drosophila* during the period extending from about 1915 to the 1920's showed that sex determination was a more complex affair than had been formerly believed. He clearly demonstrated that the sex of an individual is determined by the ratio of the number of X-chromosomes and the number of sets of autosomes in its cells. Bridges concluded that in effect femaleness is carried in the X-chromosomes and maleness in the autosomes. One of the important keys to Bridges' success in solving the problem of sex determination was his discovery of several *Drosophila* females which were triploid (3n). Triploid females possess three sets of chromosomes consisting of three

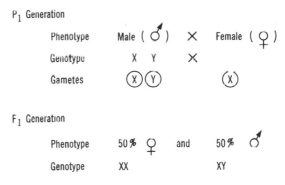

P₁ Generation

Phenotype	Male (♂)	×	Female (♀)
Genotype	X Y	×	
Gametes	Ⓧ Ⓨ		Ⓧ

F₁ Generation

Phenotype	50 % ♀	and	50 % ♂
Genotype	XX		XY

Figure 13-5. Distribution of the sex chromosomes from generation to generation.

X-chromosomes and three sets of autosomes in contrast to the usual diploid condition (2*n*) of two X-chromosomes and two sets of autosomes. The ability of triploid females to produce offspring when mated to normal diploid males offered a unique and simple experimental means to study the effects of varying and juggling the quantities and proportions of the sex chromosomes and autosomes.

A triploid female can produce four possible kinds of egg cells with regard to chromosome make-up containing: (1) one X-chromosome and one set of autosomes (A), (2) one X-chromosome and two sets of autosomes (2A), (3) two X-chromosomes and one set of autosomes (A), and (4) two X-chromosomes and two sets of autosomes (2A). A normal diploid male produces the usual two kinds of sperm containing: (1) an X-chromosome and one set of autosomes (A), and (2) a Y-chromosome and one set of autosomes (A). The possible offspring of such a mating provides an unusual variety of combinations of sex chromosomes and autosomes as indicated in the checkerboard square. (Figure 13-6).

Bridges compared the sexual characteristics of the progeny with their chromosome make-up (Table 13-1) and concluded that sex was determined by the ratio of the number of X-chromosomes to the number of sets of autosomes which an individual possesses.

The occurrence of two X-chromosomes and two sets of autosomes in a normal female (XXAA), expressed as 2X:2A, gives a ratio of 1.00. The same ratio of unity is associated with female XXYAA, despite possession of a Y-chromosome, and with the triploid female XXXAAA. The ratio A/X of 1.0 therefore appears to be correlated with female sex determination. By contrast the ratio X/A of 0.50 goes hand in hand with maleness as indicated in the normal diploid male XYAA. An intermediate ratio of 0.67 gives a so-called *intersex* which is sterile with sexual traits intermediate between the male and female. Finally the ratios 0.33 and 1.5 gave weak and sterile individuals called supermales and superfemales bearing a

Figure 13-6. Possible offspring arising from a cross between a triploid female and a diploid male of *Drosophila*.

resemblance to males and females respectively. Presumably the genes on one of the autosomal chromosomes exert a tendency for maleness (the Y-chromosome is totally inert in this respect) whereas the X-chromosomes exercise a female-forming effect. In man and mouse, however, the Y-chromosome apparently carries the genes for "maleness." The autosomal chromosomes have only a slight effect. Sex is determined mainly by the balance of the X- and Y-chromosomes in contrast to *Drosophila* where sex is decided by the balance of the X- and autosomal chromosomes.

Sex-Linked Inheritance

Genes borne on the sex chromosomes—in nearly all cases on the X-chromosomes—are called sex-linked genes. In general the term *sex linkage* is used to designate the presence of genes on the X-chromosome. The first experimental evidence supporting the proposal that certain genes are carried on the X-chromosome was presented by Morgan in 1910 as a result of genetic studies with *Drosophila*. Mor-

Table 13-1 Sexual Types of *Drosophila* Progeny Arising from a Cross between Triploid Female and Diploid Male.

Sexual Traits	Genotype	Ratio X/A
Abnormal supermale	XYAAA	0.33
Male (diploid)	XYAA	0.50
Intersex	XXYAAA	0.67
Intersex	XXAAA	0.67
Female (diploid)	XXAA	1.00
Female (diploid)	XXYAA	1.00
Female (triploid)	XXXAAA	1.00
Abnormal superfemale	XXXAA	1.50

gan isolated a naturally occurring white-eyed *Drosophila* mutant from a population of normal red-eyed flies and studied the mode of inheritance of the white-eyed condition. By means of various crosses he showed that the gene for red eyes was dominant over the allele for white eyes. However, the occurrence of the eye-color phenotype in numerous progeny was different for male and female. The data implied an involvement of the sex chromosomes. Additional evidence soon convinced Morgan that the mode of inheritance of the genes for red and white eye color in *Drosophila* could be entirely accounted for by assuming that these genes were sex linked (i.e., carried on the X-chromosomes). The hypothesis of sex-linked genes has successfully served to predict the results of certain experiments and has thus far been confirmed by every conceivable experimental test put to it.

Morgan's original observations were that a cross between the white-eyed male mutant and a homozygous red-eyed female yielded an F₁ generation of 100 per cent red-eyed flies. The F₂ generation consisted of the familiar ratio of approximately three red to one white indicating that the gene (W) for red eyes was dominant and the mutant allele (w) for white eyes was recessive. The most striking feature of the F₂ generation, however, was the fact that all the females were red-eyed, whereas half the males were red-eyed and the other half white-eyed. Until that time the inheritance of all traits studied in *Drosophila* and other organisms had shown no unequal distribution between the two sexes of the progeny. From these and other crosses Morgan finally concluded that the results could best be explained by assuming that the genes for eye color are carried on the X chromosome. The preceding mating between the white-eyed male and red-eyed female could therefore be interpreted as shown in Figure 13-7.

Although the trait for white eye is recessive, the presence of a single gene for this characteristic *in the male* will be expressed in the phenotype because the male has only a single X-chromosome. Its unlike Y-chromosome lacks the allele of this gene. Single recessive sex-linked genes express themselves in the absence of the dominant allele. As can be seen from Figure 13-7 a father transmits (1) his X-chromosome to all his daughters but to none of his sons, and (2) his Y-chromosome to all his sons but to none of his daughters. A female derives one X-chromosome from her mother and one from her father, whereas a male receives his single X-chromosome only from his mother. The white-eyed males in the F₂ generation of the example have received their gene for this trait from their normal-appearing but heterozygous red-eyed mother of the F₁ generation.

As a partial test of the hypothesis of sex-linked genes, it should be possible to produce some white-eyed females by crossing F₁ female (heterozygous for red eyes) with a white male, in effect performing a testcross or backcross (p. 308). This is precisely one of the experiments performed by Morgan, and his predicted results of 50 per cent white-eyed males and 50 per cent white-eyed females were entirely confirmed (Figure 13-8).

Numerous sex-linked genes have since been discovered. Nearly all have been found to be on the X-chromosome. Because single recessive sex-linked genes express themselves in the absence of the dominant allele (i.e., in males), sex-linked genes will therefore express themselves more frequently in males than in females. In human beings such conditions as red-green color blindness (inability to distinguish between red and green colors), hemophilia (the bleeder's disease, Chapter 25), and certain other abnormal and normal traits are among the approximately thirty known sex-linked traits. Their mode of inheritance is identical with the example given of Morgan's original experiments with white-eyed and red-eyed inheritance in *Drosophila*. Simply substitute in place of w for white-eyed *Drosophila* in Figure 13-8 the symbol r designating the recessive allele for color blindness or h for hemophilia, and the genetics of these sex-

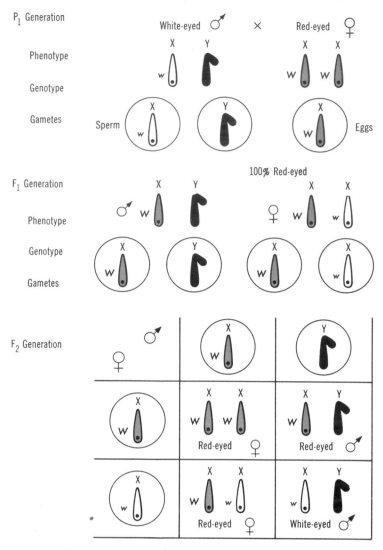

P₁ Generation

White-eyed ♂ × Red-eyed ♀

Phenotype

Genotype

Gametes — Sperm — Eggs

100% Red-eyed

F₁ Generation

Phenotype

Genotype

Gametes

F₂ Generation

Red-eyed ♀   Red-eyed ♂

Red-eyed ♀   White-eyed ♂

Phenotype   3 red-eyed: 1 white-eyed (100% red-eyed females;
50% red-eyed and 50% white-eyed males)

Figure 13-7. A cross demonstrating sex-linked inheritance of eye color in *Drosophila.*

linked traits in human beings are identical. Males suffering from recessive sex-linked diseases but having apparently normal parents must have inherited the condition from their mothers (who would have to be heterozygous for these traits) and not from their fathers. The ability of single recessive sex-linked genes to express themselves in the male as well as the segregation of X-chromosomes in gametogenesis accounts for the higher incidence of red-green color blindness in males than in females. In the United States about 8 per cent of the males are red-green color blind whereas less than 1 per cent of the females display the same condition.

In human beings the sex ratio at birth is not

exactly 1:1—boys exceed girls by about 2 per cent. For obscure reasons the ratio is apparently even more disproportionate in the initial sex ratio of unborn infants. It has in fact been estimated that probably shortly after fertilization the ratio is as high as three males to two females in view of the greater occurrence of stillborn males than females. The higher fatalities among prenatal males may be due in part to the prevalence of sex-linked defects which mainly affect males.

In species (e.g., birds, moths, and certain fishes) in which the male has two X-chromosomes and the female X and Y sex-linked genes express themselves more frequently in females than in males. A mother transmits her X-chromosome to all her sons but to none of her daughters, and her Y-chromosome to all her daughters but to none of her sons.

In a comparatively small number of organisms the Y-chromosome is also a carrier of

several genes. In *Drosophila*, for example, a number of genes or hereditary determinants have been identified on the Y-chromosomes and are therefore Y-linked. They are transmitted directly from father to son. In fact several are found only on the Y-chromosome such as those that affect the fertility of the males. The absence of the Y-chromosome is associated with males who are sterile. In man a number of genes have been postulated on a portion of the Y-chromosome which may be homologous with a section of the X-chromosome.

Nondisjunction of Sex Chromosomes

In the years 1914 to 1916 Calvin Bridges, the same geneticist who was later to establish the chromosomal basis for sex determination in *Drosphila* published some highly important genetic results. His findings firmly established that the sex-linked gene for white eyes is located on the X-chromosome. Bridges' work

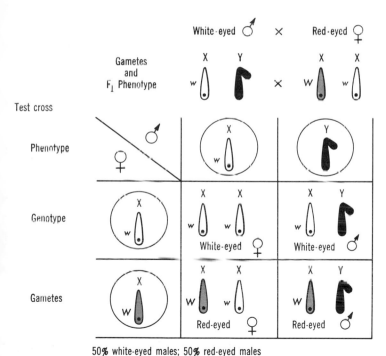

50% white-eyed males; 50% red-eyed males
50% white-eyed females; 50% red-eyed females

Figure 13-8. A backcross illustrating the sex-linked inheritance of eye color in *Drosophila*.

was a turning point in biology for it clearly and unequivocally demonstrated once and for all to the satisfaction of nearly all geneticists that genes are located on chromosomes, a concept put forth by Morgan and his colleagues some five years earlier.

At the time Bridges, working as a graduate student in Morgan's laboratory at Columbia University, observed that a cross between a mutant white-eyed *Drosophila* female and a normal red-eyed male gave unusual results. Although the offspring of this cross consisted of the predicted white-eyed sons and red-eyed daughters in accordance with sex linkage, they occasionally included the totally unexpected white-eyed females and red-eyed males. Bridges explained the unusual appearance of white-eyed females and red-eyed males in the F_1 generation of the cross by postulating that the white-eyed daughter must have two X-chromosomes bearing the recessive genes for white. These could only have been contributed by the white-eyed mother. Similarly the red-eyed son could only have derived its single X-chromosome carrying the dominant gene for red eyes from his red-eyed father.

Bridges further reasoned that this could be explained by the hypothesis that infrequently there was a failure of the two X-chromosomes to separate or disjoin during meiosis of the white-eyed female parent. In such instances (occurring spontaneously in one among 2000 to 3000 cells) the two X-chromosomes of the female instead of normally separating during the anaphase of the first meiotic division either remained in the egg or were eliminated in the polar body, a phenomenon known as *nondisjunction*. Fertilization of the two types of exceptional eggs (two X-chromosomes or no X-chromosomes) arising from meiosis associated with nondisjunction can produce four possible offspring as shown by the checkerboard square (Figure 13-9).

The two possible offspring pertinent to our present discussion are the unusual white-eyed daughter arising from the fertilization of an egg

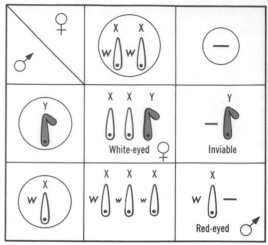

Figure 13-9. Possible offspring with regard to eye color resulting from the fertilization of two exceptional eggs (two X-chromosomes and no X-chromosomes) arising from *nondisjunction* in *Drosophila*.

bearing two X-chromosomes by a Y-carrying sperm, and the red-eyed son arising from the fertilization by an X-carrying sperm of an egg bearing no X-chromosomes. If Bridges' hypothesis is correct the white-eyed daughter should differ from normal *Drosophila* females by having a Y-chromosome in addition to her two X-chromosomes, and the red-eyed son should lack the Y-chromosome. Cytological examination by Bridges of these exceptional flies proved his predictions to be entirely correct. The other progeny bearing three X-chromosomes were poorly viable superfemales, whereas the eggs lacking the X-chromosome fertilized by the Y-carrying sperm failed to survive. In further confirmation of his theory Bridges correctly predicted the composition of offspring produced by the crossing of the exceptional females XXY to normal males. In substance Bridges' experimental results proved beyond any reasonable doubt that the gene for white eyes was carried in the X-chromosomes. In the broader sense they conclusively demonstrated by means of direct and convincing evidence that genes are located on chromosomes and that sex-linked genes were parts of the X-chromosome.

Sex-Influenced and Sex-Limited Traits

Genes that produce different effects in the two sexes are not always found on the sex chromosomes. Several genes are known which are not located on the sex chromosomes but whose phenotypic effects are influenced by the sex of the individual. Such autosomal genes which express themselves differently in the male and female are called *sex-influenced genes*. For example, the production of horns in some breeds of sheep is a sex-influenced trait accounting for horned males and hornless females. Matings between two breeds of sheep have demonstrated that the genes involved in the production of horns behave as dominant genes in the male and as recessives in the female. The heterozygous condition for the genes is sufficient to produce horns in the male whereas the homozygous recessive state is necessary to give horns to the female. In several of the instances studied the action of sex-influenced genes appears to be determined somehow by the sex hormones.

In other cases the effects of some autosomal genes are limited to one of the sexes. Such genes are called *sex-limited*. For example, in human beings a particular type of premature baldness is expressed in the male presumably in the presence of a sufficient level of male sex hormone. It is rarely if ever seen in the female. Milk production is effected in part by genes carried in the chromosomes of bulls as well as cows. Nevertheless milk production is limited to the sex possessing developed mammary glands and suitable hormones to perform this function.

Genetic Significance of Sexual Reproduction

Sexual reproduction appears to be a fundamental characteristic of living things. It displays itself in innumerable and bewildering forms. It is known to occur in so-called primitive condition, in bacteria, bacteriophages, algae, fungi, and protozoa becoming increasingly sophisticated in correspondingly higher organisms in the evolutionary scale. Sexual reproduction in certain colon bacteria as a visible mating process has only been discovered recently and stems from the earlier pioneering work of the Nobel Prize winner Joshua Lederberg. Two of the bacterial cells representing two different mating strains fuse, apparently forming a cytoplasmic bridge, and several genes of one cell are transferred to the recipient cell. Extensive studies of host-virus relationships conducted largely with bacteriophages have established that sexual reproduction in the fundamental sense of gene recombination occurs when different phage mutants multiply in the same host cell. These investigations have been carried out for the most part with the so-called T-phages which attack the colon-derived bacterial species *Escherichia coli B*.

Sexual reproduction as compared to asexual reproduction is important in several respects First, by making possible the diploid state it effectively maintains a large and varied *gene pool* (Chapter 33), accounting for a greater number of possible phenotypes in the testing ground of evolution. Second it tends to prevent the complete elimination of "defective" genes (at least when their effects are masked by the dominant genes). "Defective" genes under different environmental conditions could prove to be advantageous for survival. An example is seen in the instance of the genetic disease sickle-cell anemia (p. 290), for in the malaria-infested regions of the world the gene in the heterozygous condition has a distinct survival value. Finally, sexual reproduction serves as a means of generating new genotypes by combining different gene sets from each parent. It thereby promotes greater genetic variability among organisms, thus functioning as an important mechanism in evolution. The environment in turn acts as a selective force determining by a process of natural selection which combinations of genes are most favorably suited to survive under the given conditions. Where combination of genes occur that are unfavorable for survival of the organism in the struggle for existence, that individual will very likely perish. On the other hand those species with the most favorable complement of genes will tend to survive and become the dominant group.

INHERITANCE IN THE HUMAN SPECIES

Man as an Experimental Animal for Genetic Studies

The same principles of genetics that apply to *Drosophila,* peas, and all other organisms also govern the transmission of heritable traits in man. Wherever possible fundamental problems in human genetics have been applied to other organisms that are far more suitable to the experimental approach, for the study of heredity in man is encumbered by several serious hindrances and difficulties.

Human beings have comparatively few offspring; and their generation time, averaging approximately twenty-five to thirty years, is much too long, at least as far as the experimental geneticist is concerned. In addition, for obvious reasons, man, as a possible experimental mammal for genetic studies does not lend himself well to genotype standardization and maintenance in a uniform environment— important requirements for the experimental geneticist. Moreover planned matings among individuals are hardly determined by the scientific requirements of the geneticist.

On the other hand as experimental material for genetic investigations human beings offer certain distinct advantages. Their long life span, for example, has permitted the study of hereditary abnormalities which develop later in life, phenomena known in man but unknown in most other animals. In addition particular phenomena, for instance, color blindness and its mode of inheritance, are more easily demonstrated in man, whereas they could only have been discovered in other animals with far greater difficulty.

Techniques in Human Genetics

Various techniques have been devised which have conclusively established the existence of numerous gene-controlled traits in man. The earlier approaches to the study of inheritance in man were based on *pedigree histories* of families, usually with emphasis on conspicuous or unusual traits. The subsequent application of *statistical analysis* to human genetics has proved to be extremely valuable in determining the mode of inheritance of a number of characteristics, especially in view of the limitations noted previously. *Recent studies of identical twins and other multiple births,* as a means of attaining some degree of genotype standardization have yielded new data on the inheritance of particular human characteristics, especially relating to intelligence, special aptitudes, temperament, and certain mental diseases.

The occurrence of multiple birth such as *identical twins* (two individuals arising by division of a single fertilized egg cell and therefore possessing an identical genetic composition) in contrast to *fraternal twins* (siblings born at the same time but from different eggs fertilized by different sperm) offer an unusual opportunity to study the effects of environment on heredity. Fraternal twins are no more alike in their heredity than any brothers and sisters except that they are of the same age. They offer, however, a convenient comparison for studies of identical twins. In white populations twins occur about once in every eighty-eight births. The reasons for twin birth are not at all clear, although it is believed to be due to one or more unknown maternal genetic factors.

Despite the great promise presented by the occurrence of identical twins as a technique for studying the problem of interaction between heredity and environment, unforeseen limitations have become evident. In several instances identical twins have displayed marked physical and mental differences which are not easily explained. The prenatal environment for twins can no longer be considered as identical in view of known situations in which one member of an identical pair develops normally whereas the other lags behind. In rare cases an exchange of embryonic cells between fraternal twins during early prenatal development has been shown to result in certain similarities of blood chemistry. With these limitations in mind studies of identical twins have provided helpful information on the interaction of heredity and environment.

Inherited Physical and Mental Human Traits

Many physical features of man including the detailed structure of the face, the color and texture of the hair, skin, nails and teeth, the characteristics of eyes (including color and various defects in vision), and the structure and proportions of the skeleton and muscles have been shown to be controlled by genes. Virtually all our advances in the knowledge of human heredity have stemmed principally from clearly defined traits under the control of a single or few genes. In numerous cases, however, individual characteristics, according to our rather arbitrary designation, are determined not by a single pair of genes but by several or many pairs. The inheritance of traits of social importance—physical appearance, intelligence, good health—have proved to be extremely complex in contrast to relatively simple genetic phenomena such as the inheritance of color blindness. The main reason of course is that such characteristics as intelligence, physical appearance, and health are a composite of many simpler inherited traits.

The evidence is strongly convincing that mental ability is largely inherited. Earlier investigations of families of unusually high and low abilities as well as the more recent measurement by intelligence tests are the main types of evidence for this conclusion. The average person is supposed to have an IQ (intelligence quotient) of 100. The normal range includes all values below the average down to an IQ of 70 and above the average to about 130 or 140. IQ is the "mental age" (as determined by intelligence tests) divided by the actual chronological age multiplied by 100.

$$IQ = \frac{\text{mental age} \times 100}{\text{chronological age}}$$

For example, the average score attained by a large majority of representative ten-year-olds would constitute the normally expected performance of a child in this age group. Should an eight-year-old attain this same score then his IQ as calculated from the formula would be $10/8 \times 100 = 125$. The current view is that IQ is in large part the result of an interaction of several different genes of an additive nature. Each gene is believed to make a separate contribution to the IQ value, acting together in a cumulative but independent fashion to affect the total score.

Whereas genetic linkage studies have been extensively conducted with plants and lower animals, similar investigations with man have been comparatively rare, in view of the limitations imposed by small families and the relative randomness of matings. Studies of family records showing the occurrence of both color blindness and hemophilia, known sex-linked traits on the X-chromosome, led to the first evidence of linkage in human beings. Calculations showed that the amount of crossing-over between the two genes was 14 per cent. It has only been since 1950 that genetic linkage on the autosomes or nonsex chromosomes have been demonstrated in man.

Inherited Human Diseases

A growing list of human functional and structural diseases that are being identified as hereditary conditions is described in Chapter 11. Susceptibility to several infectious diseases has also been related to genetic phenomenon. The inheritance of blood group and Rh factor is indicated in Chapter 25.

The use of tissue-culture techniques as a tool for the study of inherited diseases and other aspects of inheritance in human beings especially from the biochemical genetic approach, shows unusual promise.

Human Diseases Associated with Change in Chromosome Number

A congenital malformation is an imperfection that is present at birth. In most instances little is known about the cause of congenital defects. Congenital anomalies may range from

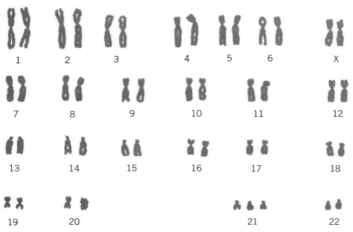

Figure 13-10. Chromosome constitution of a cell from a mongoloid human female. Chromosome 21 is triploid. The chromosomes were in the mitotic metaphase and therefore appear double. *(Courtesy Drs. M. A. Ferguson-Smith and A. W. Johnston, Ann. Inter. Med.)*

slight imperfections to radical changes which prove to be fatal. *Mongolism* is a particular congenital abnormality in man. It is recognizable at birth and characterized by a physical dwarfing and serious mental retardation. The strange appearance of an individual suffering from this condition because of slight anomalies in the eyes, nose, mouth, ears, and shape of the head accounts for the name mongolism or mongoloid idiot. Recent investigations have shown that an extra autosome, (of the pair designated as number 21) in the body cells is associated with mongolism (Figure 13-10). It is probably the result of nondisjunction (p. 327) during the first meiotic division of oögenesis. Thus in mongolism there are 45 autosomes plus the two X-chromosomes in the female, and 45 + XY in the male in contrast to 44 autosomes and two sex chromosomes in a normal individual. The age of the mother is directly related to the frequency of mongolism. In European populations the occurrence of a mongoloid child is about 1 in 2000 for mothers of 25, increasing to 1 in 50 for mothers of 45.

Other human diseases which have been associated with a change in chromosome number are *Klinefelter's syndrome* and *Turner's syndrome.* In the former the chromosomal formula is 44 autosomes plus two X-chromosomes and a Y-chromosome (44A + XXY = 47) resulting in underdeveloped males. In the latter condition (Turner's syndrome) the Y-chromosome is lacking (44A + X = 45), giving rise to an individual who looks superficially like an underdeveloped female.

Eugenics

The science of improvement of the hereditary constitution of man (or other animals) by selective breeding or other methods is called eugenics. Thus far most attempts to improve the genetic constitution of the human race and therefore the heredity of future generations of man have been eminently unsuccessful for several reasons. First, there is no common agreement on such basic questions as to what constitutes the most desirable hereditary characteristics. Which genes should be encouraged and perpetuated, and which should be discouraged and possibly eliminated? If there is a choice, should natural resistance to infection be preferred to intelligence? A new scientific discovery, for example, may completely change the biological fitness conferred by a gene. The discovery of insulin in the 1920's has permitted most diabetics to survive and lead a normal existence. Otherwise they might not have lived and produced offspring.

Second, having made the decision as to what is a desirable or undesirable trait, the next questions are: (1) what genes are most effective in producing such characteristics; and (2) how can we be certain that unsatisfactory genes are not also being transmitted in a proposed breeding program?

Third, a major difficulty centers about the tendency for inbred lines to become comparatively infertile. Crossing such stocks with other lines will therefore upset the plans for breeding a pure race.

Fourth, on theoretical grounds the fact that genetic changes in populations with long generation times, such as in man, must necessarily be slow is another difficulty in attaining eugenic progress in the human race. Moreover it is known that no appreciable changes occur in gene frequency in large populations (p. 292). In fact better standards of living have accomplished far more in terms of a healthier and more intelligent human race than most eugenic proposals.

Finally, the positive approach of encouraging reproduction between individuals of superior hereditary constitution, and the negative practice of preventing reproduction of individuals with undesirable hereditary characteristics as a means of eliminating unfavorable genes from the population have not proved feasible for a combination of reasons. These include opposition by the mores of our society as well as far-reaching legal and moral implications.

The value of sterilization (surgically altering the reproductive tract so that egg and sperm cannot unite) to decrease the incidence of hereditary defects in the population is highly questionable. Aside from the danger of misapplying the scheme for ulterior social or political motives, the effort involved would hardly justify the benefits derived. It is generally believed that most if not all individuals are heterozygous for one or more recessive defects, although they do not themselves as carriers display the abnormality. Obviously sterilization of such individuals is out of the question. Nor is sterilization of affected homozygous persons usually worthwhile since such individuals infrequently breed. A more practical and eugenically acceptable procedure would be to discourage carriers of the same defect from mating with one another as a means of effectively diminishing the occurrence of abnormal homozygous traits.

The possibility of altering the genetic composition of higher organisms including man in a *directed* fashion by means of transduction (p. 273) or artificial mutation through the use of specific chemical and physical agents remains to be developed. Such procedures may eventually prove to be feasible. There is little question that as the detailed mechanisms of gene action become more fully understood methods for the control and treatment of hereditary disease will progress.

SUPPLEMENTARY REFERENCES

Dobzhansky, T., *Evolution, Genetics, and Man*, Wiley, New York, 1955.
Penrose, L. S., *Outline of Human Genetics*, Wiley, New York, 1959.
Sager, R., and F. J. Ryan, *Cell Heredity*, Wiley, New York, 1961.
Stern, C., *Principles of Human Genetics*, second edition, Freeman, San Francisco, 1960
Wollman, E. L., and F. Jacob, "Sexuality in Bacteria," *Scientific American*, July 1956.
Also see references at the end of Chapters 11 and 12.

FIVE
THE DIVERSITY AND
INTERRELATIONSHIPS OF
LIVING THINGS

A vast array of different kinds (or species) of living things inhabits our planet. Many can be readily and conveniently classified as either animals or plants based primarily on the absence or presence of a cell wall and to a lesser extent on other characteristics (Chapter 4). Certain microorganisms, however, share the characteristics of both animals and plants. Some taxonomists prefer to classify all microorganisms within a separate kingdom, namely the *Protista*, whereas others place them within the animal or plant kingdom depending on the species. The latter type of classification is presented in this book.

Thus far approximately one million different kinds of animals and 350,000 different kinds of plants have been described more or less in accepted scientific terms. The list keeps growing each year as additional animals and plants are discovered and described. Many more undoubtedly exist.

Porcupine and fox (courtesy of Ed Cesar, National Audubon Society).

Chapter 14　The Species Concept and the Basis of Classification

GENERAL CONSIDERATIONS OF CLASSIFICATION

Artificial and Natural Systems of Classification

The earth is inhabited by an immense number of living things, and no two individuals are completely identical. It is an important goal in biology that there be a systematic, orderly classification or cataloging of this vast and changing quantity of biological material, just as a library requires that its many books be systematized and cataloged. The branch of biology that deals with classification is called *taxonomy* or systematics. Numerous and diverse systems of classification of living forms have been devised by man in the course of history. They have generally fallen into two main groups, *artificial* and *natural*. An *artificial system of classification* is based on arbitrary or artificial standards in which there is no recognition of relationships between different kinds of organisms in the sense of common or related descent. It therefore merely serves as a convenient filing system. In contrast, a *natural system of classification* is founded on the natural or evolutionary relationships among organisms, and therefore reflects as much as possible the probable evolution of these organisms.

The aim of the modern taxonomist is to devise a natural system of classification. The basic premise is that the groups of organisms that possess the greatest number of characteristics in common are more closely related. Those that share the fewest features are more distantly related. There is ample evidence to indicate that one of the main trends in the sequence of evolution has been of the *progressive* type, from organisms relatively simple in structure to those of greater complexity. Nevertheless exceptions are known to exist where the evolutionary trend has been *retrogressive* or in the opposite direction, from complexity of one or more features toward greater simplicity or *reduction*. Obviously then, extreme caution must be exercised in deciding whether a particular characteristic is simple because it is actually primitive or whether it has become simple by evolutionary reduction.

A second major hazard in interpreting evolutionary relationships is seen in the independent evolutionary acquisition of similar (although not necessarily identical) structures in organisms which are not closely related. This phenomenon is known as *convergent evolution* (Chapter 33). Such organisms may show resemblances which can easily be misinterpreted as evidences of relationship, even though they have not arisen from the same ancestral stock. The independent origin of similar eyes in certain molluscs (p. 529) and in vertebrates is an example of convergent evolution.

The present status of natural classification systems is still unsettled. Even the most highly regarded modern classification systems, although largely natural, are in certain respects artificial especially in particular fields. There are several groups (e.g., numerous microorganisms) whose relationships are not at all clear and therefore open to diverse interpretations. Some taxonomists prefer to classify all unicellular organisms into a group called the *Protista* separate from either plants or animals; others file them in the plant or animal kingdoms according to selected characteristics. Taxonomy like any other field of biology is subject to constant change. We can expect with the discovery of new information and new relationships that classification systems will accordingly undergo revisions and new interpretations.

The Species as the Unit of Classification

Many billions of individual organisms exist on our planet but we can immediately recognize that certain of these individual organisms although not absolutely identical (since no two individuals are entirely alike) closely resemble one another. We can proceed on the basis of their similarity to assemble those individual living forms sufficiently alike and closely enough related to be considered as one kind into a separate group called the *species* (plural, also *species*). For example, all living human beings are grouped within a single species. Different apes belong to several species, different monkeys to various other species, and so on.

The species is the basic unit employed in the classification of living forms and consists of a group of organisms bearing sufficiently similar characteristics. By its very nature the species as the unit of natural classification consists of a *population* (Chapters 10, 33) of individuals or a group of populations closely related in ancestry. Accordingly its members display the same structural and functional characteristics and are capable of interbreeding with one another to produce *fertile* offspring. Structural and functional similarity among individuals of a species is an expression of similarity in genetic and therefore evolutionary back-

grounds, and is often reflected in the panorama of changes during embryonic development (Chapter 31). Actually the ability to mate and produce fertile offspring, especially under natural conditions, is probably the most basic single criterion for deciding that individuals belong to the same species. It implies a close resemblance in genetic constitution and evolutionary history. The horse and the donkey, for example, may be mated to produce an offspring, the mule, which is nearly always *infertile*. For this reason alone the horse and donkey are often classified in different but closely related species. In nature interbreeding between members of different but closely related species, when possible, is an infrequent and rare occurrence. Species, therefore, exchange genes with other species rarely, or not at all, and are referred to as *genetically closed systems*.

The subunit of classification is called a *race*, *variety*, or *subspecies*. Races consist of particular populations within a species which differ to a small extent in genetic composition. Several races are usually included within a species. Races within a species are called *genetically open systems*, because they can and often do exchange genes by interbreeding, leading at times to the fusing of several races into a single population. But even the criterion of infertility for distinguishing one species from another is not entirely satisfactory. Some races within a single species are unable to produce viable or fertile offspring by interbreeding, whereas different species may at times interbreed and produce fertile offspring. Moreover, in those lower organisms where reproduction occurs only by asexual means, the taxonomist must obviously rely on criteria other than ability to mate in determining classification. The same is true in classifying fossils. By necessity these are assigned taxonomically on the basis of morphological characteristics alone.

Unfortunately for the beginning student in biology, a more exact definition cannot be given for the term species. The term (and other units of classification) designates a category or concept devised by the human mind, namely of a group of individuals closely enough related and therefore sufficiently alike to be regarded as one kind. For some types of organisms the species as the basic population unit may be self-evident, whereas for other kinds of organisms it may be obscure. The dynamic nature of living things as individuals and groups which are constantly evolving, shifting in their environment, changing qualitatively and quantitatively in their populations, makes it impossible to confine oneself to a rigid definition.

In addition to the species there are other progressively larger units in the classification system. The *genus* as the next larger unit designates a group of like or related species. Ideally each unit is essentially defined in terms of the biological evolutionary relationships of the groups of organisms to which it applies.

The Nomenclature of Classification

The earliest records of classification systems date back at least to the period of Aristotle (about 300 to 400 B.C.). Since that time numerous diverse classification systems have been devised, mostly of the artificial type, based in large part on various superficial characteristics. Some, for example, were simply alphabetical arrangements, whereas others were founded on the uses to which organisms were put by man and on certain superficial structural differences. The development of natural systems of classification is comparatively recent. It has been made possible principally as a result during the last hundred years of great advances in our knowledge and interpretation of fossil records as well as structure, function, and development of living forms at all levels of organization ranging from the molecule to the whole organism.

The present-day system of nomenclature used in classifying living things was introduced some two centuries ago principally by the Swedish physician and biologist Carolus Linnaeus (1707-1778). He is now considered to be the father of taxonomy. Linnaeus realized the need for an improved system of classification and an appropriate nomenclature. He recognized like many others that the seemingly infinite variability among living beings was not entirely haphazard, and that organisms fell into discrete kinds or groups. He called each kind a *species*, the elementary unit of classification, and to each species known to him he assigned a Latin name. At that time in the first half of the eighteenth century approximately four thousand animal species had been described, a far cry from the million or so kinds of animals known today. Rapid geographical exploration in the late eighteenth and the nineteenth centuries revealed many new kinds of organisms to the Western civilized world.

As the next higher unit of classification Linnaeus used the term *genus* (plural, *genera*) to designate a group of species which are similar in many respects and therefore presumed to be more closely related to one another than to other species. He assigned to all known organisms two Latin names, one representing the genus and the other the species. For this reason his system is known as the *binomial system of nomenclature* and is used today throughout the world by international agreement among biologists. All living human beings, for example, are members of the genus *Homo* and the species *sapiens* and are accordingly designated by the scientific name *Homo sapiens* (note that both names are always in italics and that the generic name always starts with a capital letter whereas the specific name always starts with a lowercase letter). The obvious feline characteristics of such animals as the lion, puma, tiger, jaguar, and the common cat indicate a close relationship. All are sufficiently similar to belong to the same genus (*Felis*) but are sufficiently different to be classified in separate species. They have been assigned the scientific names *Felis leo, Felis concolor, Felis tigris, Felis onca,* and *Felis domestica* respectively.

The generic name is a Latin noun and the specific name is an adjective. The specific name is usually descriptive of some characteristic of the organism which the original namer believed to be typical or unique. Occasionally

Figure 14-1. Some animals belonging to the same genus *(Felis)* but sufficiently different to be classified in separate species: common cat; tiger *(courtesy of R. Van Nostrand, National Audubon Society)*; lion *(courtesy of A. W. Ambler, National Audubon Society)*; jaguar.

the specific name is derived from the name of a person who usually first described the organism or is being honored for one reason or another. At times an abbreviation of the name of the person responsible for the binomial is also added. For example, in the scientific name for the white oak, *Quercus alba L.*, the L stands for Linnaeus who first gave the plant its indicated scientific name. This citation of authority is at times highly useful in finding the original description of the organism and avoiding confusion of identity in instances where a duplication of names has occurred. The present scientific names of many plants and animals were assigned by Linnaeus and accordingly

the first letter or an abbreviation of his name is attached to the binomial.

The use of an internationally agreed-upon scientific name for each kind of organism helps to avoid confusion and uncertainty in identifying and recording different kinds of organisms. The use of the common name of an organism although convenient has a distinct disadvantage. A given organism especially if it is widely distributed often has many common names which are strictly local in their use. Common names may not be used in other regions and may even be applied to several other distinctly different species which may or may not be related. The so-called European white water lily,

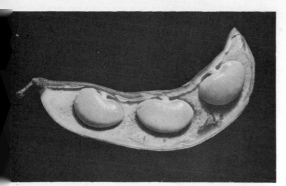

Figure 14-2. Lima beans in open pod or legume, characteristic of the family of plants Leguminosae.

for example, enjoys the use of some two hundred different common names. Conversely the term mahogany is applied to many different kinds of trees.

Linnaeus assembled similar genera into larger groups called *orders* which are further arranged into still larger related groups called *classes*. The system of units is comparable to that employed in the political organization of a nation with the town or city composing the elementary unit followed successively by progressively larger units such as the county, state, and nation.

The original categories of Linnaeus have since been enlarged in view of the vast amount of new information and newly discovered organisms. The units *family,* which falls between the genus and the order, and *phylum* (plural, *phyla),* which is the largest category of all, have subsequently been added. In addition subdivisions such as subphylum, subclass, suborder, and subfamily have been included. The sequence of categories in a descending order of inclusiveness is *phylum, class, order, family, genus,* and *species.* The differences become progressively less as one goes from the phylum to the species. On the basis of our modern interpretation of evolutionary relationships a genus ideally designates a group of like or related species. Similarly the *family* consists of a group of related genera, the *order* of related families, the *class* of related orders, and the *phylum* of related classes. Many of the names

used for the higher classification units are often based on some outstanding characteristic of the group. For example the term *Leguminosae* refers to the family of plants whose members bear their seeds in a pod or legume.

The modern classification of present-day man (*Homo sapiens*) according to this system is as follows:

Phylum — Chordata
　Subphylum — Vertebrata
　　Class — Mammalia
　　　Subclass — Placentalia
　　　　Order — Primates
　　　　　Suborder — Anthropoidea
　　　　　　Family — Hominidae
　　　　　　　Genus — Homo
　　　　　　　　Species — sapiens

The corresponding classification for the white oak tree (*Quercus alba*) is as follows:

Phylum — Tracheophyta
　Subphylum — Pteropsida
　　Class — Angiospermae
　　　Subclass — Dicotyledoneae
　　　　Order — Fagales
　　　　　Family — Fagaceae
　　　　　　Genus — Quercus
　　　　　　　Species — alba

Dynamic Status of the Species

In devising his classification of plants and animals in the eighteenth century, Linnaeus believed that the species was a distinct, unchanging natural unit of living things, divinely created "at the beginning" from which all present day organisms have linearly descended. This was a commonly held view in Linnaeus's day. Nevertheless Linnaeus happened to select as the basis for his system of classification certain fundamental characteristics (e.g., skeleton, hair, and other epidermal derivatives for larger animals, body segments for invertebrates, and reproductive structures of flowering plants) which yielded a classification scheme that was compatible with the idea of evolution. We now know of course that species are not fixed but are constantly changing dynamic units which have evolved from one another in the long history of life and will continue to do so.

The increasing difficulties of satisfactorily classifying the huge numbers of new kinds of living things discovered during the great geographical explorations of the eighteenth and nineteenth centuries soon made it evident that the concept of the species as a constant and fixed entity was not valid. Lamarck in the first half of the nineteenth century was aware that at times the differences between races and species were too difficult to distinguish. He was among the first to realize that species arose from races and that both were the result of evolutionary processes (Chapter 32). Darwin and Wallace arrived at essentially the same conclusion some thirty years later but at the same time provided a wealth of indisputable evidence in its favor as well as a reasonable theory, namely that of *natural selection* (Chapter 32), to explain its mode of action.

THE CRITERIA FOR CLASSIFICATION

Homology versus Analogy

Most of the criteria used for the present-day classification of living things are centered about anatomical and physiological characteristics. The underlying premise is that a similarity of these features among organisms is the result of a closely related biological evolution and therefore a sharing of a common ancestry. The decision as to which are the important characteristics and what interpretations we can draw with regard to evolutionary relationships and therefore classification can at times prove to be difficult and controversial.

Those structures of different organisms that correspond to one another in terms of inheritance and common ancestry and therefore in basic development and form are said to be *homologous*. In contrast those structures of different organisms that possess a similar function but are basically different in origin and structure (i.e., not homologous) are said to be *analogous*. Homologous parts in different organisms do not necessarily perform the same function. For example, the self-evident similarity in basic anatomy of the arm of man, the wing of a bird, and the foreleg of a frog strongly indicate that these structures despite their differences in function have a common inheritance and descent and are therefore homologous. In fact the fin of a now extinct ancestral fish, from which all terrestrial vertebrates including man himself are believed to have descended, has apparently provided the fundamental pattern for the limbs of these subsequently evolved terrestrial vertebrates to accomodate the functions of swimming, running, flying, and so on. A more complex and obscure homology is seen in the example of the hammer, anvil, and stirrup bones of the middle ear of mammals which have been shown to be derived from certain jaw bones of fishes (Chapter 22).

A classical example of analogy is found in comparing the wings of a bird and a butterfly. Although these structures are undoubtedly similar in function they are entirely different in organization and therefore in origin. The bird's wings with a supporting surface composed of feathers corresponds to the skeletal framework of the whole human arm or the wing of a bat (a mammal). In contrast, the wing of a butterfly essentially is made up of a membrane and is in no way structurally similar to that of a bird or a bat. Thus the wing of a bird is homologous to the arm of a man or the wing of a bat but analogous to the wing of a butterfly.

Obviously homology in contrast to analogy is indicative of an evolutionary relationship by implying descent from the same ancestral line. It thus serves as an important basis in the natural classification of living things. The cataloging of organisms on the basis of analogous structures would inevitably lead to an artificial system of classification and an incorrect interpretation of evolutionary relationships.

Although the main lines of evolutionary de-

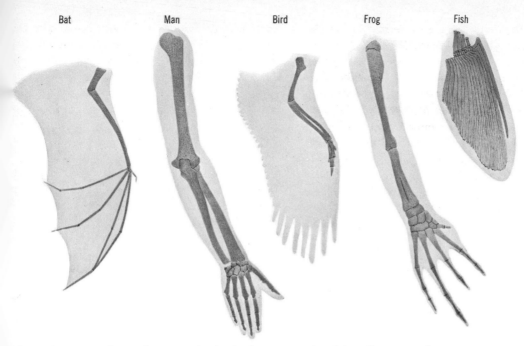

Bat Man Bird Frog Fish

Figure 14-3. Homologous bones in the forelimbs of several widely different vertebrates illustrating basic similarity in form.

velopment and relationships among living things (and therefore a corresponding natural system of classification) have been worked out to a large extent an appreciable number of special problems have not yet been entirely solved. Of particular interest is the example of the present-day Australian monotremes (p. 479) which include the duckbill and the spiny anteater. They lay eggs like reptiles but have hair and nurse their young like mammals. They are regarded by some experts as intermediate between reptiles and mammals, presumably having arisen from an ancestral species intermediate between these two major groups. Others consider the monotremes to be a separate offshoot of the reptiles which arose independently of the unidentified intermediate form that gave rise to the mammals.

Criteria for the Classification of Animals

Several specific criteria have been employed in establishing a natural system of classification for animals. The fact that different animals are superficially alike in appearance and share the same living conditions does not necessarily mean that they are closely related. For example, whales and fishes live and swim in the sea and resemble one another in form. Closer examination soon reveals that whales have no gills but breathe by lungs and have all the essential structural and functional characteristics which unquestionably identify them as mammals. The indications are that at some time in the ancient past they evolved from a small group of terrestrial mammals which returned to a watery environment. The process of natural selection has adapted them to the way of life in water as indicated by the presence of fins and the fish-like streamlined shape of the body, distinctly advantageous modifications for survival in aquatic surroundings. But the basic body structures have not been significantly changed. The presence of mammary glands, the typical four-chambered heart, and all the characteristics except the almost complete absence of hair that mark them as true mammals are easily recognizable.

In large measure the major divisions of the

animal kingdom, namely the major animal phyla, have been distinguished from one another on the basis of several fundamental anatomical characteristics. Together these different anatomical features and their accompanying processes constitute a typical design of organization and function for each particular phylum that fits into an overall cohesive evolutionary pattern. The more important of these distinguishing features are:

1. *Whether the organisms are unicellular or multicellular.* Unicellular organisms with animal cell characteristics are classified either within a separate phylum of the animal kingdom or (depending upon one's viewpoint) within a separate and third kingdom called the *Protista* (p. 335), consisting only of single-celled living things. There is little or no doubt that unicellular organisms were among the first forms of life to appear on the earth and that multicellular organisms have evolved from them.

2. *Cell differentiation.* With the notable exception among the multicellular animals of only one phylum, namely the sponges or *Porifera* (Chapter 18), distinct cell differentiation becomes evident at some time during embryonic or adult development.

3. *Number of germ layers, whether two (ectoderm and endoderm) or three (ectoderm, mesoderm, and endoderm).* In nearly all of the principal phyla representing the multicellular animals three distinct germ layers, the *ectoderm, mesoderm,* and *endoderm* (p. 439), are present during early embryonic development. They give rise subsequently to all the tissues and organs of the fully formed individual. In some of the primitive forms among the coelenterates (Chapter 18) and one or two closely related minor phyla only two germ layers, mainly ectoderm and endoderm, are present.

4. *Course and degree of development of certain organ systems.* This applies particularly to the digestive, circulatory, and nervous systems, and to a lesser extent to the skeletal system. In several of the lower animal phyla

(e.g., the coelenterates and the platyhelminthes or flatworms, (Chapter 18) digestion and circulation is accomplished in a central cavity (and in part within the cells lining its surface) having a single opening. All the other principal animal phyla possess a more complex digestive tube with an opening at each end, one for taking in food the other for eliminating undigested residues, with varying degrees of specialization. Similarly the circulatory and nervous systems display progressive degrees of structural and functional specialization including muscular pumping vessels or "hearts," and nerve cords as well as anteriorly located masses of ganglia or "brains." The skeletal system (including its origin in embryonic development, its orientation—whether external or internal—and its composition) varies among certain phyla and serves to a certain extent as a classification criterion.

5. *Presence or absence of a coelom.* The *coelom* or true body cavity separating the mesodermal tissue of the body wall and that of the digestive tract is absent in the lower animal phyla but is present in all the major higher animal phyla. The body cavity in multicellular animals varies in its characteristics and mode of origin depending on the group of animal.

6. *Presence or absence of segmentation.* Segmentation is a type of body form consisting of successive units or segments having a similar or modified structure. It definitely occurs in three animal phyla, being most distinct in the *Annelida* (Chapter 19) where segments are similar to one another. It is somewhat modified in the *Arthropoda* (Chapter 19) and is partly obscured (except for certain structures such as bone) in the *Chordata* (Chapter 20) which include the mammals.

7. *Type of Symmetry.* The proportionality or organization of nearly all living things is such that they are *symmetrical.* That is, they can be theoretically cut into two equal or equivalent halves at least as far as external appearance is concerned. Most organisms display either *radial* or *bilateral* symmetry. In *radial*

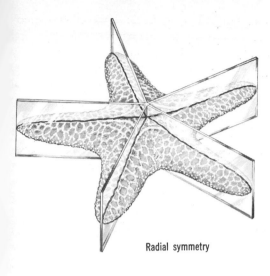

Radial symmetry

Bilateral symmetry

Figure 14-4. Diagram illustrating two principal types of symmetry in organisms: radial symmetry and bilateral symmetry.

symmetry the body parts are organized about the principal axis of the body in a radiating pattern. In other words the body is so arranged that it possesses a hypothetical central axis like the hub of an automobile wheel having two different surfaces through which a cut can be made in any plane through the vertical axis (or hub in this case) to yield two equal or equivalent halves. The starfish with an undersurface which is different from its top surface is the classic example of radial symmetry in living things. In *bilateral symmetry* the presence of a distinguishable upper or dorsal surface and a lower or ventral surface as well as an anterior and posterior region restricts the hypothetical division of the body to a single plane. The two equivalent halves are approximately mirror images of each other. In the human body this special plane is represented by the theoretical perpendicular midline or midsagittal plane of the body.

Radial symmetry tends to predominate among animals which are sessile or very slow movers. However, there is an appreciable number of radial animals that move rather effectively. Since they experience little or no

self-movement they are in one sense largely oriented to gravity, usually having an upper part and lower part; their sides are more or less uniform and thus they display radial symmetry. Bilateral symmetry on the other hand is usually associated with organisms that undergo locomotion. Since such organisms display movement, they are also usually oriented or differentiated with respect to the direction of locomotion. Thus differentiation with respect to anterior and posterior as well as dorsal and ventral regions restricts symmetry to the bilateral type.

Criteria for the Classification of Plants

In classifying the approximately 350,000 known species of the plant kingdom the same fundamental standards based on homology rather than analogy in establishing evolutionary relationships also apply. Several basic structural features including their development and their accompanying processes serve to distinguish the major plant phyla from one another, especially among the higher forms. The structural characteristics used fall into two broad classes—the *reproductive tissues* (namely those associated with sexual reproduction) and the *vegetative* or nonreproductive tissues composing all other structures of the plant body.

REPRODUCTIVE CHARACTERISTICS. The reproductive structures are shorter lived than the vegetative tissues, and are accordingly subjected for shorter time intervals to environmental influences. They are consequently less likely to become adapted to very different environmental conditions. By contrast vegetative tissues have a longer and closer relationship to their environment and as a result are more likely to change in response to external conditions. Comparisons of the structures connected with sexual reproduction (e.g., flower parts and seed types in the more advanced plants) are therefore among the most dependable bases for making judgments about the evolutionary relationships and the natural classification of plants. A number of studies have established that the tissues and organs concerned with sexual reproduction in plants have changed less during evolutionary development than the vegetative structures.

VEGETATIVE CHARACTERISTICS. 1. Examples of vegetative features used in classifying plants are the presence or absence of roots, the presence or absence of certain conducting and supporting tissues, the kind and position of leaves, and other aspects of the organization of the plant body.

2. Similarities in cell structure such as the absence or presence and number of nuclei, the type of chlorophylls and chloroplasts, and other cellular features may be indicative of relationships.

3. In lower forms the arrangement of cells, for example, in filaments, sheets, or other groups may also be useful in helping to determine natural classification.

Needless to say, any valid judgment as to the relationships among several given species of plants (or animals) is more reliable when based on several similar features rather than on a single characteristic alone.

SUPPLEMENTARY REFERENCES

Allee, W. C., *Animal Aggregations*, University of Chicago Press, Chicago, 1931.
Dobzhansky, T., *Evolution, Genetics, and Man*, Wiley, New York, 1955.
Fuller, H. J., and O. Tippo, *College Botany*, revised edition, Holt, New York, 1954.
Guthrie, M. J., and J. M. Anderson, *General Zoology*, Wiley, New York, 1957.
Mayr, E. G. Lindsay, and R. L. Usinger, *Methods and Principles of Systematic Zoology*, McGraw-Hill, New York, 1953.

Chapter 15   Plant Kingdom:

Subkingdom Thallophyta

CLASSIFICATION OF THE PLANT KINGDOM

The Old and the New

The major criteria used for classifying plants have been discussed in Chapter 14. Major revisions have been made in recent years in some of the larger categories of the plant kingdom. The older system of classification for the plant kingdom used in most books until recently is outlined below:

Division (or phylum) — Thallophyta
  Subphylum — Algae
  Subphylum — Fungi
Division (or phylum) — Bryophyta
    Class — Hepaticae (liverworts)
    Class — Musci (mosses)
Division (or phylum) — Pteridophyta
    Class — Lycopodinae (club mosses)
    Class — Equisetinae (horsetails)
    Class — Filicineae (ferns)
Division (or phylum) — Spermatophyta (seed plants)
  Subdivision — Gymnospermae (conifers and their allies)
  Subdivision — Angiospermae (flowering plants)
    Class — Dicotyledoneae
    Class — Monocotyledoneae

Extensive studies have led to several more modern and natural systems of plant classification of living and fossilized extinct plants. In one such system, outlined below, the original four divisions have been reorganized into two subkingdoms consisting of twelve phyla. This new system has gained wide acceptance, for it is believed to be more representative of probable evolutionary trends and true or natural relationships as compared to the old. In part, however, it is still artificial. No system of classification is final. As long as our knowledge of plants (and other living systems) continues to expand it can fully be expected that this new system will in time also undergo revision depending upon future findings.

Subkingdom Thallophyta
  Phyla: seven phyla of different algae, and three phyla of fungi including bacteria.
Subkingdom Embryophyta
  Phylum — Bryophyta (mosses, liverworts, and hornworts)
  Phylum — Tracheophyta (vascular plants)
    Subphylum — Psilopsida
    Subphylum — Lycopsida (club mosses)
    Subphylum — Sphenopsida (horsetails)
    Subphylum — Pteropsida
      Class — Filicineae (ferns)
      Class — Gymnospermae (conifers and their allies)
      Class — Angiospermae (flowering plants)
        Subclass — Dicotyledoneae
        Subclass — Monocotyledoneae

A descriptive survey of the plant kingdom according to this new system of classification follows:

SUBKINGDOM THALLOPHYTA

General Characteristics

The subkingdom *Thallophyta* is in large part an artificial group and consists of the above indicated ten phyla of algae and fungi. It includes numerous unrelated plants which range from microscopic forms to large multicellular types. They are usually divided in two groups: the *algae* consisting of seven phyla, and the *"fungi"* consisting of three phyla—the *bacteria*, the *slime fungi*, and the *true fungi*. Despite their designation as an artificial group, the members of the Thallophyta (or the "thallophytes" as they are called), nevertheless share several common traits. They are considered to be "lower" or more primitive plants which are relatively undifferentiated. They have no true roots, leaves, or stems, for the vascular tissues (xylem and phloem, p. 95) are notably absent. A simple plant body of this type is called a *thallus*. Moreover, the reproductive structures, whether of the sexual or asexual type, are in most cases unicellular. Finally the thallophytes, in contrast to the members of the other plant subkingdom (*Embryophyta*), form zygotes which never develop into multicellular embryos until after they leave the female sex organs.

Algae

The algae as a group are now not recognized to be a natural subdivision of the plant kingdom. They are instead an artificial and convenient collection of seven distinct and unrelated phyla which have happened to reach about the same level of development. They are believed to have evolved independently of one another and probably did not arise from a common ancestral stock, a viewpoint, however, that is still controversial. All algae possess chlorophyll and carry on photosynthesis. The multicellular types are composed of relatively un-differentiated tissues which never form true roots, stems, or leaves. Algae are predominantly aquatic, being widely distributed in fresh-water bodies of all sorts (lakes, rivers, ponds, ditches, swamps) as well as in the oceans.

The free-floating and free-swimming forms constitute the *plankton* of the oceans and lakes, whereas those that are anchored or attached to the bottom are called the *benthon*. The different species exhibit a tremendous range of sizes, shapes, and colors. They are classified into seven different phyla on the basis of a combination of characters which include types of pigments, nature of the stored food and features of the motile cells, especially of the flagella. The algae represent the primary source of food for most water-dwelling animals (p. 239) as well as a direct potential food source for man.

PHYLUM CYANOPHYTA (BLUE-GREEN ALGAE). The phylum is made up of some two thousand species, mostly fresh-water types, existing as single cells, filaments, and to an appreciable extent as colonies. Like the bacteria they are considered to be among the most primitive of all organisms. They have been shown to occur in the oldest known fossil plant remains dating back a billion years.

Their uniquely simple cell structure is also taken as evidence of their primitive nature. Most cells are surrounded by a gelatinous sheath and are bluish green in color. They display no definite nucleus with nucleolus and surrounding nuclear membrane but instead their nuclear material is dispersed in a region usually occupying the center of the cell. The cell pigments of the blue-green algae which include chlorophyll, the carotenoids, and the unique blue pigment *phycocyanin* are not organized in chloroplasts but are diffusely distributed in the outer portion of the cytoplasm. Certain species which also contain a red pigment, *phycoerythrin,* are responsible for the color of the Red Sea. Reproduction is solely by asexual means, chiefly by fission or simple cell division. No flagellate cells of any type are produced. Reserve food is stored as a

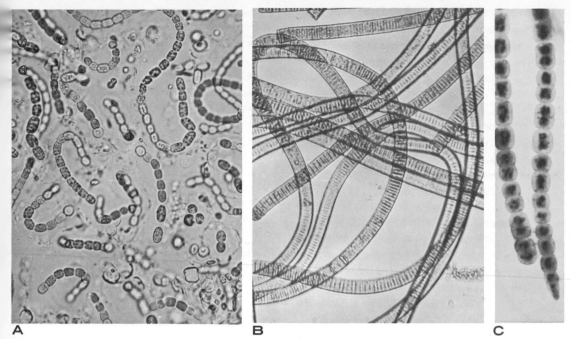

Figure 15-1. Light-microscope photographs of some blue-green algae. (A) *Nostoc*, magnification, 800X *(courtesy of H. Spencer)*. (B) *Oscillatoria*, magnification, 400X *(courtesy of H. Spencer)*. (C) *Anabaena*, magnification, 2600X *(courtesy of Dr. A. M. Glauert, J. Biophys. Biochem.)*.

carbohydrate related to starch. Examples of blue-green algae are *Nostoc, Oscillatoria,* and *Anabaena* (Figure 15-1). Some species of blue-green algae are able to carry on nitrogen fixation.

PHYLUM EUGLENOPHYTA (EUGLENOIDS). This phylum which consists of three hundred species or so is typified by the common flagellate *Euglena* described in Chapter 5. Euglenoids are mostly fresh-water types, contain a definite nucleus and bright green chloroplasts. They are unicellular flagellate cells (with one to three flagella), usually possess no rigid true cell walls, and reproduce by longitudinal cell division. Thick-walled resting cells, or *cysts,* which tide the organisms over unfavorable conditions are formed in many species. Reserve food is stored as a complex carbohydrate called *paramylum.*

The question of how one classifies primitive organisms of this type which share the characteristics of both plant and animal cells has been mentioned earlier (Chapters 4 and 5). One alternative has been to place them in a special group or kingdom, the *Protista,* with other unicellular organisms such as bacteria as well as with borderline organisms such as slime molds. You will recall that *Euglena* may also be included in the class *Flagellata* of the phylum *Protozoa* in the animal kingdom (Chapter 18).

PHYLUM CHLOROPHYTA (GREEN ALGAE). *General Features.* This phylum of some six thousand species displays certain evolutionary trends which suggest that the higher and more specialized land plants evolved from ancient green algae. The majority of the green algae are fresh water forms; some are marine; and others are terrestrial, inhabiting moist soil, rock surfaces, and tree trunks. They occur as unicellular plant bodies, colonies, or multicellular organisms (with their cells arranged in filaments or leaf-like sheets from one to several cell layers in thickness). Their chlorophylls (*a* and *b*, Chapter 7) and associated carotenoid pigments are organized in chloroplasts of diverse shape and sizes depending on the species. The cells have single definite nuclei, cell walls composed of cellulose, and reserve food in the form of starch. Depending on the species reproduction may be asexual (by cell division, by fragmentation of colonies and multicellular types, and by motile and nonmotile spores) or sexual (by fusion of gametes of equal size or unequal size). In all instances the gamete-producing structures are unicellular.

The most primitive members of the green algae are considered to be the unicellular flagellate types which are motile for most or all of their life cycles. The common alga, *Chlamydomonas* (Figure 15-2), as an example of the primitive type is a spherical single cell with a definite cellulose cell wall. It has a single large cup-shaped chloroplast containing a small protein structure called the *pyrenoid* (associated with starch formation), a red-pigmented eye spot, a centrally located nucleus, and two con-

tractile vacuoles at the anterior end near the site at which the two flagella originate. Reproduction may be asexual by the formation within the cell of two to eight motile spores (called *zoospores*) resembling the parent cell with each giving rise to a new individual; or sexual, following the formation within the cell of numerous seemingly identical gametes which resemble the parent cell. Upon liberation to the surrounding water, the gametes fuse in pairs to form zygotes. The zygote secretes a thick protective wall about itself and eventually undergoes meiosis to yield four zoospores each of which develops into a Chlamydomonas plant.

Evolutionary Trends among the Green Algae. The single-celled ancient flagellate must have evolved in several directions. *Volvox* (p. 82), for example, is considered to be the colonial descendant of a primitive flagellate green alga, and is presumably the result of evolution *from single motile cellular orga-*

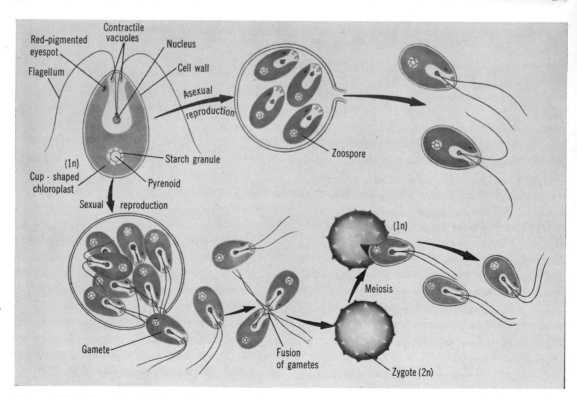

Figure 15-2. Life cycle of *Chlamydomonas*. See text for details.

nisms to motile colonies. Some of its cells are sexually reproductive, producing large stationary female gametes or eggs and numerous biflagellated male gametes or sperm cells.

A second evolutionary trend centers about the change *from motile cells to immotile single-celled and colonial organisms* through the loss of the propelling flagella. The genus *Chlorella* consisting of small spherical single cells, each possessing a cup-shaped chloroplast, is indicative of such a change (Figure 5-8). Reproduction is asexual occurring solely by the formation of two to sixteen immotile spores each giving rise to a new individual. The genus *Scenedesmus* (Figure 15-3) is another example of this trend, its members consisting of a colony of four to eight immotile cells. Asexual reproduction occurs by spores that adhere to one another thus giving rise to new colonies.

A third evolutionary trend of great significance also must have occurred, namely conversion *from an ancient motile single cell to multicellular filaments (i.e., multicellular plants)* perhaps reflecting the main line of evolution that led to the higher green plants. Among the simplest is the filamentous green algae freshwater dwelling *Ulothrix.* The latter consists of numerous cells, each of which contains a single nucleus and collar-shaped chloroplast with several pyrenoids. A specialized *hold-fast cell,* usually lacking in chlorophyll, at the base of the filament anchors the plant to its substrate. Cell division does not account for reproduction as it does in unicellular organisms but instead is responsible for growth of the filament. Reproduction in *Ulothrix* may occur asexually by the formation of four to eight zoospores (each containing four flagella) in any cells but the hold-fast cell. Each zoospore upon release to the external aquatic environment gives rise to a new filament. The production of flagellate zoospores by the nonmotile filamentous *Ulothrix* is suggestive of a flagellate ancestry. Reproduction may also occur sexually whereby a filament cell forms many similar gametes (resembling zoospores but smaller and bearing two instead of four flagella) which fuse in

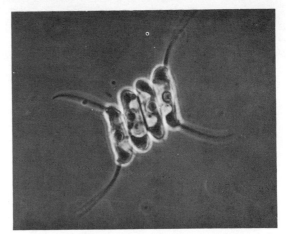

Figure 15-3. Phase-contrast-microscope photograph showing a colony of four parallel living *Scenedesmus* cells. Magnification, 1500X. *(Courtesy of Dr. T. Bisalputra, Univ. of Calif., Davis.)*

pairs to yield resting zygotes. However, the fusing gametes come from different filaments. In time each zygote undergoes meiosis to yield four zoospores, the latter eventually producing new filaments by cell division (Figure 15-4).

In the widely distributed unbranched, filamentous green alga *Oedogonium,* reproduction occurs asexually by fragmentation of the filament and by zoospores bearing a whorl of flagella. Sexual reproduction occurs by the fusion of a large nonmotile egg with a smaller motile sperm resembling a zoospore. The advanced degree of specialization in sexual reproduction is seen not only in the differentiated male and female gametes but in the specialized cells which produce them. The egg cells are formed in special single cells called *oögonia,* and the sperm in unicellular male structures, the *antheridia.* Moreover, fertilization occurs within the oögonium, when a sperm enters through a spore in the oögonial wall and fuses with the egg cell. In time the resultant zygote which develops a thick wall is liberated from the degenerating oögonium, remains dormant for several months or less, and then undergoes meiosis to produce four zoospores, each capable of growing into a new filament (Figure 15-5).

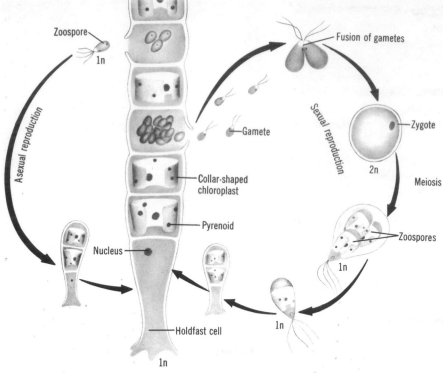

Figure 15-4. Life cycle of *Ulothrix*. See text for details.

Mention should be made of the terrestrial and widespread unicellular green algae *Protococcus,* often responsible for the green color of bark on trees. It is a spherical-shaped single-celled organism (Figure 15-6) possessing a thick cell wall, a nucleus, and a large-lobed chloroplast. Reproduction is solely by cell division. The daughter cells may separate or adhere together for a time to form a loose aggregate or colony of cells. At one time *Protococcus* was considered to be among the most primitive of the green algae. It is now regarded as an example of retrogressive evolution that has presumably been reduced from a branching filamentous ancestor, since it does at times seem to form irregular filaments.

Evolution of Sexual Reproduction in Green Algae. One of the patterns that becomes evident among the green algae is the probable evolution of sexual reproduction from asexual reproduction. According to our present views

reproduction in the most primitive algae occurred solely by cell division. Reproduction by zoospores (e.g., in *Chlamydomonas*) is believed to be a later evolutionary acquisition. Zoospores are probably the structures from which gametes originated in the evolution of sex in plants. *Ulothrix*, for example, which exhibits a primitive type of sexual reproduction, has motile gametes that are externally identical and similar in structure to the zoospores, though smaller in size.

The resemblance of gametes (at least of male gametes) to their respective zoospores is found in several kinds of green algae. In the more advanced forms (e.g., *Oedogonium*) the subsequent stages in the evolution of sexual reproduction are seen in the production of unlike gametes, the presence of male and female sex organs (the oögonium and antheridium), and retention of the nonmotile egg cell by the parent plant. These precise features—highly

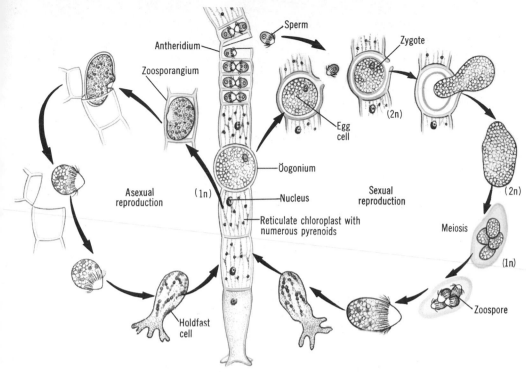

Figure 15-5. Life cycle of *Oedogonium*. See text for details.

differentiated gametes (a small motile sperm and a larger nonmotile egg), specialized sex organs, and fertilization within the parent plant —are among the fundamental aspects of sexual reproduction in higher plants. This should not be interpreted to mean that *Oedogonium* was one of the intermediate stages in the evolution of higher plants from the green algae. More exactly *Oedogonium* as a present-day living plant displays some of the characteristics of a now extinct ancient green alga that we believe eventually must have given rise to the more advanced forms.

Alternation of Generations. The origin of sexual reproduction is necessarily accompanied by two critical stages in the life history of the organism with respect to changes in its chromosome number. One is at fertilization when two haploid gametes unite to form a dip-

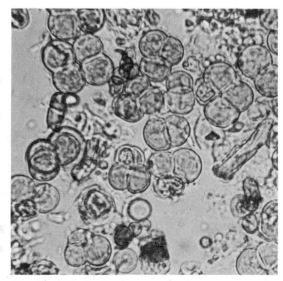

Figure 15-6. *Protococcus*, a simple green alga in groups of varying size and cell number. Magnification, 1200X. *(Courtesy of H. Spencer.)*

loid zygote; the other is at the time when the zygote (or the diploid tissues derived from it) gives rise to haploid spores by meiosis. This phenomenon of alternation of chromosome number during the life cycle of a sexually reproducing organism is spoken of as *alternation of generations*. The plant stage that produces gametes is called the *haploid* or *gametophyte generation* whereas the alternate diploid plant stage that produces diploid spores is called the *diploid* or *sporophyte generation*.

In the above sexually reproducing green algae (i.e., *Ulothrix* and *Oedogonium*), alternation of generations is not conspicuous but nevertheless is present. The filamentous plant body produces the gametes and is therefore the gametophyte generation, whereas the single-celled diploid zygote represents the sporophyte generation. As soon as the zygote undergoes meiosis to produce the haploid zoospores, the sporophyte generation has been succeeded by the gametophyte generation.

Alternation of generation in which a haploid gametophyte alternates with a diploid sporophyte takes place in all green terrestrial plants. It is much more obvious and prominent in several of the land plants, but then becomes progressively less apparent as we proceed higher in the evolutionary scale. The details of alternation of generations in green land plants and the possible evolutionary significance of the phenomenon are described in the next chapter.

PHYLUM CHRYSOPHYTA (YELLOW-GREEN ALGAE, GOLDEN-BROWN ALGAE, AND DIATOMS). The three classes constituting the *Chrysophyta* are the yellow-green algae (*Xanthophyceae*), the golden-brown algae (*Chrysophyceae*), and the diatoms (*Diatomeae*). The typical yellow or brown color of the members of this phylum, which number about six thousand species, is due to a greater proportion of yellow or brown carotinoids (p. 403) in the chloroplasts as compared to chlorophyll. Other common characters exhibited by members of the phylum include a silica-impregnated cell wall usually composed of two overlapping halves, and food reserves in the form of oil

and a complex carbohydrate called *leucosin*. The group includes motile and immotile unicellular, colonial, and filamentous types. Asexual reproduction takes place by cell division, zoospores, or immobile spores. Sexual reproduction, when it is present, occurs by the union of like gametes. The yellow-green algae and golden-brown algae are predominantly freshwater dwellers, whereas the diatoms are widely distributed in both fresh and salt water. The diatoms in fact are the most abundant of the plankton, serving as a major source of food for much of the plant and animal life in the fresh waters and the seas.

Diatoms occur in a variety of sizes and shapes (Figure 15-7) and are represented by more than five thousand different species. The transparent cell wall of the diatom is composed of an inner layer of pectin and an outer glass-like layer of silica which also happens to be a major constituent of glass. The shape of the cell (and therefore of the cell wall) ranges from oblong to circular with innumerable variations. The

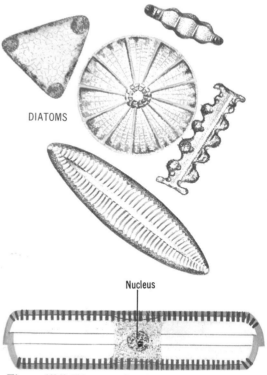

DIATOMS

Nucleus

Figure 15-7. Diatoms of various sizes and shapes.

cell wall is composed of two halves, called *valves*, with one overlapping the other like the top and bottom of a pillbox or Petri dish to make a "glass house" structure enclosing the living protoplast. The valves are ornamented with a great many striations, dots, and perforations to give a variety of beautiful patterns and designs. Diatoms reproduce principally by cell division and to a lesser extent by a sexual means involving the fusion of like gametes. In cell division each of the two newly formed daughter cells lie within one of the valves and secrete a new valve within the old to complete the "glass house."

Following the death of the cell all organic contents of the protoplast and cell wall are eventually destroyed except the glass silica valves, which usually sink to the bottom to form after innumerable centuries of accumulation great deposits of *diatomaceous earth*. Its chemical inertness and unusual physical properties have made diatomaceous earth extremely useful as a filtering and purifying agent, insulating material, soundproofing, and an abrasive. The occurrence of vast beds of diatomaceous earth on various continents of the world (one of the largest—twelve square miles and about one-half mile deep—is in California) strongly supports the notion that these areas were once under the sea where the diatomaceous deposits accumulated.

PHYLUM PYRROPHYTA (DINOFLAGELLATES). The thousand or so species of this phylum are typically unicellular flagellates bearing two long flagella and yellowish-green or golden-brown plastids. Their heavy cell walls (some species lack cell walls) are usually divided into two cellulose-like interlocking plates and contain two external grooves each accompanied by a single flagellum. They are predominantly marine organisms and together with the diatoms serve as the primary food source, the base of all food chains (Chapter 10), for most of the animal and plant life of the seas. Reproduction, as in the case of the diatoms, is mostly by cell division, whereas sexual reproduction is rare or lacking. Reserve food in the cell occurs as

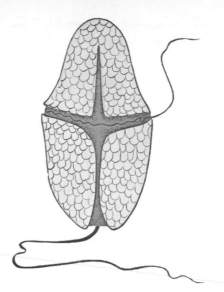

Figure 15-8. The dinoflagellate *Gymnodinium*.

starches or oils. One of the dinoflagellates, *Gymnodinium* (Figure 15-8), which secretes a red pigment, periodically increases to huge numbers (the "red tide") killing millions of fishes in the sea. Some dinoflagellates show a definite resemblance to the diatoms, and others to the protozoa.

The dinoflagellates are also classified by several animal taxonomists as members of the animal kingdom, more specifically in the class *Flagellata* (Chapter 18) of the phylum *Protozoa*.

PHYLUM PHAEOPHYTA (BROWN ALGAE). This phylum consists of a thousand or so almost entirely marine species which are distinguished from all other algae by their characteristically brown color. The latter is due to a special golden-brown pigment *fucoxanthin* (in addition to chlorophylls *a* and *c* and the usual carotinoid pigments). The plant body is always nonmotile and multicellular, ranging in size from a thallus of only a few cells to the structurally complex, so-called giant kelps a hundred or more feet long. Food reserves in the cell occur as complex carbohydrates or oils. Reproduction, depending on the species, may be by asexual fragmentation, zoospores, or immotile spores, and sexually by the union of similar or differentiated gametes. The phylum consists of many of the so-called *seaweeds* including the genus *Sargassum* often seen in the Sargasso Sea.

One of the most common brown algae is the genus *Fucus* which is widely distributed along the sea coasts in the north temperate zone. Its species are often found attached to rocks and are frequently washed up along the beaches. Like many brown algae *Fucus* shows an appreciable degree of differentiation. Its flattened

branching thallus is usually made up of several forks (known as *dichotomous* branching) is differentiated into a disc-like *hold-fast* for anchorage, a stalk called the *stipe*, and a broad flattened *frond* often containing air bladders which buoy up the plant in water (Figure 15-9).

The smaller tips of the fronds consist of spherical cavities called *conceptacles* (with small external openings) which contain the sex organs. Depending on the species the male and female sex organs (namely, the antheridia and oögonia which produce sperm and egg

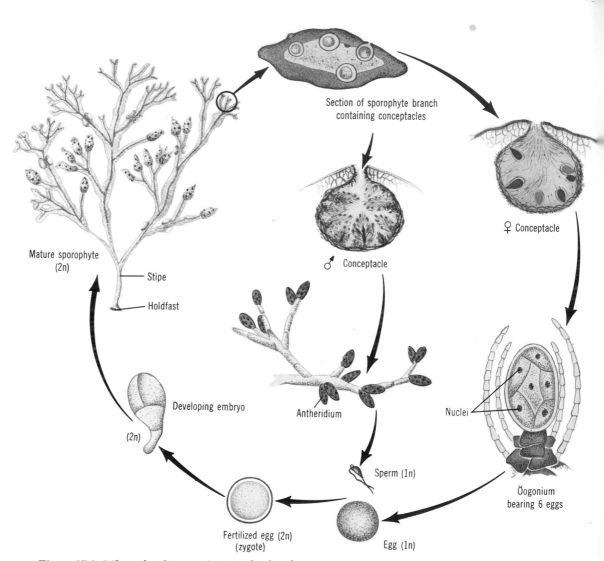

Section of sporophyte branch containing conceptacles

♂ Conceptacle

♀ Conceptacle

Mature sporophyte (2n)

Stipe

Holdfast

Developing embryo

(2n)

Antheridium

Nuclei

Öogonium bearing 6 eggs

Sperm (1n)

Fertilized egg (2n) (zygote)

Egg (1n)

Figure 15-9. Life cycle of *Fucus*. See text for details.

cells, respectively) may occur in the same conceptacle, or in different conceptacles on the same or different plants. Upon ripening the egg cells are released into the ocean where they are fertilized by the smaller motile biflagellate sperm cells. The fertilized egg cells or zygotes become attached to rocks and undergo cell division to produce new *Fucus* plants. In addition to the sexual method of reproduction indicated above, *Fucus* reproduces asexually by fragmentation. Zoospores are entirely lacking. In other types of brown algae asexual reproduction may occur by zoospores or by immobile spores, and sexually by the fusion of like gametes.

Some of the giant kelps among the brown algae display a remarkable degree of differentiation in the vegetative tissues of the thallus. They show an epidermis, cortex, cambium, and even the presence of phloem, one of the vascular tissues seen in higher plants. There is no evidence, however, that the brown algae have given rise to higher plants. The green algae are believed to be the groups from which the higher green plants evolved. The brown algae, especially the kelps, are a rich source of potassium and iodine and are used as a source of food in certain parts of the world for man and domestic animals.

PHYLUM RHODOPHYTA (RED ALGAE). The members of this phylum consisting of some three thousand species are unique in their possession of a red pigment, *phycoerythrin* (and sometimes *phycocyanin*), within their chloroplasts. They also contain chlorophylls *a* and *d* and the usual carotinoids. Like the brown algae nearly all the species are marine, nonmotile and multicellular. Food is stored within the cells in the form of an insoluble starch-like compound called *floridean starch.* Among other unusual features of the phylum are the absence of any *motile* reproductive cells (sexual or asexual) and the presence of conspicuous cytoplasmic connections between the cells of the plant body. The red algae are most abundant in the warm seas and are in general considerably smaller than the brown algae, rarely exceeding

three feet in length. In all instances sexual reproduction when it occurs takes place by the union of unlike gametes within the female sex organ. The zygote eventually gives rise to so-called *carpospores* which in many species develop into a new and additional stage in the life history before producing the sexual plants to complete the cycle.

The red algae like the brown algae serve as a food source especially in the Orient and as a substitute for animal gelatin in puddings, pies, ice cream, cosmetics, toothpaste, and so on. They are also used for the production of *agar*, an important laboratory ingredient for the solid medium used in the growth of bacteria and fungi. Many red algae tend to accumulate calcium thus becoming calcareous; and together with the coral marine microorganisms (p. 430) play a significant role in the building of coral reefs and islands.

Bacteria, Slime Fungi, and True Fungi

PHYLUM SCHIZOPHYTA (BACTERIA). *General Characteristics.* Bacteria as one of the smallest and simplest (structurally) of all living organisms are characteristically unicellular with dimensions that range from as small as 0.1 μ (1/250,000 of an inch) to as much as 5 μ. They are usually classified in the plant kingdom because of their rigid and definite cell walls which in some species contain cellulose. They are most often considered to be related to the fungi because of the absence of chlorophyll (except for the photosynthetic bacteria, p. 411) and because certain forms are known with features transitional between the bacteria and fungi. The vast majority of bacteria are heterotrophs with the notable exception of the few photosynthetic and chemoautotrophic forms (Chapter 9). *see p. 371.*

Bacterial viruses or bacteriophages, because they parasitize bacteria and for lack of a better place to put them, are often arbitrarily classified with the bacteria. Animal and plant viruses are also frequently included in the phylum *Schizophyta.* Their important characteristics have been discussed in Chapters 5 and 11.

A particular group of disease-causing microorganisms collectively called the *Rickettsia* (after their discoverer, Howard Ricketts) exhibits several characteristics including size which are intermediate between those of bacteria and bacteriophages. In virtually all instances they can only grow within the host cell. They are responsible for such diseases as typhus fever, Rocky Mountain spotted fever and several others. The Rickettsia like the bacteriophages are usually classified with the bacteria.

The unusually small size of bacteria, which makes clear differences in cell structure and shape difficult to observe, has forced the bacteriologist to rely heavily on physiological and biochemical characteristics for identification and classification purposes. Thus the types of substances which bacteria utilize or metabolize, the various products which they produce and dispose of into their external environment, their requirements for molecular oxygen, their reaction to various stains, and the types of colonies which they form commonly serve as important criteria in their classification. On the basis of both their morphological and physiological characteristics some twenty-five hundred species of bacteria have been described and classified.

Structural Features. Nearly all bacteria show one of three different general shapes (Figure 5-4). The majority are rod-shaped and are called *bacilli* (singular, *bacillus*). The second largest group are spherical- or ovoid-shaped and are termed *cocci* (singular, *coccus*). The smallest number are spiral or corkscrew-shaped and are called *spirilla* (singular, *spirillum*). At times depending on the species temporary changes in shape may occur as a result of radical changes in environment. Some bacteria, however, may exhibit different shapes at various stages in their life cycles.

Many bacteria display a nonliving slime layer called the *capsule* at the outer portion of their cell walls. It is of variable thickness and is composed largely of polysaccharides. As indicated in the discussion of transforming principle (Chapter 11) there is a definite correlation between the presence of the capsule and virulence among some of the disease-causing bacteria as in the pneumococci responsible for a type of pneumonia.

Many bacterial species also produce sheaths and spore-type walls which may serve as protection against adverse environmental conditions. It has already been indicated in Chapter 4 that bacteria possess a cell membrane, but lack an endoplasmic reticulum and mitochondria as such, and that their ribosomes are free in the cytoplasm. *lack golgi apparatus*

Most if not all the nuclear material or DNA in many bacteria and in the blue-green algae occurs as a discrete nuclear region (without a surrounding nuclear membrane) in the cytoplasm (Chapter 4). It appears to divide in coordination with the division of the cell. In some bacteria the nuclear material may be organized into several nuclear regions instead of one.

The motility of numerous bacteria in most cases is due to the action of flagella. Depending on the species, the number and distribution of flagella range from one, as in the cholera bacterium, to many flagella (Figure 5-5) covering most of the bacterial surface, as in the typhoid bacillus. The most prevalent form of reproduction is by the asexual process of cell division. The occurrence of sexual reproduction as well in at least a few known species has already been indicated (p. 329). Spore formation in bacteria generally is not regarded as a means of reproduction, but rather as a protective adaptation in most cases to unfavorable environmental conditions such as ultraviolet light, high temperatures, harmful chemicals, and so on.

Bacterial Physiology and Biochemistry. In terms of their physiological and biochemical features bacteria demonstrate a tremendous diversity. Most are heterotrophic, whereas an extremely small number are autotrophic (photoautotrophic and chemoautotrophic bacteria, Chapter 9). A few are strictly anaerobic in that they can grow only in an environment showing the complete absence or near-absence of oxygen. At the other extreme a number of bacterial species are strictly aerobic, requiring oxygen in order to grow and carry out their normal activities. Between these two extremes are innumerable species with various degrees of requirements for molecular oxygen.

As a group the bacteria are capable of enzymatically degrading virtually every type of naturally occurring organic compound and utilizing some of the products as a nutrient source. The type of organic compounds utilized by particular bacterial species and the type of metabolic products liberated to the external medium often serve as a basis for distinguishing different bacterial divisions. In general, bacteria as a group display essentially the same types of enzymatic reactions and metabolic pathways and patterns found in all other living systems. Moreover, they are often capable of additional enzymatic reactions which may distinguish them from other types of organisms and serve as the basis for classification. Their growth characteristics and nutritional requirements are governed by the same principles which affect all other organisms (Chapter 9).

Little is known at this time concerning the origin and evolutionary relationships of bacteria not only among themselves but with other types of living systems as well. One viewpoint has tended to regard them as being somewhat related to the blue-green algae in view of their similarities in cell structure. An opposing view attributes these similarities to an unrelated parallel development in the course of evolution.

Biological and Economic Importance of Bacteria. Despite the disadvantages inflicted on man by several parasitic, disease-causing bacteria, the important role of bacteria (and other microorganisms) in the economy of nature far outweighs their disadvantages. By virtue of their varied metabolic activities they have a major function in the decay of dead organic material. In this manner they serve as key links in the cyclic use and reuse of the different elements in biological systems as seen in the nitrogen cycle, carbon cycle, and others (Chapter 10). In addition within the nitrogen cycle

itself the nitrogen-fixing bacteria by transforming nitrogen gas to the level of ammonia or amino nitrogen have a central role in making available a nitrogen source for all other forms of life including plants, animals, and other microorganisms.

Bacteria also have proved to be highly useful in a variety of industrial and agricultural applications. The manufacture and processing of many products in the dairy industry—such as butter, cheese, and buttermilk—depend on the metabolic activities of certain bacteria. In the manufacture of vinegar, the alcohol produced in the fermentation of sugars and other carbohydrates is further metabolized by the bacterium *Acetobacter aceti* to acetic acid, the principal ingredient of vinegar. The production of sauerkraut and dill pickles, the tanning of leather, the processing of flax fiber by the textile industry, the curing of cocoa, coffee, and tea, the formation of the important commercial solvents (e.g., ethyl alcohol, butyl alcohol, and acetone) are examples of the industrial uses to which bacteria and their various products including enzymes have been put. The importance of bacteria as experimental material in the study of genetics and biochemical and nutritional phenomena has been indicated in Chapters 8 through 11.

In terms of their detrimental activities certain bacteria are harmful in causing diseases of man, domestic animals, and cultivated plants and in causing the spoilage of foodstuffs. Such common human diseases as tuberculosis, pneumonia, typhoid fever, leprosy, streptococcus infections, and meningitis are results of successful invasions of the body by specific bacterial species. In many of these diseases the clinical symptoms result from poisons or toxins produced by the invading bacteria. The devices by which the body resists invading organisms, including the production and action of antibodies, are described in Chapter 25.

The control and destruction of harmful bacteria have been attained in a variety of ways. The use of heat, sunlight, X-rays, ultraviolet light, and chemical agents (antiseptics, germicides, antibiotics) to kill bacteria or inhibit their growth and metabolic activities has proved to be effective in many instances. In milk pasteurization, for example, which involves heating milk to about 145°F for 30 minutes (or to 160°F for at least 15 seconds), most common types of pathogenic bacteria are destroyed. In food preservation the use of chemical agents, high osmotic concentrations (e.g., by addition of salts and sugars), low temperatures, and dehydration procedures are also effective.

PHYLUM MYXOMYCOPHYTA (SLIME FUNGI). This phylum and the phylum *Eumycophyta* (known as the *true fungi*, discussed later) differ from the bacteria in their possession of: (1) definite organized nuclei which include nuclear membranes, (2) considerably larger cells or cell-like structures, and (3) two general types of reproduction, by sexual means and asexually by spores. Like nearly all the bacteria they possess no chlorophyll.

The slime fungi or slime molds, consisting of some five hundred species, are a unique group of organisms whose origin and evolutionary relationships are still undetermined. Although most biologists classify them as plants largely because they possess a cell wall at the spore stage in their life cycle, others place them with the protozoa in the animal kingdom. They are found in moist woods growing on dead molding leaves, rotting bark and tree stumps, and damp soil. In its nonreproductive or vegetative stage the slime mold is best described as a multinucleate naked mass of raw protoplasm, a *plasmodium*, without definite form or shape, often brightly colored and extending several inches in area. It moves slowly by a flowing, amoeboid-like motion, engulfing organic food in the process, which it digests in food vacuoles.

Under certain environmental conditions the vegetative plasmodium stage transforms itself into a reproductive stage consisting of groups of thin-walled spore cases or *sporangia*. The color, shape, and size of the sporangia and whether or not they are borne on stalks de-

Figure 15-10. Sporangia of a slime mold species (*courtesy of R. E. Hutchins*).

pends upon the species (Figure 15-10). In time the mature sporangia rupture, liberating the spores. The spores under favorable conditions germinates, each producing one to four naked motile cells called *swarm cells* bearing two flagella. The flagellate cells may divide by fission or even become amoeboid, but they sooner or later fuse in pairs, thus constituting a sexual stage. Depending on the species, the zygote develops into the plasmodium to complete the life cycle (Figure 5-10) or fuses with several zygotes in the eventual formation of the plasmodium. Meiosis occurs in the sporangium, accounting for the fact that the spores and swarm cells are haploid. The plasmodium and sporangia possess the diploid number of chromosomes.

PHYLUM EUMYCOPHYTA (TRUE FUNGI). *General Features.* This phylum is composed of four classes called the *phycomycetes* (algal fungi), *ascomycetes* (sac fungi), *basidiomycetes* (basidium fungi), and *deuteromycetes* (or imperfect fungi) to make a total of seventy-five thousand described species. All or nearly all share the common characteristic of possessing a plant body composed of tubular branched or unbranched filaments called *hyphae* containing a mass of cytoplasm with many nuclei (Figure 5-1). Many hyphae form a mass called the *mycelium*. In some species cross walls, which separate masses of multinucleate cytoplasm or even cells, are present within the hyphae, whereas in others they only appear when the reproductive structures are formed. All true fungi are heterotrophic and some are parasitic. All reproduce asexually by microscopic spores usually formed in large numbers. Many in addition reproduce by sexual means.

Class Phycomycetes (Algal Fungi). The common name algal fungi applied to the organisms of this class stems from their similarity in structure and reproduction to that of certain green algae. There is no agreement, however, that they descended from these algae, since it is possible that they could also have evolved along parallel lines from certain protozoa. Most members of the phycomycetes consist of multinucleate hyphae (without cross walls) that form a loose fuzzy mycelium. Asexual reproduction takes place by spores produced in sporangia; sexual reproduction is effected by the union of like gametes or different gametes, depending on the species.

A familiar example of this class is the cottony bread mold *Rhizopus nigricans* which grows on damp bread and other foodstuffs. Of the mass of hyphae constituting the mycelium some (called *rhizoids*) penetrate the substratum, whereas others (called *sporangiophores*) form black sporangia at their tips containing numerous asexual spores. Upon liberation from the mature ruptured sporangia each of the spores under favorable conditions is capable of developing into a new mycelium. Sexual reproduction is initiated by the growth from each of two adjacent mycelia of a short hypha branch which make contact with one another. A cross wall forms near the tip of each hypha (*progamete*) to form a reproductive cell (gamete) which then fuses with the other to yield a zygote. The latter enlarges, forms a thick wall about itself, and after a period of dormancy puts forth a hypha whose tip develops into a sporangium. Each of the spores that is subse-

quently released can develop into a new mycelium to complete the life cycle (Figure 15-11). It should be noted that in this species self-fertilization does not occur. Fertilization can only take place between two different types of strains, designated as *plus* and *minus* with respect to compatibility in sexual reproduction. In certain other species this requirement does not apply.

Class Ascomycetes (Sac Fungi). The thirty thousand or more species that make up this class are unusually diverse in reproduction, size, structure, and other characteristics. All, however, share the common feature of forming as a result of sexual reproduction a sac-like structure termed the *ascus* which usually contains eight so-called *ascospores*. This is the basic unifying characteristic of all members of the class. The hyphae of ascomycetes in contrast to those of the phycomycetes are usually divided by cross walls into separate masses of cytoplasm containing one or more nuclei. In most species many asci are borne within or upon definite masses of hyphae called *ascocarps* that are usually either cup-like or globular-shaped. Asexual reproduction often takes place by asexual spores called *conidia* produced in chains at the tip of certain hyphae. Each conidium and each ascospore may germinate into a new mycelium. Some also reproduce asexually by vegetative budding (e.g., yeast, Chapter 30).

In sexual reproduction multinucleate sex organs arise from short hyphal branches. The contents of the male organ or *antheridium* are transferred to the female organ where the male and female nuclei pair off into separate cells and then undergo fusion. Each of the cells develops into an ascus, its fused or diploid nucleus dividing by meiosis and then by mitosis to yield the usual eight haploid ascospores. The life history of the pink bread mold *Neurospora*, an ascomycete which has proved to be an important experimental organism in the development of the concepts of biochemical genetics (Chapter 11), is summarized in Figure 11-12. The similarities between the repro-

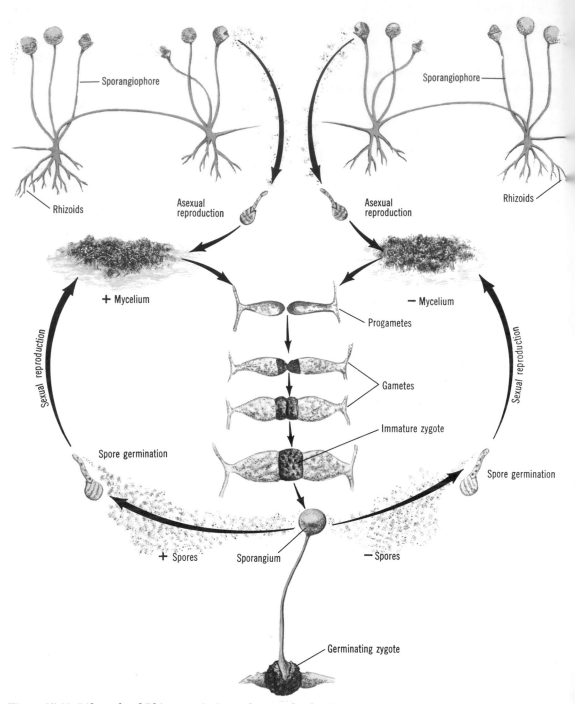

Sporangiophore

Sporangiophore

Rhizoids

Asexual reproduction

Asexual reproduction

Rhizoids

+ Mycelium

− Mycelium

Sexual reproduction

Sexual reproduction

Progametes

Gametes

Immature zygote

Spore germination

Spore germination

+ Spores

Sporangium

− Spores

Germinating zygote

Figure 15-11. Life cycle of *Rhizopus nigricans*. See text for details.

ductive features of the ascomycetes and the red algae have led to some speculation about a close evolutionary relationship between the two groups. However, certain kinds of evidence suggest that the ascomycetes probably evolved from an ancient phycomycetes type.

The ascomycetes include such species as yeast which are considered to be single-celled saprophytic fungi bearing a single ascus, and the blue and green molds which include the genus *Penicillium*. Different species of Penicillium are used for the production of the important antibiotic *penicillin* and for imparting particular odors and flavors to many cheeses. Some ascomycetes are responsible for such diseases as Dutch elm disease, chestnut blight, brown rot of store fruits, and ergot diseases of certain cultivated cereals (wheat and rye).

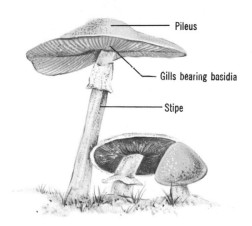

Pileus

Gills bearing basidia

Stipe

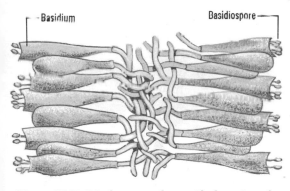

Basidium

Basidiospore

Figure 15-12. Mushroom and magnified section of a gill from the undersurface of its pileus showing basidia and basidiospores.

Class Basidiomycetes (Basidium Fungi).

Like the ascomycetes, this class, made up of twenty-five thousand or so species, has non-motile spores and cross walls in its hyphae. The unique feature common to all its species despite their great variety in form and function is a special reproductive structure, the *basidium*. The basidium consists of an enlarged club-shaped cell possessing four minute stalks, each of which bears a single haploid spore, the *basidiospore*, at its tip (Figure 15-12). The basidium usually arises from a cell containing two nuclei at the tip of a hypha. During its development the two nuclei fuse (i.e., sexual reproduction) and the resulting diploid nucleus undergoes meiotic division to yield four haploid nuclei. Each will eventually become the nucleus of a basidiospore. The basidiospores, like the ascospores of the ascomycetes, are therefore the result of sexual reproduction. Each basidiospore upon its release is capable of developing into a new basidiomycete plant. One or more other types of spores, depending on the species, also occur during the life cycle.

In general the basidiomycetes include many of the larger and more noticeable fungi such as mushrooms, toadstools, and puffballs, and the numerous disease-causing rusts and smuts which parasitize plants. The smut fungi, for example, constitute one of the major orders of the basidiomycetes and chiefly infect the grass family which includes wheat, rye, corn, oats, barley, and rice. The sooty dark appearance of the smuts is due to the masses of dark-colored so called *smutspores* or *chlamydospores* which they develop. The rust fungi, as another order of the basidiomycetes, have a reddish brown color because of their spores, attack various higher plants, and are unusual in their ability to parasitize alternately two unrelated host plants in the course of their life cycle. The wheat rust fungus, for example, infects the wheat plant and the common barberry, alternating between the two hosts. It produces at least four different types of spores, each type appearing at a particular stage in the life cycle.

The mushrooms and related fungi grow on

dead leaves and other decaying tissues and are characterized by their formation of large projecting fruiting bodies consisting of a stalk or *stipe* and an umbrella-shaped cap, the *pileus* (Figure 15-12). The undersurface of the pileus is made up of many radially arranged thin plates of hyphal tissue called *gills* which bear the basidia and their basidiospores. Some mushrooms produce heat stable organic compounds which are highly toxic to the central nervous system, often causing violent symptoms followed by death.

The similarity between the basidiomycetes and ascomycetes in hyphal structure and in reproductive methods, including the development of basidia and asci respectively, is responsible for the general opinion that the basidiomycetes evolved from the ascomycetes.

Class Deuteromycetes (Imperfect Fungi). This is the smallest class within the true fungi and consists of a miscellaneous collection of fungi which fail to exhibit any type of sexual reproduction. Several species are responsible for certain diseases of higher plants and of man, including ringworm and athlete's foot. Most imperfect fungi are presumed to have their origin in the ascomycetes, and their life histories are not completely known.

Mycorrhizae and Lichens. The intimate structural and functional association of certain fungi (many of which belong to the ascomycetes and basidiomycetes) and the roots of particular higher plants is called a *mycorrhiza*. Although some consider the mycorrhizal fungi to be parasites, the more prevalent viewpoint is that both the fungi and the higher plant roots which they inhabit derive mutual benefit from the relationship. Presumably the fungus aids in the absorption of water and other nutrients by the plant roots, whereas the higher plant provides food to the fungus.

The intimate structural and functional associations of certain fungi, nearly all of which are ascomycetes, with particular blue-green algae or green algae are called *lichens*. A lichen "plant" is therefore composed of two organisms, a specific fungus and a specific alga. Both types of organisms presumably benefit from the relationship—the fungus obtaining organic nutrients from the alga, and the alga obtaining

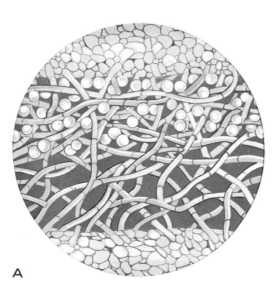

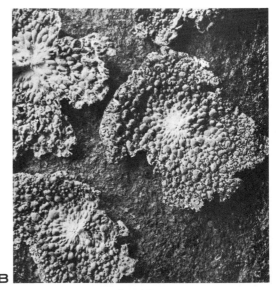

A   B

Figure 15-13. Lichens. (A) Representation of a microscopic view ot a section through a lichen showing the fungal lyphae and the spenical algae. (B) Crustose lichen *(courtesy of H. Spencer).*

water and probably some of its essential elements from the fungus. In general the bulk of the lichen is made up of the fungal hyphae. The fungus and alga of a lichen can be separated and grown separately. Approximately fifteen thousand "species" of lichens have been described. They are usually grouped into one of three shapes (crust-like, leaf-like, and shrub-like) and range in size from minute to large forms (Figure 15-13). Lichens are widely distributed on all the continents, growing on rocks, tree bark, and soil. They are well adapted to survive extremes of cold, heat, and drought. They often form an important part of the vegetation of the arctic and subarctic regions serving as pasturage for deer, ox, caribou, and other animals. They are also used commercially in various parts of the world for tanning animal hides, as a source of dyes, and for cosmetics, perfumes, and soaps.

SUPPLEMENTARY REFERENCES

Bonner, J. T., *The Cellular Slime Molds*, Princeton University Press, Princeton, N.J., 1959.
Burnet, F. M., *Viruses and Man*, Penguin, Baltimore, 1953.
Christensen, C. M., *The Molds and Man; an Introduction to the Fungi*, University of Minnesota Press, Minneapolis, 1951.
Fuller, H. J., and O. Tippo, *College Botany*, revised edition, Holt, New York, 1954.
Gibbs, R., *Botany: An Evolutionary Approach*, McGraw-Hill, New York, 1950.
Greulach, V. A., and J. E. Adams, *Plants, An Introduction to Modern Botany*, Wiley, New York, 1962.
Robbins, W. W., T. E. Weier, and C. R. Stocking, *Botany*, third edition, Wiley, New York, 1964.
Smith, G. M., *The Fresh Water Algae of the U.S.*, second edition, McGraw-Hill, New York, 1950.
Smith, G. M., *Cryptogamic Botany, Vol. I: Algae and Fungi*, McGraw-Hill, New York, 1955
Stanier, R. Y., M. Doudoroff, and E. A. Adelberg, *The Microbial World*, second edition, Pren-
Thimann, K. V., *The Life of Bacteria*, Macmillan, New York, 1955.
Tiffany, L. H., *Algae: The Grass of Many Waters*, Thomas, Springfield, Ill., 1939.
Wilson, C. L., and W. E. Loomis, *Botany*, revised edition, Dryden Press, New York, 1957.

Chapter 16

Plant Kingdom: Subkingdom Embryophyta

GENERAL CHARACTERISTICS

Although the subkingdom *Embryophyta* consists of only two phyla, the *Bryophyta* and *Tracheophyta*, it consists of nearly three hundred thousand species representing three-fourths of the plant kingdom. The two phyla are believed to have evolved independently from green algae; nevertheless they share several common characteristics despite their independent origins.

First, nearly all members of the Embryophyta are essentially true terrestrial or land plants. It is true that a few higher plants of this group are obviously aquatic types (e.g., water lilies). However, there is every indication that they evolved from terrestrial forms just as the sea-going mammals such as whales and seals surely originated from terrestrial mammalian ancestors.

Second, all develop their embryos within the female sex organs of the gametophyte stage from which they derive protection and nutrition, a situation markedly resembling that of mammals. This is in contrast to the algae, for example, where fertilization either occurs in the external medium or the zygote is liberated from the parent plant soon after fertilization as in *Oedogonium* (Chapter 15).

Third, all plants belonging to the Embryophyta possess multicellular sporangia and multicellular sex organs, the *archegonium* representing the female sex organ and the *antheridium* the male one.

Other traits of the Embryophyta include male and female gametes, the same proportions of chlorophyll and carotinoids as in the green algae, and the presence of a waterproof cuticle covering most of the aerial parts of the plant. Finally, all display a definite alternation of generations involving a *multicellular* gametophyte (haploid) and a *multicellular* sporophyte (diploid).

PHYLUM BRYOPHYTA (BRYOPHYTES)

General Characteristics

The phylum, *Bryophyta* consisting of three classes, *Hepaticae (liverworts)*, *Anthocerotae (horned liverworts)*, and the *Musci (true mosses)*, includes approximately twenty-five thousand species. In addition to the traits indicated for all members of the Embryophyta, the bryophytes in general display a prominent and independent gametophyte generation representing the main plant body. The sporophyte generation is smaller, somewhat inconspicuous, and dependent for its nutrition upon the gametophyte to which it is always attached. Bryophytes lack true roots, stems, and leaves, and require water for fertilization in order that the sperm swim to the egg.

Class Hepaticae (Liverworts)

The typical plant body (i.e., of the gametophyte) of the class, *Hepaticae* which consists of some nine thousand species, is illustrated by the widely distributed genus *Marchantia* of moist shady habitats. The plants are branched or forked, grow prostrate on the substratum, and have a clearly differentiated upper or dorsal surface and a lower or ventral surface.

The upper surface has the male and female sex organs which are borne on umbrella-like stalks or receptacles (on separate gametophytes in the case of *Marchantia*). The lower surface displays numerous thread-like rhizoids for nutrient absorption and anchorage (Figure 16-1). Several antheridia are embedded in the upper surface of the male receptacle, and each mature club-shaped antheridium is made up of a jacket of cells surrounding a mass of sperm. Under suitable conditions the antheridia release their coiled biflagellate sperm which swim to the archegonia. The latter, unlike the antheridia, are borne with their necks pointing downward on the undersurface of the lobed female receptacle. Each mature archegonium is made up of a large basal portion, the *venter*, surrounding the egg cell and a slender and elongated tubular portion called the *neck* containing an open canal through which the motile sperm reaches the egg.

Fertilization takes place within the archegonium. The resulting diploid zygote, which marks the beginning of the sporophyte generation, soon undergoes cell division to produce an embryo that develops into the mature sporophyte. The latter consists of the *foot* embedded in the female receptacle of the gametophyte, a stalk-like structure called the *seta*, and a *capsule* containing spores and certain spindle-shaped structures, *elators*. The latter change their shape in response to humidity changes thus helping to release the spores. Each spore under appropriate conditions germinates to form a new gametophyte.

Alternation of the sporophyte generation with the gametophyte generation is plainly evident and is summarized in Figure 16-1. The sporophyte generation begins with the fertilized egg and consists at first of the zygote which subsequently develops into the dependent mature sporophyte consisting of the foot,

seta, and capsule. The gametophyte generation begins with the spores within the capsule (having undergone meiosis or reduction division in their development from the spore mother cells) and is followed by the development of the prominent plant body or thallus with its receptacles bearing the sex organs.

Marchantia also reproduces asexually by means of small masses of cells called *gemmae* borne in small cup-like structures on the dorsal surface of the thallus. The gemmae are usually washed away from the parent plant and under suitable conditions develop into a new gametophyte plant body.

Class Anthocerotae (Horned Liverworts)

The class Anthocerotae, consisting of some four hundred species, displays a gametophyte thallus which is relatively small with little internal differentiation of tissues. Both archegonia and antheridia are produced on the same thallus. The sporophyte is cylindrical, long, and complex. Unlike that of *Marchantia*, it is capable of manufacturing most if not all of its organic food requirement by the photosynthetic process.

Class Musci (True Mosses)

The class Musci, composed of approximately fifteen thousand species, is characterized by a conspicuous long-lived gametophyte generation. The mature gametophyte plant body usually consists of upright stem-like axes having rhizoids at the lower end and bearing spirally arranged "leaves" (Figure 16-2). The mosses are not as strictly limited to wet habitats as are many of the liverworts.

In the life cycle of a typical moss a haploid spore marks the beginning of the gametophyte generation. It germinates to develop a branching multicellular green filament called the *protonema*, resembling some of the filamentous green algae. Several protonema branches penetrate the substratum and lose their chlorophyll to become rhizoids for anchorage of the plant and the absorption of nutrients. Other branches develop into "leafy shoots," usually

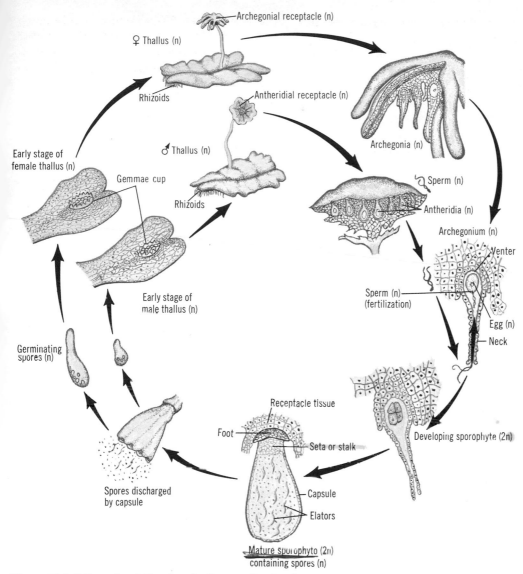

Figure 16-1. Life cycle of *Marchantia*. See text for details.

a few inches high, of the familiar moss plant.
None of the structures can be considered to be
true roots, stems, or leaves, because they lack
vascular tissue (xylem and phloem) and other
anatomical features.

The antheridia and archegonia are produced
at the tips of the leafy "shoots" either on the
same plant or on different plants depending
upon the species. The antheridia like those of
the liverworts are usually stalked and club-

shaped. They consist essentially of a jacket or
wall of cells enclosing a mass of cells which
develop into coiled sperm, each bearing two
long terminal flagella. The archegonia which
are also stalked have essentially the same
structure as the archegonia of the liverworts
except that they are more elongated.

Fertilization occurs by fusion of one of the
sperm which has entered the archegonium
with the nonmotile egg cell. The resulting

diploid zygote which represents the beginning of the sporophyte generation undergoes rapid cell division to form an embryo. In time the embryo grows and develops into a mature upright sporophyte consisting of a *foot* (which penetrates through the old archegonium into the leafy gametophyte shoot), an elongated *seta*, and a complex *capsule*. The latter possesses chloroplasts and some stomata and ap-

parently manufactures some of its food by the process of photosynthesis. Each of the diploid spore mother cells within the capsule undergoes meiosis to produce eventually four haploid spores which mark the beginning of the gametophyte generation. The release of the spores from the capsule and the germination of each under suitable conditions into a protonema completes the life cycle of the moss. The

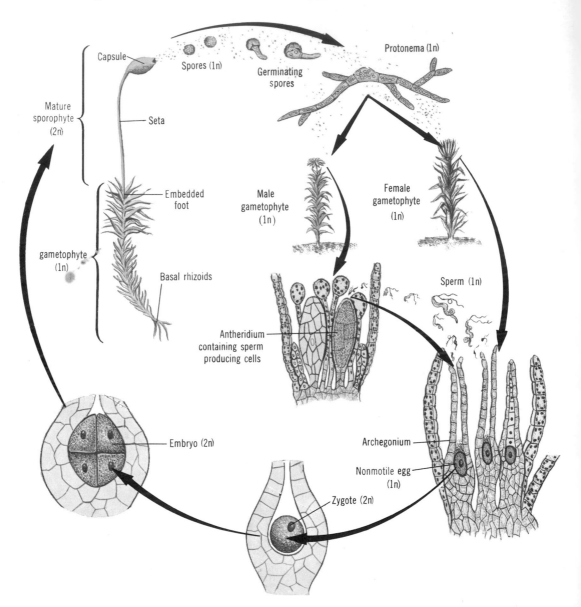

Figure 16-2. Life cycle of typical moss. See text for details.

clearly defined alternation of the prominent and independent gametophyte generation with the smaller and dependent sporophyte generation (as in the case of the liverworts) is summarized in Figure 16-2.

In some mosses asexual reproduction also takes place as it does in liverworts by means of gemmae produced at the tips of the gametophyte "leaves" and "stems."

There seems to be no common agreement concerning the evolutionary relationships of the bryophytes other than that they originated from the green algae. One school of thought considers the liverworts to be more primitive than the mosses and suggests that ancestral bryophytes gave rise to the higher plants. A more recent and increasingly favored theory considers the mosses to be more primitive than the liverworts. It proposes that higher plants did not originate from the bryophytes after all but arose independently from the green algae.

PHYLUM TRACHEOPHYTA (VASCULAR PLANTS)

General Characteristics

All members of the phylum Tracheophyta consisting of nearly three hundred thousand species are characterized by two important features: (1) the *presence of vascular tissue* composed of *xylem* and *phloem* and (2) a *sporophyte* that is *larger* than the gametophyte and *entirely independent* of it except during the early stages of development. All members of the phylum experience an alternation of generations. At times it may appear to be masked, especially in higher forms, because the gametophyte becomes very much reduced in size and may remain contained within the sporophyte generation.

The phylum is subdivided into four subphyla: the *Psilopsida, Lycopsida, Spheriopsida,* and *Pteropsida.* According to one of the newer concepts of plant relationships the subphylum Psilopsida, which is considered to be the most primitive of the four, had its origin from some ancient stock of filamentous green algae and in turn gave rise via one of its ancient and now extinct orders, the Psilophytales, to the other three subphyla.

Subphylum Psilopsida

GENERAL CHARACTERISTICS. The subphylum Psilopsida consists of two orders, one of which, the Psilophytales, is now extinct and is known only through its fossil remains. The other order is called Psilotales and is made up of two living genera. The subphylum Psilopsida is of great interest because it apparently has all the signs of being the most primitive of the vascular plants. Except for a forking or dichotomously branched stem containing vascular tissue (a solid central core of xylem surrounded by a cylinder of phloem), there is little or no organ differentiation. True roots, true leaves, and a cambium are lacking. The absence of a cambium tells us that the plant body is made up completely of primary tissues since there is no secondary growth.

ORDER PSILOPHYTALES. Judging from the wide distribution of their fossil remains within certain rock strata, the order *Psilophytales* must have been prevalent 350 to 380 million years ago during the Silurian and Devonian ages (Chapter 32). Our knowledge of these most ancient of all known vascular plants is based entirely on studies of fossils of their sporophyte stage. There is no information on their gametophytes, since such fossils have not yet been discovered.

In appearance the typical Psilophytales sporophyte (e.g., the genus *Rhynia*) was an erect forking naked stem (with the vascular tissue arrangement already indicated) possessing no leaves. The spore cases or sporangia were located on the tips of some of the branches (Figure 16-3) and the underground stem called the *rhizome* possessed rhizoids instead of roots. In certain other genera the stem had small spine-like or scale-like emergences, depending on the genus, which are considered by some to be the first beginnings of leaves.

ORDER PSILOTALES. The order Psilotales with its two genera consisting of three known living species has provided us with information about the gametophyte generation of the subphylum. In general the gametophyte looks like a small piece of cylindrical, forking rhizome bearing rhizoids (Figure 16-4). Many antheridia and archegonia, essentially similar in structure to those of the bryophytes, are scattered over the gametophyte surface. The sporophyte generation shows a marked resemblance to that of the Psilophytales.

The present tendency is to regard this highly interesting subphylum as the evolutionary link between the higher terrestrial vascular plants and certain ancient green algae from which they are believed to have arisen. More precisely it is thought that the now extinct order Psilophytales having arisen from the green algae proved in turn to be the evolutionary intermediate from which the other three subphyla (Lycopsida, Spheriopsida, and Pteropsida) arose.

Subphylum Lycopsida (Club Mosses)

GENERAL CHARACTERISTICS. The subphylum Lycopsida consisting of five orders encompasses a total of approximately one thousand species. Its more important features include a sporophyte possessing (in addition to the forked branching stem) true roots and true leaves (contain vascular tissue), the latter often being small and spirally arranged. Fossil studies indicate that the ancient and now extinct forms were much larger. Spore cases or sporangia are borne on the upper surface of particular leaves called *sporophylls*. In most cases the sporophylls are arranged at the tips of stems in clusters called *cones* or *strobili*.

ORDER LYCOPODIALES. The chief characteristics of the order Lycopodiales (the club mosses) is illustrated by the genus *Lycopodium*. The sporophyte has a moss-like appearance because of the many small spirally arranged leaves which cover the upright forked branching stems. The latter grow forth from rhizomes which also give rise to branching true roots. The vascular tissue of the stem with its solid core of xylem enclosed within a cylinder of phloem shows no cambium. All tissues are therefore primary with no secondary growth occurring. Depending on the species the sporo-

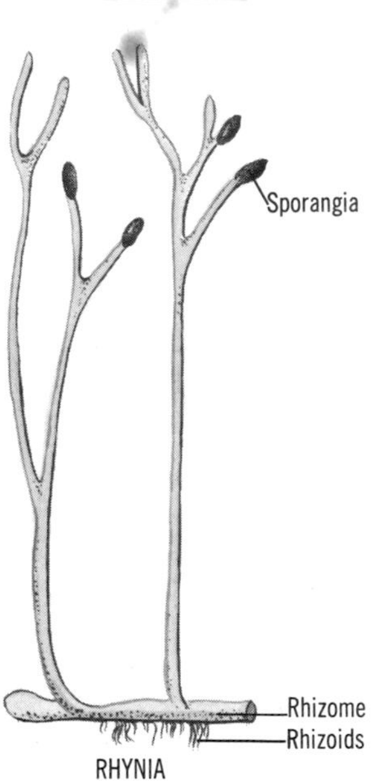

Figure 16-3. Sporophyte of *Rhynia* (order: Psilophytales).

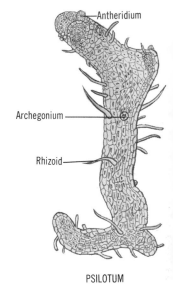

Figure 16-4. Gametophyte of order Psilotales.

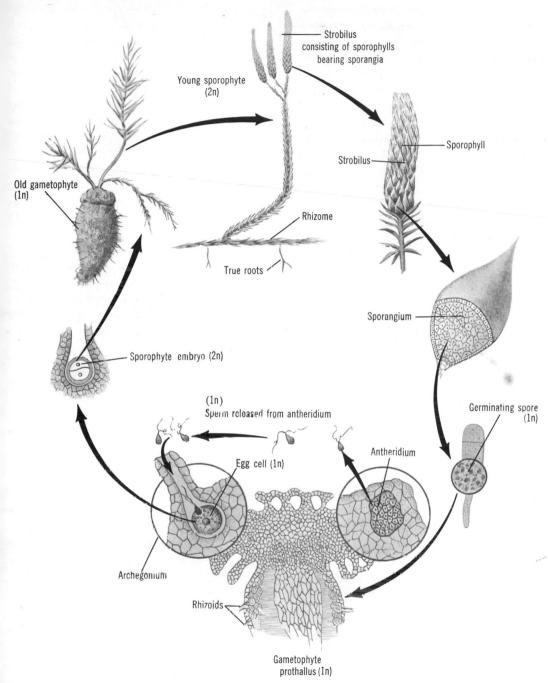

Young sporophyte
(2n)

Strobilus
consisting of sporophylls
bearing sporangia

Sporophyll

Strobilus

Old gametophyte
(1n)

Rhizome

True roots

Sporangium

Sporophyte embryo (2n)

Germinating spore
(1n)

(1n)
Sperm released from antheridium

Egg cell (1n)

Antheridium

Archegonium

Rhizoids

Gametophyte
prothallus (1n)

Figure 16-5. Life cycle of *Lycopodium*. See text for details.

phylls (i.e., bearing sporangia) may be either scattered or grouped at the tips of the stem branches to form cones or strobili. The spores within the sporangia arise by meiotic division from the spore mother cells. The colorless gametophytes called *prothalli* which are produced from the germinating spores are less than an inch in size and generally tend to be embedded in the soil. The upper surface of the gametophyte possesses archegonia and antheridia, essentially similar to those of the bryophytes, whereas the lower surface bears rhizoids. Fertilization of the egg cell by a biflagellate sperm marks the beginning of the sporophyte generation and is followed by embryo development to give rise in time to a young leafy sporophyte (Figure 16-5).

ORDER SELAGINELLALES. Many of the characteristics of the widely distributed order *Selaginellales*, the small club mosses, as represented by the sole living genus *Selaginella*, are like those of the *Lycopodiales* but with several significant differences. The more important of these differences are: (1) sporophylls are always arranged in cones or strobili, (2) two kinds of spores and two kinds of gametophytes (male and female) are produced, and (3) true vessels (p. 95) are present in some species.

The cones are located at the tips of the stem branches and consist of two types of sporophylls: the upper sporophylls (called *microsporophylls*) each bearing a small sporangium (*microsporangium*) which produces many small spores (*microspores*), and the lower sporophylls (*megasporophylls*) each bearing a larger sporangium (*megasporangium*) which produces only four large spores (*megaspores*). The haploid microspores and megaspores while still in their sporangia germinate to form male and female gametophytes respectively. The mature male gametophyte is entirely enclosed by the microspore wall and is simply made up of a single vegetative or prothallial cell and a single antheridium which produce numerous biflagellate sperm. It possesses no chlorophyll and is completely dependent upon the sporophyte for its nutrition. The mature

female gametophyte, which has ruptured the spore wall but still remains surrounded by it, consists of several archegonia embedded in several layers of cells containing chlorophyll.

At the time of fertilization the microspores are liberated from the microsporangia, and with the uptake of water their walls rupture and release the sperm. The sperm swim into the megasporangia where a sperm finds its way into an archegonium, fertilizing the egg. In time the zygote which marks the beginning of the sporophyte generation develops into an embryo which eventually becomes an independent sporophyte plant (Figure 16-6).

ORDER LEPIDODENDRALES. This order known as the giant club mosses is extinct and is presently represented only by fossil remains. All its members were trees, some reaching heights of greater than 125 feet and diameters of nearly six feet. As a group they attained their peak of development in the *Carboniferous Period* (Chapter 32) three hundred million years ago. Like *Selaginella* they produced cones and two different types of spores. In addition they possessed an active cambium that was responsible for appreciable secondary growth.

ORDER PLEUROMEIALES. Like the giant club mosses, this order is also extinct and is at present only represented by fossil remains. Its members possessed a single unbranched trunk resembling those of the giant club moss species and cones bearing two different spores.

ORDER ISOETALES. This order known as the quillworts with one living genus consists of more or less aquatic types possessing quill-like leaves and a life cycle like that of *Selaginella*. It has a cambium, microspores and macrospores, multiciliate sperm, cones or strobili, and extremely reduced male and female gametophytes among its various features.

The tissues of the ancient Lycopsida plants that existed during the Carboniferous Period are important constituents of coal.

Subphylum Sphenopsida (Horsetails)

GENERAL CHARACTERISTICS. This subphylum with its three orders, two of which are

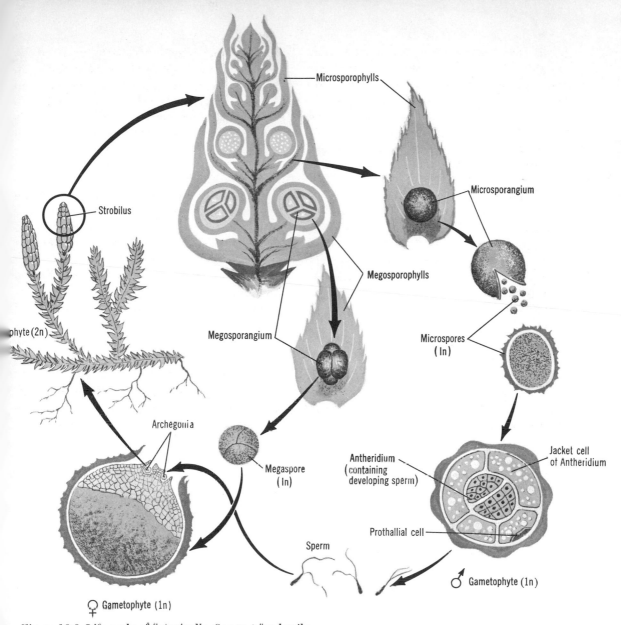

Figure 16-6. Life cycle of *Selaginella*. See text for details.

Labels in figure: Microsporophylls · Strobilus · Microsporangium · Megosporophylls · Megosporangium · Microspores (1n) · Archegonia · Megaspore (1n) · Antheridium (containing developing sperm) · Jacket cell of Antheridium · Prothallial cell · Sperm · ♂ Gametophyte (1n) · ♀ Gametophyte (1n) · ...phyte (2n)

extinct and fossilized, contains only twenty-five living species. Its sporophytes possess true roots, stems, and leaves. The leaves are simple and small and are arranged in whorls at the joints, or nodes, of the hollow and furrowed stems. The sporangia are borne in groups on specialized or modified sporophylls (probably evolved from minor lateral branches) which are arranged as cones or strobili.

In the only living genus *Equisetum* (Figure 16-7) which occurs nearly all over the world the conspicuous sporophyte of most of the twenty-five species has two kinds of aerial stems. One is a green, vegetative bushy horse tail-like stem with whorled branches. The other is a fertile, colorless, unbranched stem bearing a single cone at its tip. Both types of stems arise from a horizontal branched rhizome bear-

strobilus

fertile branches

vegetative branches

Figure 16-7. *Equisetum.*

ing whorls of scale-like leaves and at times roots. The cell walls of the stem epidermis are typically impregnated with silica thus imparting a rough, brittle, abrasive texture to the plant. The latter feature made them useful as a scouring agent for kitchen utensils and floors in the early history of America.

The strobilus consists of the terminal end of the stem axis with its closely packed nodes and whorls of shield-shaped sporophylls, each sporophyll bearing five to ten elongated sporangia on its underside. The spores arise within the sporangia after meiosis of the spore mother cells and are all of the same size and appearance (*homosporous*). By contrast some of the extinct *Equisetales* species produced two different kinds of spores (*heterosporous*). Following their release from sporangia the spores germinate to form small green, often ribbon-like, gametophytes usually bearing both antheridia and archegonia. Liberation of the spirally coiled multiciliate sperm is followed

by fertilization of the egg cell within the archegonium and the successive development of the embryo and new sporophyte plant.

Like the Lycopsida, the Equisetales attained their height of prominence during the Carboniferous Period and contributed their tissues to the formation of coal.

Subphylum Pteropsida

GENERAL CHARACTERISTICS. The subphylum Pteropsida with its two hundred and fifty thousand or so species consists of three classes: the *Filicineae* (ferns), *Gymnospermae* (conifer and its allies), and *Angiospermae* (flowering plants). The gymnosperms and angiosperms are often referred to as the *seed plants.* Approximately 95 per cent of the Pteropsida species belong to the flowering plants.

The important features which characterize all members of the Pteropsida include: (1) sporophytes with true roots, stems, and leaves; (2) leaves which are usually large and complex, having probably evolved by flattening and other modifications of an entire stem branch system; (3) sporangia usually located on the lower sporophyll surface; and (4) often small reduced gametophytes which become dependent upon the sporophyte in the gymnosperms and angiosperms. It is the present consensus of opinion among plant taxonomists that of the three classes the ferns are probably the most primitive, and that the gymnosperms which very likely evolved from an ancient and now extinct group of ferns gave rise in turn to the angiosperms.

CLASS FILICINEAE (FERNS). The ferns as a class of the subphylum Pteropsida comprise nearly ten thousand species. Among the most important special features of the ferns are: (1) the occurrence of fertilization by swimming sperm which require water for their transport; (2) the presence of numerous sporangia, usually on the lower surface of the leaves; (3) absence of seeds and large leaves; and (4) the presence of a green, independent gametophyte stage. Ferns are widely distributed and flourish most luxuriantly in moist, warm, shady habitats reaching their greatest height (approximately fifty feet and more) in the tropics.

Of the four different orders which make up the ferns the order *Filicales*, commonly called the true ferns, with its nine thousand species is usually selected as most representative of the class. The fern is most familiar to us in the conspicuous sporophyte stage. It consists of a horizontal underground stem or rhizome bearing several typical leaves or *fronds* above ground and fibrous roots from its lower surface below ground. Although no cambium is present and all tissues therefore are primary, the structure of the stem is quite advanced, possessing vascular bundles, an epidermis, cortex, and pith (p. 388). The leaves generally die at the close of each growing season whereas the rhizome remains on growing from year to year. At times the rhizome branches separate from the older portions and persist as individual new plants thus representing a form of vegetative propagation.

The underside of the fronds often bear brownish "dots" called *sori* (singular, *sorus*) which are clusters of sporangia containing haploid spores. Spore mother cells within the sporangia have undergone meiosis to produce the spores (the beginning of the gametophyte generation) all of which are either of the same type (homosporous) or of two different types (heterosporous) depending upon the species. Different species of ferns also differ in the distribution, structure, and form of their sori and sporangia. In certain ferns each sorus is covered by an outgrowth from the leaf called the *indusium* (Figure 16-8). In some ferns there are two types of leaves – special spore-bearing leaves (or sporophylls) and vegetative leaves which never produce spores.

The released spores usually germinate on the moist ground and develop first into filaments of green cells with rhizoids. Each of the filaments then develops into a small, typically heart-shaped gametophyte called the *prothallus* consisting of a flat green plate of cells bearing rhizoids and both types of sex organs on its undersurface. The mature gametophyte is

Figure 16-8. Underside of the fronds of the fern *Dryopteris cristata* showing each sorus covered with an indusium. *(Courtesy C. Neidorf, AIBS Bull.)*

usually about one-quarter inch in diameter and tends to have its archegonia (which are essentially similar to those of the bryophytes) concentrated near the notch, whereas the antheridia are scattered among the rhizoids. In some species the antheridia and archegonia are borne on separate gametophytes. The multiciliate sperm which are set free from the antheridia usually swim to other prothalli and enter the archegonia where fertilization takes place. The resulting zygote marks the beginning of the sporophyte generation and is retained within the archegonium where it develops first into an embryo and then into a new sporophyte with roots, stems, and leaves. It is during the early stages of embryonic development, at least until the first or primary root and leaf appear, that the young sporophyte is completely dependent upon the tiny gametophyte for its nutrition. The life cycle of the fern with its distinct alternation of generations is summarized in Figure 16-9. The life histories of most ferns are essentially similar.

THE CLASSES GYMNOSPERMAE AND ANGIOSPERMAE. *The Seed and the Pollen Tube.* The class *Gymnospermae* (conifers and their allies)

and the class *Angiospermae* (flowering plants) are collectively known as the *seed plants*. The key characteristics that distinguish the seed plants from all others and account for their phenomenal success as terrestrial forms are

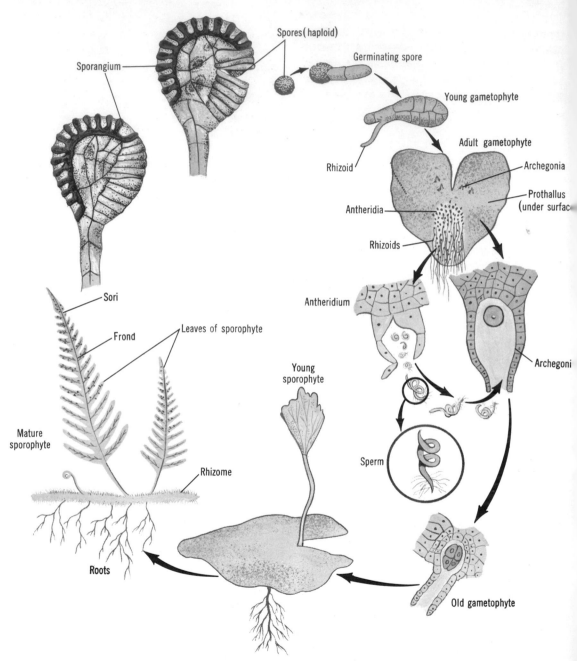

Figure 16-9. Life cycle of a fern. The sporophyte is diploid and the gametophyte is haploid.

the *production of seeds* and the *formation of a pollen tube.* The gymnosperms and angiosperms are universally heterosporous in the basic sense that one type of spore (microspore) produces a male gametophyte and the other (megaspore) a female gametophyte. The megaspore, however, is not released but is retained within the megasporangium where it develops into the female gametophyte. This entire structure, namely the megasporangium surrounded by certain maternal sporophyte tissue, the *integument,* together with the enclosed female gametophyte is collectively called an *ovule.* After fertilization an embryonic sporophyte is formed (but temporarily ceases development to enter a resting stage) and the integument is matured into a so-called *seed coat.* This entire structure consisting of the embryo in the resting stage, the enclosing megasporangium wall, and the surrounding matured integument (i.e., seed coat) is now known as the *seed.*

Under suitable conditions the embryo or young sporophyte within the seed will resume development, germinating and emerging into an older and recognizable sporophyte with true roots, stems, and leaves. The seed as an extremely efficient stage in the development of the new plant has conferred important advantages for existence in a terrestrial environment. Seeds are generally well adapted for wide dissemination and are viable for long periods of time (in some cases for hundreds of years), being resistant to dessication, extremes of temperature, and numerous toxic substances. All seeds are equipped with a built-in supply of available food assuring that the newly germinating plant will be adequately developed by the time it becomes self-supporting.

Pollen-tube formation by the male gametophyte, as the second unique characteristic of the seed plants, has also contributed to the phenomenal success of the seed plants as terrestrial organisms. It has liberated them to a large degree from dependence upon free water in order for fertilization to take place. Microspores mature into the male gametophytes known as *pollen grains* which are

disseminated in various ways. Under suitable conditions each produces a pollen tube which grows toward the nearby ovules thus transporting the male gamete to the female gametophyte.

Class Gymnospermae. In addition to seed production and pollen-tube development the gymnosperms as a class possess other characteristic features. Unlike the angiosperms (described in a later section) their ovules and resulting seeds are not borne within an enclosed structure. They are therefore said to be "naked," accounting for the name "gymnospermae" which means "naked seeds." The conspicuous sporophyte generation has true roots, stems, and leaves, and the gametophyte is dependent and extremely small. The sporophytes are mostly woody and evergreen and have an active cambium yielding considerable secondary xylem and phloem. They are economically important as a source of timber, turpentine, and resin.

The gymnosperms, which are known to have descended from an ancient line extending back into the upper Devonian Period, are made up of seven orders made up of more than sixty genera and seven hundred species. Three of the orders, *Cycadofilicales, Bennettitales,* and *Cordaitales,* are known only as fossil plants, whereas one of the orders (*Ginkgoales*) has only a single living species, *Ginkgo biloba* (maidenhair tree). The other three orders are the *Coniferales, Cycadales,* and *Gnetules.*

Order Coniferales. Coniferales (or the conifers), the major living order of gymnosperms, consist of some fifty genera and six hundred species. It includes the well-known pines, spruces, firs, larches, junipers, cedars, yews, and redwoods. All characteristically possess cones or strobili which are either male or female. Depending on the species some plants bear both types of cones (i.e., monoecious) or one type of cone (dioecious). All produce non-motile sperm which are conveyed to the egg by pollen tubes. In the great majority of conifers the leaves are scale-like or needle-like usually remaining on the plant throughout the year.

The familiar pine (genus *Pinus*) as a member of the Coniferales has a life history which includes the well-known pine tree sporophyte stage with its large branched stem and extensive root system. The male cones (also called *staminate* cones) bear only microsporangia, consist of spirally arranged microsporophylls, and are found in clusters near the ends of some branches. Two microsporangia containing haploid microspores (pollen) are borne on the undersurface of each microsporophyll. Each microspore or pollen grain at the time of shedding (pollination) is an immature male gametophyte containing two *prothallial cells,* a *tube cell,* and a *generative cell* (Figure 16-10).

The female (or *carpellate*) cones which are larger but fewer in number than the staminate cones consist of spirally arranged megasporophylls on whose upper surface are located two ovules. Each ovule is made up of a single integument (with a single opening called the *micropyle*) surrounding the megasporangium (now called the *nucellus*). Each megasporangium produces only four haploid megaspores which mark the beginning of the gametophyte generation. Three of the megaspores degenerate and the fourth develops into a small female gametophyte consisting of two or three archegonia embedded in a mass of haploid vegetative storage tissue called the *endosperm* (Figure 16-10).

Pollination, or the transport of pollen grains to the female cones, is accomplished by the wind, some of the pollen grains coming to rest in a sticky fluid near the micropyle. As the fluid dries the pollen grains are drawn down through the micropyle until they come in contact with the nucellus itself. Pollen tubes begin to grow from the pollen grains but fertilization does not occur until about a year later. As the pollen tube slowly develops the generative cell divides to form a *stalk cell* and *body cell.* The latter enters the pollen tube and eventually divides into two nonmotile *male nuclei* thus completing development of the fully matured male gametophyte. The mature male gametophyte therefore consists of six cells (two prothallial cells, tube cell, stalk cell, and two male nuclei) and is dependent on the sporophyte for its nutrition (Figure 16-10).

Meanwhile the female gametophyte has also been slowly developing. At the time of fertili-

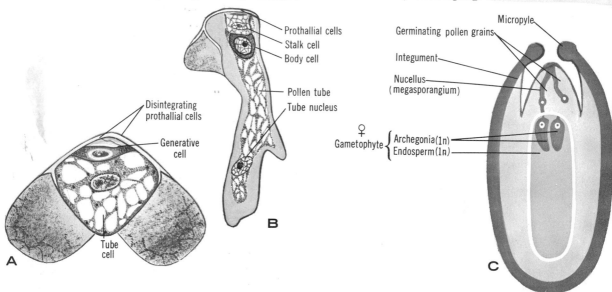

Figure 16-10. The pine (A) pollen grain or microspore (immature male gametophyte), (B) mature male gametophyte, and (C) ovule containing the mature female gametophyte (longitudinal section).

zation the tip of the pollen tube reaches one of the archegonia of the female gametophyte and one of its male nuclei fuses with the egg cell to form the zygote—the beginning of the sporophyte generation. During the cell division that follows only a single embryo develops from each female gametophyte (the remaining embryos within the gametophyte having degenerated). The embryo finally consists of several leaf-like structures called *cotyledons*, the embryo axis called the *epicotyl* (which will become the young stem of the plant) and the *hypocotyl* (which will become the primary root of the plant). The dormant embryo embedded within the haploid endosperm and successively surrounded by the nucellus and matured integument (i.e., seed coat) now collectively constitute the seed. The familiar shell of the pine seed is the modified integument. The structure of the pine seed is shown in Figure 16-11.

The Orders Cycadales, Ginkgoules, and Gnetales. The order *Cycadales* or cycads, once abundant during the upper Mesozoic Period, (Chapter 32), is probably the most primitive of the living gymnosperms. It now consists of about one hundred species of palm-like tropical and subtropical plants (Figure 16-12). Most

representatives of the group possess certain features (e.g., motile sperm, vascular bundle arrangement, and leaf structure) reminiscent of the ferns in addition to characteristics similar to those of the gymnosperms (e.g., seeds, pollen tube, and reduced gametophytes).

The order *Ginkgoales* with its single living species, *Ginkgo biloba* (maidenhair tree) is characterized by broad, lobed leaves and a life history (including motile sperm) similar to that of the Cycadales.

The order *Gnetales* in addition to its gymnosperm characteristics shows several angiosperm features such as true vessels in the secondary wood and a female gametophyte in several genera resembling that of angiosperms. In these respects it is more like the angiosperms than any other gymnosperms. The suggestion has been made that an ancient line of the Gnetales may have given rise to the angiosperms, but there is no supporting fossil record.

Class Angiospermae. The angiosperms or flowering plants are the most advanced class of the subphylum *Pteropsida* (and in fact of the

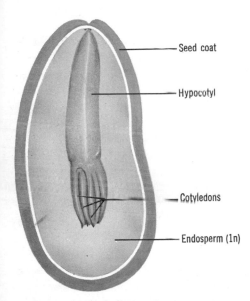

Figure 16-11. Longitudinal section of the pine seed. The epicotyl is surrounded by the cotyledons.

Seed coat

Hypocotyl

Cotyledons

Endosperm (1n)

Figure 16-12. The cycle *Cycas media* showing ovulate cones (*courtesy of Chicago Natural History Museum*).

entire plant kingdom). They are composed of approximately three hundred thousand different species divided into two subclasses, the *Dicotyledoneae* (dicotyledons) and the *Monocotyledoneae* (monocotyledons). Not only do the angiosperms exceed in number of species all other plant groups taken together, but also they are of far greater economic importance to man than any other plants. As agricultural crops they represent an important source of man's food supply and in this respect have played a central role in the development of human society. They also provide us with textiles, medicines, and oils.

Although they share many features with the gymnosperms, the angiosperms are distinguished from the latter class by the following important characteristics.

1. All angiosperms possess flowers which are essentially highly modified strobili or cones composed of microsporophylls called *stamens* and megasporophylls called *carpels*. They are often borne together in contrast to the staminate and carpellate strobili of the gymnosperms. A flower like a strobilus is therefore essentially a stem with leaves modified for carrying on reproduction.

2. The ovules and seeds of angiosperms are contained within an enclosed structure, the ovary. It has presumably arisen from the fusion in the course of evolution of one or more megasporophylls or carpels. By contrast the gymnosperms bear unenclosed or "naked" seeds on the surface of the magasporophylls. As a result in angiosperms the pollen tube must grow through the tissues of the carpel before reaching the ovule.

3. With but a few exceptions vessels are present in the xylem of all angiosperms.

4. Angiosperms undergo a double fertilization, as we shall soon see (p. 385).

5. Whereas pollination in gymnosperms is by wind, in angiosperms it is by insects and birds as well as by wind.

6. Although the angiosperms include woody plants that persist year after year (*perennials*) they also include many soft-tissued plants (*herbaceous* plants) that live for one or two years (in contrast to the gymnosperms which are all woody perennials).

The angiosperms like the gymnosperms have reduced dependent gametophytes, large, conspicuous, and almost entirely independent sporophytes, heterospory, pollen-tube formation (which eliminates the necessity of water for fertilization) seeds, and true roots, stems, and leaves.

Subclasses Dicotyledoneae and Monocotyledoneae. The angiosperms as a class are grouped into two subdivisions, the subclass *Dicotyledoneae* consisting of about 225,000 species having two cotyledons in their embryos, and the subclass *Monocotyledoneae* consisting of some 75,000 species possessing only one cotyledon in their embryos. Other important differences between the two subclasses are that the dicotyledonous plants usually have their vascular tissues in a cylinder or bundle arranged in a single circle, possess a cambium, and show net-veined leaves (Figure 16-13). Monocotyledons, on the other hand, usually have scattered vascular bundles, no cambium, and leaves with parallel veins. Also the flower parts of dicotyledons often occur in numbers of four or five or multiples thereof (as four sepals, four petals, four stamens, four carpels) whereas those of monocotyledons are usually in numbers of three or multiples of three. From an evolutionary point of view the monocotyledons, which include the grasses, lilies, irises, and orchids, are considered to be more advanced than the dicotyledons. The latter resemble the gymnosperms in their possession of a cambium and the circular arrangement of vascular tissues. Presumably the monocotyledons arose from some ancient line of dicotyledons.

LIFE CYCLE OF A TYPICAL ANGIOSPERM
Flower Structure

Strictly speaking the flower as the reproductive structure of the conspicuous angiosperm sporophyte is a modified shoot bearing reproductive organs. Some of the flower organs have

A B

Figure 16-13. The net-veined leave of (A) dicotyledons, and the parallel-veined leaves of (B) monocotyledons. *(Courtesy of H. Spencer and R. E. Hutchins.)*

presumably originated from stems and others from leaves.

A typically *complete* flower (e.g., rose and petunia) possesses all the usual flower parts. It is composed of the tip of a stem called the *receptacle* and the four types of floral organs which grow from it, the *sepals, petals, stamens,* and *pistil* (Figure 16-14). The *sepals,* collectively called the *calyx,* as the outermost of the floral organs which usually enclose the other flower parts in the bud are generally small, green, leaf-like structures. The petals, collectively called the *corolla,* which constitute the next whorl of structures are often the most conspicuously colored of the flower parts. The petals by virtue of their bright colors, sweetish nectars, and distinctive floral odors tend to attract insects which are important in pollination. Within the circumference of the corolla are the *stamens,* each usually consisting of a slender stalk or *filament* bearing at its tip an enlarged portion, the *anther,* which produces pollen. The stamens correspond to the microsporophylls of the gymnosperms. In many flowers the number of members in each of the whorls is usually the same. Surrounded by

the stamens at the center of the flower is the *pistil* composed of an enlarged lower portion, the *ovary* (consisting of one or more carpels containing the ovules), a slender structure, the *style,* rising from the ovary and the expanded tip of the style called the *stigma.* Depending on the species the pistil is composed of one or several carpels. Each of the carpels is homologous with the megasporophylls of *Pinus.* A good deal of variety occurs among the angiosperms with respect to flower structure, shape, arrangement, size, color, number of members for each of the flower parts, fusion of flowers, and so on.

Although most species of angiosperms possess complete flowers in that all of the usual flower parts (sepals, petals, stamens, and pistil) are present, there are other species that are lacking in one or several of the flower parts. In some the sepals or petals or even both may be absent. This is the case, for example, for the grains and grasses, the calla lily family and the willow family where both the calyx and corolla are absent. In other species either the stamens or pistils are lacking, a feature believed to have evolved from plants possess-

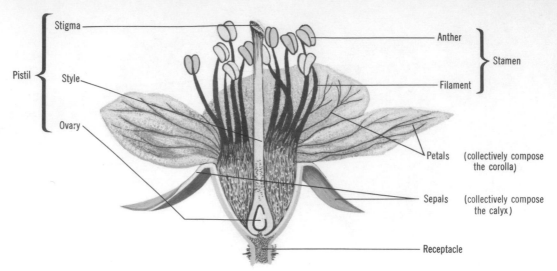

Figure 16-14. Structure of a typical complete flower.

ing complete flowers. In the walnut and oak, for example, separate staminate and pistillate flowers lacking pistils and stamens respectively are borne on the same plant.

The Male and Female Gametophytes

As in the gymnosperms the haploid pollen grains or microspores of angiosperms which are produced in the anthers arise as a result of meiosis by the spore mother cells. Liberation of the pollen grains and its transmittal by wind and insects (and very rarely by water) to the stigma of flowers of the same plant (*self-pollination*) or other plants of the same species (*cross-pollination*) marks the beginning of the process of sexual reproduction. At the time of liberation the pollen grains, each containing a *tube nucleus* and a *generative nucleus*, are already considered to be a male gametophytes. The tube nucleus regulates the subsequent growth of the pollen tube. After being deposited on the stigma the pollen grain absorbs food and water and sends forth a pollen tube which grows downward through the style towards the ovary. It is usually during the period of early growth of the pollen tube that the generative nucleus perhaps representing the vestigial remains of an antheridium divides to

produce two male nuclei or gametes. The mature male gametophyte therefore consists of the germinating pollen grain with its pollen tube, the three nuclei, and some associated cytoplasm (Figure 16-15).

The female gametophyte in angiosperms consists of a structure known as the *embryo sac* contained within each of the ovules. The latter are in turn attached by separate short stalks to the wall of an enclosing carpel, of which one or more make up the ovary. The outer structure of the ovule is composed of two integument layers (instead of one as in the gymnosperms) which covers an underlying *nucellus* representing the remains of the megasporangium wall. The latter surrounds the female gametophyte which at maturity typically contains eight nuclei (Figure 16-15). Three of the nuclei consisting of an *egg nucleus* and two so-called *synergid nuclei* are present at the end of the embryo sac near the *micropyle* (the tiny pore extending through the integuments). They probably represent the last vestiges of an archegonium. Two nuclei, the *polar nuclei,* are located near the center of the embryo sac, and three nuclei called the *antipodals* are present at the end of the embryo sac opposite the micropyle. Each ovule encloses a single embryo sac

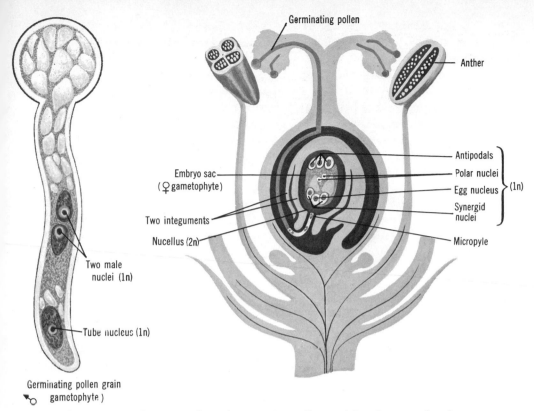

Two male
nuclei (1n)

Tube nucleus (1n)

Germinating pollen grain
(♂ gametophyte)

Germinating pollen

Anther

Embryo sac
(♀ gametophyte)

Antipodals
Polar nuclei
Egg nucleus } (1n)
Synergid
nuclei

Two integuments

Nucellus (2n)

Micropyle

Figure 16-15. Mature male gametophyte (germinating pollen grain) and mature female gametophyte (embryo sac) of an angiosperm or flowering plant.

and has developed from a single megasporangium containing a single megaspore mother cell. The latter has undergone meiosis and, of the four haploid megaspores produced, three disintegrate. The single megaspore that persists undergoes several divisions to develop eventually into the mature female gametophyte or embryo sac.

Both the male and female gametophytes are in a most reduced stage. Like those of the gymnosperms they are completely dependent upon the sporophyte generation for their nutrition, since neither the male nor the female gametophyte has chlorophyll or a means of directly obtaining nutrients from the soil. Antheridia and archegonia recognizable as such are absent in the gametophytes. Nor are mobile male gametes present. The striking predominance of the sporophyte generation (and the marked reduction of the gametophyte gen-

eration) tends to mask the phenomenon of alternation of generations. Nevertheless it is definitely present in the angiosperms – an interpretation which would have otherwise been difficult to make had it not been for our knowledge of the life cycles of the bryophytes, ferns, gymnosperms, and other lower forms.

Fertilization, Seed Development, Fruit Formation, and Seed Germination

Before fertilization can occur the pollen tube must first grow downward through the style and into the ovary where it finally penetrates the embryo sac (via the micropyle) to discharge its male or sperm nuclei. One of the two male nuclei fuses with the egg cell to form the diploid zygote marking the beginning of the sporophyte generation. The other sperm nucleus meanwhile fuses with the two polar nuclei to form a triploid (3n) nucleus which will eventually develop into the triploid endosperm (you will recall that the endosperm in gymnosperms is haploid, p. 380).

Soon after this occurrence of double fertilization, a phenomenon found only in angiosperms, the remaining five nuclei of the embryo sac (antipodals and synergids) begin to disintegrate and disappear. The diploid zygote by the processes of cell division and differentiation shortly develops into an embryo. Meanwhile the triploid endosperm nucleus also experiences successive cell divisions to form the multicellular triploid endosperm tissue which is the food storage tissue of the seed. During their development the embryo and endosperm receive food materials from the parent sporophyte plant. The foods (for the most part oils, starches, or proteins) which accumulate in the endosperm will be utilized by the embryo when the seed subsequently germinates into a young sporophyte plant. The embryo and endosperm grow and develop while the integuments become hardened and modified into a seed coat, thus collectively transforming the enlarging ovule into a developing seed (Figure 16-16).

At the same time that the seeds are forming the ovary also increases in size and the other flower parts (stamens, petals, and sepals) deteriorate and disappear. Thus the enlarging ovary with its developing seeds eventually becomes the *fruit*. A fruit therefore occurs exclusively in the flowering plants for it is a matured ovary of a flower, or a cluster of matured ovaries, including one or more of its seeds. Depending on the species fruits may reach maturity relatively soon after fertilization or they may take several years.

Although the angiosperm embryo within the seed may differ widely in appearance depending on the species, all possess the same fundamental parts. The embryo always consists of one or two *cotyledons* or *seed leaves* (depending on whether it is a monocotyledonous or dicotyledonous plant, respectively), the *epicotyl* (or *plumule*) or that part of the main embryo axis above the point of attachment of the cotyledons, and the *hypocotyl* or that portion of the axis below the cotyledons, at whose lower end is the *radicle* or rudimentary root (Figure 16-16). The cotyledons are temporary leaves that function in the digestion, absorption, and storage of food from the endosperm thus making it available to the embryo before and at the time of seed germination.

The seeds of many species normally experience a period of rest or dormancy, usually during the winter, when growth and development of the embryo are at a standstill. It is during this stage of seed dormancy that the embryonic plant (in the form of the seed embryo or primitive sporophyte stage) is best able to withstand unfavorable environmental conditions. The biochemical or physiological mechanisms responsible for seed dormancy are not well understood. Once the dormancy period has passed or broken the occurrence of favorable external conditions such as available water and oxygen and suitable temperatures results in the resumption of growth and development of the embryo into a young sporophyte, a process known as *seed germination*. Some of the stages in the germination of the common bean *(Pha-*

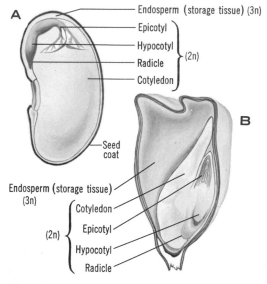

Figure 16-16. Structure of (A) the common bean seed (dicotyledon) and (B) a corn kernel, a fruit (monocotyledon).

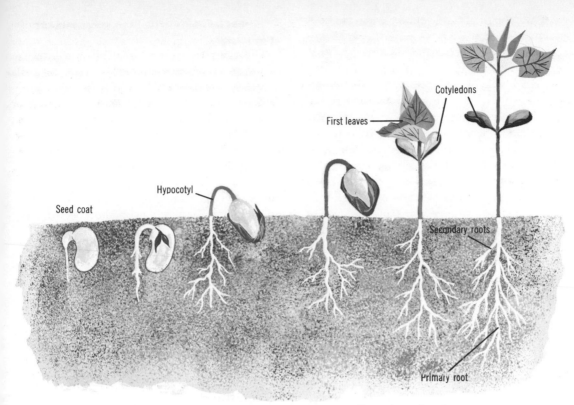

Figure 16-17. Some stages in the germination of the common bean *Phaseolus vulgaris*.

seolus vulgaris) are shown in Figure 16-17. If the cotyledons are raised above the ground during germination as in the common bean plant, they become green and carry out photosynthesis even before their food is exhausted. In other species the cotyledons may remain below the ground and therefore never carry on photosynthesis. The life cycle of an angiosperm is shown in Figure 16-18.

Anatomy of the Flowering Plant

The basic structural features of the various types of cells and tissues of flowering plants have already been described in Chapter 5. During the life of the flowering plant starting with the fertilized egg cell these various cells and tissues arise from the mitotic process, develop, and arrange themselves to form the plant body consisting of *stems* (and its branches),

roots, and *leaves*.

THE STEM. The plant stems of angiosperms are classified as either *woody* or *herbaceous*. Woody stems are usually covered with a layer of cork tissue and are tough and thick. They are characteristic of plants called *perennials* which live longer than two years. Herbaceous stems are generally soft, green, and thin, and are typical of plants that live for either one growing season (*annuals*) or two growing seasons (*biennials*). The woody plants are considered to be the more primitive, having appeared prior to the herbaceous ones in the course of evolution.

Stem Structure. General Features. In a typical woody flowering plant the mature tissues of the stem are essentially arranged as concentric cylinders around a central core of loosely packed, colorless parenchyma cells known as the *pith*. The pith often serves for storage, and in certain plants, may be completely ruptured during growth, resulting in a central hollow cavity. As seen in cross section (Figure 16-19) the pith is encircled by the multilayered xylem, also known as the *wood*, consisting of tracheids, vessels, fibers, and parenchyma. The xylem in turn is surrounded by a cylinder composed of a single layer of meristematic cells, the cambium, followed by several layers of phloem consisting of parenchyma, fibers, sieve tube cells, and companion cells. The proportions and arrangements of the various cell types composing the phloem vary in different plants. The xylem, cambium, and phloem

are collectively called the *conductive or vascular tissue.*

The xylem is largely involved in the transportation of water and dissolved mineral salts from the roots (where they are absorbed) to the other parts of the plant. The phloem appears to be the chief passageway for the transfer (or *translocation*, p. 414) of organic foods from the sites of their manufacture to regions of use and storage. The conductive tissues also function in support and protection and are without doubt the most complex in the entire plant. Depending on the species they are arranged in higher plants in the form of a cylinder or individual bundles which are con-

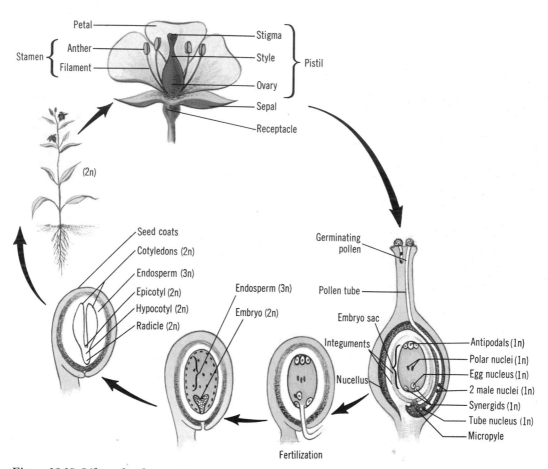

Figure 16-18. Life cycle of an angiosperm.

tinuous in the roots, stems, and branches. The outer zone (or cylinder) of parenchyma cells surrounding the phloem is called the *cortex*.

Xylem, Cambium, and Phloem. The xylem or wood derived from the apical meristems (growing points) is known as *primary xylem*, and is formed during the vertical growth of the stem as described hereafter. When derived from the cambium it is referred to as *secondary xylem*. Increase in diameter of the stem is accomplished by cell division of the cambium layer. Of the two cambium daughter cells that result, the inner one next to the xylem may develop and mature into a secondary xylem cell, whereas the outer daughter cells next to the phloem remain meristematic. The latter subsequently divide and the outer daughter cells may develop and mature into secondary phloem cells while the inner ones remain meristematic. In this manner the cambium layer gives rise to secondary xylem and secondary phloem (although not necessarily in an alternating order) and is always maintained between the two types of conductive tissue. Generally a greater quantity of secondary xylem is formed during the growing season than secondary phloem, so that the xylem, or wood, makes up the bulk of the stem. Except for the more peripheral layers close to the cambium, most of the trunk of older trees such as the maple, oak, or redwood consists of dead xylem or wood, composed largely of vessels

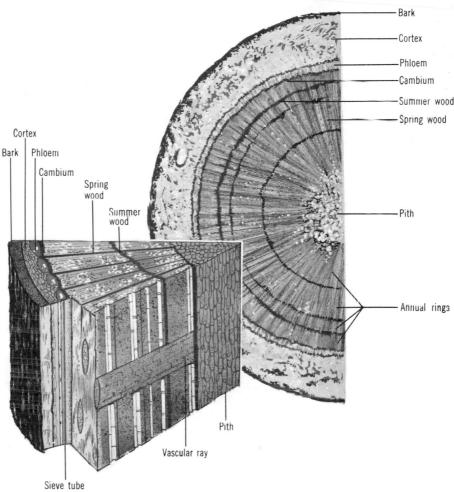

Figure 16-19. Diagram of cross-section of a woody stem.

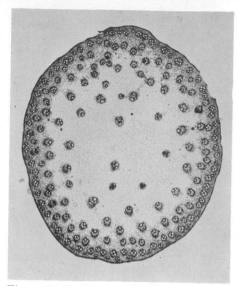

Figure 16-20. Photograph of a corn stem in cross-section showing numerous individual vascular bundles.

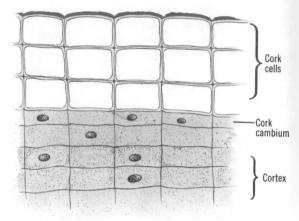

Figure 16-21. Cross-sectional view in woody stems of cortex, cork cambium, and cork.

and fibers. Commercial wood is almost exclusively secondary in nature.

In some species of herbaceous plants a cambium is present, whereas in others it is absent. In the former case the cambium is considerably less active than that of woody plants and is at times discontinuous. The net effect is the production of less secondary tissue, therefore accounting for less growth in diameter. In other instances, as in the stem of clover, the conductive tissue and cambium may be arranged in the form of isolated vascular bundles. The monocotyledonous plants (e.g., corn, wheat, and other grains and grasses), nearly all of which are herbaceous, possess no cambium tissue and therefore display no secondary growth. All their tissues are primary in origin, having developed initially from primary (or apical) meristematic cells. Their xylem and phloem are organized in individual vascular bundles dispersed through the stem (Figure 16-20).

Annual Rings. Since the spring is the most favorable part of the growing season, the cambial activity and the size of cells produced, especially of the xylem, is greatest at that time.

Thus they account for a relatively porous wood. With the progressively hotter and dryer weather of summer, cell size and the rate of division decrease, resulting in a relatively denser wood. Cell division of the cambium finally ceases with the coming of winter, and resumes again the following spring. In cross section these differences, especially between the dense wood of the summer and the porous wood of the following spring, are seen as alternating circles or rings of summer and spring wood. They reflect well-marked climatic seasons and are called *annual rings* (Figure 16-19). The youngest or most recently formed annual ring is located immediately inside the cambium.

Cortex, Cork, and Bark. Surrounding the phloem is a zone of tissue made up of several layers of loosely packed parenchyma cells, collectively called the *cortex*. It may also contain fibers either as dispersed cells, strands, or a continuous cylinder. In woody stems the cortex is surrounded by a meristematic cylinder of cells, the *cork cambium,* and finally by the cork itself (Figure 16-21). In these plants the aggregation of all the tissues encircling the cambium—phloem, cortex, cork cambium, and

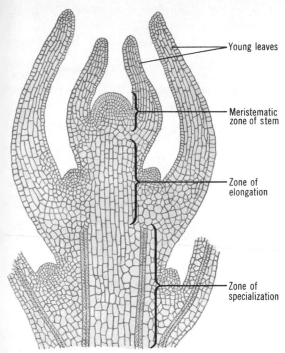

Figure 16-22. Diagram of longitudinal growth and differentiation in the stem tip.

Young leaves

Meristematic zone of stem

Zone of elongation

Zone of specialization

cork—are collectively called the *bark*. In young woody plants (before the appearance of cork tissue) and in most herbaceous plants, the cortex of the stem is covered with a continuous layer of living epidermal cells extending over the surface of the entire plant. In the older parts of roots and stems, however, which have experienced an increase in diameter as a result of cambial activity (i.e., in woody plants) the epidermis has been ruptured, sloughed off, and replaced by cork tissue.

Stem Growth. In most higher plants growth in stem length takes place principally at the tip where the apical meristem is located. Cell division of the meristematic tissue results in a movement upward of the apical region of daughter cells that are still meristematic. It leaves behind other daughter cells that mature and develop into the specialized cells of the stem. The youngest cells of the stem are therefore in the apical meristem whereas the progressively older cells are found in corre-

spondingly lower regions of the stem. In their conversion to specialized cells the daughter cells first become greatly enlarged and elongated, increasing at least 10 to 20 times the size of the meristematic cells. It accounts almost completely for the observed increase in stem length. This is followed by a process of maturation or differentiation in which some of the cells are ultimately converted into epidermal, parenchyma, conductive tissues, and so on. The sequence of changes which newly formed daughter cells undergo in the process of their transformation to mature specialized cells can be seen by proceeding downward along the stem. Thus starting at the tip of the stem and moving downward we see first the tip or *meristematic zone* followed by the *zone of elongation* and the *zone of specialization* (Figure 16-22). The zones are not sharply delineated but gradually blend into one another. The stem beneath the zone of specialization represents the fully formed mature region.

THE ROOT. *Root Structure.* The arrangement of tissues in the roots of flowering plants is essentially like that of the stem. There are, however, a number of differences. First, unlike most stems, roots have no pith. Second, the vascular or conductive tissue of the root is arranged in a somewhat different manner with the prominent xylem (for the most part vessels and tracheids) occupying the central core from which emanate a number of lateral extensions. In cross section, the xylem therefore looks like a star, or a wheel with the central core as the hub and the lateral extensions as the spokes (Figure 16-23). Parenchyma cells and phloem tissue occupy the spaces between the spokes with the cambium (when it is present as in the woody plants) separating the xylem from the phloem. Cambial division accounts for the growth in diameter of the root as it does in the stem. Third, the innermost parenchymal layer of the cortex enclosing the compactly packed conductive tissues and cambium is somewhat specialized. It is called the *endodermis* and consists largely of cells whose cell walls are moderately impregnated with the same waterproof material, suberin, characteristic of cork tissue. Fourth, at a particular region along the length of the root where absorption of water and dissolved mineral nutrients takes place, the epidermal cells covering the surface of the root possess delicate projections or extensions of cytoplasm called *root hairs*. The walls of the epidermal cells and root hairs usually lack a cuticle. The extensions may be almost a centimeter in length, are a continuous part of the epidermal cell, and may be present in high concentrations (thousands per square centimeter of root surface). They provide a tremendously increased area and are responsible for the absorption of water and dissolved nutrients from the soil, which is the main function of the root system. Studies of the root system of the rye plant have established that a single plant has 14 billion root hairs, representing a total area of more than 4000 square feet. The other principal roles of the roots in anchoring the plant and serving as food-storage organs are secondary to the role of absorption. Finally, the apical tip of the root is covered with a protective mass of cells called the *root cap*, discussed hereafter.

Root Growth. Growth in length of the root is very much like that already described for the stem but with a few added features. In addition to the usual *meristematic zone* at the tip followed by the *zone of elongation* and *zone of specialization*, the meristematic zone is covered by a thimble-shaped mass of cells called the *root cap* (Figure 16-24). Its obvious function is to protect the meristematic tip as the root pushes out among the soil particles in the course of growth. The zone of maturation more or less coincides with the region of epidermal root hairs (the active absorbing surface of the root). It may extend back several centimeters depending on the root and its rate of growth. As in the stem the increase in root length is largely the result of increase in cell size and cell number in the zone of elongation.

THE LEAF. *General Features.* The leaf is essentially a flattened and expanded portion of the stem. Its primary role is to carry on photosynthesis for which it is well suited in terms of structure and tissue arrangement. The typical leaf of a higher plant such as a dicotyledon (e.g., a bean leaf) consists of a broad, flattened *blade* which is usually attached to the stem or one of its branches by a stalk called the *petiole*. The petiole varies in length and is even absent

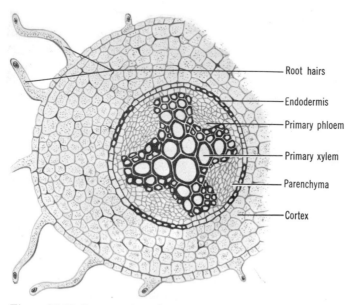

Root hairs

Endodermis

Primary phloem

Primary xylem

Parenchyma

Cortex

Figure 16-23. Cross-section of a root.

in some species. In cross section it is like a miniature stem consisting of small vascular bundles (generally lacking cambium), which at one end branch off from the vascular tissue of the stem. At the other end they connect to the principal vascular bundles of the blade in the form of the *midrib* or several large veins depending on the plant species. The vascular tissue of the midrib or the large veins in turn gives off numerous branches which grow smaller and smaller as they ramify through the leaf finally coming to an end. The veins may form a variety of patterns including a net-like design, a parallel venation, a palm-like effect, and so on depending on the species (Figure 16-13).

Leaf Structure. In cross section (Figure 16-25) the upper surface of the typical dicotyledenous leaf is covered with a single layer of colorless epidermal cells. On its outer side the epidermal cells are protected with the usual waxy, waterproof secretion of cutin which is practically impervious to such gases as oxygen, nitrogen, and carbon dioxide. Immediately below the epidermis is a densely packed layer of columnar parenchyma cells called the *palisade layer*, containing numerous chloroplasts. Beneath the palisade layer is a loose packing of chloroplast-containing parenchyma cells (interspersed with numerous intercellular spaces) collectively referred to as the *spongy* layer. The lower surface of the leaf like the upper surface is bounded by a layer of colorless epidermal cells which in most angiosperms are characteristically interspersed with numerous small specialized openings or pores.

Each pore, surrounded by two highly specialized and modified epidermal cells, the guard cells, is collectively called a *stoma* (plural, *stomata*) (Figure 16-25). Stomata may also occur (usually to a more limited extent) on the upper surface depending on the species. The guard cells are typically sausage-shaped, and usually contain a single chloroplast. In addition the portion of their cell wall bordering on the stomatal pore is considerably thickened,

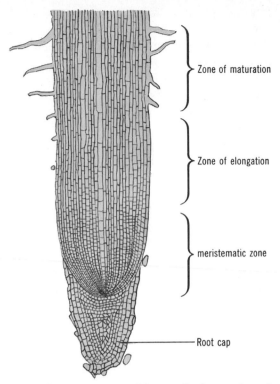

Figure 16-24. Diagram of longitudinal growth and differentiation in the root tip.

a significant feature which accounts in part for the ability of guard cells to regulate the size of the stomatal opening. The factors and possible mechanisms controlling stomatal pore size are discussed in the next chapter. The *maximal* size of the stomatal opening varies considerably according to the species of plant. It may range from as little as 20 square microns to as high as 400. Although these openings seem small they are really immense compared to the estimated size of oxygen, carbon dioxide, and water molecules. For example, calculations show that approximately 10,000 water molecules arranged in a single straight line occupy a distance of only 5μ. The number of stomata, like their size, also varies greatly. Measurements of stomatal distribution on the leaves of different plants range from as low as 1400 per sq cm (in the *Zebrina pendula*, the wandering jew) to more than 100,000 (in *Quercus coccinea*, the scarlet oak).

By connecting the intercellular spaces to the outside air the stomata have a key function in permitting the exchange of gases (oxygen, carbon dioxide, and water vapor) between the leaf and its environment. Thus by making possible the continuance of air from the outside through the pore to the interior of the leaf, they have an important influence on the rate of photosynthesis and the loss of water from plants as described in the next chapter.

The anatomy of the leaf is preeminently suited to the terrestrial photosynthesizing plant. It allows for maximal exposure to the light, in relationship to leaf volume, of the chloroplast-containing cells. Moreover, the loose, irregular arrangement of the cells constituting the spongy layer makes possible a large internal surface area, and thus permits a greater exchange of gases via the stomata between the cells and their environment.

Leaf Growth. In woody plants leaf buds form in the early fall from small masses of meristematic tissue. They open in the following spring and quickly develop to mature leaves. The transformation of the miniature leaf (from the leaf bud stage) to a mature leaf principally involves a general enlargement of most of the cells of the blade. The contribution to growth by cell division is relatively minor contrary to the situation in the stem and root as discussed earlier. Although the stem and root continue to grow as long as the plant is alive, the growth of the leaf is limited. It reaches a particular size, functions for one or a few seasons depending on the species, and then falls away by the process of *abcission* described in the next chapter.

EVOLUTIONARY TRENDS IN THE PLANT KINGDOM

Evolution of Sexual Reproduction and Alternation of Generations in Plants

The probable course of the evolution of sexual reproduction and alternation of generations in plants is reflected in a survey of the living plants of the plant kingdom. We have already indicated in the previous chapter that sexual reproduction presumably originated in some ancient green algae by the adaptive

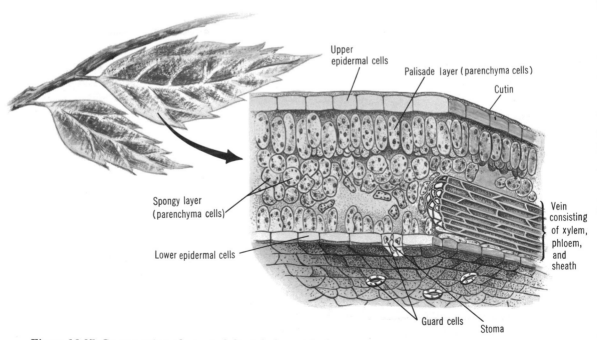

Figure 16-25. Cross-section of a typical dicotyledonous leaf.

transformation of zoospores to similar gametes. Sexual reproduction by the fusion of like gametes (as in *Ulothrix*, p. 351) is believed to have been followed by the development of sexual reproduction involving the fusion of unlike gametes as well as the formation of male and female sex organs as in *Oedogonium* (p. 351). In these forms it can be considered that an alternation of generations exists, the haploid filament representing the dominant gametophyte generation and the diploid zygote the sporophyte generation.

As we proceed to the more advanced multicellular forms of the plant kingdom, the alternation of generations at first becomes more definite as in the bryophytes; and then increasingly less so as we approach the more advanced terrestrial plants until it is barely discernible in the angiosperms. At the same time the gametophyte generation has become smaller, less dominant, and less independent whereas the sporophyte has become larger, dominant, and more independent (Figure 16-26). The gametophyte generation as the dominant generation in lower plant forms is best suited for aquatic life, whereas the sporophyte which attains its greatest and most progressive development in the advanced terrestrial plant forms is best adapted for an existence on land.

In the alternation of generations of all green land plants there must be at least one mitotic division between meiosis and fertilization (i.e., during the gametophyte stage); and at least one mitotic division between fertilization and meiosis (i.e., during the sporophyte stage).

2n

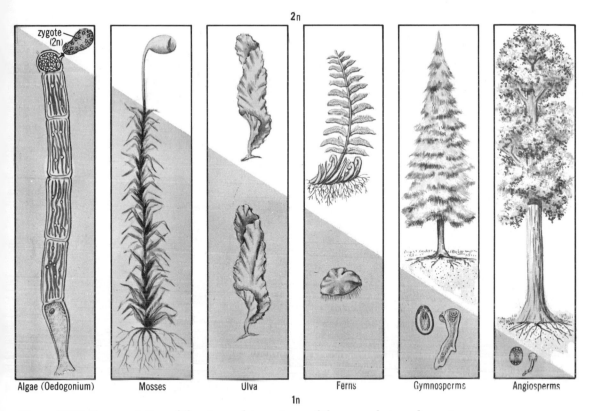

zygote (2n)

Algae (Oedogonium)   Mosses   Ulva   Ferns   Gymnosperms   Angiosperms

1n

Figure 16-26. Representation of the size and importance of the sporophyte and gametophyte generations in the plant kingdom. As we proceed to more advanced multicellular plants, the sporophyte becomes larger, dominant, and more independent, whereas the gametophyte becomes smaller, less dominant, and less independent.

In other words alternation of generations in terrestrial plants involves *two multicellular stages*, namely a *multicellular gametophyte* and a *multicellular sporophyte*.

Alternation of generations is a universal occurrence in all species of the Embryophyta and is found frequently among the algae and fungi. This fact alone would suggest that it is a phenomenon of some evolutionary significance. In this regard a favored current interpretation proposes that alternation of generations combines the genetically less stable (and therefore more readily varied) properties of the gametophyte generation with the relative genetic stability of the sporophyte generation.

The diploid sporophyte generation reproduces by forming haploid spores which represent a large variety of different genetic make-ups as a result of meiosis. The spores develop into haploid gametophytes whose different genetic combinations are now subjected to the inevitable testing or selection processes of the environment: the gametophytes that are best adapted by virtue of their genetic composition to cope with existing environmental conditions will have a better chance of reaching maturity than those not as well endowed. Thus by favoring survival of gametophytes best suited to the given environment there is in effect a natural selection for those gene combinations that have proved to be superior.

The subsequent formation of the sporophyte generation by fertilization of gametes (from gametophytes that have attained maturity) allows for the recombination of the remaining gene groups, in general those that have proved to be more advantageous for survival. Spore formation by the sporophyte generation again leads to a great variety of spores with different genetic make-ups to complete the cycle. If the environment should change, other appropriate genes would be favored.

The sporophyte generation, of course, is also subjected to the selection pressures of the environment, but is more stable than the gametophyte by virtue of its diploid genetic composition. In general the haploid gametophyte can be varied more readily than the diploid sporophyte since its expression of characteristics depend on unpaired genes as compared to paired genes in the sporophyte. Thus the gametophyte generation permits a more rapid adaptation to the changing environment and therefore a more rapid rate of evolution. By contrast the sporophyte generation provides a greater measure of evolutionary stability. In this manner the phenomenon of alteration of generations confers the evolutionary advantages of both the gametophyte and sporophyte generations upon the species.

Overall Relationships in the Plant Kingdom

The probable evolutionary progression and relationships among the various groups in the plant kingdom are summarized in Figure 16-27. The earliest and most primitive plants were probably unicellular, nonphotosynthetic bacteria-like organisms. They must have evolved to the various groups of algae and higher fungi of the present-day subkingdom *Thallophyta*. This evolutionary development presumably included a transformation from simple, undifferentiated protoplasts to highly specialized protoplasts with nuclei and other organized subcellular structures.

The main evolutionary transition to higher plants from the thallophytes is believed to have occurred by way of an ancient green algae to a now-extinct psilophytales stock. The bryophytes and present-day green algae are generally considered to be independent offshoots of the ancient green algae, and were probably not involved as connecting links between the thallophytes and the main line of evolution of higher plants. The psilophytales are thought to have given rise to the various lines composing the present-day Embryophyta. The modern seed plants as represented by the gymnosperms and angiosperms supposedly originated from certain ancient ferns and evolved separately and independently of one another along parallel lines. The present view is that the angiosperms did not arise from a

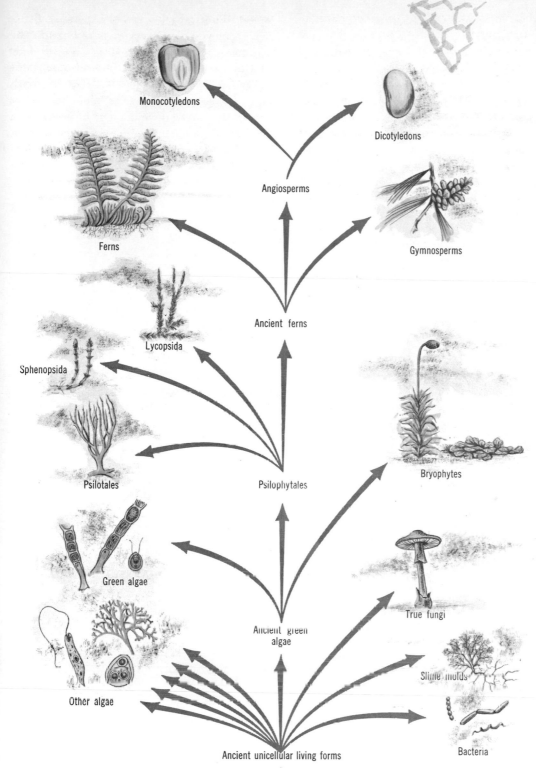

Figure 16-27. Probable evolutionary relationships within the plant kingdom.

primitive line of gymnosperms. Within the angiosperms themselves the monocotyledonous plants are regarded as an evolutionary offshoot from a dicotyledonous ancestor.

The evolution of terrestrial plants from an aqueous existence was accompanied by the progressive differentiation of various types of tissues that assured successful conquest of the land. This included the development of structures: (1) to control water loss (the impervious waxy cuticle and the stomata), (2) to transport water salts and other substances (the vascular tissue), (3) to support the plant in air (fibers in the vascular tissues), (4) to absorb effectively water and salts from the environment (root system), (5) to absorb light effectively (the leaf), and (6) to carry on reproduction and early development independently of free water. The latter has been attained by the evolutionary development of highly specialized reproductive branches (cones and flowers), pollen tubes and seeds in the seed plants, and the predominant sporophyte accompanied by the corresponding decrease in size and complexity of the gametophyte generation.

SUPPLEMENTARY REFERENCES

Bold, H. C., *The Plant Kingdom*, Prentice-Hall, Englewood Cliffs, N.J., 1960.
Foster, A. S., and E. M. Gifford, Jr., *Comparative Morphology of Vascular Plants*, Freeman, San Francisco, 1959.
Fuller, H. J., and O. Tippo, *College Botany*, revised edition, Holt, New York, 1954.
Lawrence, G. H. M., *Taxonomy of Vascular Plants*, Macmillan, New York, 1951.
Robbins, W. W., T. E. Weier, and C. R. Stocking, *Botany*, third edition, Wiley, New York, 1964.
Sporne, K. R., "The Phylogenetic Classification of the Angiosperms," *Biological Reviews*, February 1956.
Wilson, C. L., and W. E. Loomis, *Botany*, revised edition, Dryden Press, New York, 1957.

Chapter 17   Plant Kingdom:

Physiology and Biochemistry

of Flowering Plants

The angiosperms, representing the most advanced form of evolutionary development attained thus far by plants, are the dominant and economically most important class within the entire plant kingdom. From both the fundamental and practical standpoints we know more about the details of their structure and function than of any other plant group.

The basic anatomical features of the angiosperms ranging from the subcellular level to the complex organization of the whole plant have already been described in Chapters 4, 5, and 16. The same biochemical principles and similar metabolic pathways (described in Chapters 7-9) including respiration and protein and nucleic-acid metabolism (Chapter 11) apply in general to the flowering plants. The present chapter will deal mostly with the physiology and biochemistry of flowering plants.

PHOTOSYNTHESIS

General Significance

Photosynthesis is the biological process by which green plants are able to utilize the energy of sunlight to convert carbon dioxide and water to the higher energy carbon-hydrogen bonds of organic compounds such as carbohydrates, fats, and proteins. Molecular oxygen is liberated as one of the products.

Some of the overall biochemical aspects of the photosynthetic process have already been outlined in Chapter 8. All organisms by means of the respiratory process cleave and transfer hydrogen from these higher energy-containing organic compounds to yield lower energy-containing substances with the concomitant release of energy for use by the living cell. The overall energy pattern in the biological world therefore consists of (1) a transformation of the light energy of the sun by photosynthesis to the chemical form represented by the carbon-hydrogen bonds of carbohydrates and other organic compounds; and (2) its ultimate utilization and final dissipation by the activities of living cells. Sunlight therefore is the primary source of energy for nearly all living things (Chapter 6 and 10).

Approximately 80 per cent or more of the total photosynthesis on our planet occurs in the oceans. It has been estimated that each year about 150 billion tons of carbon dioxide and 60 billion tons of water enter into the photosynthetic process of our planet to produce about 110 billion tons of molecular oxygen and some 100 billion tons of organic matter (expressed as glucose). Sizable fractions of this organic material are used in respiration and other life activities of the plants themselves, whereas only a minute fraction is actually consumed as food by animals. By far the greatest portion is decomposed or decayed to carbon dioxide, water, and mineral salts through the action of microorganisms. The cessation of decay in the distant past under certain geologic and climatic conditions and the subsequent accumulation of partially decomposed plant material under great pressures of rock and earth for millions of years resulted in the formation of peat and coal.

Historical Development

Like most areas in science the beginnings of our knowledge of photosynthesis have been slow and painful, occurring at a relatively late date in the history of man. At the time of Columbus' discovery of America in 1492, nothing was known of the process.

By the date of the landing of the Pilgrims, 1662, the first principal progress in our knowledge of photosynthesis had finally been made. It was provided in an experiment classic for its simplicity and incisiveness by the Belgian physician and naturalist Van Helmont during the seventeenth century. He demonstrated that only a few ounces of soil were removed during the growth of a young willow tree from a weight of five pounds to almost 200 pounds in a tub of soil over a period of five years. The increase in plant growth obviously was not due to an equivalent removal of material from the soil (which was contrary to the accepted beliefs of that period). Instead it could be attributed almost entirely to nutrients provided by the air and water. We now know, of course, that the organic material, which composes nearly all of the dry weight of plants, arises from carbon dioxide and water.

The next major advance occurred a hundred years later in 1772 when Priestley announced his remarkable finding that green plants could restore air which had "been injured by the burning of a candle." Seven years later Ingenhousz, Dutch physician to the Austrian empress, reported that this restoration of "bad air" depended on the sunlight and was carried out only by the green parts of the plant.

In 1782 Senebier in Switzerland observed that the presence of another gas which we now know to be carbon dioxide was necessary for the purification of air by green plants in sunlight. By 1796 Ingenhousz had deduced that carbon dioxide was a reactant in the photosynthetic process and O_2 a product. Eight years later in 1804 de Saussure, also in Switzerland, concluded from his quantitative measurements of carbon dioxide uptake, oxygen production, and dry-weight increase that water also must be involved in photosynthesis. In addition he observed that in the dark green plants carry on respiration like animals, producing carbon dioxide and water from organic matter and oxygen. Thus by the early 1800's the general overall chemical equation of the photosynthetic process had been discerned except for the recognition of carbohydrates as the organic product. By 1850, about ten years before the start of the American Civil War, carbohydrates were definitely established as one of the organic products of photosynthesis.

The green pigment of plants was named chlorophyll in 1819, and its key role in the absorption of light for photosynthesis was conclusively shown by the work of Engelmann in 1880. The recognition of photosynthesis in its more fundamental terms as a biological process for converting the energy of light into a chemical form was made in Germany by von Mayer, the discoverer of the law of the conservation of energy. During the years 1910 to 1940 the magnificent studies of Willstätter and Hans Fischer in Germany elucidated the chemical structure of the chlorophylls. In 1960 the first reported synthesis of chlorophyll in the chemical laboratory was announced by Woodward of Harvard.

One of the most significant findings relating to the steps of the photosynthetic process was reported in 1905 by the British plant physiologist Blackman, who first showed that the photosynthetic process consists of at least two successive series of events, a *light reaction* followed by a *dark reaction*. The physiology and biochemistry of the light and dark reactions are described in later sections of the chapter.

Innumerable studies of photosynthesis have been continued since Blackman's contribution. Several major breakthroughs in our understanding of this process from the viewpoint of the biochemical steps and mechanisms have occurred since the end of World War II.

Physiology of Photosynthesis

SITE OF OCCURRENCE AND EXCHANGE OF GASES. In all plants with the exception of the blue-green algae photosynthesis is confined to the chloroplasts which are made up of *grana* (p. 62), consisting of highly organized layers of chlorophyll, protein, and lipid molecules. Studies with isolated chloroplasts in a completely cell-free system have demonstrated that the entire process of photosynthesis can take place within the chloroplasts themselves starting with carbon dioxide, water, and light to produce carbohydrates and molecular oxygen.

The anatomy of the leaves of angiosperms (Figure 16-25) provides several advantages to the photosynthesizing plant. First, it permits maximal exposure of many of the chloroplast-containing cells to the light as compared to the leaf volume. And second, it is responsible, by virtue of the loose, irregular structure of the spongy cells, for a large internal surface area in contact with the external environment. Thus it furnishes an extensive carbon dioxide absorbing area for the photosynthetic process.

SIZE OF THE STOMATAL APERTURE. The structure and distribution of the stomata, which serve to connect the intercellular spaces of the leaf with the outside air, have been discussed in Chapter 16. The main function of the stomata is to permit the exchange of gases (carbon dioxide, oxygen, and water vapor, which is the gaseous form of water) to occur between the leaf and its environment. The size of the stomatal openings therefore influences the photosynthetic rate by controlling the rate of gas exchange (i.e., CO_2, O_2, and H_2O) between the plant and its environment. During the evening and often during the warmest part of a summer day, the stomata are entirely closed resulting in a greatly decreased exchange of gases between the leaf and its environment. It is usually during the first half of the day and the late afternoon that the stomata are open allowing for an exchange of gases (by the diffusion process) and an appreciable rate of photosynthesis.

The stomatal aperture is primarily determined at any given time by the turgor of the guard cells. In many guard cells the cell wall bordering on the stomatal pore is considerably thicker than the other portions of the cell wall (Figure 17-1). An increase in turgor causes a greater expansion of the thinner portions of the cell wall than of the thicker portions, causing the latter to assume a concave shape similar to that of a sausage. This effect is illustrated by inflating a cylindrical balloon which has been made thicker on one side by use of rubber patching. Upon inflation it will assume a sausage shape which increases in its degree of curvature with greater internal pressure or turgor resulting in a larger stomatal aperture.

What are the factors that determine the turgidity of the guard cells and therefore the degree of opening of the stomata? In most in-

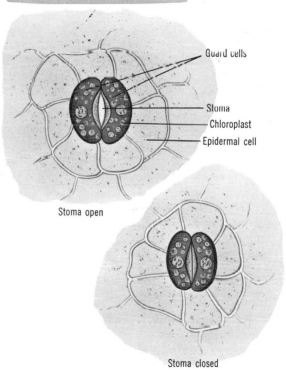

Figure 17-1. Effect of cell wall thickness under conditions of increased turgor in determining the shape of the guard cell and therefore the size of the stomatal aperture.

stances stomata open in the light and close in the dark. A number of mechanisms probably operate to make this phenomenon possible and several theories have been proposed. One of the more favored viewpoints is that exposure to light causes an increase in osmotic concentration within the chloroplast-containing guard cells as a result of photosynthesis. The higher osmotic concentration promotes a net movement of water into the guard cells and therefore an increase in their turgor, causing an increased opening of the stomata. A proposed mechanism is that photosynthesis, by favoring a net removal of carbon dioxide and therefore decreasing the concentration of carbonic acid (p. 131), causes a rise in pH. The increased pH in turn exerts a definite influence in converting starch to many molecules of glucose-1-phosphate by shifting the equilibrium of the phosphorylase reaction towards the glucose-1-phosphate. The net effect is a considerably increased osmotic concentration.

$$\text{Starch + Phosphate} \underset{}{\overset{\text{Phosphorylase}}{\rightleftharpoons}} \text{Glucose-1-phosphate}$$

The closing of the stomatal opening during the heat of a summer's day is attributed to the insufficient water present in the plant at the time. The greatest loss of water from higher plants takes place through the stomata by a process of evaporation called *transpiration* (p. 412). By early afternoon of a bright summer day a plant is usually losing water at a faster rate through transpiration than it is gaining by absorption through its roots. The guard cells under these circumstances do not have sufficient water to maintain their turgor resulting in a closing of the stomatal pores. Thus the photosynthetic rate is markedly decreased because of limted gas exchange (i.e., limited carbon-dioxide concentration) as well as a limited availability of water. Other factors undoubtedly contribute to the mechanism of stomatal opening and closing. Further investigations in this area are necessary to explain more fully the important physiological phenomenon of control and periodicity of stomatal aperture.

RELATIONSHIP OF LIGHT AND PIGMENTS IN PHOTOSYNTHESIS. *The Nature of Light.* Light as a form of energy is considered to be emitted as distinct "packets" of waves or as particles (called photons). These two viewpoints, known as the *wave theory* and *photon theory* respectively, are used collectively because they explain many of the properties of light which cannot be accounted for by either theory alone. According to the wave theory white light is made up of a mixture of light of different colors, or wavelengths as demonstrated by its resolution into a spectrum of colors through dispersion by a prism (Figure 17-2). Each of the colors corresponds to a different wavelength or range of wavelengths of light. Visible light, namely that which we can detect with our eyes, is really only a small portion of the broader physical phenomenon of radiant energy. The red-colored end of the visible spectrum is made up of longer wavelengths which become progressively smaller as we move to the opposite (violet) end of the visible spectrum. Beyond the visible red end (longer wavelength) of the radiant energy spectrum are the longer invisible *infrared* or heat waves and the even longer electric waves used in radio transmission. In the opposite direction beyond the shorter violet end of the visible spectrum are the shorter invisible ultraviolet waves followed successively by the X-rays, the gamma rays emitted by radioactive elements, and finally by the shortest of all, the cosmic rays, emitted from outer space. The major components of the spectrum of radiant energy are quantitatively expressed in terms of their wavelengths, which is the distance between the two successive crests of a wave.

The wavelengths of visible light range from about 400 mμ (violet color) to about 700 mμ (red color). The sunlight which reaches the earth's surface, ranges from about 300 mμ in the invisible X-ray region through the visible region to about 2600 mμ in the invisible infrared region.

The energy possessed by a photon is collectively called a *quantum* and may be expressed

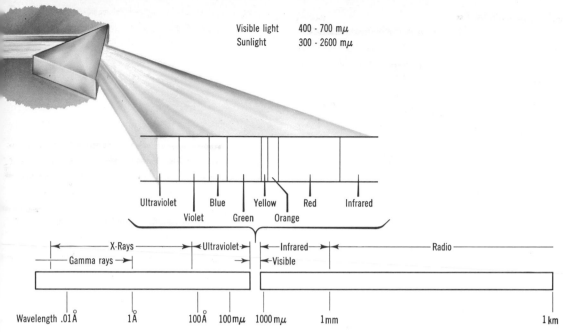

Visible light	400 - 700 mμ
Sunlight	300 - 2600 mμ

Figure 17-2. Diagram of the radiant energy spectrum showing the position of visible light and its resolution by a prism into its different component light wavelengths or colors.

in standard energy terms such as calories. The energy contained by a photon is inversely proportional to wavelengths which means that the smaller the wavelength, the greater the energy per photon. The energy value of a quantum of red light therefore is less than that of violet light. A quantum of X-ray radiation with a wavelength of 200 mμ, for example, has five times the energy of the longer infrared radiation with a wavelength of 1000 mμ.

Light Absorption and the Photosynthetic Pigments. All the evidence to date indicates that the chlorophylls participate directly in photosynthesis by absorbing certain visible wavelengths of radiant energy. The most effective wavelengths for photosynthesis are the red and the blue. A good deal of the green component of the visible light which strikes a leaf is not used in photosynthesis, because green light is not absorbed. This is indicated by the fact that the leaf is green.

The yellow and orange carotenoid pigments, consisting of the carotenes and xanthophylls (derivatives of vitamin A) are universally present in chloroplasts. They also appear to function as absorbers of light for the photosynthetic process, at least in several algae. Similarly, some of the unique pigments associated with certain algae such as the blue pigment phycocyanin of the blue-green algae (and some red algae), the brown pigment fucoxanthin of the brown algae, and the red pigment phycoerythrin of the red algae (and some blue-green algae) also seem to function as light absorbers in the photosynthetic process. However, they are unable to substitute completely for chlorophyll in its vital photosynthetic role. No plants have yet been found which can carry on photosynthesis without possessing at least one of the chlorophyll pigments.

The chemistry and distribution of the chlorophylls have been described in Chapter 7. The chlorophylls like all other organic constituents of plants are synthesized by specialized enzymatic mechanisms within the plant itself. Any impairment in the biosynthesis of the chlorophylls manifests itself as an abnormal pale green color of the leaves, a symptom which is called *chlorosis*. Our present knowledge of the conditions affecting chlorophyll biosynthesis indicates an interplay of several important factors. These include: (*a*) *genetic factors*; (*b*) *light* itself which appears to be essential for chlorophyll formation in many higher plants; (*c*) *magnesium* and *nitrogen*, since these atoms are part of the structure of the chlorophylls; (*d*) *iron*, *zinc*, *copper*, and *manganese*, a deficiency of any of these metals resulting in a characteristic chlorosis of the leaves; and (*e*) other factors such as an *adequate oxygen and water supply* and a *suitable temperature* range.

PHYSIOLOGY OF THE LIGHT AND DARK REACTIONS. The British plant physiologist Blackman in the early twentieth century employed flashing light as a means of exposing plants to short alternating periods of light and dark. He observed that the rate of photosynthesis at continuous high light intensities was the same as in flashing light when the light period of a few fractions of a second duration was alternately followed by a dark period of an equally short time interval. It was only by considerably increasing the relative length of the dark interval that he could decrease the rate of photosynthesis. He also showed that under normal conditions of light intensity, a rise in temperature caused a striking increase in the photosynthetic rate. Such observations suggested that the reaction during the dark interval, which is markedly influenced by temperature, is considerably slower than the preceding light reaction. It was from experiments of this type that Blackman concluded photosynthesis consisted of at least two phases: a rapid *light reaction* followed by a slower series of light-dependent steps called the *dark reaction*.

The dark reaction is directly unaffected by light although it depends on the products of the preceding light reaction for its activity and is markedly influenced by temperature. Stated in another way the dark reaction is the *rate-limiting reaction* or the "bottleneck" which determines the overall rate of photosynthesis, for a process can go no faster than the slowest rate of any step in its chain of events. The biochemical steps of the light and dark reactions are discussed in a later section of the chapter.

EFFECT OF CARBON DIOXIDE ON PHOTOSYNTHESIS. Carbon dioxide as one of the three primary reactants of photosynthesis (the others being water and light) is usually the factor that most often controls or limits the rate of photosynthesis under normal field conditions. A rise in concentration of carbon dioxide in the atmosphere (which averages about 0.04 per cent) is usually accompanied by a corresponding increase in the rate of photosynthesis. If the concentration of carbon dioxide is doubled (and this can be readily accomplished in a green house), then the rate of photosynthesis will be doubled, all other factors being equal. Thus an increase in the concentration of the most limiting factor (in this case the concentration of carbon dioxide) causes an increase in the photosynthetic rate until some other factor, perhaps light or water, in turn becomes limiting.

PRODUCTS OF PHOTOSYNTHESIS. Molecular oxygen and carbohydrates are the major products of photosynthesis. The evidence that the oxygen liberated arises solely from the water is described in a later section of the chapter. The oxygen diffuses out of the photosynthesizing leaf cells of higher plants into the intercellular spaces and then through the stomatal openings into the surrounding air. A portion of the oxygen released by the photosynthesizing chloroplasts may be used directly by the plant cells for respiration. During the day the average rate of photosynthesis by most plants far exceeds the rate of aerobic respiration, so that there is a net release of molecular oxygen to the atmosphere by these plants.

The most common carbohydrates that accumulate in leaf cells as a result of the photsynthetic process are starch and certain other polysaccharides. This is determined by sev-

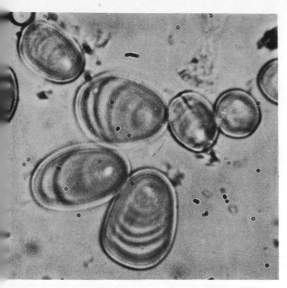

Figure 17-3. Starch granules from a potato tuber as seen in the light microscope. Magnification, 1400X. (*Courtesy of Dr. M. S. Buttrose, J. Cell. Biol.*)

eral factors, the most important being genetic as indicated by differences among plant species. Frequently, nonphotosynthesizing colorless plant cells such as those of the potato tuber will accumulate carbohydrates largely in the form of starch granules suspended in the cytoplasm (Figure 17-3). The starch is synthesized from sugars that were formed and transported from other parts of the plant.

EFFICIENCY OF PHOTOSYNTHESIS. We know that the oxidation by the respiratory process (or by any other means) of a gram-molecular weight or mole of glucose to carbon dioxide and water causes the release of 686,000 small calories (p. 189). Therefore the overall reverse process, photosynthesis, must result in the capturing of an identical amount of energy in the carbon-hydrogen bonds of a mole of glucose that has been formed.

Does a single quantum of red light (wavelength, 600 mμ), which is the most effective in photosynthesis, furnish sufficient energy in the photosynthetic process to transform a molecule of carbon dioxide to the higher-energy carbon-hydrogen bond present in the glucose molecule? In other words can 6 quanta of light provide enough energy to transform 6 molecules of carbon dioxide into a molecule of glucose in the course of photosynthesis? The answer is no, because a mole equivalent of quanta of red light possesses 40,000 calories and 6 of these would only provide 6 × 40,000 or 240,000 of the 686,000 calories present in the chemical bonds of a mole of glucose. At the very least, three times this number of quanta, namely 18 quanta equivalents per 6 moles of carbon dioxide or 3 quanta equivalents per mole of carbon dioxide, are needed. This, however, would assume an efficiency of light utilization close to 100 per cent. Actual measurements by various investigators have yielded conflicting data. The plant physiologist usually expresses the efficiency of photosynthesis in terms of the number of quanta of red light (since it is the most effective in photosynthesis) needed to convert a molecule of CO_2 to the level of carbohydrates. This is called the *quantum requirement* and has been reported to range from four (i.e., 75 per cent efficiency) to 10 (i.e., 30 per cent efficiency).

The total amount of radiant energy which annually reaches the earth's surface has been estimated to be of the order of 5×10^{20} large calories. Approximately only 1 per cent of this energy, about 5×10^{18} large calories, is transformed by the photosynthesis of the earth's green plants to the chemical energy of carbon-hydrogen bonds. Of this 80 per cent or more is actually carried out by the photosynthesizing organisms in the oceans.

Biochemistry of Photosynthesis

The biochemical approach especially at the enzymatic level has proved to be a powerful tool in unraveling several basic features and detailed mechanisms of photosynthesis. Certain broad aspects of the biochemistry of photosynthesis including its comparative features and general relationships to respiration, chemosynthesis, and nutrition have been discussed in Chapters 8, 9, and 10.

It has already been noted that the physiological evidence obtained in the early 1900's by Blackman working with intact plants showed photosynthesis to consist of two successive events, a reaction(s) dependent on light, the *light reaction* or *light phase*, followed by a series of nonlight-requiring reactions called the *dark reaction* or *dark phase*. We now know as a result of extensive biochemical investigations that the photosynthetic reactions constituting the *light phase* provide both the reducing power (as TPNH) and energy (as ATP) for the conversion of carbon dioxide to the level of carbohydrates; and that the subsequently occurring *dark phase* consists of the several enzymatic reactions by which carbon dioxide is ultimately transformed to carbohydrates.

THE LIGHT PHASE. *The Hill Reaction.* In 1937 the English biologist Dr. Robin Hill observed that cell-free suspensions of chloroplasts liberated oxygen in the presence of light without the apparent participation of carbon dioxide. His work demonstrated that photosynthesis could be fragmented into some of its component reactions. It also supported the view that the molecular oxygen released in photosynthesis originated from water, since carbon dioxide was not involved. In order for this biochemical reaction (now known as the *Hill reaction*) to occur appreciably a suitable acceptor of hydrogens or electrons such as ferric ions (Fe^{3+}) must be added:

$$2H_2O + 4Fe^{3+} \xrightarrow[\text{chloroplasts}]{\text{Light}} 4Fe^{2+} + 4H^+ + O_2$$

The 1950's witnessed the important finding that the pyridine nucleotide coenzyme TPN could also serve as an acceptor of hydrogens or electrons in the Hill reaction.

$$2H_2O + 2TPN^+ \longrightarrow 2TPNH + 2H^+ + O_2$$

The Hill reaction does not consist of a single step as the preceding equation might suggest. Instead, it represents an initial series of photosynthetic reactions involving the cleavage of water by radiant energy to yield molecular oxygen and reducing power in terms of hydrogens or electrons.

Cyclic and Noncyclic Photosynthetic Photophosphorylation. The highly significant discovery in 1954 that isolated chloroplasts upon exposure to light were also able to phosphorylate ADP to ATP represented another major advance in the elucidation of the photosynthetic mechanisms. Since that time numerous studies have led to the following present-day concept, although still incomplete, of the biochemical events composing the light phase in photosynthesis.

Photosynthesis is initiated through the absorption of the energy of light by chlorophyll in the chloroplasts. This is considered to be the primary photochemical act of photosynthesis (all other subsequent reactions of the photosynthetic process may take place in the dark). As a result, the chlorophyll of the illuminated chloroplasts is converted to a higher energy or "excited" state.

On the basis of modern physicochemical theory the "excited" chlorophyll molecules resulting from the absorption of light have had some of their electrons raised from their normal energy state to a higher energy level. They are probably very powerful reducing agents compared to unexcited chlorophyll molecules. Although the precise nature of the primary photochemical act which ultimately provides chemical energy (ATP) and reducing power (TPNH) is still largely a matter of speculation, the latest evidence indicates, as we shall soon see, that two types of chlorophyll are involved. It is believed that the "higher energy electrons," by means of certain postulated pathways within the chloroplasts, may ultimately be (*a*) returned to chlorophyll with the concomitant formation of ATP, a process referred to as *cyclic photophosphorylation,* or (*b*) transferred to TPN to form TPNH also accompanied by ATP synthesis by a process known as *noncyclic photophosphorylation.*

In the *cyclic photophosphorylation* pathway it is postulated that a stepwise transfer occurs of the "higher energy" electrons on a "downhill" energy path to their original state in chlorophyll. It results in the release of their

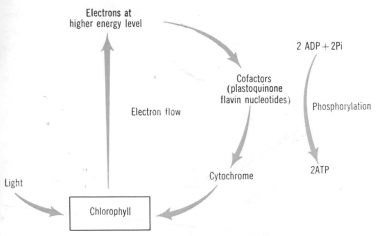

Figure 17-4. Schematic representation of cyclic photophosphorylation. See text for details.

extra energy to form ATP from ADP and inorganic phosphate. Several cofactors, including cytochrome, flavin nucleotides and possibly a substance related to coenzyme Q called *plastoquinone*, are believed to participate as electron carriers (Figure 17-4).

The cycle is completed when the electron returns to the chlorophyll molecule. A portion of the energy which is relased along the way is captured and converted to ATP with an estimated efficiency of two ATP's formed per electron transferred. The sequence proposed in Figure 17-4, therefore, represents a mechanism by which solar energy is transformed to the more biologically utilizable form of ATP. It differs from the coupled phosphorylation which accompanies terminal electron transport in mitochondria (p. 189) in several ways. ATP formation by illuminated chloroplasts occurs (1) at the expense of absorbed light energy, (2) without the consumption of molecular oxygen, and (3) without the addition of a chemical substrate to provide free energy.

The *noncyclic photophosphorylation pathway* of photosynthesis also converts light energy to ATP. In addition the pathway fulfills the second major requirement for the photosynthetic assimilation of carbon dioxide to the level of carbohydrates by producing *reducing power* in the form of TPNH. The pathway is a modified version of the Hill reaction and involves the reduction by illuminated chloroplasts of TPN to TPNH with the concomitant formation of ATP from ADP and inorganic phosphate. Water is the ultimate source of hydrogens or electrons in this biological photo-reduction of TPN to TPNH. The process also involves the release of an equivalent amount of molecular oxygen from the water molecules (Figure 17-5).

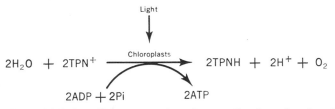

$$2H_2O \;+\; 2TPN^+ \xrightarrow[\substack{\text{Chloroplasts} \\ 2ADP + 2Pi \quad 2ATP}]{\text{Light}} 2TPNH \;+\; 2H^+ \;+\; O_2$$

Figure 17-5. Overall representation of noncyclic photophosphorylation.

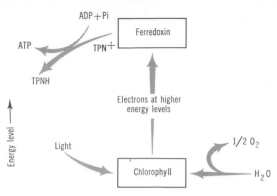

Figure 17-6. Detailed representation of noncyclic photophosphorylation. See text for details.

Our knowledge is still quite incomplete as to the intermediates, coenzymes, and biochemical events participating in the sequence of electron transfer from water to TPN within the highly organized chloroplasts. A newly discovered iron-containing protein called *ferredoxin* is now thought to be involved. One of the proposals for *noncyclic photophosphorylation* postulates a pathway whereby the higher energy electrons of "excited" chlorophyll molecules resulting from the absorption of light are transferred first to ferredoxin and then to TPN instead of returning to the chlorophyll molecules. Water molecules are believed to serve as the electron donor to reduce the "excited" or oxidized chlorophyll molecules with the concomitant liberation of molecular oxygen. Thus the "excited" or oxidized chlorophyll molecules are restored to their original state to be used again in the photosynthetic process with water acting as the primary electron source. In effect the absorption of light by chlorophyll raises the reducing power of water to a sufficiently high level so that its hydrogens or electrons can function as electron donors in the reduction of TPN to TPNH (figure 17-6).

The most recent evidence now indicates that in order for photosynthesis to occur, the two types of chlorophyll pigments in the higher green plants must absorb light. Chlorophyll *b* is "excited" by absorbing light quanta in the red region (about 660 mμ) of the spectrum and chlorophyll *a* by absorbing in the far red region (about 700 mμ). It is believed that each pigment activates a separate photochemical reaction which works in series with the other and is essential to the overall photosynthetic process.

In one such scheme suggested by Dr. D. I. Arnon of the University of California, it is postulated that the first main photochemical reaction involves the absorption of red light by chlorophyll *b*. Electrons are accordingly lifted from the low energy level of water to a higher energy state with the concomitant production of molecular oxygen. The higher energy electrons are presumed to be received by plastoquinone and then transferred to cytochrome *f* (both cofactors are known to be present in chloroplasts). The second principal photochemical reaction involves the absorption of far red light by chlorophyll *a*. It presumably lifts the electrons from the intermediary energy level of cytochrome *f* to a still higher energy level to the cofactor ferredoxin.

According to this hypothesis, if the resultant photoreduced ferredoxin is reoxidized by TPN, noncyclic photophosphorylation takes place. If the reduced ferredoxin is not oxidized by TPN but instead by plastoquinone, cyclic photophosphorylation results. In effect these two photochemical reactions involving chlorophylls *b* and *a* work in series to drive "uphill" the flow of electrons from the low energy level of water to a higher energy state. In the course of the subsequent return of these electrons to their original

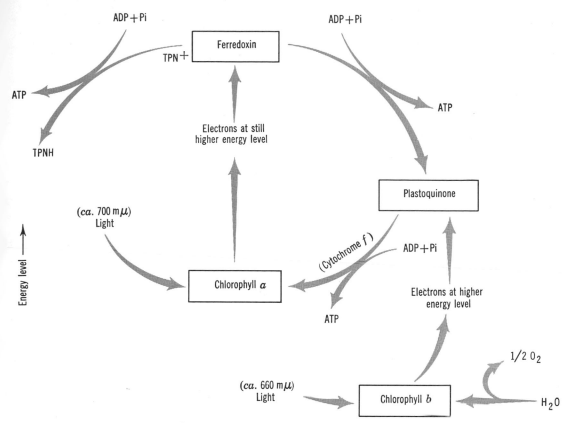

Figure 17-7. A proposed scheme for the detailed biochemical steps in the light phase of photosynthesis involving chlorophylls *a* and *b* and the cyclic and noncyclic photophosphorylation pathways. See text for details.

ground level, noncyclic or cyclic photophosphorylation takes place as indicated depending upon the pathway of electron flow. This version of the light phase of photosynthesis including the postulated sites of ATP formation and the relationship of cyclic and noncyclic photophosphorylation is summarized in Figure 17-7.

In summary, the light phase of photosynthesis is currently conceived to consist of the *cyclic photophosphorylation pathway* and the *noncyclic photophosphorylation pathway*, initiated by the separate photochemical reactions of chlorophylls *b* and *a* by red light and far red light, respectively. In this manner the light phase transforms solar energy to ATP and reducing power in the form of TPNH to be used in the subsequent dark-phase transformation of carbon dioxide to carbohydrates. The

ATP and TPNH which are present in the cell only in catalytic amounts are promptly used in several reactions including the stepwise conversion of carbon dioxide to carbohydrates.

The preceding two proposed pathways for the light phase of photosynthesis apply only to the integrated structure of the whole chloroplast or its highly organized units, the *grana* (p. 62). Although chlorophyll molecules in solution in the test tube can absorb light energy and become "excited," the energy is rapidly lost. It is usually emitted as light at a longer wavelength (a phenomenon called *fluorescence*) in the absence of the highly organized structure of chloroplast.

THE DARK PHASE. The sequence of enzymatic reactions, which appears to constitute the main route of conversion of carbon dioxide to carbohydrates and its intermediates (i.e., the dark phase of photosynthesis), was largely solved during the last decade by Dr. Melvin Calvin and his associates at the University of California. For this work Dr. Calvin was honored with the Nobel Prize in 1962. Radioactive carbon dioxide ($C^{14}O_2$) proved to be an important tool for the study of this aspect of photosynthesis. The short time exposure of green plants to radioactive carbon dioxide ($C^{14}O_2$) in the light was followed by the identification of the C^{14}-labeled products subsequently formed in the cell. It provided important clues as to the intermediates and reactions constituting the pathway of the dark phase.

Dr. Calvin and his colleagues observed that a five-second exposure to light of the green algae *Chlorella* in the presence of radioactive C^{14}-labeled carbon dioxide resulted in appreciable photosynthesis with a high concentration of radioactivity first appearing in 3-phosphoglyceric acid. The C^{14} occurred largely in the carboxyl or acid group (Figure 17-8).

The 3-phosphoglyceric acid is the same substance that serves as an important intermediate in the anaerobic respiratory pathway (p. 179). It is not difficult to conceive that by a reversal of the anaerobic respiratory pathway starting with 3-phosphoglyceric acid (and TPNH plus ATP furnished by the light of photosynthesis) carbohydrates such as glucose could be formed. In fact, distribution studies of the C^{14} label in other compounds with increasing times of exposure of the plant to $C^{14}O_2$ during photosynthesis have strongly implicated the coordinated action of certain enzymes of both the anaerobic respiratory pathway and the pentose oxidative pathway (Chapter 8). They are now thought to be directly responsible for most of the steps comprising the *dark reaction*.

According to our latest information, the dark

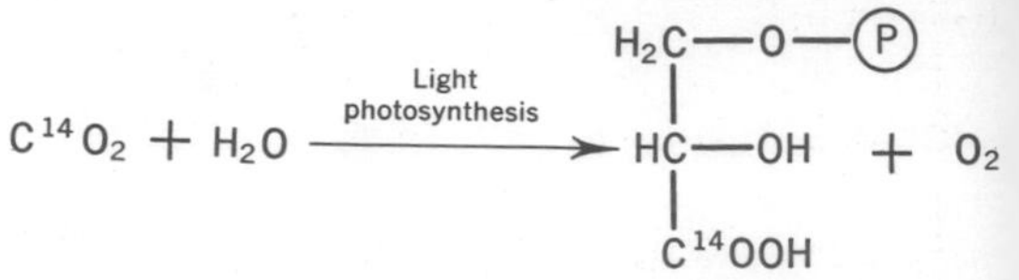

$$C^{14}O_2 + H_2O \xrightarrow[\text{photosynthesis}]{\text{Light}} \begin{array}{c} H_2C\!\!-\!\!O\!\!-\!\!\textcircled{P} \\ | \\ HC\!\!-\!\!OH \\ | \\ C^{14}OOH \end{array} + O_2$$

Figure 17-8. Early incorporation of C^{14} (by photosynthesis) from $C^{14}O_2$ into the carboxyl group of phosphoglyceric acid.

phase of photosynthesis consists of the following enzymatic events.

1. A key step involves the addition of carbon dioxide to a compound called ribulose-1, 5-diphosphate resulting in the formation of two molecules of 3-phosphoglyceric acid. The enzyme which catalyzes the reaction is called *carboxydismutase* and has been shown to be present in chloroplasts (Figure 17-9).

2. Several enzymes of the pentose oxidative pathway participate in maintaining a supply of ribulose-diphosphate. They catalyze the reactions whereby fructose-6-phosphate reacts with glyceralderhyde-3-phosphate (also called 3-phosphoglyceraldehyde) to yield first xylulose-5-phosphate, (and a four-carbon sugar phosphate). The xylulose-5-phosphate is isomerized to ribulose-5-phosphate, and then enzymatically phosphorylated by ATP to ribulose-diphosphate (a reaction which is not part of the pentose oxidative pathway as shown below.

3. The 3-phosphoglyceric acid arising from the carboxydismutase reaction is converted to the corresponding 3-phosphoglyceraldehyde presumably by a reversal of the corresponding steps in anaerobic respiration (reactions 5a and 5b, p. 179) as shown in the overall equation:

3–Phosphoglyceric acid $+$ ATP $+$ TPNH $+$ H$^+$ $\rightleftharpoons$

3–Phosphoglyceraldehyde $+$ TPN$^+$ $+$ ADP $+$ P

The required energy (ATP) and reducing power (TPNH) are ultimately provided by the previ-

 (6 carbons) $\quad$ (3 carbons)

(a) Fructose-6-phosphate $+$ 3-Phosphoglyceraldehyde $\rightleftharpoons$ Xylulose-5-phosphate $+$ 4–Carbon sugar

(b) Xylulose-5-phosphate $\rightleftharpoons$ Ribulose-5-phosphate

(c) Ribulose-5-phosphate $+$ ATP $\rightleftharpoons$ Ribulose–1, 5-diphosphate $+$ ADP

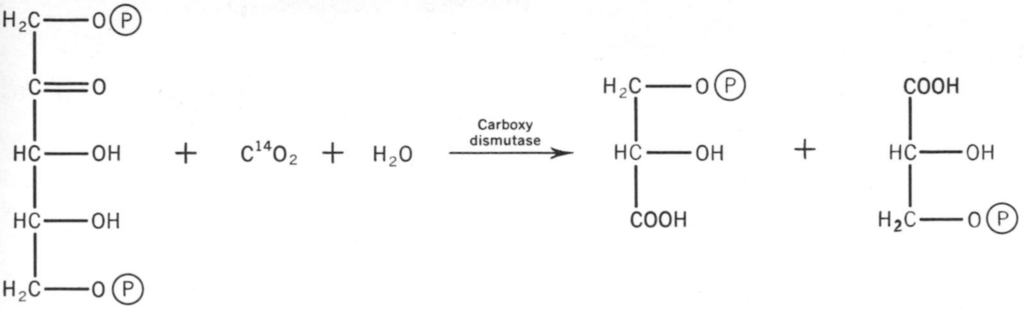

Carboxy dismutase reaction structures:

H₂C—O(P)
|
C=O
|
HC—OH   +   C¹⁴O₂   +   H₂O   →   (Carboxy dismutase)
|
HC—OH
|
H₂C—O(P)

Ribulose-1, 5-diphospate

$$\text{Ribulose-1,5-diphosphate} + C^{14}O_2 + H_2O \xrightarrow{\text{Carboxy dismutase}}$$

Products:

H₂C—O(P)
|
HC—OH
|
COOH

+

COOH
|
HC—OH
|
H₂C—O(P)

Figure 17-9. Reaction catalyzed by the enzyme carboxydismutase.

ously described events of the light phase.

4. By means of the successive action of the isomerase and aldolase enzymes (reaction 4, p. 178) in apparent reversal of the anaerobic respiratory pathway, the phosphorylated sugar, fructose-1,6-diphosphate can be formed:

3–Phosphoglyceraldehyde $\underset{\text{aldolase}}{\overset{\text{Isomerase}}{\rightleftharpoons}}$

Fructose–1, 6–diphosphate

The cyclic nature of the dark phase as we picture it at present is shown in Figure 17-10. The requirement for ATP and TPNH and the reactions in which they participate are indicated.

Comparative Biochemistry of Photosynthesis

All the enzymes constituting the dark phase of photosynthesis have been found in a wide variety of tissues and organisms, many of which are nonphotosynthetic. Therefore, it becomes increasingly apparent that the fundamental distinction between photosynthetic and nonphotosynthetic cells resides in the way in which they form ATP and reduced pyridine nucleotides. Photosynthetic cells can synthesize these compounds at the expense of light energy as well as by certain metabolic reactions that occur in the dark such as in respiration. Nonphotosynthetic cells including animal tissues and microorganisms are unable to utilize light in this manner and can derive their ATP and TPNH only from the metabolic degradation of particular energy-rich organic compounds. Therefore photosynthesis is basi-

cally the unique biological process for transforming the energy of sunlight into the energy of ATP and the reducing power of TPNH for the synthesis of cellular substances.

One theory proposes that photosynthesis probably first emerged in a primitive form capable of transforming light energy into ATP (i.e., cyclic photophosphorylation). Thus at a time when our atmosphere was still devoid of molecular oxygen it could have provided the photosynthetic cell with another source of ATP in addition to that furnished by fermentation. According to this viewpoint it was only later in the evolutionary time scale that this ancient form of photosynthesis became linked to the reduction of pyridine nucleotides, accompanying oxygen liberation and the assimilation of carbon dioxide.

A small number of photosynthetic bacteria are known which possess chlorophyll-like pigments and carry on photosynthesis. However, they fail to liberate molecular oxygen in the process. Instead they may produce other substances in its place. For example, a particular class within the photosynthetic bacteria utilizes hydrogen sulfide, H₂S, in photosynthesis, liberating elementary sulfur, S°, as a product, but not molecular oxygen. As pointed out by the esteemed microbiologist Dr. C. B. van Niel, there is nevertheless a basic similarity between bacterial and plant photosynthesis. The *net effect* of photosynthesis in both green plants and photosynthetic bacteria is to split a reducing substance (H₂O in the case of plants and H₂S in the case of the green sulfur bacteria) to form hydrogens or electrons (and ATP) for the ultimate reduction of carbon dioxide to the level of carbohydrates. In green plants the oxidized product is molecular oxygen derived from water, and in certain photosynthetic bacteria elementary sulfur from hydrogen sulfide.

On the basis of van Niel's generalized concept as well as the Hill reaction the origin of the molecular oxygen produced in photosynthesis is obviously from water and not carbon dioxide. This question was even more directly answered by use of the O^{18} isotope (p. 120) in the early 1940's. By comparing the O^{18} concentration in the molecular oxygen liberated in photosynthesis with that of the O^{18} in the carbon dioxide and water, it was found that the molecular oxygen arising during photosynthesis is derived exclusively from water.

$$6CO_2 + 12H_2O^{18} + \text{Light energy} \xrightarrow{\text{Photosynthesis}}$$
$$C_6H_{12}O_6 + 6O_2^{18} + 6H_2O$$

As further confirmation, when CO_2 heavily labeled with O^{18} was used, hardly any of the O^{18} label appeared in the liberated O_2.

WATER RELATIONSHIPS

The major constituent of all active living cells on our planet is water. One of the important developments which has better adapted higher plants to a terrestrial existence has been the evolution of the vascular system. The latter provides an appreciable advantage to land plants by making possible the efficient transfer of water from the absorbing root to the aerial parts of the plant.

Transpiration

All higher plants are continuously absorbing water from the soil in which their roots are anchored. At the same time water is being continuously evaporated from the aerial parts of the plants (principally from the leaves) to the surrounding air, a process known as *transpiration*. Transpiration occurs almost entirely by way of the stomata located in the leaves.

The leaf is essentially an organized mass of actively photosynthesizing and respiring mesophyll cells enclosed in a waterproof envelope of cutinized epidermal cells perforated by the stomata. Water evaporates from

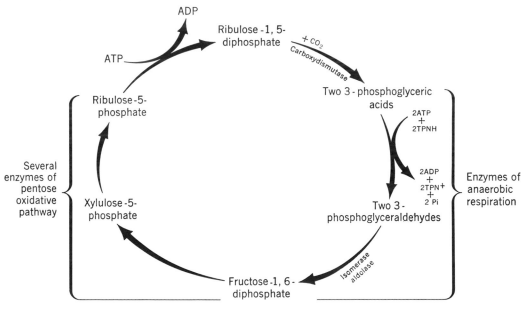

Figure 17-10. Cyclic sequence of enzymatic reactions constituting the dark phase of photosynthesis. See text for details.

the numerous mesophyll cells into the intercellular air spaces of the leaf (where it collects in the gaseous form of water vapor). Thus a diffusion gradient is created favoring a net movement of water outward through the stomata into the external air. If the moisture content of the external air is high, the diffusion gradient for water vapor between the inside and outside air of the leaf is less. Transpiration or the evaporation of water from the leaves is therefore decreased. Transpiration takes place as long as the stomata remain open. It is only when the stomata are almost entirely closed as a result of a loss in turgidity of the stomatal guard cells that transpiration ceases. Under normal circumstances of adequate water supply the rate of transpiration exhibits a typical daily pattern that reflects the degree of opening of the stomal apertures. It is greatest during the day and declines considerably, often to the point of cessation, at night.

Transpiration is responsible for immense losses of water from higher plants and therefore indirectly from the soil. A single corn plant, for example, during its normal life span of three months or so has been shown to transpire as much as 50 gallons of water, corresponding to a loss of more than 300,000 gallons of water by an acre of corn plants! When such water losses are extrapolated to great expanses of vegetation such as large forests, it becomes obvious how the process of transpiration may exert profound influences on regional climates. It affects the moisture content of the air and therefore the temperature and rainfall of a given area.

Aside from its effect in raising the temperature of the leaf, light exerts a powerful positive action on the turgidity of the guard cells and therefore on the extent of the stomatal opening as discussed previously. When the rate of transpiration exceeds the rate of water absorption by roots (often because of an inadequate water supply in the soil) wilting occurs and may be followed by death. Under conditions when the leaves begin to wilt, the guard cells lose their turgidity, the stomata close, and transpiration ceases despite the presence of light. In addition to light intensity and water supply, such factors as wind velocity, humidity of the external air, and temperature influence the rate of transpiration.

Whether or not transpiration contributes distinct benefits to higher plants is a controversial question among plant physiologists. Perhaps the phenomenon is an incidental one occurring because the stomata are open, and is of no advantage to the plant. There is some agreement that the process of transpiration aids in the upward movement of dissolved salts in the xylem once the salts have entered the roots. In some species of plants it probably prevents dangerously high temperatures in leaves, lowering these temperatures on hot days by several degrees since evaporation has a cooling effect.

Ascent of Plant Sap

Transpiration has been invoked in several theories to account in part for the rise of water and dissolved substances, or sap, in tall trees as much as several hundred feet high. According to the *transpiration-cohesion-tension theory*, transpiration creates a diffusion pressure gradient for water, a so-called "pulling force". It is presumably responsible together with the large cohesive forces that exist between water molecules for a mass lifting of a water column through the xylem elements of the tree. These "pulling forces" have actually been measured in actively transpiring plants (and in model systems), and shown to exceed by several-fold the normal pressure of the atmosphere. The latter will raise water only some 33 feet.

Other forces, believed to be of secondary importance, also seem to contribute to the ascent of plant sap. One is called *root pressure*, the force held responsible for the exudation of plant sap from the stump that remains when the stem of a plant is severed close to the ground (Figure 17-11). Measurements of root pressure, made by attaching a manometer to the cut end of the stump, show considerable variation in different species, but never magnitudes (no more than two or three atmospheres) that could account for the rise of sap in tall trees.

Absorption of Water and Salts

The absorption from the soil of water and dissolved inorganic nutrients by the roots is not entirely understood. It is known, however, to involve both *diffusion* (Chapter 6) and energy-requiring *active-transport* mechanisms (p. 112). The delicate root hairs themselves, which are relatively short-lived and cover a portion of the region of maturation of the root, are the actual absorbing structures of the plant. The important factors involved in the absorption of salts and water and the ascent of sap in plants are summarized in Figure 17-12.

Translocation

The upward movement in the plant of water and its dissolved materials including at times organic substances such as sugars apparently occurs principally through the xylem. There is evidence, however, that at certain times of the year especially in the early spring the phloem may also function in this capacity depending on the species. The process by which organic materials (in solution and suspension), synthesized for the most part in the leaves (and to some extent in the roots), are transferred to other parts of the plant (usually downward) is called *translocation*. It occurs chiefly by way of the phloem. Translocation upward in the plant also occurs in the phloem, as it seems to do in the xylem, depending on the species and the time of year.

PLANT HORMONES

Plant hormones, like animal hormones, are produced in one part of the organism and transmitted to another part. They act in extremely small quantities and influence particular physiological processes of the target organs and tissues. Plants, unlike animals, do not produce their hormones in special glands but often in rapidly growing embryonic tissues or in older cells of leaves.

Growth Hormones

The plant hormones that function in the regulation of plant growth are collectively known as the *growth hormones* or *growth regulators*. They consist of the *auxins* and the *gibberellins*.

AUXINS. The auxins are synthesized by young physiologically active cells, especially by the meristematic or growing apices of stems and roots including buds, young leaves, and developing flowers. They are usually transported in one direction away from the more apical tips or portions of the plant in which they are produced toward the zone of elongation and the more basal portions of the plant. Although several auxins have been isolated from plant tissues and chemically identified, the most widely distributed of these, and probably the most important, is indole-3-acetic acid. It is apparently derived from the amino acid tryptophan (Figure 17-13).

Indole-3-acetic acid has been shown to influence several cellular processes. It is necessary for the elongation of cells in the zone of elonga-

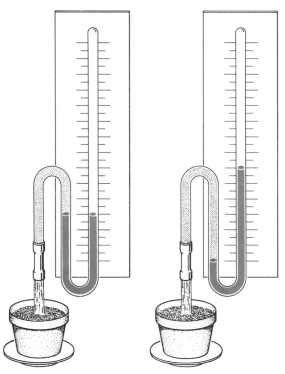

Figure 17-11. Demonstration of root pressure. The difference in height of mercury in the two arms of the manometer is a measure of root pressure.

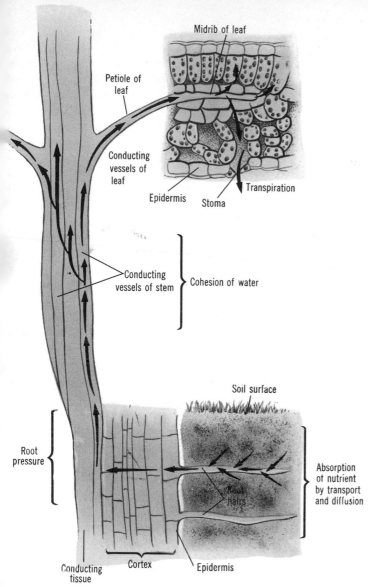

Figure 17-12. Schematic representation of the entry of salts and water into a plant, and the ascent of sap by root pressure, transpiration, and cohesion.

tion of growing stems and roots. It apparently stimulates the cell-elongation process by affecting the deposition of cellulose and increasing the plasticity of the cell walls, thus allowing for a greater absorption of water by the plant cells. If, for example, the tip of a young growing stem is severed, growth of the stem will markedly decrease and finally cease. If the tip is replaced, stem growth is largely restored for at least several hours. If the severed tip instead is placed in contact with a small block of agar for a number of hours, and the agar block containing the hormone is then transferred to the cut end of the stem, stem growth resumes but at a slower rate.

Indole-3-acetic acid also has a stimulatory effect on cell division—initiating, enhancing, and regulating cell division of roots and their branches, stems, buds, and the cambium. The need for the hormone is strikingly demon-

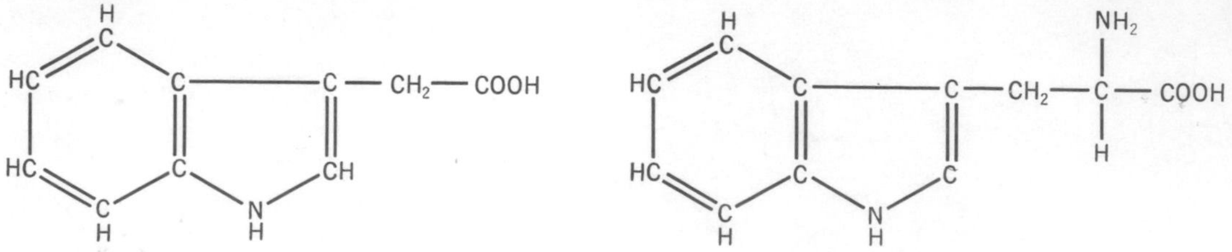

Indole-3-acetic acid

Tryptophan

Figure 17-13. Indole-3-acetic acid; tryptophan.

strated in the tissue culture of plant cells where its addition is required in order for cell division to occur. In general roots require significantly lower concentrations of auxin than do stems in order to promote cell division and growth. This greater sensitivity of the roots is also reflected by the inhibitory effect of higher concentrations of applied indole-3-acetic acid which may still be stimulatory to the growth of stems. Sufficiently larger concentrations of the plant hormone finally prove to be inhibitory to stem growth as well.

Tropisms. The direction of curvature or growth movements of plants in response to certain environmental factors are called *tropisms.* They are attributed to a resulting differential distribution of auxins in the plant tissues concerned. For example, the growth or curvature of a plant stem toward a light source (as in the case of a plant placed in a box having a small lateral aperture for the entrance of light, Figure 17-14) is called *phototropism.* It is apparently due to the uneven distribution of auxin in the stem. The side of the stem away from the light possesses significantly more auxin than the side of the stem exposed to the light. It therefore has a greater rate of growth, thus accounting for the observed curvature.

Similarly the eventual upward curvature of the stem after a plant has been placed on its side (in the dark) is ascribed to a greater auxin concentration on the lower side (due to the force of gravity) than the upper side. The resulting greater rate of growth on the lower side of the stem accounts for the observed upward curvature or growth movement (*geotropism*). The opposite curvature of the root (of the

laterally placed plant), namely its growth downward, presumably is due to the inhibitory effect of the higher auxin concentrations on the lower side of the horizontally placed roots (Figure 17-15).

Abscission. A decrease in auxins is responsible in part for the fall of leaves, flowers, and fruits, a process known as *abscission.* In the abscission of leaves, for example, the shortening daylight period and the diminishing auxin supply moving downward from the leaf blades to the leaf petioles result in the formation at the base of the petiole of a zone of specialized parenchyma cells known as the *abscission layer* (Figure 17-17). Its thin cell walls finally

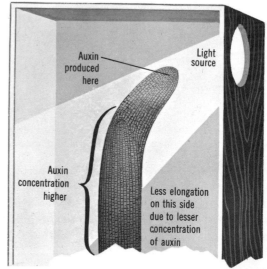

Figure 17-14. Demonstration of phototropism. The side of the stem exposed to the light has more auxin than the opposite side, thus accounting for the stem curvature.

Figure 17-15. Demonstration of geotropism. See text for details.

separate. Leaf fall usually soon follows when the vascular bundles of the petiole which still hold the leaf to the stem are ruptured by the mechanical action of the wind.

In certain agricultural situations it is desirable to delay the fall of premature fruit as in apple trees and orange trees. Spraying of the young fruits with a solution of an appropriate growth regulator, usually with the synthetic substance 2,4-dichlorophenoxyacetic acid, prevents their drop until they are ready for harvest. In contrast, by spraying with a suitable

chemical analogue (i.e., an "antiauxin") which has the opposite effect of auxin, leaves and fruit can be made to fall prematurely where desirable (e.g., in preparation for the mechanical harvesting of cotton). The effects of auxin on the onset of flowering and on the development of fruit are discussed in a later section.

Growth Regulators and Weed Killers. Our knowledge of the effects of auxins has been put to good commercial use in a number of agricultural practices. The rapid and extensive formation of roots on stem cuttings can be promoted by the application of powders, pastes, and solutions containing small concentrations of auxins or chemically related synthetic substances called *growth regulators* (e.g., indolebutyric acid and α-naphthalene acetic acid).

Mention also should be made here of the weed killers such as the synthetic substance 2,4-dichlorophenoxyacetic acid commonly called 2,4-D. This compound in a certain concentration range is highly toxic to certain plants especially dicotyledonous or broadleaved plants, but is relatively nonpoisonous to monocotyledonous or narrow-leaved plants. This type of differential toxicity has served as the basis for the extensive use of 2,4-D as a weed killer for the destruction of broad-leaved weeds in lawns and in certain monocotyledonous crops as the cereals or grains.

Gibberellins. These are a related group of organic substances, originally discovered and isolated by Japanese research workers from the ascomycete fungus *Gibberella fujikuroi* which infects rice seedlings. The fact that rice seedlings infected by the fungus tended to be extremely elongated was one of the initial

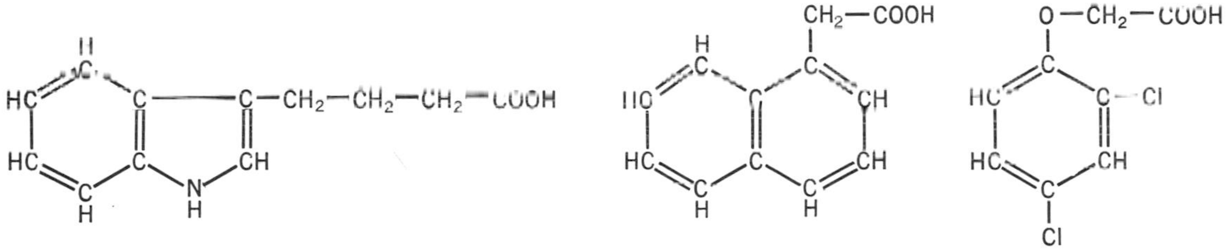

| Indolebutyric acid (IBA) | α-naphthaleneacetic acid (NAA) | 2, 4-dichlorophenoxyacetic acid (2, 4-D) |

Figure 17-16. Indolebutyric acid; α-naphthaleneacetic acid; 2,4-dichlorophenoxyacetic acid (or 2,4-D).

observations that led to the eventual discovery of the gibberellins. The substance *gibberellic acid* (Figure 17-18) as representative of this group of substances has a powerful growth-regulating effect when applied to some higher plants. It causes an extreme elongation of the stem, a marked stimulation of flowering, and larger fruit formation.

Gibberellin-like substances are now being found in increasing number of tissues of higher plants. The evidence is accumulating that they are actually involved in the normal physiology of higher plants.

Effect of Hormones and Other Factors on Flowering

The onset of flowering is a poorly understood process and is in part induced by auxins, other hormones, and additional factors as indicated below. Gibberellins are involved

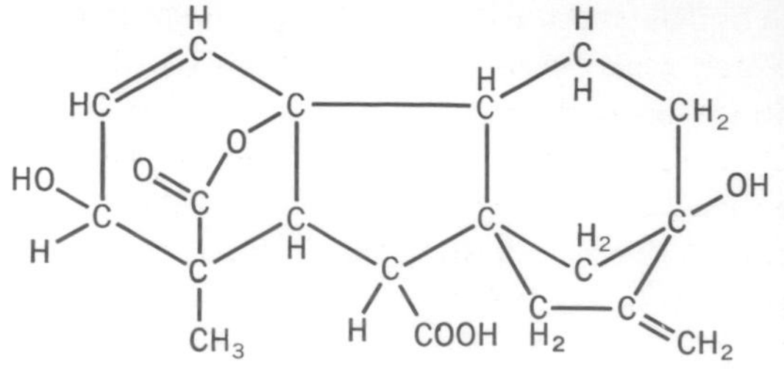

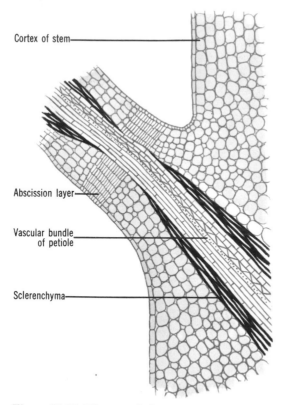

Gibberellic acid

Figure 17-18. Gibberellic acid.

in initiating the formation of flowers in some plants (long-day plants, p. 419), and both gibberellins and auxins are involved in subsequent fruit development. This is obviously only a part of a more complex picture. The auxin effect on fruit development now serves as the basis for an important agricultural practice. When auxins or related substances (e.g., the synthetic growth regulator naphthalene acetic acid) are applied to the pistils or ovaries of flowers, mature parthenocarpic (Chapter 30) but seedless fruits develop. This can be readily shown, for example, with watermelons and tomatoes.

PHOTOPERIODISM. A number of experimental studies also clearly point to the production of a diffusible chemical agent or hormone tentatively called *florigen* which somehow initiates flowering. Nevertheless all attempts thus far to isolate and identify this chemical substance and its mechanism of action have been futile.

We do know, however, that there is a close relationship between the duration of daily exposure of the plant to light and the onset of flowering, a phenomenon known as *photoperiodism*. Moreover, experimental results indicate that plants exposed to a suitable photoperiod produce in their leaves the unidentified hormonal substance florigen, which is then transmitted to the flower buds where it initiates flowering.

On the basis of the length of their photoperiod all angiosperms can be divided into three groups: (1) so-called *short-day plants* (e.g., asters, dahlias, poinsettias, violets) which produce flowers only when their daily photo-

Cortex of stem

Abscission layer

Vascular bundle of petiole

Sclerenchyma

Figure 17-17. Diagram of abscission layer at base of petiole.

period is shorter than a certain critical period which varies with the species (e.g., cockleburs flower when the day length is 16 hours or less); (2) *long-day plants* which produce flowers only when their photoperiod is longer than a certain critical period (spinach, for example, flowers when the day length is 10 hours or more); and (3) *indeterminate plants* (e.g., sunflower, tomato, dandelion, carnation) which flower independently of the photoperiod.

Short-day plants usually flower in early spring or late summer or fall. Long-day plants flower in late spring and early summer. Both short-day and long-day plants are found in the temperate zones, whereas at the higher latitudes, north and south of 60°, the prevalent species are long-day plants. In contrast, the indeterminate plants are widely distributed over the planet irrespective of the length of day. Short-day plants can be made to flower during the long summer days by shading during a portion of the day. Long-day plants can be induced to flower during the short-day winter months by supplementing their light exposure through the use of artificial lighting. Such practices are widely used in the commercial flower-raising industry.

Extensive investigations of photoperiodism since its discovery in 1920 have revealed certain basic relationships. First, the photoperiodic response (i.e., initiating of flowering) does not after all depend on the length of the light period but on the *length of the dark period* instead. Reproduction through flowering is controlled in effect by the length of the night. Thus short-day plants are in reality "long-night" plants, requiring a minimal uninterrupted dark period. Long-day plants are "short-night" plants, requiring a dark period whose duration does not exceed a particular maximum. In some plants one night of suitable length is sufficient to bring about flowering. Interruption of the dark period, even by a momentary flash of light, has been shown to be effective in preventing initiation of flowering. Soybean plants, for example, soon flower when grown under conditions of 16 hours of darkness and 8 hours of light. Flowering is suppressed, however, if

Figure 17-19. Flowering response in the kalanchoe plant. *Left:* grown under conditions of an uninterrupted dark period; *center:* same conditions as at left but with a one-minute interruption with red light at midnight; *right:* same conditions as center plant but the red-light interruption was followed by one minute of exposure to far-red light which nullifies the action of red light. *(Courtesy of Agricultural Research Service, Plant Ind. Sta., U.S. Dept. Agricult.)*

the routine 16-hour periods of darkness are interrupted by a moderately intense light for a few seconds.

Second, by means of grafting experiments it has been possible to demonstrate that an unidentified substance, which we have called florigen, is responsible for flower initiation. It is produced in the photoperiodically stimulated leaves and is transmitted to the flower buds. It is also effective on flower buds of a grafted plant of the same species whose leaves are exposed to an unfavorable photoperiod.

Third, the quality of light used in stimulating or in interrupting the photoperiodic response is most important. It has provided us with valuable clues about the mechanisms of the photoperiodic response. The fact alone that flowering can be suppressed by a small amount of light implies involvement of a light-sensitive pigment. We now know from studies of the flowering response at various wavelengths that interruption of the long dark period of a short-day plant by red light (in the wavelength region of 660 mμ) is most effective in inhibiting the flowering response. If the plants, however, are subsequently exposed to a flash of "far-red" light (in the wavelength region of 730 mμ), flowering is stimulated (Figure 17-19).

Such results have led to the proposal that the photoperiodic response is initiated by a receptor pigment called *phytochrome*. The latter is postulated to exist in two forms, as a *red-absorbing pigment* and as a *far-red-absorbing* pigment, which are interchanged by light. Exposure to red light (660 mμ), or to sunlight, converts some of the red-absorbing pigment to the far-red-absorbing form, whereas exposure to far-red light (770 mμ), or to darkness, favors the reverse reaction.

$$\text{Red-absorbing pigment} \underset{\text{Far-red light or darkness}}{\overset{\text{Red light or sunlight}}{\rightleftharpoons}}$$

$$\text{Far-red-absorbing pigment}$$

The predominant form in sunlight is the far-red pigment which is the controlling factor for flowering. For flowering to occur in short-day plants (e.g., soybean), the period of darkness must be sufficiently long to (*a*) decrease the far-red-absorbing pigment to a low level by conversion to the red-absorbing form, and (*b*) maintain this low level for some hours. If the darkness should be interrupted with just a little red light, the far-red-absorbing pigment produced suppresses the flowering reaction.

The unidentified flowering stimulus (i.e., florigen) produced in the leaf during the period of darkness in short-day plants moves from the leaf to the cells of the stem and its branches where flowering is induced. In general the mechanisms responsible for the complex process of flowering are still largely unsolved.

Interestingly enough, when applied to long-day plants exposed to an unfavorable photoperiod, the gibberellins nevertheless initiate flower formation but are without effect on short-day plants. We do know that temperature must play a central role in the initiation of flowers, as it also does in seed germination, for prior exposure to low temperatures is necessary in order to elicit the photoperiodic response.

Finally, it should be mentioned that the antagonistic action of red and far-red light on the flowering response is also evident in several other aspects of plant development. These include leaf expansion, stem elongation, seed germination, and possibly the onset of leaf fall and dormancy in the autumn in many plants. Leaf expansion, for example, is strongly promoted by exposure to a dose of red light but is prevented if followed immediately by exposure to far-red light. On the other hand, stem elongation is inhibited by red light, an effect which is antagonized by far-red light. The foregoing phytochrome explanation also has been invoked to account for these phenomena.

SUPPLEMENTARY REFERENCES

Bonner, J., and A. W. Galston, *Principles of Plant Physiology*, Freeman, San Francisco, 1952.
Borthwick, H. A., and S. B. Hendricks, "Photoperiodism in Plants," *Science*, October 28 (1960).
Calvin, M., *The Path of Carbon in Photosynthesis*, Prentice-Hall, Englewood Cliffs, N. J., 1957.
Galston, A. W., *The Life of The Green Plant*, second edition, Prentice-Hall, Englewood Cliffs, N. J., 1964.
Hendricks, S. B., "Metabolic Control of Timing," *Science*, July 5 (1963).
Hill, R., and C. D. Whittingham, *Photosynthesis*, revised edition, Wiley, New York, 1957.
James, W. O., *An Introduction to Plant Physiology*, fifth edition, Clarendon Press, Oxford, England, 1957.
Meyer, B. S., D. B. Anderson, and R. N. Bohning, *Introduction to Plant Physiology*, Van Nostrand, Princeton, N J., 1960.
Naylor, A. W., "The Control of Flowering," *Scientific American*, May 1952.
Salisbury, F. B., "Plant Growth Substances," *Scientific American*, April 1957.
Salisbury, F. B., "The Flowering Process," *Scientific American*, April 1958.
Veen, R. van der, and G. Meijer, *Light and Plant Growth*, Macmillan, New York, 1959.

Chapter 18

Animal Kingdom:

Protozoa to Nematoda

INTRODUCTION

The major criteria used for classifying animals have been discussed in Chapter 14. Some two dozen animal phyla have been described. The quantity is necessarily stated as an approximation, since there is no complete agreement among taxonomists on the status of all phyla. For example, some authorities may classify certain animals in one particular phylum whereas other taxonomists may classify them instead among two and more phyla. Of the total animal phyla, however, about ten are generally considered to be the major ones, comprising the greater proportion of known animals. The outstanding characteristics of the major animal phyla are described in this and the next two chapters.

PHYLUM PROTOZOA

General Features

The most prominent feature of members of this group is that all are single-celled organisms. Nearly all are also of microscopic size ranging from 100 to 300 μ. A few, however, attain sizes as large as 3 and even 4 cm in their longest dimension. The protozoans display a wide range of complexity and specialization in form and function within a single cell. As already indicated some authorities classify all single-celled organisms within a separate kingdom, the *Protista*.

At least twenty-five thousand different species of *Protozoa* have been described and there is little doubt that many more exist. A conservative estimate is that at the very least there are approximately one hundred thousand species and probably many more. The phylum is subdivided by most taxonomists, into five classes called *Sarcodina, Ciliata, Suctoria, Sporozoa,* and *Flagellata.* Although all members of the class Sporozoa are parasitic and there are numerous parasitic species in the other classes, the vast majority of protozoans are free-living forms. The principal features of each class are described below.

Most protozoa have failed to leave a record of their past as fossils because of their soft bodies and small size. A few that form skeletons of silica have been found in rock deposits dating as far back as a half billion years and more.

Class Sarcodina

All members of the class *Sarcodina* are characterized by the distinctive capacity to form temporary protoplasmic extensions called *pseudopodia.* The term *Sarcodina* is derived from "sarcode," which was originally applied to undifferentiated protoplasm. The class includes the simplest forms of protozoa, although not the most primitive, and is best illustrated by the

Figure 18-1. Glass model of a member of the *Fora-minifera, Globigerina bulloides,* which builds a many-chambered shell of limestone. *(Courtesy of Amer. Mus. Natural History.)*

genus *Amoeba* and related genera. The salient features of the amoeba organism including its food vacuole and contractile vacuole as well as its ability to form pseudopodia have already been described (p. 80). Many amoebae are free-living animals occurring in marine and fresh-water environments. One of the species is responsible for the serious disease of humans called *amoebic dysentery.*

Reproduction is largely by mitotic cell division, although there is some evidence for sexual reproduction. Under adverse conditions some species form cysts. Other amoeboid genera possess external skeletons or shells composed of calcium carbonate, silica, and other materials. The pseudopodia are extended through one or more openings in the shell depending upon the genus. The so-called *Foraminifera,* for example (Figure 18-1), have calcareous skeletons which they secrete. Other amoeboid protozoa called *Radiolaria* form intricate and beautiful skeletons of silica. The skeletons of Foraminifera and Radiolaria may become converted on the ocean floors

into chalk and flint, respectively. Nearly all Foraminifera are marine organisms and in regions such as the North Atlantic the shells of these dead organisms accumulating over millions of years compose an appreciable portion of the silt of the ocean floors. They may also make a major contribution as a result of geologic upheaval in the formation of land masses—some of them several hundred feet thick, as in the instance of the White Cliffs of Dover in the British Isles.

Class Ciliata

The protozoans of the class *Ciliata* are characterized by cilia which partially or completely cover the external surface of the cell. Nearly all members are also distinguished by the unique possession of two types of nuclei, a large *macronucleus,* and at least one small *micronucleus,* with significant differences in function. They are on the whole the largest and most complex of the protozoa and commonly occur in either fresh water or salt water and as parasites. The genus *Paramecium* commonly found in fresh water habitats illustrates the important features of the group.

The *Paramecium,* unlike the *Amoeba,* has a definite and fixed shape resembling that of a spindle with a bluntly rounded anterior and a more pointed posterior end. The entire external surface of the *Paramecium* cell is covered by several thousand rhythmically beating cilia whose coordinated action propels the organism in a spiral course. The cilia project through tiny holes in the outer covering, or *pellicle,* and are attached near the periphery of the cytoplasm to certain *basal granules.* These in turn are interconnected by longitudinal so-called *neuro-fibrils.* The basal granules and neurofibrils somehow account for the integrated beating motion of the cilia. Dispersed on the cell surface among the cilia and presumably serving in a protective capacity are spindle-shaped bodies called *trichocysts* which discharge slender, hair-like filaments.

The food supply of the *Paramecium,* consisting mostly of bacteria, is swept into the cell by

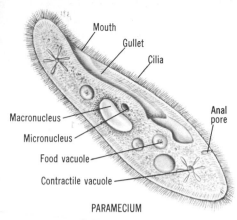

Mouth
Gullet
Cilia
Anal pore
Macronucleus
Micronucleus
Food vacuole
Contractile vacuole

PARAMECIUM

Figure 18-2. The *Paramecium*.

way of a cilia-lined mouth or *oral groove*. The latter is connected to a gullet or so-called *cytopharynx* at the base of which a *food vacuole* forms. Ingested material is enzymatically digested in the food vacuole which has meanwhile become detached moving through the cytoplasm of the cell. The *anal spot* is the specialized site at which undigested remains are eliminated. As in all protozoa, respiration is accomplished by the diffusion inward of oxygen and outward of carbon dioxide. Ammonia as the principal nitrogenous waste product also leaves the organism by diffusion. The two *contractile vacuoles,* each (with its radiating canals which collect fluid) at opposite ends of the cell, serve to expel the large excess of water that constantly enters the organism from its hypotonic environment.

The *micronucleus,* which contains recognizable chromosomes, functions primarily in reproduction, asexual and sexual. The *macronucleus,* on the other hand, appears to be more directly involved in controlling metabolism, growth, development, and most other processes of the organism. In asexual reproduction the micronucleus experiences mitotic division whereas the macronucleus elongates and amitotically pinches in two. At about the same time or shortly afterwards, the cell constricts to yield two daughter cells of approximately equal size.

Sexual reproduction in *Paramecia* is of a particular type called *conjugation*: two organisms of similar external appearance but different physiological mating strains, analogous to the male and female of higher animals, pair and exchange portions of their micronuclei through a regular series of events.

Although most ciliates are free-living forms found in either fresh or salt water, numerous parasitic types have been observed in the digestive tract of many hosts including pigs, sheep, cattle, and man. Many of the ciliates are similar to the *Paramecium* but some have achieved an even greater complexity.

Class Suctoria

Members of the class *Suctoria* constitute only a small group of *Protozoa* and are closely related to the *Ciliata*. They are characterized by the presence of cilia only during the immature phase of the life cycle, thus accounting for motility in young individuals. In adults, however, the cilia have been replaced by tentacles used for capturing food and feeding. The representative suctorian (e.g., the genus *Podophryl*) is usually anchored by a stalk-like structure and is therefore sessile, with tentacles radiating from the central cell body. Reproduction takes place asexually by cell division and sexually by conjugation.

Class Sporozoa

All members of the class *Sporozoa* are parasites. They have been found in the tissues of nearly all the animal phyla and exhibit highly complex reproductive cycles involving different hosts. They have little or no means of motility or specialized structures for the ingestion of food in most of the stages of their intricate life cycles. The term sporozoa ("seed or spore animals") is derived from the fact that spores (cells with special protective coverings capable of withstanding extreme heat, cold, dessication, and other unfavorable conditions) are conspicuous stages in their life cycles. One of the genera known as *Plasmodium* is made up of numerous species, four of which are known to be responsible for human malaria and mosquitoes of the genus *Anopheles* are the only two hosts essential for the successful completion of the life cycle of the malaria-causing organism. (Figure 18-3).

MALARIA. The malaria-causing *Plasmodium* species enters the human blood stream in the form of an elongate spindle-shaped cell (*sporozoite*) from the salivary gland of the *Anopheles* mosquito when it bites man. The

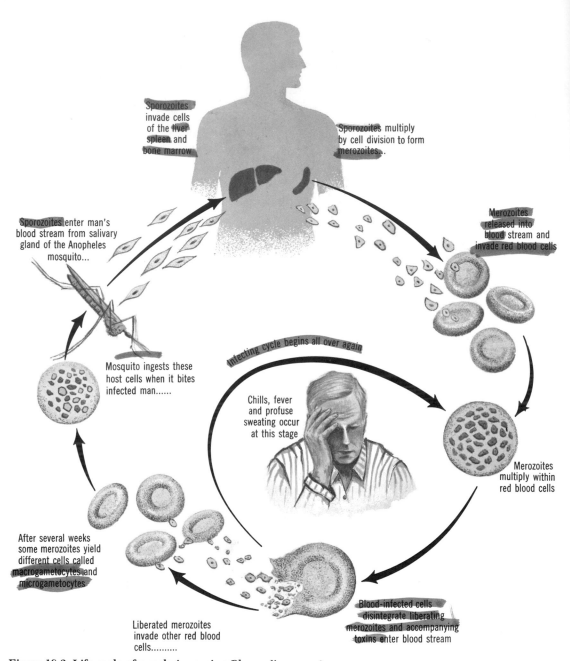

Sporozoites invade cells of the liver spleen and bone marrow

Sporozoites multiply by cell division to form merozoites...

Sporozoites enter man's blood stream from salivary gland of the Anopheles mosquito...

Merozoites released into blood stream and invade red blood cells

Mosquito ingests these host cells when it bites infected man......

Infecting cycle begins all over again

Chills, fever and profuse sweating occur at this stage

Merozoites multiply within red blood cells

After several weeks some merozoites yield different cells called macrogametocytes and microgametocytes

Liberated merozoites invade other red blood cells..........

Blood-infected cells disintegrate liberating merozoites and accompanying toxins enter blood stream

Figure 18-3. Life cycle of a malaria-causing *Plasmodium* species.

sporozoites soon disappear from the circulating blood and invade the cells of the liver, spleen, and bone marrow. There they rapidly multiply by cell division to produce many smaller spore-like cells called *merozoites*. Within a week or two the merozoites are released to the blood stream where each invades a red blood cell. Within the red blood cell the merozoite experiences several successive divisions to yield approximately 10 to 20 merozoites per red blood cell during a period of about 36 to 72 hours depending in part upon the infecting species of *Plasmodium*. This type of asexual reproduction by the parasite occurs synchronously in millions upon millions of the patient's red blood cells. Upon completion of merozoite production, a large number of erythrocytes are ruptured or disintegrated with the liberation of merozoites and accompanying toxins into the blood stream. This phenomenon coincides with the periodic occurrence in patients of chills, fever, and profuse sweating, which is apparently caused by the release of toxins from the synchronously disintegrating red blood cells. Each liberated merozoite invades another red blood cell, and the cycle repeats itself until the natural defense mechanisms of the body begin to control the disease within a matter of several weeks.

After several cycles of asexual reproduction during the course of several weeks, some merozoites, instead of continuing to produce like cells, yield two different cell types called *macrogametocytes* and *microgametocytes*. These cells remain in the red blood cells of the human host until they are ingested by the *Anopheles* mosquito. The macrogametocytes and microgametocytes resume their development within the mosquito's stomach to form female and male gametes, respectively. Fertilization occurs in the stomach. The resulting zygotes migrate through the digestive tract wall to its outer surface where they encyst themselves and produce large numbers of sporozoites. The eventual rupturing of the cysts and subsequent migration of sporozoites to the salivary glands where they remain and are injected into man by the bite of the mosquito completes the life cycle of the *Plasmodium*. The first symptoms of the disease appear within two to three weeks after the initial infection.

Quinine, a drug extracted from the bark of the cinchona tree, has been used for many years to control the disease. Since World War II several synthetic drugs such as *atabrine, primaquine,* and *chloroquine* have proved to be more effective antimalarial agents with the added advantage of having fewer toxic side effects. None of the drugs effects a final cure even though the blood appears to be cleared of the parasite. The most effective long-term control is attained by destroying the breeding places of the *Anopheles* mosquito and by screening in buildings. The relationship of the hereditary blood-cell disorder, *sickle-cell anemia* as well as the conferring of partial immunity to malaria are indicated in Chapter 25.

Different species of sporozoans infect different hosts including numerous domestic animals such as chickens, turkeys, dogs, and cats.

Class Flagellata

The class *Flagellata* includes all single-celled organisms which possess in most stages of their life cycles one or more flagella used in locomotion. In most other respects, they show a wide diversity of characteristics and combine in part several of the features of both plants and animals. Accordingly, they are also classified by many plant taxonomists within the plant kingdom. Some contain chlorophyll and are therefore photosynthetic, deriving all of their nutrition like green plants from carbon dioxide, water, and inorganic mineral salts. Others are entirely heterotrophic, actually ingesting particles of organic matter upon which they almost completely depend for their nutrition. Various gradations in nutrition between these two extremes are observed among members of the class. However, the absence of a cell wall, the usual presence of a pellicle, and the occurrence in some of an amoeboid-like stage in their life cycle are reminiscent of unicellular animal-like features. A familiar example of the flagellates is seen in members of the genus *Euglena*, which are also classified in the plant kingdom within the phylum *Euglenophyta* (Chapter 15).

The colonial flagellate genus *Volvox*, described earlier (p. 82), consists of numerous seemingly identical plant-like cells resembling *Euglena*. They possess two flagella instead of one, two contractile vacuoles, chlorophyll, and no gullet. The organism reproduces asexually by successive division of cells which subsequently give rise to several colonies. It also reproduces sexually by the fusion of a male and female gamete to form a zygote which eventually develops into a colony. As pointed out previously (p. 82) the first signs of functional differentiation have already made their appearance. Whether the cells of *Volvox* can be considered to be a highly progressive colony of individual cells or instead a rudimentary multicellular organism is difficult to say and is in part a matter of one's viewpoint. Like *Euglena*, *Volvox* is also classified in the plant kingdom, namely with the green algae (phylum *Chlorophyta*, Chapter 15).

The predominantly marine flagellate forms, the *dinoflagellates*, may also be included in this class. Many plant taxonomists, however, classify them within a separate phylum (*Pyrrophyta*, Chapter 15) of the plant kingdom. An appreciable number of flagellates are parasitic, the most notorious being several species of the genus *Trypanosoma* responsible for the disease *African sleeping sickness*.

In general, the flagellates are regarded as the most primitive of the present-day unicellular organisms. In favor of the viewpoint is their possession of both plant and animal characteristics, as if they were transitional between the two types. There is also some speculation that multicellular organisms, especially plants and possibly animals, may well have had their origin from colonies of ancient flagellate types resembling the present day *Volvox*.

It should be noted that the five classes of *Protozoa* described are principally distin-

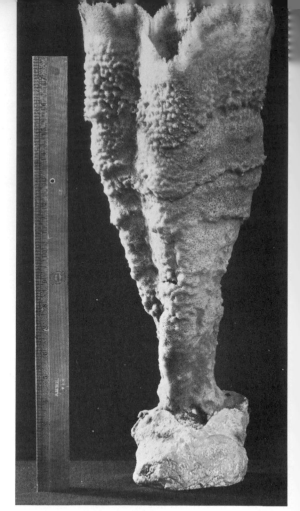

Figure 18-4. The sponge *Tubra phyicifera*. *(Courtesy of Amer. Mus. Natural History.)*

guished by their mode of locomotion: *Sarcodina* (pseudopods), *Ciliata* (cilia), *Suctoria* (cilia when young), *Sporozoa* (no movement, at least in the asexually reproducing stage), and *Flagellata* (flagella). All the other major animal phyla (described hereafter) consist of multicellular forms.

PHYLUM PORIFERA

The *Porifera* or sponges are regarded as the simplest and most primitive of the multicellular animals. They are not considered to be on the main line of animal evolution (see Figure 18-4, Chapter 20). Upon first examination, sponges

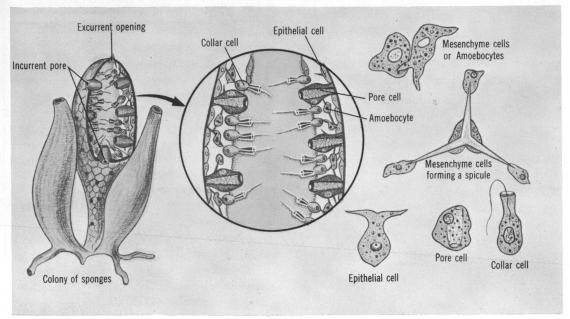

Figure 18-5. Diagram of a section through a simple sponge, and its various types of cells.

appear to be no more than a colony of cells. Nevertheless, the cells are of several differentiated types but are arranged neither as well-defined tissue layers nor as organs. Many sponges are irregularly formed without a definite body plan, whereas a few have recognizable forms. Nearly all have an internal skeleton.

The phylum consists of approximately fifteen thousand species (mostly marine forms firmly attached to the ocean floor of the shallow waters in which they grow) and is characterized by the presence of an internal cavity ranging in complexity from a single large space to an extensive system of internal canals depending upon the species (Figure 18-5). The internal cavities are connected to the surface by many tiny openings or pores (therefore, the name *Porifera*) which serve as the sites of entry of water into the organism. Water leaves by way of other larger but fewer openings. The phylum includes three classes depending on the principal substances composing the internal skeleton—calcium carbonate, silica, and protein fibers. The latter includes those sponges that are used as a source of bath sponges.

The outer surface of the sponge and part of the surface of the internal cavities are lined with flattened epithelial cells. A large portion of the internal cavity surface is lined with so-called flagellated *collar cells* which ingest microorganisms and food particles entering the canals in the inflow of water. Between the external covering and the internal layer of collar cells is a jelly-like matrix containing wandering amoeba-like cells called *amoebocytes or mesenchyme cells*. They may occur in almost any part of the sponge body and are capable of differentiating into other cell types. Some of the mesenchyme cells secrete needles or *spicules* of calcium carbonate, silica, or structural protein (depending upon the species) which form an internal supporting skeletal framework.

The presence of neurosensory cells and neuron cells organized in the form of a primitive nervous system coordinates in part the flow of water in and out of the sponge by affecting the contractile cells. The latter control the diameter of the minute pores and exit openings.

The amoebocytes apparently receive digested food from the flagellate cells and by their migratory activity distribute it to all parts of the sponge. Reproduction occurs asexually in some forms by budding. Sexual reproduction is more widespread and occurs by the union of egg and sperm, usually from different sponges, within one of the internal cavities. The developing zygote, as a mass of flagellate cells, is discharged to the external environment by the outflowing water, becomes attached and eventually develops into a recognizable sponge.

Some sponges have an unusual ability to regenerate from a small fragment. In several types the cells, which can be almost completely separated by squeezing through silk cloth, show the remarkable ability to reassociate, at first into small multicellular masses eventually forming large sponges like the original.

PHYLUM COELENTERATA

General Features

The phylum *Coelenterata* consists of three classes and some ten thousand species which are predominantly marine animals including jellyfish, corals, and sea anemones. There are a few fresh-water forms such as *Hydra*. Coelenterates are characterized by a primitive plan of organization of radial symmetry which is centered about the single internal digestive cavity. The latter typically has only one external opening serving as both mouth and anus about which are located several tentacles, extensions of the body wall. The body wall only in the most primitive forms consists of two main layers of cells, the outer *epidermis* and inner *gastrodermis* (corresponding to the ectoderm and endoderm, respectively), separated by a noncellular jelly-like secretion called *mesoglea*. In jellyfish the mesoglea represents a major portion of the organism and is responsible for the jelly-like quality of the animal. In all other coelenterates a middle rudimentary layer is present containing cells which are probably analogous to cells of mesodermal origin in higher animals. The final unique feature of the

Coelenterata is the possession by all species of special nonliving stinging capsules called *nematocysts* produced by special cells and equipped with a hollow thread. The latter can be shot out rapidly like a harpoon, paralyzing minute animals which are then brought to the mouth by the tentacles. Nearly twenty different types of nematocysts have been described (some species having more than one type) and have proved useful in the classification of coelenterates. All coelenterates, whether sessile or free-swimming, feed mostly on the animal life including small fish of their watery environments.

Coelenterates in comparison to sponges are clearly more advanced, displaying a higher level of organization as well as a more definite form and symmetry. In coelenterates cellular differentiation has given rise to two principal layers of cells showing the presence of definite muscular, nerve, and reproductive tissues and possibly even organs of a primitive type, namely the tentacles.

Hydra

The relatively simple and widely distributed fresh-water genus *Hydra* is often used to illustrate the structure and activities of the Coelenterata. *Hydra* is a small animal, and to the naked eye has a whitish thread-like form which can rapidly contract to the size of a pinhead. Under the microscope it is seen to resemble a two-layered hollow cylinder at whose open end is a circle of tentacles of varying number (Figure 18-6). The central body cavity called the *gastrovascular cavity* serves primarily for digestion and distribution of food materials.

The epidermis of the body wall consists of several different cell types, of which so-called *epitheliomuscular* cells are present in the greatest majority. In addition to functioning in a protective and covering role, epitheliomuscular cells possess longitudinal contractile processes whose coordinated contraction produces a shortening of the body. Similar cells in the endodermis have circularly oriented contractile processes and are responsible for lengthening and constriction of the body. The epidermis also includes glandular cells, nematocyst-producing cells, nerve cells, sensory receptor cells, and small undifferentiated interstitial cells. Nerve cells and receptor cells form an interconnecting network which innervates the epitheliomuscular cells of both epidermis and gastrodermis, accounting for the coordination of muscular activity. In contrast to that of vertebrates, the nerve cells of *Hydra* can transmit nerve impulses from cell to cell in either direction along a nerve pathway.

The gastrodermis is made up mainly of large epithelial or muscular flagellate cells which form pseudopodia for ingesting undigested particles of food from the gastrovascular cavity. Digestion is initiated within the gastrovascular cavity by the enzyme secretions of special glandular cells of the epidermis and is completed within the food vacuoles of the above-mentioned flagellate, amoeboid cells. Undigested residues are eventually discarded by these cells into the gastrovascular cavity and, together with any other resistant materials, are discharged through the mouth to the exterior by a series of violent body contractions. The products of digestion eventually reach all parts of the body by circulating through the gastrovascular cavity as a result of flagellate activity, wave-like contractions of the body canal and diffusion. Oxygen uptake and the excretion of metabolic wastes including carbon dioxide and nitrogenous by-products take place by diffusion.

Hydra reproduce by asexual or sexual means. Asexual reproduction occurs by budding: one or more small elevations showing on the middle or lower portion of the body soon develops an extension of the gastrovascular cavity, a mouth, and tentacles and takes on the appearance of a tiny hydra; the bud usually separates from the parent, which has been providing its nutrition, by a constriction to yield a new and independent *Hydra*.

Most species are *hermaphroditic*, producing both ovaries and testes, whereas some species are *dioecious*. Both the testes and ovaries develop as small swellings from the epidermis.

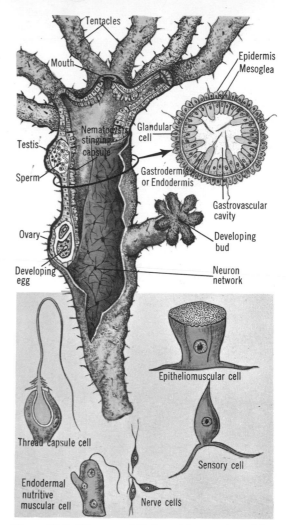

Figure 18-6. Diagram of *Hydra* with a portion of the body wall removed to illustrate various structures and cell types.

The mature sperm which are periodically released swim about in the water and may fertilize an egg cell by entering the ovary through an opening in the epidermal wall. The zygote or fertilized egg cell proceeds to divide and form a cyst-like cover which soon surrounds a solid sphere of embryo cells consisting of an outer ectoderm layer and an inner solid mass of endoderm. The developing embryo detaches itself from the parent and eventually develops into a miniature hydra. *Hydra,* like the coelenterates in general, have a striking ability for

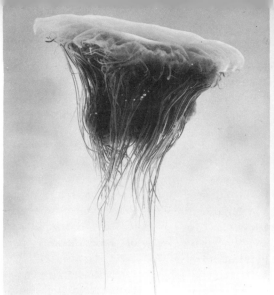

Figure 18-7. The sea anemone *Condylactis gigantea* (belonging to the class Anthozoa of the coelenterates) occurs only in the polyp stage. *(Courtesy of Amer. Mus. Natural History.)*

Figure 18-8. A jellyfish of the class Scyphozoa of the coelenterates which occurs only in the medusa stage. *(From Goodnight, Goodnight, and Armcost, Fig. 12-11b, p. 249, Wiley.)*

regeneration, two complete individuals being formed within a few days from a severed organism.

ALTERNATION OF GENERATIONS. Actually the more representative genera of the Coelenterata show an *alternation of generations* consisting of two morphologically different types of individuals or generations called the sedentary *hydroid* or *polyp* and the free-swimming *medusa*. Individuals of the hydroid or polyp type reproduce *asexually* by budding to yield progeny of the medusa type. Medusae reproduce *sexually* to form offspring that are hydroids. Thus one generation reproduces asexually, and the next sexually accounting for the alternation of generations. For some genera, such as Hydra, where alternation of generations does not occur, there may be only polyps and in others only medusae. The two types differ in appearance, the polyp resembling the general structure of a Hydra—tubular in shape with a mouth and surrounding tentacles at one end (Figure 18-7). The medusa, as illustrated by the free-living jellyfish, looks more like a free-swimming, delicate and transparent, inverted saucer with tentacles around its edges (Figure 18-8).

Corals

The variations and complexities of the coelenterates differ considerably, depending on the species, genus, and class. Some genera produce a hard surrounding cup-like limy skeleton which is secreted by the epidermal cells. These are the true corals, comprising many species which abound in the tropical and subtropical seas. The corals, more so than any other animal with the possible exception of man, have had a highly significant role in the geologic history of the earth. The skeletons of corals in the tropical oceans have been largely responsible for the formation of large reefs and even islands bordering on continents and other islands. The many coral reefs, atolls, and islands of the South Pacific, and in particular the Great Barrier Reef, a ridge many miles wide and extending more than a thousand miles along the eastern shoreline of Australia, are the result of build-up of coral skeletons during great passages of time.

The three classes constituting the Coelenterata follow.

1. *Hydrozoa*—In this class the polyp is usually the predominant and conspicuous form although some form colonies that produce

medusae. *Hydra*, Portuguese Man-of-War, and *Obelia* belong to this class.

2. *Scyphozoa*— In this class the medusae are the predominant and conspicuous form as exemplified by the jellyfish.

3. *Anthozoa*— Members of this class have no medusa stage, usually form complex polyps, and are all marine organisms. They include the corals, sea anemones, and sea pansies.

A phylum, the *Ctenophora*, more commonly known as "sea walnuts" or "comb jellies" and consisting only of approximately one hundred species, strongly resembles the Coelenterata in several respects but differs in others. All its members are marine animals usually floating near the surface of the sea. They are characterized by eight rows of swimming *combs* or *plates* composed of fused cilia, by which the organism moves. In addition to radial symmetry, an epidermis, and gastrodermis, as seen in the coelenterates, the ctenophores possess a definite but primitive mesoderm cell layer from which the muscular elements arise. Many have a pair of tentacles, but almost all lack nematocysts. They feed on small animals in the sea and have a branching gastrovascular cavity. Some are luminescent, giving off weak blue-green light.

PHYLUM PLATYHELMINTHES (FLATWORMS)

General Features

The phylum *Platyhelminthes* which is composed of three classes totaling some ten thousand species, possesses several important advanced features. Many of the basic characteristics can be illustrated by referring to the free-living class *Turbellaria*, although its features are not universal for the Platyhelminthes. The other two classes, *Trematoda* and *Cestoda*, consist entirely of parasitic species. They are therefore less suitable for describing the important features of the phylum because of their highly specialized structure adaptations to the parasitic existence.

First, members of the Platyhelminthes characteristically display bilateral symmetry, for they have definite dorsal (upper) and ventral (lower) surfaces and anterior (head) and posterior (tail) ends. Second, they have a well-defined mesoderm which differentiates into specialized tissues and organs. Unlike higher phyla, however, they do not possess a cavity or coelom between the body wall and the digestive cavity. Third, they have a more or less developed head region with special sensory receptors for light (the eyes or eyespots) as well as a concentration of nervous tissue consisting of two ganglia or the "brain." Finally, they display highly specialized and complex reproductive and excretory organs. They resemble the coelenterates, however, in still having a digestive cavity with only a single opening which serves as both mouth and anus.

Class Turbellaria

Among the most familiar members of the class *Turbellaria* are the *planarians*. A good example is the species *Dugesia tigrina* which is widely distributed in North America, occurring in many ponds and streams. The organism is a small gray worm, about 2 cm long, having a triangular-shaped head with two eyespots on its dorsal surface. The eyespots are at most only sensitive to varying intensities of light and form no image. Locomotion is attained by both the beating of the cilia in the thin layer of mucus on the epidermis and by muscular contractions of the body. On the ventral surface near the central portion of the body is the mouth leading into the pharynx which opens into the branching gastrovascular cavity. The pharynx is a muscular, tube-like proboscis structure which is extended from the mouth during feeding. It is also used for disposing of undigested wastes (Figure 18-9).

The gastrovascular cavity is made up of three main branches and lesser divisions extending throughout the body. Animals and other food particles are broken into small fragments by the muscular action of the pharynx, engulfed by the pseudopodia of the special cells lining the gastrovascular cavity, and digested within the food vacuoles formed in these cells.

Much of the mesoderm in planaria consists of loose amoeboid cells and contains the excretory system, reproductive system, gland cells, and muscular layers. The lymph-like fluid which fills the space between the mesodermal cells, aided by muscular movements, serves in a circulatory role. It helps to distribute the products of digestion as well as oxygen absorbed through the epidermis.

The excretory system which functions chiefly in regulating the water content of the tissues consists of a branching network of fine tubules distributed throughout most of the mesoderm. At one end the tubules fuse to form larger tubes which drain to the exterior by means of several small pores. At the other end each tubule terminates in a single so-called *flame cell* consisting of a hollow center continuous with the duct of the tubules and containing a tuft of flickering cilia (Figure 18-10). Presumably the beating cilia produce a current of fluid with metabolic wastes in solution which flows towards the pores. Metabolic wastes are probably excreted mainly by the cells lining the gastrovascular cavity.

The nervous system includes a concentration of nerve cells or "brain" located beneath the eyes, comprising two ganglia and two nerve cords extending through the mesodermal tissue along the ventral side to the posterior end of the body. The two nerve cords are connected throughout their length by cross strands, like the steps of a ladder. Nerves also extend from the brain and cords to all parts of the body. In addition to the eyes several other different types of sensory cells specialized for the reception of chemical and tactile stimuli (e.g., food substances, touch and water currents) are distributed over the body surface, especially at the two pointed projections at the side of the head.

Planaria is monoecious, each individual worm having both male and female organs

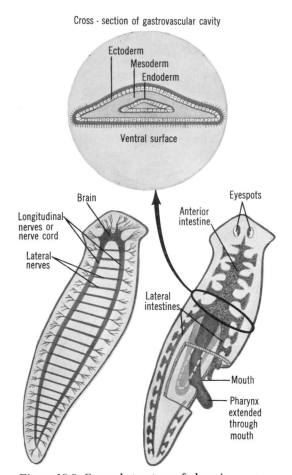

Cross - section of gastrovascular cavity

Ectoderm
Mesoderm
Endoderm

Ventral surface

Brain

Longitudinal nerves or nerve cord

Lateral nerves

Anterior intestine

Eyespots

Lateral intestines

Mouth

Pharynx extended through mouth

Figure 18-9. General structure of planaria.

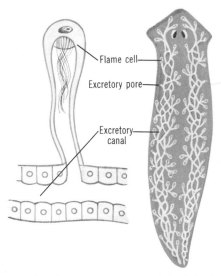

Flame cell

Excretory pore

Excretory canal

Figure 18-10. Excretory system of planaria including the flame cells.

(arising from the mesoderm) which are highly specialized and complex. Copulation involves the mutual exchange of sperm, whereby two individual worms come together at their ventral surfaces and the penis of each is inserted into a ventral genital opening of the other. Self-fertilization is prevented in part by the structure of the reproductive systems. Several fertilized eggs and hundreds to thousands of yolk cells are soon enclosed in a cocoon-like structure and released through the ventral genital opening to the exterior. The zygotes in time develop into embryos utilizing the stored yolk material within the cocoon which eventually ruptures, discharging young planaria worms.

Planaria also manifests remarkable powers of regeneration forming a complete and perfect individual from only a small piece of animal. Many species of planaria in addition exhibit a form of asexual reproduction in which the worm simply constricts and divides into a headpiece and tailpiece. The two pieces quickly regenerate the missing tissues and organs to form two complete organisms.

Classes Trematoda and Cestoda

The other two classes of the phylum *Platyhelminthes*, namely the *Trematoda* (flukes) and *Cestoda* (tapeworms) are very different in appearance and habit as a result of their adaptation to a parasitic existence. They include numerous parasites which are harmful to man and domesticated animals, and possess several of the structural modifications characteristic of parasites. In general, members of the Trematoda or flukeworms have undergone less extreme structural modifications than those of the Cestoda or tapeworms in adapting to parasitism. The most outstanding modifications experienced by the trematodes in adaptation to parasitism are replacement of the epidermis and cilia by a cuticle and development of hooks and suckers for attachment to the host. Most lack eyespots and other specialized sense organs but have well developed digestive, excretory, and in particular reproductive organs. Many of the trematodes have com-

plex life histories and require the participation of several specific hosts. They range from those that live on the external surfaces of other animals to those that inhabit the internal recesses of the host. The human liver fluke, whose life cycle is described in an earlier chapter (Figure 10-10), is a well-known example which illustrates some of the adaptations that have been made to the parasitic way of life.

Members of the Cestoda have earned the common name of tapeworms from their characteristic long, ribbon-like appearance, which may be many feet long. One of the largest tapeworms to infect man has been known to reach a length of 60 feet. They are typically restricted to the intestines of their hosts. They have degenerated to such an extreme degree in their long standing evolutionary adaptation to parasitism that in addition to their possession of the major parasitic traits displayed by the Trematoda they entirely lack their own digestive tract including a mouth. They are completely dependent upon their host for digested food. However, they possess well-developed reproductive and excretory systems which are basically like those of the other members of the Platyhelminthes. The body consists of a head provided with hooks and suckers, and a series of body "segments" called *proglottids* (Figure 18-11). The latter are produced from the neck region by a process resembling budding, the youngest proglottids being nearest the head and the oldest progressively farther away. Each mature proglottid has both male and female sex organs, and as it grows older it becomes engorged with eggs containing embryo worms.

PHYLUM NEMERTINEA

This phylum of approximately six hundred species consists of mostly flattened and greatly elongated marine forms ("ribbon", "band" or "proboscis" worms) which live mainly on the ocean floor. In comparison to the Platyhelminthes they show certain advances which become even more developed in higher animal phyla. For this reason the phylum, although not usually considered to be a major one, is worth considering in an introductory textbook.

The three most outstanding new features of members of this phylum are a digestive tract with an anal opening, a blood-vascular system, and a unique protrusible structure called the *proboscis*. The digestive tract is a straight tube leading from an anterior mouth for taking in food to a posterior anus for eliminating undigested materials. The blood-vascular system consists of three main blood vessels extending throughout the length of the body which unite at both the anterior and posterior ends. In most species the blood is usually colorless (although some have red blood cells containing a form of hemoglobin) and is circulated largely by muscular contractions of the animal as it swims. The unique proboscis is a tubular organ, located in a sheath dorsal to the mouth opening. It is used to capture food and bring it to the mouth for ingestion. The proboscis actually is not an integral part of the digestive tract, un-

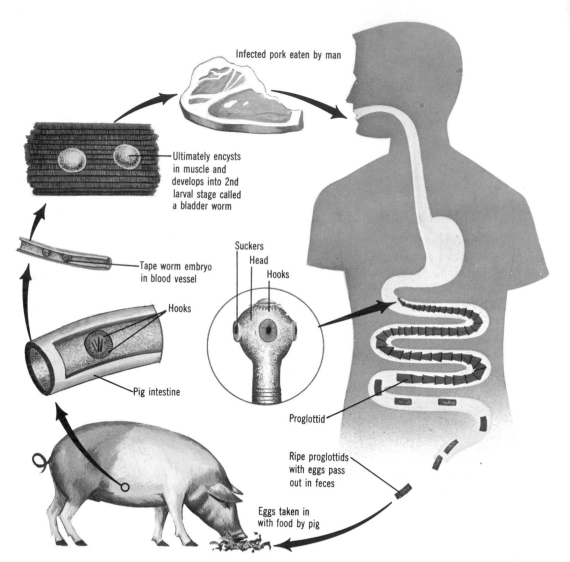

Infected pork eaten by man

Ultimately encysts in muscle and develops into 2nd larval stage called a bladder worm

Tape worm embryo in blood vessel

Hooks

Pig intestine

Suckers

Head

Hooks

Proglottid

Ripe proglottids with eggs pass out in feces

Eggs taken in with food by pig

Figure 18-11. Life cycle of a tapeworm infecting man. Note that the first larval stage consisting of an embryo with hooks occurs in the pig intestine.

like the proboscis of planaria which is part of the pharynx. The central nervous system of the Nemertinea is more highly developed than that of the Platyhelminthes, consisting of a "brain" (composed of two ganglia) and three longitudinal and connecting nerve cords (Figure 18-12).

In several important respects, however, the Nemertinea resemble the Platyhelminthes. Both phyla display bilateral symmetry; they develop from three embryonic layers (ectoderm, mesoderm, and endoderm) without the formation of a body cavity; and they possess excretory organs that are fundamentally similar, although more specialized in the Nemertinea.

Most members of the Nemertinea are dioecious with fertilization occurring in the open water or within the body of the female depending on the species. A ciliated free-swimming larva is usually one of the stages of development, later undergoing metamorphosis to form the adult.

PHYLUM NEMATODA (ROUNDWORMS)

Members of the phylum *Nematoda* which constitute about ten thousand species are tiny, cylindrical, thread-like worms with bodies pointed at both ends. They are called *round worms* and occur almost everywhere in fantastically high numbers, particularly in fresh water, salt water, and soil. With the exception of the *Arthropoda* (Chapter 19) and *Protozoa* they probably exceed in numbers all other animals. Many are parasitic on plants as well as animals at one time or another. A significantly large number are also free-living during all stages of their life cycle.

Undoubtedly the most advanced feature of the nematoda is the presence of a primitive type of body cavity between the gut wall and body wall. It is not a true body cavity, unlike that of most higher animal phyla, in the sense that it has developed from the embryonic blastocoel (Chapter 31) and is not lined by mesodermal tissue. For this reason its body cavity is called a *pseudocoelom*.

All nematodes show a marked similarity in anatomy (Figure 18-13). The adult form of the species *Ascaris lumbricoides* as more or less representative of the phylum is a parasite inhabiting the small intestine of man. The body, which ranges in length from about 5 to 15 inches, is a relatively simple cylindrical tube, tapered at both ends and covered with a heavy cuticle secreted by the underlying epidermis. The cuticle must be periodically shed to permit growth of the individual. The body cavity or pseudocool between the body wall and digestive tract contains a lymph-like fluid which presumably serves in the transport of nutrients and wastes. Portions of the excretory and reproductive systems are also present within the body cavity.

The digestive tract of nematodes typically

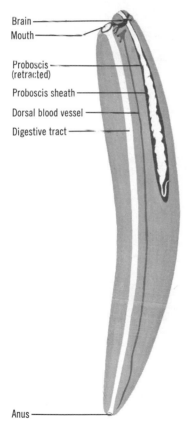

Brain —
Mouth —

Proboscis —
(retracted)

Proboscis sheath —

Dorsal blood vessel —

Digestive tract —

Anus —

Figure 18-12. Diagram of structure of a typical nemertean.

consists of an anteriorly located *mouth* encircled by sense organs, a muscular *pharynx*, a straight elongated *intestine*, a *rectum*, and a posterior *anus*. The epithelial cells lining the intestine function in digestion and in the storage of carbohydrates and lipids, transferring nutrients to the fluid of the pseudocoel for distribution to the various parts of the worm. No blood-vascular system is present. In a parasite such as *Ascaris lumbricoides* the predigested food mixture of the host passes into the parasite's intestine where it is absorbed.

The nervous system is made up of a nerve ring surrounding the pharynx from which nerve cords and fibers extend in various directions innervating the muscle cells and sense organs.

The excretory organ is somewhat unique consisting of a modified system of cells with internal canals which fuse at the anterior end to form a single tube. The latter empties to the exterior by way of a so-called *excretory pore*.

Most nematode species are dioecious—either male or female. Copulation usually results in the occurrence of fertilization in the oviducts. The resultant zygotes become surrounded by

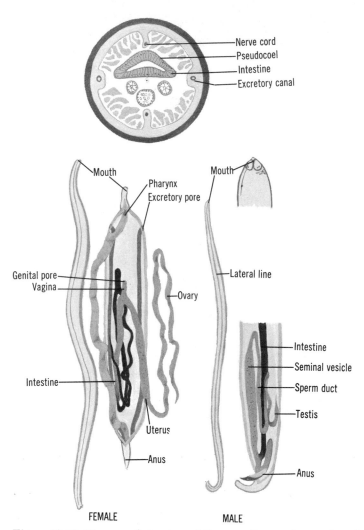

Figure 18-13. Diagram of structure of the parasite roundworm *Ascaris lumbricoides*.

a proteinaceous shell and are released via the digestive tract. Embryo development occurs within the shell—the young worms finally hatching after the eggs have been ingested by the proper host, as in the case of *Ascaris lumbricoides* within the intestine of man. The young worms subsequently penetrate the intestinal mucosa and enter the circulatory system thus passing to the liver, heart, and lungs. They eventually reach the intestine where they undergo final maturation to the adult stage.

The commonly known hookworms, pinworms, and trichina worms are other important examples of the approximately fifty species of nematodes known to be parasitic to man. The bizarre disease *elephantiasis* is caused by a nematode species which is transmitted to man by the bite of a mosquito. The parasitic worm by virtue of sheer numbers clogs the lymph passages of the human host, usually resulting in huge swellings of the extremities. The leg of an individual infected by this parasite may come to weigh as much as one hundred pounds.

The tremendous abundance of nematodes is illustrated by the estimate that an acre of good soil houses approximately three billion nematode individuals of various species.

SUPPLEMENTARY REFERENCES

Borradaile, L. A., F. A. Potts, L. E. S. Eastham, and J. T. Saunders, *The Invertebrata*, second edition, Cambridge University Press, New York, 1955.

Buchsbaum, R., *Animals without Backbones*, revised edition, University of Chicago Press, Chicago, 1960.

Hegner, R. W., *Parade of the Animal Kingdom*, Macmillan, New York, 1937.

Hyman, L. H., *The Invertebrates*, Vols. 1-3, McGraw-Hill, New York, 1940-1951.

Mayr, E., E. B. Lindsley, and R. L. Usinger, *Methods and Principles of Systematic Zoology*, McGraw-Hill, New York, 1953.

Chapter 19   Animal Kingdom: Phyla Mollusca, Annelida, and Arthropoda

ANIMAL PHYLA CHARACTERIZED BY A TRUE BODY CAVITY

Modes of Formation of a True Body Cavity

The remaining phyla of the animal kingdom are progressively more advanced than those that have already been described. One of their most outstanding features in addition to bilateral symmetry and the development of three embryonic layers (ectoderm, mesoderm, and endoderm) is the possession of a true body cavity or coelom. They are accordingly referred to as *eucoelomate* animals. By definition a coelom is a body cavity that surrounds the digestive tract and is lined by a layer of mesoderm tissue.

There are two fundamentally different modes of formation of the mesoderm and coelom (Figure 19-1) which are evident only during early embryonic development. The manner of mesoderm and coelom formation serves as one of the important criteria for grouping the eucoelomate animals into two major divergent branches whose evolution has proceeded independently of one another. In one branch composed of the major phyla *Mollusca, Annelida,* and *Arthropoda,* as well as several minor phyla, certain cells early in the cleavage process first give rise to a solid mass of mesodermal cells. They subsequently develop cavities to form the coelom, a type known as the *schizocoelom.* In the other main branch con-

sisting of the major phyla *Echinodermata* and *Chordata* (discussed in the next chapter), the mesoderm arises from the wall of the embryonic gut as hollow outgrowths or pouches which eventually form a coelom, a type known as the *enterocoelom.* To date the culmination of evolutionary development (in terms of numbers of species and individuals and adaptability to various environmental conditions) is represented by the phylum *Arthropoda* in the schizocoelous branch and the phylum *Chordata* in the enterocoelous branch.

PHYLUM MOLLUSCA

External Features

Members of the phylum *Mollusca* consist of nearly one hundred thousand known species arranged in five classes, the *Amphineura* (e.g., chitons covered with eight segmented dorsal shell plates), the *Scaphopoda* (e.g., tooth shells), the *Gastropoda* (e.g., snails and slugs), the *Pelecypoda* (e.g., clams, mussels, oysters), and the *Cephalopoda* (e.g., squids, octopuses, nautiluses). They are widely distributed, being found in the depths of the oceans, the arid deserts, fresh water, the moist tropics, and at the tops of mountains. The three most important classes are the *Gastropoda, Pelecypoda,* and *Cephalopoda,* all displaying great diversity of structural adaptations which account for their successful way of life.

Most molluscs are free-living, creeping, or burrowing marine animals. Some such as the cephalopods, represented by the octopuses, are more active free-swimming types. All have soft bodies which in most species are protected by a heavy shell or exoskeleton. Because of the latter structure, they have proved to be excellent fossils. Their presence in Cambrian rocks (Chapter 32) laid down six hundred million years ago has provided firm evidence that the molluscs have arisen from an extremely ancient line in the primitive sea.

In addition to the characteristics of bilateral symmetry and three embryonic layers, all molluscs possess a basic body plan which clearly distinguishes them from the other animal phyla. The body is essentially made up of a *head* which in most species is well-developed with sense organs, a *visceral region*

containing most of the internal organs, a ventral muscular *foot* used for locomotion, and covering the entire animal an envelope of glandular epithelial tissue called the *mantle* which in many cases secretes the predominantly calcium carbonate shell (Figure 19-2).

In the pelecypods (e.g., the clam or mussel) the shell is composed of two valves hinged together at the dorsal side. The foot is thrust out between the margins of the shell for purposes of locomotion. Certain adductor muscles passing through the mantle are attached to valves at particular areas and are responsible for the opening and closing of the valves at the ventral edges by relaxation and contraction, respectively. If a small foreign body such as a sand grain, a small piece of shell or a parasite comes to rest between the mantle and shell, a copious secretion occurs enveloping the

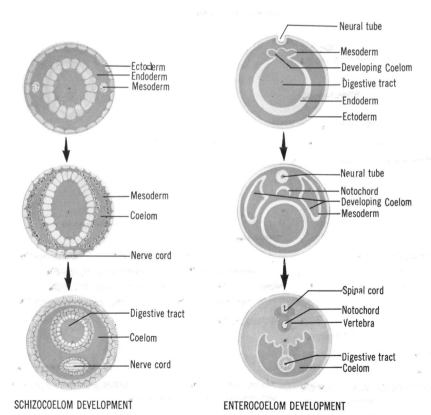

SCHIZOCOELOM DEVELOPMENT ENTEROCOELOM DEVELOPMENT

Figure 19-1. Diagram of development of the schizocoelom (in the earthworm) and enterocoelom (in a vertebrate) in the eucoelomate animals. See text for details.

foreign particle in successive layers of shell-like material. Thus it results in the formation of a pearl. Certain species, particularly the pearl oyster, *Pinctada*, are used in Japan for the "culturing" of pearls by inserting a small piece of shell into a pocket of the mantle. In gastropods, as represented by snails and slugs, the visceral region is usually coiled in a spiral and is covered by a shell frequently displaying a corresponding spiral configuration. In these animals the head is well developed, and the broad muscular foot is well adapted for creeping.

Many of the molluscs (in fact all the modern classes with the exception of the pelecypods) possess a unique organ, the rasping tongue-like *radula* consisting of a strip of tissue with rows of horny teeth. It is really functional only in chitons and gastropods and is vestigial in the cephalopods. The radula is operated in a saw-like fashion by the action of specific muscles and is used for obtaining food. In the case of some carnivorous snails, it serves for drilling holes in the shells of bivalves (or pelecypods).

The digestive tract of all molluscs is con-

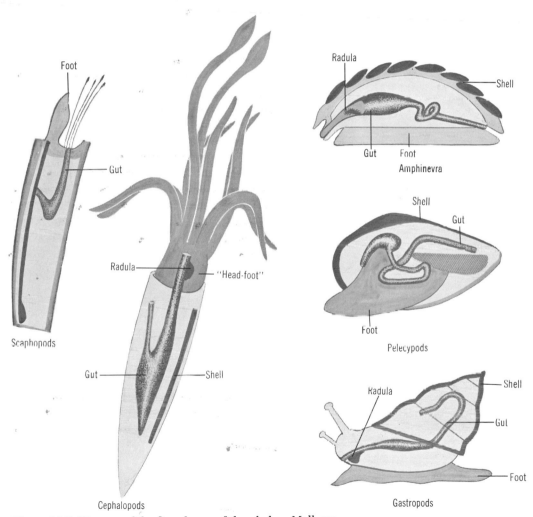

Figure 19-2. Diagram of the five classes of the phylum Mollusca.

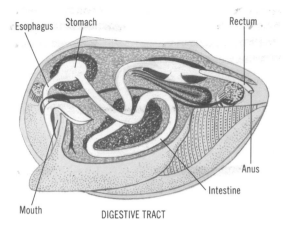

Esophagus   Stomach   Rectum

Mouth   DIGESTIVE TRACT
Anus
Intestine

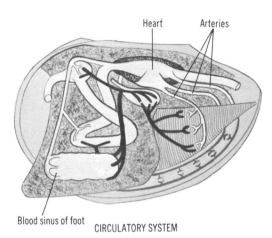

Heart   Arteries

Blood sinus of foot   CIRCULATORY SYSTEM

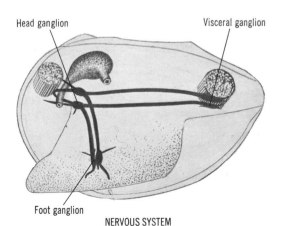

Head ganglion   Visceral ganglion

Foot ganglion
NERVOUS SYSTEM

Figure 19-3. Diagram of the digestive, circulatory, and nervous systems in the clam.

stituted essentially of a mouth, esophagus, stomach, intestine, rectum, anus, and important glandular appendages. Relatively appreciable modifications are evident among the species. Digestion in general is initiated within the passages of the alimentary tract and is completed intracellularly by cells of the lining.

The molluscs with the exception of the cephalopods exhibit a well-developed, "open-type" circulatory system (Chapter 25) consisting of a beating heart and numerous distributing blood vessels leading to the various organs of the body. Within the organs, however, the blood flows through spaces or *sinuses* rather than capillaries. Nutrients and oxygen diffuse directly into the intracellular fluid without going through the walls of the blood vessels. The cephalopods have an exceptionally well-developed circulatory system of the "closed" type (with capillaries) which is presumably related to its more active way of life compared to the other classes of molluscs.

Among the most remarkable adaptations effected in some molluscs during the course of their evolution are their lung-like organs. These consist of the mantle cavity and the richly vascularized mantle itself which is the site of gas exchange in the terrestrial gastropods and in some of the aquatic ones. In all other molluscs including the marine gastropods, the gills are the primary organs for gas exchange between the water and the circulating blood. Since numerous fresh-water snails also "breathe" by means of these "lungs," it is presumed that they probably descended from terrestrial forms —just as aquatic mammals like the whale and seal are considered to have evolved from land mammals.

The excretory organs of molluscs are fundamentally paired tubules called *nephridia* which are differentiated into tubular and bladder-like portions. The nephridia which lead from the coelom and drain by way of external openings remove soluble wastes from the intracellular fluid and blood.

The nervous system in many molluscs consists of three basic pairs of interconnected ganglia located in the head, foot, and visceral mass with nerves extending to the muscles and sensory surfaces of the body. In cephalopods, however, as represented by the squids, the nervous system has evolved into a highly developed and specialized ganglionic mass, the brain, with nerves extending to all parts of the body. A diagrammatic representation of the digestive, circulatory, and nervous systems of the clam (Figure 19-3) is shown to illustrate these systems in the molluscs.

In many molluscs, the sexes are separate, and the reproductive processes vary greatly depending upon the species. The ovaries and testes are generally branching structures within the visceral mass. For some, fertilization occurs externally, and for others, internally. In certain species such as the common marine hard-shell clam, *Venus mercenaria*, and in numerous marine snails the zygotes first develop into free-swimming ciliated larvae called *trochophores* (Figure 19-4). In many molluscs the trochophore is soon converted into a second larval stage, the *veliger*, which eventually metamorphoses into the adult. Many of the fresh-water mussels have life cycles involving a larval stage parasitic on fresh-water fishes.

The wide variety of organisms constituting the phylum *Mollusca* is the result of evolutionary adaptations in different directions from a common ancestral form in response to environmental conditions in different habitats.

Class Amphineura

This class, as exemplified by the chitons or "armadillo snails," is regarded as the most primitive of the five classes. It is thought to be more similar than any other present-day type to the common ancestral form from which all other molluscs have evolved. Its members are only modified to a small extent in their general features, showing the molluscan characteristics in a simple form. The chitons are sluggish animals which live in shallow water and feed upon algae rasped from rocks by the

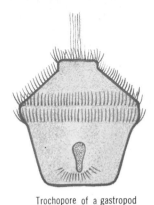

Trochopore of a gastropod

Figure 19-4. Trocophore of a marine snail.

action of the radula. They are characterized by a shell consisting of eight dorsal plates (Figure 19-5). Their various internal systems (digestive, circulatory, excretory, reproductive, and nervous) although similar to those of other molluscs are considered to be of a relatively primitive type.

Class Scaphopoda

Members of this class are elongated molluscs covered by a curved tapering shell open at both ends, with a foot which is modified into a digging organ protruding from one end. These structural features represent a particular set of adaptations to a burrowing existence in which scaphopods lie partially buried in the sand. They feed on small organisms in the water that is conducted in and out of the mantle cavity.

Class Pelecypoda

The pelecypods represent still another set of adaptations to a burrowing existence, being bivalved and laterally compressed (Figure 19-5). The head is not well developed and the species usually have poorly developed sense organs. In general, they are motile to a limited extent and lead a more or less sedentary existence, although a few species swim fairly well. As one adaptation to their sedentary life, they filter microorganisms for purposes of

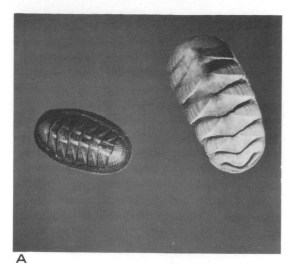

A

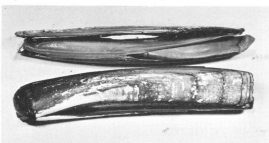

B

C

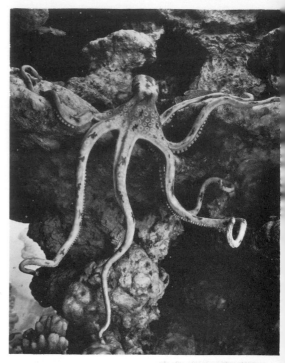

D

Figure 19-5. Representations of the various molluscs. (A) Chitons (class Amphineura) (*courtesy of Amer. Mus. Natural History*); (B) razor clam (class Pelecypoda) (*courtesy of Carolina Biol. Supply Co.*); (C) land snail (class Gastropoda) (*courtesy of L. M. Chace*); (D) octopus model and nautilus model (class Cephalopoda) (*courtesy of Amer. Mus. Natural History*). The class Scaphspoda is not shown.

feeding from the water environment by means of the gills which initially evolved as a respiratory structure. The pelecypods range in size from tiny species 2 to 3 mm in diameter to giant clams (*Tridacna*) of the tropical Pacific reaching diameters of approximately six feet and weights as high as five hundred pounds.

Class Gastropoda

Members of the *Gastropoda*, the largest of the molluscan classes, reflect the evolution of a wide diversity of structures in different habitats. Their distribution in environments ranging from the aquatic to the terrestrial and the accompanying adaptation from gill-type respiratory organs to a lung-like kind have already been mentioned. Most species typically display the soft body within a specially coiled shell. Some, however, such as the garden slugs, have lost their shells in the course of evolution. In all likelihood the ancestral gastropods lived in the sea, since the present-day primitive types are marine, and the more specialized forms are of the fresh-water kind or terrestrial.

Class Cephalopoda

The cephalopods are the most highly organized and modified of the molluscs in adaptation to a free-swimming, active, predaceous existence. Of particular interest are the remarkably developed nervous system and eyes. The image-forming eyes of the squid are complete with cornea, lens, and retina. (See Figure 22-9). In their apparent resemblance to those of chordates, such as mammals, the cephalopod eye represents an extraordinary example of independent evolution of similar structures in relatively unrelated organisms.

Despite the extremely modified evolutionary adaptations seen in the cephalopods, the fundamental plan of organization of the primitive ancestral mollusc can still be discerned. The visceral mass has become elongated, and the foot has evolved into several muscular tentacles bearing rows of adhesive cups. At one extreme in some species, such as the octopus, the shell has entirely disappeared, whereas at the other

Figure 19-6. Giant squid (*courtesy of Amer. Mus. Natural History*).

extreme, as in the nautilus, there is a large shell (Figure 19-5).

The characteristics of the squid are fairly representative of the cephalopods. The torpedo-shaped body (Figure 19-6) is covered by a tough muscular mantle. At the open end of the body are the tentacles or foot and the head with its mouth and well-developed vertebrate-like eyes. The anus of the U-shaped digestive tract opens into the mantle cavity. The squid swims through the water by (1) a pair of fins located at the opposite or posterior end of the trunk and (2) by draining water into the mantle cavity and expelling it through a nozzle-like tube, the *siphon*, derived from the foot and located on the ventral surface near the eyes. When necessary the squid can move through the water with great speed by the rapid and forceful ejection of water through the siphon, a form of jet propulsion. It can swim either backward or forward by simply changing the direction of the siphon. The fins and tentacles serve as steering and stabilizing devices. The squid also possess an *ink sac* opening into the rectum which functions as a protective device in escaping predators by releasing a stream of ink to the water being pumped from the mantle cavity, thus hiding its movements. Different species of squids range in size from about an inch in body length to the giant form which has been reported to have a body length as long as 18 feet with 34-foot-long tentacles.

The phyla *Mollusca* and *Annelida* (described below) are considered to have decended undoubtedly from a common ancestor in view of the similarity of several important features including general level of organization, larval types, and embryonic cleavage patterns.

PHYLUM ANNELIDA

General Features

The phylum *Annelida* is composed of four classes totaling some ten thousand species.

The annelids consist largely of marine worms that burrow or crawl upon the ocean floor, especially near the shore. Many marine species build small tubes which they permanently inhabit, whereas other species live in a succession of temporary tubes. Some species are even free-swimming, at least during the breeding part of their life cycle. Others have adapted to fresh water and even to terrestrial conditions. In the latter example, sufficient moisture must be present for survival of the organism. Many of us are familiar with such annelids as the earthworm and, to a lesser extent, the sandworm and leech. The earthworm as a terrestrial species, however, possesses several features which are quite unlike those of most annelids. The most striking feature of the annelids is a body structure consisting of cylindrical segments of similar structure, internally as well as externally, and separated from one another by transverse partitions. The segments at both ends, however, have undergone sufficient differentiation to be distinguished as a head (made up of three segments) and a hind end (one segment). All other segments of

the body are more or less alike. Externally, segmentation is evinced by the obvious rings and often by the presence of many pairs of appendages. Internally it is shown by the segmentation and pairing of internal organs. However, the digestive tube, the principal longitudinal blood vessels, and the nerve cords extend without interruption throughout the length of the annelid body. The excretory organs, called *nephridia*, are also characteristically paired and repeated in most body segments. Segmentation in one form or another is present in all the more advanced animal phyla having evolved independently in the annelid-arthropod line and in the chordate line (which includes man).

Like the coelom of the Mollusca, that of the Annelida is schizocoelous (p. 439) in origin. However, it is uniquely separated into compartments by the transverse partitions or *septa* of the segments. In addition, the annelids characteristically display a dorsal anterior brain connected to a ventral nerve cord which in turn is made of paired ganglia in each segment.

Like the preceding Mollusca, the Annelida display three embryonic layers and are bilaterally symmetrical. Its members also have a closed circulatory system complete with a group of "hearts" which pump the blood through the body. Many annelids use the moist skin for the exchange of the respiratory gases, lacking any other type of respiratory system, although some marine species have gills.

Class Polychaeta ("Many-Bristled")

The polychaetes as a group probably best characterize the annelid level of organization. The earliest fossil records of the annelids, like those of the molluscs, date back to the Cambrian Period, thus suggesting descent from an ancient marine annelid line. These fossil remains show a distinct resemblance to one of the present-day annelid class, *Polychaeta*. The latter constitutes the largest and probably the most primitive of the four annelid classes. These annelids, depending on the species, may be mud and sand burrowers, inhabitors of artificial tubes which they build from secreted material, or free-swimming types.

The common "sandworm" or "clamworm" *Nereis virens* (Figure 19-7) is typical of this class as well as of the phylum. Most polychaetes are distinguished primarily by the presence on each segment of a pair of external laterally placed, fleshy, paddle-like structures called *parapodia* (singular, *parapodium*) which serve in the dual roles of locomotion and gaseous exchange. Numerous bundles of chitinous bristles protrude from the parapodia and are probably useful in protecting the animal as well as holding him in his burrow. The relatively large surface of the parapodia and their rich supply of capillaries make them well suited as respiratory organs. The body wall of all annelids and many of the lower worms is covered externally by a delicate, noncellular *cuticle* secreted by the underlying epidermal cells.

Members of the Polychaeta also possess a clearly differentiated head composed of three segments, well equipped with several sense organs including eyes and tentacles. The latter apparently serve in a tactile function. The body of the sandworm like that of all annelids is a long, slender, rounded cylinder made up of many segments. It is essentially a succession of similar segments with certain specializations and modifications at each end. Body growth typically involves the addition of successive new segments at the posterior end just ahead of the segment bearing the anus.

The long digestive tract is a straight tube extending from the ventrally located mouth at the anterior end to the anus at the extreme posterior end. The mouth leads into the pharynx, an eversible organ having two jaws, which is used like a proboscis for seizing prey. The pharynx is followed successively by an esophagus and a long simple tube called the stomach-intestine which terminates at the anus. The coelom itself is partitioned into compartments by the transverse separating walls or septa of the segments and is filled with a lymph-like fluid containing ameboid cells.

Figure 19-7. Clamworm or sandworm (*courtesy of N. Y. Zoological Society*).

The circulatory system is of the "closed" type, since the blood is confined throughout its circuit to the blood vessels. The latter consists of a main dorsal and ventral longitudinal blood vessel connected to smaller branches that lead to capillaries in various parts of the body. Muscular contractions or pulsations of the larger blood vessels are responsible for propelling the blood through the circulatory system. The red color of the blood is due to the presence of hemoglobin-like pigment which, unlike that of vertebrates, is not contained in blood cells but is dissolved in the plasma itself.

Every segment, except those near the ends of the body, has a pair of small coiled nephridia located almost completely within the coelom and consisting of coiled tubes. At one end of each nephridium is a ciliated, funnel-shaped opening which presumably collects dissolved metabolic waste products from the coelomic fluid. The opposite end of the tube empties to the exterior through a pore in the body wall.

The nervous system is typically made up of a large ganglion, the brain (situated in the dorsal region of the head), connected by nerves encircling the pharynx to a ventral nerve cord (with segmental ganglia) which traverses the length of the body. Smaller nerve fibers, similar in number and distribution in nearly all the segments, radiate from the nerve cord to muscles and sense organs.

Nereis, like most of the polychaetes, is dioecious. The temporary ovaries and testes form in each of the two sexes at each breeding season from certain cells lining the coelomic cavity. Egg cells and sperm are emitted in huge numbers to the sea water where fertilization occurs. The zygote in many species of Polychaeta develop into a ciliated free-swimming larval stage, the *trochophore*, similar to that seen in certain classes of the Mollusca. It eventually metamorphoses into a young adult.

Class Oligochaeta

Members of this class consisting of well over two thousand species are confined almost exclusively to fresh water and to moist terrestrial habitats. With the exception of the familiar earthworm belonging to the genus

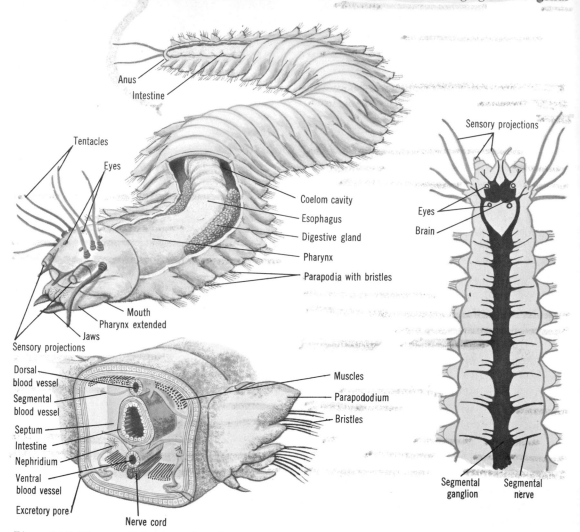

Figure 19-8. Diagram of structure of sandworm.

Lumbricus, they are for the most part quite small in size. Most species of earthworms are rarely longer than ten inches, although certain tropical earthworms attain the enormous size of ten feet in length. At the opposite extreme are the fresh-water worms measuring less than a millimeter in length.

The name of the class is derived from the fact that its members have few and inconspicuous bristles. Unlike the polychaete, the oligochaete, as represented by the earthworm, lacks parapodia but still has some of its vestigial remains called *setae*. It moves largely by muscular movements aided by the setae. The earthworm has a poorly differentiated head region and lacks eyes, tentacles, and other head appendages (Figure 19-9). In fact a careful examination is necessary to distinguish the head from the tail of the earthworm. The number of segments in a full-sized earthworm is not definite and varies between 120 and 175. All segments—except the first segment which contains the mouth and the most posterior segment which contains the anus—are externally more or less similar. Actually the external surfaces of segments 31 to 37 are characteristically glandular and swollen to give a girdlelike appearance. This region is called the *clitellum* (Figure 19-10) and secretes the mucous sheath in which fertilization and subsequent embryonic development take place. Earthworms have outstanding regenerative powers and are capable of replacing damaged or destroyed segments or groups of segments to an extent that depends on the region of the body. Beneath the epidermis the earthworm's body wall is a layer of *circular muscle* whose contraction decreases the diameter but increases the length of the body. Gaseous exchange between the blood and environment occurs through the skin.

The circulatory system of the earthworm, is essentially similar to that of the sandworm. It has in addition several secondary longitudinal vessels and five pairs of vessels, so-called "hearts," which surround the esophagus connecting the main dorsal with the main ventral blood vessels.

The excretory system and nervous system are comparable to those of the sandworm. The only major difference is the notable lack of highly specialized sense organs in the head region of the earthworm. The majority, if not all, of the sense receptors are apparently located in the surface layers of the body wall with the greatest concentration at the anterior end.

The earthworm's digestive system has the usual structures already described for the sandworm. In addition a portion immediately following the esophagus is differentiated into a *crop* (for storage of food) and a muscular *gizzard* (for grinding food). Also present are several pairs of *calciferous glands* which secrete calcium carbonate into the esophagus. They presumably function in the neutralization of acid soil in the gut as well as in the elimination of excess carbonate from the blood. These additional adaptations are apparently well suited to the soil-burrowing existence of the earthworm. The earthworm's source of nutrition is the decaying organic matter of the soil. It is ingested by passing an enormous quantity of soil through the digestive tract. Undigested residues are eliminated via the anus as familiar worm castings. As a result of these activities, the earth is turned, bringing lower levels of soil up to the surface. Thus it accounts for an increased aeration of the soil as well as an improvement in its chemical composition—two distinct benefits which enhance the productivity of the soil. Charles Darwin estimated that the activity of earthworms accounted for a turnover of as much as eighteen tons per acre per year.

Unlike most annelids which release their gametes in the surrounding water where chance fertilization occurs, the earthworm in adapting to a terrestrial habitat has experienced several important changes in reproduction. The earthworm is monoecious, having both ovaries and testes in the same individual, which are part of the permanently developed reproductive systems. The two pairs of testes are located in segments 10 and 11, counting from the anterior end of the body, whereas the pair of ovaries are in segment 13. Self-fertilization cannot take place because of the structural organization of the reproductive system.

Copulation, which usually occurs only at night during moist weather, consists of the coming together of two individuals along their ventral surfaces in a temporary union. Mucous secretions by both worms at this time form a protective sheath about the two partners. Between the sheath and body walls are small grove-like channels which serve as pathways for the transfer of sperm from the *seminal vesicles* (site of maturation of sperm) of each to the *seminal receptacles* (site of storage for

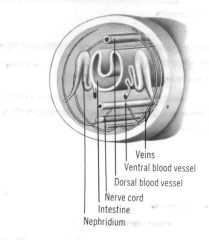

Veins
Ventral blood vessel
Dorsal blood vessel
Nerve cord
Intestine
Nephridium

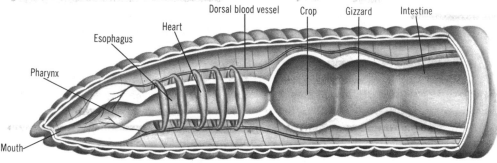

Dorsal blood vessel Crop Gizzard Intestine
Heart
Esophagus
Pharynx
Mouth

CIRCULATORY AND DIGESTIVE SYSTEM

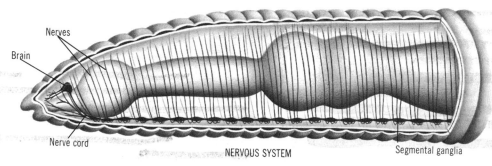

Nerves
Brain
Nerve cord
NERVOUS SYSTEM
Segmental ganglia

Figure 19-9. Diagram of digestive, circulatory, nervous, and excretory systems of the earthworm.

sperm until subsequent fertilization) of the other. Following the exchange of sperm during copulation, the mates separate. Fertilization, which subsequently occurs only after the eggs have reached maturity and been released, takes place in a unique manner. A special mucous sheath, secreted by glandular cells of the clitellum (Figure 19-10) is moved anteriorly by muscular contractions of the body. As it passes segment 14, it receives mature egg cells from the oviduct openings, and as it passes segment 9, it receives from the openings of the seminal receptacles sperm obtained during copulation. Fertilization occurs within the sheath as it continues to slide forward until it finally slips off the anterior end of the worm. The sheath which is usually left behind in the burrow becomes sealed to form a capsule or cocoon containing several zygotes. The latter develop into miniature earthworms before emerging.

Class Hirudinea

The third major class of annelids is the *Hirudinea* or leeches made up chiefly of aquatic forms, although some are marine and others terrestrial (Figure 19-11). Many members of this class have a parasitic or semiparasitic existence feeding on the blood of vertebrate hosts. Although the leeches display the basic body plan of annelids, they have undergone considerable modification and specialization in adapting to their parasitic way of life. They lack parapodia and setae and generally have suckers for locomotion, attachment, and feeding. Some possess horny jaws for making incisions in the skin of the host. The anticoagulant *hirudin* (Chapter 25) is secreted by their salivary glands thus preventing the coagulation of host blood while they are feeding. The digestive tract bears many side pouches for the prolonged storage of blood thus permitting the animal to live for long periods, as much as several months, on a single feeding.

Class Archiannelida

This class of annelids represents a miscellaneous collection of a small group of simpli-

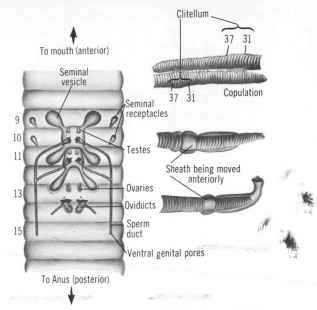

Figure 19-10. Diagrams of reproductive system and copulation in the earthworm. See text for details.

fied, possibly primitive, marine worms. Its members show internal but not external segmentation and form a typical trochophore larva during the course of development to the adult stage. It is generally considered to be representative of a primitive annelid type, although it could possibly reflect a secondary simplification by evolution.

PHYLUM ARTHROPODA

General Features

The phylum *Arthropoda* consists of five principal classes (and two minor classes). Its members are by far the most successful group of organisms that inhabit the earth. They are found everywhere—in both fresh and salt water, on land and in the air, extending from the torrid equator to the frigid polar regions, from great heights in the atmosphere to far depths in the oceans. The phylum consists of at least one million species of unexcelled diversity, of which approximately 800,000 alone are insects. Among the familiar arthropods are included spiders, millipedes, centipedes, crabs, lobsters, crayfish, shrimp, and

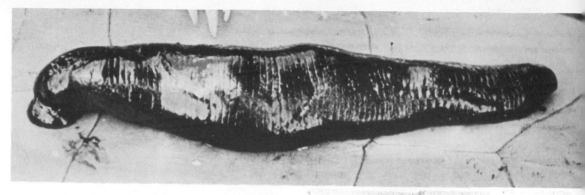

Figure 19-11. American medicinal leech, class Hirudinea (*courtesy of L. M. Chace*).

many others. They far exceed the total number of species, approximately 150,000, of all the other animal phyla as well as the 350,000 plant species. Arthropods are the arch biological competitors of man, eating and destroying his food and shelter, carrying disease, and parasitizing his body. Although several are favorable to man's existence, serving as food and a destroyer of certain parasites, these benefits are far outweighed by the damage inflicted by most other arthropods. They range in size from microscopic to enormous forms such as the giant crab which may measure up to twelve feet in diameter. The complexity of their structure and behavior is matched only by that of the vertebrates.

The fundamental structures which the arthropods share in common with the annelids leave little doubt that both phyla evolved from the same ancestor, probably some five hundred million years ago. The two phyla consist of animals characterized by bilateral symmetry, three germinal layers, a schizocoelom, segmentation, and organ systems that are fundamentally alike.

In addition, the arthropods have evolved serveral important new characteristics which clearly distinguish them as a definite and unique phylum. First, they display jointed appendages—limbs composed of several parts which are hinged together in particular ways to permit specific movements—accounting for the term *Arthropoda* ("joint-footed"). The

Arthropoda is the only invertebrate phylum with this characteristic. Jointed appendages permit great freedom of movement and have been adapted for jumping, hopping, flying, crawling, swimming, walking, clasping, digging, and biting.

Second, like annelids, arthropods have segmented bodies except that the segments have tended to become modified, specialized, and in part fused. As a result the arthropod body is typically composed of three recognizable regions—the *head, thorax,* and *abdomen.* In general, the head consists of six fused segments with each segment except the first usually possessing a pair of jointed appendages which serve as sensory organs or feeding devices. For example, in the majority of arthropods the first segment of the head lacks appendages, the second segment has a pair of antennae or feelers, the third may also bear antennae, the fourth has jaws or *mandibles,* and the fifth and sixth segments each display a pair of auxiliary jaws or *maxillae* for the handling of food. Depending on the species, the jaws also may be considerably modified into sucking tubes and piercing organs. The number of segments in the thorax and abdomen varies according to the class and species. The thorax of insects, for example, is made up of three segments, whereas that of crustaceans consists of six. The thoracic segments nearly always have attached appendages, whereas the abdominal segments may or may not bear

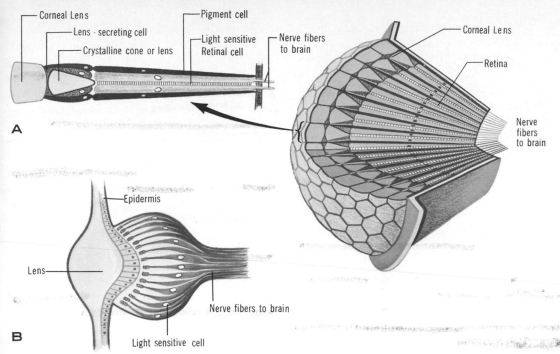

Figure 19-12. Diagram of arthropod eyes: (A) compound eye of an insect consisting of many visual units; (B) simple eye of a spider. *(Adapted from R. Buchsbaum, Animals without Backbones, rev. ed., Univ. Chicago Press, 1960.)*

appendages, according to the species.

Third, and perhaps one of the most significant evolutionary advances typifying the arthropods, is the modification of the soft cuticle (as represented, for example, in annelids) to an exoskeleton thickened and hardened by the impregnation of certain substances such as structural proteins and chitin, a nitrogen-containing polysaccharide. In certain crustaceans calcium salt deposits are also included in the structure of the exoskeleton. The exoskeleton must be regularly shed or *molted* to permit growth. In contrast, those molluscs that are enclosed by an exoskeleton can continually increase in size without molting, because they are capable of continually enlarging their skeleton.

Other general characteristics of the arthropods include:

1. A *greatly reduced coelom* as compared with that of the annelids.

2. An *open circulatory system* resembling that described for most molluscs. The blood is carried from the dorsal pulsating heart by arteries emptying into extensive body spaces, collectively called the *hemocoel*, where it permeates the various internal tissues and organs. It eventually returns by veins to a large cavity surrounding the heart. The blood enters the heart itself by way of several valve-like openings.

3. In general, a *more highly developed and centralized nervous system* than that of annelids with elaborately evolved sensory receptors, especially the eyes, resulting in an organism that is better adapted to cope with its environment. Depending on the species, the head may contain either or both of two kinds of eyes—the *simple eye* and *compound eye*. The compound eye is unique to the arthropods and consists of a group of many visual units. Each visual unit is complete with a corneal structure, its own separate light-sensitive retinal cell with nerve fibers extending to the brain, pigment cell, and lens (Figure 19-12). In contrast, the simple eye possesses a single lens which

functions in conjunction with many light-sensitive cells (Chapter 22).

Arthropod Evolution

It is presumed that the development of the hardened external cuticle or skeleton was a major influence in directing the evolution of an ancient worm-like ancestor with a soft cuticle to the present-day arthropods. Other evolutionary changes, developed by chance and perpetuated by natural selection, must have been correlated with the development of the exoskeleton in order for the new forms to survive and propagate. These necessarily included (1) the complex process of molting (under the intricate control of the endocrine system) to permit growth, and, (2) the development of flexible joints between groups of the externally hardened segments, as well as segmental appendages with definite joints to permit locomotion. These changes were eventually correlated with the evolution of specifically acting groups of muscles in the form of flexor and extensor types, replacing the circularly and longitudinally arranged body wall muscle layers displayed by the annelids. The formation of the exoskeleton very likely set the stage for the evolutionary selection of the additional changes indicated above.

Regional specialization, such as the development of the head with its specialized sense organs and mouth parts, and appendages adapted for specific functions such as swimming, walking, and flying, probably evolved subsequently.

The invasion of the land by descendants of aquatic arthropods was favored by the presence of an exoskeleton generally impervious to water, and of segmented appendages for walking which were also capable of supporting the weight of the body. The limited supply of water available on land was a strong selective factor in favoring the evolution of those arthropod lines whose excretory organs eliminated excreta in a relatively dry state (i.e., uric acid, Chapter 28). Similarly the evolution of tracheal respiratory systems (p. 459) in terrestrial arthropods (in contrast to the gills of aquatic forms)

undoubtedly proved to be a distinct advantage to the land types, because they function with very little loss of water by evaporation and are therefore far less wasteful of water. The insects as judged by their almost infinite diversity and immense numbers are considered to be the most successful class of arthropods. They possess all the advantageous features essential for existence in a terrestrial habitat and in addition have evolved complex behavior patterns and the ability to fly, two characteristics which are probably major factors in their phenomenal biological success.

Class Crustacea

The class *Crustacea* is represented by such well-known organisms as the lobster, crayfish, shrimp, crab, and barnacle. It consists, in large part, of approximately fifty thousand known species of marine forms, to a lesser extent, fresh-water types, and a small number of terrestrial arthropods.

THE LOBSTER. The lobster lives in the sea (in contrast to the closely related crayfish who inhabits fresh water) and is regarded as a typical crustacean. In its general external structure, the segmented body of the lobster is typically enclosed in an exoskeleton (which thins out at the joints permitting maximum flexibility) to form the three main specialized body regions—the head fused to the thorax (collectively called the *cephalothorax*) and the abdomen (Figure 19-14). The exoskeleton, which consists primarily of the characteristic chitin and tough scleroproteins, covers the entire external surface of the crustacean including its most delicate external parts such as the feathery gills. It even extends as a lining into the anterior and posterior ends of the digestive tract. In the periodic process of molting or shedding, the lobster, like other arthropods, dissolves some of the material of its skeleton and secretes a new, flexible, thin skeleton beneath the old one before discarding the latter. In time the new skeleton hardens. Touch-sensitive bristles are scattered over the body, especially on the appendages and

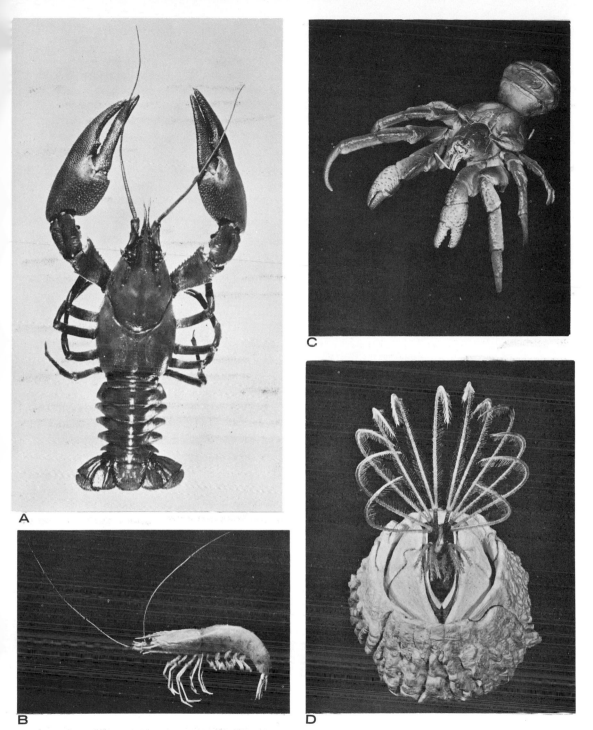

Figure 19-13. Some crustaceans. (A) Crayfish (*courtesy of Carolina Biol. Supply Co.*); (B) model of shrimp (*courtesy of Amer. Mus. Natural History*); (C) robber crab (*Birgus latro*) (*courtesy of Amer. Mus. Natural History*); (D) model of barnacle (*courtesy of Amer. Mus. Natural History*).

tail region, and extend to the external surface through tiny perforations in the exoskeleton.

The body consists of 21 segments (6 making up the head, 8 the thorax, and 7 the abdomen) to which are attached a total of 19 pairs of appendages (each pair on a separate segment) possessing various forms and specialized functions. The first segment of the head, although it bears no appendages, has a pair of compound eyes on long movable stalks which can be extended or retracted thus conferring a considerable range to the field of vision. Two pairs of antennae or sensory appendages, different in form and specialized for tactile and chemical stimulation, are located on the second and third segments. Each of the segments four to nine possesses a pair of highly specialized appendages which are modified for the manipulation and chewing of food and are accordingly called the *jaw* or *mouth parts*. More specifically, the so-called *mandibles or jaws* for chewing are present on the fourth segment, two pairs of *maxillae* for passing food to the mouth on the last two segments of the head, and three pairs of *maxillipeds* for manipulating food on the first three segments of the thorax. The fourth thoracic segment possesses as its appendages an enormous pair of pincer-bearing claws, the *chelipeds*, for grasping food and for defense, whereas each of the remaining four thoracic segments bears a pair of walking appendages, the *periopods*. On the first five segments of the abdomen are situated five pairs of paddle-like appendages, the *swimmerets*, which are used primarily in circulating water to the gills and, to a lesser extent, as an aid in swimming in a forward direction. Actually, in the male the first pair of swimmerets are considerably modified as copulatory organs for transferring sperm to the female; in the female they are greatly reduced in size. The sixth abdominal segment bears a pair of fan-like appendages, the *uropods*, which together with the flap-like seventh abdominal segment (which has no appendages) form the broad tail fin used in swimming.

The feather-like delicate gills of the lobster, as lateral outgrowths of the body wall, lie in certain chambers of the thoracic region and are protected by extensions of the exoskeleton. The digestive tract consists of the *mouth*, a short *esophagus*, a *complex stomach* which includes a so-called *gastric mill* consisting of teeth-like structures that complete the mastication of food, large *digestive glands* containing tubular cavities into which the finely divided food particles are passed for digestion and absorption, an *intestine* which has little or no function in digestion and absorption, and an *anus*.

The circulatory system, like that of the molluscs, is of the "open type" with a beating heart and connecting arteries that terminate in *sinuses* or *hemocoelic* spaces whose circulatory fluid or haemolymph is drained by a system of vessels to the gills for gas exchange and returned to the heart. The blood which has a remarkably rapid clotting time contains the bluish oxygen-carrying pigment, *hemocyanin* (Chapter 25) and colorless leucocytes.

Excretion of nitrogenous wastes is performed by a pair of compound tubular structures or kidneys called the *green glands* leading to a small bladder that empties near the antennae.

The nervous system which roughly resembles that of the annelids consists of a relatively large bilobed "brain" connected to the nerves of the eyes and antennae and to the *ventral nerve cord*, with smaller nerves extending from these structures to the various parts of the segments and appendages.

The reproductive system in the male consists of a pair of partially fused testes located in the thorax and connected by a pair of vas deferens ducts to the outside. In the female the pair of ovaries produce eggs which pass via oviducts to the outside. In copulation the male and female come together ventrally, packets of sperm, or *spermatophores*, are released through the male genital openings and transferred by the modified first pair of swimmerets of the male to a superficial, pouch-like storage cavity,

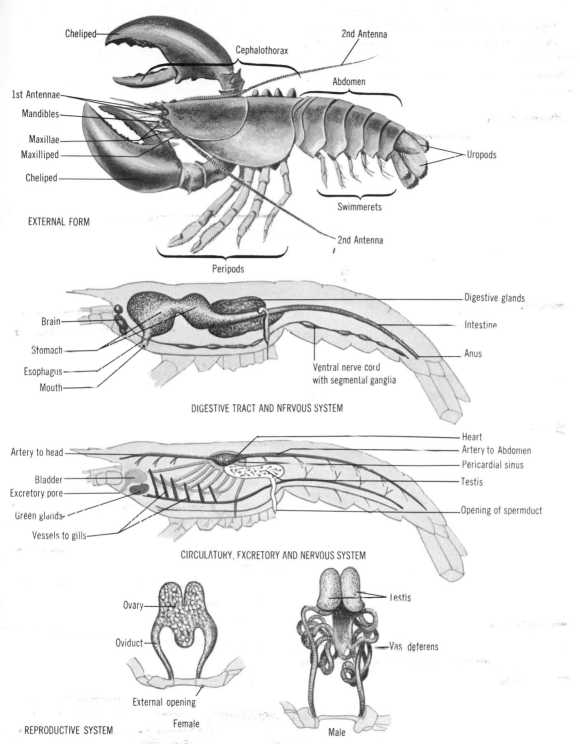

EXTERNAL FORM

Cheliped

Cephalothorax

2nd Antenna

Abdomen

1st Antennae

Mandibles

Maxillae

Maxilliped

Cheliped

Uropods

Swimmerets

2nd Antenna

Peripods

DIGESTIVE TRACT AND NERVOUS SYSTEM

Digestive glands

Brain

Intestine

Stomach

Anus

Esophagus

Mouth

Ventral nerve cord
with segmental ganglia

CIRCULATORY, EXCRETORY AND NERVOUS SYSTEM

Heart

Artery to head

Artery to Abdomen

Pericardial sinus

Bladder

Testis

Excretory pore

Green glands

Opening of spermduct

Vessels to gills

REPRODUCTIVE SYSTEM

Ovary

Testis

Oviduct

Vas deferens

External opening

Female

Male

Figure 19-14. The external and internal anatomy of the lobster. See text for details.

the *seminal receptacle,* in the female. At an appropriate time the eggs are emitted from the oviduct and fertilized by the sperm which are simultaneously issued from the seminal receptacle. The fertilized eggs develop into independent larvae which eventually transfer into adults.

Class Trilobita

This is a now extinct class whose fossilized remains are widely distributed. The body, which consisted of a head, thorax, and abdomen, was divided into three lobes by two longitudinal furrows. *Trilobita* flourished in the Cambrian and Silurian Periods both, presumably as bottom dwellers in the prehistoric seas. Several taxonomists classify this group within a separate subphylum rather than as a class. (Also see Chapter 32.)

Class Onychophora

The great significance to the biologist of this small group of obscure animals existing mostly in the tropics is the fact that they have characteristics of both annelids and arthropods. The best known of the group is the genus *Peripatus* which includes the "walking worm" (Figure 19-15) whose worm-like body has numerous paired short blunt legs or appendages. Its eyes, muscular body wall, and segmentally arranged ciliated nephridial tubules are reminiscent of annelids, whereas the chitinous exoskeleton, the jaws, hemocoel, reduced coelom, and tracheal system are characteristic of the arthropods. This unique mixture of annelid and arthropod traits has been sufficient reason for some biologists to rank them as a separate phylum, rather than as belonging just to the arthropods.

Class Insecta

BASIC FEATURES. The insects are considered to be the most advanced class of modern arthropods. In terms of number alone, either from the point of view of species or individuals, they are by far the dominant form of terrestrial animal life. Their diversity is unmatched. Numerous factors have contributed to their

Figure 19-15. "Walking worm" (genus *Peripatus*), a unique mixture of annelid and arthropod traits (*courtesy of Carolina Biol. Supply Co.*).

success. Present-day insects are quite small, ranging from about one-eighth to about two inches in length. Their small size and accompanying small food requirement have been highly advantageous to their existence. Many possess wings and are the only invertebrates that can fly, making possible an increased feeding and breeding range as well as a way of coping with predators.

Although all insects have the same fundamental structure, various species show extreme modifications. Among their common characteristics are clearly defined and separate head, throax, and abdominal regions. The head consisting of six fused segments contains a pair of compound eyes and one or more simple eyes. The second head segment bears a single pair of antennae, whereas other appendages are complex mouth parts varying greatly in structure depending on whether they function in biting as in the grasshopper, sucking as in the butterfly, or piercing and sucking as in the mosquito. The thorax is characteristically made up of three segments, each possessing a pair of walking legs. The great majority of insects bear wings, usually a pair on each of the last two thoracic segments. The nature of the wings may differ considerably and is used as an important basis for classifying the different groups of insects. In the beetle, for example, the front wings have become a protective cover, whereas in the dragonfly both pairs are membranous. In mosquitoes and houseflies the second wing pair is greatly decreased in size and is no longer used for flying but for balancing instead. The number of abdominal segments varies somewhat and ranges downward from a maximum of 11 with no appendages usually present. Respiration occurs by a system of tracheal tubes which carry oxygen to almost every cell of the body. Finally, many insects have complex life histories involving several complete changes in body form (i.e., *metamorphosis*, p. 461) from the egg to the adult.

Insects have been classified into some two dozen different orders depending on the absence or presence of wings, type of mouth parts, character of metamorphosis, the nature of their external reproductive organs, and so forth. The overwhelming diversity of insect forms is compounded by the fact that several widely different types characteristic of the different stages in the life history (e.g., the worm-like larva stage and the winged adult stage of butterflies) often occur within a single species, a phenomenon termed *polymorphism.* This is more fully illustrated in the later discussion on metamorphosis.

THE GRASSHOPPER. The locust, commonly called the "grasshopper," is widely distributed in virtually all parts of the world. It is often used, because of its several primitive insect characteristics, to illustrate more or less the basic form and function of a typical insect. Its external body plan (Figure 19-16) and structure conform to the generalized features indicated for insects as a class. Between the two lateral compound eyes the grasshopper also bears three simple eyes or *ocelli*, whose functions are not clearly understood. The single pair of antennae are regarded as true segmental appendages that have evolved into sense organs in contrast to the compound eyes and ocelli which are not appendages. The mouth parts of the grasshopper are of the biting type and include segmental appendages as well as outgrowths of the head. They include a pair of chewing jaws (*mandibles*), a pair of flap-like structures (*maxillae*) for manipulating food, an upper and lower lip-like structure (*labrum* and *labium*, respectively), and a tongue-like organ (*hypopharynx*). Its fore wings are tough and leathery, and its hind wings thin and membranous.

The first of its eleven abdominal segments has two laterally placed, flattened *tympanic membranes* which respond to sound waves.

Paired *spiracles,* the external openings of the respiratory tracheal system, are present on all thoracic segments as well as on each of the first eight abdominal segments and open and close rhythmically with the breathing movements of the body. The breathing system or branched tracheal tubules ramify throughout the body becoming smaller and smaller, as they lead away from the spiracles, until they are in contact with the body cells providing them with oxygen and removing carbon dioxide. Portions of the tracheae also expand into compressible abdominal air sacs which act as bellows as a result of the alternate contractions and relaxations of the muscular abdomen thus aiding in the movement of air through the respiratory system.

The circulatory system is of the "open" type resembling that of the crustaceans with the important exception that it does not function in the distribution of respiratory gases. The latter role has been taken over by the tracheal system. The colorless blood, which lacks a respiratory pigment and serves mainly as a circulating medium for food and wastes, is pumped by a tube-like beating heart into the blood cavity or *hemocoel*. Here the blood bathes the various tissues and organs of the body giving up nutrients and taking on metabolic waste products. The latter are excreted by many thread-like, coiled *Malpighian tubules*, the chief excretory organs of insects, which extend from the hemocoel into the intestine. The metabolic wastes are then passed out of the body with the feces. Uric acid is the chief nitrogenous excretory product (Chapter 28).

The digestive tract itself consists of a *buccal cavity*, or mouth, with salivary glands, a short *esophagus*, a thin-walled *crop* which extends into the thorax and functions as a temporary storage organ, a *gizzard* for grinding food, a *stomach* where nearly all the digestion occurs (as a result of digestive enzymes secreted by several pairs of glands called the *gastric caeca*), an *intestine*, a *rectum*, and an *anus* (Figure 19-16). Absorption of nutrients occurs principally in the stomach and anterior region

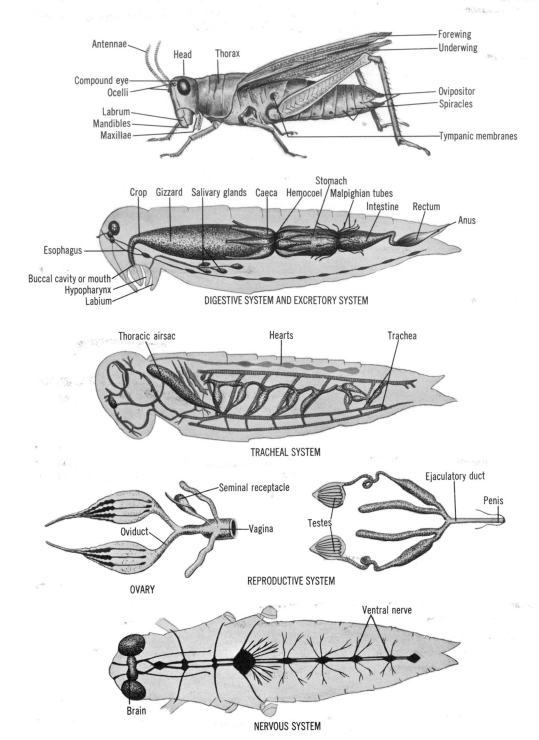

Figure 19-16. The external and internal anatomy of the grasshopper. See text for details.

of the intestine.

The nervous system of the grasshopper is essentially similar to that of crustaceans as represented by the lobster. The large brain located in the head region is composed of several fused ganglia and is connected by two large nerves to a ventral nerve cord extending into the abdomen with nerves radiating to most parts of the body.

The reproductive system of the male is made up of two testes (located near the intestine) from which sperm are eventually transferred to a common ejaculatory duct traversing an external eversible *penis* at the tip of the abdomen. In the female the eggs are formed in two ovaries and are passed by a common oviduct to the vagina. The latter possesses a small sac-like *seminal receptacle* which receives and stores sperm furnished by the male during copulation, usually in the late summer or early fall. At an appropriate time eggs pass through the vagina, are fertilized by the stored sperm, and the resulting zygotes deposited in the soil by an external female structure, the *ovipositor*. (The ovipositor in the honeybee has evolved into the *sting*.) The zygotes start embryonic development almost immediately, becoming well-formed embryos before they experience a rest period, the embryonic *diapause*, which tides them over the winter. Development is resumed in the spring with the embryos hatching by early summer as young grasshoppers or *nymphs*. The latter resemble small adults without wings and in time experience a succession of molts before attaining maximal size.

We have used the grasshopper as an illustrative animal to describe the fundamental features of the representative insect. However, it should be noted that innumerable variations and modifications of external body structures and internal organ systems have occurred in the course of evolution thus accounting for the many types of present-day insects.

Insect Metamorphosis

The life histories of insects may be quite different. At one extreme are the present-day primitive insects (e.g., the grasshopper, cockroach and leafhopper) whose life cycles exhibit no metamorphosis. The young hatch from the eggs in the almost exact image of the adult, except for their smaller size and immature sexual condition. At the other extreme are at least five known orders of insects whose members experience drastic changes in form and function in the course of their development from the embryo to the adult stage, a phenomenon known as *complete metamorphosis*. Between these two extremes there range various kinds of life cycles among the insects.

One of the best known examples of complete metamorphosis is provided by the order *Lepidoptera*, represented by moths and butterflies. Their life cycles involve at least four distinct stages: (1) the *embryonic stage*, (2) the *larva* or feeding stage (the caterpillar) arising from the embryo and representing a completely different organism from the adult in nearly all features of form and function; (3) the *pupa* forming from the larva after several molts and representing a quiescent and nonfeeding stage; (the cocoon); and (4) the *adult* which forms during the latter portion of the pupa stage finally emerging with the splitting of the pupal skin (Figure 19-17). The process of metamorphosis in insects, like the process of molting in crustaceans, is under the control of particular hormones produced by neurosecretory cells and transported by the blood. Certain neurosecretory cells in the brain of insects secrete the *brain hormone*, possibly identical with cholesterol, which stimulates the so-called *prothoracic gland*. The latter in turn secretes *ecdysone*, a *growth* and *differentiation* hormone identified as a steroid. By initiating the complex processes of growth and differentiation leading to molting and the transformation from the larval to the pupal stage, *ecdysone* thereby initiates the post-embryonic growth and development of insects.

Another hormone termed the *juvenile hormone* secreted by a third endocrine gland, called the *corpus allatum*, lying near the brain, stimulates larval development, but inhibits metamorphosis. It also permits molting to occur during the larval stage. In effect the juvenile hormone permits growth but prevents maturation. It thus prevents changes of form during molting and assures that the larva will reach an adequate size before pupating. The juvenile hormone is not secreted during the final larval stage, thus allowing pupation to occur. In insects such as the grasshopper it is not secreted in the later nymph stage, allowing the insect to attain adulthood. Molting therefore is controlled through the regulatory release of the brain hormone, whereas maturation is controlled through the regulatory release of the juvenile hormone.

One of the most exciting new findings is the demonstration that the injection of pure ecdy-

sone in the larvae of the midge *Chironomus tentans* causes prompt (within 15 minutes) and characteristic chromosomal puffs to appear as observed on the giant chromosomes of the salivary gland (Figure 19-18). The chromosomal changes are identical to those that take place during pupation. Such results suggest (but do not establish or prove) that the activity of certain genes may possibly be under the control of specific chemical agents such as particular hormones. In this case we might speculate that ecdysone has as its principal target particular chromosomal regions or genes that ultimately characterize growth and molting.

Behavior Patterns of Insects

The wide diversity in form and function that exists among the insects is also seen in

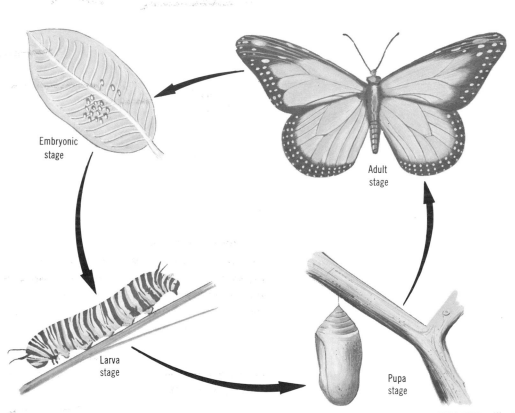

Embryonic stage

Adult stage

Larva stage

Pupa stage

Figure 19-17. Principal stages in the life cycle of a representative member of the order Lepidoptera (e.g., moths and butterflies) which undergoes complete metamorphosis. See text for details.

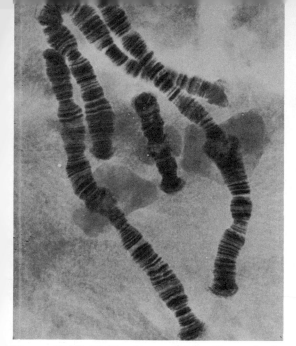

Figure 19-18. Light micrograph of salivary gland chromosomes of the midge *Chironomous tentans* showing regions of puffing. Note in particular the puffed middle portion of the short chromosome in the center of the field. The longer chromosomes at the right and left also show regions of puffing. Magnification 750X (*courtesy of Dr. W. Beerman, J. Cell. Biol.*).

Figure 19-19. The honeybee (*courtesy of Wallace Kirkland*).

their patterns of behavior. These range from insects of relatively simple habit to species with highly developed social organizations as exemplified by honeybees. In the remarkable social organization of the honeybees there are two types of females. The fertile *queen* produces zygotes from which develop all individuals of the colony, and the sterile *worker* cares for the queen, tends and feeds the young, maintains the beehive, and collects and processes food. The male or *drone* develops parthenogenetically (Chapter 30) from unfertilized eggs and is therefore haploid. Fertilized eggs produce either queens or workers depending in part on their diet. If a substance, "royal jelly," is included in the diet of female larvae, future queens will develop.

The amazing social organization of honeybees and their remarkable ability to communicate to their companions direction, distance, and kind of food or flowers available are due to inherited reflexes or instincts. Information about direction and distance of flowers (i.e., pollen and nectar) is apparently conveyed by certain types of dances performed by the returning scouting bees. A "circling" dance indicates that the food is relatively near (less than one hundred meters away), a "waggle" dance that it is a farther distance. Direction of the food source and the quantity involved are also indicated by the dance which is joined in by other workers. These astounding discoveries of the behavior of bees are largely the result of the work of the eminent Austrian biologist Karl von Frisch and have since been confirmed by other researchers.

Classes Chilopoda and Diplopoda

Although the *Chilopoda* (or centipedes) and the *Diplopoda* (or millipedes) show several similarities, they are nevertheless significantly different in certain important respects to warrant classification into two distinct classes. They are reminiscent of both annelids and insects. Representatives of both display elongated bodies, indefinite number of segments with many paired jointed appendages, tracheal breathing system, similar mouth parts, and a defined head with antennae and several simple eyes.

Centipedes, however, are somewhat flattened and carnivorous. Each of the segments

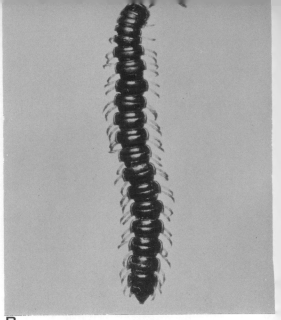

A   B

Figure 19-20. (A) Giant centipede from Colombia (approximately 7 inches long) (*courtesy of N. Y. Zoological Society*). (B) Millipede (*courtesy of U.S. Dept. of Agric.*).

except the last two possesses a pair of walking legs. The gonads and genital openings are situated in the same general position as in the insects (Figure 10-20). By contrast, millipedes are more worm-like, cylindrical, and herbivorous. Each *apparent* segment (really made up of two fused segments) bears two pairs of walking legs. Their reproductive ducts are differently located, opening anteriorly rather than posteriorly as in the centipedes and insects.

Class Arachnida

The arachnids as represented by spiders, daddy longlegs, ticks, mites, scorpions, and others are distinctly different from insects with which they are often confused. Arachnids have a cephalothorax joined to the abdomen, simple eyes, and no antennae. One of the basic features of this phylum is the presence of six pairs of appendages on the cephalothorax. The first two pair are the pincer-like *chelicerae* and the *pedipalps*, respectively, and the remaining four pair are walking legs in contrast to the three pairs of legs of insects. In spiders the first pair of appendages, the *chelicerae*, are sharp-pointed pincer-like claws and the second pair are sensory organs. In

male spiders the pedipalps are modified for transferring sperm to the female at mating. In scorpions the pedipalps are instead pincer-like for coping with prey. Although the abdomen bears no segmental appendages, there are several pairs of blunt projections near the anus, the *spinnerets*, containing small tubes through which silk is secreted by silk glands within the abdomen.

The respiratory organs of scorpions and the great majority of spiders consist of so-called *book lungs* (Figure 19-22) which are internal cavities with many thin, hollow plates among which the blood circulates. The hollow plates contain air spaces connecting to the outside by a slit-like, spiracular opening. Some spiders also have tracheal systems resembling those of insects. Although most spiders are beneficial to man by destroying insects, other arachnids such as ticks and mites are parasites and a definite hindrance.

Class Merostomata

Before leaving the arthropods mention should be made of another small class, the *Merostomata*. They are sometimes grouped together with the arachnids to compose a

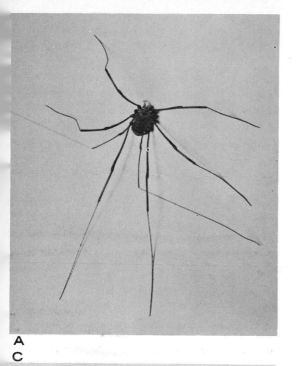

A

B

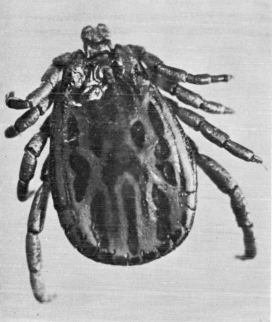

C

D

Figure 19-21. Some representatives of the class Arachnida. (A) Daddy longlegs (*courtesy of H. Spencer*). (B) Spider (*courtesy of Carolina Biol. Supply Co.*). (C) Winter tick (*courtesy of P. A. Knipping*). (D) Scorpion (*courtesy of Amer. Mus. of Natural History*).

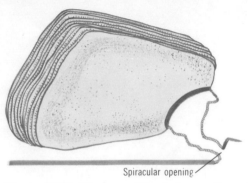

Figure 19-22. Diagram of book lungs of a spider.

Figure 19-23. Horseshoe crab (*Limulus polyphemus*) (*courtesy of H. Spencer*).

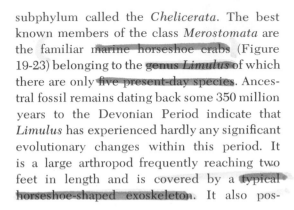

Spiracular opening

subphylum called the *Chelicerata*. The best known members of the class *Merostomata* are the familiar marine horseshoe crabs (Figure 19-23) belonging to the genus *Limulus* of which there are only five present-day species. Ancestral fossil remains dating back some 350 million years to the Devonian Period indicate that *Limulus* has experienced hardly any significant evolutionary changes within this period. It is a large arthropod frequently reaching two feet in length and is covered by a typical horseshoe-shaped exoskeleton. It also possesses compound as well as simple eyes, an unsegmented abdomen, and a long pointed tail. It lives in shallow coastal waters and feeds on small forms of other marine life. Aside from these unique features, its basic resemblance to arachnids is seen in its general body organization—a cephalothorax with six pairs of appendages including chelicerae. As its respiratory system, *Limulus* has many leaflike gills which bear a resemblance to the gilllike book lungs of the terrestrial arachnids.

SUPPLEMENTARY REFERENCES

Borradaile, L. A., F. A. Potts, L. E. S. Eastham, and J. T. Saunders, *The Invertebrata*, second edition, Cambridge University Press, New York, 1955.
Brown, F. A. (Editor), *Selected Invertebrate Types*, Wiley, New York, 1950.
Buchsbaum, R., *Animals without Backbones*, revised edition, University of Chicago Press, Chicago, 1960.
von Frisch, K., *Bees—Their Vision, Chemical Senses and Language*, Cornell University Press, Ithaca, N. Y., 1950.
Frost, S. W., *General Entomology*, McGraw-Hill, New York, 1942.
Hyman, L. H., *The Invertebrates*, Vols. 1-4, McGraw-Hill, New York, 1940-1959.
Imms, A. D., *A General Textbook of Entomology*, fourth edition, Methuen, London, 1938.
Krogh, A., "The Language of the Bees," *Scientific American*, August 1948.
Mayr, E., E. B. Lindsley, and R. L. Usinger, *Methods and Principles of Systematic Zoology*, McGraw-Hill, New York, 1953.
Schneiderman, H. A., and L. I. Gilbert, "Control of Growth and Development of Insects," *Science*, January 24, 1964.
Williams, C., *Morphogenesis and the Metamorphosis of Insects*, Harvey Lecture No. 47, Academic Press, New York, 1953.

Chapter 20   Animal Kingdom:

Phyla Echinodermata and Chordata

INTRODUCTION

The phyla *Echinodermata* and *Chordata* constitute the second main branch of the animal phyla possessing a true body cavity or coelom. The members of these two phyla have a body cavity of the type known as the *entercoelom* in contrast to the *schizocoelom* displayed by the *Mollusca, Annelida*, and *Arthropoda* as discussed in the previous chapter.

PHYLUM ECHINODERMATA

Basic Features

The echinoderms as *spiny-skinned*, solely marine animals constitute some six thousand species arranged in five classes. Their two most unique characteristics are the presence in the adult form of *radial symmetry* and a highly unusual method of locomotion made possible by a *water-vascular system*. As typified by the familiar star fish *Asterias* (see Figure 20-2A), the body consists of a central disc from which radiate usually five or more arms or rays, depending on the species. The radial symmetry of the echinoderms, reminiscent of the coelenterates, is considered to be a later evolutionary development, expecially in view of the fact that the larvae are bilaterally symmetrical. Echinoderms have apparently tended to change from bilaterally symmetrical free-swimming ancestral forms to attached forms.

In their other features, the echinoderms show strong similarities to animal phyla of a higher degree of organization. As eucoelomate animals they possess a well-developed coelom and are *triloblastic*, that is, they arise from three distinct embryonic germ layers—the ectoderm, mesoderm, and endoderm. The arrangement of tissues in the body wall and the wall of the gut is the same as in other "higher" animal forms including the vertebrates. Nearly all echinoderms bear an endoskeleton consisting of a series of hard calcareous plates (frequently containing spiny projections) in the soft tissues of the body wall. Although the principal classes of echinoderms are unusually different in their habits and appearance (e.g., sea lilies, starfish, serpent stars, sea urchins, sand dollars, and sea cucumbers), their internal organization essentially is similar.

The Common Starfish

The common starfish *Asterias vulgaris*, representative of the class *Asteroidea* found chiefly in the coastal waters of the Atlantic north of Cape Cod, often is used to illustrate the important features of the phylum. Its body consists of a central disc and five radiating arms or rays. The upper surface of the body is covered with short skeletal spiny structures, among which are two other types of structures. These are the *pedicellariae* which are minute pincer-like structures keeping the body surface free of foreign material and the *papulae* which are thin-walled, tiny finger-like protrusions communicating with the coelom and functioning in breathing (gas exchange) and excretion (Figure 20-1). The mouth is located on the undersurface of the starfish, occupying the center of the disc.

One of the unique features of the echinoderms is their *water-vascular* system which is a sea-water circulatory system used for locomotion. It consists collectively of a circular canal (on the undersurface of the central disc) from which emanate five radial canals, one extending along the undersurface of each arm.

Numerous pairs of tiny, hollow, thin-walled cylinders, the *tube feet*, ending in suckers are connected by separate short branches to each radial canal. At the base of each tube foot is a bulbous muscular sac, the *ampulla*. By contraction the ampulla forces water into the tube foot, making it turgid and causing it to extend. Sea water enters the water-vascular system through a *sieve plate* located at one side of the upper disc surface between two of the arms. By coordinated action of the tube feet, the starfish is able to move, attaching itself to various objects including food. In feeding on its principal food, which is molluscs

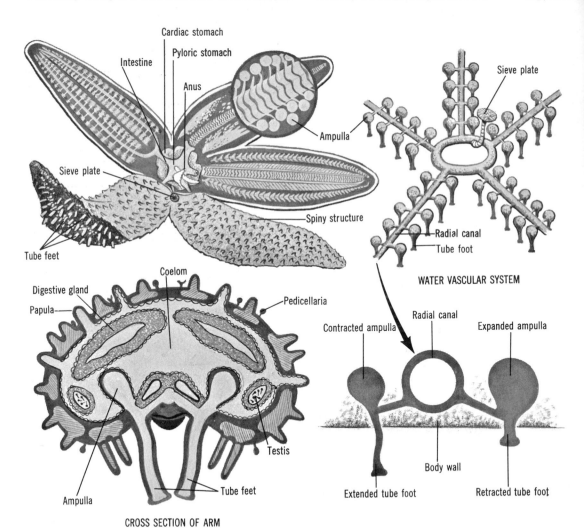

CROSS SECTION OF ARM

Figure 20-1. Various structural features of the starfish.

such as clams, oysters, and other bivalves, the starfish grasps its prey with the tube feet suckers on the undersurface of the arms, and by sustained powerful muscular contractions slowly pries apart the valves of the mollusc. A slight opening of only a few millimeters between the valves is sufficient to permit the starfish to insert its stomach (which has now been turned inside out and everted through the mouth) into the mantle cavity of the bivalve where it releases powerful digestive juices. The soft tissues of the mollusc are broken down and completely ingested by the starfish, which then withdraws its stomach and moves away, leaving in its wake an empty shell.

The digestive tract of the starfish consists of the mouth connecting to the large lower cardiac stomach leading to the small upper pyloric stomach which in turn opens into the intestine. The latter drains to the exterior via the anus on the upper surface of the disc. Included in the digestive system are five pairs of a series of connected sac-like invaginations, one pair extending into each arm, whose powerful digestive enzyme secretions drain first into the pyloric stomach and then into the cardiac stomach where they are mainly active.

The colorless fluid in the extensive coelomic body cavities bathes the body tissues like the hemocoelic fluid of an arthropod. Neither functional blood vessels nor a beating heart is present. Except for the presence of amoeboid cells and small concentrations of protein and nutrients the composition of starfish blood is remarkably like that of sea water. Blood circulation is accomplished by the flagellate epithelial cells lining the body cavity.

The nervous system, reflecting the general radial symmetry of the body, is made up essentially of a circular nerve cord located in the disc connected to a series of five radial nerve cords, one extending into each arm. The sensory organs consist of receptors scattered throughout the epidermis as well as light-sensitive eyespots and sensory tentacles at the top of each arm.

In the male and female the reproductive system consists of five pairs of gonads (ovaries or testes) one pair in each arm with ducts opening to the outside in the angles between the arms. Egg cells and sperm are discharged into the sea water where fertilization takes place. The zygotes develop rapidly into a bilateral ciliated larval stage. The larvae, after several weeks of swimming and feeding, sink to the bottom and undergo metamorphosis to tiny starfish. Starfish have outstanding regenerative powers, regrowing injured or destroyed arms.

Other Echinoderm Classes

The basic features of the starfish (class *Asteroidea*) are present in the other four echinoderm classes (Figure 20-2) despite apparent external differences in most cases. Members of the class *Ophiuroidea*, as represented by serpent and basket stars, show obvious similarities (long slender arms, small discs) to the starfish and clearly are echinoderms.

In the class *Echinoidea*, the sea urchin, a common representative, has a globular body covered with spurs, a lower oral surface bearing a central mouth with five large teeth, modified tube feet, papulae, pedicellariae, and certain body areas which correspond to the arms of a starfish.

In the class *Holothuroidea*, typified by the sea cucumber, the apparent bilaterally symmetrical, elongated body (extending from mouth to anus) masks a fundamentally radial symmetry. Ten branched tentacles surround the mouth of the sea cucumber and the scattered tube feet are connected internally to five radial internal canals. Its similarities to the starfish in the water-vascular system, circulatory system, and certain other features mark it definitely as an echinoderm.

Most representatives of the class *Crinoidea* have a flower-like appearance (e.g., sea lily) because of their five branched arms and frequent attachment to the bottom by a stalk connected to the lower disc surface. As indicated by the fossil record they were far more abun-

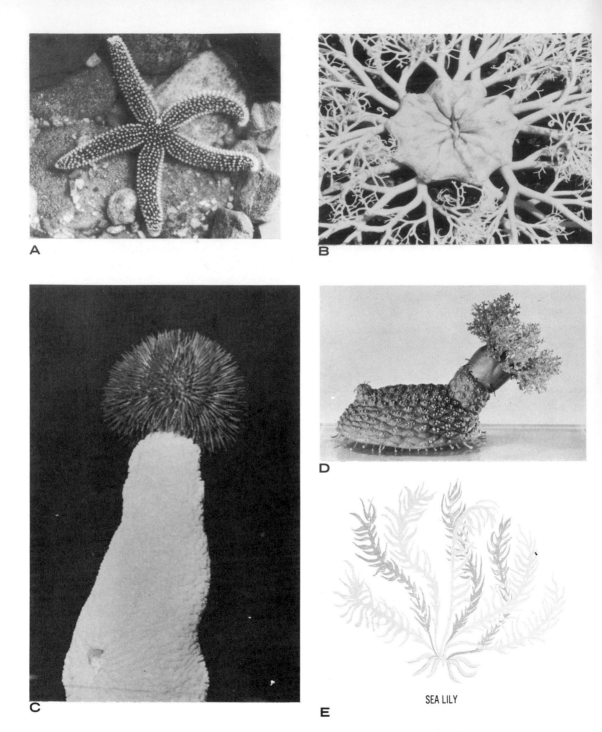

A

B

C

D

SEA LILY

E

Figure 20-2. Representatives of four of the five echinoderm classes: (A) familiar starfish, class Asteroidea (*courtesy of H. Spencer*); (B) basket star, class Ophiuroidea (*courtesy of Ward's Nat. Sci. Est.*); (C) sea urchin, class Echinoidea, perched on top of coral (*courtesy of N. Y. Zoological Society*); (D) model of sea cucumber, class Holothuroidea (*courtesy of Amer. Mus. Natural History*); (E) sea lily, class Crinoidea.

dant in past geologic eras starting with the end of the Cambrian period.

PHYLUM CHORDATA

Basic Features

The group of animals constituting the phylum *Chordata* includes the subphylum *Vertebrata* (fishes, amphibians, reptiles, birds, and mammals) and three invertebrate subphyla as well. Although the chordates are far less numerous in numbers (approximately fifty thousand species) than the arthropods, they rival them in diversity of structure and their adaptations to more modes of existence extending from the poles to the equator on land, in the sea, in fresh water, and in the air. In terms of their ability to remain active at low temperatures, the chordates tend to be superior to the arthropods. In diversity of size the chordates, unlike the arthropods, range from minute forms such as fishes less than a half inch long to whales approximately 100 feet in length and 150 tons in weight.

Although the chordates have many features noted among the invertebrate phyla including bilateral symmetry, three primary germ layers, segmental arrangement of body parts, a well-developed true coelom or body cavity, and a complete digestive tract, they possess three unique body characteristics that distinguish them from all other animal groups. At some period of their life all chordates possess: (1) the dorsally located pliant connective tissue *notochord*, from which the phylum has obtained its name; the notochord appears in the embryos of all chordates and in some is present as such throughout life, whereas in vertebrates it is replaced by the vertebral column or backbone; (2) the hollow, dorsal *neural tube* located just above the notochord and representing the central nervous system; and (3) the set of *pharyngeal gill slits* which in aquatic forms function throughout life as the gills or respiratory organs. In terrestrial chordates they are transient, nonfunctional embryonic structures usually failing to open to the outside. They have become modified to produce other structures (e.g., the middle ear) which better fit the animal to a terrestrial existence. In addition to these three exclusive features, most chordates exhibit a heart which pumps blood through a closed circulatory system, a tail-like portion of the body, and separate sexes.

The chordates are usually subdivided into four subphyla—the *Hemichordata, Urochordata, Cephalochordata,* and *Vertebrata*. It should be noted, however, that one of these, the *Hemichordata*, is also ranked as a separate phylum by several biologists because its members either possess the three unique characteristics in a relatively rudimentary condition or because some lack the true neural tube and notochord as indicated below.

Subphylum Hemichordata

The subphylum *Hemichordata* consists of a minor group of exclusively marine forms (some one hundred species) which are probably best represented by the acorn worms. Their bodies consist of a tongue-like *proboscis* for burrowing, a *"collar"* containing the mouth, and the *trunk* possessing the pharynx with many pharyngeal clefts, long intestine, and gonads (Figure 20-3). The two principal nerve trunks bear some resemblance to the central nervous system of the typical chordates; and a limited and very primitive notochord-like structure functions in a supportive role. The hemichordates exhibit expecially in the larval stages some of the features of the echinoderms, probably a reflection of a common ancestry.

Subphylum Urochordata (or Tunicata)

The subphylum consists of some two thousand known marine species and are commonly known as tunicates, ascidians, or "sea-squirts." In addition to their unmistakable basic chordate characteristics in the larval stage, they are typified in the adult stage by an attached or sessile existence with features that are hardly recognizable as belonging to the chordates. In the larval or "tadpole" stage the actively swimming embryo has a well-developed notochord and neural tube in its tail. In the course of metamorphosis, however, the notochord disappears, the central nervous system is modified into a ganglionic mass, and the organism is transformed into one with an attached mode of existence.

The adult tunicate (Figure 20-4) is covered entirely with a tough, elastic cellulose membrane called the *tunic* or *test* which is penetrated by two tubes: an *incurrent siphon* through which water enters carrying food as minute organisms and oxygen and an *excurrent siphon* that carries outgoing water and contains feces, gametes, and zygotes. The opening of the incurrent siphon is actually the mouth which leads to an enlarged pharynx or *branchial sac* specialized for food collection and aeration of blood. Entering water passes through the many small holes in the branchial sac wall, into the extensive body cavity termed the *atrium*, and finally out of the body via the excurrent siphon. The branchial sac is connected to the rest of the digestive tract which consists successively of the esophagus, stomach, intestine, and anus, the latter draining into the atrium. The circulatory system consists of a beating heart and tubular-like cavities through which the blood circulates.

Most tunicates are monoecious. Their gametes are discharged by the single ovary and testis into the atrium and passed out of the body via the excurrent siphon. Fertilization may take place in the atrium or in the external environment where development occurs. In certain species the asexual process of budding produces colonies of ascidians, called compound ascidians.

Subphylum Cephalochordata

This small phylum of marine animals is made up of some thirty species arranged in a single class, the *Amphioxi*, often collectively referred to as "Amphioxus" or *lancelets*. Its members are quite small, about two inches in length, with the general shape of a slender fish (Figure 20-5). The well-developed notochord extending

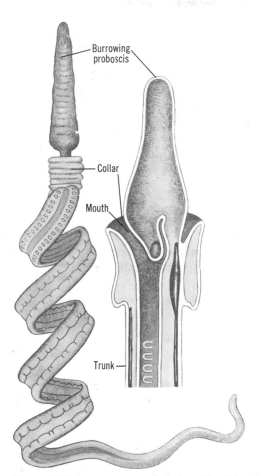

Burrowing proboscis

Collar

Mouth

Trunk

Figure 20-3. Acorn worm, subphylum Hemichordata.

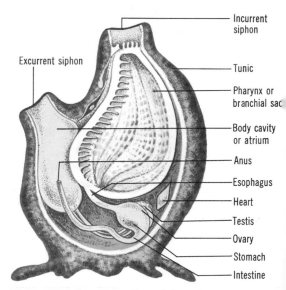

Excurrent siphon

Incurrent siphon

Tunic

Pharynx or branchial sac

Body cavity or atrium

Anus

Esophagus

Heart

Testis

Ovary

Stomach

Intestine

Figure 20-4. Structure of an adult tunicate.

as a semirigid internal supporting skeleton from one end of the animal to the other, the hollow nerve cord which is slightly enlarged into a "brain" at its anterior end, and the numerous gills which function in breathing leave no doubt as to the chordate nature of the group. No clearly defined brain—nor head for that matter—is present. The animal possesses no eyes but bears a pigmented eyespot at its anterior end near the spinal cord. The body plan closely resembles that of the vertebrates with similar but simple organ systems. The digestive tract is made up of pharynx or branchial sac perforated by many pairs of gill slits, an intestine leading to the posteriorly located anus, and a digestive gland, the liver, attached by a duct to the anterior end of the intestine.

The closed circulatory system consists of two main longitudinal vessels whose peristaltic contractions serve as the main driving force for the pumping of blood. The reproductive organs of the separate sexes are made up of paired gonads and project from the side walls into the atrium in which the gametes are discharged. All indications suggest that amphioxus is representative of some ancient descendant of the tunicates and that the vertebrates may well have originated from a form related to it.

Subphylum Vertebrata (or Craniata)

BASIC FEATURES. The members of the *Vertebrata* as the largest and most advanced group within the chordates are uniquely distinguished by the presence of a vertebral column or backbone, composed of internal living skeleton of bone or cartilage. Accordingly, the members of this group are called *vertebrates* by contrast to all other multicellular animals which are known as *invertebrates*. Although the notochord appears in all vertebrates during embryonic development, in the more advanced vertebrates it is replaced by the vertebrae, and in the less advanced vertebrates it persists throughout life as a cord running through the center of each vertebra. In addition, the great majority of vertebrates are distinguished by: (1) the presence of a definite brain formed by the differentiation of the anterior end of the neural tube and enclosed within the skull or cranium; (2) usually two pairs of jointed appendages, either fins or limbs; (3) a closed blood-vascular system with a well-developed ventral pumping heart and blood containing red blood cells; (4) gill slits which are permanent in the lower vertebrates, but transitory in the higher forms which develop lungs; (5) a portion of the body extending rearward as a *tail*; (6) a large coelom containing the vital organs; (7) dorsally located kidneys; (8) paired eyes and ears; and (9) a single pair of gonads in the separate sexes.

The eight different classes constituting the subphylum vertebrata are usually grouped into two superclasses: the *Pisces* or aquatic fishes bearing gills and fins; and the *Tetrapoda*, made

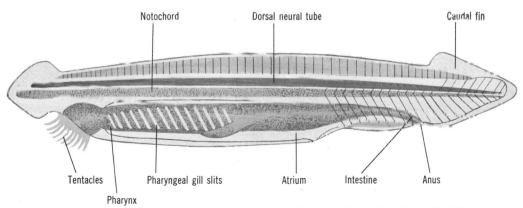

Figure 20-5. Diagram of amphioxus *(adapted from R. Buchsbaum, Animals without Backbones, rev. ed., Univ. Chicago Press, 1960).*

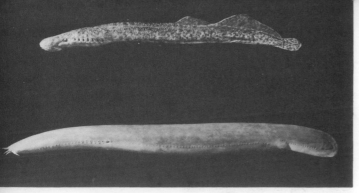

Figure 20-6. The jawless fishes, class Agnatha: (*top*) lamprey and (*bottom*) hagfish (*courtesy of Amer. Mus. Natural History*).

up of the nonaquatic or terrestrial forms. The Pisces or fishes consist of the four classes: *Agnatha, Placodermi, Chondrichthyes,* and *Osteichthyes.* The four terrestrial classes are the *Amphibia, Reptilia, Aves,* and *Mammalia.* This arrangement or classification of the vertebral classes represents part of the basis for the interpretation that vertebrates evolved from an aquatic to a terrestrial mode of existence.

SUPERCLASS PISCES. *Class Agnatha (Jawless Fishes).* This class now consists of only two groups of living representatives, the lampreys and the hagfishes, which are presumed to be the final survivors of an extremely ancient group of agnathans, the first of the vertebrates. Fossil remains indicate that agnathans were well represented during the early Devonian Period. The present-day lampreys and hagfishes (Figure 20-6) are distinguished by the absence of bone and of both jaws and appendages. They bear rudimentary vertebrae (and skeletal parts composed of cartilage) and a persistent notochord. They are eel-shaped fishes with smooth-scaled skin and possess a round, jawless, sucker-like mouth, at their anterior end by which they attach and feed on other fishes, abrading and rasping their way into the flesh with their inner mouth parts. Among their other features, the agnathans have a single nostril on the dorsal side of the head between the eyes, a pair of simple semicircular canals, (Chapter 22) nearby, a relatively well-developed brain, seven pairs of gills, and general body structures that are far more complex than those of amphioxus. The sea

lamprey, belonging to the genus *Petromyzon,* has remarkable powers of adapting itself to fresh-water conditions. With the opening of waterways that connect the Great Lakes to the ocean, the sea lamprey gradually migrated from the ocean and became a serious menace to the important fresh-water fish of the Great Lakes.

Class Placodermi (The First Jawed Fishes). This is an extinct and ancient group whose members, as indicated by the fossil remains are considered to be the earliest fishes or vertebrates with jaws. They gave rise to all later fishes and apparently arose from early agnathans. Their mobile jaws presumably evolved from a pair of hinged gill supports or arches. They gradually replaced most of the agnathans by the middle of the Devonian Period.

Class Chondrichthyes (Cartilaginous Fishes). This class, including such fishes as sharks, skates, and rays, is distinguished principally by a completely cartilaginous skeleton. They have jaws and teeth, and paired appendages or fins. They experience internal fertilization, with many species retaining the eggs in the oviduct during development. The sharks as streamlined elongated fish inhabiting the surface waters are believed to be among the earliest of the Chondrichthyes from which the flattened, bottom-water-dwelling rays and skates evolved. The chondrichthyans bear five to seven pairs of gills and a scaly skin. By the high level of dissolved urea in their blood, many uniquely maintain a high osmotic concentration of the blood to meet the problem of water loss to the hypertonic sea water (Chapter 28).

The chondrichthyans or cartilaginous fishes and the osteichthyans or bony fishes (the next class described) apparently evolved simultaneously and independently from the placoderms, which they finally replaced by the end of the Devonian Period. The early chondrichthyans had bony skeletons from which the present-day cartilaginous skeleton in this group arose. All indications are that the chondrichthyans were originally adapted to life in sea water from which very few fresh-water forms have since evolved.

Class Osteichthyes (Bony Fishes). The oste-

Figure 20-7. Skate (*courtesy of N. Y. Zoological Society*), class Chondrichthyes (cartilaginous fishes); and shark (*courtesy of Marineland of Florida*).

ichthyans were also originally specialized for life in sea water but have also evolved over the millions of years to become dominant vertebrates of both the fresh waters and the seas.

The osteichthyans are characterized by an adult skeleton consisting chiefly of bone. The general anatomy of a typical bony fish is shown in Figure 20-8. The entire gill region, containing four pairs of gills (by contrast to the five to seven pairs in cartilaginous fishes), is covered by a single bony flap, the *operculum*, with a single exit at its free edge. Usually the body is completely covered by an armor of overlapping scales. In many other respects including internal anatomy (with the possible exception of the *swim* or air bladder in the bony fishes), the bony fish is generally similar to the shark.

Surprisingly enough, lungs in addition to gills very likely were present in most of the early osteichthyans as they arose in the middle Devonian Period. They probably served as a supplementary means of obtaining oxygen as they still do in the relatively rare present-day lungfishes (p. 248). In most bony fishes, however, the lung lost its breathing role and evolved into the swim or air bladder (Figure 20-9). The air bladder functions (by increasing or decreasing its content of CO_2, O_2, and N_2 gases) in regulating the buoyancy of the body, thus maintaining the organism at various depths.

The early bony fishes are believed to have consisted of two groups: the so-called *ray-finned* fishes from which the present-day bony fishes (with primitive lung transformed to swim

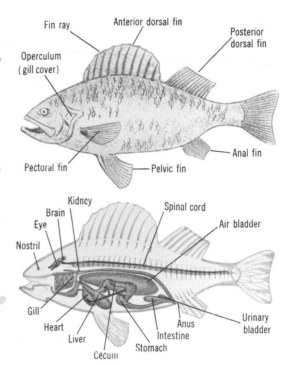

Figure 20-8. Anatomy of a bony fish, the perch (class Osteichthyes).

bladder) have probably evolved, and the *lobe-finned* fishes (having an appreciable fleshy portion or "lobe" to their fins) from which both the existing lungfishes and all terrestrial vertebrates have probably descended. Until relatively recently, it was commonly believed that the ancient lobe-finned bony fish (order *Crossopterygii*) had been extinct for many millions of years. But since 1939 several living specimens of one of the lobe-finned groups, the *Coelacanths*, have been caught off the coast of South Africa and Madagascar. Their fin bones are comparable to those of the limbs in amphibians. It should be made clear that the coelacanths still in existence are not the "ancient lobe-finned fish" from which terrestrial vertebrates evolved but a persistent marine side branch from the ancient stock.

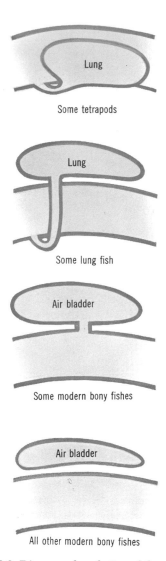

Figure 20-9. Diagram of evolution of the swim bladder in most bony fishes.

SUPERCLASS TETRAPODA. *Class Amphibia.* Most of the evidence clearly supports the interpretation that the earliest terrestrial vertebrates were primitive amphibians which arose from certain ancient lobe-finned fishes, probably sometime during the latter part of the Devonian Period, and that all terrestrial vertebrates eventually descended from this primitive form. There is little doubt that the bony skeleton (including that of the paired fins) and lungs of their fish ancestors made it possible to support a body in the air and obtain oxygen, respectively, thus bettering their chances for success in the invasion of the land.

The present-day amphibians are the least numerous of the terrestrial vertebrates and the least adapted of the subphylum to land dwelling. As their name indicates they have a dual life, living both in and out of water. Nearly all members of the class have a smooth, moist, glandular skin without scales which supplements the lungs in the process of respiration. At best they are really semiterrestrial forms, their moist skins being subject to rapid drying and their larval stages being aquatic in habit.

Modern amphibians fall into two main orders consisting of the more primitive salamanders and newts (collectively called *Caudata*) bearing tails, and the more highly specialized frogs and toads (collectively called *Anura*) which lose their tails in the adult stage. A third small and unimportant order of living amphibians also exists, called the *Apoda*, which are entirely without limbs and are worm-like in appearance.

The larval stages of the salamander and newt group are very much like the adult stages except for the loss of gills and the appearance of lungs during metamorphosis (one type of salamander is lungless). In frogs and toads the larval or tadpole stage is fish-like in appearance with a tail, gills, and the absence of forelegs. The course of metamorphosis, which is in part controlled by secretions of the thyroid gland, is marked by the loss of both the tail and the gills, as well as other changes to produce the adult.

Additional characteristics of the Amphibia include two pairs of legs (except for the Apoda), a three-chambered heart (two atria, one ventricle) with partial separation of aerated and unaerated blood, and external fertilization (except for salamanders).

Class Reptilia. Strictly speaking, the Amphibia are intermediate in the transformation of aquatic vertebrates to the truly terrestrial type. The first land vertebrates are in reality the reptiles who, unlike the amphibians, are in no way dependent upon an aquatic existence for completion of any phase of their life cycle. They are completely adapted for terrestrial life, living even under desert conditions. They undoubtedly evolved from a primitive and now extinct form of amphibian.

Modern reptiles are found in both water and land habitats; and are grouped into four orders representing the remaining lines of development of some fifteen groups that existed as the predominant animals at least 150 million years ago in the "age of reptiles" (Chapter 32). Like the amphibians, the reptiles are cold-blooded. Their body temperature fluctuates with that of the environment, and except for regions with extremely cold climates (where they are not present), they are widely distributed especially in tropical and temperate areas including hot, dry deserts. Unlike the Amphibia, they are covered with scales or horny epidermal plates and undergo no larval stage—the young resembling the adults.

The complete adaptation to terrestrial conditions by the reptiles was made possible by important evolutionary changes in reproduction, development, respiration, and circulation. In particular, internal fertilization and embryonic development within a protected and adequately supplied environment were key adaptations in the conquest of land by the reptiles. In most reptiles the fertilized egg cells which are laid on land have rigid calcified or leathery shells, a large supply of yolk and water, a rapidly developing protective *amnion* which prevents water loss, and the *allantois* (Chapter 31) which functions in both a respiratory and excretory capacity. The longer period of embryonic development lends more assurance that the newly hatched offspring are able to care for

Figure 20-10. Cast of coelacanth *(courtesy of Amer. Mus. Natural History).*

themselves. In some reptiles the zygotes are retained within the body of the female where complete embryonic development occurs in a specialized region of the mother's reproductive tract, the young leaving her body as they hatch.

The breathing system of reptiles is more efficient than that of amphibians in view of the participation of ribs and muscles in the inspiration and expiration processes. Moreover, the effectiveness of the respiratory process has been improved by the development in most reptiles of an unfinished wall in the heart, which partially divides the heart into two incomplete ventricles thus further separating oxygenated from nonoxygenated blood. In crocodiles and alligators the two ventricles have actually been completely separated. The evolution of the heart in vertebrates is discussed in Chapter 26.

Other changes that favored a terrestrial existence included a tendency for longer, more powerful, and more ventrally located legs that made it possible for the reptile to support its body off the ground.

Reptilian Orders. Of the four surviving present-day orders of reptiles, three—the *Chelonia, Crocodilia,* and *Squamata*—are fairly abundant, whereas the fourth, the *Rhynchocephalia,* consisting of a single species (*Sphenodon punctuatum*), found only in New Zealand, is close to extinction. The *Chelonia,* consisting of turtles, tortoises, and terrapins, is a primitive order whose most characteristic feature is the pos-

Figure 20-11. Sea turtle (*courtesy of Marineland of Florida*).

session of an external body shell. Those that have returned to the water, such as the great sea turtle, have adapted in part to an aquatic existence as evidenced by modification of their appendages into flippers (Figure 20-11). They are, nevertheless, basically terrestrial animals for they breathe by lungs and come on land during the egg-laying season.

Members of the *Crocodilia*, which include the crocodiles and alligators, are also reptiles that have returned to the water. Like the Chelonia, they breath air and lay their eggs on land. Some of their anatomical features, such as a divided heart ventricle and a nearly complete diaphragm between the thoracic and abdominal cavities, suggest that they are among the most advanced of the reptiles.

The *Squamata*, consisting of lizards and snakes, are the most abundant reptiles, composed of some four thousand species. Lizards are four-legged animals, whereas the more recently evolved snakes have no limbs (with the exception of a few such as pythons which possess tiny vestiges). In snakes the enormous mouth is equipped with sharp inward-curving fangs or teeth and a long-forked sensitive tongue, significant adaptations in the successful quest for food.

Class Aves (The Birds). There is no doubt that some ancient reptilian forms are the ancestors from which the birds and the mammals independently evolved. Birds are the only animals to bear feathers—their unique and characteristic feature. The strong resemblance of birds to reptiles is seen in numerous characteristics including the structure of the skull, the presence of scales on the legs, and the shelled egg with its extraembryonic membranes. The ancient riddle of which came first, the egg or the hen, has obviously been answered by the animal taxonomist. The egg came first, for its essential features in birds were present in reptiles from which the birds descended.

Although they are remarkably well adapted for flight, not all living birds are able to fly. Some, such as the penguin, have lost this ability but have compensated by being able to swim extremely well. Other flightless birds include the existing ostriches, kiwis, emus, and several others. Among the many characteristics of birds which suit them to flight, the most important have been feathered wings and a lighter and more compact body framework. The wings evolved by modification of the reptilian forelimbs and the body framework by several adaptations including: (1) the evolutionary transformation of scales to the light feathers which function in flight by virtue of their supporting surface and minimum weight (they also insulate against the extremes of heat and cold); (2) the development of light, hollow bones; and (3) the reduction of leg and wing muscles, the wings being moved by the powerful back and chest or pectoral muscles.

Other important adaptations occurred in the evolutionary ascent of birds from their reptilian ancestors including the development of acute hearing, a better physical equilibrium, and extremely keen vision—significant attributes during swift flight that were attained in part by a greater development of particular parts of the brain. In addition, birds have a high and sustained metabolic rate made possible largely by (1) the evolution of a four-chambered heart with complete separation of aerated and non-aerated bloods, and (2) an efficient breathing system consisting of lungs and usually nine large thin-walled chambers, the *air sacs*, occupying the spaces between the internal organs and even extending into some of the hollow bones (see Figure 27-8). Like mammals, birds

Figure 20-12. Blacksnakes emerging from eggs originally left in a hole in the ground for the sun to hatch (*courtesy of L. M. Chace*).

are warm-blooded and undergo internal fertilization; but unlike mammals they undergo embryonic development outside the body. In contrast to reptiles, birds possess a bill or beak, lack teeth, and in most cases lack a penis. The unusual development of the cerebral regions of the brain largely reflects the complex instinctive behavior patterns of birds as evinced by nest building, care of the young, and seasonal migration.

The approximately twenty-five different orders of living birds constitute a total of some nine thousand species.

Class Mammalia. Of the several characteristics which distinguish the mammals from all other vertebrate groups, the two outstanding ones are the presence of *hair* serving in insulation and temperature control, and *mammary glands* by which they nurse their young. By virtue of these and other important features indicated below we very modestly consider the mammals (more precisely the primates within this class) to be the culmination of advanced development within the vertebrates and, for that matter, within the entire animal kingdom.

The additional significant characteristics which have evolved that distinguish mammals from their extinct and primitive reptilian ancestors include: (1) warm-bloodedness (as in birds) contributed in part by a four-chambered heart, efficient respiratory system, and temperature-regulating mechanisms; (2) embryonic development within a specialized portion of the duct of the female reproductive tract (with the ex-

ception of the monotremes, below) and increased care and sustenance of the young; (3) an unusually large brain with an accompanying increase in intelligence and complexity of behavior patterns; (4) a complete separation of the thoracic and abdominal cavities by a muscular diaphragm, thus an increased efficiency of the breathing system; (5) better means of locomotion as a result of changes in limbs and joints; and (6) more efficient teeth and more sensitive sense organs such as eyes and ears.

Subdivisions of the Mammalia. The mammals are classified into three subclasses of living representatives consisting of some eighteen orders and fifteen thousand species. The subclass *Prototheria* consists of the primitive egg-laying mammals which include the monotremes —the duck-billed *Platypus* and the spiny anteaters (Figure 20-13).

In the subclass *Marsupialia,* as represented by the kangaroo of Australia and opossum of North America, the offspring are born in a very immature state because of a rudimentary placenta and are transferred to the abdominal marsupium or pouch of the mother. Here they obtain their nutrition from the mammary glands of the mother, attaining full development equivalent to the later embryonic life of more advanced mammals. They usually stay on for even longer periods, leaving the pouch to obtain food and returning to it under adverse circumstances.

In the subclass *Placentalia,* whose representatives make up sixteen of the eighteen orders of living mammals, the chief characteristic, as the name implies, is the possession of a well-developed placenta (Chapter 31). The most common orders of the Placentalia are:

Insectivora ("insect eaters")—moles and shrews
Chiroptera—bats
Primates—lemurs, monkeys, apes, and man
Edentata—armadillos and sloths
Rodentia—squirrels, rats, mice, beavers, and other rodents
Cetacea—whales, dolphins, and porpoises
Carnivora ("meat eaters")—cats, lions, dogs, wolves, bears, and others

Figure 20-13. The duck-billed platypus *(courtesy of Amer. Mus. Natural History)*; anteater *(courtesy of N. Y. Zoological Society)*, of the mammalian subclass Prototheria.

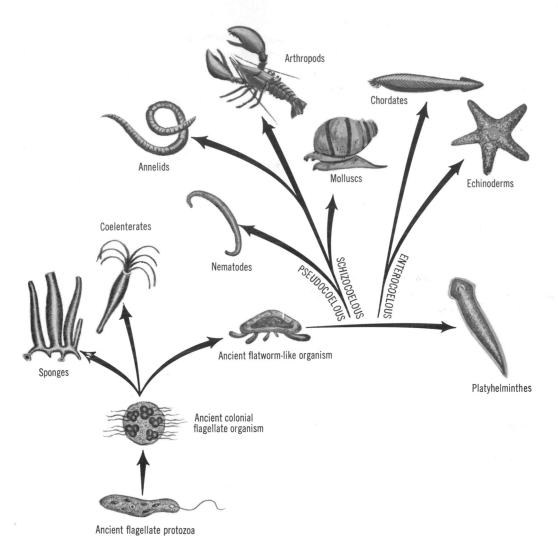

Figure 20-14. Diagram of the probable evolutionary relationships among the major animal phyla.

Proboscidea—elephant

Perissodactyla—odd-toed hoofed animals, such as horses and zebras

Artiodactyla—even-toed hoofed animals, such as swine, deer, and cattle

BROAD RELATIONSHIPS AMONG THE ANIMAL PHYLA

It should be evident in looking back at the relationships among the major animal phyla that the evolution of these groups did not occur, in many cases, as a straight-line series of successive events with one phylum giving rise to another. In numerous instances, different phyla gave rise to diverging or branching successions of phyla like the branching of a river into its tributaries or a tree into its limbs. Many of the branches represent the final groups, some having become extinct, others remaining unchanged. In the course of evolution, several of the phyla or some of their subdivisions have

given rise to new types of organisms, becoming extinct themselves in the process, whereas others have remained relatively unchanged during the passage of vast periods of time.

Attempts to reconstruct the sequence of evolutionary changes in the animal kingdom (and plant kingdom) have led to several different views of the relationships among phyla. One of the more favored interpretations is that multicellular animals arose from some primitive flagellate protozoa. According to this viewpoint, summarized in Figure 20-14, it is presumed that the flagellate protozoa evolved to produce first a colonial organism; and that from the latter there subsequently evolved three separate branches of multicellular animals —the sponges, the coelenterates, and an ancestral worm most closely related to the present-day flatworms. It is believed that this primitive, flatworm-like ancestor (which lacked a body cavity just as the present flatworms do) ultimately gave rise to two major branches

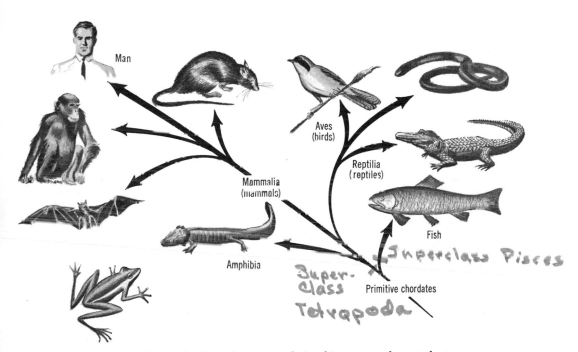

Figure 20-15. Diagram of the probable evolutionary relationships among the vertebrates.

of animal forms in the evolutionary tree. One branch evolved into the higher worms (as represented by the roundworms, annelids, arthropods, and molluscs. Whereas the other branch gave rise to the echinoderms and the chordates. The probable evolutionary relationships among the vertebrates are indicated in Figure 20-15. The conquest of land by the arthropods and by certain of the vertebrates starting with the Amphibia involved the solution of such common problems as general water loss, support of the animal body in the air, and the ability to reproduce and undergo embryonic development in an evironment of a limited water supply.

SUPPLEMENTARY REFERENCES

Orr, R. T., *Vertebrate Biology,* Saunders, Philadelphia, 1961.

Romer, A. S., *Man and the Vertebrates,* third edition, University of Chicago Press, Chicago, 1941.

Romer, A. S., *The Vertebrate Body,* third edition, Saunders, Philadelphia, 1962.

Storer, T. I., and R. L. Usinger, *General Zoology,* third edition, McGraw-Hill, New York, 1957.

Walter, H. E., and L. P. Sayles, *Biology of the Vertebrates,* third edition, Macmillan, New York, 1950.

Young, J. Z., *The Life of Vertebrates,* second edition, Oxford University Press, New York, 1962.

SIX

BIOLOGY OF COMPLEX ANIMALS
WITH EMPHASIS ON MAN

Man is the culmination of a vast biological evolutionary process that began with the origin of life an estimated two billion years ago. The course of development of every human being, especially during the embryonic stage starting with the fertilized egg, reflects in part the history of man's evolution on the planet Earth. The human body, in its various stages of growth and development starting with the fertilized egg, provides us with a kaleidoscope, as it were, of a variety of structures and activities which in itself is almost a study of comparative biology. In the adult individual alone these structures extend from essentially isolated single units, such as white blood cells which resemble single-celled protozoans, through innumerable stages of complexity to the whole man with his uniquely developed brain.

Coney Island (courtesy of Andreas Feininger).

Chapter 21   Coordination:

The Nervous System

INTRODUCTION

Integration and Control

GENERAL FEATURES. The human body like most advanced multicellular animals is comparable to a vast city with its population of thousands of billions of cells living and functioning together harmoniously in a smoothly running, well-coordinated organization or community. As in any large city, factory, or other type of organized system, one or more kinds of control and communication are essential to assure an integration of activity.

The term *integration* in biology, as elsewhere, means a summing up or putting together, the attainment of unity out of diversity. In another sense integration by its very nature is more than merely a summing-up process. As a result of integration new and often unpredictable features appear, especially in biological phenomena, which at times are difficult to explain on the basis of our knowledge of the individual parts. In the integrative process the whole has become equal to more than the sum of its parts, for a new dimension has been added, as it were. This is particularly true for the action of the nervous system, as we shall soon see.

TYPES OF INTEGRATION AND CONTROL. The *nervous system* is one of the most important of several recognized means for control and integration of body function. By its action it is also largely responsible for the unique and remarkable ability of many animals, despite extreme changes in external conditions, to maintain a stability or constancy of their internal environment, a physiological phenomenon known as *homeostasis*. The relative constancy of internal environment depends on a complex interplay of numerous dynamic processes, ranging from the molecular to the gross levels, that are sensitive to external as well as internal conditions. Maintenance and alteration of these dynamic processes are mediated in part through the action of the nervous system.

As specific organic substances ranging in complexity from relatively simple compounds to intricate proteins, *hormones* also play a major role in body control, integration, and maintenance of the internal environment (Chapter 23). They are secreted directly into the blood stream by the so-called *endocrine glands* which in some cases are stimulated into action by the nervous system and in others by chemical changes in the body. Hormones act in extremely small quantities to influence the growth, responses, and several activities of other tissues and target organs apparently by affecting cell metabolism. The action of the nervous system is more rapid, but its influence is of considerably shorter duration than the hormonal (or *endocrine*) system. A closer comparison, however, of the nervous and endocrine systems, as we shall see in Chapter 23 indicates that they share more similarities than heretofore believed.

We have recently come to realize that the phenomena of *molecular feedback*, *enzyme adaptation*, or *induction* and *enzyme repression* (Chapter 11) have important roles in the regulation of cell metabolism and therefore in the control and integration of the whole organism—plant, animal, or microbial. Still another mode of integration and control is seen in the as yet obscure chemical regulatory mechanisms that are apparently responsible for the differentiation and specialization of cells, especially during embryonic development (Chapter 31). The nervous system is without doubt the least understood of all the body systems.

The flowering plants respond to changes in environment mainly by *growth movements* called *tropisms* apparently as a result of the asymmetrical distribution of the plant growth hormone *auxin* (Chapter 17). Some plants also respond by turgor movements as seen for example in the opening and closing of floral organs of certain species, and in the leaf movement of the sensitive plant *Mimosa*. In the latter case any one of several stimuli (e.g., touch) presumably generates an electric impulse which eventually reaches certain cells at the base of each leaflet causing a turgor loss from cells on one side with the resultant closing together of the leaflets. The latter gradually return to their original position as turgor is slowly established in the cells. The photosensitive pigment *phytochrome* and other plant hormones such as *florigen* and the *gibberellins* (Chapter 17) are apparently also responsible for the coordination of other particular plant activities. In addition there is evidence that the phenomena of molecular feedback, enzyme induction, and enzyme repression also apply to the flowering plants.

STRUCTURAL AND FUNCTIONAL ORGANIZATION OF THE NERVOUS SYSTEM

General Features and Evolutionary Trends

Any qualitative or quantitative change in environment that can be detected by an organism is defined as a *stimulus*. The ability to respond to a stimulus or change in environment, a characteristic called *responsiveness or irritability*, is a fundamental feature of living systems. The response which is essentially similar in all organisms consists of three successive steps: receipt of the stimulus, conduction of the resultant signal, and reaction to the signal. For example, in a unicellular organism such as an amoeba the reaction to a foreign nonedible object is usually a movement away from it. In this case the response is performed entirely within the protoplasm of the single cell. Among some of the unicellular organisms (e.g., in several of the ciliates), there are actually specialized areas in the protoplasm for detecting changes in the environment, additional areas for transmitting the excitations to various parts of the cell, and other areas for effecting a response.

In the course of evolution of the more advanced multicellular animals, the ability of the organism to respond to particular stimuli has become highly developed in specialized tissues and organs. These include: (*a*) certain specialized nervous tissues or closely associated cells or organs, called *receptors*, which are sensitive to particular kinds of stimuli in the environment (e.g., the eyes and ears for light and sound, respectively); (*b*) the nervous system itself to propagate, transmit, and integrate the resultant signal or *nerve impulse* initiated by the stimulus at the receptor; and (*c*) the *effector* organs or tissue such as muscles and glands which react to the nerve impulse by being either stimulated or repressed in their activities. In this respect the nervous system links *receptors* to *effectors* by conducting and integrating nerve impulses from the former to the latter.

The first recognizable nervous system among present-day living forms consists simply of a network of somewhat similar nerve-like cells ramifying through most of the organism as seen in the lower group of the multicellular invertebrate animals, the *Coelenterata* (Chapter 18), which include jellyfish, corals, and

Hydra. Nerve impulse conduction is slow and can occur in either direction depending on where the stimulus acts. Nevertheless, certain cells of the nervous system appear to be functionally different. Some (receptors) are more sensitive to particular chemical and mechanical changes in the environment, others transmit the excitation to different parts of the body, and others (effectors) respond to the excitation by undergoing movement. Within the coelenterates a higher degree of development of the nervous system is illustrated in the familiar umbrella-shaped medusas or jellyfish. Here the nerve network is largely grouped into two parallel bundles of nerve cells or nerve rings. The jellyfish also possesses the first true sense organs: eye-like structures (*ocelli*) which are sensitive to light and so called *statocysts* which are sensitive to changes in position.

The successively more advanced invertebrate groups show progressive changes towards specialization in structure and function of the nervous system. In several of the flatworm species (Chapter 18), as bilaterally symmetrical animals, in addition to a network of nerve cells distributed throughout most of the body, there are the true beginnings of a centralized nervous system as well as differentiation into so-called *afferent* and *efferent neurons* (p. 500), which transmit nerve impulses from receptors and to acceptors, respectively. In planaria, for example, some of the nerve cells are clustered together, tending to form longitudinal nerve cords. The nerve cells in these cords serve as links between stimulus and response. The nerve cords fuse at the anterior portion of the body with other aggregates of nerve cells called *ganglia* (p. 494), but these are not yet considered to be a brain (Figure 21-1). Some specialized receptor cells and tissues are also present. These features have endowed many of the flatworms with more varied behavior and more rapid responses than the coelenterates.

The trend toward a more specialized and centralized nervous system including the condensation of the nervous system from a diffuse net and the development of chains of ganglia, becomes more evident in the annelids (Chapter 19). Moreover, in certain annelids such as the polychaete worms (e.g., *Nereis*), the head ganglia are no longer merely sensory relay centers (as they are in the oligochaetes such as the earthworm) but they also exercise some

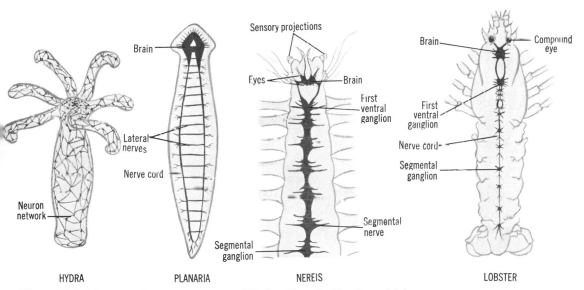

Figure 21-1. Diagrams of nervous systems of Hydra, Planaria, Nereis, and lobster.

control over several of the animal's activities. It is among the molluscs (Chapter 19) that one can trace the further progressive transformation of ganglia from the level of controlling centers for the activities of the animal (as in the gastropods such as the snail) to a highly complex and able brain (as in the cephalopods such as the octopus and the squid). Such development has been associated with a correspondingly advanced and complex behavior including unusual learning ability.

The arthropods (which include the insects, crabs, and lobsters, Chapter 19) as the most complex of the invertebrates have a fully developed central nervous system consisting of two ventrally located, solid nerve cords and a "brain". The latter is represented by a ring of two ganglia surrounding the esophagus or food-pipe portion of the digestive tract (Figure 21-1).

It is within the vertebrates, especially the mammals and in particular man, that the greatest specialization and development of the brain has occurred. The brain, and to a secondary extent the spinal cord, is considered to be the most advanced structural and functional feature of the nervous system. The vertebrate brain is essentially a large ganglionic mass—an overdeveloped portion of the anterior region of the spinal cord. The spinal cord in all vertebrates is a single, hollow structure running lengthwise down the back (dorsal part) of the body.

The brain of the most primitive vertebrates (as represented by the primitive fishes) is made up essentially of three enlargements of the spinal cord called the *forebrain, midbrain,* and the *hindbrain,* extending upward into the skull cavity (Figure 21-2). This basic organization of the brain has been so modified, even in fishes, during the course of evolution by the development of successive swellings and enlargements that it can no longer be easily distinguished in many vertebrates. In the human brain, which is the most highly developed of all, the three original regions are best recognized during an early stage of embryonic development prior to rapid modification by subsequent enlargement

and differentiation. Man's brain is the product of at least a billion years of evolution and is considered to be the greatest enigma in modern science today.

In general the evolutionary trends within the animal kingdom have been toward the development of (*a*) a centralized nervous system whose nerve fibers have formed cords which function primarily in the conduction of nerve impulses; (*b*) a localization of cell bodies into ganglia and their aggregation to form a brain accompanied by advanced and complex types of behavior; (*c*) the retreat of the centralized nervous system deeper into the protective reaches of the body; and (*d*) the elaboration of the receptors or sense organs (Chapter 22) and the effectors (the muscles and glands).

General Functions

The nervous system is a principal means of communication between the body parts, serving to integrate their many activities. It performs this highly specialized function by receiving various stimuli to which it responds by transmitting messages or so-called *nerve impulses* to different tissues and organs. Its action results in adjustments which are more favorable for the survival of the multicellular animal body.

All messages carried by the nervous system of mammals are transmitted within a fraction of a second or seconds. They must always pass through the brain or spinal cord or both, just as all telephone messages entering or leaving a factory must be relayed by way of the switchboard. The flow of information in the nervous system occurs as nerve impulses and goes not only from the brain and spinal cord to all parts of the body, but also via different nerve circuits from all parts of the body to the brain and spinal cord. In many instances it is precise, detailed information of which we are unaware (such as how much sugar, oxygen, and carbon dioxide are present in the blood). In other instances it is manifested at the conscious level as emotions and interpretations as a result of the integrative activity of different parts of the brain. Messages from the brain and spinal cord in turn control the body's response to this information. It is worth noting that the level of complexity of these two examples is of an entirely different order. On the one hand we have a relatively good working knowledge of the physiology of the nervous system with regard to such phenomena as the effects of carbon dioxide concentration in the blood. On the other we are as yet entirely unable to explain or correlate the physiology of the neuron and such dependent phenomena as thought, emotions, and interpretation in man.

Nearly all our responses at both the conscious and unconscious levels including physical movement, thoughts, emotions, memories, and personality traits are made possible through the functioning of the nervous system. Aside from its general role in controlling and integrating the activities of different parts of the body, the nervous system in one respect has a broad and unique function. It is our principal, if not the only, direct means of contact with the external living and nonliving environment about us. Our entire awareness of the existence of things as well as our responses to objects and events in the world surrounding us are necessarily mediated by the nervous system, accounting for our every thought, sensation, and movement. A defect or impairment in any portion of the nervous system could therefore impose limitations on our contacts with the outside world. Destruction of the eyes, or their nerves (optic nerves) leading to the brain, means we can no longer see what is happening around us. Defects in the nerve cells leading from the specialized taste buds in the tongue will result in a loss of ability to taste certain substances.

We know there are numerous physical phenomena that cannot be detected directly by means of our sense organs and nervous system. Magnetic fields, X-rays, radio waves, cosmic rays, and atomic radiation are instances of this type. We are only aware that they exist

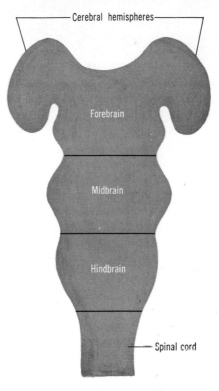

Figure 21-2. Organization of the brain of the most primitive vertebrates (i.e., primitive fishes) showing forebrain, midbrain, and hindbrain.

because we have been sufficiently clever to transform some of their effects by various devices into phenomena (such as heat, visible light, sound, and so on) which we can now detect or decipher through the action of the nervous system.

Our complete dependence on the nervous system and associated structures for knowledge of the world about us raises an interesting philosophical question. Is it possible that the world may be quite different from what we picture it to be because of limitations and possibly aberrations in our nervous system? The answer is very likely "no." Our perceptions of the external world must be close to reality, for otherwise how could we have evolved and survived in the inexorable process of natural selection of the last two billion years?

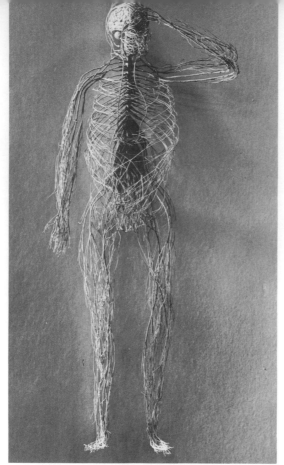

Figure 21-3. Model of nervous system of man (courtesy of Amer. Mus. Natural History).

Overall Organization of the Nervous System in Higher Animals Including Man

Man as the most complex and advanced of the multicellular animals possesses a nervous system made up of approximately ten to twelve billion specialized cells called nerve cells or neurons. These cells, consisting of cell bodies and their extending fibers, are organized in a vast and complex communication network (Figure 21-3) like a telephone system that coordinates the activities of a great factory. Depending on their location neurons may occur as single cells linked to one another through their fibers or processes (called axons and dendrites) in linear or branching sequence, or the fibers may be organized as a nerve, bundle of fibers, or nerve trunk which is made up of several to many fibers bound together within a common sheath of connective tissue.

Neurons never occur as isolated single cells or isolated clusters of cells but are always linked to other nerve cells as part of the vast and branching nervous system.

In all vertebrates including man the nervous system is made up of (1) a central structure consisting of the brain and spinal cord, collectively called the central nervous system, which serves as a central exchange or switchboard; and (2) a connecting vast and intricate branching network of nerve cells and fibers, collectively called the peripheral nervous system, which ramifies and extends to each and every part of the body.

The central nervous system of man is made up of the brain and spinal cord, whereas the peripheral nervous system consists of 12 pairs of cranial nerves and 31 pairs of symmetrical spinal nerves and their many branches. The cranial nerves originate in different sections of the brain and extend to various parts of the head, the neck, and to the internal organs or viscera of the chest and abdomen. The spinal nerves originate in pairs at various locations along the length of the spinal cord and form branches which extend into the arms, legs, and trunk of the body. The peripheral nervous system is in turn subdivided into two groups, the somatic nervous system and the visceral nervous system (also called the involuntary or autonomic nervous system). The somatic nervous system innervates the skeletal muscles, skin, and certain other body parts and is therefore responsible for the movement of various parts of the body through reflex actions (p. 499) as well as under the control of the will. The visceral nervous system innervates cardiac muscle, smooth muscle, and glands and therefore governs and controls the functions of the viscera (heart, gut, glands, etc.) which are carried out automatically and ordinarily at the level of unawareness (or unconscious level). These include rate of heart beat, contraction of the smooth muscle of the digestive tract, blood vessels, urinary bladder and other internal organs, and secretion by the digestive glands and sweat glands. The visceral nervous system thus has an indispensable role in maintaining

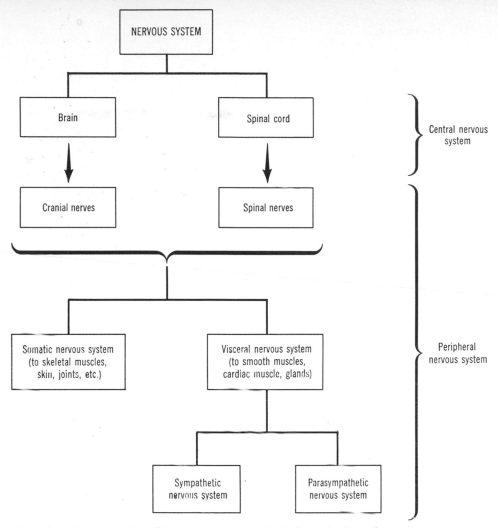

Figure 21-4. Overall organization of the nervous system in higher animals such as man.

the constancy of the internal environment.

On the basis of structural and functional differences, the visceral nervous system is subdivided into two parts, the *sympathetic nervous system* and the *parasympathetic nervous system*. Anatomically the nerve fibers of the sympathetic and parasympathetic nervous systems differ from each other in arising from different sections of the brain and spinal cord as well as in certain other aspects (p. 503). Most internal organs are innervated by nerve fibers from both the sympathetic and parasympathetic nervous systems. Functionally, the two divisions of the visceral nervous system have opposite effects. For some internal or-

gans nerve impulses arriving by way of the sympathetic nerves will be stimulatory whereas those arriving via the corresponding parasympathetic nerves will inhibit the same activity. For other organs the effects will be reversed, the sympathetic being inhibitory and the parasympathetic stimulatory.

A diagram of the overall organization of the nervous system in higher animals including man is shown in Figure 21-4. A more detailed discussion of the structure and function of these various subdivisions is presented in later sections of the chapter.

It should be noted that the central and peripheral nervous systems are not independent and

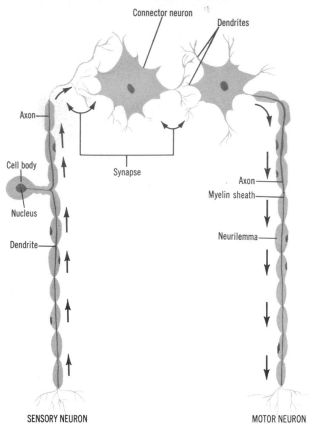

Connector neuron
Dendrites
Axon
Cell body
Synapse
Nucleus
Axon
Myelin sheath
Dendrite
Neurilemma

SENSORY NEURON — MOTOR NEURON

Figure 21-5. Drawings of sensory, connector, and motor neurons in a reflex arc showing various cellular structures, the synapses, and the direction of nerve impulse transmission.

separate entities. From one point of view the peripheral system is an extension of fibers from the central nervous system like the branches of a tree from their trunk. All messages or nerve impulses transmitted by way of the peripheral nervous system must eventually pass along a nerve pathway that always includes one or more neurons in the central nervous system.

Detailed Structure and Function of the Nervous System

Within the nervous system itself we know most about the structure and function of the neuron. It is only when we deal with progressively increasing numbers of neurons that our knowledge of the complexities of structure and function of the nervous system becomes pro-

gressively less. By the time we reach the highly complex brain with its vast and intricate organization, our understanding of its action is virtually nil.

ANATOMY OF THE NEURON. The neuron or nerve cell is the structural and functional unit of the nervous system. It consists of the main body of the cell, called the cell body, containing the usual nuclear and cytoplasmic structures and one or more specialized cytoplasmic extensions called fibers or processes. The cell bodies and fibers of neurons vary so widely in size and shape that it is almost impossible to describe a "typical" or generalized neuron. Cell bodies range in diameter from 4 to 25 microns, whereas the processes or fibers and their branches may extend in length from a few microns to as much as two or three feet. There is in fact still some disagreement about the terminology applied to the neurons, especially to its fibers or processes. Some neurons (e.g., motor neurons, p. 500) possess a long, slender, cytoplasmic process known as the *axon* with branches near its terminal end, and one or more shorter cytoplasmic processes called *dendrites*, usually arising from the opposite part of the cell body (Figure 21-5). The dendrites transmit nerve impulses towards the cell body, whereas the axon transmits nerve impulses away from the cell body. Other neurons (e.g., sensory neurons, p. 500) have only a single process or fiber which divides close to the cell body into two main branches. (Figure 21-5). Which of these branches corresponds to the axon and which is the dendrite? The most desirable definitions rest on a functional basis: the portion of the neuron that transmits nerve impulses towards the cell body is the *dendrite*, whereas the branch transmitting the nerve impulse away from the cell body corresponds to the *axon*.

The fibers or processes of many neurons of vertebrates are each enveloped for most of their length in a whitish, noncellular, stratified sheath of fatty materials called the *myelin sheath*, (Figure 21-6). The latter is somewhat like the insulation of an electrical wire, which is often surrounded by a *cellular* sheath called the *neurilemma*. Both sheaths are interrupted at regular intervals along their length by constrictions or nodes. The presence or absence of a myelin sheath as well as its thickness depends on the given nerve cell. Neurons in the brain and spinal cord lack the neurilemma sheath but possess a myelin sheath.

Several functions have been proposed for the myelin sheath although none have been clearly established. The major roles which have been suggested are that the myelin sheath serves as (1) a type of insulation that prevents the indiscriminate distribution of the nerve impulse to adjacent nerve fibers, (2) a food or energy supply for the nerve cell, and (3) a means of enhancing the rate of conduction of the nerve impulse since myelinated neurons conduct impulses at a fast speed, as much as 10- to 20-fold greater than nonmyelinated cells. Many nerve physiologists believe that the main function of the myelin sheath is to enhance the rate of nerve impulse travel. Disintegration of the myelin sheath in the central nervous system and its replacement by scar tissue impairs nerve impulse transmission, and occurs in the disease *multiple sclerosis*.

NERVE REGENERATION. Nerve cells lack the ability to multiply in contrast to other tissues. Once a neuron or its cell body is destroyed it cannot be replaced. However, neurons can regenerate several axons and dendrites provided the cell bodies are not damaged and a neurilemma sheath is present. The exact role of the neurilemma sheath in nerve regeneration is not known. In a matter of weeks the portion of the nerve process that has been severed from the cell body has usually become completely disintegrated while the neurilemma sheath continues to be maintained. Usually a new dendrite or axon will slowly grow out into the hollow neurilemma sheath, replacing the degenerate cut portion of the nerve process. Nerve fiber regeneration when it occurs may take months,

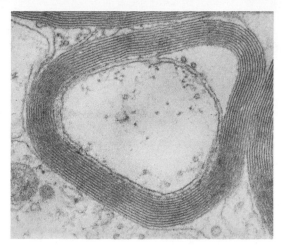

Figure 21-6. Electron micrograph of transverse section of myelinated nerve fiber showing the lamellar nature of the myelin sheath, magnification 72,000X *(courtesy of J. F. Metuzals, Journal of Ultra Structural Research).*

eventually restoring normal function to the tissue or organ originally affected by the nerve damage. In many instances of cut peripheral nerve fibers this type of regeneration takes place only if the cut ends of the nerve are held together in close proximity to one another, otherwise the regenerating nerve fibers grow astray. The fact that injured brain and spinal cord nerve fibers fail to show regeneration and are therefore permanently damaged has been attributed principally to the universal absence of the neurilemma sheath in the neurons of the central nervous system.

All parts of the neuron are clearly under control of the nucleus located in the cell body. It seems apparent that one or more factors that maintain organization and therefore prevent degeneration must be transmitted from the nucleus to the different parts of the nerve cell, because any portion that is severed from the cell body begins to degenerate within a few hours.

THE SYNAPSE. Neurons never occur as single isolated units but are always part of a linear or branched sequence of other nerve cells to constitute the central and peripheral nervous systems. Consecutive neurons are always so arranged that the axon endings of one are "connected" to the dendrites of the next. Actually there is no protoplasmic continuity or physical contact between the axon of one neuron and the dendrites of the next. Instead there is a narrow anatomical gap which together with the nearby specialized parts of the neurons is collectively called the *synapse*. As we shall soon see, nerve impulses are normally transmitted in only one direction—from dendrites to cell body to axon to synapse to dendrites of the successive neuron and so on. (More precisely, at the synapse the nerve impulses arriving at the axon endings are terminated and new impulses are started up at the dendrites of the successive neuron.)

GANGLIA AND NUCLEI. The nerve trunk, mentioned earlier, is in reality a bundle of many axons and dendrites bound together in a connective tissue sheath. The cell bodies, whose dendrites and axons compose a nerve fiber, are in turn grouped together in aggregates, which are called *ganglia* when they occur in the peripheral nervous system, and *nuclei*[1] when located in the central nervous system. The gray matter of the brain and spinal cord consists of cell bodies while the white matter is made up of fibers consisting of axons and dendrites.

THE NERVE IMPULSE. *General Features.* Messages are transmitted via neurons from one part of the body to the other by means of a self-propagating transient wave of electrical activity or electrical signal, called the *nerve impulse*, which travels along the length of a neuron. Thus neurons function by propagating nerve impulses, an invisible act, in response to an appropriate stimulus. In contrast, muscle tissues, for example, function by contracting, a visible act, in response to a given stimulus.

In certain limited ways the nerve impulse is comparable to the brief electrical signal or current (the dot and dash of the Morse code) sent along a telegraph communications system. It should be noted, however, that a nerve impulse is never identical with an electrical impulse or electrical current. It is probably best defined as an electrochemical phenomenon. Its fastest observed rate of travel is at best about 350 feet per second or about 4 miles per minute in a nerve fiber (its slowest rate about 1 mile per hour) in contrast to the rate of 100,000 miles per second which can be achieved by an electric current (stream of electrons) through wire. A second very important difference is the fact that the nerve impulse is generated or self-propagated by the very neurons which transmit it, as we shall soon see. In some respects a nerve impulse resembles a burning spark traveling along the length of a fuse. The physical-chemical change instigating the electric impulse in one section of a nerve cell causes a similar change in the adjacent section and so on until the impulse reaches the end of the fiber.

What accounts for the electrical phenomena of neurons, and exactly how are nerve impulses propagated along the entire length of any nerve circuit? The answers lie in the structure and chemistry of the neuron and in the composition of the natural fluid surrounding it. A major portion of our knowledge of the nature of the nerve impulse has developed from studies with certain giant nerve cells of a marine mollusc, the *squid* (p. 445), found in large numbers in the coastal waters of the North Atlantic. Although the squid normally swims by using its fins, it can also dart rapidly backward or forward by ejecting a jet of water. Two sets of giant nerve fibers control the muscle that are responsible for the jet propulsion mechanism. Their giant axons, which are as large as 1 mm in diameter (and therefore at least 50 times as large as the biggest axons in our own bodies and those of other vertebrates) have proved to be excellent material for the study of the electrical properties of nerve fibers or processes. Subsequent investigations have shown that nerve conduction mechanisms in

[1] It is unfortunate that the term *nucleus* is used in biology in two different ways: (1) most widely to designate the key structure of the cell, and (2) in a highly specialized category, namely as aggregates of cell bodies (of neurons) in the central nervous system.

vertebrates are fundamentally the same as those observed in squid and other invertebrates.

Resting and Active Membrane Potentials and Action Currents. We can think of a nerve axon as a long hollow cylinder representing the cell membrane filled with cytoplasm which differs in chemical composition from the surrounding extracellular fluid. The giant axons of squids, because of their large size, lend themselves well to the insertion of certain microelectrical equipment called electrodes into the cytoplasm (and into the extracellular fluid). In this manner it has been possible to show that the outer surface of a squid axon, when not transmitting a nerve impulse, is electrically more positive than the inside by about 0.07 volts. It is as if a series of tiny batteries, each with its positive poles turned toward the outside surface and its negative poles toward the inside surface, were lined up side by side in the axon membrane (Figure 21-7). This net difference in charge between the inner and outer surface of a nonconducting neuron is called the *resting membrane potential.*

The passage of a nerve impulse along the neuron is directly associated with a significant change in the resting membrane potential. Under normal conditions a nerve impulse is initiated by an appropriate stimulus applied at the dendrite end of the neuron resulting in a remarkable localized change in the resting membrane potential. The latter rapidly disappears and is replaced for a brief instant (about 0.001 of a second) by a new potential called the *active membrane potential* in which the inner membrane surface has become more positive than the outside, usually by about 0.05 volts. It is as if the tiny hypothetical batteries just indicated had been replaced for a fleeting fraction of a second by somewhat weaker batteries turned the other way around with their positive poles now on the inside and the negative poles on the outside of the cell membrane. The change is very brief, however, and only a portion of the neuron (0.1 to 10 cm) is in the active membrane potential state at any one time. The cell membrane quickly returns to the original resting potential state once the nerve impulse has passed.

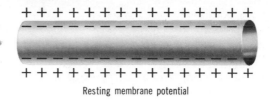

Resting membrane potential

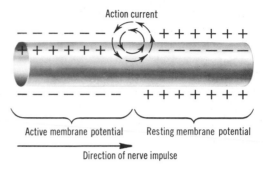

Action current

Active membrane potential   Resting membrane potential

Direction of nerve impulse

Figure 21-7. Diagram of axon showing electrical charge distribution on the outside and inside surfaces of the membrane illustrating the *resting membrane potential*, the *active membrane potential*, and *action currents* and their relationship to the generation of the nerve impulse.

These changes between the resting potential and active potential of the nerve cell membrane are believed to be the fundamental mechanism for propagation of the nerve impulse. The difference in potential between the active and resting regions of the cell membrane causes electric currents called *action currents* to flow in the external medium as well as within the nerve fiber itself. Action currents flow around cyclic pathways which pass inward from the outer membrane surface at the active membrane potential region, then along the inside membrane surface to the resting potential region just ahead of the impulse, and finally out through the membrane and back through the external fluid to the active membrane potential region to complete the circuit (Figure 21-7). The flow of the action current through the resting potential membrane region just ahead of the nerve impulse causes the membrane potential in that region to change from the resting to the active state. The action current then advances into the next successive region along the membrane, the entire process repeating itself. It is actually the migration of the change in potential from the resting to the active state in successive regions of the cell membrane that constitutes the moving nerve impulse.

The Membrane Theory. What is responsible for the difference in charge between the inside and outside of a neuron membrane which accounts for both the resting and active membrane potentials? According to the *membrane theory,* nerve membrane potentials arise because of differences between the concentrations of certain ions on the two sides of the membrane. Of the numerous ions present in the nerve cell and the surrounding fluid, two types in particular are of great importance in the nerve impulse mechanism. Chemical analysis has demonstrated that sodium ions (Na^+) are tenfold higher in concentration outside than inside the membrane surface, whereas potassium ions (K^+) are 20 times more concentrated inside than outside. (In addition there is a predominance of large negative organic ions inside the neuron in contrast to the negligible concentrations of these ions outside the membrane; the reverse situation is true for chloride ions (Cl^-).

The resting membrane is much more permeable to potassium ions than to the sodium and organic ions. In the resting or nonconducting state the nerve cell membrane permits only a small net movement into the cell of sodium ions, accounting for their high concentration on the outside surface. For the same reason the organic ions remain concentrated within the cells. According to the membrane theory, diffusion outward of a relatively small number of potassium ions (leaving the negative organic ions behind) is sufficient to generate the observed resting membrane potential of 0.07 volts. The passage of a nerve impulse is associated with a considerably greater increase in permeability to sodium ions than to potassium ions. The consequent rapid net movement of the positive sodium ions inward (leaving the negative chloride ions behind) not only abolishes the resting potential (called *depolarization*) but makes the inside momentarily more positive than the outside to give an active membrane potential of 0.05 volts. Soon after passage of the nerve impulse the resting membrane potential is restored (*repolarization*). The membrane rapidly becomes again impermeable to sodium, and a small quantity of potassium diffuses out of the fiber to reinstate the internal negatively charged condition of the resting state. The neuron is now ready to conduct another impulse.

The chemical and physical basis for the remarkably rapid and specific change in membrane permeability to sodium ions but not to the closely related potassium ions is another of the unsolved problems of biology. Whatever the explanation, experiments indicate that the observed large permeability changes are caused by a slight change in membrane potentials brought about by the outward flow of the action current through the membrane ahead of the advancing impulse. Action currents depolarize the membrane ahead of the advancing nerve impulse, initiating permeability changes and thus accounting for the movement of the nerve impulse. The changes in membrane potentials and membrane permeability are therefore mutually and inextricably related.

It seems obvious from what has been said that small quantities of sodium and potassium respectively must enter and leave the nerve fiber each time a nerve impulse is propagated. Actual measurements have shown that each impulse changes the internal sodium and potassium concentrations by extremely small values. Although a nerve can conduct many impulses before its chemical composition is greatly changed, sodium must eventually be moved back out and potassium back in. The energy required to return these ions uphill against their respective concentration gradients in contrast to downhill transfer occurring during impulse propagation is presumably generated by metabolic processes in the nerve cell. The mechanisms of this "metabolic pump" for moving sodium ions out of the neuron into the external fluid containing ten-fold greater sodium ion concentrations, and potassium ions into the cell already containing considerably higher potassium concentrations, are not yet established. Present indications are that this metabolic pump is a type of active transport and that its fuel may well be the energy-rich ATP (Chapter 8) produced by the respiratory activity of the cell. In partial support of this proposal is the observation that a limitation in the oxygen supply is known to cause a rapid decrease in the ability of nerve cells to conduct nerve impulses.

In summary, a neuron in the resting state has a net positive electrical charge on the outer surface of its cell membrane and a net negative electrical charge on its inner surface. The membrane is said to be electrically polarized, and the net difference in charge is called an electrical potential, in this instance the *resting membrane potential.* The charges are due to an energy-requiring process of accumulation of positive ions (Na^+) on the external membrane surface and certain organic negative ions on the internal surface, as a result of the metabolic activities of the nerve cell. The two sets of oppositely charged ions cannot mix and therefore cannot neutralize one another because the cell membrane is relatively impermeable to them in the resting state. A nerve impulse is initiated by a stimulus which depolarizes the membrane at its site of application, usually at the dendrite end of the neuron. The subsequent inward passage of current at the point initially depolarized and the outward passage of current through adjacent regions of the membrane depolarizes the neighboring regions and increases their permeability to sodium ions. In this manner the simultaneous increase in membrane permeability and sodium move-ment into the neuron in successive regions along the length of the nerve cell constitutes a wave of electrical depolarization or migrating electrochemical reaction called the nerve impulse. The increased permeability to sodium ions rapidly disappears and the original internal negatively charged condition of the resting state is presumably restored by the subsequent movement of potassium ions (K^+) from the inside to the outside of the cell.

Other Physiological Features of the Nerve Impulse. The time interval required for restoration of the resting membrane potential before another nerve impulse can be transmitted by the neuron is called the *refractory period.* In mammalian nerves the observed refractory period ranges from 0.001 to 0.005 seconds, which means that approximately 200 to 1000 impulses per second can be fired along a nerve.

In order to initiate a nerve impulse a stimulus of certain minimum intensity must be applied. If the minimum threshold of stimulus strength is equaled or exceeded a nerve impulse will be started; and once started, the nerve impulse travels at a speed that is entirely independent of the intensity of stimulus. Its rate depends only on the physical and metabolic state of the nerve itself. This relationship is called the *all-or-none law.* Actually it is possible for two or more stimuli in rapid succession to initiate a nerve impulse even though each stimulus of itself is below the minimum threshold of intensity. This adding together of sub-minimal stimuli to elicit an impulse is called *summation.* In terms of the membrane theory, in order to initiate a nerve impulse the potential of the nerve fiber must be sufficiently altered (whether by a single stimulus or by summation) to cause a certain minimum increase in sodium permeability. The stimulus which initiates the nerve impulse is comparable to pulling the trigger of a gun or lighting a fuse. Sufficient force to pull the trigger must be applied for the gun to fire. Once the threshold trigger force is equaled or exceeded, pulling the trigger harder will not make the bullet travel any faster.

Similarly the rate of travel of a burning spark along a fuse will be the same whether the fuse is ignited either by a single match or a powerful blowtorch. The speed of movement of the burning spark depends only on the physical and chemical condition of the fuse.

The intensity of stimulation necessary to initiate a nerve impulse varies with the nature of the receptor nerve tissue and the stimulus itself. For example, the eye as an extremely sensitive and specific receptor organ is stimulated by extremely low intensities of visible light. A nerve impulse is thus initiated that passes along the optic nerve connecting the eye to the brain. However, the same or a far greater intensity of light applied to the ear will not set off an impulse along the auditory nerve connecting the organ of hearing to the brain.

Qualitative and Quantitative Effects of Nerve Impulses. Once a nerve impulse is started, no matter what the stimulus or how applied, it is essentially the same as any other nerve impulse that occurs in any other part of the nervous system. If the all-or-none law is valid and all nerve impulses are alike, how can we account for our ability to distinguish both qualitative and quantitative effects? The answer is that these effects can be attributed to several factors including the number of nerve endings stimulated, the nerve pathways traveled, and the frequency of nerve impulses (the number of impulses per second and their spacing in time). The most important factor of all is the sorting out of this information (an integrative process) by the brain. The latter functions as a giant complex control panel with different regions specializing in receiving different kinds of information. For example, stimulation of the eye by visible light results in the sensation of light. The same light applied to the hand, if of sufficient intensity, initiates impulses which go to another area of the brain to give a sensation of heat.

Nerve Impulse Transmission across the Synapse. Nerve stimulation normally occurs at the dendrite end of the neuron. The resulting nerve impulse is subsequently transmitted along the membrane surface of the neuron via the cell body and axon to the terminal axon branches which form a synapse with the dendrites of the next neuron. Should the nerve be stimulated anywhere along its length two nerve impulses will be initiated, each traveling in the opposite direction. The one moving in the wrong direction (toward the dendrites) will terminate at the synapse and be extinguished, since it cannot be transmitted to the next neuron. The other impulse traveling in the normal direction along the axon will arrive at the synapse and cause an impulse to be initiated in the next successive neuron.

How is the effect of an impulse transmitted across the synapse? It is generally believed that an impulse arriving at the termination of an axon liberates one or more chemicals at the axon endings. These chemicals are referred to as *transmitters* and diffuse across the minute gap at the synapse to the membrane of the next neuron causing changes in its permeability to certain ions. Depending on the nature of the chemical transmitter the permeability changes may result in an increased depolarization of the membrane, thus initiating a nerve impulse. The particular chemical transmitter in the sympathetic ganglia has been shown to be the ester *acetylcholine* (p. 505). Diffusion of transmitter across the synapse gap is significantly slower than the rate of impulse transmission along the neuron. The fact that an impulse moving in the opposite direction, from cell body to dendrites, cannot be transmitted across the synapse is ascribed to the inability of the dendrite endings to secrete the transmitter.

NERVE CELL METABOLISM. A good deal is now known about the general enzymology and metabolism of nerve tissue, an area which is advancing rapidly. Despite our extensive knowledge of the metabolism of nervous tissues, the correlation of these biochemical events with the unique characteristics and functions of nerves are not at all clear. Within the brain cells it has been recognized that there are wide differences in chemical properties among different neurons. For example, some neurons are relatively resistant to lack of oxygen, whereas others are extremely sensitive, losing function within a matter of seconds.

THE REFLEX AND THE REFLEX ARC. Most of our body activities and reactions to environmental changes, both internal and external, are automatic or involuntary. Such responses that occur outside of our awareness are immediate and rapid and are collectively called *reflexes*. Reflexes are usually classified into two broad subdivisions, the *simple or unconditioned reflex* and the *conditioned reflex*.

Simple Reflex. A *simple reflex* is an inborn, inherited, or unlearned response to a stimulus or change in environment. A *conditioned reflex* on the other hand is a response that is dependent on past experience, training, or learning. A familiar example of a simple reflex is the knee jerk in which the leg is involuntarily and momentarily extended as a result of a sharp tap below the kneecap. Certain stretch-sensitive receptor nerve endings are stimulated, starting up one or more successive nerve impulses which quickly travel by way of a particular pathway of neurons (including a portion of the central nervous system) to specific muscles of the thigh, causing them to contract and straighten the knee. The quick closing of the eyelid when an object suddenly approaches the eye, or the rapid withdrawal of the hand when it is burned or pricked even before there is an awareness of pain are also illustrations of simple reflexes. Innumerable simple reflexes are continually occurring in the body, controlling, for example, secretions of certain glands, breathing, muscular activity of large portions of the digestive tract, heart rate, and so on.

The Conditioned Reflex. Conditioned reflexes, unlike the simple or unconditioned reflex, are not inborn but are acquired and dependent on past experience and training. A *conditioned reflex* is the response acquired as a result of training or experience to a stimulus that originally failed to evoke the reaction. It was first clearly demonstrated by the eminent Russian physiologist Pavlov in the early part of

this century. Most of our basic information concerning this phenomenon is the result of his investigations. He showed that conditioned reflexes can be developed experimentally to an extraordinary degree.

Under normal circumstances the secretion of saliva when food is ingested is a simple reflex or response initiated by the stimulation of the taste buds in the mouth. Pavlov, working with dogs, demonstrated that if an additional stimulus is regularly furnished, such as the ringing of a bell, whenever food was given to the animals, in time the mere ringing of the bell without even the sight or smell of food would result in the secretion of saliva. In this way a conditioned reflex was established. A previously ineffective stimulus (the ringing of the bell), by association with a stimulus (food) that evoked a response, had become effective in eliciting the response, namely the secretion of saliva by the salivary glands. Stated in another way, a conditioned reflex represents an inborn response which has been displaced to a new stimulus. It is a more complex integrative process than a simple reflex.

The functions of both the simple and conditioned reflexes in everyday survival as automatic mechanisms of response and protection are obvious. Such responses as coughing and sneezing which expel small intruding foreign objects, and the closing of the eyelids when the eyes are suddenly approached are examples of the defensive role of reflexes.

The Reflex Arc. The structural and functional basis of the simple reflex is called the *reflex arc*. It is believed to consist of an arrangement of three or more neurons in a pathway which invariably passes through the central nervous system. The simplest kind of reflex arc might consist of only two neurons, although very few of this type are considered to exist in higher animals. A reflex, therefore, may also be defined as the response that results from a nerve impulse passing along a reflex arc. Some investigators believe that the reflex arc as the cellular mechanism of reflex action explains all nervous coordination. Others, however, feel that it is much too oversimplified to account for the complex action of the nervous system.

In a theoretically simple reflex are consisting of a few neurons (see Figures 21-5 and 21-8), the nerve impulse is normally initiated in the dendrites of the so-called *afferent or sensory neuron* located within the receptor organ or tissue. The impulses travel along the sensory neuron until they reach the terminal branches of the axon at the synapse. Impulses are thus initiated in the second neuron in the arc called the *connector neuron*. The latter is always located in the central nervous system. The nerve impulse then proceeds along the length of the connector neuron, to its axon endings, and at the synapse initiates an impulse in the third nerve cell called the *efferent or motor neuron*. The terminal axon branches of the motor neuron end in the effector organ, that is, in a muscle or gland which responds to the incoming nerve impulses.

In brief sensory or afferent neurons therefore transmit nerve impulses toward the central nervous system, whereas motor or efferent neurons transmit impulses away from the central nervous system. The connector neuron serves as the link between the sensory and motor neurons. The reflex or response made by the effector organ as a result of the arriving nerve impulse is either a muscular contraction or glandular secretion, depending on the effector involved. Nerve impulse conduction normally occurs in only one direction, from receptor via the central nervous system to effector, since the synapses do not permit the reverse movement of impulses from one neuron to another.

The above account of a single isolated reflex arc has been used for purposes of simplicity and description to indicate the structural and functional basis of a simple reflex. Unfortunately it tends to impart the erroneous impressions that (a) only a single isolated reflex arc is involved as the result of a single stimulus, and (b) an organism is a relatively passive protoplasmic mass whose responses are governed solely by environmental stimuli.

With regard to the first point, reflex actions of higher animals almost always involve an appreciable number of reflex arcs, rather than one. For example, should a person receive a sudden and unexpected burn on his fingertip,

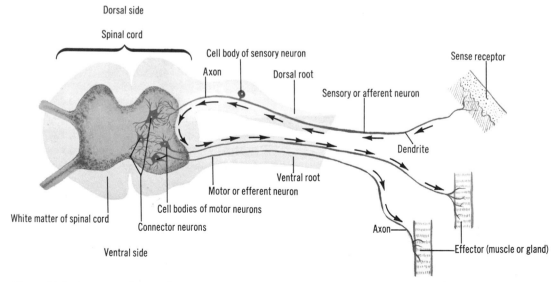

Figure 21-8. Anatomy of a spinal nerve in man and its attachment to the spinal cord (shown in cross-section) with reference to the reflex arc and pathway of nerve impulse transmission (indicated by the arrows). See text for details.

not only would he jerk his hand as a result of a simple reflex, but he would also respond in other ways. He would probably turn his head to the source of danger, ejaculate an exclamation of some kind, and very likely experience a series of sensations and reactions including pain, fear, emotional tension, and so on. Obviously numerous muscles including those of the arm, shoulders, neck, head, trunk, tongue, larynx, and respiratory tract as well as several mental processes have participated in his total reaction. What started out as a simple stimulus (i.e., a slight, highly localized burn) has evoked a rather extensive reflex behavior involving the integration of the rest of the nervous system.

This multiplicity of reactions is explained by nerve integrative processes as well as by other structural aspects of the reflex arc. The reflex arc nearly always becomes involved in more complex nervous system activity. Axons of sensory neurons in many cases have several branches, each of which may form a synapse with other connector neurons at different levels in the spinal cord and brain. A sensory neuron therefore has potential connections with many effectors and can evoke activity in many parts of the body, thus simultaneously eliciting a number of responses at one time. For example, one of the numerous axon branches of a sensory neuron may have a synapse with a second afferent neuron which extends upward in the spinal cord as part of a bundle of neuron processes (called an *ascending tract*) to end in some specific region of the brain. This particular reflex arc is considerably more complex. Not only does it consist of two successive afferent neurons and at least one connector neuron in the brain, but it also has a relay of at least two successive efferent neurons. One efferent neuron transmits the message in a descending bundle of neuron processes (called a *descending tract*) from the brain to the spinal cord and the other transmits it from the cord to the effector organ. The dendrites and cell body of the first efferent neuron are in the brain, whereas its axon extends down-

ward as part of the descending tract. The axon of the second efferent neuron whose cell body lies in the gray matter of the spinal cord extends into a spinal nerve to end eventually in an effector tissue (muscle or gland).

A single sensory neuron may have synapses with other neurons, thus accounting for the ability of a single and highly localized stimulus such as a pin prick to elicit several responses or reflexes. Similarly a single motor neuron may have synapses with numerous other neurons, thus accounting for the ability of different stimuli in different parts of the body to elicit the same response. As an example of the latter an injury to any part of the body may evoke the same use of the muscles of the larynx to emit a cry of pain.

With regard to the second point cited above it seems that the organism itself has appreciable control over what will constitute stimulation, a concept that is gaining wider acceptance. Responses or reflexes are apparently regulated and controlled by mechanisms that are still not clear. The body's receptors are continually being bombarded by innumerable stimuli. Nevertheless, compared to the much larger number of impinging stimuli, only a relatively limited number of responses or reflexes occurs, indicative of some control or inhibitory mechanism at work. It is believed that this control is exercised at least in part through a regulatory feedback type of mechanism to the receptors by the central nervous system. All proposed theories are in common agreement that if inhibition is involved, the unknown inhibitory mechanism probably occurs at the synapse rather than along the processes of the nerve cell. Similarly, there is an unknown phenomenon that is the opposite of *inhibition*, namely an enhancement or strengthened response of particular reflexes which is called *reinforcement or facilitation*.

REFLEX CENTER. The term *reflex center* refers to an aggregate of neurons (often including synapses) in the spinal cord or brain which control the activity of a particular group of effectors. For example, the reflex center in the *medulla oblongata* region of the brain

(p. 508) for breathing consists of a group of neurons which control the impulses being conducted to different muscles of the chest responsible for breathing action. The cells of the reflex center are in turn regulated by appropriate afferent impulses. Much of the brain and spinal cord are made up of reflex centers affecting body activities.

Overall Organization of the Peripheral Nervous System

THE SPINAL AND CRANIAL NERVES. Within the peripheral nervous system, the cell processes (i.e., dendrites and axons) of many sensory neurons, motor neurons, or both, depending on their location in the body, are in most instances bound together with connective tissue to constitute larger nerves or nerve trunks. *Sensory nerves* and *motor nerves* are made up only of processes of sensory neurons and motor neurons, respectively. *Mixed nerves* possess the processes of both types of neurons. All 31 pairs of spinal nerves in man are mixed nerves, whereas some cranial nerves are mixed and others are made up exclusively of either sensory neurons or motor neurons. The 12 pairs of cranial nerves arise from the undersurface of the brain and pass through small openings in the skull to their respective destinations.

The spinal nerves are attached at more or less regular intervals along the length of the spinal cord (Figure 21-8). Just before it joins the spinal cord, each spinal nerve divides into two branches or roots. The *dorsal or sensory root,* contains only sensory neurons and connects with the dorsal (or back) portion of the spinal cord. The *ventral or motor root,* contains only motor neurons and connects with the ventral portion. Since the dorsal root of a spinal nerve is made up only of sensory neurons, it represents the functional point of entry of nerve impulses into the spinal cord. Each dorsal root contains a single ganglion or bundle of cell bodies of the sensory neurons of each spinal nerve. The axons of the sensory neurons enter the dorsal side of the spinal cord which in cross section has a central butterfly-shaped region of gray matter. The latter consists of two dorsal horns and two ventral horns surrounded by whitish vertically placed bundles of axons and dendrites (Figure 21-8). The gray dorsal horns of the spinal cord are made up largely of the cell bodies of the connector neurons, whereas the gray ventral horns consist for the most part of the cell bodies of the motor neurons. The axons of the motor neurons leave the spinal cord to become the ventral root of the spinal nerve, joining with the dorsal root to make up the main trunk of the spinal nerve. The latter progressively subdivides into branches which innervate various parts of the body.

The role of the dorsal and ventral roots in conducting impulses to and from the spinal cord, respectively, can be demonstrated by severing the nerve and observing the effects. When the dorsal root is cut no impulses will reach the cord from that part of the body innervated by the severed spinal nerve. As a result that part of the body experiences a complete loss of sensation without any paralysis of the muscles. If the cut end of the dorsal root attached to the cord is stimulated, or if impulses are sent from the brain, a response will take place since the ventral root is still intact. When the ventral root is cut instead, complete paralysis of the muscles innervated by that nerve ensues because no impulses can reach the muscle from the cord. However, the senses of pressure, temperature, pain, and so on are unaffected since the dorsal root is still intact, allowing for the passage of sensory impulses to the central nervous system. If the peripheral cut end of the ventral root not attached to the spinal cord is stimulated, the muscles of that part of the body innervated by the cut nerve will respond. When the spinal nerve, which is a union of the dorsal and ventral roots, is cut, that portion of the body affected will suffer both a loss of sensation and a paralysis of the muscles.

On the basis of structure and function the peripheral nervous system consists of two subdivisions, namely the *somatic nervous system* and the *visceral or autonomic nervous system.* Both subdivisions are also represented

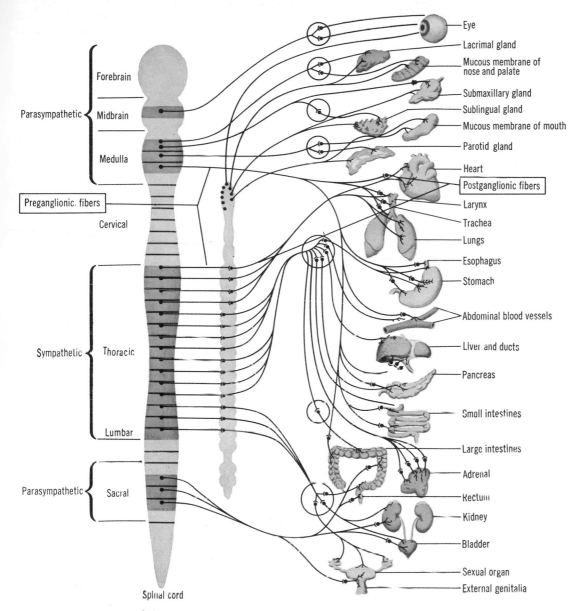

Figure 21-9. Diagram of the visceral or autonomic nervous system. See text for details (*adapted from T. I. Storer, and R. L. Usinger, Elements of Zoology, McGraw-Hill, 1955*).

in the brain and spinal cord.

THE VISCERAL NERVOUS SYSTEM. The same basic structural and functional relationships including reflexes and reflex arcs as described in the previous sections apply to both the voluntary and visceral nervous systems.

Anatomy of the Visceral Nervous System. The two subdivisions of the visceral nervous system (namely the *sympathetic* and *parasympathetic* nervous systems) are structurally and functionally different in some features but similar in others. The peripheral part of the sympathetic nervous system is exclusively confined to the spinal nerves that leave the spinal cord in the regions of the chest and abdomen, called the *thoraco-lumbar* division. However, the peripheral part of the parasympathetic nervous system is included only within several of the cranial nerves and the spinal nerves that leave the lowest portion of the spinal cord, collectively called the *craniosacral* division (Figure 21-9). Both systems characteristically possess two successive efferent or motor neurons on every reflex arc to each organ or tissue which they innervate. The ganglia of the second or distal efferent neurons in the sympathetic nervous system lie relatively close to the spinal cord, forming two vertical rows or chains of ganglia with connecting fibers between them (the sympathetic trunks), one row on each side of the cord (Figure 21-9). In the parasympathetic nervous system the ganglia of the second or distal efferent neurons are farther away from the spinal cord, tending to be near or in the organs which they innervate. In both systems the processes of the efferent neurons leading from the spinal cord to the ganglia are called *preganglionic* fibers. The processes of the second efferent neurons leading from the ganglia to the cardiac muscle, smooth muscle, and glands are known as *postganglionic* fibers. The preganglionic fibers of the parasympathetic nervous system are necessarily long because they extend from the brain and spinal cord for a considerable distance in their particular autonomic nerves to ganglia that lie in or near the tissues innervated. Their postganglionic fibers are characteristically short. The reverse situation is true for the sympathetic nervous system, the preganglionic fibers being short and the postganglionic fibers long.

The cell bodies of the preganglionic neurons of the sympathetic and parasympathetic nervous systems in the spinal nerves are located in the gray matter of the spinal cord (except for those of the parasympathetic preganglionic neurons of the cranial nerves which are in the brain). The axons of the preganglionic neurons depart from the spinal cord by way of the ventral roots of the appropriate spinal nerves. One of the noteworthy features of the anatomy of the sympathetic nervous system is that in all cases each axon of a sympathetic preganglionic axon synapses with several postganglionic neurons leading to a number of scattered tissues. By contrast each parasympathetic preganglionic neuron has synapses only with postganglionic neurons to a single structure. These structural facts account for the observation that, whereas sympathetic stimulation in all cases elicits responses by several organs, parasympathetic stimulation often invokes a response from only one organ. Nevertheless nearly all internal receptor organs and tissues are innervated by both the sympathetic and parasympathetic divisions of the visceral nervous system.

The main anatomical differences between the somatic and visceral nervous systems of the peripheral nervous system can be summarized as follows. The somatic system has only one efferent neuron from the central nervous system to effector tissues (e.g., skeletal muscle), whereas the visceral system has two efferent neurons (preganglionic and postganglionic) to its effectors. Synapses and cell bodies of the efferent or motor neurons of the somatic nervous system are always located within the central nervous system. Those for the postganglionic neurons of the visceral system always occur in ganglia outside the brain and spinal cord.

Functions of the Visceral Nervous System. By regulating smooth muscle, cardiac muscle, and many glands the visceral nervous system controls the activity of the internal organs. Thus it plays an important role in the adaptation of the body to its immediate needs and in the maintenance of a stable or relatively constant internal body environment, increasing or decreasing the activity of each internal organ in an integrated fashion. Visceral reflex arcs are usually activated by several different stimuli including stretch, pressure, and chemical factors. As we shall soon see, groups of certain neurons in the brain and spinal cord serve as integrating or reflex centers for the activities of the sympathetic and parasympathetic systems. They regulate such body functions as breathing, water balance, heat control, sexual responses, and so on. The afferent or sensory neurons of most reflex arcs involving internal organs function similarly to those of the somatic reflexes. These and numerous other relationships have emphasized the role of the entire nervous system as an integrated unit. Neither the visceral nor the somatic nervous system serves independently of each other or of the central nervous system.

How do the roles of the sympathetic and parasympathetic divisions of the visceral nervous system differ? We now know that these two divisions have opposite effects on the activities of each internal organ innervated. They either stimulate or inhibit according to the needs of the body. In this manner the sympathetic and parasympathetic portions of the autonomic nervous system tend to effect a balance which contributes to the stability of the internal environment.

In most body activities, including heart rate, blood pressure, and activity of the sweat glands and adrenal glands, nerve impulses arriving via the sympathetic nervous system have a stimulating effect. Nerve impulses received by way of the parasympathetic system depress or inhibit these activities. Thus the sympathetic nervous system, among its functions, can act in an emergency role, enabling the body to cope with situations of stress by promoting maximal energy production (and minimal bleeding). The parasympathetic division of the autonomic nervous system, among its functions, is primarily concerned in making adjustments that bring about or maintain a constancy of internal environment. For certain other body activities, however, including the action of smooth muscle in the walls of the digestive tract and secretion by the salivary glands, the effects are precisely the opposite. The sympathetic system inhibits and the parasympathetic system stimulates. In general the

parasympathetic system tends to build up and protect the resources of the body by slowing down most activities and increasing that of the digestive tract. By contrast the sympathetic system tends to promote the use of these reserves by promoting maximal energy production.

Active Secretions of the Visceral Nervous System. What are the mechanisms by which the sympathetic and parasympathetic nervous systems exert their opposite effects? The pioneering experiments of Otto Loewi some forty years ago furnished the first important clues. He showed that the effects of the visceral nerves on the vertebrate heart rate are due directly to the action of certain chemical substances liberated by the nerve endings as a result of the arrival of nerve impulses. Loewi removed the beating hearts of two frogs, filled their chambers with a dilute chemical solution of inorganic salts, and inhibited the beat of one heart by stimulating its attached parasympathetic nerve, the *vagus* nerve. After transferring some of the fluid from the inhibited heart to the second heart the latter's rate of beat was also inhibited (although its vagus nerve had not been stimulated). Stimulation of the vagus nerve in the first beating heart had resulted in the release of a chemical substance which was inhibitory to the second heart. Loewi proposed that the axon branches of the vagus nerve terminating in the heart released this inhibitory substance when the nerve impulse arrived at the axon endings. These experiments earned him the honor of the Nobel Prize.

The vast evidence that has since been collected indicates that the mechanism of action of the visceral nervous system on receptor organs is dependent on the nerve impulse-induced secretion of certain chemicals by the terminal axon branches of the postganglionic neurons. The original inhibitory substance first detected by Loewi in the inhibited frog heart has since been identified as the ester *acetylcholine.* Acetylcholine, which is also the transmitter responsible for nerve impulse

Sympathetic — inhibits
Parasympathetic — stimulates

transmission across the synapse in sympathetic ganglia, is liberated at the terminals of post-ganglionic parasympathetic neurons that innervate the internal organs. Similarly a chemical substance called *sympathin*, which consists primarily of *norepinephrine* (also called *noradrenalin*, Chapter 23), is known to be released by sympathetic postganglionic nerve endings by arriving nerve impulses. It apparently accounts for the effects of the sympathetic system on the activities of effector tissues.

If acetylcholine is released at parasympathetic nerve endings, why does it not accumulate and produce generalized body disturbances in terms of continuous stimulation or inhibition, as the case may be, of muscular and glandular activity, resulting in spasms, exhaustion, paralysis, and finally death? The answer is that acetylcholine fails to be accumulated or distributed because of the ubiquitous enzyme *cholinesterase* which very rapidly destroys it by hydrolysis.

During World War II a deadly nerve gas was prepared (but fortunately not used) which inhibited the enzyme. It was shown to cause the generalized chaotic parasympathetic effects (soon followed by death) expected from a distribution and accumulation of acetylcholine. The sympathin released by the sympathetic postganglionic nerve endings lasts somewhat longer than acetylcholine, but it is eventually destroyed by oxidation reactions.

Central Nervous System

The central nervous system consisting of the brain and spinal cord performs a key function in the vastly intricate nervous system. It serves as the central clearing house or switchboard controlling, directing, and integrating all messages (i.e., nerve impulses) transmitted by the nervous system within the body.

PROTECTIVE STRUCTURES OF THE CENTRAL NERVOUS SYSTEM. The brain and spinal cord as vital and delicate organs of the human body are well fortified against injury by two types of protective coverings and by an external and internal cushion of fluid. The outermost covering that encases the brain is the skull or cranial bones, whereas the cord is largely enclosed within the spinal canal formed by the bony neural arches of the vertebrae. The underlying or inner covering of the brain and spinal cord consists of three distinct layers or membranes called *meninges*. They are made up for the most part of connective tissue and separated from each other by a space. The space between the inner and middle meninges is filled with a lymph-like liquid called *cerebrospinal fluid* which thus serves as an external protective cushion of fluid. It also fills certain large chambers within the brain called *ventricles* as well as the hollow central or spinal canal inside the cord. Thus it acts as an internal cushion of fluid. Cerebrospinal fluid resembles lymph in composition and is produced largely by the filtration of blood from the mass of capillaries found in each of the ventricles of the brain.

THE SPINAL CORD. The spinal cord in the average adult human is an oval-shaped hollow cylinder, 17 to 18 inches long, which tapers slightly as it extends downward through the protective canal formed by the bony neural arches of the vertebrae of the spinal column. In cross section the cord displays an inner butterfly-shaped or H-shaped core of gray matter through whose center passes a canal; the outer portion is composed of white matter. As in the other parts of the nervous system, the gray matter consists of neuron cell bodies and nonmyelinated fibers or processes. The dorsal horns of the butterfly region mostly contain the cell bodies of the connector neurons. The ventral horns contain cell bodies of the efferent or motor neurons of the spinal nerves.

The white matter of the spinal cord is made up of bundles of myelinated nerve fibers (wrapped in connective tissue sheaths) which are called *tracts* instead of nerves in the central nervous system. Each of the many different tracts apparently serves a specific function. Some transmit impulses upward and others

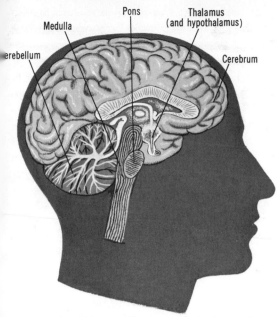

Figure 21-10. Principal regions of the brain of man (midbrain not shown).

Medulla   Pons   Thalamus (and hypothalamus)

Cerebellum   Cerebrum

downward (*ascending* and *descending* tracts, respectively) to and from different parts of the brain and body. All tracts, ascending and descending, *cross over* from one side of the spinal cord to the other somewhere along their pathways to and from the brain. Thus the right side of the brain receives impulses arising from the left side of the body and in general regulates the activities of the left side of the body. The corresponding relationship applies to the left side of the brain and the right side of the body. The significance of the curious phenomenon of *crossing over* of the tracts has not yet been satisfactorily explained.

The two main functions of the spinal cord are to serve: (1) as a pathway for the conduction of impulses between the peripheral nervous system and the brain, and (2) as a reflex center for a great many reflexes or responses much like a telephone switchboard sorts out and relays incoming calls or messages to their proper destination.

THE BRAIN OF MAN. The adult human brain, a most complex and highly developed organ,

has an average weight of about three pounds. It tends to weigh less in women, small people, and elderly persons. Its different parts have been classified in several ways. For the purposes of this book we shall describe only six main regions of the brain, namely the *medulla oblongata, cerebellum, pons, midbrain, thalamus,* and *cerebrum* (Figure 21-10). The relationship of the structures of man's brain to the original three main brain regions (hindbrain, midbrain, and forebrain) can be represented according to the following simplified classification:

Forebrain $\begin{cases} \text{Cerebrum} \\ \text{Thalamus and hypothalamus} \end{cases}$

Midbrain $\begin{cases} \text{Midbrain consisting of tracts, 4} \\ \text{protuberances involving certain} \\ \text{auditory and optic functions,} \\ \text{and reflex centers participating} \\ \text{in muscular coordination} \end{cases}$

Hindbrain $\begin{cases} \text{Pons} \\ \text{Cerebellum} \\ \text{Medulla oblongata} \end{cases}$

The medulla oblongata, pons, and midbrain are often collectively referred to as the *brainstem,* due to its general location and shape.

The structural organization of the brain is in general correlated with the degree or level at which each part functions. The lower anatomical regions of the brain deal with automatic functions (e.g., heart rate, respiration, and so on) whereas successively higher regions of the brain are concerned with correspondingly more integrated and advanced activities. The latter includes coordinated muscular activity, voluntary motion, complicated and skilled activities, and most progressive of all, the processes of reasoning and abstract thought. It is generally believed that the lower regions of the brain which are similar in most mammals are the more primitive brain portions. The evolution of higher mammals has been accompanied by an increased development in size and function of the anterior portion of the brain. More precisely it has occurred in that region of the forebrain which in man has culminated in the enormous cerebrum. Although the more primitive parts of the brain (i.e., the brainstem) still carry out their original functions, in man they are subject to various degrees of control and regulation by the higher centers.

Hindbrain. Medulla Oblongata. As an enlarged extension of the anterior portion of the spinal cord the medulla oblongata is the lowermost part of the brain which connects to the spinal cord. It measures about an inch in length and consists mostly of ascending and descending tracts of white matter with some gray matter in its interior. The enlarged cavity within the medulla oblongata representing the expanded portion of the spinal canal is called a *ventricle,* one of four which occur in the brain. The gray matter scattered within the interior of the medulla contains several vital reflex centers including those that control the rate of heart beat, breathing, and constriction and dilation of the blood vessels. Other reflex centers include those responsible for vomiting, coughing, sneezing, hiccoughing, and swallowing.

The Cerebellum. Above the medulla and extending laterally from it is the *cerebellum,* the second largest portion of the brain. It is exceeded in size only by the cerebrum but nevertheless constitutes only 10 per cent of the weight of the brain. It is composed of a central worm-shaped structure called the *vermis* and two large lateral masses or hemispheres. Each hemisphere is made up of an interior of white matter or tracts (which link the cerebellum to other parts of the brain and spinal cord) and an exterior of gray matter (mainly neuron cell bodies), called the *cortex,* arranged in numerous folds or convolutions. The cerebellum does not itself directly control body activities. Instead the impulses from its gray matter somehow operate to coordinate the activities of several other brain centers regulating and integrating certain body functions, particularly skeletal muscle activity. Although it plays no

apparent part in initiating such movements the cerebellum is responsible through impulses from its gray matter for harmonious group action of the skeletal muscles, accounting for normal movements that are smooth, timed, steady, precise, and graded in terms of force, extent, and rate.

An animal whose cerebellum has been removed displays no actual paralysis, but its movements are jerky, shaky, and poorly regulated. Injury or disease of the cerebellum in man results in the same general disorder of voluntary muscular control, typified by an unevenness and jerkiness of movement. More recent evidence indicates that the cerebellum is also concerned in the integration of the sensations of touch, hearing, and sight. The various functions of the cerebellum in coordinating specific body activities have in fact been localized or mapped in distinctly defined areas of its cortex.

The Pons. The small structure that lies just above the medulla, consisting also largely of white matter and some scattered gray matter, is called the *pons* or *bridge.* It has a bridge-like appearance because it consists largely of transverse tracts which serve to conduct impulses between the *cerebellum, medulla oblongata,* and the *cerebrum* described below. These particular bundles of nerve fibers or tracts within the central nervous system that extend from some parts of the *cerebrum* into other parts of the brain or spinal cord are called *projection tracts.*

The Midbrain. Just above the pons and immediately below the lower part of the cerebrum (midway between its two hemispheres) is the *midbrain,* a mass of projection tracts made up mostly of white matter surrounding a central cavity. The dorsal portion of the midbrain also possesses a prominent mass of gray matter which collaborates with the cerebellum in controlling muscular coordination. The ventral portion of the midbrain, consisting of two rope-like masses of white matter or tracts, constitutes the main connection between the hindbrain (medulla oblongata, pons, and cerebellum) and the forebrain. The dorsal portion of the midbrain displays four rounded protuberances in which lie certain auditory and visual reflex centers. These protuberances mediate such reflexes as constriction of the pupil of the eye (when exposed to strong light) and the pricking up of an animal's ears (in response to sound).

In summary the pons and midbrain (composed mostly of projection tracts) serve largely as conduction pathways between the spinal cord and other parts of the brain. The midbrain possesses certain visual and auditory reflex centers as well as particular nerve centers which collaborate with the cerebellum in muscular coordination.

The Forebrain. Thalamus and Hypothalamus. The thalamus and hypothalamus together with certain secondary structures collectively represent the posterior portion of the forebrain which lies above the midbrain and below the cerebrum. Actually the thalamus and hypothalamus make up most of the walls of another ventricle. The latter is little more than a slit connecting the ventricle in the medulla oblongata by way of a small canal in the midbrain to the large right and left ventricles in the cerebrum. The thalamus serves as a relay station, receiving nearly all the impulses arriving from the different sensory areas of the body before passing them on to the cortex of the cerebrum where they give rise to conscious sensations.

The hypothalamus is the principal region of the brain possessing the visceral reflex centers for controlling and integrating the metabolism and various activities of the internal organs and tissues. It regulates body temperature, smooth muscle activity, water balance, appetite, blood pressure, and possibly carbohydrate and fat metabolism.

With regard to temperature regulation the front part of the hypothalamus possesses reflex centers which act to prevent overheating, whereas the rear of the hypothalamus (and front of the midbrain) protects against cold. The body reacts to heat by increasing blood circulation to the skin, thus accelerating heat loss by perspiring and by a faster rate of breathing. It reacts to cold by decreasing blood circulation to the skin, thus minimizing heat loss, and by exercising, shivering, and ingesting more food. The mechanisms of fever production are thought to be associated with the release from damaged body cells of a substance that affects the temperature regulating centers of the hypothalamus.

The hypothalamus apparently also participates in producing sleep and maintaining the waking state. It determines the sexual drive, and develops such basic sensations as hunger, thirst, fear, and rage. These basic sensations, however, are not determined simply by the foregoing vaguely described anatomic and physiological relationships. Instead the relationships with other parts of the brain (as indicated, for example, by the effect of emotions) are far more complex and not well understood by any means. Several indications point to the thalamus and hypothalamus as the more primitive regions of the forebrain, functioning at a certain crude level of integration. The cruder sensations and emotions such as pain, the temperature extremes of hot and cold, hunger, thirst, fear, and rage can be primitively perceived and "interpreted" for existence at a primitive level by the thalamus and hypothalamus but to a far lesser and more poorly refined extent than by the cerebral cortex.

Finally, as we shall see in Chapter 23 on the endocrine system, the hypothalamus is also the center of control for anterior pituitary function and the producer of certain hormones.

The Cerebrum. The cerebrum, by far the largest part of the human brain, consists of more than half the 10 billion neurons of the entire nervous system. It is also the largest brain region of apes and monkeys, but is a less prominent structure in the brains of lower vertebrates (Figure 21-11). In man the cerebrum represents the highest form of organization and integration of the nervous system yet achieved by any form of life on our planet. It is the unique organ of the human species, for its various activities account for the basic differences between man and all other existing animals as well as those that preceded him in the evolutionary sequence. Within the cerebrum resides the most advanced functions of the nervous system including memory, intelligence, insight, personality, and judgment and the most highly developed centers for various sensations including sight, hearing, smell, taste, and so on.

Structure—The surface or *cortex* of the cerebrum in man covers and overlaps most of the other brain structures, extending to a depth of about 0.1 to 0.2 inch and covering an area of about 400 square inches. It is composed of gray matter of some two billion cell bodies in a vast interconnecting mass arranged in folds or convolutions (like the surface of a walnut kernel) which appreciably increase its surface area. The cerebrum is divided by a deep longitudinal groove into two halves called *hemispheres* which are not completely separated from each other but are connected together by the underlying white matter. The underlying white matter of the cerebrum is composed for the most part of nerve tracts connecting different parts of the cortex to each other as well as to other parts of the brain and spinal cord. Within the white matter are several well-defined islands of gray matter whose exact functions are not yet known. There is some evidence that they aid in controlling voluntary muscular movements. The cortex of each

hemisphere displays prominent fissures and is divided for convenience of description into five lobes. The lateral ventricles are found one in each cerebral hemisphere and are connected by means of a canal to the ventricle formed by the walls of the thalamus and hypothalamus.

Function—Our knowledge of cerebral function has been obtained over the years in a variety of ways. These have included examining the effects of removing or destroying different cerebral areas in experimental animals, observing the reactions evoked by stimulating exposed cerebral regions in humans and animals, studying the symptoms of patients with known brain damage, and using a relatively recent technique for measuring electrical changes called *brain action potentials* in the brains of intact, living individuals. Microscopic investigations have contributed important information establishing that there are more than 100 different structural areas in the cortex. These many studies have collectively established a number of important facts concerning several functions of the cortex and other brain regions. While we know that certain areas of the cerebral cortex are responsible for specific roles (Figure 21-12) it seems highly likely that many other functions are completely dependent on the cortex as a whole.

Sensory areas of the cerebral cortex—It has been possible to plot or map particular cerebral

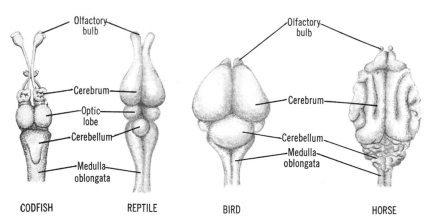

CODFISH   REPTILE   BIRD   HORSE

Figure 21-11. Comparative anatomy of the vertebrate brain *(adapted from A. S. Romer, The Vertebrate Body, second edition, Saunders, 1955).*

areas or locations, called *sensory areas*, associated with the reception of certain sensory impulses arriving from the peripheral nervous system via different parts of the central nervous system. Sensory regions of the surface of the cerebral cortex such as the *visual area* (responsible for sight), the *auditory area* (hearing), the *olfactory area* (smell), and the *gustatory area* (taste), and so-called *somatosensory areas* (touch, pain, pressure, perception of body position, and so on) have been located and mapped as shown in Figures 21-12 and 21-13.

Destruction or damage to any specific sensory area will cause a loss in ability to experience that particular sensation despite the fact that all other parts of the cerebral cortex as well as the specific sense organs are functioning normally. Destruction of the visual sensory areas, for example, will cause blindness just as certainly as would the loss of both eyes. We know that the sensory areas are connected to other parts of the cortex as well as to different regions of the brain and spinal cord. Any conscious sensation, although we ascribe it to a particular cortical area, is very probably the result of widespread cortical activity as well as the integrated functioning of other numerous parts of the nervous system as a unified whole. The cortex, moreover, does not merely register the separate sensations as they occur but in addition evaluates, compares and puts them together into meaningful concepts. When we view an object, for example, not only do we get a sense of light and dark but we also experience, as a result probably of widespread cerebral cortex activity, qualitative and quantitive effects in terms of size and shape of the object, its colors, and various degrees of light intensity. Even more important we interpret these different properties not as separate and isolated entities but as a unified, integrated, whole object such as a pencil or an automobile, as the case may be.

Motor areas of the cerebral cortex—Innumerable experiments and observations have also led to the mapping on the cerebral cortex of distinct areas responsible for the voluntary

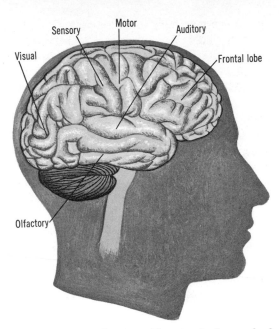

Figure 21-12. Localization of function in the cerebral cortex of man.

contraction of the different skeletal muscles (Figure 21-13). They are called the *motor areas* of the cortex because nerve impulses from these localized regions eventually pass by way of motor neurons to specific skeletal muscles, causing them to contract. It can be shown, for instance, that a mild electric shock to the motor areas of an exposed cortex will cause a spasmodic contraction of specific skeletal muscle groups (on the opposite side of the body). There is also evidence that impulses from the cortical motor area, when transmitted through a different pathway, exert an inhibitory instead of a stimulating effect on muscular movement.

Although it might seem that nerve impulses originate in the cerebral cortex, for example in the motor areas, to give rise to voluntary movements, there is appreciable evidence that the motor area must first integrate afferent impulses in order to transmit efferent impulses. In effect the motor areas as well as the sensory areas are still fundamentally integrating centers which do not initiate nerve impulses but serve to regulate and transmit them along the usual efferent nerve pathways. Of some interest is the fact that motor areas (and sensory areas) of the cortex are in a distinct sequence but in a reverse or upsidedown topographical order compared to that of the skeletal muscles which they control (Figure 21-13). Moreover, the size of the motor area for each group of muscles appears to be proportional to the complexity of the movements performed and to the extent of use rather than to the size or bulk of the muscles. For example, the motor areas concerned with the fingers or the facial muscles are larger than those for the muscles of the abdominal walls. Man's outstanding manual dexterity—his remarkable ability to use his hands—is dependent on the development of the appropriate area of his cerebrum.

Association areas of the cerebral cortex— Although extensive regions of known function have been mapped for the surface of the human cerebral cortex there are still large areas, known as *association areas*, which have defied all attempts at localization of function. The association areas, which in man represent a major portion of the cerebral cortical surface, are believed to be responsible for the highly advanced traits of memory, intelligence, learning, foresight, imagination, emotions, verbalization (expression of concepts in words), and various other mental processes. All attempts to solve the great riddle of the association areas and to explain intellectual and mental phenomena in terms of neural mechanisms as we understand them today have thus far met with failure. At most we can only speculate from limited evidence. One widely held theory states that memory can be ascribed to some unidentified plastic change produced in the

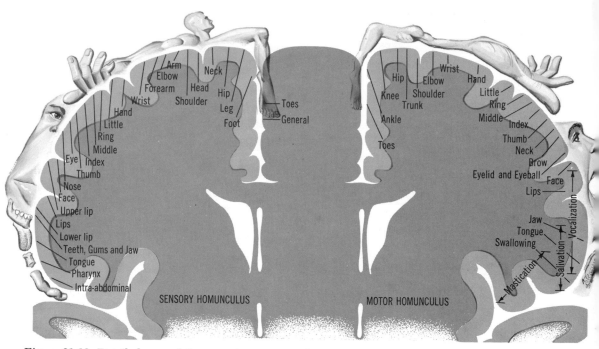

Figure 21-13. Detailed map of the somatic sensory and motor functions in the cerebral cortex of man. The left side of the figure represents a section through the sensory area (see Figure 21-12) whereas the right side is a section through the motor area. The distorted size of the body parts (a "homunculus") corresponds to the size of the cerebral area controlling the particular body part. These cerebral areas are in turn proportional to the complexity of movements and extent of use rather than to the size of the muscles (*adapted from W. Penfield and T. Rasmussen, The Cerebral Cortex of Man, Macmillan, 1950*).

association areas of the cerebral cortex, presumably by facilitating nerve impulse transmission across snyapses as a result of previous use or activation of particular nerve pathways.

The reticular system—A newly proposed theory now contends that the highest levels of integration and mental processes do not after all reside solely in the neurons of the cerebral cortex as long supposed. Instead it proposes that these functions are significantly aided by a region extending through the central portion of the brainstem, the so-called *reticular system.* This is supposed to be attained by an intricate and poorly understood interchange of nerve impulses between nerve cells of the cerebral cortex and those of the reticular system. The reticular system according to this hypothesis is primarily concerned in arousing or "awakening" the cerebral cortex to receive and interpret incoming sensory signals. It presumably serves not only to alert the cortex but contributes to the regulation of all motor activities of the body as well. In this particular respect it is roughly comparable to a traffic control center helping to direct the flow of messages to the brain and alerting the conscious centers to activity.

Our information of brain biochemistry, particularly with reference to mental and emotional conditions, is still at a primitive stage although a major research effort is being made in this field. Recent studies of brain function suggest that emotions, moods, and behavior may be significantly influenced by certain compounds normally found in the brain. Two such substances have been identified as specific amines (p. 141), namely *noreptnephrine* and *serotonin* (Chapters 23 and 25).

Many facts about severe mental diseases and deficiencies suggest the existence of specific metabolic disturbances possibly related to genetic phenomena, although the exact mechanisms are not known. Two types of drugs or chemotherapeutic agents have been developed for treatment or alleviation of emotional illnesses. The *tranquilizers* have a calming or tranquilizing effect, whereas the *antidepressants* elevate mood and restore drive and zest for living. The physiological or biochemical basis for mental diseases and for the relief-giving effects of these drugs, however, are unknown.

Electrical brain waves—In 1929 it was discovered that the cerebral cortex is almost constantly experiencing small rhythmical changes in electric charge or potential, commonly called *brain waves.* These can be detected and measured by means of electrodes applied to the scalp. Brain waves seem to be due to an inherent electrical activity of the nerve cells of the cerebrum, especially of the cortex. They are apparently not caused by nerve impulses arriving at the cerebrum from lower levels of the nervous system. The instrument used for recording brain waves is called an *electroencephalograph*. Most normal individuals show several regular types of brain waves. These include the so-called *alpha-waves,* which are best recorded from the skull overlying the cortical visual sensory area when the eyes are shut and when the visual field is uniform; the *beta-waves,* of lower intensity; and a third group of considerably greater strength, the *delta-waves,* which appear during sleep. In general, visual activity, muscular activity, and mental activity are responsible for drastic changes in the frequency, regularity, and height of the brain waves. The electroencephalograph has proven to be a valuable diagnostic tool in distinguishing between several kinds of brain disease and damage which characteristically alter the brain wave pattern. It has been especially useful in diagnosing the condition known as *epilepsy.* Epilepsy may be due to certain types of brain damage or to a genetic defect and is characterized by irregular periods of convulsions and spasms.

In closing this chapter it is worth reemphasizing that the neural mechanisms which account for learning, memory, intelligence, and all other associations made by the brain are still obscure. Man's expectation is that his brain, which is transforming the world, is clever enough to understand itself. The hope is that someday in the not too distant future our growing knowledge of biochemistry, genetics, biophysics, mathematics, and information theory (the manner in which information is transmitted, coded, stored, and integrated) will ultimately unravel the complex mechanisms that account for brain function.

SUPPLEMENTARY REFERENCES

Adrian, E. D., *The Mechanism of Nervous Action*, Oxford University Press, London, 1955.
Babkin, B. P., *Pavlov*, University of Chicago Press, Chicago, 1949.
Brazier, M. A. B., *The Electrical Activity of the Nervous System*, Macmillan, New York, 1950
Carlson, A. J., and V. Johnson, *The Machinery of the Body*, fifth edition, University of Chicago Press, Chicago, 1962.
Eccles, J. C., "The Physiology of Imagination," *Scientific American*, September 1958.
Gerard, R. W., "What Is Memory?." *Scientific American*, September 1953.
Gray, G. W., "The Great Ravelled Knot," *Scientific American*, October 1948.
Halstead, W. C., *Brain and Intelligence*, University of Chicago Press, Chicago, 1947.
Herrick, C. J., *Neurological Foundations of Animal Behavior*, Holt, New York, 1924.
Katz, B., "The Nerve Impulse," *Scientific American*, November 1952.
Snider, R. S., "The Cerebellum," *Scientific American*, August 1958.

Chapter 22

Coordination:

The Receptors or

Sense Organs

INTRODUCTION

General Features

A *sense organ or receptor* is best defined as specialized nervous tissue or other tissue in intimate contact with a nerve cell that is sensitive to a specific stimulus or change in the environment. All receptors when stripped down to their barest essentials are the dendrites of sensory neurons or highly specialized sensitive cells in close association within them.

The millions of receptors of the body, ranging in complexity from simple naked nerve fibers to highly specialized structures such as the eye, are therefore really part of the nervous system or closely associated with it. The eye itself, for instance, which is specifically sensitive to visible light, has evolved as a highly developed and specialized portion of the brain. Receptors perform the vital function of informing the body at both the conscious and unconscious levels of changes in its external and internal environments. Thus they enable the body to respond by protecting itself and thereby improving its chances of survival.

Several important features with respect to this role should be emphasized. First, specific receptors are particularly sensitive to specific stimuli. In other words a particular sense organ requires far less of a particular kind of energy to stimulate it than of any other. However, it can also respond to other stimuli if they are of sufficient strength or intensity. For example, although the eyes and ears are receptors for light and sound, pressure on the eyeball causes a sensation of light, and irritation due to disease causes a ringing in the ears.

Second, specific sensitivity to specific stimuli is due to (a) specialized structure of the receptor cell (e.g., photopigments in photoreceptors), and (b) auxiliary structures that efficiently channel the adequate stimuli and protect against other stimuli (e.g., sound waves normally reach the organ of hearing or organ of corti, which is protected by a bony structure, by way of a particular pathway).

Third, the kind of sensation that is elicited depends only on *what* nerve pathways are activated and not how they are activated. Under normal conditions specific stimuli induce a local excitatory state in specific receptors which in turn initiate signals in the form of action potentials, or nerve impulses, that travel along the connecting nerves. All nerve impulses, whether they give rise to conscious or unconscious responses, are essentially alike regardless of the stimulus that initiated them. The nerve impulses are transmitted to the central nervous system where they are sorted, channelized, and deciphered. At the level of unawareness or unconsciousness, certain pressure-sensitive receptors in the lungs, for example, keep the breathing centers of the brain informed about the breathing process. Others in the large artery (the aorta, Chapter 26) leading from the heart are responsible for keeping the heart centers in the brain aware of blood pressure. At the level of awareness or consciousness the quality of sensation depends on the arrival of nerve impulses at particular sensory areas of the brain. As an illustration, the region of the cerebrum receiving impulses from an olfactory receptor interprets them as a specific odor or aroma. In other words it does not matter how a receptor is stimulated because it will always lead to the activation of certain nerve pathways and to a sensation appropriate to the adequate stimuli.

Finally, the arrival of nerve impulses at the brain or spinal cord results in a rapid sending out of instructions via nerve impulses to the appropriate effectors (muscles and glands), evoking a response to the environmental change.

Overall Evolution of the Receptors

The specialization in structure and function of cells, tissues, and organs which has accompanied the evolution of multicellular animals applies equally well to the sense organs or receptors. A unicellular organism such as an amoeba responds to contact with a nonedible, foreign object by moving away. Obviously it receives the stimulus, transmits the resulting disturbance or message, and carries out a suitable response. As a single cell it encompasses the combined functions of the receptor organs, nervous system, and effector organs of higher animals.

The first real separation of receptor function from conduction is seen in the lower multicellular invertebrates, the *Coelenterata*. Perhaps the most primitive nerve cell development is illustrated in the jellyfish *Aurelia*, belonging to this group. Here we find so-called *neurosensory cells* which not only receive the stimuli but also transmit them directly to the effectors, the muscle cells. In most other organisms of the *Coelenterata*, however, separation of the roles of reception and conduction has occurred, for there are now distinct conducting cells or neurons composing the nerve

network as observed in *Hydra*. As an additional evolutionary change the cell bodies of the original neurosensory cells which are no longer located at the surface now maintain their contact with the external environment by means of dendrite-like extensions. Cells of this type have apparently evolved into the sensory neurons of higher animals whose dendrites serve as the primary receptors.

Other progressive changes among the more advanced members of the animal kingdom have included: (*a*) the development of specialized cells about certain sensory dendrites which augment their sensitivity to particular stimuli; and (*b*) the appearance of still other highly specialized cells which serve as the actual receptors. In these instances the associated neurons function solely as conductors to the central nervous system.

In all cases ranging from the extreme of the primitive neurosensory cell found in jellyfish to that of a complex sense organ such as the mammalian eye with its collection of auxiliary structures, the common denominator is the responsive cell capable of reacting to an external environmental change or stimulus.

TYPES OF RECEPTORS

Classification of Receptors

The commonly described "five senses"— touch, smell, taste, hearing, and vision—in reality represent an incomplete list of the senses. We now recognize at least 11 distinct sensations or senses in higher animals, including man: touch, smell, taste, hearing, vision, warmth, cold, equilibrium, pain, awareness of position and movement (called *proprioception*), and *visceral sensations* (such as hunger, nausea, sexual sensations, and so on). The different sensations are initiated by stimulation of various specialized sensory receptors. The latter can be grouped according to the nature of the stimulus into three main subdivisions: (1) the *chemical receptors* (those for taste and smell) which are sensitive to chemical stimuli; (2) the *mech-*

anical receptors (those for touch and pressure, pain, temperature, sound, and motion) which are sensitive to mechanical stimuli; and (3) the *photoreceptors* (the eyes) which are sensitive to certain ranges of wavelengths of electromagnetic radiation (Chapter 17) such as visible light.

CHEMICAL RECEPTORS. The ability to detect chemical changes in the environment is a general property of protoplasm. This property is in fact the sole basis for the detection of foods and harmful chemicals by many single-celled organisms, lower invertebrates, and several advanced aquatic invertebrates. In addition numerous aquatic invertebrates such as certain marine molluscs have simple local receptors that examine or analyze the water drawn in by the organism. Among the invertebrates the greatest specialization in the chemical receptors is seen in the insects. Special smell receptors are present on the antennae. Special taste receptors occur at the mouth region and, in some insects such as the housefly, on the legs.

Flavor in foods is the result of a combination of taste and smell which are two different entities. They are associated with two different types of receptors giving rise to impulses that are transmitted by different nerve pathways to different regions of the brain.

Taste. The receptors for taste in higher vertebrates such as man are called *taste buds.* They consist of barrel-shaped clusters of specialized slender cells located on the surface of the tongue. In mammals the many taste buds are embedded within the numerous small, localized mucous membrane elevations of the tongue called *papillae.* Each receptor cell of a taste bud has a fine hair-like projection extending toward the small pore of its taste bud which opens on the surface of the tongue (Figure 22-1). Several sensory neuron dendrite branches are distributed among the receptor cells of each taste bud. A substance must first be dissolved in water or saliva, in which form it enters the microscopic pores of the taste buds, in order to act as a chemical stimulus of particular receptor cells. Thus nerve im-

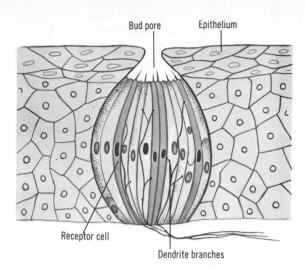

Figure 22-1. Structure of a taste bud on the tongue of man.

pulses are initiated in the nearby sensory neurons and eventually give rise to the sensation of taste.

In man there are four fundamental sensations of taste—*sweet, salty, sour,* and *bitter*—for which there are separate taste buds located on different parts of the tongue. Taste buds sensitive to sweetness and saltiness tend to be concentrated at the tip of the tongue (Figure 22-2). Those for sourness (acids) are mostly distributed along the sides, and those for bitterness are found at the back of the tongue. The distribution of taste buds varies widely among the different vertebrate groups. In fishes they are often scattered over the surface of the head as well as the mouth. In amphibians such as the frog they are found for the most part within the mouth and pharynx. In reptiles and birds they occur within the pharynx, and in mammals they are confined largely to the surface of the tongue.

Although all the taste buds are structurally alike, they are nevertheless physiologically different in sensitivity as well as specificity. In man, bitterness (as tested by one's sensitivity to the drug quinine) can be detected in a dilution of one part in 2,000,000; sweetness, 1 part in 200; sourness (hydrochloric acid), 1 part in 130,000; and saltiness (table salt or sodium chloride), 1 part in 400. The taste for sourness is a response to acids (Chapter 6), and appears to be the most specific of the four taste sensations. We seem to experience other taste sensations because of a blending of these fundamental sensations with one another and with the sensations of smell (see following section), as well as a stimulation of other nerve endings in the mouth.

Smell. The receptors for smell are specialized ciliated cells functioning in the dual role of receptor and conductor. They are embedded in the mucous membranes which line the main upper passages of the nose and nasal cavities (Figure 22-3). The first requirement for any material to arouse the sensation of smell is that it reach the nasal passages in gaseous form. It must therefore be volatile, giving off particles of molecular size which are carried in the air by diffusion and air currents to the smell receptors within the nasal cavities. Here they are first dissolved in the mucous secretions before they can stimulate the appropriate receptor. There are an almost infinite variety of odors, and there seems to be no correlation between the chemical or physical properties of materials and the sensations of smell which they elicit.

The sensitivity of the smell receptors are in general several thousandfold greater than that of the taste receptors. In many animals where the sense of smell is of central importance for survival in terms of detecting enemies and seeking out food, an appreciable portion of the brain is devoted to this function. Man, with a relatively poorly developed sense of smell compared to such animals, can nevertheless detect certain substances in the air in dilutions of one part in 50 billion. Interestingly enough the smell receptors, although extremely sensitive in detecting the slightest of odors, are also apparently easily fatigued. For this reason odors which are at first quite strong are not sensed at all after a few minutes time.

MECHANICAL RECEPTORS. The kinds of sense organs or receptors that are sensitive to mechanical stimulation show a wide diversity. They range on the one hand from free nerve endings through a variety of intermediate types of increasing complexity to the highly specialized organ, the ear. The touch and pressure mechanical receptors near the body surface may well have been among the first receptor tissues to appear in primitive animals living in the seas. They undoubtedly served to sense obstacles as well as vibrations produced by other organisms, and probably permitted the animal to orient itself to some degree to the pull of gravity. Subsequent invasion of the land by animals from the oceans must have been accompanied by the evolution of touch and pressure receptors showing greater sensitivity to sound waves transmitted through the medium of air.

In many insects and aquatic invertebrates the touch and sound receptors are sensitive vibratory hairs. Insects also have other special sound receptors.

Touch and Pressure Receptors. The sensa-

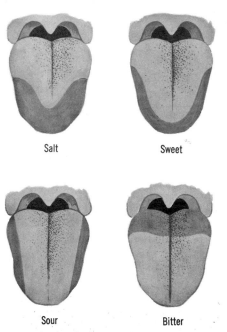

Salt

Sweet

Sour

Bitter

Figure 22-2. Localization of different taste buds on the tongue of man.

tion of touch is elicited by a light momentary contact such as a light brushing of the skin. The sensation of pressure is usually experienced upon sustained and more intense contact. Some consider the sensations of touch and pressure to be different degrees of the same sensation elicited by the same receptors. Others ascribe the sense of touch exclusively to specialized encapsulated nerve endings in the skin and to nerve endings in the hair roots which are stimulated when a hair is bent. According to this view the presence of other specialized types of encapsulated receptors found in deeper parts of the skin are the receptors for pressure. The touch receptors are not uniformly distributed over the surface of the body but are more concentrated in particular areas such as at the finger tips and lips. Certain receptors sensitive to pressure or tension are found in the carotid arteries (Chapter 26) and respond to changes in blood pressure.

Located within the skeletal muscles, tendons, and joints are at least three different kinds of pressure receptors collectively known as *proprioceptors* (Figure 22-4). Stimulation of the proprioceptors gives rise to the sensation of awareness of position and movement of body parts. The stretching of a tendon or the contraction or stretching of a muscle stimulates the proprioceptors. Our sense of physical balance is a complex phenomenon attributed to several factors, including the proprioceptors, pressure receptors in the soles of our feet, the equilibrium organs of the inner ear, and our sense of vision.

Temperature Receptors. The sensations of heat and cold are due to the stimulation of separate and specific encapsulated nerve endings or receptors which are unevenly distributed in the skin and mucous membranes of the body (Figure 22-4). Extremely hot objects also stimulate the pain receptors as well as normal heat receptors.

Pain Receptors. The receptors for pain are simply free naked nerve dendrites. They respond not only to a mechanical stimulus but also to any other type of stimulation — chemical,

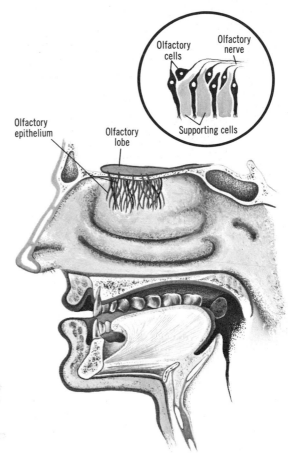

Figure 22-3. Diagram of the nasal passages and cavities in man showing the location of the receptors for smell (in the olfactory epithelium). Inset: cross section of a portion of the olfactory epithelium.

thermal, or otherwise — as long as it is of sufficient intensity. Compared to the receptors for touch, pressure, and temperature, those for pain are the most numerous, occurring in all tissues of the body except the brain. The brain, ironically enough, is therefore insensitive to pain. Of the foregoing receptors, only those for pain are also located within the deeper tissues and organs of the body. Thus pain may arise from stimulation of the pain receptors in the skin, in the skeletal muscles, tendons, joints, and in the internal organs such as the intestines, kidneys, and so on.

The presence of pain receptors obviously

favors survival of the organism by informing it of environmental changes potentially dangerous to health and life. At times, for reasons that are not entirely clear, the cerebrum erroneously interprets the source of pain, when it arises from the stimulation of deeper structures in the body such as the skeletal muscles and internal organs. In these instances, the brain refers the stimulus to an external surface area, a phenomenon known as *referred pain*. For example, pains originating in the heart will at times be referred to the inner surface of the left arm.

In summary, at least five different kinds of receptors in man responsible for the senses of touch, pressure, pain, heat, and cold are located for the most part in the skin and mucous membranes. As already indicated, some are simply free nerve endings whereas others are specifically encapsulated in specialized tissues. In all cases they represent the dendrite portions of sensory neurons that ultimately connect up to the spinal nerves. By contrast, the receptors for taste and smell are exclusively restricted to the tongue and nasal cavities, respectively, and are connected to particular cranial nerves.

Visceral Sensations. The mechanism of initiation of certain visceral sensations such as thirst, hunger, and appetite are not too well understood. For lack of a better place they are tentatively classified in this book under mechanical receptors. The sensations of thirst, hunger, and appetite originate in the internal organs but no specific receptors have as yet been identified. Thirst is associated with the reduced water content of the body. Hunger is a localized sensation associated with a lack of food. It is apparently initiated by the rhythmic contractions of the muscles in the walls of the stomach. Appetite, although somewhat similar to hunger, is a more generalized and pleasant sensation and represents an enjoyable desire for food.

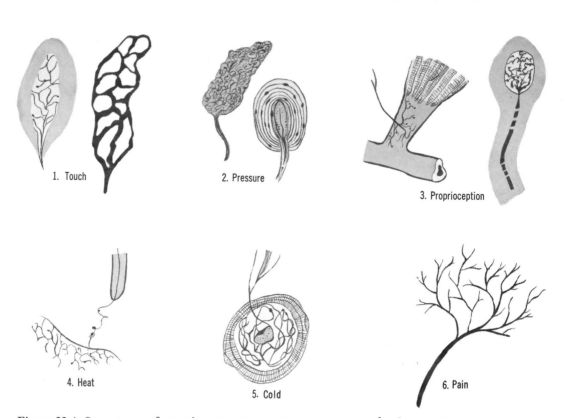

1. Touch   2. Pressure   3. Proprioception

4. Heat   5. Cold   6. Pain

Figure 22-4. Some types of proprioceptors, temperature receptors, and pain receptors.

The Ear. The ear is the receptor organ member of the *auditory apparatus*, which consists of the ears, the auditory nerves, and the auditory areas of the cerebrum. The ear is highly sensitive for the reception of sound waves, which are best defined as vibrations of any physical medium—gas, liquid, or solid—in which they are propagated.

The ear of man as an example of the mammalian ear is made up of three regions: the *outer* ear, *middle* ear, and *inner* ear. The outer and middle ears are basically auxiliary structures which receive, amplify, and transmit sound waves. The actual sensory receptors for the sound waves are found only in the inner ear. The inner ear therefore possesses the actual sense organ for hearing.

Outer Ear. The outer ear (Figure 22-5) in humans consists of three parts: (1) a trumpet-shaped flap of elastic cartilage and skin called the *pinna* located on the side of the head; (2) a short funnel-shaped passage or tube, about an inch in length, called the *outer auditory canal* leading from the pinna into one of the bones of the head; and (3) a thin, semitransparent, elliptical, flexible membrane called the *eardrum* or *tympanic membrane* (about 0.4 inches in diameter) stretching across the inner end of the auditory canal and separating it from the middle ear. In many mammals the pinna may be moved or "perked up" by well-developed muscles so as to "collect" sound waves.

Middle Ear. The middle ear which connects the outer ear to the inner ear is a small, hollow, air-filled cavity within one of the bones of the head. It is lined with an epithelial membrane and contains three tiny bones joined together, commonly called the *hammer, anvil,* and *stirrup* because of their shapes (Figure 22-5). The "handle" end of the hammer bone is attached to the inner surface of the tympanic membrane. Its opposite end is connected by a small joint to the anvil which in turn is joined to the stirrup. The foot plate of the stirrup fits into the so-called *oval window,* a membrane-covered opening leading into the inner ear. A second opening which is also covered by a thin membrane connects the middle and inner ears and is called the *round window.* Three additional openings from other sources, making a total of five, lead into the middle ear: one from the external auditory canal covered over by the

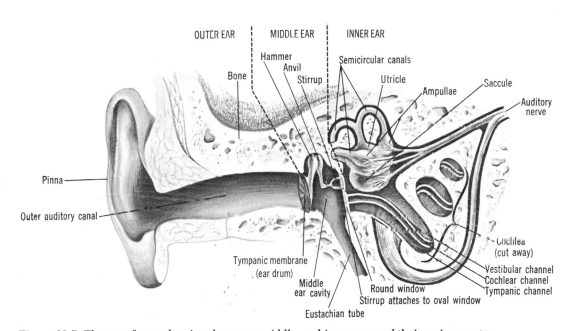

OUTER EAR | MIDDLE EAR | INNER EAR

Hammer
Anvil
Bone
Stirrup

Semicircular canals
Utricle
Ampullae
Saccule
Auditory nerve

Pinna

Outer auditory canal

Tympanic membrane (ear drum)

Middle ear cavity

Eustachian tube

Round window
Stirrup attaches to oval window

Cochlea (cut away)
Vestibular channel
Cochlear channel
Tympanic channel

Figure 22-5. The ear of man showing the outer, middle, and inner ears and their various parts.

tympanic membrane has already been mentioned; one from a network of small irregular honeycomb spaces called the mastoid sinuses located in one of the surrounding bones of the head; and one from the so-called Eustachian tube lined with an epithelial membrane and connecting that part of the throat behind the nose (called the nasopharynx) to the middle ear.

The collapsible Eustachian tube by serving as an air passage has an important function in equalizing pressure on both sides of the tympanic membrane. Abrupt changes in external pressure might otherwise cause the membrane to rupture. The Eustachian tube normally remains closed except during swallowing or yawning. These activities permit a pressure change in the middle ear, thus balancing the pressure on the external surface of the tympanic membrane. Sudden pressure changes on the tympanic membrane brought about by loud explosions, or by rapid ascent or descent in an elevator or airplane, can be offset by deliberately swallowing at the time. Unfortunately the Eustachian tube can also be a passageway for the spread of infections from the nose to the middle ear and connecting structures such as the mastoid sinuses.

Inner Ear. In its overall structure the inner ear consists of both a bony and membranous labyrinth or complex series of passageways and cavities. Within one of the bones of the head are housed the separate receptors for hearing and equilibrium. In general the bony portion of the labyrinth entirely encloses and protects the similarly shaped membranous labyrinth. A layer of lymph-like fluid separates the two, serving as a protective cushion or buffer. Of the different sense organs contained in the inner ear only one, called the cochlea because of its outward resemblance to a snail shell, is concerned with the sense of hearing. The others, namely the saccule, utricle, and its attached semicircular canals have to do with the sensation of physical equilibrium and orientation (Figure 22-5). These are described in a later section.

The cochlea—The cochlea has an outer bony structure in the shape of a snail's shell. It is similar to that which might have been formed by winding a tube slightly more than an inch in length spirally for two and one-half turns around a central, cone-shaped pillar of bone. The larger spiral turns are at the base of the cochlea and the smaller ones are at the apex. Within the bony cochlea are three similarly shaped, spiraling membranous channels running the full length of the cochlea. The organization and arrangement of these channels are best visualized by hypothetically unwinding the spirals of the cochlea as shown in Figure 22-6. The uppermost channel known as the vestibular channel is attached at its base end to the oval window into whose membrane the stirrup bone of the middle ear is inserted. At its other end located at the apex of the cochlea the vestibular channel has a small opening which communicates with the lowermost channel called the tympanic channel. The base end of the tympanic canal terminates in the membrane-covered round window leading into the middle ear. Both the tympanic and vestibular channels are filled with a clear fluid called perilymph which comes from the cerebrospinal fluid. The third and smallest channel called the cochlear channel, which rests between the other two, is filled with a clear fluid called endolymph. It is separated from the overlying vestibular channel by a membrane called the vestibular membrane and from the underlying tympanic channel by a ledgelike projection of the bony cochlear wall plus a membrane, the basilar membrane.

The actual receptors for hearing are present in the cochlear channel as several rows of specialized "hair" cells, approximately 24,000 in number. They contain numerous cilia projecting into the endolymph from the free end of each cell. The rows of hair cells together with supporting cells and surrounding dendrites constitute the structure called the organ of Corti. It rests on the basilar membrane within the cochlear channel. The cell bodies from which the dendrites originate make up a

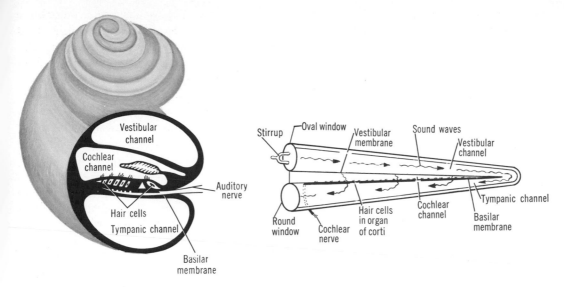

CROSS SECTION OF COCHLEA   DIAGRAM OF HYPOTHETICALLY UNCOILED COCHLEA

Figure 22-6. (A) Cross-sectional view of the cochlea; (B) schematic representation of the organization of its channels when hypothetically unwinding the cochlea.

ganglion within one of the numerous passages of the inner ear; their axons constitute the auditory nerve, a branch of one of the cranial nerves.

The ultimate conversion of sound waves into vibrations of the endolymph fluid within the cochlear channel mechanically stimulates the cilia of the hair cells of the organ of Corti causing them to initiate impulses in the surrounding dendrites. The arrival of these impulses via the auditory nerve to the auditory area of the cerebral cortex gives rise to the sensation of hearing.

Evolution of the Vertebrate Ear. Our present knowledge of the evolutionary development of the ear in vertebrates indicates that the outer and middle ears are relatively recent acquisitions. All vertebrates possess an inner ear whereas the progressive additions of the middle and outer ears, starting with the amphibia, achieve their most advanced states in the higher animal forms.

Although the outer and middle ears function solely in hearing, certain parts of the inner ear not involved in hearing play a central role in our sense of physical balance or equilibrium.

Interestingly enough, the inner ear of vertebrates appears to have been originally concerned with balance. Its anatomical and functional development as an organ of hearing is considered to be a more recent evolutionary development. For example, the typical present-day fish as the least developed of the contemporary vertebrates exhibits organs of equilibrium in its inner ear which are remarkably similar to those of man. However, its receptors for hearing are hardly existent, having just begun to make their appearance from a portion of the equilibrium apparatus. The capacity of fishes for hearing is therefore extremely primitive and poorly developed. A somewhat similar situation also prevails for the amphibians. It is among the reptiles, however, that the first striking advances in the hearing capacities of vertebrates have occurred, achieving their highest development in the mammals. Throughout the evolutionary progression of the auditory apparatus, however, the organs of balance in the inner ear have remained more or less unchanged, being essentially the same in all vertebrates.

In a typical modern fish the organ of hearing

(Figure 22-7) is represented only by the equivalent of an inner ear connected to the exterior by a reduced passageway, namely one of the *pharyngeal gill slits* (p. 471) or the *spiracle*. In higher vertebrates it has contributed in the course of evolution to the middle ear. In many amphibians and in most reptiles the external opening of the pharyngeal cleft has been closed off by a tympanic membrane lying flush with the body surface. Attached to its inner surface is a small modified jaw bone (which in higher forms evolved into the stirrup) leading to the inner ear. A Eustachian tube is also present. An essentially similar type of middle ear arrangement is also found in many birds. Although most modern amphibians (e.g., the frog) possess this basic complement of middle ear parts (including the tympanic membrane), several such as the salamander and newt have lost the middle ear cavity as well as the Eustachian tube and tympanic membrane (but not the middle ear bone). Within the reptiles themselves certain exceptions also exist. On the one hand the snake (like the salamander and newt) has lost the tympanic membrane, middle ear cavity, and Eustachian tube. On the other hand in crocodiles and alligators and certain lizards the tympanic membrane is no longer at the body surface but instead is located at the base of a shallow canal opening to the

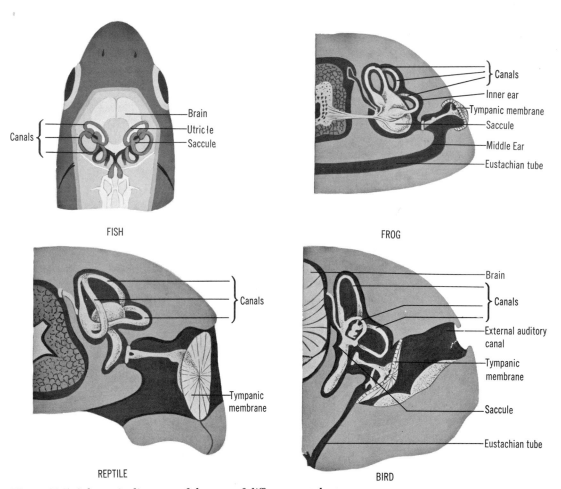

Figure 22-7. Schematic diagrams of the ears of different vertebrates.

exterior. In mammals this has evolved into the deep and tubular external auditory canal accompanied by the pinna. A further basic evolutionary change experienced by mammals has been the incorporation of two additional bones (hammer and anvil) into the sound-transmitting apparatus of the middle ear.

Physiology of Hearing. The process of hearing depends on a succession of events which start with the entry of sound waves into the external auditory canal causing the tympanic membrane to vibrate. The small pinna in man in contrast to larger ones of many mammals probably makes little or no contribution to collecting or reflecting the sound waves that enter the ear. The vibrations of the tympanic membrane are mechanically transmitted (and magnified) by the hammer, anvil, and stirrup bones of the middle ear to the oval window membrane of the vestibular channel in the cochlea of the middle ear. The vibrations of the oval membrane set up movement or pressure waves in the perilymph of the vestibular and tympanic channels. These pressure waves are in turn transmitted via the basilar and vestibular membranes to the endolymph of the cochlear channel, mechanically stimulating the hair cells of the organ of Corti. Impulses are thus initiated in the surrounding dendrites and transmitted ultimately by way of the auditory nerve to the auditory sensory area of the cerebral cortex resulting in the sensation of hearing. Fluids are for all practical purposes incompressible, and vibrations or pressure waves in the perilymph are compensated for and finally dissipated by corresponding inward and outward bulgings of the round window membrane at the base of the tympanic channel. In brief, sound waves are normally transmitted through air, bone, and fluids of the ear, finally stimulating nerve endings; thus nerve impulses are initiated which are transmitted to the auditory sensory area of the brain to give the sensation of sound.

Several aspects of hearing are not yet understood with certainty. Sound as perceived by the human ear has three properties: (1) *pitch* or *frequency* which is the number of cycles or double vibrations per second reaching the human ear, (2) *loudness* or the intensity power or amplitude of the cycles or vibrations, and (3) *quality* or "timbre" which is dependent on secondary tones produced along with the fundamental sound waves. According to the usually accepted theory we are able to distinguish between differences in pitch or frequency because vibrations of different frequencies cause some hair cells to be stimulated more strongly than others. The result is a sending of nerve impulses to correspondingly specific sites in the cerebral cortex, presumably accounting for our ability to discriminate between differences in pitch.

In contrast a second theory, which is less generally accepted, compares the ear to a telephone system. It proposes that the cochlea does not distinguish between differences in sound frequencies, as claimed by the first theory, but suggests that the organ of Corti cells vibrates as a whole instead of selectively. The resulting frequency of nerve impulses received by the auditory sensory area of the cerebrum is thought to be the basis for discrimination of pitch in place of the ear itself. It may well be that our ability to distinguish differences in pitch will prove to be dependent on an analysis by both the cochlea and the auditory region of the brain.

Depending on age and other factors the range of audible frequencies varies considerably among different species of animals and among individuals of a given species such as man. The human ear can detect sounds ranging in frequency from about 20 to 20,000 cycles per second. It is most sensitive to sounds between 1000 and 2000 cycles per second. Most sounds made by a mouse are usually of frequencies greater than 20,000 cycles per second and are therefore inaudible to the human ear; the cat, however, can hear noises of such high frequencies.

The range of frequency of sound waves used by bats is from about 30,000 to 70,000 vibrations a second and therefore beyond the limit of human hearing. The bat cochlea can even be stimulated by sounds with frequencies as high as 100,000 cycles per second. Being unable to see, bats are made aware of the position of obstacles by means of sound waves originally emitted by the bats and reflected back to them from the objects in their path. They are able to avoid obstacles only when they can emit these high-frequency sounds and hear the echos reflected back from the obstacles lying ahead. If either the ears or mouth of bats is tightly covered, they become helpless and avoid obstacles only with the frequency that would be expected from chance alone.

Deafness. Any impairment or defectiveness in the ability to hear sounds normally heard by the average individual is known as *deafness*. The common disorders of hearing are usually classified into three types. (1) *Conduction deafness* is due to defects in the sound-transmitting mechanisms as a result of an obstruction in the external auditory canal, damage to the ear drum, damage or stiffness of the middle ear bones by excessive deposition of calcium salts, or blockage of the Eustachian tube. (2) *Perception deafness* is often due to damage of the cochlea, usually of the receptor hair cells of the organ of Corti. Boiler makers, airplane pilots, and artillerymen often are deaf to particular frequencies of sound apparently because of destruction to specific groups of hair cells in the organ of Corti. Deafness caused by damage to the auditory nerve is also included in the perception deafness group. (3) *Central deafness* is usually due to a physical or psychological disorder in the auditory sensory region of the cerebral cortex or the brain tracts leading to it.

Organs of Equilibrium within the Inner Ear. In addition to the cochlea as the primary organ of hearing, the inner ear contains three organs, the *saccule, utricle,* and *semicircular canals,* that play a major role in our sense of equilibrium and awareness of position (Figure 22-8).

In its overall structure the inner ear is a complex labyrinth of bony as well as membranous passages and cavities. The separate but connecting *utricle* and *saccule* sacs are housed within a single division of the bony labyrinth called the *vestibule,* located between the cochlea and the semicircular channels (Figure 22-8).

Within the utricle and saccule sacs, which are only about an eighth of an inch in their longest diameter, are also special receptor "hair" cells and nerve endings, collectively called *macula,* projecting into an overlying gelatinous mass. The latter contains many small, bone-like fragments called *otoliths* made up of calcium carbonate and protein. Any changes in position of the head or body, which cause the otoliths to stimulate the hair cells, initiate nerve impulses traveling to the brain. These ultimately evoke muscular reflexes that tend to right or restore the body to its normal position. Stimulation of the visual receptors and proprioceptors also induces the same type of reflex or response. The nerve endings from the various organs of equilibrium in the inner ear ultimately lead into the same cranial nerve as the auditory nerve extending from the cochlea.

Within the three bony semicircular canals, each lying in a plane approximately perpendicular to the other two, are the corresponding membranous semicircular canals. The latter are hollow tubes containing endolymph fluid and connecting to the utricle. One end of each canal near its junction with the utricle is enlarged into a swelling called the *ampulla.* Within each ampulla is a small elevation of receptor hair cells and nerve endings collectively called the *crista,* projecting into an overlying gelatinous mass. Since the semicircular canals are at right angles to each other, movement of the head in any direction will cause movement of endolymph in one or more of the semicircular canals. Thus the hair cells of the crista will be stimulated initiating impulses that are transmitted to the brain. Nerve impulses arising in the receptor cells of the semicircular canals give rise to a sensation of movement and imbalance and to reflexes that tend to right the body.

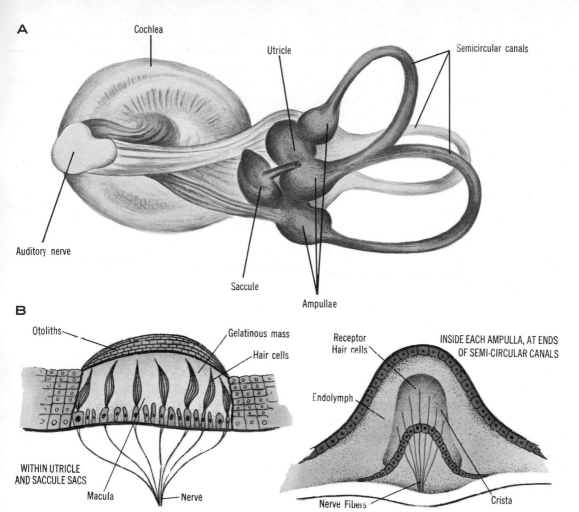

A

Cochlea

Utricle

Semicircular canals

Auditory nerve

Saccule

Ampullae

B

Otoliths

Gelatinous mass

Hair cells

Receptor
Hair cells

INSIDE EACH AMPULLA, AT ENDS
OF SEMI-CIRCULAR CANALS

Endolymph

WITHIN UTRICLE
AND SACCULE SACS

Macula — Nerve

Nerve Fibers

Crista

Figure 22-8. (A) Anatomical relationship of the cochlea, saccule, utricle, and semicircular canals; (B) structure of the saccule, utricle, and semicircular canals.

PHOTORECEPTORS. *Sensitivity to Light.* Light is a form of electromagnetic radiation which is made visible to us by means of a highly specialized receptor organ, the eye. More precisely, visible light or the visible spectrum is arbitrarily defined as the wavelengths of electromagnetic radiation that range between 400 and 700 millimicrons (or 4000 to 7000 angstrom units) because they can be ordinarily detected by the human eye. Sensitivity to light is widespread among living things. Many biologists in fact regard sensitivity to light, especially in the ultraviolet region (100 to 3900 mμ), and to a lesser extent in the visible region, as a common property of protoplasm.

The vertebrate eye is probably the most sensitive biological detector of visible light. The eye, however, is not equally sensitive to all wavelengths within the visible spectrum. It is most sensitive to light waves of approximately 500 mμ, as little as 5 to 15 quanta resulting in visual sensation as shown by the late Selig Hecht of Columbia University. We do not become suddenly blind at wavelengths immediately below 400 or above 700 mμ. Actually the specialized light receptor cells within the eye still initiate visual processes of a sort at wavelengths as low as approximately 350 mμ to those as high as 800 mμ. Beyond these extremes the vertebrate eye is no more sensitive to electromagnetic radiation than is the unspecialized surface of the skin. For many insects, however, the range of visible light extends into the ultraviolet where the human eye has no particular sensitivity.

Basic Features of Visual Function. Although there is a wide diversity of photoreceptors or eye structures among the invertebrates and vertebrates of the animal kingdom, a common basic pattern for visual function has become evident.

The first step involves the absorption of light energy by the receptor cell. In order for this to occur a suitable absorbing material, namely a colored substance or pigment, must be present. One of the most important features of the light-perception mechanism is centered about the nature of the absorbing pigment, for its specific absorption properties determine sensitivity to the different wavelengths of light. All photo-pigments that have been identified in any animal are composed without exception of a specific protein to which the carotenoid pigment, retinene, the aldehyde of vitamin A, is attached. The present evidence also indicates that the carotenoid pigments may well be the light-perceiving or light-sensitive substances of plant tissues and green flagellates, too. In animals the sensitivity to light is often enhanced by lens-like structures in the receptors for concentrating and focusing the light. Most animals have complicated eyes consisting essentially of a specialized pigmented surface or *retina* usually associated with a lens or lens-like structure. The lens may be within a single cell or made up of a large number of cells depending on the species.

The absorption of light by the photosensitive pigment of the receptors raises the energy level of the capturing molecules to an excited state. Thus chemical reactions are started which act as stimuli to initiate nerve impulses.

The latter process constitutes the second basic step for visual function.

In higher animals such as ourselves the third basic step begins with the arrival of the impulses at the visual sensory areas of the cerebral cortex. Here they are integrated and analyzed to yield a visual sensation that is followed by an appropriate response.

Photoreceptors of Various Organisms. Most of our knowledge of the visual processes of animals centers about the vertebrates, a few arthropods, and to a lesser extent the squids. We do know, however, that the eyes are not the only means for the reception of light. In some unicellular organisms or protists (e.g., *Euglena*) there are certain highly specialized pigmented areas, so-called eyespots, which appear to function as sensitive receptors for light. Eyespots are not to be considered as eyes and at most probably indicate to the organism whether light is absent or present. The behavior of *Euglena* is to keep in bright light where it can photosynthesize maximally.

The degree to which photoreceptors have developed or evolved in the animal kingdom varies considerably. Among certain species of such diverse invertebrate phyla as the molluscs (e.g., the octopus), arthropods (e.g., the spider), and echinoderms (e.g., the starfish) there has independently evolved a photoreceptor organ or eye consisting essentially of *pigmented*

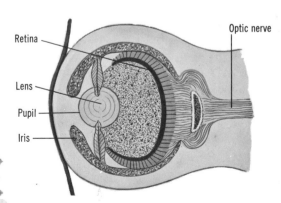

Figure 22-9. The squid eye. Note its resemblance to the human eye (Figure 22-11). See text for details.

light-absorbing nerve cells and a thickened epithelium or *lens* for concentrating the light on the pigmented cells. In the molluscs, for example, the eye may range from no more than a pigmented spot in some representative forms to an intricate structure in others (e.g., squid and octopus), resembling in many respects the mammalian eye. The image-forming eye of the squid (Figure 22-9) and of vertebrates, with its cornea, lens, and retina, is an outstanding example of independent evolution of like structures in relatively unrelated organisms (p. 337).

The ability to discern clear images depends on several factors. These include a suitably shaped lens and a large number of sensitive receptor cells organized as a retina on which the lens can focus an image. In many lower animal forms in which these requirements are not fulfilled, vision may consist only of the ability to distinguish light from dark, movement of objects, and in insects crude but discernible images. The more advanced eyes, namely those that can form discernible or useful images, must have evolved independently in some of the more complex molluscs (e.g., cephalopods), in particular spiders, and in certain primitive, nonextinct vertebrates from which all other vertebrates including ourselves arose.

Among the arthropods, the insects and crustaceans (e.g., lobsters and crabs), in addition to simple eyes, possess so-called *compound eyes* (See Figure 19-12) composed of many smaller "eyes" or visual units, each consisting of a small package of light-sensitive cells and a lens. Each visual unit receives light from a slightly different portion of the animal's environment, resulting in the creation of a roughly recognizable overall image.

Color vision, the ability to distinguish between different wavelengths, is present among numerous insects, fishes, reptiles, and birds but is limited to only a few mammals, including man.

THE HUMAN EYE. The adult human eye, measuring approximately one inch in diameter, consists of a hollow sphere called the *eyeball*, approximately five-sixths of which is enclosed in the bony eye socket of the skull. In addition there are accessory structures which include the *eyebrows*, *eyelids*, the *tear gland apparatus*, the *conjunctiva* (a delicate protective membrane covering the exposed part of the eyeball), and the *six small ocular muscles* attaching each eye to its socket. The ocular muscles account for the ability of the eye to rotate in various directions (Figure 22-10).

Structure of the Eye. The eyeball itself is composed essentially of three coats or layers (Figure 22-11).

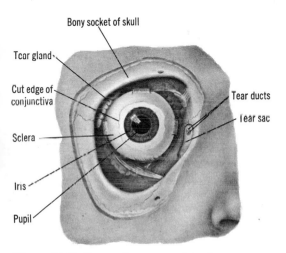

Bony socket of skull
Tear gland
Cut edge of conjunctiva
Sclera
Iris
Pupil
Tear ducts
Tear sac

Figure 22-10. External anatomy of the human eye.

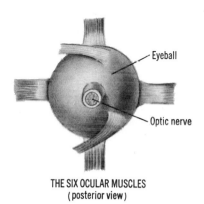

Eyeball
Optic nerve

THE SIX OCULAR MUSCLES
(posterior view)

Outer Layer. The outermost coat called the *fibrous tunic* is divided into two regions: (1) the *cornea* or the transparent and most anterior portion made up of several cell layers covering the exposed portion of the eyeball and representing about one-sixth of the surface; and (2) the *sclera,* a firm, white, dense semirigid membrane which covers the remainder of the eye giving shape to the eyeball and protecting its inner parts. The ocular muscles extend from the sclera to the eye socket. The cornea itself is actually composed of five separate layers of cells including an inner and outer epithlial layer. Most of the energy metabolism of this structure depends on the aerobic metabolism of glucose. Since the cornea possesses no direct blood supply (also true for the lens), the diffusion of O_2 from the atmosphere and nutrients from the *aqueous humor* is essential.

Middle Layer. The middle layer of the eyeball is called the *vascular tunic* and consists of three regions: the *choroid coat,* the *ciliary body,* and the *iris.* The choroid coat, which is a thin, dark membrane containing many blood vessels and a large quantity of pigment, closely adheres to the undersurface of the sclera. It therefore invests about five-sixths of the eyeball. At its anterior portion, that is, at the exposed portion of the eyeball, the choroid coat has been modified into the *ciliary body* which lies at the junction of the choroid and the *iris* or colored portion of the eye. The ciliary body, consists of several parts including the involuntary *ciliary muscle* which is responsible for changing the shape of the lens.

The iris is a thin, colored, doughnut-shaped structure consisting of involuntary circular and radial smooth muscle fibers arranged about a circular central opening called the *pupil.* The iris is suspended between the cornea and the lens and is attached at its outer margin to the ciliary body. It has a major role in determining the amount of light entering the vertebrate eye by regulating the size of the pupil through the reflex response of the iris muscles. The circular fibers of the iris are supplied by the parasympathetic fibers of the visceral ner-

vous system and act to narrow the pupil. The radiating fibers are connected to the sympathetic fibers and serve to enlarge the pupil. The muscles of the iris also aid in the formation of clear images on the retina. Constriction of the pupil by contraction of the circular muscle fibers of the iris normally accompanies the viewing of nearby objects. In this manner divergent rays from the viewed object are prevented from entering the eye through the periphery of the cornea and lens. The entry of such rays would cause a blurred image because they could not be brought into focus properly on the retina. In many nocturnal animals (e.g., the cat) the narrowed pupil is slit-like rather than circular. In some fishes the pupil remains unchanged since the iris does not adjust the size of the pupil in these animals.

The eye is probably the only organ of the body possessing both voluntary and involuntary muscles. The voluntary muscles consist of the six ocular muscles permitting movement of the eyeball in any desired direction under control of the will. The involuntary muscles are those of the iris which regulate the size of the pupil, and the ciliary muscle which accounts for accommodation by affecting curvature of both the lens and the cornea.

Inner Coat. The third and inner coat of the eyeball, called the *retina,* is the photosensitive structure of the eye. It is considered to be a modified portion of the primitive brain and is primarily nervous in structure and function. The retina is an incomplete coat in that it does not have an anterior portion (i.e., it does not exist at the exposed part of the eyeball). It contains the actual receptors for vision and consists of two major layers, an *outer pigmented layer* of epithelial cells lying in contact with the choroid coat and an *inner sensory layer* made up of several kinds of cells arranged in three principal sublayers. Interestingly enough, the retina has the highest known rate of oxygen consumption (per unit weight) of any tissue in the body. The pigmented layer contains at least the enzymes necessary for the synthesis of rhodopsin (p. 534), prevents internal reflec-

night vision

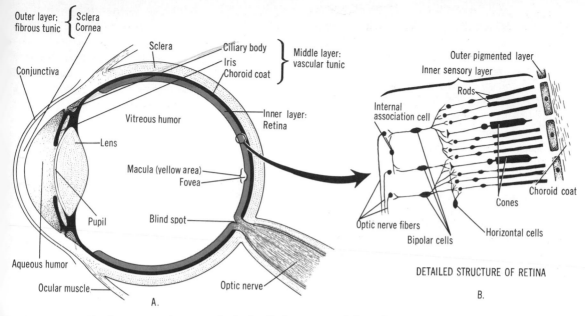

Figure 22-11. The human eye (cross section); detailed structure of the retina.

tions of light within the eye, and possesses melanin, the same (pigment occurring in the skin.) The presence of melanin in the iris is also responsible for brown eyes. In blue eyes melanin is absent from the iris, the blue color arising from absorption of longer wavelengths as light is reflected back from the iris.

Two kinds of receptor cells, the *rods* and *cones,* so called because of their shapes, constitute the sublayer that lies adjacent to the pigmented layer. The rods are characteristically long and narrow whereas the cones are short and thick (Figure 22-11). The rods and cones as the highly specialized and sensitive receptors for visual light stimuli are modified neurons. The outer segment of the rod and cone is the special portion of the cell sensitive to light whereas the inner portion is very much like a typical nerve cell. The other two principal sublayers of the inner sensory layer, proceeding from the rods and cones toward the center of the eyeball, consist successively of bipolar and horizontal cells and of the retinal ganglion cells whose axons converge just before

leaving the eye to constitute the *optic nerve.* The latter transmits impulses to the visual sensory area of the cerebral cortex.

The fovea and the distribution of cones and rods—At about the exact geometric center of the surface of the retina is a small, yellowish area, the *macula,* which contains a tiny depression about one millimeter in diameter called the *fovea.* The fovea is the region of keenest vision, the area on which an image of an object is normally focused, like light rays in a camera. It accounts for acute visual perception of details and of color. It is structurally unique also in that the light-sensitive layer consists only of densely packed cones. Except for the cone layer and underlying pigmented layer, all other layers of the retina in the fovea are extremely thin or absent. Vision in the region of the retina surrounding the fovea is far less sensitive to detail and color and becomes progressively more ill defined and less acute as one proceeds from the center of the retina to its more peripheral areas. This correlates well with the distribution in the retina of the esti-

rods – light.
cones – details

Coordination: The Receptors or Sense Organs 531

mated 7 million cones. The cones are most highly concentrated in the fovea, becoming correspondingly less numerous with increasing distance from the center of the retina toward the peripheral areas.

By contrast the estimated 120 million rods of the retina of the eye, which are primarily responsible for "night vision" or vision in dim light, tend to increase in concentration with increasing distance from the fovea. They reach a maximum about 20 degrees from the fovea and then decrease.

Vision in dim light is best attained by viewing an object indirectly, that is, slightly sideways so as to focus the image more toward the periphery of the retina where the rods are more plentiful. Although the rods are considerably more sensitive than the cones to lower light intensity, they fail to elicit a color sensation, a response arising exclusively in the cones. Rods produce visual reactions only in terms of black and white or mixtures of the two.

The blind spot — The area of convergence of the nerve processes of the retina before penetrating the rear of the eyeball as the optic nerve enroute to the brain is called the *optic disc* or *blind spot*. The optic disc is a creamy white, light-insensitive, circular indentation on the retinal surface. It is somewhat off-center, lying to the nasal side of the fovea and containing neither rods nor cones. An entering artery and departing vein via the blind spot ramify throughout the retina.

The lens — Within the eyeball itself, just behind the pupil, lies the elastic, pale yellow *lens,* a transparent biconvex structure about one-third of an inch in diameter. It is clear and glassy in appearance and is composed of an outer layer of epithelial cells enveloping an elastic protein coat or capsule which contains a clear, viscous, gel-like fluid. The lens is constructed of numerous layers of protein fibers and is surrounded by an inert membrane of unknown composition. Its thick gel-like interior contains 25 per cent protein and at least 10 per cent lipid. Defective lens metabolism often manifests itself by an opacity called *cataract,*

the result of a change in protein metabolism which is evinced by the formation of fibrous aggregates in the lens.

The lens is suspended in position by a series of fibers collectively called the *suspensory ligament* connecting the entire circumference of the lens to the *ciliary body* which also connects the iris to the choroid coat (Figure 22-11). The portion of the ciliary body that contains a mass of involuntary smooth muscle fibers is called the *ciliary muscle.* It is the principal agent responsible for changing the shape of the lens, thus permitting the lens to vary its light-focusing properties depending on the objects being viewed. Not only does the lens function to focus light, but it also serves as a light filter not permitting light wavelengths less than about 400 mμ to reach the retina. Changes in curvature or shape of the lens (an involuntary reflex initiated by the light itself) and therefore the extent to which the lens focuses light are determined by the degrees of contraction of the ciliary muscle. The lens is flattened for focusing on distant objects, but assumes a more spherical shape (i.e., its curvature is increased) for focusing on nearby objects.

Operationally a man-made camera shares many similarities with the mammalian eye. Both employ a lens to focus light from objects on the photographic plate or retina as the case may be. One important mechanical difference is that the camera is focused by changing the distance between lens and film. The eye is focused by adjusting the shape of the lens. In both instances by virtue of the properties of light passing through a lens the light rays cross each other and the image formed is always inverted. The shutter as the camera mechanism for admitting or shutting out light corresponds operationally to the eyelid of the eye. The diaphragm as the light regulating mechanism of the man-made camera is functionally equivalent to the iris. In photographic film the light-sensitive material is a chemical, usually silver bromide crystals. It is dispersed in gelatin and corresponds to the rods and cones of the retina of the eye.

The ability of the eye to bring objects at various distances into focus is known as *accommodation*. It is accomplished in terrestrial vertebrates by means of the lens and the cornea. In reptiles (except snakes), birds and mammals accommodation by the lens is brought about by changing the shape of the lens through the action of the muscles of the ciliary body as already indicated.

Interestingly enough in fishes and amphibia accommodation is brought about not by changes in curvature of the lens but through movement of the lens backward or forward by means of special muscles within the eye. In these animals the structural and functional analogy of the eye and camera is therefore more complete.

The Chambers of the Eye and their Media. The eye is a hollow sphere containing two main chambers. In the front portion of the eyeball between the cornea and the lens is the first main chamber of the eye. (Actually it is subdivided by the iris and ciliary body into an anterior space and a posterior space.) It is filled with a clear, limpid, water fluid called the *aqueous humor*. The second but larger main chamber between the lens and retina is occupied by a transparent jelly-like material called *vitreous humor*. In order to reach the retina, light rays must therefore pass successively through the cornea, aqueous humor, the lens, and the vitreous humor.

Physiology of Vision. The cornea, aqueous humor, lens, and vitreous humor are essential for transmission and focusing of light on the light-sensitive cells. The rods and cones, the optic nerve, and the brain are concerned with light reception and vision. In the final analysis the sense of vision is accomplished by the brain. Stimulation of the light-sensitive rods and cones of the retina gives rise to a barrage of nerve impulses which are conducted to the visual areas of the cerebral cortex. Here the features of viewed objects—degree of light and dark, color, form, and motion—are recorded, integrated and intepreted to yield the overall sensation of vision.

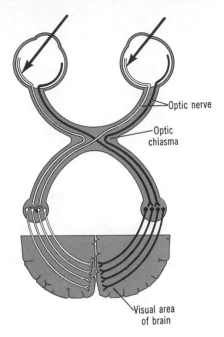

Figure 22-12. The optic chiasma or site at which the optic nerves, one from each eye, partially cross.

The image of an object that falls on the retina is in an inverted position and reversed from side to side just as is the image that falls on a photographic plate. Yet we do not see the image as upside down and reversed. The sensation of vision that occurs in the brain includes the mental process whereby the sensation is projected out of the body to the viewed object. In the process of interpretation the image is again inverted and reversed from side to side, causing the object to appear as it actually is in its true position.

An impulse arising in a rod or cone is transmitted to the brain by way of the optic nerve. In mammals the two optic nerves, one from each eye, partially cross at a site known as the *optic chiasma* as they pass to the visual areas of the cerebrum (Figure 22-12). Not all axons within the optic nerves cross at the optic chiasma. Some cross over to the opposite side, and others remain uncrossed. As a result the visual center on each of the two sides of the cerebral cortex receives impulses from half the retina of one eye and half the retina of the other eye instead of impulses from the entire retina of one eye. More exactly, axons from the nasal half of each retina cross over and enter the brain on the opposite side while axons from lateral or temporal side of each retina do not cross and therefore enter the brain on their own side. Therefore each of the two visual centers of the cortex receives impulses from the nasal half of the retina of one eye (located on the opposite side of the head) and temporal half of the retina of the other eye (located on the same side of the head).

The partial crossover of the optic nerves occurs only in mammals. In all other vertebrates all axons in each optic nerve cross to the opposite side. An object "viewed" by the left eye is interpreted on the right side of the brain, and vice versa.

Stereoscopic or Binocular Vision. In most vertebrates the eyes are directed laterally so that each eye usually has a different field of vision. In such animals the brain must therefore record and coordinate two entirely different visual scenes. In many mammals and in birds of prey where the eyes are directed forward the two fields of vision overlap to a large extent giving rise to one composite image instead of two, a response known as *stereoscopic or binocular vision.* The ability to judge distance or depth is largely ascribed to binocular vision. It reaches a high state of development in primates including man, and is contributed in part by the *partial* crossover of the optic nerves just described. The movement of the two eyeballs is normally and reflexly coordinated. Both eyes act in unison so that they are directed inward toward the viewed object, a phenomenon known as *convergence.* It is brought about by the balanced action of the external eye muscles. Actually the two fields of vision in such animals, although very similar, are not identical since the two eyes view the object from different angles. The two slightly different images produce nerve impulses which are intergrated into a single composite visual image by the brain. Other factors also contribute to the estimation of depth and distance including relative size of objects, distinctness of detail, and so on.

Biochemistry of Vision. The means by which light falling on the rods and cones of the retina acts as stimulus to initiate impulses that ultimately result in the sensation of vision are not entirely clear. Several important and unique biochemical phenomena, especially in the rods, have been uncovered, however, which promise to elucidate the mechanism of action of these light receptor cells.

Our present knowledge indicates that the biochemical steps in visual stimulation involve (1) an initial light-dependent chemical reaction (i.e., photochemical reaction) in which one or more specific pigments absorb light and are chemically transformed in the process; (2) initiation of a nerve impulse, presumably by one or more of the pigment products of the previous photochemical reaction; and (3) regeneration of the pigment to its original state so that it can be used again in subsequent visual stimulation. Step 1 is considered to be the only photochemical reaction in the process.

Night Vision. The rod cells contain a unique reddish pigment called *rhodopsin* or *visual purple* which is a conjugated protein—a complex of a specific protein known as *opsin* and the aldehyde form of vitamin A (called *retinene*). Various lines of evidence indicate that the rhodopsin of the rods is the photosensitive pigment responsible for night vision. Rhodopsin, upon exposure to light, is bleached almost immediately to opsin plus retinene (collectively called *visual yellow*). We are not completely certain which of the photochemical products of rhodopsin, if any, serve as the stimulus that gives rise to nerve impulses resulting in night vision. The reverse reaction, namely reconversion of the visual yellow to the visual purple state occurring in the dark is a relatively slower and more complex process involving several enzymatic reactions as indicated below. During this time the individual is relatively insensitive to light—at least until the normal level of rhodopsin is restored. We have all experienced the common difficulty of initially distinguishing seats in a darkened movie house after entering from a well-lit lobby or a bright outdoors. Within a few minutes our ability to see in the dark is correspondingly restored.

The retinene that appears upon bleaching of rhodopsin cannot recombine directly with opsin to form active rhodopsin but is first reduced to the alcohol form of vitamin A by DPNH, isomerized, and reoxidized by DPN to a particular isomer called *11-cis-retinene*. This may be accomplished in the dark by means of the enzyme alcohol dehynogenase (p. 180) for which DPN serves as a cofactor, and an isomerase. The result is the regeneration of rhodopsin as outlined in Figure 22-13.

In man maximal sensitivity to night vision is attained after a period of about 3/4 of an hour in the dark. A deficiency of vitamin A in the diet results in defective vision in dim light but not in bright light, a condition known as *night blindness*. The observation known since ancient times that night blindness in humans is alleviated by feeding liver or liver extracts was shown some 40 years ago to be due to the presence of vitamin A.

Day Vision and Color Vision. Far less is known about the physiological or biochemical mechanism of action of the cones as the receptors responsible for color and detailed vision. The cones are considerably less sensitive to light than the rods and require 50- to 100-fold greater light intensity in order to be stimulated. One of the more widely accepted theories has postulated for years that there must be at least three closely related pigments in cones, each sensitive to one of the three primary colors thus accounting for color vision. It is only very recently, however, that this has been established. Experiments at Hopkins and Harvard with retinas from humans and monkeys have demonstrated for the first time the existence of three kinds of primary color receptors—a blue-sensitive cone, a

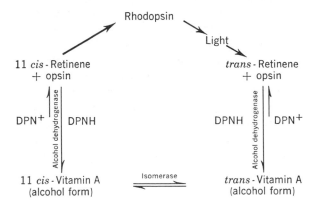

Figure 22-13. Some biochemical transformations associated with night vision.

green-sensitive cone, and a red-sensitive cone —which are collectively responsible for color vision. The evidence also indicates that the green-, red-, and probably the blue-sensitive pigments consist of the same 11-*cis*-retinene as in rhodopsin but bound to different proteins or opsins, thus accounting for their different light-absorbing properties.

Vision in Other Animals. Most vertebrates have both rods and cones in their retinas, although a few species have but one of the two types. The owl, for example, has only rods (and pupils which can open wider than those of man) and therefore possesses only vision in dim light. The owl's eyes are greatly enlarged but cannot be turned in their sockets, thus requiring that the entire head be turned in order to change direction of sight. By contrast, birds that are active during the day, such as the pigeon, have only cones and therefore enjoy detailed as well as color vision. The eyes of birds are relatively huge, a fact not readily apparent because the lids conceal most of the eyeball. In several ways the eye of the bird is optically superior to that of man, but the range of visual experience of the bird is undoubtedly inferior owing to the relative simplicity of its brain.

Many reptiles and fishes have color vision, whereas frogs, salamanders, and most mammals with the notable exception of man and some primates are unable to distinguish colors.

For example, the dog, cat, cow, and the horse are color blind. Numerous animals have an internal mirror-like surface in the pigmented layer behind the retina called the *tapetum* which is responsible for the "glowing" eyes of cats and dogs at night. In these animals the tapetum, consisting of crystals of zinc and the amino acid cysteine, serves to reflect dim light not absorbed during passage through the retina. Thus it allows the light to impinge again on the light receptor cells. The tapetum considerably increases the sensitivity of vision in poor light. In many fish, amphibia, and reptiles it consists largely of guanine crystals, the same substance that is one of the purine bases in DNA and RNA structure (Chapter 7).

Freshwater fish, in contrast to mammals, birds, amphibians, and salt-water fish, have a retinal pigment in place of rhodopsin called *porphyropsin*. The salmon which develops in fresh water but migrates to the ocean contains both pigments in its retina.

Common Defects in Vision. For various reasons eyes may be unable to focus light properly on the retina, thus giving rise to a blurred image. *Visual acuity*, or the degree of sharpness or distinctness of vision, is usually measured by the ability of an individual to see letters of an established size that can be viewed by a normal eye at a distance of 20 feet. In the commonly used Snellen test normal visual acuity is rated as 20/20, which means that the eye under test sees the standard size letters as seen by the normal eye at 20 feet. Ratings of 20/40 or 20/80, for example, mean that the eye must be at 20 feet to see clearly letters that can be seen by the normal eye at 40 or 80 feet, representing a visual acuity of 20/40 or 50 per cent, or 20/80 or 25 per cent of normal.

Among the most common defects in vision are *nearsightedness* (myopia), *farsightedness* (hyperopia), and *astigmatism*. In *nearsightedness* the light rays are focused at a point in front of rather than on the retina (Figure 22-14), usually because the eyeball is longer than usual. It can be corrected by placing a concave or *divergent* lens in front of the eye, thus suffi-

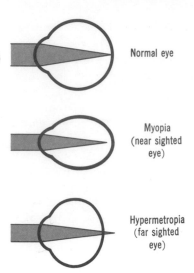

Figure 22-14. Diagram of near-sightedness and far-sightedness.

ciently decreasing the extent of bending or refraction of light rays entering the eye so that they focus on the retina. In *farsightedness*, which is just the opposite, the light rays are focused at a point beyond the retina, usually because the horizontal axis of the eye is shorter than usual. It can be corrected by use of a convex or *convergent* lens which causes a greater converging of the light rays entering the eye. As most people reach middle age they tend to become farsighted because of a progressive decrease in elasticity of the lens which is therefore less able to bulge or assume maximum curvature. The resulting decrease in accommodation adversely affects near vision. In *astigmatism* the irregularities in the curvature of the cornea, or more usually in the lens, result in part of the retinal image being out of focus. It can be corrected by lenses which compensate for the irregular curvature.

Blindness, the loss of the sensation of vision, may be partial or complete. It may result from either a loss in transparency of any of the media of the eye through which light passes, defects in the retina, defects in the nerve pathway leading from the eye to the brain, or impaired function of the visual centers in the brain.

SUPPLEMENTARY REFERENCES

Beidler, L. M., "Our Taste Receptors," *Scientific Monthly,* December 1952.

Haagen-Smit, A.J., "Smell and Taste," *Scientific American*, March 1952.

Kalmus, H., "The Chemical Senses," *Scientific American*, April 1958.

Katz, B., "The Nerve Impulse," *Scientific American*, November 1952.

Le Grand, Yves, *Light, Color and Vision*, Chapman and Hall, London, 1957.

Sperry, R. W., "The Eye and Brain," *Scientific American*, May 1956.

Von Békésy, G., "The Ear." *Scientific American*, August 1957.

Wald, G., "Eye and Camera," *Scientific American*, August 1950.

Wald, G., "The Molecular Basis of Visual Excitation," *American Scientist*, January 1954.

Chapter 23   Coordination:

The Endocrine System

INTRODUCTION

The various activities of the body are controlled and integrated by at least two known major means: the *nervous system* and the *endocrine system.* The phenomena of *molecular feedback, enzyme repression, and enzyme induction* (Chapter 11) may also well prove to be major mechanisms for attaining metabolic regulation.

In man as in all other mammals the endocrine system consists collectively of some 10 different specialized glands of various embryonic origins located in particular parts of the body (Figure 23-1). The glands have no ducts and liberate their secretions known as *hormones* directly into the blood stream. For this reason the glands composing the endocrine system are also referred to as the *ductless glands.*

Most of our knowledge of endocrine systems centers about the vertebrates, in particular the mammals. A number of endocrine tissues and hormones (unrelated to those of mammals) have been shown to be present among the more advanced invertebrates such as insects, crustaceans, and certain molluscs. For example, the intimate involvement of several hormones in the metamorphosis of some insect species has already been described (Chapter 19). For most other invertebrates, however, there is as yet no evidence for the existence of endocrine glands. This is not to say that such animals lack processes of chemical coordina-

tion. There is not the slightest doubt that these organisms are significantly regulated by various chemical substances or hormones. In all probability such chemicals are produced in scattered cells or small groups of cells that have not evolved into definite and discernible glands.

The plant hormones have already been discussed in Chapter 17.

Chemical Nature of Hormones

Hormones are organic substances of varying structural complexity which are carried by the blood to other parts of the body where they exert their specific effects. They may either stimulate or inhibit a function but in general do not initiate a process. For example, sugars may be metabolized in the absence of the hormone insulin, and oxidative processes still go on in the absence of thyroid hormone, but they do not proceed at normal rates. In the most simple terms hormones are "chemical messengers" that pass from the glands via the blood stream to the target organ or process. In a broader sense, however, they can no longer be regarded merely as chemical messengers of the blood. They are important regulating substances that control virtually every aspect of the metabolism of living cells. A few hormones have relatively simple structures (e.g., adrenaline). Others as the sex hormones belong to the fatty group of substances known as *steroids* (Chapter 7), whereas most are proteins or polypeptides whose chemical structures are only now being elucidated. In general, hormones fall into two chemical classes. They are either *steroids* or *amino-acid derivatives* which include proteins, peptides, and modified amino acids.

Hormone Function

Hormones are effective in remarkably small quantities. For example, the injection of a few micrograms of adrenaline (p. 549) into a dog causes a definite increase in the rate of heart beat. There is little doubt that all hormones exert their action by affecting the

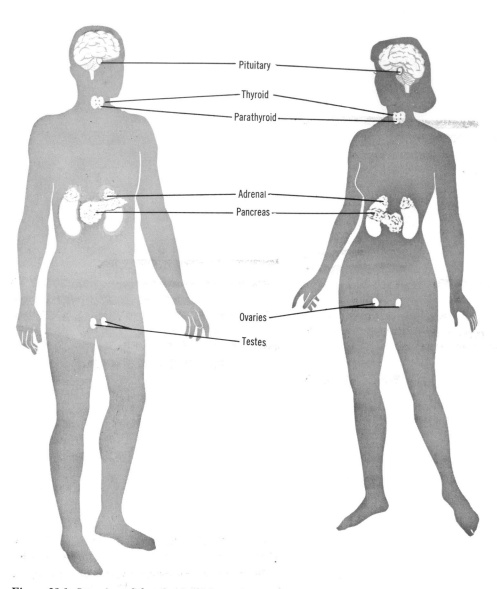

Figure 23-1. Location of the glands of the endocrine system in man.

fundamental metabolism of their target cells and tissues. They therefore have a marked influence on the basic life processes including growth, development, reproduction, energy utilization, cell permeability, and so on. Nevertheless there is still no conclusive evidence as to the mechanism or manner by which a hormone produces its effects, despite the tremendous research efforts in this area over the years. The fact that hormones, like vitamins and micronutrient elements, function in extremely small quantities would appear to implicate them in a catalytic role, possibly as components of enzyme systems; but as yet there are no definite data that clearly support this view. The mechanism of hormone action at the molecular level is one of the major unsolved riddles of biology.

Although the endocrine system and nervous system share the common function of integration and control of body activities, there are several obvious distinctions in the manner in which they act. In general the action of hormones occurs more slowly and is longer lasting as compared to that of the nervous system which effects high-speed and short-duration responses. The endocrine system uses the blood to carry hormones to the effector tissues. The nervous system uses a sequence of neurons as the system of communication that finally secretes chemicals (e.g., acetylcholine and sympathin) to elicit the typical response in the effector organ.

A closer comparison of the nervous and endocrine systems, however, indicates that they share more similarities than heretofore believed. In some respects the nerve cell resembles an endocrine cell. Both types secrete certain chemicals which act on a target organ or tissue. In contrast to the endocrine cell the nerve cell is in direct contact with its target organ. In addition some endocrine tissues, for example, the *adrenal medulla* (p. 548), secrete the same hormones or chemicals (noradrenalin or sympathin) as the nerve cells. The adrenal medulla is actually a modified portion of the sympathetic nervous system, and several of the pituitary secretions are in reality secretions of modified nerve cells or indirectly regulated by nervous mechanisms residing in the hypothalamus region of the brain. Here are specific instances in which endocrine function strongly resembles nerve function.

The endocrine system like the nervous system tends to maintain a dynamic balance within the internal environment of the animal and contributes to the response of the animal to its external environment. Most effector organs, with the possible exception of a large portion of the skeletal muscles, are regulated by both the endocrine and nervous systems. Finally, hormones also play an important role in the growth, development, and differentiation of the tissues of the animal. In most cases they do not exert their physiological action in an independent manner but act in an interrelationship with other hormones.

Control of Endocrine Secretion

The secretion of hormones by the endocrine glands is controlled by a complex of *chemical* and *nervous factors*. The secretory activity of most of the endocrine glands seem to be regulated by certain substances carried by the blood. In some instances these chemical factors are hormones themselves. In other cases they are relatively simple substances such as sugars (e.g., blood glucose stimulates the flow of insulin by the pancreas) and acids (e.g., the secretion of secretin by the small intestine is stimulated by the acid chyme entering from the stomach). In a few glands (e.g., the adrenal medulla) secretory activities are regulated directly by the visceral nervous system.

Scope of Hormone Action

It becomes evident from what has already been said that hormones do not act as isolated factors, although we may have classified them as such largely for the sake of convenience. Endocrine function in reality is based on an intricate complex of interactions including antagonisms and enhancements at various levels in the makeup of the organism. Some hormones appear to be highly specific in their action with respect to the target tissue (e.g., the follicle-stimulating hormone and the luteinizing hormone, p. 554). Others such as the thyroid hormone, insulin, the adrenal cortical hormones, and others affect a wide variety of cells. Moreover, the interrelationships between the nervous system and the endocrine system are far more involved than formerly believed as indicated above.

Most vertebrates from fishes to mammals have similar but not necessarily identical hormones. The effects of hormones, however, may vary considerably depending on the species. For example, one of the ovarian hormones, estrogen (p. 558), has striking effects on the feathering of certain fowl (leghorn chicken) but no effect on others (pigeon).

What Is a Hormone?

Finally, it should be noted that with our ever-growing knowledge of biological function, the boundaries for our original definition of a hormone tend to become blurred and unwieldy. We know, for example, that certain substances such as carbon dioxide and urea move out of the blood and have important effects in regulating normal physiological activities. Although it is true that carbon dioxide is produced by most if not all body tissues, urea is of a more restricted origin, being primarily formed in the liver and kidney. Nevertheless we do not ordinarily regard such substances as hormones. We have also learned that certain hormones formerly considered to be produced by a specific gland may also be synthesized in other parts of the body. Some steroid hormones, for example, are produced in certain organs and even in plants.

THE THYROID GLAND

Location and Structure

The thyroid gland consists of two lateral lobes and a connecting isthmus of tissue and in the human adult has an average weight of 25 to 30 grams. It is located in the midportion of the neck slightly below the *larynx* or voice box, just anterior to the upper portion of the *trachea* or windpipe. The gland is well supplied with blood, has a connective tissue framework, and contains many microscopic cavities or *vesicles*. The latter are lined with a single layer of cuboidal epithelial cells which are the actual secretory cells responsible for the production of the thyroid hormones (Figure 23-2). The hollow center of each vesicle is filled with a gelatinous collodial material made up mostly of a large complex glycoprotein called *thyroglobulin* (see following section).

The Thyroid Hormones

The thyroid gland has the remarkable ability to store and accumulate iodine which is a constituent of the thyroid hormones. At least one-quarter of the total body iodine is concentrated within the gland itself. Experiments with radioactive iodine (I^{131}) have demonstrated that within a few hours following injection of sodium iodide as much as 70 per cent accumulates in the thyroid gland. It is now known that the thyroid hormone consists of at least four physiologically active iodinated organic compounds collectively called *iodo-*

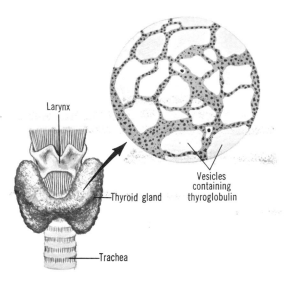

Larynx

Thyroid gland

Vesicles containing thyroglobulin

Trachea

Figure 23-2. Gross and microscopic structure of the thyroid gland in man.

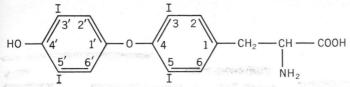

Figure 23-3. Thyroxine.

thyromines. The most abundant of the four is called *thyroxine* which until recently was believed to be the only physiologically active component or hormone secreted by the gland. The structure of thyroxine is the iodinated derivative of the essential amino acid L-*tyrosine* and is shown in Figure 23-3. Of the other three iodothyromines, two are almost identical in their chemical structure, having only 3 iodine atoms (on the above-numbered 3, 5, and 3′, and 3, 3′, 5′ positions), whereas the other has 2 iodine atoms (at the 3 and 3′ positions) instead of the 4 iodine atoms possessed by thyroxine. The 3, 5, 3′ iodinated form in fact has five- to tenfold as much biological activity as thyroxine, whereas the remaining two are less active than thyroxine. The mixture of the foregoing 4 iodothyromines is now considered to be the hormones produced by the thyroid gland.

The iodothyromines are present in the vesicles of the gland in both the free state and as part of the large gylcoprotein thyroglobulin. Thyroglobulin itself has no hormonal activity. However, in the normal course of events it is hydrolyzed to yield the active iodothyromines or thyroid hormones which are apparently the only iodinated compounds secreted into the blood stream by the gland. The thyroid hormones are not transported by the blood in a free form but combine largely with one of the blood proteins, namely alpha-globulin which therefore serves as a carrier.

THYROID HORMONE FUNCTION. *Physiological and Biochemical Effects.* The thyroid hormones stimulate the rate of oxygen consumption or oxidative metabolism and resulting heat production of the various cells and tissues of the body. The thyroid gland also has a second important function, namely a regulatory role (by its effects on cellular metabolism) in the general processes of growth and development of all cells and tissues. These include sexual development, maturation of bones and teeth, mental development, energy metabolism and so on.

The mechanism of action of the hormones at the molecular level is still not established. We do know that in isolated tissues and mitochondria added thyroxine, by possibly affecting the permeability of the mitochondrial membrane, has the ability to disjoin or uncouple the formation of ATP, which normally accompanies the terminal steps of aerobic respiration (Chapter 8). This effect is called *uncoupling of oxidative phosphorylation.* Thus a portion of the energy derived from oxidative metabolism instead of being stored as ATP would be wasted as heat. Excessive heat production is known to accompany the occurrence of an overactive thyroid in the whole animal. Whether or not the uncoupling mechanism of thyroxine on oxidative phosphorylation observed in isolated tissues and mitochondria also applies in the intact organism is not yet clear.

The thyroid hormones influence a wide diversity of tissues and organs, probably more so than any other hormone. In amphibians they also have a remarkable action in accelerating the rate of metamorphosis or development to the adult stage. Tadpoles treated with the thyroid hormones rapidly undergo differentiation and development to the adult frog stage. Conversely, tadpoles whose thyroid tissue has been removed do not metamorphose but grow to a large size remaining in the tadpole stage.

HYPO- AND HYPERTHYROIDISM. As with all other hormones nearly all our knowledge of the functions of the thyroid secretions is derived from experiments with laboratory animals in which the gland has been removed or excessive quantities of the hormone have been administered. A second important source has been clinical observations of patients. The phenomenon of an insufficient secretion by the thyroid gland is known as *hypothyroidism,* whereas that of an excessive secretion is called *hyperthyroidism.* Hypothyroidism may be due to a variety of factors including atrophy of the gland, deficient dietary supply of iodine, or an inadequate development of the glandular tissues for whatever the reasons may be. Hypothyroidism at birth gives rise to the dwarfed condition called *cretinism* which is typified by retarded physical, sexual, and mental development and a significantly lowered metabolic rate. Early administration of the thyroid hormones by mouth or injection is necessary to prevent permanent effects.

The occurrence of hypothyroidism in adults produces the condition called *myxedema,* characterized by a lowered metabolic rate, thickness and puffiness of the skin, coarseness and brittleness of the hair and fingernails, and a general physical and mental lethargy. There is usually a weight gain, loss of hair, slower pulse rate, reduced blood pressure, and a decreased body temperature. The reasons for the inadequate development of the thyroid gland in cretins or its atrophy in patients suffering from myxedema are not known. The administration of adequate doses of the thyroid extracts quickly restores normal function to individuals with myxedema.

Any enlargement of the thyroid gland is designated by the term *goiter.* One of the causes of *simple goiter* is a dietary deficiency of iodine. At one time it was quite prevalent in geographic areas where the soil and water were deficient in the element (for example, in the mountain villages of the Alps and Pyrenees). The wider distribution of foods grown in different areas and the addition of iodine to certain foods (e.g., table salt) and drinking water have reduced its incidence.

Hyperthyroidism is accompanied by physio-logical effects and symptoms which are the opposite of those observed in hypothyroidism. One of the most severe conditions of hyperthyroidism is called *Graves' disease* or *exophthalmic goiter.* It is characterized by an enlargement of the entire gland, an elevated metabolic rate, weight loss, profuse perspiration, higher pulse rate, and a typical protrusion of the eyeballs called *exophthalmos* (Figure 23-4). The condition may be treated by surgical removal of a portion of the thyroid gland, administration of radioactive iodine which accumulates in the thyroid destroying some of its tissues, or use of certain thyroid-inhibiting drugs which interfere with the synthesis of thyroid hormones. Hyperthyroidism may also be caused by a tumor or growth of the thyroid gland.

Control of Thyroid Secretion

The secretion of thyroid hormones is apparently controlled by the thyroid-stimulating hormone (known as the *thyrotrophic hormone*) secreted by the anterior pituitary gland (p. 553). The thyrotrophic hormone is produced in larger quantities as a result of decreased levels of thyroxin in the blood. The rise of thyroxin in the bloodstream in turn inhibits, by a negative feedback mechanism (p. 288), the production of the thyrotrophic hormone, thus decreasing stimulation of the thyroid.

Regulation of the level of thyroid hormones once secreted into the blood stream is affected in part by the liver through enzymatic mechanisms involving the removal of iodine and the amino group from the hormones.

THE PARATHYROID GLANDS

Location and Structure

The parathyroid glands in man consist of two pairs of small oval glands of densely packed cells (each gland averaging about 5 mm in diameter) attached to the thyroid gland. The glands are absent in fishes, but are present in amphibians, reptiles, birds, and mammals in either one or two pairs, depending on the species. Their close anatomical relationship to the thyroid gland is apparently not matched by any relationship in function.

The Parathyroid Hormone and Its Function

The parathyroid hormone is a protein (perhaps several proteins although this is not certain) of undetermined structure which regulates the levels of calcium and phosphorous in the blood. Unlike the thyroid hormones it is destroyed by protein-digesting enzymes and must therefore be administered only by injection and not by mouth. By affecting the concentrations of inorganic calcium and phosphorous in the blood the hormone indirectly regulates the levels of these substances in all other cells and body fluids (i.e., the internal environment of the organism).

An overabundant supply of parathyroid hormone as a result of overdosage of parathyroid extract or a tumor of the glands is characterized by an increase blood calcium level, lowered blood phosphate concentration, and an increased excretion of calcium by the kidneys. An insufficiency of parathyroid hormone in experimental animals and man, usually as a result of removal of the glands, causes a marked decrease in blood calcium concentration. It is followed within a few days by increased irritability or excitability in nerve and muscle (known as *tetany*), convulsions, and death. Administration of calcium salts by mouth or by injection temporarily relieves the condition, as do injections of parathyroid gland extracts.

The exact mechanism by which parathyroid hormone exerts its effects is not clear. In hypoparathyroidism the resultant decrease in blood calcium levels is accompanied by a characteristic increase in blood phosphate concentration. The hormone apparently maintains a normal level of calcium and phosphate in the blood by its action on both bone metabolism and kidney function. In general an increase in blood calcium is accompanied by a

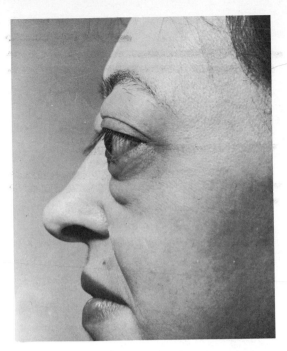

Figure 23-4. A patient with exophthalmic goiter. Note the typical protrusion of the eyeballs, called *exophthalmos*. (*Courtesy of R. W. Carlin.*)

decrease in phosphate concentration so that the product of their concentrations is roughly constant. Parathyroid hormone causes an increase in the calcium concentration of the blood at the expense of the major reserves of calcium, namely the bone. The hormone somehow stimulates the action of the bone-dissolving cells (Chapter 29), thus enhancing demineralization or decalcification of the bony matrix. The resulting dissolution of bone also releases phosphate which is liberated together with calcium. Under these conditions the removal of excess phosphate from the blood by the kidneys is apparently stimulated by parathyroid hormone. The net result of the action of the hormone in stimulating both bone demineralization and phosphate excretion by the kidney is to increase the level of the blood calcium.

In hyperparathyroidism the maintenance of a high blood calcium at the expense of bone often leads to an indiscriminate calcification of the soft tissues of the body.

It should be noted that vitamin D is related in some unknown fashion to parathyroid function and calcium and phosphate metabolism. For example, it can be shown that high doses of vitamin D can maintain normal blood calcium concentrations in hypoparathyroidism.

Control of Parathyroid Secretion

The parathyroid glands apparently secrete their hormone in response to the calcium level of the blood. A decreased calcium concentration in the blood leads to an increased secretion of the parathyroid hormone, whereas an increased blood calcium content gives rise to a decline in hormone secretion. Our information to date fails to support the idea that hormones from other glands, including the anterior pituitary, have a role in regulating the activity of the parathyroid glands.

THE PANCREAS
(ISLETS OF LANGERHANS)

Location and Structure

The pancreas in human adults is an elongated gland weighing about three ounces. It lies behind the stomach close to the posterior abdominal wall, and functions both as a digestive gland and an endocrine gland.

The bulk of the pancreas consists of glandular cells which secrete a mixture of several digestive enzymes that drain by way of a duct into the small intestine (Chapter 24). The pancreas also contains scattered, rounded microscopic clusters or islets of tissue approximately 0.3 mm in diameter (Figure 23-5) and about a million or so in number. The islets are not connected with any ducts, and perform an important endocrine function. They were discovered by Langerhans in 1869, although their role was not known until many years later, and are accordingly called *islets of Langerhans*. In some fishes the islets are anatomically distinct and are aggregated into separate so-called *principal islets* made up almost exclusively of

endocrine tissue. In other fishes no pancreas is found but the equivalents of islet tissue are embedded in particular sections of the wall of the intestine, and in some species even in parts of the liver. They probably represent the most primitive physiological equivalents of islet tissue.

The islets of Langerhans in mammals consist of four known types of cells. The so-called *beta (β)-cells* constitute the majority in the islets and are responsible for secretion of the hormone *insulin*. About 20 per cent of the islet cells are the *alpha (α)-cells* which are generally believed to secrete a second hormone called *glucagon*. The functions of the small percentage of remaining cells, called the C-cells and D-cells, are not known. All vertebrates appear to have β-cells or their equivalent for the secretion of insulin. Both α- and β-cells have been identified in the islet tissue of several but not all species of fishes. Some amphibians have only β-cells whereas other possess both α- and β-cells in their islets. Reptiles and birds have both types in their islets with α-cells being the most numerous in contrast to mammals where β-cells are the predominant type.

Insulin

The term *insulin* was given in 1916 to the unidentified, highly unstable active hormone of the islets of Langerhans. Using dogs, Banting and Best in 1921 were the first to obtain a stable preparation of insulin. Heretofore the main obstacle to obtaining insulin was its rapid destruction by the digestive juices of the pancreas upon disruption of the gland. Banting and Best succeeded where others had failed. They made use of the observation that surgical tying off of the pancreatic duct results within a few weeks in degeneration of the pancreas cells which produce pancreatic juice. Subsequent extraction of such a gland yielded stable insulin preparations. Insulin, as a proteinaceous hormone, is now known to consist of 51 amino-acid residues in the form of two linked peptide chains with a molecular

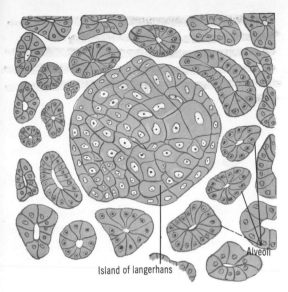

Figure 23-5. Diagram of a microscopic section of the pancreas and its scattered microscopic islets of langerhans.

weight of 6000 (Figure 7-5). It is rapidly destroyed by protein-digesting enzymes and must therefore be administered by injection and not by mouth to avoid its destruction in the digestive tract.

Numerous correlations between the degree of β-cell degeneration and insulin content of the pancreas have implicated these cells in the production of the hormone. Such correlations include: (*a*) earlier clinical studies of patients suffering from the disease *Diabetes mellitus*, commonly called diabetes, a condition characterized by the excessive loss of glucose through the urine. Diabetic individuals show a lower insulin level and abnormal or fewer β-cells in their pancreas; (*b*) observations that artificially maintained high concentrations of blood glucose in laboratory animals lead to degeneration of only the β-cells in the islets, no extractable pancreatic insulin, and eventually to a lasting diabetou and (*c*) data that the drug *alloxan* which selectively destroys the β-cells of the pancreas by a still unexplained mechanism also gives rise to a decrease in extractable insulin and to diabetes.

FUNCTION OF INSULIN. Insulin and glu-

cagon (together with certain other hormones from the thyroid, adrenal, and pituitary glands) play a central role in regulating the carbohydrate metabolism of the body. The mechanisms of action of insulin and of glucagon, however, are still relatively obscure. Both pancreatic hormones, by affecting carbohydrate metabolism in the liver and other cells of the body, have a major function in maintaining blood glucose at a constant level, about 100 mg per 100 ml of blood in mammals. The major sources of blood glucose are first the diet and second such tissues (in particular the liver) which store carbohydrate (in the form of glycogen). The glycogen of skeletal muscle is normally not released as glucose to the bloodstream but is utilized in the muscle tissue itself.

Insulin decreases the concentration of blood glucose by promoting (*a*) its metabolic utilization in cell respiration and fatty acid synthesis, and (*b*) its deposition in the storage form of glycogen, particularly in skeletal muscle tissue and very probably in liver. In mammals whose pancreas has been removed, in diabetics, and in alloxan-treated animals the resultant underutilization of glucose is reflected in several ways. The blood glucose level is elevated, the liver glycogen content is lowered, and fatty-acid synthesis is decreased. Despite the high concentrations of blood glucose, the cells of the body ironically enough respond as if none were present since insulin is not available for enhancing utilization. The liver reacts as if utilizable glucose were lacking in the blood stream and continues to transform its glycogen to blood glucose. The high levels of blood glucose soon exceed the threshold for kidney excretion and the sugar now "spills over" into the urine.

Under these circumstances the cells resort to fat as an energy source, but the oxidation of fatty acids does not proceed to completion. As a consequence there is an accumulation in the blood (and urine) of keto-acid fragments or *ketone bodies* of fatty-acid metabolism, a condition known as *ketosis*. If left untreated, ketosis eventually results in death. Other changes accompanying removal of the pancreas include a reduced rate of respiration and lowered body protein. The latter condition is due in part to a metabolic breakdown and conversion of proteins to glucose and to a decrease in protein synthesis from amino acids.

Diabetes and starvation share several biochemical similarities. In both instances glucose is not being metabolized in muscle and liver at a normal rate. Instead fatty acids serve as the energy source with the eventual accumulation in the blood of ketone bodies leading to ketosis. However, the diabetic has excessively high concentrations of blood glucose, whereas the starving individual has normal or slightly subnormal levels of blood glucose derived primarily from fatty-acid metabolism.

In contrast to a deficiency of insulin, injection of the hormone causes a rapid decline in blood glucose level, an elevated deposition of glycogen in liver and muscle, and a generally increased utilization of glucose in metabolism. How does insulin stimulate the conversion of glucose to glycogen? One theory proposes that insulin stimulates the movement of glucose across the cell membrane into the cell by somehow increasing permeability to various sugars. Although there is appreciable evidence in favor of this view, there is also experimental support for a second major theory. It contends that insulin influences the early stages of glucose metabolism by possibly affecting hexokinase, the enzyme responsible for the conversion of glucose by ATP to glucose-6-phosphate (Chapter 8).

Elevated glucose levels in the blood apparently serve as the stimulus for insulin secretion by the β-cells of the pancreas. A lowering in blood glucose concentration is accompanied by a decrease or cessation in insulin secretion.

Glucagon

The evidence that glucagon originates in the α-cells of the pancreas islets is somewhat similar to that just indicated for insulin production from the β-cells: (a) certain chemical agents cause a selective destruction of the α-cells which is accompanied by a decreased glucagon content of the pancreas, and (b) glucagon content and α-cell population are directly correlated in different parts of dog and bird pancreas where the α-cell distribution varies. Glucagon (from beef pancreas) is a relatively small protein molecule with molecular weight of approximately 4000, and consists of a single straight chain of 29 amino-acid residues.

The hormone has the opposite effect of insulin, tending to increase the level of blood glucose by somehow promoting the conversion of liver glycogen (but not of muscle glycogen) to glucose. The liver therefore appears to be the primary target organ for glucagon. Glucagon is believed to act by somehow enhancing the activity of the enzyme (phosphorylase) responsible for the breakdown of glycogen to glucose-1-phosphate. It possibly prevents enzyme inactivation or stimulates its activity. Adrenalin and several hormones of the adrenal cortex also serve to increase the blood glucose level by stimulating the breakdown of liver glycogen. Their action accounts for the observation that surgical removal of the pancreas gives rise only to those symptoms that reflect an insulin deficiency even though glucagon is now also lacking.

THE ADRENAL GLANDS

Location and Structure

The two adrenal glands in man each weigh about 5 g, measure 1 to 2 inches in length, and are somewhat pyramidal in shape, lying one near the top of each kidney. The adrenal glands have a rich blood supply, are innervated by the sympathetic nervous system, and consist of two parts that are embryonically, anatomically, and functionally different. In the typical mammal the gland consists of an external reddish-brown *cortex* which surrounds an internal grayish *medulla* (Figure 23-6). Thus far it has not been possible to account for the significance, if any, of the close anatomical relationship between the cortex and medulla. In some fish the equivalent of the adrenal cortex is

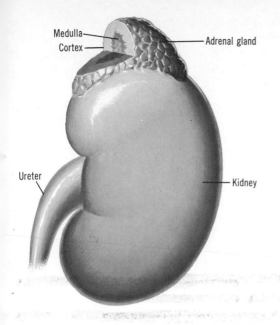

Figure 23-6. Diagram of an adrenal gland in man showing its cortex and medulla.

present as distinct and separate bodies from the adrenal medulla.

Hormones of the Adrenal Medulla

The closely packed cells of the adrenal medulla in man consist of two distinct cell types. These are the *adrenaline-secreting* cells and the *noradrenaline-secreting* cells which are responsible for the production of the two hormones, *adrenaline* or *epinephrine* and *noradrenaline* or *norepinephrine*, respectively (Figure 23-7).

In man 70 to 90 per cent of the hormonal activity of adrenal medulla extracts is adrenaline. In the baboon no noradrenaline is present, whereas in the whale (and the chicken) noradrenaline accounts for 80 per cent of the hormonal activity in the secretions of the adrenal medulla.

ADRENALINE AND NORADRENALINE FUNCTION. The two hormones have related but individual physiological effects. Moreover, their release from the secretory cells in the medulla is controlled by two different centers

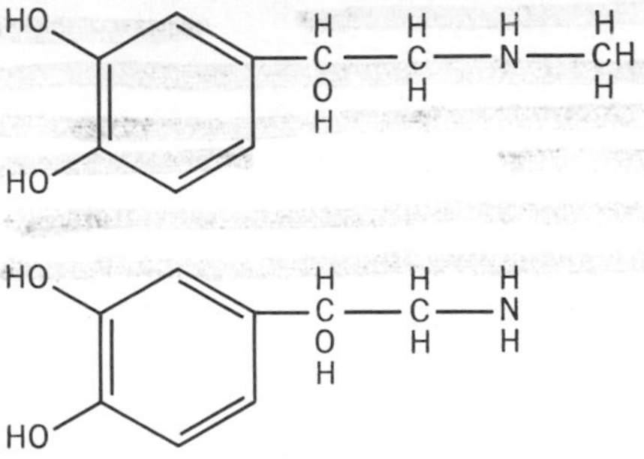

Figure 23-7. Adrenaline and noradrenaline.

in the hypothalamus which can be differentially stimulated. In general the two hormones of the adrenal medulla exert the same physiological effects as those that are brought about by stimulation of the sympathetic nervous system. It has only recently been established that the chemical substance liberated by the sympathetic nerve endings is noradrenaline, and not adrenaline as formerly believed.

The two hormones of the adrenal medulla like the sympathetic nervous system tend to rally the body to situations of stress or emergency. They are responsible in part for the physiological adaptation of the organism to certain demands of the environment. The remarkably close relationship between the adrenal medulla and the nervous system is also indicated by several other lines of evidence. These include their common embryonic origin from neural crest cells (Chapter 31), their production of similar chemical compounds (i.e., noradrenaline), the cytological resemblance of adrenal medulla secretory cells to certain modified neurons, and the dependence of medulla hormone function on stimulation from the sympathetic nervous system. In essence the adrenal medulla consists of modified postganglionic neurons of the sympathetic nervous system.

Of the two, adrenaline functions most closely as the so-called "emergency" hormone for the body. It has a decided effect in elevating the glucose level in the bloodstream by somehow enhancing enzymatic conversion of liver glycogen to glucose. The rise in blood glucose is accompanied by an increase in oxygen consumption, body temperature, and heat production. Adrenaline also tends to increase the blood flow in skeletal muscle, heart, and viscera by dilating the blood vessels. It is responsible as well in part for the relaxation of smooth muscles of the digestive tract and bronchial tubes of the lung, while causing contraction of certain other muscles. In this fashion it serves to shunt or direct the circulation of blood where necessary during exertion or increased activity. Adrenaline also augments blood pressure and cardiac output as well as stepping up the rate of heart beat.

In contrast, the effects of noradrenaline are less extreme. Noradrenaline has no appreciable influence on carbohydrate metabolism or oxygen consumption and exerts little or no action on the cardiac output and heart rate. It produces milder inhibitory effects on smooth musculature and fails to relax the muscles of the bronchial tubes. It does raise the blood pressure, but, unlike adrenaline, it is responsible for constriction instead of dilation of the blood vessels.

Although there are data suggesting that adrenaline (and noradrenaline to a lesser extent) acts indirectly at the enzymatic level by inducing the formation of a factor necessary for the activity of the enzyme phosphorylase, the evidence is not entirely clear. Both hormones are metabolized and inactivated by several enzymatic processes in the body and finally excreted in the urine in modified form.

The adrenal medulla unlike the thyroid, parathyroid, pancreas, and adrenal cortex is not essential for life since it can be removed surgically without causing drastic effects.

The Adrenal Cortex

HORMONES. The adrenal cortex of mammals is made up of several zones of cells, depending on the species, and is essential for life. As early as 1885 the fatal condition known as *Addison's disease*, characterized by a typically abnormal

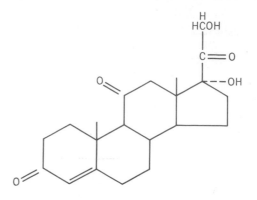

Figure 23-8. Cortisone.

skin pigmentation, gastrointestinal disturbances, weakness, and anemia, was correctly attributed to pathological changes in the adrenal (cortex) glands. By the late 1930's and early 1940's it was recognized that adrenal cortex extracts contained a multiplicity of active steroid hormones collectively called "cortin."

By 1958 some 45 different steroids had been isolated from extracts of the adrenal cortex. Of this number only 6 have significant adrenal cortical hormonal activity. They are *cortisone, corticosterone, deoxycorticosterone, aldosterone, hydrocortisone (cortisol),* and 11-dehydrocorticosterone. The structure of cortisone is shown in Figure 23-8. The other steroids have closely related structures. Several of the steroids isolated from the adrenal cortex have male hormone-like effects. Two female hormones have also been obtained. The adrenal cortex is rich in ascorbic acid (vitamin C) whose role is unknown, and cholesterol, the chief compound from which the steroid hormones are synthesized.

FUNCTIONS OF THE ADRENAL CORTICAL HORMONES. Innumerable studies based on experiments with animals and on observations of patients suffering from an undersecretion or oversecretion of the gland have indicated that the adrenal cortex functions in several diverse physiological areas. The primary effects of the adrenal cortical hormones fall in the following main groups.

1. *Carbohydrate and Protein Metabolism.* A number of adrenal cortical hormones, more specifically *cortisone, cortisol,* and *corticosterone,* exert their influence primarily on carbohydrate metabolism. They are therefore often *referred to as the glucocorticoid* hormones. They increase the blood glucose level at the expense of liver glycogen and enhance the conversion of protein (and fat) to carbohydrates. The mechanism by which this is accomplished is not clear. They somehow inhibit protein synthesis from amino acids as well as increase the availability of amino acids from protein breakdown, thereby furnishing a greater amino-acid supply for carbohydrate formation by the liver.

2. *Mineral, Salt, and Water Metabolism.* The cortical hormones that have a regulatory effect on the relative concentrations of mineral ions (especially sodium and potassium) in the body fluids, and therefore on the water content of the tissues, are referred to as *mineral corticoids.* Aldosterone and deoxycorticosterone are highly potent in this respect. An insufficiency of the mineral corticoids results in an increased excretion into the urine of sodium ions, chloride ions, and water, accompanied by a fall in blood sodium, chloride, and bicarbonate. A concomitant rise in potassium ions at the expense of the body cells and tissue fluids also occurs. The loss of bicarbonate reflects itself in a lowered pH or *acidosis* of the blood. Administration of the mineral corticoid hormones has the opposite effects, resulting in an increase in blood sodium and chloride concentrations, greater retention of water by the body, a decrease in potassium concentration, and a restoration of pH of the blood to its more normally alkaline level. Hormones from certain other glands (e.g., the pituitary gland) directly or indirectly participate in the control of salt and water metabolism.

3. *Sexual Development.* Under certain circumstances the adrenal cortex appears to secrete steroids which are similar in their effects to male hormones. For example, adrenal cortical tumors in females may give rise to masculine characteristics as illustrated by the bearded lady of the circus. The interrelationships of the adrenal cortex with the gonads (reproductive organs) which produce sex hormones are quite complex and poorly understood. Although the female sex hormones have also been detected in adrenal cortical extracts, it is believed that they are simply intermediates in the formation of the adrenocortical steriod hormones.

4. *Inflammation, Allergy, and Other Effects.* Several of the cortical hormones have a marked influence in preventing the appearance of an inflammation (Chapter 25) and accompanying breakdown of connective tissue. Cortisol and, to a lesser extent, cortisone are effective in this respect. Some cortical hormones (e.g., cortisol) also counteract the symptoms of allergic or hypersensitive reactions (Chapter 25). Accordingly they have been used in the treatment of several kinds of acute inflammatory and allergic diseases, especially of the eye. They are also employed to control the symptoms of particular arthritic conditions and rheumatic fever.

The steroid secretions of the adrenal cortex also exercise several other influences on body functions including a role in decreasing the level of red and white blood cells and stimulating the secretions of the digestive tract.

The means by which cortical hormones produce their effects are not understood. One theory postulates that the gland permits the organism to withstand or better adapt to the stress conditions of its environment, especially to infectious or toxic changes. In support of this view are the observations that an individual with an insufficient adrenal cortical supply, as compared to a normal subject, is less able to withstand such conditions as extreme heat or cold, shock, hemorrhage, other physical trauma, infections, exposure to toxic chemicals, and even the effects of other hormones.

CONTROL OF THE ADRENAL CORTEX. The development and function of the adrenal cortex is under the control of a hormone called the *adrenocorticotrophic hormone (ACTH)* secreted by the anterior portion of the pituitary gland. Although ACTH seems to function in the development of the entire cortex, it principally stimulates glucocorticoid secretion, having only a small effect on mineral corticoid production. The secretion of ACTH by the anterior pituitary is apparently stimulated by a diminished glucocorticoid concentration in the blood. The ACTH in turn stimulates adrenal cortical secretion. Thus a classic negative feedback relationship exists between the pituitary and adrenal cortex whereby the increasing glucocorticoid level in the blood reciprocally inhibits further ACTH secretion by the pituitary.

Oversecretion by the adrenal cortex as a result of excessive secretion by the pituitary of ACTH, gives rise to *Cushing's disease.* The symptoms include high blood pressure, salt retention, swelling of the tissues with water, demineralization of the bones, and loss of sexual function. Oversecretion by the adrenal cortex may also result from a tumor in the cortical cells. The symptoms that manifest themselves will depend on the kinds of hormones secreted by the tumor. If glucosteroids such as cortisol are predominantly produced, changes in metabolism accompanied by weakness and wasting of muscle and certain types of obesity occur. If greater concentrations of the male-like hormones are secreted, females begin to attain masculine characteristics and males show a greater accentuation of the male sexual characteristics.

THE PITUITARY GLAND (OR HYPOPHYSIS)

Location and Structure

The *pituitary gland* or *hypophysis* is a rounded body about the size of a large pea weighing approximately 5 g and consisting of two lobes. It is located at the base of the brain over the roof of the mouth and is directly attached, at the undersurface of the cerebrum, to the hypothalamus portion of the brain by a small stalk. The two lobes constituting the pituitary are essentially two different endocrine glands, as are the adrenal medulla and adrenal cortex, and the thyroid and parathyroid glands. The lower or *posterior lobe*, also referred to as the *neurohypophysis*, is derived from brain tissue and bears structural resemblances to nervous tissue. The upper or *anterior lobe*, now preferably called the *adenohypophysis*, is derived from the epithelial tissue of the mouth. In the course of embryonic development the neurohypophysis moves downward, becoming posterior in position to the adenohypophysis which has developed upward to assume an anterior location relative to the neurohypophysis.

Adenohypophysis (or Anterior Pituitary Gland)

The adenohypophysis is often referred to as the "master gland" of the endocrine system because of its important effects in regulating and maintaining the development and function of other endocrine glands. It therefore has a key part in integrating growth and metabolism, and in the development and functioning of the reproductive system including the secondary sexual characteristics, to name but a few of its roles. The adenohypophysis in mammals is made up of several different cell types and in gross appearance is seen to consist of several subdivisions.

HORMONES OF THE ADENOHYPOPHYSIS (OR ANTERIOR PITUITARY GLAND). The adenohypophysis in humans secretes at least six distinct hormones. All are proteins except for the adrenocorticotrophic hormone (ACTH) which is a polypeptide. In contrast the neurohypophysis secretes two known hormones. Nearly all the known pituitary hormones have been purified to a high degree and their chemical and physiological properties well described. The pituitaries of cattle and pigs from slaughter houses have served as an indispensable source for these studies. The known hormonal functions of the adenohypophysis can be fully ascribed to the collective physiological effects of these separate hormones. The nature and function of the six known hormones of the adenohypophysis are as follows:

1. *Thyrotrophic or Thyroid-Stimulating Hormone (TSH)*. The hormone has been purified to a considerable extent and shown to be a glycoprotein with a molecular weight of less than 10,000. It controls various aspects of thyroid gland function, including development and maintenance. TSH also stimulates iodine accumulation, the conversion of iodine into the thyroid hormones, and their release from the gland into circulation. The operation of a negative feedback mechanism in regulating TSH secretion was indicated previously. It is thought that certain nerve secretions from specific areas of the hypothalamus are transmitted by way of the pituitary stalk to regulate the secretion of TSH.

2. *Adrenocorticotrophic Hormone (ACTH)*. ACTH regulates the development and secretion of the adrenal cortex in the same way that TSH controls the thyroid gland. The secretion of ACTH and adrenal cortical hormones (principally the glucocorticoid secretions) are mutually effected by a negative feedback mechanism. In addition as in the case of TSH secretion there is evidence of nerve secretions from certain hypothalamus areas of the brain which influence the secretion of ACTH. Such a mechanism suggests a basis for the release of ACTH by several different stimuli including emotional stress, extreme temperatures, poisons, drugs, and various other substances. The ACTH molecule has been well characterized as a polypeptide of molecular weight 4500 containing 39 amino acids. Some 15 of these amino acids can be removed leaving a basic chain of 24 amino acids which still retains most of the hormonal activity. The ACTH amino-acid composition of beef and sheep is the same, whereas that of hog is slightly different.

3. *Growth Hormone*. The growth hormone (also called *somatropin* or *STH*) stimulates both body weight and the rate of growth of the skeleton. The skeletal and muscular tissues are the most responsive in this respect. The striking retardation in growth of younger experimental animals as a result of surgical removal of the pituitary gland was one of the earliest findings relating to the function of the pituitary. The means by which STH stimulates body growth and skeletal development are not known.

The growth hormone from several mammals including man has been purified, crystallized, and characterized as a protein. Beef crystalline growth hormone has a molecular weight of about 48,000 and is composed of 416 amino-acid residues, whereas the molecular weight of the growth hormone from humans is approximately 27,000. As much as 25 per cent of the bovine hormone may be removed by using digestive enzymes without impairing hormonal activity. Slight differences in the amino-acid content of the growth hormone from different species have been shown.

Undersecretion of the growth hormone during the years of skeletal growth of an individual results in *dwarfism*. Dwarfism, in contrast to cretinism arising from thyroid insufficiency, is not accompanied by physical deformity, mental inferiority, or retardation. An adult dwarf may attain a height no taller than 3 or 4 feet and is usually sexually immature. The development of growth-hormone insufficiency during adult life is a much rarer condition.

Oversecretion of the growth hormone *prior to adulthood* results in *gigantism*, a condition typified by a general overgrowth of the skeleton giving rise to individuals of gigantic stature, as tall as 7 or 8 feet or more in height. Oversecretion of the hormone *after the attainment of full skeletal growth* gives rise to the condition called *acromegaly*. The disease is manifested by a characteristic enlargement or overgrowth of the bones of the hands, feet, and in particular the jaws, cheeks, and face as well as an increase in the overlying soft tissues (Figure 23-9). To date there is no evidence of the biological mechanism that controls secretion of growth hormone.

4. *The Three Gonadotrophic Hormones*. Early observations of atrophy and impaired development of the reproductive system following the degeneration or surgical removal of the pituitary gland indicated that the gland was also essential for normal sexual development and function. Over the years three distinct hormones necessary for sexual development and activity have been isolated in highly purified form from the anterior pituitary gland and partially characterized. All are proteins. They are referred to as the *gonadotrophic hormones* since they control the growth and development of the gonads (i.e., ovaries in the female and testes in the male). Secretion of the gonadotrophic hormones is apparently controlled by feedback mechanisms and by nerve secretions from the hypothalamus.

The gonadotrophic hormones are secreted by the adendoypophysis in only slight amounts until the period before the onset of puberty. They are then produced in progressively larger concentrations, thus initiating the onset of sexual development characteristic of puberty. In the female they subsequently account for the cyclic changes (menstrual cycle, Chapter 30) that recur in the ovaries and womb throughout the years of sexual maturity. In the male they regulate the formation of sperm and the production of the male sex hormone, *testosterone* (p. 559). The details of the interrelationships between the gonadotrophic hormones and the sex hormones produced by the ovaries and testes are discussed in a later section of this chapter. The following are gonadotrophic hormones.

(*a*) *Follicle-Stimulating Hormone (FSH)*. In the female starting at puberty and continuing throughout the years of female sexual maturity, FSH promotes certain changes during a portion of each menstrual cycle. It stimulates the development and maturation of an ovarian follicle (Chapter 30) which produces the egg cell and one of the female sex hormones, *estrogen*.

Figure 23-9. An individual with acromegaly, the result of an oversecretion of growth hormone by the anterior pituitary gland after attainment of full skeletal growth. (*Courtesy of World Wide Photos.*)

In the male starting at puberty FSH induces spermatogenesis by the germinal epithelial cells in the seminiferous tubule of the testes (Chapter 30). FSH has been highly purified from sheep and hog and shown to be glycoprotein with molecular weights of 67,000 and 29,000, respectively.

(*b*) *Luteinizing Hormone (LH)*. In the female LH is involved in the further development of the egg cell as well as its release by rupturing of the ovarian follicle. The hormone is also responsible for stimulating the development of the *corpus luteum* (Chapter 30) and production by the latter of a hormone, *progesterone* (p. 559). Progesterone and estrogen are the two principal sex hormones in the female responsible for sexual drive and the development of the secondary sexual characteristics (e.g., mammary gland development, rounded contours, and so on).

In the male LH stimulates the formation and secretion of the male sex hormone testosterone by specialized cells in the testes. Testosterone is primarily responsible for the sexual drive and development of the secondary sexual characteristics of the male (e.g., enlargement of the penis, deeper voice, hair on the body, and so on). The luteinizing hormone has been highly purified from sheep and pig and also shown to be a glycoprotein with a molecular weight of 40,000 and 100,000 from these sources, respectively.

(c) *Lactogenic or Luteotrophic Hormone (LTH)*. This hormone, also known as *prolactin*, apparently functions only in the female. It was originally described as the hormone necessary for the initiation of milk secretion in the mammary gland of the mother shortly after giving birth. It is now known that LTH also functions together with estrogen in promoting development of the mammary glands. The hormone also serves together with LH to maintain the *corpus luteum* (and therefore progesterone secretion) which is so vital for the maintenance of pregnancy. Unlike the other two gonadotrophic hormones (FSH and LH), LTH is not a glycoprotein but a simple protein, as obtained from sheep and pig, with a molecular weight of approximately 25,000.

The factors controlling the release of the gonadotrophic hormones seem to be clearest in the case of FSH. Secretion of FSH is inhibited by the sex hormones, indicating a negative feedback control mechanism. There is also evidence of nervous control, presumably by neural secretions from the hypothalamus.

By contrast the secretion of LH (unlike that of FSH) seems to be stimulated by female sex hormones. The factors causing the release of LTH are even more poorly defined. At best there is suggestive evidence that it is regulated by special secretions from the hypothalamus which exerts an *inhibitory* effect in contrast to the general stimulating effect noted for other adenohypophysical hormones.

The mechanism of the "biological clock" by which the secretion of the gonadotrophic hormones is initiated at the age of 10 or 11 or so (in humans), thus inducing the maturation of the sex organs, is not known.

5. *Intermedin or Melanocyte-Stimulating Hormones (MSH)*. Two distinct hormones known as the melanocyte-stimulating hormones (MSH) have been purified from several vertebrates. They stimulate the distribution and concentration of the *melanin* pigment granules in the epidermal cells of the skin. Both hormones are polypeptides containing 15 and 18 amino-acid residues, respectively. In frogs and tadpoles MSH accounts principally for the generalized blackening of the skin. Removal of the pituitary in these animals results in a concentration of the pigment near the center of the cells thus lending a lighter or silvery color effect to the skin. Whether or not MSH plays a role in pigmentation in humans is not known. Other types of pigments in addition to melanin are also affected (e.g., the pigments responsible for the bright colors of bird feathers). It should be noted that additional factors including nerve effects, sex hormones, thyroxine, and certain other anterior pituitary hormones exercise an influence on pigmentation.

The central role of the anterior pituitary gland in controlling several endocrine glands and other body tissues is summarized in Figure 23-10.

Neurohypophysis (or Posterior Pituitary Gland)

The neurohypophysis of man, by its release of at least two known and distinct hormones called *vasopressin* (or the antidiuretic hormone) and *oxytocin*, exerts certain important physiological actions which are described below.

Of great interest is the realization that oxytocin and vasopressin are not actually synthesized in the neurohypophysis. Instead they are manufactured in the neurons of the hypothalamus region of the brain and migrate through the axons to the neurohypophysis where they are stored. It is generally believed that nerve impulses control the synthesis of these hormones in the hypothalamus as well as their release from the neurohypophysis.

HORMONES OF THE NEUROHYPOPHYSIS (OR POSTERIOR PITUITARY LOBE). The recent Nobel Prize-winning work of Du Vigneaud and his collaborators at the Cornell Medical School on

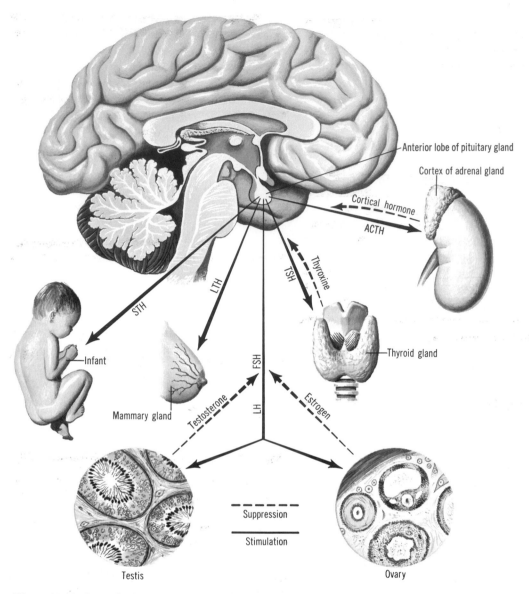

Figure 23-10. Central role of the adenohypophysis or anterior pituitary gland. See text for details.

the separation, chemical identification, and synthesis of the hormones of the neurohypophysis has made it possible to study the physiological action of each substance. *Oxytocin* is composed of 8 amino-acid residues, of which 5 form a ring structure (Figure 23-11).

Vasopressin is nearly the same as oxytocin but has a phenylalanine amino-acid residue in place of isoleucine at position 1 and an argi-

nine amino-acid residue in place of leucine at position 2 in Figure 23-11.

The neurohypophysis of most mammals including man secretes only oxytocin and vasopressin. That of birds, reptiles, amphibians, and bony fishes also secretes oxytocin; but instead of vasopressin it secretes a second hormone more like oxytocin called *vasotocin.* The latter has an arginine amino acid residue at position 2 in place of leucine. In all a total of four different specific hormones, which includes oxytocin and vasopressin, have been extracted from the neurohypophysis of a large variety of vertebrate pituitary glands and shown to have a marked chemical similarity. Each is composed of 8 amino acid residues of which 5 form a ring structure as shown for oxytocin. The substitution by certain amino acids in place of isoleucine and leucine in positions 1 and 2 represents the only differences that account for the other three natural hormones in this group. The physiological functions of the neurohypophyseal hormones in mammals are as follows.

(1) *Oxytocin* has a unique and striking effect in causing a powerful contraction of the uterus. This is probably indicative of its general function in promoting the contraction of smooth musculature of the body. The smooth musculature of the urinary bladder and intestines, for example, is also affected but the greatest response is elicited in the uterine muscle especially during the latter stages of pregnancy. The hormone is frequently administered by injection during and after birth to stimulate contraction of the uterus and constriction of blood vessels, thus facilitating the birth process and impeding the loss of blood.

The normal ejection of milk from the mammary gland of the lactating female is initiated by the mechanical stimulation applied to the nipple by the sucking infant. The mechanism for this action resides in the effect of oxytocin in stimulating smooth muscle contraction. The sucking of the nipple gives rise to nerve impulses which are transmitted to the hypothalamus causing oxytocin release from the pituitary. Milk *ejection* is therefore a response to the release of oxytocin from the neurohypophysis, and is different from milk *secretion* which is a response to the lactogenic hormone secreted by the adenohypophysis.

(2) *Vasopressin* is also referred to as the *antidiuretic hormone* because of its striking influence in decreasing the loss or excretion of water from the body by way of the urine.

$$S \qquad\qquad S$$
Cys·Tyr·Ileu·Glu(NH$_2$)·Asp(NH$_2$)·Cys·Pro·Leu·Gly(NH$_2$)

Figure 23-11. Oxytocin.

Apparently changes in the osmotic concentration of the blood and body fluids stimulate particularly sensitive neurons in the hypothalamus resulting in the release of the hormone from the neurohypophysis. An undersecretion of vasopressin results in the disease *Diabetes insipidus* (Chapter 28), which is characterized by the daily excretion of huge volumes of urine. It is usually accompanied by lesions in the pituitary gland or hypothalamus and can be controlled by injections of vasopressin.

A secondary function of vasopressin resides in its ability to cause constriction of the musculature of the arterioles and capillaries, including the coronary and pulmonary vessels, thus causing some rise in blood pressure.

THE FEMALE AND MALE SEX HORMONES

General Features

The specialized organs which eventually produce the *reproductive cells* (or *germ* cells) are termed the *gonads*. In higher animals the male gonad produces the sperm cells and is called the *testis*. The female gonad which produces the egg cells or ova is called the *ovary*. The mature gonads of both sexes have a dual role. Not only are they the centers for production of the germ cells but they also act in an endocrine capacity. They serve as the primary sources of the sex hormones which control the maturation and function of the reproductive system and certain other tissues of the body.

In essence the sex hormones in at least two important ways make possible the successful completion of fertilization. First, they regulate the mature development of the ducts and auxiliary glands which will assure the proper passage of the sex cells. Second, they stimulate the development of the so-called secondary sexual characteristics which are associated with "maleness" and "femaleness" and contribute to the behavorial responses (e.g., sexual desire) in both sexes, bringing them together in sexual reproduction. The gonads and their hormonal secretions are not necessary for the life of the organism although they are obviously essential for continuation of the species.

From what has already been said about the gonadotrophic hormones it is apparent that the maturation, maintenance, and functioning of the gonads (for the formation of reproductive cells and secretion of the sex hormones) are almost exclusively under the control of the anterior pituitary gland. The complex relationships of the gonadotrophic hormones of the pituitary and their periodic interactions with the gonads constitute an intricate control mechanism. The latter accounts for the reproductive cycles in the female characterized by regular changes in the female genital tract as well as behavorial responses (collectively called the *estrus* cycle in most mammals and the *menstrual cycle* in man and other primates (Chapter 30)).

Female Sex Hormones

The principal function of the female sex hormones is the maintenance of the reproductive tract for (a) the normal passage of the egg cell and its fertilization, and (b) the subsequent embryonic formation and development of the fertilized egg into a new individual. The ovary secretes two types of female sex hormones called *estrogen* and *progesterone* which are steroids.

ESTROGEN. Estrogen is a collective name for four different but closely related steroid hormones secreted by the maturing ovarian follicle (Chapter 30). Not all four hormones are necessarily secreted by any given animal species, the quantity and kinds of estrogen depending on the source. The most common ovarian estrogen of many mammals is considered to be estradiol-17β whose structure is shown in Figure 23-12. Starting shortly before puberty and continuing throughout the sexually mature life of the female the secretion of estrogen from the developing follicle is

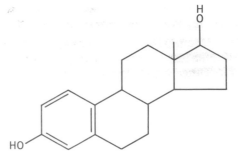

Figure 23-12. Estradiol-17β, a common estrogen of many mammals.

periodically stimulated by the follicle-stimulating hormone of the pituitary gland. Estrogen is responsible for the mature growth, development, and maintenance of the female reproductive tract, the secondary sex organs (breasts, vagina, uterus), and other secondary sexual characteristics (the rounded feminine contours of the body, deposition of body fat, typical pelvic enlargement, appearance of pubic hair, and so on). It very likely also contributes to the sexual desire of the female. Estrogen promotes repair of the uterine lining following menstruation (Chapter 30) in preparation for possible implantation of a fertilized egg. Although the hormone helps control the development and functioning of the mammary gland, it appears to inhibit lactation by inhibiting the formation or secretion of the lactogenic hormone by the pituitary gland. Estrogen tends in general to decrease secretion of the gonadotrophic hormones of the pituitary.

The biochemical basis for the numerous functions of estrogen is still not known. Several mechanisms including the involvement of the hormone as an electron or hydrogen carrier between DPN and TPN have been suggested. None, however, have been conclusively established.

Another important source of estrogen in humans and many other mammals, second to the developing follicle of the ovary, is the *placenta* (Chapter 31), a structure which develops in pregnant females from both the embryo and maternal tissues. Estrogen is also

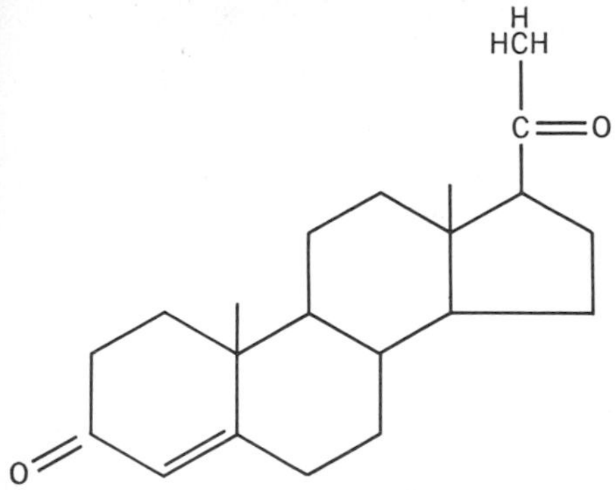

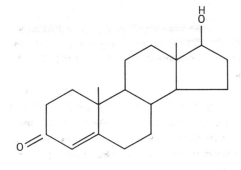

Figure 23-13. Progesterone, an important ovarian female sex hormone.

Figure 23-14. Testosterone, the principal male sex hormone of most mammals, including man.

present in the adrenal cortex. The hormone has been found to occur much more widely in nature than heretofore believed. Not only has it been isolated from various invertebrates but also from plants. Some 30 families of higher plants have been shown to contain one or more forms of estrogen. Whether they perform a significant role in plants or are simply nonfunctional by-products of steroid metabolism is not known.

PROGESTERONE. Progesterone (Figure 23-13), the second principal ovarian female sex hormone, is also a steroid somewhat related in chemical structure to estrogen. It is secreted during the latter half of the menstrual cycle in human females chiefly by the temporary endocrine tissue, the *corpus luteum* (Chapter 30), which rapidly develops in the ruptured follicle shortly after the release of the egg cell.

Progesterone further promotes the development of the uterine lining, already initiated by estrogen during the first half of the menstrual cycle, in preparation for implantation of the fertilized egg. At this particular phase of the female menstrual cycle it takes over the general functions of estrogen (when the latter is being secreted at a minimum level) in maintaining the mature female reproductive tract and the secondary sexual characteristics. Thus, together with estrogen, progesterone is responsible for the sequence of changes of the repeating menstrual cycle that occur in the female reproductive tract starting at puberty and extending through the reproductive life of the female. Like some of the adrenal cortical hormones, progesterone also seems to promote retention of sodium salts and water, presumably by affecting kidney function.

Progesterone is also found in the mammalian placenta, the adrenal cortex, and the testes of some mammals (e.g., the pig). The occurrence of the hormone in the adrenal cortex and testes is probably due to its role as an intermediate in the synthesis of other steroid hormones.

RELAXIN. There is evidence for a second hormone produced by the mammalian corpus luteum called *relaxin* which is a polypeptide instead of a steroid. It specifically causes relaxation of the pubic ligament and possibly contributes to mammary gland development and inhibition of uterine muscle contraction. It could prove to have a significant role in determining the time of birth.

Male Sex Hormones

The male sex hormones are usually referred to as *androgens*. The steroid *testosterone* (Figure 23-14) is the principal male sex hormone secreted by the testes of most mammals including man. More specifically it is secreted by modified connective tissue cells called *interstitial cells* located between the seminiferous tubules (Chapter 30). A second less predominant male sex hormone is also secreted by the testes of most mammalian species, although in some species (e.g., the rat) it is the major type. The male sex hormones have not only been obtained from the testes but from the adrenal cortex, the placenta, and the ovaries as well.

The male sex hormones are responsible for the mature development and maintenance of the various ducts and accessory glands of the male reproductive tract as well as the secondary male sexual characteristics including sexual desire. Starting at puberty the male sex hormones promote the mature development of the penis, appearance of hair on the face and other parts of the body, a more prominent larynx and accompanying deeper voice, greater muscular development and strength, and sexual desire. *Testes removal* or *castration* in the human male prior to the onset of puberty results in the failure of the secondary sexual characteristics to appear. After puberty, castration causes an attentuation of the sexual characteristics.

A biological antagonism exists between the male and female sex hormones since they have opposite physiological actions on many structures. For example, the resultant development in experimental female animals of male secondary sexual characteristics following the administration of male sex hormones can be inhibited by the simultaneous administration of female sex hormones.

The negative feedback mechanism of control which operates between the pituitary and the gonads is evident from the observation that the secretion of LH (and FSH) is diminished in response to the level of male sex hormone in the blood.

OTHER HORMONES

Gastrointestinal Hormones. The hormones concerned with the integration of the digestive process are discussed in the next chapter on the digestive system.

Hormonal Secretion of the Pineal Apparatus. The so-called *pineal apparatus* is a small body lying deep in the brain which may serve in an endocrine function. Several different hormonal secretions have been ascribed to it but none have as yet been conclusively established.

Insect Metamorphosis Hormones. The principal hormones involved in insect metamorphosis have been discussed in Chapter 19.

SUPPLEMENTARY REFERENCES

Beach, F., *Hormones and Behavior,* Hoeber, New York, 1947.
Csapo, A., "Progesterone," *Scientific American,* April 1958.
Gorbman, A., and H. A. Bern, *A Textbook of Comparative Endocrinology,* Wiley, New York, 1962.
Levine, R., and M. S. Goldstein, "The Action of Insulin," *Scientific American,* May 1958.
Rasmussen, H., "The Parathyroid Hormone," *Scientific American,* April 1961.
Wilkins, L., "The Thyroid Gland," *Scientific American,* March 1960.
Williams, R. H., *Textbook of Endocrinology,* third edition, Saunders, Philadelphia, 1962.
Young, W. C., Editor, *Sex and Internal Secretions,* third edition, Williams and Wilkins, Baltimore, 1961.
Zuckerman, S., "Hormones," *Scientific American,* March 1957.

Chapter 24　　　Digestion

INTRODUCTARY AND COMPARATIVE ASPECTS

Cellular metabolism is the basis for all the activities that characterize living systems. In order for metabolism to take place energy and matter, collectively called food or nutrients (Chapter 9), must ultimately be presented to the organized components of the cell in a suitable state.

Unicellular organisms obtain their nutrients directly from their external aqueous environment. The nutrients already in solution to which the cell is permeable are usually readily taken up. The nutrients that are present as relatively larger and more complex particles may be handled in one or more of several ways depending on the organism. Many bacteria and fungi, and several protozoans often secrete to the external medium certain enzymes which catalyze the breakdown (usually by hydrolysis) of these larger nutrient molecules to smaller molecular products, a process known as *extracellular digestion*. The small molecules may now be readily absorbed by the cell. In other single-celled organisms, including numerous protozoans the main process of digestion occurs within the cell (*intracellular digestion*) and is carried out in food vacuoles within the organism itself. Solid food particles are taken into the cell in various ways (e.g., by being surrounded or engulfed as in *Amoeba*, or passing through the cell membrane as in *Paramecium*)

where they become enclosed in temporary food vacuoles in which enzymatic digestion occurs. Some of the products of digestion are subsequently utilized in various metabolic reactions of the cell.

The sponges as the simplest and the least advanced of the multicellular animals possess no specialized digestive organs. Flagellated collar cells lining the internal chambers of the sponge engulf small particles of food which are subsequently digested within the food vacuoles of these cells in much the same manner as in many protozoans.

In higher multicellular animals a highly specialized and complex system of organs and tissues known as the *digestive system* has evolved. Its principal function is to convert or digest foods or nutrients to a physical and chemical state suitable for proper absorption into the circulatory system for ultimate utilization by the cells of the body. Digestion in the annelids and all higher animals is entirely extracellular. Strictly speaking, however, digestion *within* higher animal cells is not at all unusual. The breakdown of stored food such as glycogen in the liver and fats in adipose tissue for further metabolism or transfer to other cells is essentially a digestive process. Similarly the enzymatic hydrolysis of proteins within cells is also a process of digestion.

The first major advance toward a specialized digestive system is seen in the coelenterates and flatworms (Figure 24-1). Members of both phyla have a central digestive or gastrovascular sac or cavity with only a single opening which serves for ingestion of food material as well as for egestion of undigested remains. Digestion is partially extracellular but largely intracellular. Some of the cells lining the gastrovascular cavity secrete digestive enzymes which hydrolyze the contained food particles to a limited extent. The partially digested particles are subsequently taken into separate cells lining the cavity where digestion is completed within food vacuoles in a fashion similar to that in sponges. The gastrovascular cavity of flatworms as exemplified by *Planaria,* however, is considerably more intricate than that of coelenterates, for it is a branched system of blind pockets which ramifies throughout the body and connects by channels to the mouth.

All other major animal phyla from the annelids upward possess a tubular type of digestive tract that extends from mouth to anal opening essentially similar to that of vertebrates. Such an arrangement permits a one-way passage of food materials and allows for the important possibility of a succession of specialized structural and functional modifications of the digestive tube along its length. Starting with the mouth the digestive system includes all the organs and tissues that are directly or indirectly concerned with one or more of the following: (1) physical and chemical conversion of foods to smaller size particles and molecules, namely *digestion;* (2) *absorption of digested materials* from the alimentary canal into the circulatory system (blood vessels and lymphatics); and (3) *elimination of undigested food residues* by way of the anal opening. The chemical steps of digestion are based entirely on specific enzyme-catalyzed hydrolysis reactions (Chapter 7). Oxidation-reduction reactions are not involved. In the earthworm, for example, the digestive tract consists of a *pharynx, esophagus,* a thin-walled distensible chamber (the *crop*), a thick muscular-walled grinding chamber (the *gizzard*), a *long intestine* where digestion and absorption are completed, and an *anal opening.* During its passage through the digestive tract the food is mixed with the juices from several types of digestive glands. A generally similar digestive tract is found in most other higher multicellular animals, be it insect or man (Figure 24-1). It is noteworthy that all the animal phyla above the evolutionary level of the flatworms possess a true coelom or body cavity between the digestive tract and the body wall (with the exception of the nematodes which have a pseudocoel).

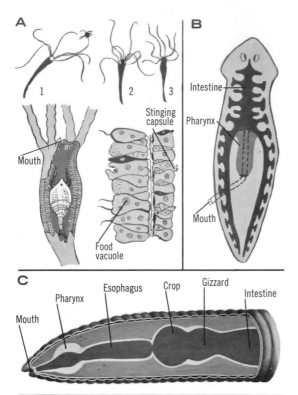

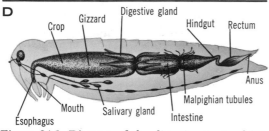

Figure 24-1. Diagram of the digestive tracts of (A) Hydra, (B) Planaria, (C) earthworm, and (D) the grasshopper.

STRUCTURE AND FUNCTION OF THE DIGESTIVE SYSTEM OF MAN

For the sake of description the organization of the alimentary canal in man (and other vertebrates) can be conveniently divided into the (1) mouth, (2) pharynx, (3) esophagus, (4) stomach, (5) small intestine and associated glands (namely pancreas and liver), (6) large intestine, and (7) rectum. The various parts of the digestive system of man are shown in Figure 24-2.

The Mouth

The mouth cavity of nearly all vertebrates including man as the site of entrance of food into the digestive tract is bounded by an upper and lower jaw with external folds of skin constituting the lips. In birds, turtles, and several primitive mammals the lips are replaced by a horny beak or bill. The entire mouth cavity, which like the rest of the digestive tract is lined with an epithelial lining, is bounded on its sides by the cheeks and by the teeth projecting from the jaw bones, on its floor by the tongue, and on its roof by the *hard* and *soft palate*. The hard palate consists of several bones and lies above the soft palate. The soft palate is made up of muscle arranged in the shape of an arch which separates the nasal cavities from the throat or pharynx.

TONGUE. The tongue is covered with an epithelial lining and is made up of several sets of skeletal muscle. The orientation of its muscle fibers in different directions accounts for its ability to move in different planes, an activity controlled by the will. The tongue is richly supplied with sensory nerves serving the many sense organs of taste and touch which are imbedded in its surface (Chapter 23). Its major digestive function in man is in the manipulation of food for chewing by the teeth and for shaping of the chewed food into a spherical mass called the *bolus*. The tongue then pushes it into the pharynx to initiate swallowing. In other vertebrates the tongue may be elongated and greatly extensible thus permitting it to play a role in the actual collection of food as in

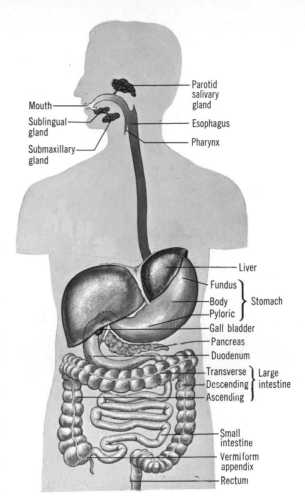

Figure 24-2. The digestive system of man.

the catching of insects by the frog. In man it is also an important aid to speech.

TEETH. All vertebrates with the exception of a small group of primitive forms have teeth, or have arisen from toothed ancestors. The general evolutionary trend has been toward a decrease in the total number of teeth as well as in the number of generations of teeth during the lifetime of the individual. In lower vertebrates such as fishes several scores of teeth are present at any one time and are constantly being replaced as previously formed teeth are lost. By the time man is reached in the evolutionary scale the number of teeth has been reduced to 32 (8 on each half of the upper and lower jaws) with a second or permanent generation of teeth occurring only for the frontally located ones. The original rear teeth (molars) which develop relatively later are never replaced once they are lost. The trend towards a decreased number of teeth reaches its culmination in modern birds and certain reptiles who are totally devoid of teeth.

The evolution of permanent teeth in the higher vertebrates has also been accompanied by a tendency for firmer fastening of the teeth to the jawbones. This has been attained usually by the anchoring of the bases or roots of the teeth within sockets of the jaw bone, a situation characteristic of all mammals and some reptiles.

Despite differences and variations in gross shape all vertebrate teeth with few exceptions have a fundamentally common structure. In some organisms the teeth differ in form and shape in different regions of the mouth. The latter situation is particularly characteristic of mammals (with a few exceptions such as the whale). Chisel-like *incisors* are present at the front of the jaws followed successively by conical, pointed *canines*, and *premolars* and *molars* with grinding surfaces.

In mammals such as man the typical tooth (Figure 24-3) is divided into three regions: the *crown*, which protrudes in the mouth cavity above the gum, the *neck*, which is surrounded by the gum, and the *root*, which is embedded in a socket of the jawbone. The outermost layer of the crown consists of an exceedingly hard surface called *enamel* which is composed largely of crystals of calcium apatite and small quantities of calcium phosphate. The bulk of the tooth lies beneath the enamel and consists of a thick outer layer called *dentine* whose composition is somewhat similar to bone. The dentine surrounds the interior of the tooth called the *pulp* which is made up of connective tissue, blood vessels, and nerves. The tooth is fastened to the jaw bone within the socket by means of a bone-like cement located on the outer surface of the dentine. In man each half of the upper and lower jaw proceeding in order from the front to the rear has two chisel-shaped teeth for cutting food called *incisors*, one pointed conical tooth for tearing food called the *canine*, and two *premolars* and three *molars* with grinding surfaces for crushing and grinding food to make a total of 32 teeth.

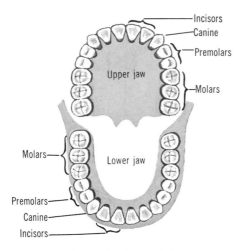

Figure 24-3. The teeth of man. (*Above*) diagram of a longitudinal section through a molar; (*below*) each half of the upper and lower jaws has 8 teeth to make a total of 32 as shown.

The rearmost molar is called a *wisdom tooth* and is usually nonfunctional.

SALIVARY GLANDS. In man *saliva* is largely the collective secretion of three pairs of *salivary glands*, called the *parotid, sublingual,* and *submaxillary* glands, composed of clusters of cells whose ducts open into the mouth cavity. Saliva consists of both thin watery and thicker viscous mucous fluids which serve principally to moisten and lubricate ingested food. In humans and most other mammals it also contains a starch-digesting enzyme called *ptyalin* or *salivary amylase* which catalyzes the hydrolysis of starch to the disaccharide maltose. Interestingly enough salivary amylase is not present in the saliva of the dog, cat, or horse. The parotid glands lie below and in front of the ear and secrete only the thin watery type of saliva. In the virus infection *mumps* these glands become painfully inflamed and swollen. The sublingual glands are located beneath the tongue towards the front of the mouth cavity and secrete only the mucous type of saliva. The submaxillary glands are also situated beneath the tongue but towards the rear of the mouth cavity at the angle of the lower jaw. Their saliva consist of both the thin watery and thick mucous types of saliva. Human saliva, which also contains mucus secreted by small glands scattered diffusely over the surface of the mouth cavity, is slightly acid ranging between pH 6.4 and 6.8. About 1200 to 1500 ml of saliva is secreted by the average adult in 24 hours.

The quantity of starch which is digested to maltose through the action of salivary amylase is not certain. Although the enzyme displays appreciable activity under mildly acid conditions such as those prevailing in the mouth, food ordinarily spends a short time in the mouth before being transferred to the stomach. The strongly acid contents of the stomach (approximately pH 2) would be expected to inactivate quite rapidly the salivary amylase of the saliva-moistened bolus, thus terminating salivary digestion. On the other hand the time required especially in large meals for the penetration of food by the acid juices of the stomach may permit starch digestion by the enzyme to occur for a considerably longer period.

Vertebrates in general display a variety of glands which secrete fluids and occasionally enzymes into the mouth cavity. In some snakes certain glands produce poisons or toxins. The venom from their poison glands is usually not directly poured into the mouth but instead flow through canals or grooves of modified teeth from which they are emitted.

Food taken into the mouth cavity is quickly reduced to a soft mass by the collective action of the lips, jaws, teeth, cheeks, and tongue in preparation for swallowing. During this process of *mastication* the food mass is permeated with saliva. In the act of swallowing, the masticated food is first shaped into a bolus, placed on the tongue, and pushed backward into the pharynx.

The Pharynx or Throat

The region of the alimentary canal in vertebrates between the mouth and the foodpipe or esophagus is called the *pharynx* or *throat*. It is also the crossing-over point between the digestive tract and respiratory tract, serving as the common passage way for the transmission of food from the mouth to the esophagus and air to the larynx. The general structure of the pharynx is described in Chapter 27.

The pharynx plays an important role in swallowing, a phenomenon in which the muscular walls of the pharynx contract, squeezing the bolus and forcing it downward into the esophagus. At the same time other involuntary mechanical movements take place which assure that the food will not move into the nose, larynx, or back again into the mouth: the soft palate is raised thus preventing the food from entering the nose; the larynx is elevated causing the epiglottis to close over the glottis or entrance to the air passageways over which the bolus must pass enroute to the dorsally located esophagus; and the base of the tongue and the muscular walls surrounding the entrance to the pharynx block the movement of the bolus back into the mouth cavity.

The Esophagus

The *esophagus* or *foodpipe* in man is a collapsible muscular tube about 10 inches long extending from the pharynx downward between the lungs, behind the heart and trachea, and through the diaphragm directly to the stomach. Food is carried through the esophagus by a series of rhythmical automatic ring-like contractions of the muscular walls known as *peristalsis* traveling downward and sweeping before it any food contained within the tube. Peristalsis also occurs in the stomach and intestines and is in fact a characteristic action of most hollow muscular tubes of the body.

The site at which the esophagus joins and empties into the stomach is called the *cardiac sphincter.* Ordinarily this region is in a contracted state thus closing off the stomach from the esophagus and preventing regurgitation of the stomach contents into the esophagus. However, as part of the swallowing reflex, which is accompanied by peristaltic waves passing down the esophagus, the cardiac sphincter relaxes, permitting an opening, like a hole in a doughnut, through which the food is swept into the stomach.

The Stomach

The stomach is essentially a more dilated and muscular structure of the alimentary canal which is connected at its upper or proximal end to the esophagus and at the lower or distal end to the small intestine. It functions in the storage of food, the further breaking up of food into smaller particles through its powerful muscular movements, and digestion through the action of the digestive juices which it secretes.

The stomach is situated largely in the upper left side of the abdominal cavity beneath the diaphragm and extends at its lower part toward the mid-region of the abdomen under the liver. It consists of three main regions (see Figure 24-2): the *fundus* which is the upper enlarged dome-shaped portion of the stomach lying in contact with the diaphragm; the *body* or central region; and the *pyloric region* which is the lower constricted horizontal portion connecting to the small intestine. At the junction between the pyloric region of the stomach and the small intestine is a muscular valve of circular smooth muscle, called the *pyloric sphincter.*

The size of the stomach varies according to the size of the individual and the extent to which it has been distended by the presence of food. When filled with food its walls may be considerably distended, accommodating a maximal volume of $2\frac{1}{2}$ to 4 quarts in the average adult male and somewhat less in the female. The relatively large capacity of the stomach accounts for its function as a reservoir. A comparatively large volume of food may be received by the stomach in amounts that can be efficiently and with proper tonicity fed slowly into the intestine. It is mainly responsible for the ability to satisfy our food requirements in two to three meals per day instead of more frequent meals as in the case of an individual whose stomach has been surgically reduced in size or removed. When empty, the stomach has a more tubular shape resembling the letter J and is about the size of a large sausage. Its walls are partially collapsed and its rich inner epithelial lining containing numerous gastric glands takes the form of longitudinal folds.

The muscular walls of the stomach contain smooth muscle fibers arranged longitudinally in an outer layer, circularly in a middle layer, and obliquely in an inner layer. They are collectively responsible for the peristalsis and powerful grinding action of the stomach. The inner surface of the stomach is lined with a mucous lining of columnar epithelial cells in which are scattered an estimated 10 to 35 million tubular gastric glands. The latter pour their secretions, called *gastric juice,* through small ducts into the stomach cavity. The gastric glands of the fundus and body of the mammalian stomach contain three structurally and functionally different types of cells: one cell type produces mucus; another the digestive enzymes found in gastric juice; and the third, remarkably enough, hydrochloric acid. By contrast, in amphibians both the principal digesting enzyme (pepsinogen) and hydrochloric acid are mainly produced by a single cell type (*oxyntic* cell) in the gastric glands. The gastric glands of the pyloric region secrete only mucus, possessing neither the enzyme-producing nor the hydrochloric-acid-producing cells.

GASTRIC JUICE. Gastric juice, as the collective secretions of the gastric glands, is a mixture of several substances. In humans it consists principally of water, the mucoprotein *mucin* which is responsible for the thick viscous nature of mucus, the protein digesting enzyme *pepsin,* and hydrochloric acid. As indicated in a later section the gastric juices of certain animals, but not man, also contain the enzyme *rennin* which acts specifically upon *casein,* the protein in milk.

Mucin. Mucin, secreted in varying quantities forms a coating over the stomach lining and functions in an important protective capacity. Because of its properties of buffering or binding acid as well as inhibiting the enzymatic action of pepsin, it plays an essential role in helping to prevent the digestion of the protein composing the wall of the stomach (and intestines). The fact that mucin is steadily renewed and only slowly digested is added assurance that the digestive enzymes are mechanically separated from the tissues of the digestive tract. Within the gland cells themselves the digestive enzymes produced are as a rule isolated in an inactive form in so-called secretory vacuoles or *zymogen granules* which prevent the mixing of these enzymes with the cell contents. (Figure 24-4)

Pepsin. Several digestive enzymes are produced and secreted by the various glands of the digestive tract in an enzymatically inactive form, and are usually activated upon mixing with the other digestive juices. This is true for *pepsin* which is secreted in an inactive form called *pepsinogen* by special glandular

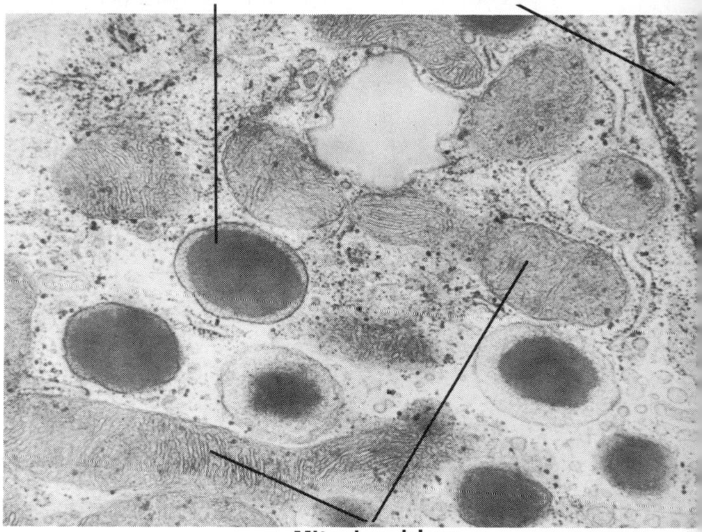

Figure 24-4. Electron micrograph of part of an oxyntic cell from the gastric glands of bullfrog showing zymogen granules (accounting for pepsin activity of the gastric juice), nucleus, and mitochondria. Magnification, 45,750X. (*Courtesy of Dr. A. W. Sedar, J. Biophys. Biochem. Cytol.*)

cells of the stomach. Pepsinogen is activated to pepsin when exposed to the acid medium of the stomach or to some already activated pepsin. In the activation process a polypeptide which apparently is responsible for pepsin inhibition is released from the pepsinogen.

Pepsin catalyzes the hydrolysis of proteins to yield smaller fragments or polypeptides and peptides. Little or no free amino acids are produced by its action. It shows optimal enzymatic activity at about pH 2 which is the pH of the stomach contents as a result of the hydrochloric acid component of the gastric juice.

Hydrochloric Acid. Hydrochloric acid is probably the most unusual component of the gastric juice. It is secreted by specialized glandular cells in a remarkably concentrated form (approximately 0.15M) having a pH of about 1.0 which represents a hydrogen ion concentration a million times greater than that of plasma. The final pH of gastric juice is about 2.0 (one-tenth the hydrogen ion concentration) as a result of dilution. The most important function of the hydrochloric acid in the digestive process appears to be in furnishing suitably acid conditions both for the activation of pepsinogen to pepsin and optimal digestive activity of the latter. The inordinately low pH caused by hydrochloric acid is also responsible for the precipitation of many soluble proteins. As a result the latter remain for a longer time in the stomach and are therefore subjected to a longer period of digestion by pepsin. The strong acidity also functions to kill many microorganisms, thus preventing bacterial invasion and putrefaction of food.

Rennin. Rennin apparently is not present in human gastric juice but occurs in the stomach secretions of several other mammals in the infant stage (e.g., calves). It acts specifically upon casein, the protein of milk, causing it to precipitate and therefore to stay in the stomach longer. Rennin extracted from the *fourth stomach* of calves (see Figure 24-5) has been used for centuries in cheese making. The resulting flocculent precipitate of milk is called the *curd* and the clear fluid the *whey.* Actually rennin acts by splitting the milk protein into two smaller soluble fragments, one of which combines with the calcium that is normally present to form an insoluble calcium protein or curd. The proteins are then acted upon in the stomach by pepsin. In humans, milk protein is coagulated by pepsin which also initiates protein digestion.

STOMACH FUNCTION. Our modern knowledge of stomach function is based on the work of the American Army surgeon William Beaumont. In 1833 Beaumont performed classic studies on the effects of dietary and emotional factors on the secretion of gastric juice in a patient, Alexis St. Martin. The latter had suffered an accidental shotgun discharge that caused a permanent opening leading from the surface of the abdomen to the stomach. It thus afforded a remarkable opportunity at that time to investigate the functioning of the stomach. In the course of his studies with this unusual patient Beaumont demonstrated the acidity and digestive properties of gastric juice. Subsequent experiments over the years by numerous other workers, including Pavlov (Chapter 21), of gastric juice secretion with experimental animals, and with individuals who have swallowed suitably designed rubber tubes for obtaining samples of stomach contents in the absence and presence of food, conclusively established many of the features of gastric secretion.

The quantity and composition of gastric juice formed varies somewhat depending in part on the type and amount of food ingested. In general about two quarts of gastric juice are produced daily on a so-called average diet in the human adults. The peristaltic movements of the stomach, especially in the lower half of the stomach body and pyloric region, break up solid food masses and mix them thoroughly with the gastric juice. Eventually a nearly homogenous semifluid called *chyme* is formed.

The suitable consistency of food is apparently one of the prime factors determining how soon it will leave the stomach. Fluids pass through the stomach quite rapidly, often in 20 minutes or less. Solid foods, which take much longer, must first be converted to chyme, and on the average are completely emptied into the small intestine within 3 or 4 hours. When food has attained a consistency appropriate for discharge

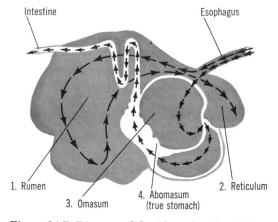

Figure 24-5. Diagram of the "four-chambered stomach" of a cow, showing the route of ingested food. See text for details.

into the small intestine it is progressively evacuated by the stronger descending peristaltic contractions of the pyloric region of the stomach through the pyloric opening into the small intestine.

STOMACHS OF OTHER VERTEBRATES. In general the digestive tracts of vertebrates are more or less alike in their basic organization and function, although variations and adaptations occur. Among certain mammals, as in sheep and cattle, the stomach is commonly made up of several distinct subdivisions each with special functions. Cows, for example, as cud-chewing animals have a "four-chambered stomach" (Figure 24-5). The first three chambers are actually modifications of the esophagus, whereas the fourth is the true stomach. The four chambers, are not connected in series to one another. The *first chamber,* called the *rumen,* stores food as it is eaten. The food is then gradually moved to the *second chamber*

called the *reticulum* where it is further softened by mixing with digestive juices. Small masses of the softened food are then passed directly back as *cud* by way of the esophagus to the mouth where they are thoroughly chewed and mixed with saliva. The cud is swallowed again but now moves from the esophagus directly to the *third chamber* called the *omasum* and from there into the *fourth chamber* or *true stomach.* It is in the fourth stomach called the *abomasum* that characteristic gastric digestion occurs. And it is in the fourth stomach of suckling calves that a rich concentration of rennin is found.

Birds also exhibit special adaptations of the esophagus and stomach. The so-called saccular *crop,* a dilated region at the lower end of the esophagus, is used for food storage. The stomach is also modified into two divisions—an upper glandular region and a lower muscular-walled grinding structure called the *gizzard* (Figure 24-6).

Figure 24-6. Digestive tract of birds.

Small Intestine

The small intestine in the average adult is a tubular organ measuring about 21 feet long and approximately 1 inch in diameter. It is arranged in coils and loops which fill a large part of the abdominal cavity and is attached through most of its length to the dorsal abdominal wall by membranous structures collectively called the *mesentery*. The latter also support the blood vessels, lymphatics, and nerves that service the intestinal walls.

The first 12 inches or so of the small intestine leading from the stomach is called the *duodenum*. The rest is arbitrarily divided into two sections—an upper portion called the *jejunum* extending about 7 or 8 feet, and the lower portion or *ileum* which is about 12 feet long.

The small intestine is well adapted for its important role as the principal organ of the alimentary tract in which digestion and absorption of food occur. Like most of the alimentary canal it is essentially constructed of three layers of tissue—an *inner epithelial layer* or mucosa with an underlying coat of connective tissue in which are embedded the main blood vessels of the digestive tract, a *middle muscular layer* consisting of an inner system of circularly arranged smooth muscle fibers and an outer one of longitudinal fibers (in contrast to the three muscular coats of the stomach), and an *outer connective tissue layer*.

The inner epithelial lining of the small intestine provides an enormous surface for the absorption of nutrients. This is attained not only by virtue of its great length and its folds or convolutions but most important of all because of its innumerable finger-like semimicroscopic projections called *villi*. A huge number of tiny villi are distributed over the entire surface of the small intestine lining, giving it a soft, velvety appearance. Each villus consists of a blood capillary, a small lymph vessel called a *lacteal* (Chapter 25), and an outer covering of a single-cell layer of specialized columnar epithelial cells which are continuous with the intestinal lining and embedded intestinal glands (Figure 24-7).

The villi are in effect highly specialized absorptive organs whose epithelial cells are entirely responsible for the absorption of water and the products of digestion from the small intestine. They exhibit properties of selective absorption, and there is little doubt that their action also includes an *active energy-requiring transport* mechanism (p. 112). It has been estimated that the small intestine of man possesses approximately 5 million villi, making up a surface of about 10 square meters—or more than five times the skin surface. The villi appear to be in ceaseless motion, moving from side to side as well as lengthening and shortening. Presumably these movements mix the intestinal fluids in the immediate neighborhood of the villi, thus helping the processes of digestion and absorption. The large intestine and the stomach are completely devoid of villi. Lying between the villi are microscopic pockets and indentations representing intestinal glands which possess mucous and digestive enzymes collectively called *intestinal juice*.

DIGESTION IN THE SMALL INTESTINE. In addition to the intestinal glands contained within the lining of the small intestine, the pancreas and liver as separate and accessory organs are also important glands which pour their juices by way of ducts directly into the small intestine.

PANCREAS. The pancreas in man is a diffuse, fish-shaped organ ranging from 6 to 9 inches in length, an inch or so in width, and slightly less in thickness. It is situated partially behind the stomach within the curvature of the small intestine (Figure 24-2). It is common to all vertebrates, and functions in two separate and different roles: *(a)* it secretes pancreatic juice for digestive purposes by way of a duct that leads into the small intestine, and *(b)* it serves as an endocrine gland by virtue of specialized scattered clusters of cells *(islets of Langerhans)* which secrete two different hormones into the blood stream, *insulin* and *glucagon* (Chapter 23), essential for normal carbohydrate metabolism.

The cells that produce pancreatic juice compose the bulk of the pancreas and are

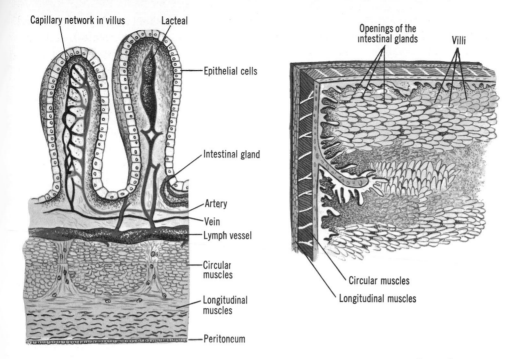

Figure 24-7. Microscopic view of the villi and embedded intestinal glands on the surface of the lining of the small intestine.

drained by a system of microscopic ducts. The tiny ducts unite to form larger tubes eventually joining to the main pancreatic duct which runs the length of the entire gland. In humans the main pancreatic duct enters the wall of the duodenum about 3 to 4 inches below the pyloric sphincter where it joins the *common bile duct* leading from the liver to form a common chamber draining into the intestine (Figure 24-2).

Pancreatic juice contains several important enzymes concerned with the digestion of carbohydrates, fats, and proteins as indicated below. The daily volume secreted by the average adult is about 500 to 800 ml. Pancreatic juice is alkaline (pH 7 to 8) and thus partially neutralizes the acid contents emerging from the stomach, at the same time providing a more suitable pH for the action of its digestive enzymes. The starch-digesting enzyme of the pancreatic juice is called *amylase*. It is similar in enzymatic action and in several of its prop-

erties to salivary amylase, catalyzing the hydrolysis of starch to maltose. Pancreatic amylase is extremely active and is the most important enzyme involved in the digestion of starch in the alimentary canal.

Pancreatic juice also contains the enzyme *lipase* which catalyzes the hydrolysis of (a) neutral fat in part to its di- and monoglycerides as well as to glycerol and fatty acids, and (b) a wide variety of other esters to their acid and alcohol components. It is the principal enzyme responsible for the hydrolysis of fats in the digestive process. Pancreatic lipase is apparently secreted in an inactive precursor form which is then converted by an unknown mechanism in the small intestine to an active fat-digesting enzyme.

The pancreas also secretes several important protein-digesting enzymes in inactive precursor states which are activated in the small intestine. These include the inactive *trypsinogen, chymotrypsinogen,* and *procarboxypeptidase* which are transformed to the corresponding protein-digesting enzymes, *trypsin, chymotrypsin,* and *carboxypeptidase.* Trypsinogen is activated or "unmasked" to trypsin by the enzyme *enterokinase* secreted by intestinal glands in the lining of the small intestine, or by the action of trypsin itself. Activation occurs through an enzymatic process, which involves the liberation of an inhibitory polypeptide, similar to the conversion of pepsinogen to pepsin. Chymotrypsinogen and procarboxypeptidase are rapidly transformed to the active chymotrypsin and carboxypeptidase, respectively, by trypsin. Each of the 3 protein-digesting enzymes catalyzes the hydrolysis of different peptide bonds in proteins, polypeptides, and simpler peptides to yield a mixture of different peptides and amino acids. Additional protein- and peptide-digesting enzymes which hydrolyze other specific types of peptide bonds are also apparently present in pancreatic juice although these have not yet been well characterized.

The pancreatic juice also contains a ribonucleic-acid-digesting enzyme responsible for the hydrolysis of RNA to smaller fragments or mononucleotides.

LIVER. The liver as the largest gland of the body performs a variety of important functions, as indicated previously (Chapter 9). With respect to its digestive function the liver is the site of formation of *bile,* a complex, clear yellow- or orange-colored fluid of slightly alkaline reaction. The chief constituents of bile are water (97 per cent), bile pigments (various breakdown products of hemoglobin after the globin and iron have been removed), bile salts, lecithin, cholesterol, inorganic salts, and mucin.

Bile is continuously produced, largely from blood constituents, by the cells of the liver and is carried by a system of ducts of progressively larger size to the principal duct of the liver known as the *hepatic duct.* The latter merges with the *cystic duct* from the gall bladder to form the *common bile duct* (Figure 24-2), which enters the duodenum via a common opening with the pancreatic duct as described previously. The gall bladder itself is a pear-shaped

muscular sac of approximately 50 ml capacity attached to the undersurface of the liver. Bile passes from the hepatic duct into the common bile duct but is prevented from entering the small intestine by a smooth muscle sphincter valve at the common opening shared with the pancreatic duct. As a result, the continuously secreted bile is forced along the cystic duct into the gall bladder where it is stored until needed. During its period of storage in the gall bladder, the bile is concentrated severalfold by the absorption of water (and salts). In some instances a complex insoluble precipitate appears, resulting in the formation of so-called *gall stones* which usually are composed of 80 per cent or more cholesterol.

In normal adults the daily production of bile probably ranges between 500 and 1000 ml. Bile serves in the excretion of certain waste products and in the process of digestion. In excretion it acts as a vehicle for the removal of excess calcium, certain breakdown products of hemoglobin from wornout red blood cells, and other wastes. It participates in *lipid digestion* (although it contains no known fat-digesting enzymes) and *lipid absorption* by promoting emulsification and solubilization of lipids including the fat-soluble vitamins, and the fatty acids liberated in fat digestion. The fat-emulsifying and -solubilizing action of bile is attributed to the property of its bile salts (chiefly salts of glycocholic and taurocholic acids in humans) in lowering surface tension, thus promoting the division of fatty materials into small globules. As a result the total surface area of fats and oils exposed to the action of pancreatic lipase is increased considerably. In addition, bile aids general digestion in the small intestine by virtue of its alkalinity which helps neutralize the acid chyme arriving from the stomach.

The role of bile salts in aiding in the digestion of fats is secondary to its important function in enhancing the absorption by the villi of fat-digestion products and other lipid-soluble substances, including the fat-soluble vitamins. It has been shown, for example, that despite the exclusion of bile from the intestine the great majority of neutral fats are nevertheless digested to monoglycerides, diglycerides, glycerol, and fatty acids. Under these circumstances, however, a large proportion of the fat-digestion products and other fat-soluble substances are not absorbed but are eliminated instead in the feces. This is particularly evident in the absorption of vitamin K which is necessary to ensure the normal rate of blood clotting (Chapter 25).

The exact mechanism by which bile salts enhance lipid absorption is not clear. They are apparently associated with some lipids during their absorption or passage through the epithelial cell layer of the villi, and are returned by the portal blood to the liver where they are excreted again into the bile. Thus the bile salts are utilized over and over again with a small loss appearing in the feces.

DIGESTIVE GLANDS OF THE SMALL INTESTINE. The numerous digestive glands embedded within the wall of the small intestine (Figure 24-7) consist of several types of secretory cells. Together they secrete a mixture of digestive fluids collectively called *intestinal juice* or *succus entericus*. Intestinal juice is slightly alkaline and contains large quantities of mucus as well as several different enzymes, most of which have not been isolated in pure form or fully characterized. The daily volume of intestinal juice secreted by the average adult is approximately 3000 ml. The role of mucus in lubrication and protection during the digestive process has already been discussed. In addition to the enzyme enterokinase intestinal juice contains a number of peptide-hydrolyzing enzymes called *peptidases* which complete the digestion of the various protein fragments or peptides to amino acids. Several enzymes are also present which account for the final digestion of carbohydrates to the monosaccharide level. These include *maltase* for the hydrolysis of maltose to glucose, *sucrase* for sucrose to glucose and fructose, and *lactase* for the milk sugar lactose to glucose and galactose. In addition a lipase as well as a number of enzymes for the hydrolysis of nucleic acids, nucleotides, and nucleosides occur in the intestinal juice. Recent evidence suggests that these intestinal enzymes may be functioning chiefly in the columnar cells and that activity found in the intestinal juice is of little importance.

The principal enzymes of the digestive tract and their major properties are summarized in Table 24-1.

MUSCULAR ACTIVITY OF THE SMALL INTESTINE. Several types of movement occur in the small intestine as a result of its muscular activity. These include *peristalsis,* a movement essentially like that area described for the esophagus. As they travel downward the muscular contractions propel the chyme along the intestinal tube somewhat like pinching a rubber tube full of a viscous fluid and sliding the fingers along it.

Thorough kneading and mixing of the chyme with the digestive juices in the intestine takes place by so-called *segmental contractions* of the smooth musculature of the intestinal walls. The process is characterized by rings of contraction occurring simultaneously every few inches along successive segments of the intestine. As these original contractions relax, new contractions appear in the formerly uncontracted portion of each segment, a phenomenon occurring several times per minute. Segmental contractions also ensure that the chyme will be brought into contact with the intestinal lining for suitable absorption of the digestion products by the villi. The passage of chyme within the small intestine to the large intestine usually takes about 8 hours.

The Large Intestine

STRUCTURE. The large intestine is essentially an inverted U-shaped tube within the abdominal cavity. It is considerably shorter than the small intestine, having a length of only 5 to 6 feet in the average adult. Its diameter, however, is approximately $2\frac{1}{2}$ inches (but decreases towards the lower end of the tube), noticeably larger than that of the small intestine. The large intestine consists of a vertical *ascending* portion extending upward along the right side of the abdomen, a *transverse* portion which passes horizontally across the upper part of the abdomen below the liver and stomach and above the small intestine, and a *descending* vertical portion extending downward along the left side of the abdomen to the *rectum,* the terminal portion of the digestive tract (Figure 24-2). The small intestine connects with the ascending portion of the large intestine at the lower right side of the abdomen some 2 to 3 inches above the beginning of the colon. This "blind" portion of the large intestine below the T-shaped junction with the small intestine is called the *cecum.* At its very end is a small blind structure called the *veriform appendix.* The opening of the small intestine into the colon is guarded by a ring or sphincter of smooth muscle called the *ileocolic valve.* It controls the passage of chyme into the large intestine, and at the same time prevents the reverse flow of material back into the small intestine. Thus it protects the latter from the rich bacterial population in the large intestine. In man, the cecum and appendix

Table 24-1   Principal Digestive Enzymes in Man

Enzyme	Gland	Optimum pH	Substrate	Product
Salivary amylase	Salivary glands	Slightly acid (pH 6.4–6.8)	Starch	Maltose
Pepsin (secreted as pepsinogen)	Gastric glands	Very acid (pH 2.0)	Proteins	Polypeptides and peptides
Amylase	Pancreas	Slightly alkaline (pH 7–8)	Starch	Maltose
Lipase	"	"	Fats	Glycerol, fatty acids, mono- and diglycerides
Trypsin (secreted as trypsinogen)	"	"	Proteins, poly-peptides, peptides	Peptides and free amino acids
Chymotrypsin (secreted as chymotrypsinogen)	"	"		
Carboxypeptidase (secreted as procarboxypeptidase)	"	"		
Maltase	"	"	Maltose	Glucose
Ribonuclease	"	"	Ribonucleic acid (RNA)	Nucleotides
Enterokinase	Intestinal glands	Slightly alkaline (pH 7.5–8.5)	Trypsinogen	Trypsin
Peptidases	"	"	Peptides	Free amino acids
Maltase	"	"	Maltose	Glucose
Sucrase	"	"	Sucrose	Glucose and fructose
Lactase	"	"	Lactose	Glucose and galactose
Lipase	"	"	Fats	Fatty acids, glycerol, mono- and disaccharides
Nucleases	"	"	Nucleic acids (RNA and DNA)	Nucleotides, nucleosides, and bases

have no important function. In herbivores (animals subsisting solely on a diet of grasses and other plants) such as the horse, cow, and rabbit, the cecum is quite large and is an important site for the digestion of cellulose by the rich and specialized bacterial population which it houses. Painful inflammation of the appendix in man as a result of infection is called *appendicitis* and is usually treated by surgical removal of the appendix.

FUNCTION. The large intestine performs several important functions. One of its most significant roles is in the absorption of water (and salts) from the fluid residual chyme which enters from the small intestine. The water which is absorbed includes not only that originally present in food but the large volume contributed by the secretions of the salivary glands, stomach, pancreas, liver, and intestinal glands as well.

A too rapid passage of chyme through the colon does not permit adequate reabsorption of water and is evinced by the condition of *diarrhea*. It is usually caused by excessive muscular activity of the walls of the large intestine often as a result of a physical irritation, infection, drug action, or emotional upset. If permitted to go unchecked it will lead to dehydration and excessive loss of salts which can prove to be fatal, especially in infants. At the other extreme an unusually slow passage of chyme through the large intestine may be responsible for excessive removal of water resulting in *constipation*, which is characterized by a relatively drier and therefore harder mass of undigested residues. As a result of the highly efficient processes of digestion and absorption that take place largely in the small intestine, little or no *usable* foods, other than water and salts, reach the large intestine.

A second important role of the large intestine is performed by the huge and varied bacterial population that it contains. The ability of many intestinal bacterial strains to synthesize certain vitamins, amino acids, and other growth factors which we absorb in part from the colon helps us to meet some of our nutritional require-ments. As an illustration of the nutritional contribution of intestinal bacteria, one can cite the appearance of incipient symptoms of vitamin deficiencies which arise from the destruction of these bacteria by excessive and prolonged use of antibiotics. Some bacterial strains housed in the large intestine are also responsible for the breakdown of a portion of the small quantities of undigested or partially degraded protein which reach the colon. As a result they liberate such substances as indole, skatole, and hydrogen sulfide which account for the characteristic odor of feces.

The large intestine shows considerably less muscular activity than the small intestine. The regular and frequently occurring segmental contractions and peristalsis seen in the small intestine do not occur in the colon. Instead there may be an occasional muscular movement resembling segmental contraction; but at intervals of several hours there are strong massive peristaltic waves which move the contents of the colon toward the rectum.

The Rectum

The last 6 to 8 inches of the intestinal tract are called the *rectum*. The opening of the rectum to the exterior is called the *anus* and is guarded by two muscular sphincters—an internal one of smooth muscle and an outer one of striated muscle. As the rectum is filled and compacted with feces it distends until it is sufficiently stimulated to give rise to the defecation reflex. Under ordinary circumstances this reflex can be consciously inhibited in individuals other than infants. Defecation consists of a powerful peristaltic contraction of the descending portion of the colon and rectum accompanied by a voluntary contraction of the abdominal muscles and a relaxation of the anal sphincters. The feces which is eliminated consists of a compacted mixture of undigested food residues, remains of the bile pigments, minerals, epithelial cells of the intestinal mucosa, and bacteria. It also contains an appreciable quantity of materials (fats, nitrogenous substances, and minerals) eliminated or excreted from the blood. Bacteria constitute about 10 to as much as 50 per cent of the feces. The indigestible food substance consisting mostly of the cellulose of plant materials is usually called "roughage" and serves to stimulate further the secretory and muscular activity of the intestinal wall.

Absorption of Nutrients from the Digestive Tract

In general the epithelial cells of the intestine are impermeable, or nearly so, to the large molecules of carbohydrates (starch), proteins, fats, and nucleic acids. More recent evidence indicates that disaccharides are absorbed as such. Digestion of these larger molecules produces smaller size products, including simple sugars, glycerin, fatty acids, monoglycerides, diglycerides, amino acids, and nucleosides, which pass much more freely across the intestinal mucosa.

For all practical purposes virtually all absorption in the digestive tract takes place through the villi of the small intestine with the exception of water which is mainly absorbed from the large intestine. Some absorption of water, alcohol, and small quantities of mineral salts also occurs in the stomach. Certain drugs and hormones can be absorbed from the mouth. Very little digestible substances reach the large intestine.

ACTIVE TRANSPORT IN INTESTINAL ABSORPTION. The absorption of small molecules, including the final products of digestion, across the epithelial cells of the villi of the small intestine cannot be explained by diffusion alone. Most of the evidence indicates that the intestinal epithelial cells possess active transport mechanisms (p. 112) capable of transporting substances from the intestine to the blood and lymph of the villi regardless of the concentration gradient.

It should be noted that the absorption process is a highly selective one in the sense that some substances are absorbed more rapidly than others, whereas other molecules despite their small size are hardly absorbed at all. For example, magnesium sulfate (Epsom salts), whose molecules are considerably smaller than those of simple sugars and most amino acids, is for all practical purposes not absorbed from the digestive tract. This is one of the reasons for its effectiveness as a laxative or cathartic.

ABSORPTION OF ORGANIC NUTRIENTS. Considerable absorption of the simple sugars and dissacharides apparently takes place by the active transport mechanism. The result is an efficient transfer of these sugars via the epithelial cells of the villi to the blood of the capillaries.

The form and manner in which the digestion product of fats are absorbed from the small intestine are not entirely clear. It is evident, however, that these products enter the lymph vessels or so-called *lacteals* of the villi rather than the capillaries. They appear in the lymph as regenerated triglycerides or fats and ultimately enter the blood stream via the large lymph vessels which empty into the subclavian veins (Chapter 26). The name *lacteal* refers to the milky appearance which the lymph vessels assume during absorption, caused by the suspension of fat droplets in the lymph. There are strong indications that incompletely digested fats such as mono- and diglycerides may also be absorbed without undergoing further breakdown. It now appears that shorter chain fatty acids (containing less than 10 carbon atoms), and possibly glycerin which is water soluble, are chiefly absorbed by the capillaries rather than the lacteals of the villi. As in sugar absorption, the absorption of the products of fat digestion also depends on the metabolism of the intestinal epithelial cells, and therefore probably involves active transport mechanisms. The role of the bile salts in the absorption of fat-digestion products as well as other lipid-soluble substances has already been discussed.

Amino acids as the major end products of protein digestion are rapidly and almost exclusively absorbed in the small intestine, entering the blood stream directly by way of the blood capillaries of the villi. Different amino acids are known to be absorbed at different rates, but the exact mechanisms by which amino-acid absorption takes place are not known. Appreciable amounts of peptides and, under special circumstances, proteins (e.g., milk proteins and egg white, particularly in infants) may also pass through the epithelial cells of the small intestine and appear in the blood.

Digestion of nucleic acids occurs mainly in the duodenum. The nucleotides liberated from nucleic acids by the action of ribonucleases and deoxyribonucleases are further enzymatically hydrolyzed to nucleosides and inorganic phosphate. The nucleosides are probably absorbed as such from the small intestine, although little is known about the process.

ABSORPTION OF METAL IONS. The absorption of certain metal ions, especially those of calcium, magnesium, and iron, present special problems. Many calcium salts are insoluble, especially at the alkaline pH of the small intestine, and only soluble ionic calcium is known to pass through the intestinal epithelial cells. Lactose and vitamin D enhance the absorption of calcium salts (and magnesium salts) although the mechanisms by which they act are not clear. Iron, like calcium, forms several insoluble salts, and only a small fraction of the ingested iron is absorbed from the intestine. For reasons which are not clear, iron in the ferrous state is more readily absorbed than is the ferric form.

Integration and Control of Digestive Juice Flow

At least two types of mechanisms, *neural* and *hormonal*, are responsible for the integration and control of digestive juice secretion. The extent to which each participates varies with the particular gland.

CONTROL OF SALIVA SECRETION. The secretion of saliva is entirely under the control of the visceral nervous system and is regulated by nerve impulses arising from both simple and conditioned reflexes. No hormonal factors appear to be involved. Simple reflexes caused by mechanical factors, such as the presence of materials in the mouth whether they are foods or inert foreign bodies (e.g., pebbles), stimulate the flow of saliva. Conditioned reflexes induced by the thought, sight, taste, or smell of food are also responsible for the copious production and secretion of saliva.

CONTROL OF GASTRIC JUICE SECRETION. The secretion of gastric juice is under the control of both neural and hormonal factors. Nerve impulses arriving via the visceral nervous system usually initiate the flow of gastric juice in the stomach. The presence of material in the mouth is apparently responsible for the simple reflexes resulting in gastric secretion. The thought of food and the sensations of sight, taste, and smell also stimulate the flow of gastric secretions. The arrival of food in the stomach causes a further increase in the secretion of gastric juice, largely as a result of the action of a hormone called *gastrin* produced by the pyloric region of the stomach. Gastrin, like any other hormone, is released and circulated in the blood stream. Upon reaching the stomach it induces copious secretion of gastric juice by the gastric glands. The chemical identity of gastrin has not yet been definitely established. It is thought that mechanical distention of the stomach and the presence of polypeptides released in the partial digestion of proteins by pepsin further enhance the flow of gastrin.

The entry of lipids into the duodenum apparently causes the liberation by the intestinal wall of a hormone called *enterogastrone* which *inhibits* rather than stimulates gastric juice secretion. Enterogastrone activity has been obtained in extracts of intestinal epithelial cells, but the responsible substance has not yet been chemically characterized. Here is an example of a hormone whose action is inhibitory rather than stimulatory.

CONTROL OF PANCREATIC JUICE SECRETION. The secretion of pancreatic juice is regulated by both hormonal and neural mechanisms. The entrance of acid chyme from the stomach into the duodenum causes the release of a polypeptide hormone called *secretin* from cells of the duodenal wall into the blood circulation. The arrival of secretin at the pancreas by way of the blood stream stimulates the secretion of copious volumes of pancreatic juice rich in bicarbonate. The pancreatic juice, however, is low in digestive enzyme activity. Secretin is also effective, but to a lesser extent, in stimulating the flow of bile from the gall bladder and intestinal juice from the glands in the walls of the small intestine.

A second intestinal hormone called *pancreozymin,* unlike secretin, stimulates the secretion of pancreatic juice rich in digestive enzyme activity, although the volume of pancreatic juice is not strikingly increased. A similar effect is also attained by a neural mechanism initiated by stimulation of nerve endings in the stomach.

CONTROL OF BILE SECRETION. The entry from the stomach of fatty foods into the upper segment of the small intestine promotes the

Table 24-2 Summary of Neural and Hormonal Factors Affecting the Flow of Digestive Juices

Digestive juice	Factors affecting secretion	Principal site of formation	Principal site of action	Principal phenomena effected
Saliva	Simple reflex (mechanical factors in mouth)	. . .	Salivary glands	Secretion of saliva
	Conditioned reflex (thought, sight, taste, and smell)	. . .		
Gastric juice	Simple reflex (mechanical factors)	. . .	Gastric glands	Secretion of gastric juice
	Conditioned reflex (thought, sight, taste, and smell)	. . .		
	Polypeptides	From partially digested proteins in pyloric region of stomach	"	" " " "
	Gastrin	Pyloric region of stomach	"	" " " "
	Enterogastrone (stimulated by presence of lipids)	Duodenum	"	Inhibition of gastric juice secretion
Pancreatic juice	Reflex (probably simple reflex)	. . .	Pancreas	Secretion of pancreatic juice rich in digestive enzymes
	Pancreozymin	Duodenum	"	Secretion of pancreatic juice rich in digestive enzymes
	Secretin	"	"	Secretion of large volume of pancreatic juice low in digestive enzymes
Bile	Reflex (probably simple reflex)	. . .	Gall-bladder	Contraction and emptying
	Cholecystokinin	Duodenum	"	" " "
Intestinal juice	Role of nervous system as yet unknown			
	Enterocrinin	Duodenum	Intestinal glands	Secretion of intestinal juice
	Duocrinin	"		" " " "

release into the blood stream of an intestinal hormone called *cholecystokinin*. The latter causes the gall bladder to contract discharging its contents into the cystic and common bile ducts. At the same time, the sphincter muscle at the common opening of the bile duct and pancreatic ducts into the duodenum relaxes to permit free passage into the duodenum. Emptying of the gall bladder seems to be in part also under the control of the nervous system, probably the result of a simple reflex.

CONTROL OF INTESTINAL JUICE SECRETION.
The mechanism for the control of intestinal juice secretion is not clear. Somehow the presence of chyme in the small intestine stimulates the flow of intestinal juice. There is some evidence for the participation of two specific hormones called *enterocrinin* and *duocrinin* secreted by the intestinal lining into the blood stream for enhancing the secretion of intestinal juice. The neural and hormonal factors affecting digestive juice flow are summarized in Table 24-2.

SUPPLEMENTARY REFERENCES

Beaumont, W., *Experiments and Observations on the Gastric Juice and the Physiology of Digestion*, Harvard University Press, Cambridge, Mass., 1929.
Best, C. H., and N. B. Taylor, *The Physiological Basis of Medical Practise*, Williams and Wilkins, Baltimore, 1945.
Carlson, A. J., and V. Johnson, *The Machinery of the Body*, fifth edition, University of Chicago Press, Chicago, 1962.
Scheer, B. T., *Comparative Physiology*, Wiley, New York, 1948.

Chapter 25

Circulation:

Composition and Function of Blood

GENERAL FEATURES OF CIRCULATION
Environmental and Evolutionary Aspects

Most single-celled organisms obtain food and oxygen for their metabolic needs directly and continuously from their aqueous environment. The resulting waste products of metabolism, including carbon dioxide, are in turn transferred out of the cells directly to the external surroundings. Renewal of the external environment in the immediate vicinity of cells continually occurs by diffusion, and is aided considerably by currents arising from temperature differences and organism movement. Thus unicellular organisms are assured of a constant supply of nutrients and adequate removal of metabolic waste products.

In some of the lower multicellular animals such as sponges and coelenterates the exchange of nutrients and waste substances between organism and the external aqueous medium is virtually as free as in unicellular animals. The water in which these animals live is usually propelled through definite body channels by ciliary motion or by muscular movements. In this manner the aqueous external environment circulates through the organisms, bringing food and oxygen to the many cells and removing carbon dioxide and other excretion products.

Somewhat higher in the evolutionary scheme of things we find a number of animal forms, such as flatworms (*Platyhelminthes*), pos-

sessing a body fluid called *hemolymph*, which flows irregularly back and forth through the spaces between the loosely packed cells as a result of the muscular movements of the organism. In effect the flatworms, like the sponges and coelenterates (as well as the nematodes), have no special circulatory system. The loose arrangement and thin layering of their cells are such that diffusion is adequate for the exchange of nutrients and waste products.

All other major animal phyla (annelids, molluscs, arthropods, echinoderms, and chordates) possess vascular circulatory systems which tend to be progressively more complex and specialized as one advances in the evolutionary scale. For example, present in many molluscs, and in most arthropods, such as the lobster, is a muscular organ, the heart, which pumps the hemolymph through arteries directly to tissue spaces in each organ of the body, thus providing nutrients and removing metabolic waste products. In the lobster, the hemolymph, before finally returning to the heart, flows first through the gills, withdrawing oxygen from the water and releasing carbon dioxide. This type of vascular organization is classified as an *open circulatory system* since the vessels are not completely continuous, and the blood passes out of the vessels into the tissue spaces through part of its circuit (Figure 25-1).

In some worms and in all vertebrates including man, the circulatory system consists of predominantly closed tubes in which the blood pumped by the heart flows from arteries to veins by way of the *capillaries*, the microscopic blood vessels composed of a single layer of cells. It is during the passage of blood within the capillaries that the interchange of nutrients and waste products between the blood and the tissue fluids occurs, resulting in definite changes in the composition of the blood stream. The arteries and veins essentially serve to convey the blood to and from the capillaries. This kind of system which does not permit whole blood to come in direct contact with the cells (although some blood components pass out of the vessels) is therefore classified as a *closed circulatory system*. It is regarded as the most advanced evolutionary type, having a greater efficiency with respect to rate of blood flow, maintenance of blood pressure, and economy of blood volume. The heart, as part of the circulatory system, is responsible for propelling the blood to all parts of the body at adequate speeds and pressure.

An additional network of vessels exists for many of the higher animals equipped with the closed type of circulatory system. This is the *lymphatic system* which transports *lymph*, the fluid existing in the internal spaces among cells and tissues, ultimately returning it to the blood stream. Thus man as well as most other vertebrates possesses two kinds of circulatory fluids, blood and lymph, both fluids which have evolved from the hemolymph of the more primitive open circulatory system. In some organisms (e.g. the frog) a separate heart exists for the lymphatic system.

A few biologists still regard blood and lymph as a tiny portion of the sea which became enclosed and modified within the bodies of the more advanced multicellular animals during the course of evolutionary development. The 0.9 per cent salt concentration of the blood is considerably less than the present-day 3 per cent salt concentration of the oceans. A few believe that when the first ancient terrestrial mammals appeared the salt concentration of the seas must have been significantly less than 3 per cent and, therefore, somewhat closer to that of the blood. However, the facts are that blood does not represent the sea trapped within us. Blood evolved independently and differently in several groups and happens to be similar in only *some* respects to sea water.

Role of Blood

Blood has the following important functions. (1) It supplies the various cells and tissues with nutrients and oxygen for growth, repair, and other life activities. (2) It transports the waste products of cellular metabolism, including carbon dioxide, to the excretory organs where they are eliminated. (3) Its white blood cells, antibodies, and other protective substances are an important defense against disease and injury. (4) It helps regulate and equalize body temperature by evenly and rapidly

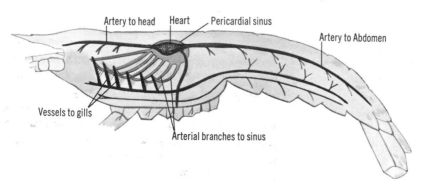

Figure 25-1. Diagram of the open circulatory system of the lobster.

distributing the heat that is stored to a large extent in the body fluids. (5) It bathes the various body cells and tissues in fluid, thus regulating the water, acid, base, and salt contents of all tissues including itself, at the same time exercising a significant effect on osmotic concentrations throughout the body. (6) It transports the secretions of the endocrine glands, the hormones (Chapter 23), which are so necessary for the regulation and coordination of the activities of the various cells and tissues. (7) It maintains its own integrity and composition, halting its own escape by the complex blood-clotting mechanism.

In short, the broad overall role of the blood in addition to serving as a transporting agent is to maintain the stability of the general internal environment of the body. In so doing, this important fluid remains remarkably constant in its physical and chemical properties, fluctuating only within a narrow margin in its chemical composition.

DETAILED COMPOSITION AND FUNCTIONS OF BLOOD

Whole Blood

Blood is a highly complex, seemingly homogeneous fluid composed of a large variety of dissolved and suspended inorganic and organic substances as well as three kinds of free cells—the *red blood cells* (erythrocytes), the *white blood cells* (leucocytes), and the *blood platelets*. The presence of these cells accounts for the designation of blood as a tissue. In higher animals such as man, blood constitutes about 8 per cent of the body weight. An individual weighing 165 pounds has about 6 quarts of blood. Well-oxygenated blood, such as usually occurs in the arteries, is scarlet. Less-oxygenated blood is dark red, almost black, or, as seen in the veins, has a blue color. Blood is opaque, is five to six times more viscous than water, and has a specific gravity that ranges from 1.05 to 1.06 with a pH of 7.39.

When blood is transferred from a person's vein to a test tube and clotting is prevented by

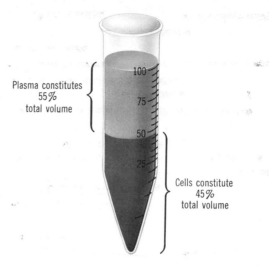

Figure 25-2. Volume relationship of plasma and formed elements in human blood.

adding certain chemicals called anticoagulants, it separates into two layers within a short time. This separation is easily and rapidly effected by centrifuging for a few minutes. The resulting upper layer, which is yellow and generally transparent or slightly opalescent, contains colloidal proteins, as well as many organic and inorganic substances in solution, and is called *plasma*. It constitutes 55 per cent by volume of the blood (Figure 25-2). The lower layer consists predominantly of erythrocytes with relatively small numbers of leucocytes and blood platelets. They are collectively called the *formed elements* and make up the remaining 45 per cent of the blood. The formed elements have a specific gravity of 1.09 as compared to 1.03 for that of the plasma, thus accounting for their separation by gravitation or centrifugation.

Plasma

WATER AND PROTEINS. Water constitutes 90 per cent by weight of the plasma. The second principal constituent is represented by the various proteins which collectively make up 7 to 8 per cent of the plasma. The plasma proteins are usually classified into four general subdivisions: *serum albumins* (4.2 per cent), *serum globulins* (2.6 per cent), *fibrinogen* (0.3 per cent), and the remainder constituting 1 per cent or less of the plasma. The serum globulins have been separated into various fractions designated as *alpha, beta,* and *gamma* globulins. Some are antibodies (p. 597) and therefore confer immunity against certain diseases. A practical application of this knowledge has been the use of the *gamma-globulin* fraction to prevent or to attenuate the effects of certain diseases such as measles.

Actually more than 70 different proteins have already been shown to be present in the plasma including lipoproteins, glyco- and mucoproteins, metalloproteins, approximately 20 different enzymes, several proteins involved in clotting, and antibodies. Recent evidence indicates that a number of the plasma proteins act as vehicles or carriers for many substances of relatively small molecular size transported by the blood. For example, inorganic iron has been shown to be bound to a special protein in the plasma; and it is this protein that provides the means of transporting the iron in the body to its various destinations. Similarly specific plasma proteins serve as carriers for numerous other substances including fats and sugars.

The plasma proteins perform a number of key functions. In addition to conferring immunity and serving as vehicles for relatively smaller molecules transported by the blood, they are principally responsible for maintaining the osmotic concentration of the blood since they normally do not pass out of the blood stream into surrounding cells and tissues. In this manner the plasma proteins contribute to the maintenance of blood pressure and to the water balance between the plasma and tissue fluids.

The plasma proteins are apparently in a state of dynamic equilibrium in the sense that they are being continuously formed and broken down. In addition, striking increases of certain enzymes in the plasma occur as a result of certain abnormal conditions in other cells and tissues. Within a few hours following a heart attack (Chapter 26), there is a marked increase within the blood plasma of the enzymes transaminase and lactic dehydrogenase arising from the affected heart muscle. These phenomena are now used as valuable clinical tools in the diagnosis of this condition.

SALTS. The total inorganic salt concentration of the plasma is 0.9 per cent with a preponderance of chloride, sodium, and calcium ions and lesser quantities of potassium and magnesium ions. Together these five ions help maintain an ionic equilibrium which is essential to the proper functioning of cells. Smaller concentrations of bicarbonate, sulfate, and phosphate are also present as well as trace amounts of iron, copper, and iodide ions.

GLUCOSE AND OTHER SIMPLE SUGARS. The concentration of glucose in the plasma normally averages about 0.1 per cent, ranging from about 0.08 to 0.14 per cent. Glucose is absorbed by the capillaries in the intestine, stored principally as animal starch (glycogen) in the liver and skeletal muscle, and is carried to all parts of the body by the blood to be used as a principal energy source in cellular metabolism. Certain nerve cells in the brain are particularly sensitive when the glucose level of the blood falls to 0.04 per cent or less, resulting in involuntary muscle contractions, convulsions, and eventually death. Small concentrations of certain other simple sugars are also present in the blood.

OTHER PLASMA CONSTITUENTS. The remaining 2 to 3 per cent of the plasma is made up of a variety of substances including amino acids, vitamins, fatty substances or lipids (such as neutral fats and cholesterol), hormones, urea, uric acid, and other metabolic waste products. In addition plasma contains dissolved oxygen, carbon dioxide, and nitrogen gas, and undoubtedly numerous unidentified substances.

Formed Elements

THE RED BLOOD CELL. The red blood cell or *erythrocyte* is by far the most prevalent of the formed elements. Its average concentration is approximately 5,400,000 cells per cubic millimeter of blood in the adult male compared to

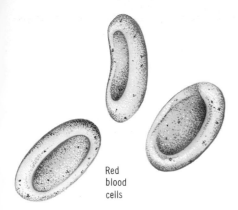

Figure 25-3. The red blood cell of man.

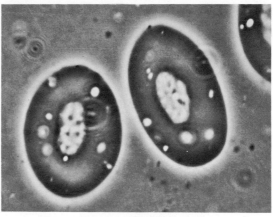

Figure 25-4. Frog erythrocytes as seen with the phase-contrast microscope. Note the biconvex elliptical shape and the centrally located nucleus. Magnification, 3000X. (*Courtesy of Dr. H. G. Davies, J. Biophys. Biochem. Cytol.*)

about 4,800,000 per cubic millimeter in the human adult female. The primary role of erythrocytes is to carry molecular oxygen to all cells and tissues of the body. Additional functions of red blood cells include regulation of the acid-base balance of the blood (and, therefore, indirectly of the other body cells), and transport of some carbon dioxide. In addition the breakdown products of hemoglobin contribute to the formation of the bile pigments.

Structure and Composition. Under the microscope the mature mammalian red cell is seen to be a biconcave disc, reddish yellow in color, and possessing no nucleus. The erythrocyte in man has an average diameter of 7 to 8 microns, and a thickness ranging from 1μ at its thinnest central portion to a maximum of 2μ near its edge, resembling a doughnut with its hole in the center covered by a membrane (Figure 25-3). It moves with the flow of the blood stream, being immobile in the sense that it cannot propel itself under its own power. In contrast to mammalian erythrocytes, those of the other vertebrates including fishes, amphibians, reptiles, and birds possess a nucleus and usually are larger, biconvex, and elliptical. (Figure 25-4)

The human red erythrocyte has a highly oriented structure of lipids, proteins, and hemoglobin consisting of approximately 64 per cent water, 28 per cent hemoglobin (approximately 100 million hemoglobin molecules), 7 per cent lipids or fatty materials, and the remaining 3 per cent sugars, salts, enzymes, and other proteins. Hemoglobin is easily removed when the cell is broken or "lysed" by exposure to a hypotonic medium such as water or to certain chemicals. The resulting structure is called a *"ghost"* or *stroma*, and consists of an interlacing network of proteins and lipids with the same shape as the intact cell. The flexible stroma is responsible for retaining the erythrocytic form, allowing the cell to bend and twist (and return to its original shape) during its passage through capillaries smaller than itself. Despite the absence of a nucleus, the mature erythrocyte is a living cell with an active metabolism of its own.

Nature and Function of Hemoglobin. Erythrocytes contain the reddish oxygen-transporting pigment *hemoglobin* which is responsible for the red color of blood. Hemoglobin has the remarkable property of attaching dissolved molecular oxygen to itself and giving it up again when the concentration or pressure of oxygen in the surroundings is low. This and related aspects are discussed more fully in Chapter 27 on the respiratory system. In this manner it picks up oxygen in the lungs and transports it via the blood stream to all the organs of the body where it releases the oxygen to the cells. Under normal circumstances the red blood cells never leave the blood stream or circulatory system, even in the course of picking up oxygen in the lungs and releasing it to the cells and tissues of the body. Hemoglobin enables our blood to carry approximately sixty times the amount of oxygen that an equal volume of water or plasma could transport in solution. Without the evolutionary acquisition of hemoglobin, all other factors being equal, we would have needed sixty times (360 quarts) our normal volume of blood to carry the same quantities of oxygen.

The mammalian red cell has a high concentration of hemoglobin near its surface thus facilitating a rapid entry or departure of oxygen. Calculations show that if erythrocytes were spherical instead of disc-like, approximately nine times as many would be needed to distribute oxygen to the cells at the same rate. If hemoglobin were simply dissolved or suspended in the plasma, as it is in some invertebrates, the marked increase in blood viscosity would make it much more difficult for the heart to pump blood. In higher animals, including man, hemoglobin functions as an oxygen-transporting pigment only when it is contained within the red blood cells. If hemoglobin is released into the plasma by disruption of erythrocytes it is rapidly broken down by certain cells and tissues of the body. Some of its degradation products are eventually excreted by the kidney and others secreted as a component of liver bile.

Hemoglobin is actually a combination of an iron-containing *protoporphyrin* compound, *heme* (Chapter 7), and a specific protein, *globin*. In hemoglobin the iron is present in a chemically reduced state as the ferrous ion (Fe^{2+}). Hemoglobin belongs to a family of molecules that include *myoglobin*, found in muscle; certain metabolic enzymes and enzyme components known as *cytochromes*, present in nearly all living organisms; the red pigment *leghemoglobin*, found in the nitrogen-fixing root nodules of legumes; and *chlorophyll*, the green photosynthetic pigment of plants (Chapter 7).

The hemoglobin molecule itself has a molecular weight of about 67,000 and actually comprises four hemes attached to the specific protein globin. Since each of the four hemes contains an iron atom that serves as the point of loose physical attachment for a single molecule of oxygen, a mammalian hemoglobin molecule can carry a maximum of four molecules of molecular oxygen. When hemoglobin (abbreviated as Hb) transports oxygen, it is called oxyhemoglobin (Hb · O_2). It has long been known that carbon monoxide, the deadly gas present in automobile exhaust fumes and illuminating gas, binds strongly to the iron of hemoglobin. Carbon monoxide has a much greater affinity for hemoglobin iron than does oxygen and, consequently, can displace molecular oxygen from oxyhemoglobin. The presence of 0.5 per cent carbon monoxide in the air will render more than half the bloodstream's hemoglobin useless in its oxygen-carrying role for at least several hours following exposure.

Hemoglobin also functions as a carrier of a small quantity of carbon dioxide, conveying it as a waste product from the tissues to the lungs for excretion. The carbon dioxide is not transported by the hemoglobin's iron, but instead is carried in part in combination with the protein portion of the hemoglobin molecule. The conditions affecting the transport and exchange of oxygen and carbon dioxide are discussed more fully in Chapter 27.

Life History of the Red Blood Cell. The average life of a red blood cell is about 120 days. Erythrocytes under normal conditions are being continuously destroyed and new ones produced at the same rate of about 140 million per minute. During embryo development the formation of the red blood cells takes place principally in the liver and spleen. In man, after birth, it is formed exclusively in the red bone marrow located near the ends of the long bones and in the flat bones such as the ribs and breastbone. Prior to entering the blood stream erythrocytes appear as undifferentiated

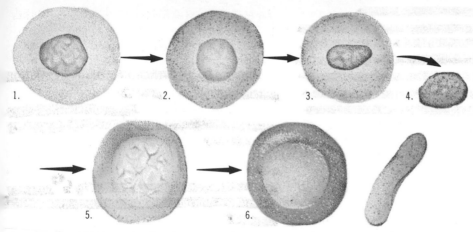

Figure 25-5. Stages in the development and maturation of the red blood cell of man illustrating the disappearance of the nucleus and formation of hemoglobin.

cells, each with a nucleus but without hemoglobin. As these cells mature they undergo a series of changes (Figure 25-5) which include disappearance of the nucleus (probably by extrusion or dissolution) and hemoglobin formation. The red blood cells, upon reaching maturity, escape into the blood stream from the special connective tissue network of red bone marrow in which they develop.

The concentration or partial pressure (Chapter 27) of molecular oxygen in the external environment markedly influences erythrocyte formation. The lower the partial pressure of oxygen, the greater the number of red blood cells in the blood stream and the greater the production of hemoglobin. The red blood cell count is observed to rise within a few days at high altitudes, such as the top of a mountain, with as much as a 20 to 50 per cent increase occurring after two weeks at 15,000 feet. The rise in erythrocyte concentration is due to a lowered oxygen tension and not to an overall decrease in general pressure as demonstrated by experiments in a pressure chamber where lowering the partial pressure of oxygen but maintaining the overall pressure will cause the same effect. On the other hand the increased number of red blood cells in the blood stream resulting from rapid ascent in an airplane (i.e.,

rapid decrease in total pressure) is due to the release of erythrocytes stored in the spleen.

Destruction of old red blood cells and those damaged by toxins and infections occurs chiefly in the spleen and the liver. A portion of the hemoglobin is ultimately converted into bile pigments. Most of the iron is retained and apparently returned to the bone marrow to be again incorporated into new red blood cells.

Blood Pigments in the Animal Kingdom. Of the several different kinds of respiratory pigments found in the animal kingdom, hemoglobin is the most common blood pigment. It occurs in all vertebrates, largely in the erythrocytes rather than in the free state in the blood but is less widely distributed among the invertebrates. It is present in the tissues of some species throughout most levels of the animal kingdom down to some of the one-cell organisms, such as the *Paramecium*, where it has been reported to be present in the cytoplasm. The fact that only one or two of the hundreds of thousands of insect species possess hemoglobin (similarly, only a few of the hundred thousand or so species of molluscs contain the pigment) has provoked speculation regarding its evolutionary significance.

Actually there are a large number of different kinds of hemoglobin, differing from species to species. In all types of hemoglobin, however, the heme components are similar whereas the protein portions are different. The heme itself is present in most, if not all, living organisms as part of the structure of some of the respiratory enzymes. Myoglobin as a specialized form of hemoglobin is found in both skeletal and heart muscle of the more highly evolved animals but only in the heart muscle (as well as in erythrocytes) of the more primitive vertebrates. In higher animals, including man, myoglobin functions by holding oxygen in reserve, releasing it to the muscle tissues according to their metabolic needs. Meat is red because of the red blood cells in its capillaries as well as the myoglobin in the muscle fibers.

Some biologists regard the first appearance of hemoglobin in primitive living cells during the early history of the earth as the result of a chance combination of heme with a suitable protein, globin. Hemoglobin at first may have had no function in the anaerobic environment that existed during the early stages of the earth's history (Chapter 3). But later its useful property as an oxygen carrier or an oxygen store must have assured its preservation through natural selection.

There are no colorless oxygen-carrying proteins. Several different kinds of respiratory pigments are found in the blood of various invertebrates. Green-colored blood occurs in certain annelid worms living in the sea and is due to the presence of a respiratory pigment called *chlorocruorin* (molecular weight 3,400,000). It is very closely related to hemoglobin, consisting of a specific protein united to a slightly different heme. The blue color of blood in lobsters, crabs, octopuses, and snails is due to a respiratory nonporphyrin-containing protein, *hemocyanin* (molecular weight 6,700,000), with copper as a component of its molecule. A respiratory blood pigment called *hemerythrin*, a pink, nonporphyrin, iron-containing protein ranging in molecular weight from 17,000 to 70,000 is found in a few marine invertebrates. In some invertebrates there is no

oxygen-carrying pigment in the blood; oxygen is transported in simple solution in the blood in quantities sufficient to meet the metabolic needs of the various body cells.

Abnormal Blood Conditions Involving Hemoglobin. The term *anemia* is used to describe any condition in which the red blood cell count or the amount of hemoglobin per cell is less than normal. Extensive loss of blood as a result of injury results in anemia. Since nearly all the iron in the blood is found in red blood cells as part of the hemoglobin structure, a dietary deficiency of iron can also cause a characteristic anemia. Moreover, hemoglobin formation and erythrocyte development are adversely affected by other nutritional deficiencies, including that of certain vitamins such as folic acid, ascorbic acid, niacin, and riboflavin. Of particular interest are the following two specific anemias.

Pernicious Anemia. The severe blood disease, *pernicious anemia*, characterized by a lowered red blood cell count and the presence of immature and fragile erythrocytes, is accompanied by serious changes in the digestive and nervous systems. The disease is due to inadequate absorption from the digestive tract of vitamin B_{12}. The relationship of pernicious anemia to a liver-rich diet, vitamin B_{12}, and *intrinsic factors* has already been discussed in Chapter 9.

Sickle-Cell Anemia. The erythrocytes of some humans possess an abnormal form of hemoglobin called *hemoglobin S*, which is produced under the influence of a particular pair of abnormal genes. Erythrocytes containing hemoglobin S are normal in appearance as long as they have an ample supply of oxygen. However, when they lose oxygen during the capillary transfer of the gas to the tissues, the red blood cells become crescent or sickle-shaped. The sickled cells clog the blood vessels and are subsequently destroyed, resulting in a serious condition known as *sickle-cell anemia.*

Both genes for this abnormal trait must be present (i.e., the homozygous condition) for sickle-cell anemia symptoms to appear. An individual having only one gene for hemoglobin S and another for normal hemoglobin (i.e., the heterozygous condition) carries a sickling tendency without showing symptoms of the disease. He may become ill only under unusual conditions, such as at high altitudes.

It has recently been demonstrated that the only chemical difference between normal hemoglobin and hemoglobin S is the replacement of a single amino acid in a total of the nearly 300 amino acids constituting part of the hemoglobin molecule. In hemoglobin S the amino acid *valine* has taken the place of another amino acid, *glutamic acid*, at a specific site in the protein structure, leaving the rest of the hemoglobin molecule unchanged. The action of the sickle-cell genes in altering the synthesis of the protein moiety of hemoglobin, by specifically substituting a single amino acid for another, results in such a radically modified hemoglobin as to produce the severe sickle-cell disease.

The high incidence of the sickle-cell gene among populations living in climates where malaria is quite common (the central belt near the equator on the African continent, Greece, Turkey, southern Italy) suggests that the gene might have survival value from the evolutionary viewpoint. In some of these areas the single gene for this trait is present in as much as 40 per cent of the population. We now know that children who are heterozygous with respect to the sickle-cell gene are relatively more resistant to malaria at a time in their lives when they are most susceptible to the ravages of this disease. If they survive they build up immunity to the disease. Why the sickle-cell trait should impart greater resistance to malaria, a disease, incidentally, in which the parasite is found in the red blood cells, is not well understood.

Several other abnormal forms of hemoglobin due to the action of certain other genes have also been characterized.

THE WHITE BLOOD CELLS. White blood cells or *leucocytes* are metabolically among the most active of the formed elements. They are devoid of hemoglobin, colorless, contain a nucleus, and the majority are larger than erythrocytes, measuring from 8 to 15 μ in diameter depending on the type. When observed in the living state under the microscope, white blood cells are in continuous motion. They are irregularly shaped, extremely active, and move under their own power against the flow of the blood stream by amoeboid motion, extending pseudopods into which the rest of the cell flows. Unlike erythrocytes, leucocytes pass out of the blood stream into the intracellular spaces by squeezing between neighboring cells of the capillary walls.

Both mature erythrocytes and leucocytes are incapable of reproduction in the blood stream. The concentration of white blood cells ranges from 5 to 10 thousand per cubic mm of blood in the adult, being outnumbered about 700 to 1 by the red blood cell population. Considerable fluctuations may occur in the white blood cell count during the course of a single day, due in part to violent exercise, extreme emotional states, and other factors. The count is usually about two times as high in infants, and throughout childhood is consistently higher than in the adult.

Classification of Leucocytes. White blood cells are generally classified on the basis of structural differences into two broad groups: (*a*) those leucocytes with a single nucleus and a clear cytoplasm and (*b*) those having a lobed or incompletely partitioned nucleus, and a cytoplasm containing fine granules which adsorb certain dyes or stains. These two main classes are further divided into subclasses depending on other structural and staining properties.

The first group (*a*) is made up of two types of cells, the *lymphocytes* and *monocytes*, both arising from the lymphatic tissue. The lymphocytes range in diameter from 8 to approximately 12 μ, and constitute about 25 per cent of the total number of leucocytes in blood. The monocytes represent 5 to 7 per cent of the white blood cells, range in size from 10 to 15 μ in diameter, and are quite mobile (Figure 25-6).

White blood cells of the second group (b) have their origin in the red bone marrow, contain cytoplasmic granules, and display a nucleus with 2 or more lobes. They are divided into three types according to the staining reactions of their cytoplasmic granules (Figure 25-6). One type, the *neutrophils*, represents the majority of the white blood cells, constituting 65 to 70 per cent or more of the total number of leucocytes. Their name is derived from the intense stain that neutral dyes confer on the cytoplasmic granules. Neutrophils are approximately 10 to 12 μ in diameter, and are the most active of all the white blood cells in terms of motility and ingestion of foreign particles. A second type, the *eosinophils*, is stained by the acid dye, eosin, and constitutes 2 to 4 per cent of the total white count. The third type, the *basophils*, is stained by basic dyes and constitutes about 0.15 per cent of the total white cells.

Ordinarily leucocytes do not survive more than a few hours after removal from the body. This is in contrast to their normal lifetime of three to four days in the blood stream. Recent investigations have shown, however, that if placed in a properly controlled laboratory environment in a quiescent state, white blood cells can survive for weeks.

Role of the White Blood Cells. The primary function of the white blood cells is to protect the body against invading microorganisms. The ability of leucocytes to destroy microorganisms depends in part on their motility and their capacity to ingest foreign particles. In these respects neutrophils as well as monocytes are the most active. By forming pseudopods or streaming extensions of protoplasm, they engulf and destroy foreign particles, including bacteria. This ingestion process is called *phagocytosis* (Figure 25-7) and was first described in 1883 by the Russian zoologist Metchnikoff.

In a region of the body where bacteria have entered—for example, at a wound—the capillaries dilate in response to the invading microorganisms thus bringing more blood to the area. The result is a reddish appearance of the tissue commonly called an *inflammation* (it may also be induced by a chemical or physical irritant). The consequent slowing of the blood stream in an inflamed area is accompanied by the exudation from the distended blood vessels of plasma, white blood cells, and occasionally erythrocytes. The white blood cells are somehow attracted to the source of irritation, especially during bacterial invasion, and accordingly migrate to the site. A dense aggregation of neutrophils collects and prevents the infection from spreading by surrounding the threatened area and engulfing the invaders. The germs are ingested alive in much the same manner that an amoeba engulfs food particles. At times as many as 10 or more bacteria may be seen within a single leucocyte. Those microorganisms that are not effectively phagocytized may give rise to an infection or disease and are called *pathogenic* agents.

Once ingested by a white blood cell the

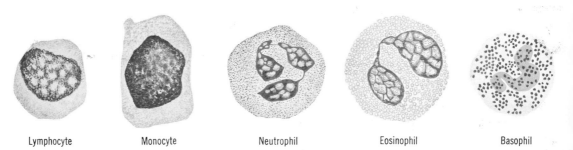

| Lymphocyte | Monocyte | Neutrophil | Eosinophil | Basophil |

Figure 25-6. The five different types of leucocytes in man.

microorganism is usually destroyed, probably through the action of hydrolyzing or digesting enzymes. Certain pathogenic bacteria, however, may be phagocytized but not destroyed. Instead they continue to live and even multiply within the leucocyte, which may now serve as a means of dissemination of the pathogenic agent.

In the course of their struggle against the invading microorganism, numerous white blood cells are killed. They may accumulate in the infected area together with exuded plasma, destroyed tissue cells, and some escaped erythrocytes, which are collectively called *pus.*

Lymphocytes appear to be quite effective against specific disease-causing bacteria. Of great importance is the indication that the lymphocytes are responsible at least in part for the manufacture of both the beta- and gamma-globins of the plasma, and therefore for the immunity substances (antibodies) described in a later section of this chapter. Lymphocytes have also been involved in scar-tissue formation, contributing to the scar or becoming part of regenerated connective tissue.

The eosinophils and the basophils are not very mobile and show only a slight tendency to engulf foreign particles. Their role is not well established. They apparently have some relationship to disease resistance since their concentrations in the blood stream are specifically increased during certain infections. This phenomenon has proven to be a useful clinical tool in facilitating the diagnosis of certain diseases. For example, the concentration of eosinophils is significantly increased during infection by trichinosis or hookworm, as well as in allergic states such as asthma.

Leukemia is a cancer or malignancy of the white blood cells. It is characterized by an uncontrolled and frequently immense increase in the concentration of leukocytes (up to one million per cubic mm) with the appearance of immature forms in the blood stream. This condition, which is eventually fatal, is accompanied by anemia because the bone marrow cells that normally produce erythrocytes are

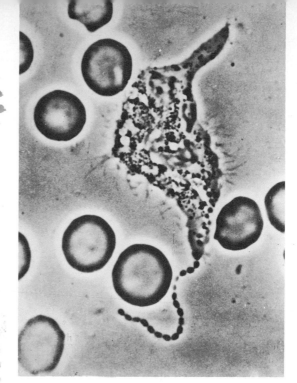

Figure 25-7. A leucocyte from human blood ingesting a chain of streptococcus bacteria (*courtesy of Charles Pfizer and Co.*).

displaced by leukemia cells.

BLOOD PLATELETS. The blood platelets are small, oval fragments of specialized bone marrow cells, measuring from 2 to 4 μ in diameter and generally lacking nuclei (Figure 25-8). They average about 250,000 per cubic mm of blood and play a central role in initiating the early steps in the formation of a blood clot, as described later. Their metabolic activity has recently been found to be equal to, if not greater than, that of the white blood cells. They are extremely fragile, and apparently experience a life span of approximately 10 days.

The Mechanism of Blood Clotting. The formation of a blood clot or *thrombus* essentially involves the conversion of the specific plasma protein, *fibrinogen,* from the sol state to the gel *fibrin.* Fibrin forms as a network of microscopic interlacing fibers that enmesh the formed elements contributing to the solidity of the clot. The clot is initially a gelatinous

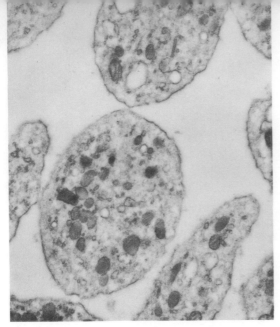

Figure 25-8. Electron micrograph of platelets from human blood. Magnification, 25,000X. (*Courtesy of Dr. N. F. Rodman, Jr., J. Cell Biol.*)

mass which in time shrinks and hardens, squeezing out a straw-colored fluid, the *serum*. Serum is almost identical to plasma except that it lacks fibrinogen.

Contrary to popular belief, blood does not necessarily undergo clotting upon exposure to air. The mechanism of blood clotting is initated by injury of tissue, such as the cutting of a blood vessel, and involves a sequence of steps, with each step dependent on the one before it.

What triggers the final step in which fibrinogen is directly transformed to the gel state, fibrin, to form the clot itself? The answer is that a specific enzyme, *thrombin* (or *thrombase*), acts on fibrinogen, catalyzing its conversion to the gel state. Thrombin is ordinarily present in the blood in an inactive state known as *prothrombin* or *prothrombase*. Prothrombin formation occurs in the liver and shows a definite requirement for vitamin K. How is prothrombin in the blood converted to the active form thrombin? Two factors are necessary, namely calcium ions, which are normally present in the blood, and *thromboplastin*, a lipoprotein. Thromboplastin is usually not

found as such in the blood stream but instead exists in an inactive precursor form as one of the normal globulin components of plasma called *thromboplastinogen*. It is converted in the presence of certain necessary plasma globulin components known as *antihemophilic factors* to the active state, thromboplastin, by the liberation from injured tissues and disrupted blood platelets of an enzyme, *thromboplastinogenase*. Therefore, the liberation of thromboplastinogenase from the platelets, and to a lesser extent from damaged cells or tissues, initiates a chain of reactions that finally form the blood clot. The clot remains as a scab until the damage is repaired and then sloughs off.

In summary, the enzyme *thromboplastinogenase* (liberated from injured tissues and disrupted blood platelets) and the *antihemophilic factors* are responsible for the conversion of *thromboplastinogen* to *thromboplastin*. The latter in conjunction with *calcium ions* activates prothrombin to the enzyme *thrombin*, which in turn catalyzes the conversion of *fibrinogen* to *fibrin*, thus forming the clot (Figure 25-9).

A good deal of progress has been made in the study of the blood-clotting mechanism, but several aspects are still not well understood.

Prevention of Clotting. The normal clotting of blood has the obvious function of preventing loss of life by preventing the loss of this important fluid from the body. Oddly enough the abnormal clotting of blood within the blood vessels has proved to be one of the major causes of death and disablement in our society. When an artery becomes obstructed by a clot the supply of oxygen and nutrients to the dependent tissues is cut off, resulting in a chain of events that may bring quick death. While a vein clot is less dangerous, it can have very serious consequences by causing waste products to accumulate in the surrounding tissues of the affected areas. It may also travel to the lungs via the heart and prove to be fatal by eventually blocking off a vital artery.

More deaths occur in the United States from

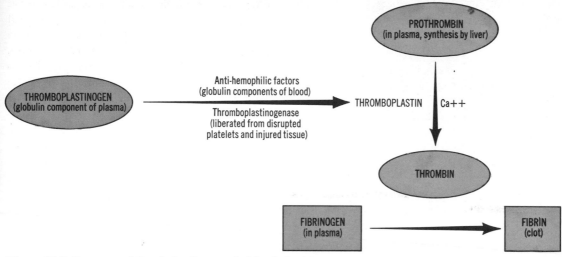

Figure 25-9. Summary of the chain of events in blood clotting.

the pathological formation of clots in blood vessels than from any other single disorder. Blood clots that obstruct the arteries nourishing the heart are chiefly responsible for death by heart attack (*coronary thrombosis*, Chapter 26). Blockage of blood vessels in the brain and lungs by blood clots also claims a large number of lives annually. Nearly half the annual deaths in the United States are of cardiovascular origin, among which obstructions by blood clots (called *embolisms*) are undoubtedly in the majority.

The medical experiences of World War II taught us that getting wounded men and surgical cases out of bed early during convalescence significantly hastened recovery. Patients who walked within a few hours after surgery gained strength more quickly, returned to their normal status sooner, and had fewer complications, including a reduced risk of blood clots. Injury and bed rest result in a decreased rate of circulation in various parts of the body, leading to a settling out of blood cells and a tendency to form clots, thus increasing the risk of embolism.

Since each step in the chain of events leading to blood coagulation depends on the reaction before it, clotting can be prevented by blocking any one of the steps involved. The substances that inhibit or prevent coagulation are called *anticoagulants* and can be made to serve some very useful purposes. In the laboratory one simple means of preventing clotting is to remove calcium ions from the blood, thus blocking the conversion of prothrombin to thrombin. This can be accomplished by the addition of certain organic compounds (e.g., citric acid) which combine with the calcium ions in the drawn blood.

During the last 20 years, the use of certain anticoagulants has provided a practical means of controlling abnormal clotting and thus saving lives. The following are among the more important anticoagulants.

Dicumarol. One of the most effective anticoagulants in current use is the compound *dicumarol.* The direct chain of events leading to its discovery started in 1934. At that time a distraught farmer brought to the biochemistry department of the University of Wisconsin two buckets of blood from one of his many cows dying of an unidentified hemorrhagic disease. Previous studies of the frequent outbreaks of hemorrhages in cattle over large areas of northwestern United States and Canada had traced the cause to the continuous ingestion of spoiled sweet clover in hay. The hemorrhaging was attributed to a suppression of prothrombin formation in the liver. Dr. K. P. Link, a biochemist, and his collaborators at the University of Wisconsin undertook to study the problem in 1934 at the time of the farmer's dramatic visit to the campus. By 1940 they had isolated, identified, and synthesized the substance in spoiled sweet clover responsible for hemorrhaging. Since it belonged to a family of organic compounds called *coumarins* which are present in all leguminous plants including sweet clover, they named the compound dicumarol.

When taken by mouth, dicumarol requires 24 hours to act, causing a pronounced reduction of the clotting ability of the blood. Continued dosage induces bleeding from slight scratches, with further doses producing spontaneous hemorrhaging. When taken in proper amounts, however, it results in lowered coagulability. Dicumarol prevents or inhibits the synthesis of prothrombin in the liver.

The fat-soluble vitamin, K is specifically required for prothrombin formation by the liver. Internal hemorrhages occur as a result of dietary insufficiency or inadequate absorption of vitamin K from the digestive tract. Dicumarol, by the virtue of its chemical structure and its inhibition of prothrombin synthesis (which can be counteracted by the administration of vitamin K) is implicated as an antivitamin or antimetabolite (p. 163) of the vitamin. Dicumarol supposedly acts by competing with vitamin K at certain presumed enzymatic steps in liver cells where the vitamin participates in the biosynthesis of prothrombin. Dicumarol cannot dissolve a clot or thrombus once it has formed. Instead it serves to prevent further growth of the clot since a blood clot is in a dynamic state tending to be built up and broken down simultaneously. For this reason it has proven to be a valuable aid for victims of heart attack.

Warfarin. Other compounds have been synthesized similar to dicumarol including a substance called *warfarin*, which has proved to be one of the most effective rat killers known. Warfarin has been responsible for the eradi-

cation of rat populations in such places as docks and granaries, heretofore invulnerable to all other rat poisons. Estimates place the number of rats in the United States at approximately 180 million, about the same as the human population. The destruction of food and other property by rats as well as their role in spreading diseases such as bubonic plague, typhus, infectious jaundice, and food poisoning make them an inordinately serious menace.

Rats become very easily bait-shy. When they ingest any poison and survive, they never eat it again. Rat colonies also have official tasters, and, if they become ill, the others avoid the contaminating food. They are unable, however, to cope with warfarin. Small doses taken with bait such as corn during a period of about 5 days kill them by internal hemorrhage slowly and gently as if going to sleep. Rats watching other rats die continue to eat the bait until they are themselves dead a few days later. The mechanism of action of warfarin as a rat killer is essentially the same as that of dicumarol, namely the inhibition of prothrombin formation in the liver by competition with vitamin K.

Heparin. Another anticoagulant is the complex, naturally occurring carbohydrate derivative known as *heparin,* which can be extracted from liver and certain other tissues. Its powerful anticoagulating action, in the animal (or in blood contained in a test tube), is immediate, unlike dicumarol which takes a few days to exercise its effect within the animal. Under normal circumstances there is little or no heparin in blood, although it appears in appreciable quantities during certain types of shock. The purified substance is used during blood transfusions and after operations to prevent the formation of clots. While there is no common agreement as to which step in the blood-clotting sequence of reactions is affected by heparin, its action has been ascribed by several researchers to an inhibition of the conversion of prothrombin to thrombin.

Hirudin. This anticoagulant is secreted by certain glands of blood feeders such as leeches, bedbugs, and fleas. It apparently acts as a typical antithrombin agent by interfering with the formation or activity of thrombin.

Hemophilia. Hemophilia is a hereditary disease (Chapter 13), caused by a sex-linked recessive gene (i.e., present on the X chromosome) and manifests itself to a larger extent in males than females. It is characterized by an extremely slow rate of clotting, sometimes taking several hours, and results in severe bleeding or hemorrhages from the smallest scratches or wounds. In females homozygous for the hemophilic gene, the disease can prove to be fatal at the time of menstrual flow. The occurrence of hemophilia in a number of the royal families of Europe, including the Romanoffs and the Bourbons, has been traced back to Queen Victoria of England as the primary source of the gene among royalty. Actually the disease is not restricted to royalty but is found among various other classes as well. Recent evidence indicates that the homophilic gene in some manner prevents the formation of one of the antihemophilic globulins which together with thromboplastinogenase are necessary for the conversion of thromboplastinogen to thromboplastin. Hemorrhages in hemophilic patients can be controlled by injection of this protein, by transfusion with normal blood, or by administration of thrombin or thromboplastin.

Menstrual Bleeding. Menstrual blood (Chapter 30) generally does not coagulate since it contains little or no thrombin or fibrinogen. It probably represents blood that has already formed clots and whose fibrin has subsequently been dissolved by certain proteolytic enzymes in the womb lining (or endometrium).

THE ROLE OF BLOOD AND RELATED TISSUES IN IMMUNITY, ALLERGY, AND DEFENSE AGAINST DISEASE

Defenses of the Body

The higher multicellular animal body employs several means of defense against harmful agents in its environment. The physical barriers of the body as the first line of defense

Portion of nucleus of macrophage

Phagocytized cell

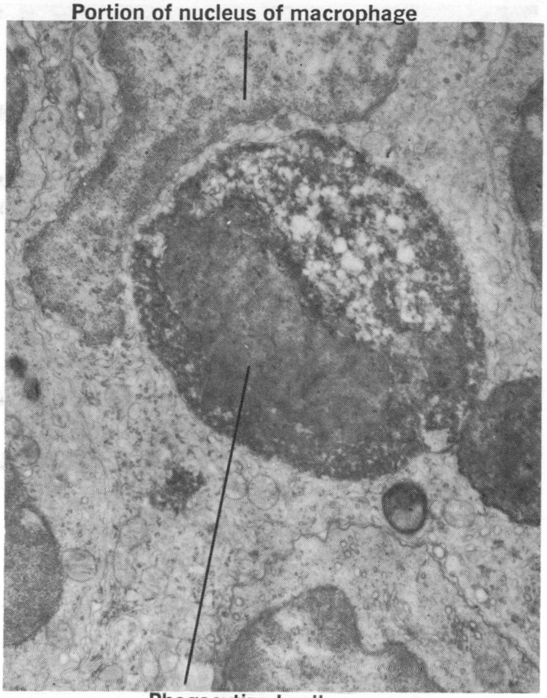

Figure 25-10. Electron micrograph of a portion of macrophage cell from mouse spleen containing a phagocytized cell. Magnification, 18,000X. (*Courtesy of Dr. D. C. Swartzendruber, J. Cell Biol.*)

include the skin and other membrane coverings (e.g., epithelial surfaces of the respiratory, digestive, and urogenital passages), the secretions of the digestive tract, and the high acidity of the stomach.

Once the physical barriers of the body have been penetrated, the second line of defense comes into play. This is made up largely of the white blood cells and certain cells known as macrophages. Macrophage cells are widely distributed throughout the body, being found in bone marrow, lymph nodes, lung, spleen, liver lining, and all loose connective tissue. The macrophages are collectively designated as the *reticuloendothelial system* since they resemble certain embryonic reticular cells as well as the endothelial cells of the circulatory system (Chapter 26). Some macrophage cells actually migrate or wander, whereas others are stationary or fixed in their locations. White blood cells and macrophages protect against pathogenic organisms (and their poisons or toxins) and other foreign substances in two important ways. They carry on phagocytosis (Figure 25-10), described earlier, and are also intimately involved in the production of specific antibacterial and antiviral substances of tissues and body fluids. Thus they confer the important characteristic of specific resistance or *immunity* on the organism in contrast to the nonspecific physical protective action of the body coverings.

The term *immunity* refers to the specific reactions by which invading microorganisms and their toxic products or other substances foreign to the animal are inhibited, inactivated, or destroyed. *Immunology* is the field of study concerned with these specific reactions. Although we have considerable information about many aspects of this field at many levels, our state of knowledge of this broad and fundamental area of biology at the molecular level is still extremely limited. The vast importance of immunological reactions in the well-being and survival of higher multicellular animals is self-evident. The present discussion will center mainly about the principal mechanisms by which the body acquires immunity.

IMMUNOLOGICAL ROLE OF WHITE BLOOD CELLS AND THE RETICULOENDOTHELIAL SYSTEM. The white blood cells (in particular the lymphocytes) and macrophages play a major role in the immunological defense mechanisms of the body. They produce specific proteins called *antibodies* in response to the introduction of microorganisms and other foreign biological materials designated as *antigens*. Antibodies are specific agents which are chiefly responsible for the inactivation or destruction of antigens. Of particular interest are the recent experiments demonstrating the formation of antibodies by lymph node cells (Chapter 26) removed from the mammalian body (i.e., *in vitro*).

The Nature of Antigens and Antibodies. Antigens. An antigen is any substance that is capable of inducing the production of specific antibodies. An antigen reacts or combines specifically with the antibodies produced, for the latter are induced with a particular configuration that is believed to be complementary, like a lock and key relationship, to a portion of the antigen. When the term antigen is applied to cells and tissue extracts, it is used in a collective sense since these materials contain many different antigens, each having its own immunological specificity and capacity to elicit antibody formation.

In general, antigens are natural products of molecular weights greater than 5000, which possess one or more aspects of their chemical structure which is foreign to the test animal. With few exceptions virtually all proteins not produced by the test animal have been shown to be antigens. Many polysaccharides have also been shown to be antigenic. The fact that some relatively simple compounds of a nonprotein or noncarbohydrate nature, including drugs and antibiotics, appear to function as antigens has been tentatively attributed to a union of the chemical substance with a tissue protein, which thus becomes capable of inducing antibody production.

Our present concept of antigens is that they possess particular chemical groupings or moieties called *determinant groups* or *haptens*, which are responsible for the specific reaction between antigen and antibody. In one sense antigens can be regarded as macromolecules whose specific determinant group reacts with the antibody. Such determinant groups when dissociated from the protein moiety may still have the capacity to react with their appropriate antibodies *but may lack the ability to induce antibody formation.* If the hapten is chemically combined with a protein, the resulting conjugated protein will induce the formation of antibodies which are specific for the hapten even though different proteins are used. In other words, the same hapten confers a common antigenic specificity to different proteins. Several determinant groups have already been isolated from natural antigens. For example, one of the antigenically active components of the blood group A substance (p. 603) is apparently a polysaccharide.

Antibodies. Antibodies are specific proteins that occur in the body fluids (the blood, lymph, and, under certain conditions, the cerebrospinal fluid) as a direct result of the introduction of or immunization with a specific antigen. They are principally characterized by their affinity for the specific antigen. Antibodies are typical globulins, which behave chemically like any other serum proteins. In some cases they may contain carbohydrate moieties, and perhaps lipids, and in many instances have molecular weights of about 160,000. Although the majority of antibodies are found in the gamma-globulin protein of blood serum, other antibodies also occur in the other globulin fractions. Except for their specific reactive ability with an antigen of a given species, antibodies always appear to be chemically the same as the comparable nonimmune globulin.

The combining sites of antibodies are envisaged as small, specifically shaped pockets in the surface of the antibody globulin molecules. The particular configuration of the combining sites is seemingly complementary to the determining portion of the antigens that induced their formation comparable to a lock and key arrangement (Figure 25-11). The antigen molecule in turn is pictured as having many active chemical sites or determinant groups protruding from the surface as specific configurations. The latter determine antigenic specificity and fit specifically into the pocket-like combining sites of the antibody. It seems quite clear that antibodies are synthesized from amino acids and not formed by modifications of already existing globulins. One major theory proposes that globulin synthesis is somehow altered by the presence of the antigen which in an unknown manner directs the production of new globulin molecules or antibodies. It has been estimated that the combining sites occupy only about 1 per cent of the total antibody surface. The number of antibody molecules produced is usually greater, in some instances several millionfold, than the number of antigen molecules injected.

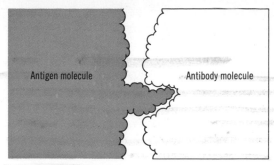

Figure 25-11. Diagram of the "lock-and-key" configuration of the combining sites of antibody and antigen.

In general, two broad groups of antibodies are recognized: so-called *natural* antibodies which are formed without apparent antigenic stimulation, and *acquired* antibodies which appear only after exposure to a known antigen. Some immunologists feel that all gamma globulins are actually antibodies formed in response to various environmental and infectious antigens and that there are no such things as nonimmune globulins. The alpha and beta blood group antibodies which are involved in blood type reactions (p. 603) are examples of the natural type. The antibodies that are developed during the course of "immunization" are examples of the acquired type. Most of our information about antibodies is based on studies of the acquired type.

The quantity of acquired antibody formed following exposure to a foreign antigenic material depends on several factors. These include the nature and amount of the antigen, the route of introduction, the amount injected, the time elapsed after the last exposure, and the animal species involved. In many instances antibody production will reach a maximum within several days or weeks after injection of the antigen and maintain itself for varying periods of time. The antibody in the serum usually becomes evident within 5 to 7 days after injection of the antigen, although this also varies depending on the foregoing factors. The response to reinjection of antigen as compared to that caused by initial injection results in the appearance of antibody at a more rapid rate, greater concentration, greater activity, and longer existence (Figure 25-12).

The Antibody-Antigen Reaction. Most antibody molecules are believed to have only two reactive or combining sites in contrast to the many more reactive sites possessed by antigen molecules. According to this concept an antibody molecule may therefore attach to a maximum of two antigens, whereas an antigen molecule may combine with many more antibody molecules as shown in Figure 25-13.

The combination or binding of antibodies to antigens is manifested in several different ways. One of the most common is the formation of a visible aggregate or precipitate. It is usually called *agglutination* when antigens such as large visible particles, or whole cells (e.g., bacteria or red blood cells) are aggregated. It is called *precipitation* when soluble antigen molecules become insoluble. Frequently when bacteria have combined with antibody they are more effectively phagocytized by white blood cells and macrophages, a phenomenon called *opsonization.* Another manifestation of antibody-antigen reaction is the disruption, or *lysis,* of cells. This is often observed with red blood cells (resulting in a release of hemoglobin) and with certain types of bacteria, and involves a rupturing or fragmentation of the cells.

The occurrence of opsonization and lysis requires, in addition to suitable antibody, a component of normal serum called *complement.* Complement is somehow involved in the indicated reactions, being absorbed by a combination of antigen with antibody. Complement also has other activities including the ability under certain conditions to cause the precipitation of soluble antigen-antibody complexes. The intricate nature of complement has made it difficult to characterize chemically.

Finally another manifestation of the antibody-antigen reaction is seen in the rejection of grafted tissues between two animals who are not identical in their genetic make-ups. For example, under normal circumstances successful tissue or organ grafts have occurred only

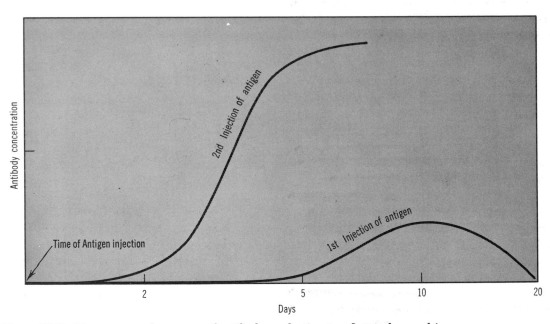

Figure 25-12. Time course of response of antibody production to a first and second injection of antigen.

where the donor and recipient individuals were identical twins. In all other instances with the sole exception cited in the section below, the grafted foreign tissue is eventually rejected.

THE THYMUS GLAND AND THE IMMUNITY RESPONSE. The recent independent experiments of several research groups in this country and abroad have revealed the central role of the thymus gland in immunity responses. In mammalian embryos shortly before birth the thymus gland, located in the chest cavity near the lower end of the trachea (Figure 25-14), is a prominent mass of lymphoid tissue making up nearly 1 per cent of the body weight. During early childhood the gland is still conspicuous, but progressively decreases in size until it has almost completely disappeared by the time adulthood is attained.

Removal of the thymus gland by surgical techniques in *newly born mammals* (e.g., mice), but not in adolescent or adult animals, may result in death of the animals from infection within several weeks. Such animals in contrast to the normal ones have little or no gamma globulin (or antibody fraction) in their blood plasma. Most surprising of all, they are able to accept skin grafts from other individuals as well as unrelated strains of mice for considerably longer periods. By contrast in untreated or normal mice ordinarily grafted foreign tissues are soon rejected as a result of the anti-bodies normally produced in the individual.

The current interpretation is that the thymus gland during the latter stages of embryonic development and for a time following birth produces lymphoid cells and possibly certain substances. These are believed to be transported to other lymphoid tissues of the body such as the lymph nodes, which are principally responsible for antibody production during most of the lifetime of the individual. Sufficiently early removal of the thymus gland, as described above for newly born mice, can almost entirely prevent antibody production and thus block the formation of an important line of defense against disease.

IMMUNITY AND HYPERSENSITIVITY. Pathogenic organisms are characterized by their ability to establish themselves and multiply in the tissues of the host ("invasiveness") and to be successfully transferred to fresh potential hosts ("infectivity"). They produce disease in numerous ways, including the production of poisons or toxins which may poison various tissues of the body, the derangement of cellular metabolism, and certain other destructive changes. The diffusible toxins formed by particular pathogenic bacteria such as those causing food poisoning (botulism), scarlet fever, diphtheria, and tetanus are neutralized by their appropriate antibodies. Such diffusible bacterial toxins, called *exotoxins*, have been shown to be proteins which are readily neutralized by their corresponding antibodies. By contrast, the toxins (called *endotoxins*) present in the cell walls of certain bacteria which are released when the bacteria die probably also interact with their appropriate antibodies. However, they are still highly toxic presumably because combination does not occur with the portion of the molecule that is poisonous. *Resistance* or *immunity* to a particular disease is an important biological manifestation of the antibody-antigen reaction.

A second major biological manifestation of the antibody-antigen reaction is *hypersensitivity*—the strong physiological response of the body tissues to the harmful effects of the anti-

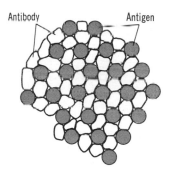

Figure 25-13. Diagram of the combination of antigen molecules with many more antibody molecules.

body-antigen reaction as a result of exposure to sufficient quantities of specific antigen.

Immunity. Immunity to specific infectious diseases is usually classified into two types, *natural* and *acquired.*

Natural immunity is resistance to a specific disease without previous known exposure to the causative agent. For example, the several races of man show various degrees of susceptibility to such diseases as tuberculosis and diphtheria. Several species of animals also display different types of natural immunity. Although our knowledge of the mechanism of natural immunity is extremely meager, we know that heredity plays a role in determining natural immunity as do such factors as age, sex, and nutrition, and various other environmental influences. In humans, the ability to produce gamma globulin is clearly under genetic control.

Acquired immunity is the resistance which is attained to particular infectious diseases during the individual's lifetime. One principal way to acquire resistance is to experience the disease. Another is by preventive treatment as discussed later. Although it is widely believed that antibody is the principal means by which the body acquires immunity, conclusive evidence for such a role exists only for some of the infectious diseases.

In general, acquired immunity to disease is evinced by the absence or a marked decrease in disease symptoms. It is ordinarily determined with experimental animals or sample populations by first injecting the antigen (in order to induce antibody formation) into numerous host individuals. These animals as well as an appropriate group of untreated animals (called *controls*) are then inoculated with the disease-causing organism, and the subsequent occurrence or frequency of disease between the two groups is compared. Immunity is demonstrated by a significant increase in resistance to the infectious agent as a result of prior injection of the antigen.

Active Immunity. The immunity that is

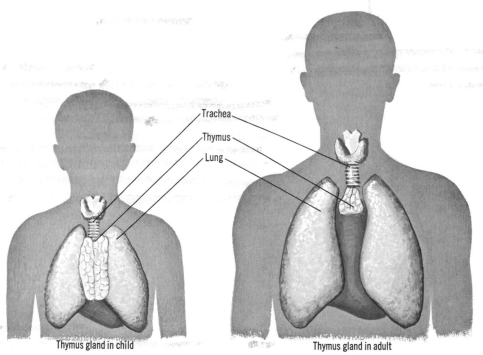

Figure 25-14. Location and size of the thymus gland in a child and adult.

conferred by a specific infection or by introducing an antigen (also referred to as a *vaccine*) into the tissues is called *active immunization*. Under these conditions the tissues of the host animal participate by synthesizing a relatively large amount of new protein (i.e., antibodies) under the stimulus of the antigen.

Active resistance or immunity may be acquired through apparent and inapparent infections or through deliberate immunizing procedures or vaccination. Vaccines may consist of: (1) Soluble microbial toxins which have been rendered less toxic by certain chemical and physical treatment. The resulting less toxic antigen is referred to as *toxoid*. (2) Bacteria and viruses killed by heat, ultraviolet irradiation, or chemicals as in the instances of cholera and plague bacteria and rabies, influenza, and mumps virus as well as the Salk vaccine for infantile paralysis. (3) Antigens isolated from disease-causing agents as in the case of the polysaccharides obtained from pneumonia bacteria. And (4) attenuated or avirulent living microorganisms as in the instances of those agents responsible for smallpox, anthrax, and tuberculosis and the Sabin vaccine for infantile paralysis. Smallpox vaccine originally introduced in England by Jenner in 1798 is a preparation of attenuated living virus obtained from the pustules of calves which have been artificially infected with the virus. The vaccine causes only a mild and brief infection in man with the appearance of a single skin lesion at the site of inoculation.

Active immunity usually takes several weeks to develop and is generally used as a preventive measure in such diseases as whooping cough, smallpox, rabies, yellow fever, infantile paralysis, diphtheria, measles, tetanus, and plague by injection of the appropriate antigen or vaccine.

Passive Immunity. Resistance or immunity to certain diseases which can be conferred by injecting antibodies from an immune animal into a nonimmune individual is called *artificially acquired passive immunity*. Under these circumstances the host animal does not play an active role in the production of the immune state. The serum or serum fractions containing the antibodies used for conferring passive immunity are obtained from animals or humans that have recovered from an infection or have been actively immunized by injection of a specific antigen. Passive immunization is usually employed to combat or protect against an infection that is already present or imminent. Horse serum or rabbit serum containing the desired antibodies are often used in these instances during the presumptive incubation period of such infections as tetanus, diphtheria, measles, mumps, infectious hepatitis, German measles, small pox, and rabies. Such antibodies when injected into a human may exist in the circulation for one to three weeks in progressively decreasing concentrations. By contrast active immunity usually lasts for a year or more, sometimes for life, depending on the specific antigen.

Passive immunity can also be transferred naturally from mother to fetus through the placenta (Chapter 31) and is probably of importance in protecting the young infant during the first weeks following birth against several infectious diseases such as measles, mumps, diphtheria, and others. In some species such as the mouse, rat, and dog, and perhaps humans, antibodies are transmitted for several days to the newborn from the mother through suckling.

Hypersensitivity. The physiological response of the body tissues to the harmful effects of the antibody-antigen reaction is called *hypersensitivity*. It may give a wide range of clinical symptoms including breathing difficulty, constriction of the small veins, and damage to the blood vessels The visible manifestations may be poorly understood shock reactions of various kinds called *anaphylactic shock* and appreciably milder reactions called *allergy*. Hypersensitivity can be classified into two broad groups, the *immediate* type and the *delayed* type. The immediate type usually occurs within minutes or hours and has as its basis the reaction between antigen and specific antibody in the serum. The mechanism of the delayed type of reaction, which ordinarily occurs between 24 to 48 hours following exposure to an antigen, is still obscure. It involves white blood cells and may occur in the absence of detectable serum antibody.

The severity of the hypersensitivity reaction depends principally on the degree of sensitivity of the individual and the amount of antigen introduced into the body. Hypersensitivity of the immediate type usually involves a prior primary response whereby appropriate antibodies are formed soon after the introduction of an antigen. The process usually takes 10 days or less. Reintroduction of an antigen into an individual previously sensitized to the same antigen may now elicit an antigen-antibody reaction which affects certain tissues, mainly smooth muscle and blood vessels, to give many symptoms of hypersensitivity. In effect the initial or primary dose of antigen has *sensitized* the organism so that subsequent inoculation of the same antigen and its combination with suitable antibody gives rise to a harmful effect on the body tissues. It should be noted, however, that in certain instances of sensitization (e.g., tubercular sensitivity) antibodies are not detectable in the serum.

The mechanism by which the antigen-antibody combination gives rise to immediate-type hypersensitivity is not well understood. The present evidence suggests that in hypersensitivity the union of antigen and antibody results in the release from tissues of physiologically active substances which act on blood vessels and smooth muscle to give a variety of effects. One popular but controversial theory has implicated the release of the chemical *histamine* (the decarboxylated product of the amino acid histidine) from particular body cells, as a result of the antibody-antigen reaction, in amounts that are sufficiently toxic to account for the observed symptoms. Allergies, as a manifestation of hypersensitivity, occur predominantly in humans and are often limited to particular regions of the body such as the skin (rashes and hives), the respiratory tract (asthmatic attacks), upper respiratory membranes and eyes (hay fever), the joints (accumulation of fluids), and the digestive tract (gastrointestinal upsets). Allergies to a vast list of substances have been described but the interpretations and data to account for them have been many and conflicting.

Serum sickness is a particular form of anaphylactic shock which usually occurs in humans one to two weeks after the administration of foreign serum (e.g., horse serum as an anti-tetanus or antidiphtheria measure) or at times after the administration of other foreign antigens. The delay in appearance of the symptoms probably represents the time necessary for the formation of the antibodies and their reaction with the antigen still remaining in the body.

Desensitization is a process by which resistance to hypersensitivity may be temporarily induced. It is often accomplished by repeated injections of antigen into a sensitive individual, and may be consistently or variably attained depending on the type of hypersensitivity and the individual. One common but controversial explanation is that such treatments diminish the concentration of circulating antibody, presumably by combination of antigen with antibody to the point where the tissues fail to respond to additional antigen. The subsequent return of sensitivity is attributed to the eventual replenishment of antibodies. Other mechanisms have been proposed, but none really provides a satisfactory explanation of desensitization.

Blood Groups

The complex nature of blood is further illustrated by the phenomenon of blood types. In 1900 Karl Landsteiner, a young Viennese pathologist, discovered that human blood was not the same in all individuals. On the basis of the frequent occurrence of clumping of red blood cells upon mixing the blood of two different individuals, he found that human blood can be classified into four well-defined groups described below. Prior to Landsteiner's Nobel Prize-winning research, many deaths resulted from the mixing of incompatible blood during transfusion. His work led to a better understanding and to the successful use of blood transfusion.

BLOOD GROUP ANTIGENS AND ANTIBODIES. Blood grouping is founded on the presence or absence of specific antigens located on the surface of red blood cells. Two of these antigens designated as A and B are present on the erythrocytes of each individual's blood in one of four possible combinations and are carbohydrate-containing peptides. When an individual has only one of the antigens the blood group is called A or B, depending on which is present. When both are present the blood type is known as AB; and when both are absent the classification is designated by the letter O to indicate zero. The blood of all humans falls into one of these groups.

On the other hand blood plasma contains one, both, or neither of two antibodies, which are complementary to the erythrocytic A and B antigens. The serum of blood type A always contains the specific protein designated as *beta* (β); blood type B has the *alpha-(α)* protein; type AB has neither; and type O has both α- and β-proteins. The α-protein is considered to be an antibody (Anti-A) directed against blood group substance A, whereas the β-protein is considered to be the antibody (Anti B) directed against blood group substance B. The mixing together of A-group red cells and α-antibodies from the plasma of group B would result in an aggregation or clumping reaction of erythrocytes. Mixing of B-group red cells and β-antibodies from the plasma of group A blood would behave in the same manner. Obviously group A blood does not contain α-protein nor does B blood have β-protein. AB blood has neither, whereas O type has both α- and β-proteins. Therefore the four different blood groups with respect to both the antigen and antibody are: A_β, B_α, AB, and $O_{\alpha, \beta}$. The β-protein will cause type B or type AB erythrocytes to clump; and α-protein will cause type A or type AB erythrocytes to clump in a typical antigen-antibody reaction.

BLOOD TRANSFUSION. If a group A individual should inadvertently receive a transfusion of type B blood, his anti-B plasma will react with the incoming erythrocyte B antigen, resulting in the clumping of the donor's red blood cells. Similarly the A antigen of a donor's blood would be expected to react with the α-antibody of a B type patient causing clumping of the former's red blood cells. Obviously these bloods should never be mixed. Actually the main concern in blood transfusions is the clumping of the donor's red blood cells in the vessels of the recipient. The recipient's erythrocytes generally escape clumping since the donor's plasma antibodies are sufficiently diluted during transfusion. Individuals belonging to group AB are "universal recipients" since they contain neither the α- nor the β-proteins and will therefore produce no clumping of any donor's red blood cells. Individuals of the O group are regarded as "universal donors" since they contain neither A nor B antigens which means that their red blood cells will not be clumped no matter what the composition of the receiver's blood.

The clumping of blood cells as a result of mixing incompatible bloods during transfusion can lead to serious complications and death. Aside from the possibility of clogging the smaller blood vessels and thus impairing circulation in vital areas, the subsequent breakdown of the clumped cells may cause kidney damage through obstruction of the kidney tubules by heme degradation products.

THE GENETICS OF BLOOD GROUPS. The inheritance of blood groups is determined by a single pair of genes for which there are three alleles. These genes apparently control the synthesis of the specific A and B blood group substances in red blood cells, and thus are responsible for the four types of blood groups in man. The gene L^A (named after Landsteiner) produces A substance; L^B produces B substance; and L^O genes neither A nor B substances. Blood group A is determined by the genotype $L^A L^A$ or $L^A L^O$, and group B by $L^B L^B$ or $L^B L^O$. Group AB arises from the genotype

$L^A L^B$, and group O from $L^O L^O$. Obviously the L^A and L^B genes are neither dominant nor recessive to each other, whereas the L^O gene is considered to be recessive to L^A and L^B.

Current investigations now indicate that O individuals do in fact have an antigen related to the AB blood-group substances called the H substance. It is thought to be a precursor of the AB blood-group substances. However, the ability to convert H substance to either A or B substance is genetically lacking in individuals of the O type.

Blood groups of the A, B, AB, and O type are also found in certain primates such as chimpanzees and gorillas which are considered to be closely related to man himself. Additional antigens other than A and B are also present on the red blood cells of humans and various other mammals and birds. A blood-group classification based on antigens different from A and B has been demonstrated in a large number of mammals and birds including cattle, dogs, cats, sheep, pigs, and chickens.

Rh FACTOR. The *Rh factor* is still another genetically determined type of antigen found in red blood cells which is responsible for their clumping under particular conditions. The antigen was first discovered by Landsteiner and Weiner in 1940 in the rhesus monkey (thus accounting for the designation Rh) 40 years after Landsteiner's monumental discovery of blood groups, and was shown to be similar in human blood. The individuals who possess the antigen are called Rh-positive and make up about 85 per cent of the white population, whereas the remaining 15 per cent are called Rh-negative (the latter group actually possess other Rh antigens of different specificities which are less important clinically). The introduction of Rh-positive blood into the blood stream of an Rh-negative individual stimulates the production of specific antibodies by the latter within approximately two weeks.

This phenomenon may have serious consequences in the developing embryo (or fetus) of an Rh-negative mother and an Rh-positive father, for it can result in a blood condition fatal to the fetus or the newborn child. If the blood of the fetus is Rh-positive, a trait inherited from the father, antibody formation to Rh-positive erythrocytes is usually stimulated in the mother's Rh-negative blood since there is a slight mixing of the fetal and maternal bloods. Therefore, during subsequent pregnancies any mixing of the mother's blood, now containing the Rh antibodies with that of an Rh-positive fetus, will cause extensive clumping and subsequent destruction of the fetal red blood cells. This condition is frequently fatal to the fetus before birth or to the newborn child shortly afterward. The genetics of the Rh factor is far more complex than that of the other blood groups. There are at least eight Rh blood genes including those for Rh-positive and Rh-negative characteristics, and their interrelationships have not yet been completely clarified.

SUPPLEMENTARY REFERENCES

Best, C. H., and N. B. Taylor, *The Physiological Basis of Medical Practise*, fifth edition, Williams and Wilkins, Baltimore, 1950.

Carlson, A. J., and V. Johnson, *The Machinery of the Body*, fifth edition, University of Chicago Press, Chicago, 1962.

Cushing, J. E., and D. H. Campbell, *Principles of Immunology*, McGraw-Hill, New York, 1957.

Fox, H. M., "Blood Pigments," *Scientific American*, March 1950.

Heilbrunn, L. V., *An Outline of General Physiology*, Saunders, Philadelphia, 1955.

Humphrey, J. H., and R. C. White, *Immunology for Students of Medicine*, Davis, Philadelphia, 1963.

Prosser, C. L., Editor, *Comparative Animal Physiology*, second edition, Saunders, Philadelphia, 1961.

Raffel, S., *Immunity*, second edition, Appleton-Century-Crofts, New York, 1961.

Surgenor, D. M., "Blood," *Scientific American*, February 1954.

Chapter 26   Circulation: Structure and Action
of the Circulatory System

INTRODUCTION

General Features

The circulatory system of higher animals such as man consists primarily of the heart, arteries, capillaries, and veins. The lymphatics are also included as secondary structures. In order for blood to perform its functions (Chapter 25) it must continuously circulate through the body. Interruption of blood flow to the brain, for example, causes a loss of consciousness within five seconds, an irreparable destruction of the mental processes within a matter of minutes, and death shortly afterward. In other tissues the failure of blood to flow may result in extensive damage often followed by death.

The heart is the pump that propels blood throughout the body. It is usually regarded as being synonymous with life itself, the last heart beat marking the onset of death. The arteries and veins function essentially as the conduits for transporting the blood to and from the different regions of the body. Arteries carry blood away from the heart, branching and growing smaller and thinner until they ultimately become the capillaries—microscopic blood vessels whose walls are made up of a single layer of flat epithelial cells called the endothelium. The interchange of substances between the blood and the various cells of the body occurs during the passage of the blood through the capillaries. The capillaries in turn fuse into larger and larger vessels, the veins, which convey the blood back to the heart.

The principal role of the blood and the circulatory system is to maintain a suitable environment for the 300 trillion cells of the human body by delivering nutrients and regulatory substances, and by removing the products of metabolism. Since this is accomplished solely by the capillaries, these vessels are regarded as the important physiological units of the circulatory system and not merely as connecting networks between arteries and veins.

Developmental Aspects

From the embryological standpoint the capillaries are the basic circulatory structures which ultimately give rise to all the other blood vessels. In the early embryonic stages the circulatory system is essentially composed of a network of endothelial tubes or capillaries containing the primitive blood stream. The outer surface of many of these tubes contains a large number of star-shaped cells which migrated originally from the surrounding tissues during earlier developmental steps. With successive embryonic development many of the star-shaped cells become progressively transformed into typical smooth muscle cells, ultimately contributing to the formation of the walls of the arteries and veins. It is therefore reasonable to regard the capillaries as immature or embryonic tissue, perhaps of a primitive nature, with a decided capacity for growth. This characteristic is exhibited when capillaries of mature tissue give rise to new arteries and veins in response to injury and disease.

We have already mentioned in the preceding chapter that the appearance of a closed type of blood circulation, accompanied in most vertebrates by an additional closed circulatory network of vessels, the *lymphatic system*, represents the culmination of a long chain of evolutionary events.

DETAILED STRUCTURE AND FUNCTION OF THE CIRCULATORY SYSTEM

The Heart

THE WORK OF THE HEART. The heart, by means of its pumping action, propels blood throughout the entire human body continuously for 24 hours a day, year after year during the average 70-year lifetime of an individual. It is essentially a double pump consisting of two pumps fused together and beating in unison. The right pump, or the right side of the heart, receives blood returning from all parts of the body (except the lungs) and sends it by way of the *pulmonary arteries* to the lungs where carbon dioxide is released and oxygen taken up. The freshly aerated blood returns from the lungs via the *pulmonary veins* to the left pump, or left side of the heart, which in turn propels it out through the largest artery of the circulatory system, the *aorta*, to all other parts of the body. The right side of the heart is therefore primarily concerned with blood circulation to the lungs, known as *pulmonary circulation*, whereas the left side of the heart in pumping blood to all the other systems is concerned with *systemic* circulation.

The remarkable and almost legendary characteristics of the heart are illustrated by innumerable statistics and analogies. As a pump weighing approximately 11 ounces — the size of the average grapefruit — the adult human heart continuously circulates 6 quarts of viscous fluid, the blood, through a vascular network which, when laid end to end as a single tube, would extend some 60,000 miles, a distance equal to 2.5 times the earth's circumference. In a resting individual it pumps approximately 5 quarts of blood per minute or 75 gallons per hour, sufficient to fill an average auto gas tank about four times per hour. With moderate activity the output is doubled, and during strenuous exercise it may be increased several-fold. In terms of work done over a 12-hour period, it performs the equivalent of raising a 25-ton weight one foot high. The heart beats at a steady tempo more than 100,000 times a day and 36 million times a year. In an average lifetime of 70 years, it beats approximately 2.5 billion times, pumping nearly 18 million barrels or more than 400,000 tons of blood and doing enough work to raise a weight of 45 tons to a height of 5 miles.

GROSS STRUCTURE AND ACTION OF THE HEART. The heart is an almost completely muscular organ. From an evolutionary viewpoint it is essentially a highly modified blood vessel with thick muscular walls. It lies in the central portion of the chest cavity directly behind the breast bone and is slightly tilted so that its lower portion is situated to the left. Between the heart itself and its protective encasing sac of connective tissue known as the *pericardium* is a layer of fluid which minimizes the friction on the outer surface of the beating heart.

The main pumping chambers of the human heart are the two *ventricles*, one on the right side and one on the left, which are separated from one another by a thick muscular dividing wall. Each ventricle is connected to its own antechamber called the *atrium* (Figure 26-1) which serves as a collecting point for blood, holding it in readiness for almost instantaneous delivery to the ventricles for each coming heart beat. Blood low in oxygen and high in carbon dioxide enters the right atrium of the heart via the two largest veins of the body, the *superior vena cava* and the *inferior vena cava*. It then passes into the right ventricle and is propelled by way of the pulmonary artery to the lungs where carbon dioxide is discharged and oxygen taken up. The aerated blood returns from the lungs through the pulmonary vein, reentering the heart directly through the left atrium. It then flows into the left ventricle which pumps the blood out through the aorta and ultimately to almost all parts of the body (Figure 26-1).

The opening from the right atrium to the right ventricle is guarded by the *tricuspid valve* made up of three flaps of connective tissue whose free edges are attached by connective tissue strings (Figure 26-1) to the ventricle wall. Thus blood is permitted to flow from atrium to ventricle but not in the reverse direction. The corresponding inlet valve between the left atrium and left ventricle is similar in structure and action except that it consists of two flaps instead of three and is accordingly called the *bicuspid or mitral valve*. Each ventricle is also equipped with an outlet valve (*semilunar* valve) of a different construction opening away from the heart at the sites where the pulmonary artery and the aorta connect to the right and left ventricles, respectively.

When the ventricles fill with blood and begin to contract, the pressure produced in the ventricles causes the inlet valves between the atria and the ventricles to snap shut like the closing of a door, producing typical sounds that can be assessed by the trained physician. Almost concomitantly the outlet valves open, permitting the discharge of blood from the right and left ventricles to the pulmonary artery and aorta, respectively. The subsequent relaxation of the heart and the consequent fall in pressure within the ventricles are followed by the closing of the outlet valves (also accompanied by its characteristic sounds) and the opening of the inlet valves permitting blood to enter from the atria. Defective or leaky valves, upon closing, produce additional sounds or "murmurs" which may furnish important clues regarding the nature of the valvular defect.

The atria do not function primarily as pumps

Figure 26-1. Diagrams illustrating various features of the heart of man.

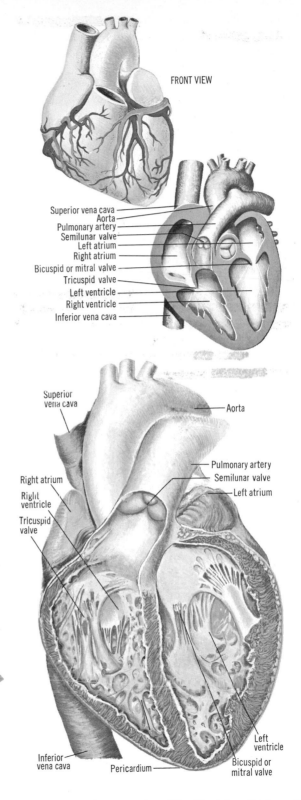

FRONT VIEW

Superior vena cava
Aorta
Pulmonary artery
Semilunar valve
Left atrium
Right atrium
Bicuspid or mitral valve
Tricuspid valve
Left ventricle
Right ventricle
Inferior vena cava

Superior vena cava
Aorta
Right atrium
Right ventricle
Tricuspid valve
Pulmonary artery
Semilunar valve
Left atrium
Inferior vena cava
Pericardium
Left ventricle
Bicuspid or mitral valve

but instead serve chiefly as blood reservoirs for the ventricles. Atrial contraction provides only a minor contribution to the filling of the ventricles. It completes the transfer of the remaining blood, most of which has already flowed into the ventricles by the elastic recoil from the preceding ventricular contraction.

Although the average volume of each ventricle is about 5 ounces, the muscular wall of the left ventricle is considerably thicker than that of the right. Accordingly the left ventricle is a more powerful pump and therefore well suited for its job of propelling blood on a longer route through the body. Blood from the right ventricle passes only to the lungs, a much shorter route, and needs a pressurehead of only about 20 per cent of that on the left.

THE FUNDAMENTAL CONTRIBUTION OF WILLIAM HARVEY. Our basic knowledge of blood circulation and the heart's role as a pump comes primarily from the epoch-making work of the English physician William Harvey in the seventeenth century. For fifteen centuries prior to Harvey's classic studies, anatomy and physiology were almost completely dominated by the views of the great second-century Greek physician, Galen. In the area of blood circulation Galen's pronouncements that blood rich in nutrients was formed in the liver and simply ebbed to and fro in the veins were uncritically accepted as established facts. According to this view arterial blood was simply in a more purified state as a result of acquiring a vital essence, *pneuma*, during the passage of blood through the lungs and through presumed invisible pores in the wall separating the heart chambers. The role of the heart was not known other than that it represented the "seat of the soul."

Harvey performed numerous careful dissections and experiments on animals both living and dead. He reasoned from the arrangement of valves in the heart and veins that blood could move in only one direction. Harvey observed that blocking or constricting the aorta distended the left portion of the beating heart with blood, and that a similar accumulation of blood occurred in the right heart by blocking the pulmonary artery. Constriction of both the inferior and superior vena cavae caused a collapse of the right heart, whereas the same treatment to the pulmonary veins resulted in the collapse of the left heart. Harvey's observations led him to the correct conclusions about the blood flow through the heart despite the accepted dogma of his day.

The fact that only one end of a cut artery spurts blood and that blood flows from only one end of a cut vein further indicated that arterial flow is away from the heart and venous flow is toward the heart. Although Harvey's work implied a connection between the arteries and veins, he had no way of knowing about the capillaries. They were discovered by the Italian microscopist Marcello Malpighi in 1661, 33 years after the publication of Harvey's famous work (*On the Motion of the Heart and Blood in Animals*). Harvey obviously could not appreciate the significance of pulmonary circulation since the discovery of oxygen and its importance to most organisms were not recognized until Lavoisier's work in the eighteenth century.

MICROSCOPIC STRUCTURE AND ACTION OF HEART MUSCLE. The cardiac muscle tissue composing the heart, as seen under the microscope, consists of long narrow networks of multinucleate, cross-striated, branching fibers tied together by connective tissue with tiny blood vessels filling the spaces between them (Figure 26-2). The muscle fibers themselves are constructed of many smaller fibers, called *myofibrils* (similar to those described in detail for skeletal muscle, Chapter 29), which display alternate light and dark crossbands or striations at regularly spaced intervals. Between the fibrils are a rich concentration of spherical bodies called *sarcosomes* which structurally and functionally correspond to the mitochondria of other cells.

A detailed picture of the physiology, biochemistry, and microscopic anatomy of striated muscle is presented in Chapter 29.

CONTROL OF THE HEART BEAT. The average heart rate differs considerably among different members of the animal kingdom. For example, the heart of a whale beats 5 times per minute, that of the canary approximately 1000 times per minute, whereas the human heart beats about 70 times per minute. The rate is slightly lower during sleep and can be appreciably increased by physical or emotional excitement.

What is the mechanism by which the heart maintains and changes its rhythmic beat? All evidence indicates that the beat originates in the heart itself. This view is supported by the innumerable observations over the centuries that various animal hearts may continue to beat even after removal from the body. Each heart beat originates from a small mass of highly specialized muscle tissue called the "pacemaker" or *sino-atrial (S-A) node* situated in the rear upper right wall of the right atrium. The application of heat or cold to this region results in an increase or decrease, respectively, of the heart rate, whereas the same treatment to other parts of the heart has no effect.

The S-A node is a unique type of muscle tissue endowed with some of the properties characteristic of nerve cells. It has the ability to generate and transmit an electrochemical disturbance, somewhat similar to a nerve impulse, which travels across the muscular walls of the two atria exciting the muscle fibers and resulting in their coordinated and progressive contraction, starting first in the right atrial wall and spreading rapidly to the left atrium. In this manner the impulse rapidly reaches another knot of nodal tissue located between the atria and the ventricles called the *atrial-ventricular (A-V) node*. The impulse is then rapidly transmitted via a specialized network of similar conducting nodal tissue to every muscle fiber of the two ventricles, resulting in their coordinated and almost simultaneous contraction. Relaxation of the atrial walls begins to take place at about the time that the ventricles have started contraction.

Each heart beat consists of the progressive and coordinated contraction (*systole*) of the heart expelling blood into the arteries followed by its relaxation (*diastole*) and resultant re-

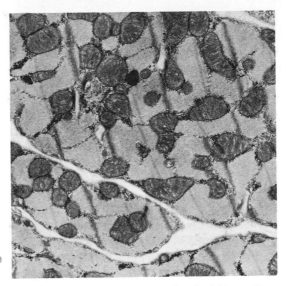

Figure 26-2. Electron micrograph of rabbit cardiac muscle showing the striated muscle fibers and the interspersed rich concentration of large spherical sarcosomes or mitochondria with their internal cristae. Magnification, 19,550X. (*Courtesy of B. O. Spurlock.*)

filling of the heart chambers by blood from the veins. The systole consists of both the atrial and ventricular contractions. Under resting conditions, the human heart experiences about 70 beats per minute, each beat occupying 0.85 seconds. The atrial systole lasts approximately 0.15 seconds followed by the ventricular systole which takes about 0.30 seconds. For the next 0.40 seconds the entire heart remains in the relaxed state before the cycle is resumed once again by initiation of contraction in the S-A node (Figure 26-3).

By the late nineteenth century it was conclusively established that the contraction of cardiac muscle, unlike skeletal muscle, does not depend on the nervous system. Experiments demonstrated that the mammalian heart could maintain its beat for a prolonged period as long as it was supplied with blood, despite the severing of its two sets of nerves. Regulation or modification of the heart beat, however, is in part accomplished by the nervous system and occurs by way of the "pacemaker." The S-A node is provided with nerve endings from both the sympathetic and parasympathetic nervous systems. Impulses arriving along the vagus nerves of the parasympathetic nervous system slow down the pumping action of the heart, whereas impulses arriving via the corresponding nerves of the sympathetic nervous system accelerate the rate. Our present state of knowledge indicates that the parasympathetic nerves play a prominent role by their "braking" action—an increased frequency of impulses along the vagus nerves accounting for a decrease in heart rate, and a decreased impulse frequency causing an acceleration of the beat. The two sets of nerves can be traced back ultimately to a specific nerve center in the medulla oblongata region of the brain which sends out the impulses controlling the heart rate. The heart rate center is in turn influenced by impulses transmitted from other parts of the body including those from higher centers of the brain. Thus anger, fear, and other emotional states may exert a profound effect on the heart rate. Destruction of the S-A node results in a marked slowing up of the heart. Observations indicate that cutting the heart nerves or destroying the "pacemaker" will decrease but not halt the beat. This suggests that cardiac muscle un-

like skeletal muscle has an inherent ability to contract rhythmically. This is clearly demonstrated by experiments in which isolated pieces of heart muscle suspended in an artificial nutrient medium continue to beat in a slow rhythmic fashion.

Obviously the complete story of heart beat control is a complex one and is the result of the interplay of several factors. Although cardiac muscle possesses an inherent power of rhythmic contraction, the heart beat itself is initiated by the S-A node whose action is in part under the influence of the nervous system as just described. In addition higher temperatures, lower blood pH as a result of a higher concentration of CO_2 (and therefore higher carbonic acid levels), and certain hormones such as adrenalin and the thyroid hormone also increase the heart beat by apparently acting directly on the S-A node. Other endocrine secretions including insulin, certain pituitary and sex hormones, inorganic ions, and undoubtedly still undiscovered factors also affect the heart rate.

Each heart beat normally pumps 75 ml of blood, which is equivalent to about 5 liters of blood per minute—almost equal to the total amount of blood in the body. Not all the blood

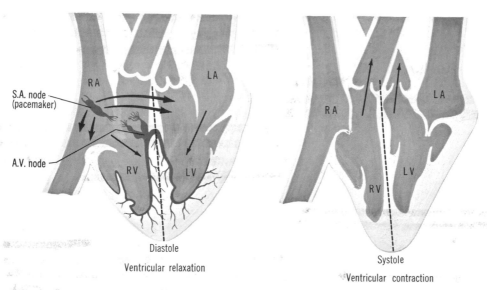

S.A. node (pacemaker)

A.V. node

RA

LA

RV

LV

Diastole
Ventricular relaxation

RA

LA

RV

LV

Systole
Ventricular contraction

Figure 26-3. Diagram of relaxation (diastole) and contraction (systole) in the heartbeat cycle.

of the body passes through the heart in one minute, however. The blood on shorter routes, such as those nourishing the cardiac muscle, will circulate through the heart a number of times in 60 seconds whereas the blood on longer routes, such as to the legs, will not yet have returned to the heart during this time. Under physical or emotional stress the volume of blood pumped by the heart in a given time may be increased severalfold. This increase is attained not only by an accelerated heart rate but also by an increase in the volume of blood pumped during each ventricular systole. Within limits the greater the stretching of cardiac muscle fibers prior to contraction the greater the force of contraction and therefore the greater the amount of blood ejected during ventricular systole. The extent of cardiac muscle stretching in turn depends on the amount of blood which has flowed into the ventricle by the end of the diastole. In brief we have a self-regulatory mechanism whereby the volume of blood entering the heart plays an important role in determining the contraction strength of the heart beat and therefore its output. If the heart muscle is stretched too far by a flow of excess blood into the ventricle because of leaky valves, the con-

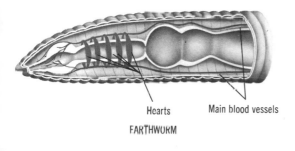

Hearts   Main blood vessels

EARTHWORM

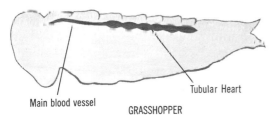

Main blood vessel   Tubular Heart

GRASSHOPPER

Figure 26-4. Diagram of the hearts and main blood vessels of the earthworm and grasshopper.

tractions may actually weaken and even cease, resulting in death.

EVOLUTION AND EMBRYOLOGY OF THE HEART. *Invertebrate Hearts.* The heart probably evolved in the lower multicellular animal forms from local portions of blood vessels whose muscular walls experienced rhythmic contractions or pulsations. The contractions propelled blood through the vessels and thus to all parts of the body. The indications are that the heart evolved differently and independently in several animal groups. The earthworm, for example, at its anterior portion has five pairs of aortic arches which connect the main dorsal longitudinal blood vessel to the main ventral longitudinal blood vessel (Figure 26-4). The ten aortic arches are in reality ten hearts, for by their rhythmic pulsating action they pump blood from the dorsal to the ventral side of the worm. The grasshopper, on the other hand, has a single tubular heart located in the upper portion of its body which pumps blood by way of only one vessel toward the head. From the head the blood leaves the vessel and flows into the large spaces and cavities of the body, eventually returning to the heart. Among certain molluscs such as the squid there are three hearts: a body heart for pumping blood to the body in general, and two individual gill hearts for forcing blood through the gills and from there by vessels to the body heart.

Vertebrate Hearts. The human heart during early embryonic formation is a simple pulsating tube having arisen from the fusion of two other thin-walled tubes beneath the developing head. The remarkable changes which it subsequently undergoes reflect in part the evolutionary development of the heart from the lower to the most advanced vertebrates.

Fish Heart. By the fourth week of embryonic life the human heart has some resemblance to a fish heart, consisting of a straight muscular tube essentially divided into two major chambers, the common atrium and the common ventricle. Blood proceeds from the veins first into the atrium and then into the ventricle before entering the large arteries (Figure 26-5).

In the fish, poorly oxygenated blood is pumped by the heart through a large ventrally located artery to the capillaries of the gills where oxygen is taken up and carbon dioxide released. The gill capillaries then rejoin to form arteries (instead of veins), finally giving rise to a single large artery on the dorsal side of the body. Oxygenated blood is transported through the large dorsal artery to all other tissues of the body via arterial branches and the usual capillaries, eventually returning to the heart by way of the veins as unaerated blood. This single type of circulation in fishes as contrasted to the double type (pulmonary and systemic circulation) in higher vertebrates, such as birds and mammals, has a limited efficiency. In the former, the heart must maintain blood circulation despite the elevated resistance of two capillary networks connected in series before the blood is returned to the heart.

Amphibian Heart. The earlier stage in development in which the mammalian heart is so strikingly similar to that of the fish is transformed shortly to that of an embryonic heart somewhat resembling the amphibian heart. The successful colonization of the land by vertebrates was accompanied by an evolutionary change from gill to lung respiration.

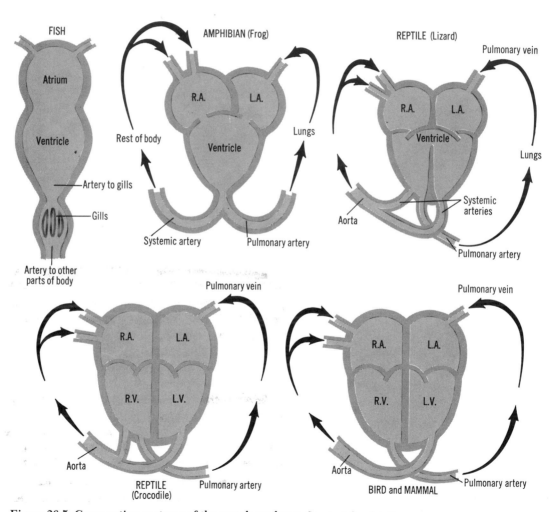

Figure 26-5. Comparative anatomy of the vertebrate heart. See text for details.

This probably went hand in hand with a number of important evolutionary anatomical modifications in the circulatory system, principally in the heart and the large arteries leading from the heart.

In a representative amphibian, such as the frog, the heart is transitional between the lower and higher vertebrates, exhibiting a partial transformation from the more primitive single circulation to the onset of separate pulmonary and systemic circulations. The frog heart consists of two atria which have come to be anterior and dorsal to the single ventricle. Blood is pumped by the single ventricle into the main artery which branches into the pulmonary arteries (leading to the two lungs) and other arteries leading to various parts of the body (systemic circulation). Blood from the pulmonary arteries eventually passes into lung capillaries taking on oxygen and giving off carbon dioxide, and finally drains into the left atrium by way of the pulmonary veins. Unaerated blood from the rest of the body flows into the right atrium. Since unaerated blood from the right atrium enters the common ventricle first, followed by aerated blood from the left atrium, a layering of the bloods occurs. At ventricular contraction the unaerated blood layer (partially mixed with aerated blood) is pushed out first, and tends to flow into the pulmonary branches of the arterial system. The aerated blood layer (also partially mixed with aerated blood) leaves the heart last, tending to flow into the systemic arteries since the pulmonary arteries are already filled with unaerated blood (Figure 26-5).

Reptilian Heart. More advanced transitional stages in the evolutionary development of the heart are exhibited in some of the present-day reptiles. In the lower reptiles, such as the lizard, there are still two atria and essentially one ventricle, although an incomplete partition in the ventricle is evident. In some higher reptiles, such as the crocodile and the alligator, which are regarded as descendants of a primitive ancestor that gave rise to the birds, the ventricle has been divided by a complete partition yielding two ventricles and thus a four-chambered heart. No mixing of aerated and unaerated blood occurs in the heart of the crocodile or alligator, but there is still some mixing in the dorsal aorta. This happens because there are three arteries leaving the crocodile heart, a systemic artery, and a pulmonary artery (both transporting unaerated blood from the right ventricle), and a systemic artery carrying aerated blood from the left ventricle. The two systemic arteries unite to form the dorsal aorta and thus account for the mixed blood in systemic circulation (Figure 26-5).

Bird Heart and Mammalian Heart. The complete separation of aerated and unaerated blood is finally attained in birds and mammals (Figure 26-5). In birds it occured by the evolutionary disappearance of the systemic artery connected to the right ventricle. In mammals it was achieved during the course of evolution in a slightly different manner. Mammals probably arose from a now extinct reptilian ancestor who had only two instead of three arteries—a systemic artery and a pulmonary artery leaving the single heart ventricle. It seems likely that the evolutionary appearance of a complete ventricular partition to create the right and left ventricles connected to the pulmonary and systemic arteries, respectively, constituted the last major step in the development of the mammalian heart. During embryonic development the human heart undergoes various rapid transitional stages which bear a definite resemblance to some of the evolutionary stages just described. By the end of the second month of embryonic formation the typically four-chambered mammalian heart with all its essential structures has already appeared.

The evolutionary achievement of complete separation of aerated and unaerated bloods in birds and mammals has afforded these animals a greater advantage for survival. We know that the relatively recent evolutionary acquisition of aerobic respiration resulted in a twenty-fold greater release and availability of energy for the different activities of living cells (Chapter 8). The complete separation of aerated and unaerated blood in the circulatory system assures the deliverance of more oxygen to the various tissues of birds and mammals as compared to that of the lower vertebrates. The consequent higher rate of aerobic metabolism accounts in part for the greater availability of useful energy and greater heat production and therefore for the ability to maintain a body temperature higher than that of the environment as in the *warm-blooded* animals (birds and mammals) in contrast to *cold-blooded* animals such as the fishes, amphibians, and reptiles.

ELECTROCARDIOGRAPH. The electrocardiograph is a sensitive electrical instrument (a galvanometer) for measuring and recording at the surface of the body the changes in electrical charge or potential associated with the systole and diastole phases of each heart beat. The actual recordings of these typical changes in electrical potential accompanying the various stages of the heart beat are called an *electrocardiogram* and consist of characteristic deflections or waves. A number of heart disorders may manifest themselves by typical electrocardiogram patterns thus making the instrument an extremely useful diagnostic tool.

THE RIDDLE OF HEART ATTACK AND ATHEROSCLEROSIS. About 10 per cent of the total blood pumped by the heart is received by the cardiac muscles through the two coronary arteries given off by the aorta at the point where it leaves the heart. The coronary arteries curl around the surface of the heart dividing into smaller and smaller branches (Figure 26-1) and eventually into capillaries that permeate every muscle fiber of the heart. The capillaries connect to the usual system of uniting veins which finally drain into a single large vein leading directly into the right atrium.

Any impairment in the delivery of oxygenated blood to a portion of the heart muscle will seriously disrupt the metabolism of the cardiac muscle fibers concerned, causing appreciable damage within a very short time. The sudden blocking of one of the coronary arteries

or its large branches by a blood clot results in a *heart attack,* a condition accompanied by intense chest pains caused by a shortage of oxygen to the affected cardiac muscle fibers. A heart attack may prove to be fatal depending on the amount of heart tissue deprived of oxygenated blood. The rapid deterioration of the affected muscle fibers of heart attack pateints is envinced by the release, starting usually within 24 hours, of a number of enzymes such as transaminase and lactic dehydrogenase into the blood stream. The appearance of a certain electrocardiogram pattern and the striking increase of these enzymes in the blood stream together with other symptoms (chest pains, breathlessness, collapse, electrocardiogram pattern) are important aids in the diagnosis of a heart attack. During recovery the localized necrotic muscle fibers are slowly replaced by scar tissue.

The heart attack was first recognized as a medical problem about 1913 and was frequently misdiagnosed until well into the 1930's as acute indigestion or gall bladder disease. It is now known to be the leading killer in the United States, causing about one-sixth of all American deaths, and approximately one-fourth of all deaths among men over 35. The basic affliction in a large majority of heart attacks is *atherosclerosis* which is the most common form of hardening of the arteries. In atherosclerosis the arteries become narrowed by fatty deposits that gradually harden into tough, fibrous plaques. The presence of these plaques beneath the endothelium lining of the artery, especially in the coronary arteries and its branches, somehow sets the stage for blood-clot formation and possible resultant heart attack (Figure 26-6). Why arterial plaques should initiate the blood-clotting mechanism is not clearly understood. It is conceivable, although not yet proved, that they offer a sufficiently rough surface to cause a disruption of the blood platelets thus starting the clotting process.

The gradual narrowing of the bore of a coronary artery over a period of years by atherosclerosis leads to the growth of new blood vessels from other arteries into the affected tissues, giving rise in this fashion to a collateral circulation—a biological safety adaptation assuring an adequate blood supply to the heart muscle. The phenomenon also illustrates the remarkable ability of large blood vessels to grow and permeate under certain circumstances into tissue where they formerly did not exist.

Atherosclerosis itself is now recognized to be extremely widespread among adult males of our Western culture. Some estimates indicate that approximately 40 per cent of all men over 40 have this condition in one or more main branches of their coronary arteries. The causes are still obscure although most of the evidence indicates a disturbance in lipid metabolism. Arterial plaques themselves are known to be rich in fats and especially in the fatty substance *cholesterol* (Chapter 7), the raw material for making the sex hormones and other hormones of similar chemical structure known as steroids. Undoubtedly a complex interplay of numerous factors are involved in atherosclerosis. Recent evidence indicates that increased cholesterol levels in the blood are correlated with an increased incidence of atherosclerosis. The contention by some research workers that a high intake of animal fats in the diet is responsible for increased blood cholesterol levels and that plant oils have the opposite effect is still highly controversial and unsettled. Although heredity seems to play a major role, we are still very uncertain as to what extent inherited tendencies are influenced by diet and environment. The female sex hormones apparently provide some protection since atherosclerosis occurs to a considerably lesser extent among women. It is also known that elevated blood pressure and excess weight definitely have unfavorable effects.

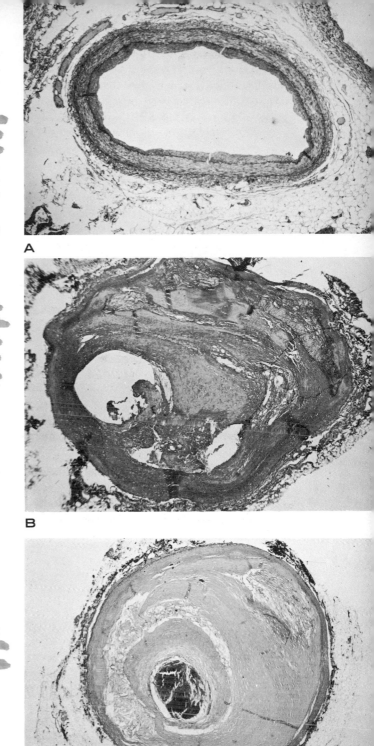

A

B

C

Figure 26-6. Atherosclerosis and the heart attack. Cross-sectional view in man of (A) a normal coronary artery; (B) a coronary artery with hardened deposits or plaques in the inner lining; and (C) an atherosclerotic coronary artery blocked by blood clot. (*Courtesy of the American Heart Association.*)

HEART SURGERY. The last two decades have witnessed remarkable advances in the surgical treatment of certain heart and vascular disorders. Surgical operations within the opened chambers of the heart itself—an area considered once to be beyond the scope of surgery—as a means of repairing various defects in the structure of valves and the walls of the heart have proved to be highly successful for a number of conditions which were formerly regarded as hopeless. Replacement of worn-out portions of some of the large arteries and veins with synthetic materials has also yielded successful results.

The Blood Vessels

ARTERIES AND ARTERIOLES. Arteries transport blood away from the heart. They vary considerably in size from the largest artery, the *aorta* (1 inch in diameter), which subdivides like the branches of a tree into smaller and smaller arteries, to those of almost microscopic dimensions, the *arterioles* (about 0.2 mm in diameter). Arteries are characterized by thick, muscular, strong elastic walls made up of esentially three layers of tissue: the *outer layer* consisting of a thick coat of fibrous connective tissue, the *middle layer* made up of smooth muscle and elastic tissue, and the *inner layer* consisting of an elastic membrane and the *endothelium* which lines the inner surface of the artery.

The typically long and tapered smooth muscle cells have tended in the course of development to wind around the arterial wall, and are capable of a slow, sustained contraction, thus accounting for the narrowing of vessel diameter. The arterial muscles are connected to two sets of visceral nerves, one set controlling constriction and the other controlling dilation of the arteries. The endothelium is actually a continuous sheath of flat epithelial cells constituting the inner surface or lining of the entire circulatory system including the heart, arteries, arterioles, veins, and capillaries (Figure 26-7). The blood of the entire body, therefore, essentially circulates within this continuous, branching tube of epithelial cells.

CAPILLARIES. The arterioles lead into a branching series of microscopic vessels, the *capillaries*, which are made up only of a single layer of endothelial cells. Capillaries are present in all tissues of the body, being found in the highest concentration in the most metabolically active regions. They have an average diameter of about 7 microns (the size of a red blood cell), at times being smaller or larger depending on location, among other factors. Their total number defies the imagination. It has been estimated that if all the

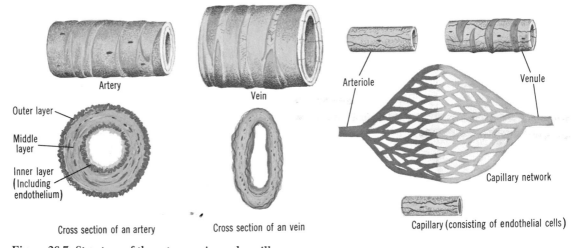

Artery

Vein

Arteriole

Venule

Outer layer

Middle layer

Inner layer (Including endothelium)

Capillary network

Cross section of an artery

Cross section of an vein

Capillary (consisting of endothelial cells)

Figure 26-7. Structure of the artery, vein, and capillary.

capillaries in the human body were put end to end, their overall length would be about 50,000 miles. Since their total volume is greater than that of the blood, all capillaries of the body are obviously not open at the same time. At any given moment blood may be flowing through one capillary network and not through another, with a shift occurring according to the needs of the tissues.

Although most of the evidence indicates that the exchange of nutrients, waste products, and regulatory substances which occurs between the blood of the capillaries and the various cells and tissues takes place in large part by diffusion, it is quite probable that the energy-requiring process of *active transport* (p. 112) also occurs. Extensive data have been collected demonstrating that the concentration of oxygen and nutrients in the capillary blood is greater than in the surrounding cells, thus accounting for a net movement of these substances out of the blood and into the cells and tissues. Similarly, the concentration of metabolic waste products and carbon dioxide in the surrounding cells and tissues is greater than that of the capillary blood, resulting in a net movement of these substances into the blood stream. By the time blood has flowed through the capillaries and reached the first small veins, a significant amount of exchange has taken place.

VEINS. The capillaries in turn unite into larger vessels, the *veins*, whose branches join to form larger and larger veins which ultimately carry blood back to the right side of the heart. The veins, like the arteries, are essentially composed of the same three layers but with certain modifications (Figure 26-7). Veins have a middle layer which is thinner and far less developed than arteries of comparable size. Their bore is somewhat larger in view of their smaller quantity of muscle. Veins, unlike arteries, have neither nerve connections nor an inner elastic membrane. A number of veins, especially those of the abdomen and lower limbs, however, possess a system of internal valves along their length to prevent the backflow of blood.

THE ARTERIAL PATHWAY. As previously indicated the first branches given off by the aorta are the two coronary arteries which curl around the surface of the heart. The aorta then forms an arch by ascending dorsally for a short distance toward the spinal column before descending through the chest cavity and passing into the abdomen. Three major arterial branches are given off from the aortal arch. The first is the *innominate* artery which divides almost immediately into (*a*) the *right subclavian* artery carrying blood to the right shoulder and arm, and (*b*) the *right common carotid* ascending through the right side of the neck and providing blood to the right side of the head. The second major branch arising from the aortal arch is the *left common carotid* artery supplying blood to the left side of the head. The third major branch is the *left subclavian* artery conveying blood to the left shoulder and arm regions (Figure 26-8).

In descending through the chest cavity the aorta gives off some small branches (not shown in Figure 26-8) which transport blood to the chest walls. A number of large arteries arise from the aorta during its passage through the abdomen. The first of these is the *coeliac artery* which ultimately subdivides into smaller arteries carrying blood to the liver, stomach, pancreas, spleen, and a portion of the small intestine. The next large vessel is the *superior mesenteric* artery leading to the remaining portion of the small intestine and to a segment of the large intestine. The aorta next sends out two *renal* arteries, one to each kidney. The last major and most posterior arterial branch coming off the aorta in the abdominal region is the *inferior mesenteric* artery which provides blood to a section of the large intestine and the rectum.

The aorta finally forks in the lower abdomen into the *right* and *left iliac* arteries, each of which subdivides into the *internal* and *external iliac* arteries. The internal iliac arteries supply blood to the various tissues of the pelvic region, whereas the right and left external iliacs extend into the legs where they become the *right* and *left femoral* arteries, respectively (Figure 26-8).

The only exception to the rule that arteries carry aerated blood is the pulmonary artery which transports *unaerated* blood from the right atrium to the lungs. Aerated blood from the lungs is ultimately returned to the heart by way of the pulmonary vein which drains into the left atrium. The pulmonary vein therefore is the only exception to the rule that veins convey *unaerated* blood toward the heart.

THE VENOUS PATHWAY. The venous counterparts to some of the large arteries are seen in various parts of the body (Figure 26-8). Blood is drained from each side of the head by a pair of large veins, the *right internal* and *external jugular* veins and the *left external* and *internal*

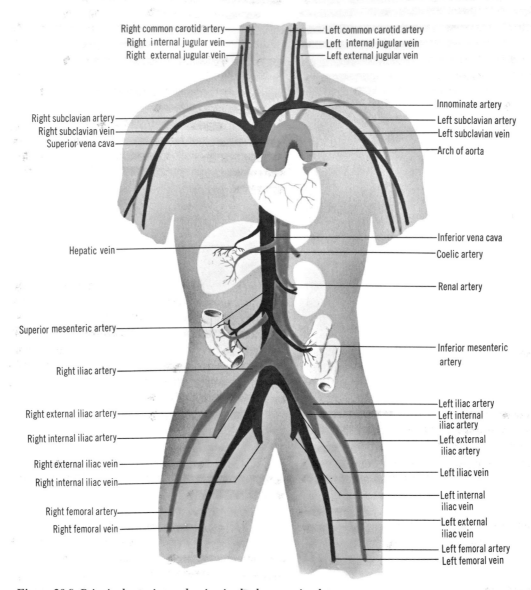

Right common carotid artery
Right internal jugular vein
Right external jugular vein
Left common carotid artery
Left internal jugular vein
Left external jugular vein

Right subclavian artery
Right subclavian vein
Superior vena cava
Innominate artery
Left subclavian artery
Left subclavian vein
Arch of aorta

Hepatic vein
Inferior vena cava
Coelic artery
Renal artery

Superior mesenteric artery
Inferior mesenteric artery

Right iliac artery

Right external iliac artery
Left iliac artery
Left internal iliac artery
Left external iliac artery

Right internal iliac artery

Right external iliac vein
Left iliac vein

Right internal iliac vein
Left internal iliac vein

Right femoral artery
Left external iliac vein
Right femoral vein
Left femoral artery
Left femoral vein

Figure 26-8. Principal arteries and veins in the human circulatory system.

jugular veins, the venous counterparts of the carotid arteries. Each set of jugular veins unites with the corresponding subclavian veins which in turn join together to form the *superior vena cava* transporting blood to the right atrium.

The *right* and *left femoral* veins returning blood from the right and left legs, respectively, become the *external iliacs* in the pelvic region where they join with their corresponding *internal iliac* veins to form the *right* and *left iliac* veins (all are counterparts of the arteries of the same name). The latter two large veins then unite in the lower portion of the abdomen to form the *inferior vena cava* which ultimately drains into the right atrium. In its ascent through the abdomen the inferior vena cava receives a *renal* vein from each of the kidneys, and more anteriorly, the *hepatic* vein from the liver.

VENOUS BLOOD FLOW IN THE LIVER. The return of blood to the heart from the major organs of the digestive tract (stomach, small intestine, and large intestine) and the spleen in vertebrates has a unique aspect. The blood leaving these organs, instead of draining directly into the inferior vena cava, flows into veins connecting to a large blood vessel, the *hepatic portal vein*, leading to the liver. Within the liver the hepatic portal vein subdivides into smaller veins and ultimately into capillaries which then unite into veins again. The veins leaving the liver join together to form the *hepatic vein* which drains directly into the inferior vena cava. Here we have a distinctive situation in which capillaries (of the major organs of the digestive tract) drain to a large vein (hepatic portal vein) which then ramifies into capillaries again (in the liver) finally giving rise to a large vein once more (hepatic vein).

It is during the passage of blood through the densely packed capillaries of the liver that the removal and storage of a significant portion of the freshly absorbed digestion products (amino acids, simple sugars, and vitamins) by the liver occurs. The subsequent release of these stored materials to the capillaries by the liver under appropriate conditions results in an enrichment of the blood leaving the liver. It should not be overlooked that the liver in addition to receiving unaerated blood via the hepatic portal vein receives aerated blood from the hepatic artery, a branch of the coeliac artery.

BLOOD PRESSURE. The force of blood against the walls of blood vessels is known as *blood pressure*. The pressure of blood in the circulatory system, like the pressure of any fluid within a confined volume, depends on (*a*) localized changes of the circulatory space as a result of contraction and relaxation of the heart, arteries, arterioles, and even the capillaries; (*b*) net shifts in blood volume depending on the amounts of blood entering and leaving a vessel, including the important considerations of the amount of blood and the force with which it is pumped out by the heart in a given period of time; and (*c*) other factors such as the total blood volume, vessel elasticity, and blood viscosity.

Blood pressure varies appreciably in different parts of the circulatory system. The highest pressure is encountered in the largest artery of the body, the *aorta*, close to the heart, where it normally ranges to 140 mm of mercury. It progressively decreases in the arteries and *arterioles* more distant from the heart, becoming lower in the capillaries and still lower in the veins. It is lowest in the inferior and superior vena cava veins reaching zero mm of mercury or even less just before they enter the right atrium. The sharpest drop in blood pressure (as much as 70 mm of mercury) takes place in the arterioles and capillaries where the friction of the blood against the blood vessel walls is greatest, due largely to the marked increase in wall surface per unit volume of blood. Blood pressure variations are roughly indicated by the rate and force with which blood escapes from cut vessels, in rapid forceful spurts from an artery and in a slow flow from capillaries and veins. Arterial blood pressure undergoes a rhythmic change reaching a maximum during ventricular systole when blood is pumped into the arteries, and decreasing during ventricular diastole. The highest arterial blood pressure experienced during the contraction stage of the heart ventricles is accordingly called *systolic pressure*, and the lowest (due to ventricular diastole), *diastolic pressure*.

Measurement of Blood Pressure. The first reported determination of blood pressure was made in 1733 by the famous English biologist and clergyman Stephen Hales, who connected a vertical glass tube to one of the carotid arteries of a resting horse. The blood reached a height of 9 feet 6 inches in the glass tubing, its level fluctuating in a rhythmic fashion—rising with each ventricular systole and falling with each diastole.

Today, blood pressure may be determined indirectly and far more conveniently by observing the applied external pressure necessary to collapse the artery in the upper left arm of a patient in the sitting position. External pressure is applied by inflating an airtight rubber cuff tied around the arm. Readings are then taken on a mercury manometer at those pressures which just permit the reflow of blood into the rest of the arm. The reflow of blood under these conditions at ventricular systole and at ventricular diastole create characteristic sounds which can be heard by means of a stethoscope placed over the arm artery below the rubber cuff. In this manner the two measurements of blood pressure (*systolic* and *diastolic pressures*) are obtained. The normal systolic pressure in man and in most other mammals ranges from about 120 to 140 mm of mercury, whereas diastolic pressure ranges from about 75 to 90. These vary considerably, however, and are affected by numerous factors including age, sex, heredity, and physical and emotional states.

PULSE. As each ventricular systole causes the spurting of blood into the aorta, the elastic walls of the aorta at the site of impact distend and then contract. The result is a transmission along the arterial walls of a wave of alternate stretchings and contractions to all arteries and arterioles, a phenomenon called the *pulse wave* or the *pulse*. The pulse is not due to the arrival of blood at the wrist, but to the transmission along the elastic arterial walls of the impact of blood suddenly entering the aorta. It is most conveniently detected by placing one's finger over an artery located near the body surface such as at the wrist of the left arm. The pulse travels independently of blood flow about 10 to 15 times more rapidly than blood itself. Its velocity is approximately the same throughout the arterial system, in contrast to the progressively decreased blood pressure in arteries farther away from the heart.

VELOCITY OF BLOOD FLOW. Obviously the amount of blood returned to the heart (by the superior and inferior vena cavae) must in general equal the quantity pumped out by the left ventricle in any given time. The rate of blood flow varies in different vessels, being high in the larger arteries (about 400 to 500 mm per second in the aorta), decreasing somewhat along the arterial system, becoming greatly reduced in the capillaries (less than 1 mm per second), and increasing again to an appreciable rate in the large veins (about 150 mm per second).

These differences in velocity of flow are governed largely by the changes in the total vessel cross-sectional area encountered by the blood during its passage through the circulatory system. In a model system of tubes of increasing diameter connected end to end, the flow of fluid from smaller diameter to larger, diameter tubes is decreased in the larger tubes (Figure 26-9). The same principal holds if the larger tubes are replaced by a group of smaller diameter tubes arranged in parallel provided their *total* cross-sectional area exceeds the diameter of the inlet tube. This is essentially the type of relationship that exists in the circulatory system. As the large arteries proceed away from the heart, they branch into thousands of progressively smaller arteries, ultimately giving rise to arterioles, each of which leads to numerous capillaries. Although each of these branches has a diameter smaller than that of the vessel from which they originated, the total cross-sectional area of these branches is greater (Figure 26-9). As expected a decreased rate of blood flow in the branches

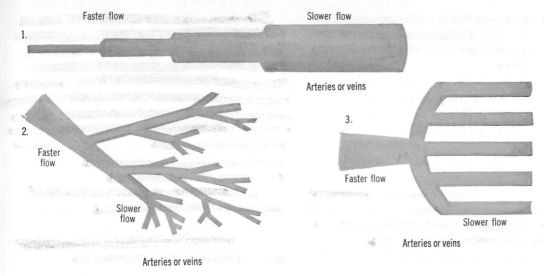

Figure 26-9. Dependence of the velocity of flow of a fluid, including blood, upon the total cross-sectional area of the conducting tubes. See text for details.

is the result. The tremendous increase in total cross-sectional area at those points where arterioles give rise to capillaries accounts for the correspondingly sudden and marked decrease in the rate of blood flow. Since the transfer of nutrients, hormones, and metabolic wastes between the blood and tissues occurs solely at the capillaries, the slow rate of blood flow is advantageous in allowing adequate time for exchange.

Conversely the joining of capillaries to form veins, which unite into large veins resulting in an overall decrease of total cross-sectional area of the vessels as they return to the heart, is accompanied by an increased rate of blood flow.

The flow of blood in the arteries is of a spasmodic intermittent nature, being most rapid during ventricular contraction and slower during ventricular diastole. The spurting type of blood flow is most marked in the aorta, becoming less spasmodic and less intermittent in the arteries farther away from the heart until it is finally transformed into a steady and continuous flow in the capillaries and veins. The pulsating, elastic, arterial walls during ventricular diastole serve to push the blood

along until the next ventricular systole. The difference between the rates of flow of arterial blood during systole and diastole becomes less and less farther and farther from the heart.

In addition to the pumping action of the heart two other factors facilitate the movement of blood through the veins. First, contractions of surrounding skeletal muscle cause the veins to collapse, forcing the blood to move toward the heart since the valves present in the large veins of the arms and legs prevent flow in the opposite direction. For example, exercise by walking or running acts as an important aid in returning blood from the legs against the pull of gravity. Second, in the process of breathing the lowered pressure within the chest cavity during the inspiration phase also lowers the pressure of blood within the chest veins and the atria accounting for an increased flow of venous blood toward the heart.

DISTRIBUTION OF BLOOD. The metabolic activities, and therefore the blood supply required, in different parts of the body may vary markedly within short periods of time. The use of certain muscles, the processes of digestion and absorption, and other energy-requiring activities by different tissues of the body are synonymous with a need by these active cells for an increased blood supply to provide more nutrients and to remove metabolic wastes.

The differential distribution of blood at various times to different parts of the body according to their needs is primarily determined by the diameter of the arterioles which lead to the capillaries in these areas. This makes it possible to divert blood from one tissue and direct it to another where it may be more urgently required. Arteriole diameters are controlled by the contraction and relaxation of the smooth muscle fibers arranged in circular rings in the arteriolar walls. The state of contraction or relaxation of the arteriolar muscle fibers (and therefore the quantity of blood flowing into these vessels and their connecting capillaries) is under the direct influence of both nervous and chemical factors. In addition to affecting blood supply, the diameter of the arterioles also has a direct influence on blood pressure in the tissues served by the arterioles.

Smooth muscle of arterioles, like heart muscle, is supplied with two sets of nerves from the visceral nervous system. Impulses received along one set of nerve fibers result in constriction of the arterioles in the internal organs, thus reducing the blood supply to the capillaries arising from these arterioles and therefore to that area or organ of the body. It also increases the local blood pressure. Impulses arriving along the second set of nerves, however, cause the arteriolar muscle to relax and thus account for vascular dilation. The increased diameter of the arterioles is responsible for the increased flow of blood and the decreased blood pressure in the connecting capillaries of that region. Impulses transmitted along the two sets of nerves originate from particular nerve centers in the medulla oblongata which are in turn affected by impulses from higher nerve centers and other parts of the body. A high concentration of carbon dioxide in the blood stream exerts a direct effect on these nerve centers in the medulla, resulting in arteriolar constriction.

The muscle fibers of the arterioles are also directly affected by certain chemicals such as adrenaline and carbon dioxide since the arterioles respond to these compounds whether or not their nerves have been severed. The increased acidity, arising in part from higher concentrations of carbonic acid as a result of an increased metabolism, directly causes the smooth muscle fibers to relax. In this manner it increases the local supply of blood (as well as decreases the blood pressure) in the active area. Carbon dioxide therefore has a dual action. It may affect certain nerve centers, and in local areas under metabolic stress increased concentrations may directly dilate the arterioles without mediation of the nervous system, thus increasing the blood supply to that particular region. However, through its action on the central nervous system, carbon dioxide has the overall effect of constricting the arterioles. Thus it brings about a general rise in blood pressure and a fall in blood supply to other than the highly active tissues.

Adrenaline is also responsible for different responses of the arteriolar muscle fibers depending on the location of the blood vessels. It causes dilation of the arterioles serving the skeletal muscles, on the one hand, and constriction of the arterioles in the muscles of the internal organs such as the digestive system on the other.

Our knowledge of circulatory control—more specifically blood supply and blood pressure regulation—is far from complete. Various research studies are beginning to uncover an intricate array of additional chemical factors which add up to an extremely complex picture. There is evidence that a number of substances (e.g., heparin and histamine) obtained from tissues may be serving as local regulatory factors in blood circulation by inhibiting the ability of some of the small blood vessel muscles to constrict. We know that steroid hormones produced by the cortex of the adrenal gland (Chapter 23) indirectly affect circulation. We have also known for some time that *vasopressin,* a hormone secreted by the posterior lobe of the pituitary gland, exerts a direct effect in stimulating arteriolar constriction.

In addition, an enzyme formed in the kidneys has been shown to exert a highly significant influence on capillary circulation. The early experiments, performed more than 50 years ago, demonstrating that kidney tissue extracts raised the blood pressure of laboratory animals have been extended and amplified to the point where we have fairly detailed information concerning the mechanisms involved. Our current knowledge indicates that an enzyme formed in the kidney and another in the blood act successively on a protein substrate in the blood stream to yield an eight-amino-acid polypeptide called *Angiotensin II*, one of the most active compounds known for elevating blood pressure. The identity of Angiotensin II has been confirmed by a long and arduous chemical synthesis, and its physiological properties verified.

In summary, the control of blood flow, blood distribution, and blood pressure is determined by a complex interrelationship of both nervous and chemical factors which act primarily by controlling the constriction and dilation of the blood vessel musculature. Chemical factors probably play an even more important role than nervous regulation in the control of the smaller blood vessels, since many of their smooth muscle cells have no direct innervation. Actually the mechanism of nervous controls is basically explained in chemical terms since the autonomic nervous system affects muscle action and therefore blood vessel bore through the secretion of sympathin and acetylcholine by appropriate nerve endings.

THE LYMPHATIC SYSTEM. Lymph, also called *tissue fluid*, is derived primarily from blood plasma which has filtered through the capillary walls into the internal spaces surrounding all cells. It differs from blood plasma in having about half the protein concentration. Variations exist in the concentrations of other substances in the lymph as compared to plasma depending on additions and withdrawals made by the surrounding cells. Lymph may have white blood cells which have passed out the capillaries and, in particular, lymphocytes which are produced in the lymphatic system itself.

While some lymph may reenter the blood stream directly by way of the capillaries, most of it instead passes into a separate network of vessels collectively called the *lymphatics* or *lymphatic system* (Figure 26-10). The lymphatics are found in all parts of the body and range in size from that of capillaries to that of larger veins. They strongly resemble capillaries and veins in wall structure and the possession by the larger lymphatic vessels of valves which prevent backflow. One important difference, however, is that the lymphatics do not enjoy a continuous closed circulation. Instead the microscopic lymph vessels which correspond to capillaries terminate in a dead end. Lymph is largely taken up by the microscopic vessels and moves slowly in one direction to the larger and larger lymph vessels, which ultimately converge into two large trunks in the upper portion of the torso. Each lymphatic trunk drains into the right and left subclavian veins, respectively, thus returning fluid directly to the venous blood stream. Most of the lymph actually enters the blood by way of the left subclavian vein.

In man and other mammals the flow of lymph through lymphatic vessels, like the flow of blood through the veins, is ascribed principally to the contraction and relaxation of skeletal muscle in the surrounding tissues and to the breathing movements of the organism. The flow of lymph from the area of the intestines is in addition uniquely facilitated by the rhythmic wave-like motion or contraction of the millions of finger-like microscopic projections, the *villi*, present on the inner surface (see Figure 24-7) of the intestinal wall.

In many of the lower vertebrates (e.g., the frog) lymph is propelled by a number of "lymph hearts"—thickened muscular portions in the walls of some lymph vessels which propel the lymph by their pulsating action. The evolutionary significance of the absence of "lymph hearts" in mammals is not clear.

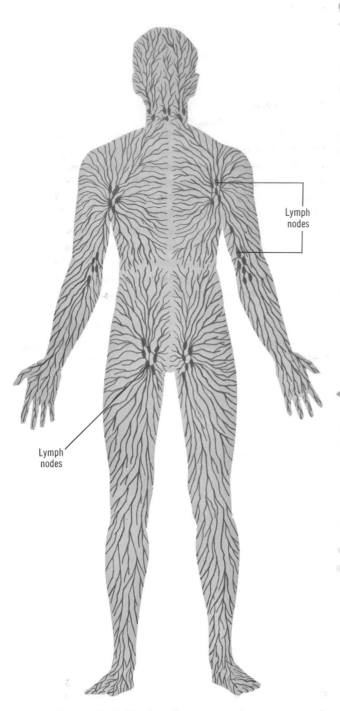

At many points in the body, where the smaller lymph vessels unite to form larger ones, are lumpy masses or aggregations of cells known as *lymph nodes* (Figure 26-11). These play an important role in the body's defense against disease by producing lymphocytes and antibodies as well as filtering out bacteria and foreign particles.

The lymphatic system performs a nvmber of important functions. First, it has a significant role in returning tissue fluids to the blood stream. Although it is true that the blood capillaries also take up some of the intracellular fluid, the major contribution in this respect is made by the lymphatics. Second, by virtue of the greater permeability of the microscopic lymph vessels (as compared to the blood capillaries) to large protein molecules, fats, and even solid particles, the lymphatic system serves to return and transport proteins and fats to the blood stream. It is a well-established fact that most of the products of fat digestion are absorbed from the small intestine by the lymphatic networks in the villi (amino acids and sugars are taken up by the blood capillaries). Third, the lymphatic system aids in the fight against invading microorganisms through the production of lymphocytes and antibodies, and the filtering action of the lymph nodes. It should be noted that lymphocytes also originate in a similar lymphoid tissue found in the spleen, tonsils, and certain other organs. Finally, filtration by the lymph nodes serves not only to remove microorganisms from the body fluids but also any foreign particles (e.g., dust and soot), including cancer cells, which may have broken loose from other tissues and eventually entered the lymph stream. In some instances the trapping of bacteria in the lymph nodes may result in an infection and swelling of the nodes; or in the case of freely circulating cancer cells, the trapping and subsequent proliferation of the malignant tissues in the lymph nodes.

THE SPLEEN. The spleen is probably best classified as an organ belong to the circulatory system. In man it is somewhat larger than the

Lymph nodes

Lymph nodes

Figure 26-10. The lymphatic system in man.

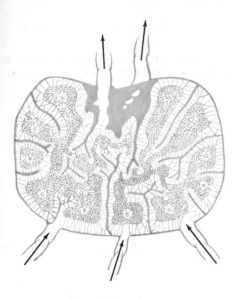

Figure 26-11. Diagram of a lymph node.

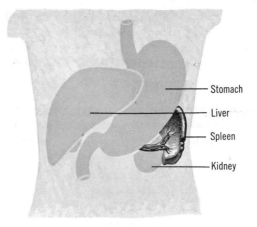

Figure 26-12. The spleen in man.

kidneys, about the size of a clenched fist, reddish-brown in color, and situated in the dorsal upper left region of the abdomen behind the stomach and above the left kidney (Figure 26-12). It contains a large amount of smooth muscle, and its internal structure is permeated by small areas of lymphoid tissue and many cavities connected directly to the blood vascular system.

Clarification of the spleen's function was finally made after years of research effort, and it is likely that other functions for this organ will be uncovered in the future. The spleen appears to serve uniquely as a blood reservoir, containing blood of a high red cell concentration within its cavities. Contraction of its smooth muscles as a result of hemorrhage, physical or emotional stress, low oxygen tension in the blood, carbon monoxide poisoning, or higher environmental temperatures decreases the volume of the organ, thus squeezing the stored blood contained in the cavities directly into the blood stream. In addition, the spleen produces lymphocytes, destroys worn-out red blood cells (as does the liver), and in the embryo contributes to the production of red blood cells.

The spleen, however, is not essential under normal conditions, since it can be removed without causing any serious effects. It is probable that under certain stress conditions as mentioned, it might well be critical in determining survival of the organism.

CHANGES IN THE CIRCULATORY SYSTEM AFTER BIRTH. A number of dramatic and remarkable changes take place in the circulatory system of the newborn child. Our information concerning the mechanisms initiating birth and the accompanying radical changes in the circulatory system are meager and for the most part at the speculative stage. The lungs of the fetus (or embryo) during pregnancy are partially collapsed and nonfunctional as far as breathing is concerned, receiving just enough blood to meet their metabolic needs. Blood flow to and from the fetal lungs is limited by the partially collapsed state of the pulmonary blood vessels as well as by the presence of two temporary structural by-passes, one in the fetal heart and one between the pulmonary artery and the aorta. The fetal heart possesses a flap-like oval opening in the wall separating the right and left atria which permits only right-to-left flow (Figure 26-13). It accounts for the transfer of a large portion of blood directly from the right to the left heart without passing through the lungs. Some blood, however, does flow from the right atrium into the right ventricle, but upon being pumped into the pulmonary artery is in large part almost immediately shunted directly into the aorta by means of an embryonic vessel, the *arterial duct,* or *ductus arteriosus,* connecting the pulmonary artery to the aorta (Figure 26-13).

With the tying-off and cutting of the umbilical cord at birth a series of drastic and rapid changes occur. The newborn infant's lungs expand for the first time to initiate the breathing cycle. The phenomenon is usually ascribed to stimulation of the respiratory center in the brain by the accumulating carbon dioxide in the blood stream. It is accompanied by a dilation of the pulmonary blood vessels permitting a greater flow of blood through the pulmonary artery to the expanded lungs instead of a shunting through the arterial duct to the aorta. The consequently greater flow of blood from the lungs via the pulmonary vein to the left atrium and the resulting higher pressure of the increased blood volume tend to close the oval opening in the atrial wall by pushing the protruding wall flap over it. The bore of the arterial duct is quickly blocked off by the rapid growth of endothelial lining, and the wall flap closing the oval window eventually grows permanently

into place. Most of these amazing changes normally occur within a few minutes following birth. In due course the remains of the arterial duct and the umbilical vessels are converted to connective tissue.

At times the oval opening or arterial duct may fail to close completely. These impairments usually do not cause an insufficient aeration of the blood. Other types of circulatory defects, however, such as a large opening in the wall separating the ventricles and a partial obstruction to blood flow in the pulmonary artery, may result in an inadequate aeration of the blood. In these cases the insufficiently oxygenated hemoglobin as seen in the skin capillaries has a bluish cast instead of the normal scarlet color of oxyhemaglobin. Children suffering from this condition are known as "blue babies."

During the prenatal stage the blood of the fully formed embryo or *fetus* receives its oxygen and nutrients by diffusion from the maternal blood stream, and discharges its metabolic waste products including carbon dioxide by diffusion into the mother's blood. This exchange of nutrients and wastes takes place in the placenta (Chapter 31) where the capillaries of the fetus and the blood of the mother are in close proximity. The placenta which thus performs the nutritional, respiratory, and excretory functions of the fetus is itself a combination of embryonic and maternal tissues connecting the fetus by means of the umbilical cord to the wall of the womb. Fetal blood is conveyed through the umbilical cord to the placenta via two umbilical arteries which arise as branches from the lower part of the aorta. Oxygenated blood from the placenta is transported to the fetus by way of the umbilical vein which eventually drains into the inferior vena cava.

FETAL AND MATERNAL HEMOGLOBINS. The transfer of oxygen from the oxyhemaglobin of the maternal blood to the hemoglobin of the fetal blood by diffusion is of considerable interest since the blood in the umbilical vein proceeding from the placenta to the fetus has a higher oxygen saturation than the maternal blood in the placenta from which it obtains

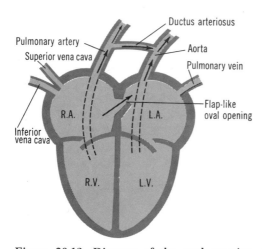

Figure 26-13. Diagram of the oval opening and arterial duct in the heart of a newborn child. See text for details.

it oxygen. This apparent paradox has been resolved by the finding that fetal hemoglobin possesses certain chemical and physical properties different from that of hemoglobin in an older animal. It is able to absorb a significantly larger volume of oxygen under given conditions as compared to adult hemoglobin accounting for the greater oxygen saturation of fetal blood.

For example, at body temperature, 30 mm of oxygen, and pH 6.8, fetal blood is 58 per cent saturated with oxygen, whereas maternal blood is only 33 per cent saturated. Fetal hemoglobin ordinarily begins to disappear from the blood after birth and is usually completely replaced by the adult type within 4 to 6 months.

SUPPLEMENTARY REFERENCES

Best, C. H., and N. B. Taylor, *The Physiological Basis of Medical Practise,* fifth edition, Williams and Wilkins, Baltimore, 1950.

Carlson, A. J., and V. Johnson, *The Machinery of the Body,* fifth edition, University of Chicago Press, Chicago, 1962.

Prosser, C. L., Editor, *Comparative Animal Physiology,* second edition, Saunders, Philadelphia, 1961.

Rogers, T. A., *Elementary Human Physiology,* Wiley, New York, 1961.

Zweifach, B. W., "The Microcirculation of the Blood," *Scientific American,* January 1959.

Chapter 27   Respiration

GENERAL CONSIDERATIONS

Definitions

RESPIRATION. Unfortunately for the beginning student in biology the term *respiration* has several different meanings. As used in cell metabolism (Chapter 8), respiration refers to the integrated series of chemical reactions by which the living cell obtains energy for its various life functions from particular food or nutrients.

All higher animals carry on aerobic respiration (Chapter 8) and must therefore have a means for expediting the necessary exchange of oxygen and carbon dioxide between the organism and its external environment, a process which is also called *respiration*. Accordingly, the organs and tissues of the body that function together as a system to accomplish the rapid exchange of respiratory gases between the organism and its external environment is called the *respiratory system*. It is in this sense rather than from the viewpoint of cell metabolism that the term respiration or respiratory system is used in the present chapter. The widespread application of the term to the process of breathing, namely inhaling and exhaling, is also broadly included within this meaning.

PARTIAL PRESSURES OF GASES. *Exchange of Gases between the Blood and Its Environment.* The concentration of gases in a mixture can be expressed in several ways. Air, for example, is an excellent illustration of a natural gas mixture. Its gaseous components can be expressed on a percentage basis or on the basis of their *partial pressures* (or *tensions*). The latter is the contribution that each gas makes to the total pressure of the gas mixture. On a percentage basis air consists of almost 80 per cent nitrogen (N_2), approximately 20 per cent oxygen (O_2), 0.04 per cent carbon dioxide (CO_2), and small concentrations of several other gases. The pressure of air under conditions of standard temperature and standard atmospheric pressure is balanced by the pressure of a column of mercury 760 mm high (or by a column of water 32 feet high) and can therefore be designated in these convenient terms. Since nitrogen represents 80 per cent of the atmosphere its partial pressure in the air is $80/100 \times 760$ mm = 608 mm of mercury. Similarly, the partial pressure of oxygen would be $20/100 \times 760$ = 156 mm of mercury, and that of carbon dioxide $.04/100 \times 760$ = 0.3 mm of mercury. The use of partial pressures as a convenient means of designating gas concentrations is applied to gases whether they are dissolved in other gases, liquids, or solids.

Basic Features of a Respiratory System

In unicellular animals and small aquatic organisms (such as the coelenterates and flatworms) no specialized respiratory system is needed. The exchange of oxygen and carbon dioxide between the organism and its watery environment is carried out directly and adequately by diffusion. In the more complex animal forms the direct exchange of respiratory gases between organism and environment can obviously no longer suitably fulfill the needs of all the body cells in this respect. The multicellular organisms that evolved an adequate respiratory organ or respiratory system therefore must have had a distinct advantage in survival and propagation of the species.

Several different types of respiratory systems are found among the various multicellular species of the animal kingdom. All, however, share at least two basic features in common. Whatever the form of respiratory organ or respiratory system each and every type must be well provided with a *transportation system*, namely the blood-vascular system, that carries oxygen to and carbon dioxide away from the cells of the body. The second important requisite is an *extensive* and *thin epithelial surface* (in close contact with a rich supply of capillaries), a structural arrangement that permits a rapid entry of fresh oxygen into the transportation or blood system and a rapid elimination of carbon dioxide at the same time. The respiratory epithelium is constantly maintained in a moist condition, thus assuring that sufficient water is present for dissolving the oxygen and carbon dioxide in their passage between the blood and external environment.

The extensive surface area of the respiratory system is necessary to meet the requirements of the organism for obtaining an adequate supply of oxygen and disposing of waste carbon dioxide. The human body at rest, for example, must obtain 250 ml of oxygen each minute from the surrounding atmosphere, and may require up to 10 times as much during physical exertion. In order to do so it must present to the atmosphere a large and well-vascularized surface for gaseous exchange in the form of a respiratory system which meets the two basic requirements indicated earlier. This is precisely what it does in the form of the internal surfaces (*pulmonary alveoli,* p. 634) of the lungs with its rich supply of capillaries, collectively equivalent to a total surface area of approximately 100 square meters—some 50 times as great as the body surface.

To the best of our knowledge the operation of the gas transport-exchange system (uptake and release of oxygen and carbon dioxide) is based on the physical principle of diffusion no matter what type of respiratory organ is involved. Under normal circumstances the aerobic metabolism of a cell results in a decrease of oxygen and an elevation of carbon dioxide tensions. The passage near the cell of blood possessing relatively high oxygen and low carbon dioxide tensions will be accompanied by an exchange of gases. Oxygen will diffuse from the region of its higher partial pressure (the blood) into the cell, and carbon dioxide will move from the region of its higher partial pressure (the cell) into the blood. Blood arrives at the gills or lungs, as the case may be, with a deficiency of oxygen and a surplus of carbon dioxide in contrast to the opposite conditions which exist on the atmosphere side of the respiratory membrane. By virtue of the pressure gradient, oxygen from the external environment diffuses into the blood, whereas surplus carbon dioxide by the same token is discharged from the blood.

The remarkable ability of hemoglobin in the red blood cells to take up and carry molecular oxygen is an all-important factor in the transport of oxygen. Hemoglobin accounts for the ability of blood to transport 60 times as much oxygen (20 ml per 100 ml of blood) as the oxygen-carrying capacity of blood plasma (0.3 ml per 100 ml) where the gas is present in simple physical solution.

In effect, respiration consists of three phases: The first phase involves the exchange of gases between the blood and external environment or the air; the second consists of the transport by the blood of gases between the lungs and cells of the body; and the third is represented by the exchange of gases between the blood and body cells. The latter phase fulfills the

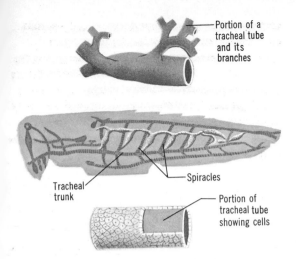

Figure 27-1. Diagram of the tracheal respiratory system of the grasshopper. (*Adapted from T. I. Storer, General Zoology, second edition, McGraw-Hill, 1951.*)

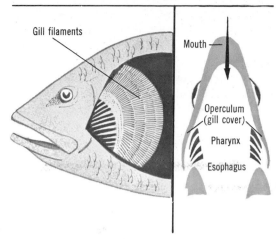

Figure 27-2. Diagram of the gills in a bony fish.

ultimate function of the respiratory system in that it provides oxygen to the many cells and tissues of the body and rids them of waste carbon dioxide.

Types of Respiratory Systems

The outer integument or skin is the most common, if not the only, device used for respiration by several of the invertebrates and lowest vertebrates as well as the embryos and larvae of fishes and amphibians. It is probably the most primitive type of respiratory membrane. In the earthworm, for example, the moist skin is the respiratory organ. Oxygen transport to all cells of the body as well as carbon dioxide removal to the skin is performed by the blood of the circulatory system. In amphibians the skin is in fact still a principal respiratory organ in addition to the gills in the tadpole and the lungs in the adult. It is also employed to a slight extent in terrestrial vertebrates. In the turtle, pigeon, and man, for example, the major respiratory organs are the lungs but some gaseous exchange takes place through the skin. The epithelium of the mouth and pharynx is also used by amphibians as a respiratory organ.

In most insects oxygen is carried directly to the cells and tissues, and carbon dioxide is removed by a branching system of air tubes called trachea (Figure 27-1). The latter open to the outside by a pair of small pores called *spiracles* located in each body segment. The pulsating abdominal walls of the insect are responsible for drawing air into the trachea and forcing it out. In the grasshopper, for example, of the ten pairs of spiracles on the sides of its body, the four front pair open as the abdomen expands, drawing air into the body, and the other six pair close. With the subsequent contraction of the abdomen the front four pairs close and the hind six pairs open, forcing the air through the tubes to the cells and tissues and eventually out of the body.

As a general rule the two major respiratory organs of vertebrates are *gills* and *lungs.* Gills are best adapted for obtaining oxygen from an external aqueous medium and releasing carbon dioxide to it, whereas the lungs are best designed for operating in an external medium of air. Gills are tufted or layered outgrowths covered by a very thin layer of cells beneath which is a rich concentration of blood capillaries (Figure 27-2). They are found in fishes and some amphibians and occur along the sides of pouches in the region of the pharynx. As the respiratory organs which perform the same function as lungs, the gills obtain the oxygen dissolved in water. Water enters the pharynx by way of the mouth and is forced through the gill slits over the gill surfaces to the outside. Gas exchange between the water and the blood, consisting of the uptake of oxygen and giving off of carbon dioxide, occurs at the gills through the process of diffusion.

THE RESPIRATORY SYSTEM OF MAN

Structure

All organs that make possible the exchange of oxygen and carbon dioxide between the organism and its environment constitute the respiratory system. In man and other mammals it includes the *lungs* and the *air passageways* which lead to them (Figure 27-3).

AIR PASSAGEWAYS. These consist of the *nose, pharynx, larynx, trachea, bronchi,* and *bronchioles.* The interior of the nose is hollow and is divided by a wall or septum into two lateral halves, the right and left nasal cavities. Each nasal cavity is lined with a mucous membrane consisting largely of ciliated epithelial cells and is subdivided essentially into three passageways by the projection of several bones from the lateral walls of the internal nose. Air enters the nasal cavities by way of the nostrils or *anterior nares.* During its passage through the internal nose it is warmed, moistened, and filtered of dust and foreign particles by the mucous membrane. The air is also chemically examined by the specialized smell receptor cells located in the mucous membrane in a small upper recess of the nasal cavity. The nasal cavities lead into the throat or *pharynx* by two internal openings called *posterior nares.*

The *pharynx* or throat as a muscular passage lined with mucous membrane, channelizes air to the larynx or voice box and food from the mouth to the esophagus or foodpipe. The seven

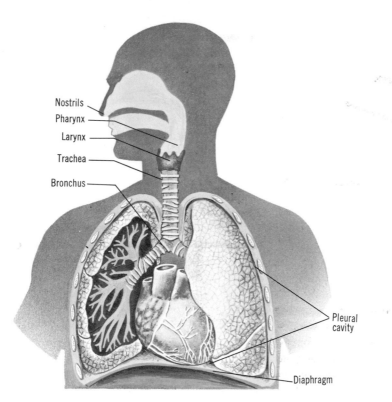

Nostrils
Pharynx
Larynx
Trachea
Bronchus
Pleural cavity
Diaphragm

Figure 27-3. Respiratory system of man (including "bronchial tree" of right lung).

openings found in the pharynx include the two posterior nares, the two Eustachian tubes each leading from the middle ear, the mouth, the opening into the larynx, and the opening into the esophagus. The tonsils and adenoids are located in the pharynx.

The *larynx* or *voice box*, situated in the neck just below the pharynx, is a complex cartilage structure surrounding the upper end of the trachea or windpipe. It connects the pharynx above and the trachea below it, and is made up of nine cartilage sections bound together by an elastic membrane and two groups of muscles which control its movement. One of the cartilage sections composing the larynx, called the *epiglottis*, has a muscularly controlled, hinge-like action and serves as a lid which automatically covers the opening of the larynx during the act of swallowing. Thus it serves to prevent the entry of foods or liquids into the larynx during their passage to the esophagus. The cavity or space within the larynx called the *glottis* is lined with mucous membrane which is continuous with that of the pharynx and trachea, and contains stretched across it two thin-edged fibrous bands called the *vocal cords*.

The larynx is responsible for voice or sound production, a function determined by the vibrations of the vocal cords produced by the passage of air through the voice box. Sound has three properties — *loudness*, *pitch*, and *quality* (Chapter 22). The production of loudness depends on the energy with which the vocal cords vibrate, the greater the movements of the cords the louder the sound. Pitch is determined by the length and tension of the vocal cords. Long, relaxed vocal cords are responsible for low-pitched notes whereas short, tense cords produce high notes. Women and children, in contrast to men, have shorter cords and therefore high pitched voices. Changes in tension and position of the vocal cords are attained by the action of muscles attached to several of the cartilage sections of the larynx. The quality or timbre of voice production depends on the number and intensity of the overtones or harmonics and is aided by the nose, trachea, and chest acting as sounding boards or resonating chambers.

The *trachea* or *windpipe* is a tubular structure about 4 to 5 inches long with a diameter of approximately 1 inch. It is located in front of (or ventral to) the esophagus and extends from the larynx downward through the neck just into the chest cavity or *thorax* where it divides into the *right* and *left bronchi*. In cross section the trachea wall is made up of three tissue layers: an *inner layer of epithelial cells* consisting of several layers of ciliated cells and underlying mucus-secreting cells; a *middle layer of incomplete rings of cartilage with smooth muscle fibers* stretching between them; and an *outer dense elastic connective tissue layer*. The trachea wall contains a series of some 15 to 20 C-shaped cartilage rings (they are incomplete dorsally where the trachea is adjacent to the esophagus) which prevent the trachea from collapsing, thus maintaining an open passageway for air (Figure 27-3). The tissues between the cartilage rings and in the dorsal cartilage gaps consist largely of a strong fibroelastic membrane containing smooth muscle fibers. The inner surface of the trachea is lined with ciliated columnar epithelial cells whose cilia beat upward, tending to create air and mucus currents which impede the entry of small foreign bodies into the air passageway.

The right and left bronchi enter the right and left lungs respectively and almost immediately divide and subdivide into progressively smaller and smaller bronchi branches. The right lung consists of three primary lobes and the left lung of two primary lobes (Figure 27-3) so that the right bronchus initially divides into three main branches, one to each lobe, before further subdividing, whereas the left bronchus divides into two main branches.

The bronchial tubes have the same type of structure as the trachea, including cartilage rings and an inner ciliated epithelial lining. As the bronchi subdivide into smaller and smaller tubes the cartilage rings are progressively replaced by irregularly distributed and isolated cartilage plates which become smaller and fewer in number. When the smaller bronchi attain a diameter of 1 mm or less, the cartilage is entirely lacking and the tubes are now called *bronchioles*. Their walls, made up essentially of circularly arranged smooth muscle, are lined on their inner surface with epithelial tissue similar to that of the trachea and bronchi. The muscle of bronchioles is innervated by nerves from both the sympathetic and parasympathetic nervous systems which are the basis of the usual reflex response (Chapter 21) for adjusting the diameters of the bronchioles. Marked bronchiolar constriction is responsible for the respiratory distress which is so characteristic of asthmatic attacks.

The trachea, the two connecting bronchi, and their many branches show a striking similarity to an inverted miniature tree and for this reason are often referred to collectively as the *"bronchial tree"* (Figure 27-3). No interchange of gases can occur across its relatively thick walls. Its primary function is to serve as a passageway by which air can reach the interior units of the lungs, namely the *alveoli* (see following section), just as the arteries and veins of the circulatory system conduct the blood to and from the capillaries.

THE LUNGS. *Microscopic Structure.* As they proceed deeper and deeper into the lungs, the bronchiole tubes continue to divide and subdivide, each finally opening into one of the many *air sacs* that constitute the functional units of the lung. Each air sac looks like a cluster of grapes (Figure 27-4) and consists of several microscopic out-pocketings (usually four to six) in its wall structure; these are called *alveoli*. The total number of alveoli in both lungs is estimated at nearly a billion. It is at the alveolar surfaces, which are lined with a rich supply of capillaries, that the interchange of gases between the air and blood occurs. By the time the final bronchiole has reached the air sac, only the internal layer of epithelial cells remains. The walls of the alveoli are composed simply of a single layer of squamous epithelial cells which

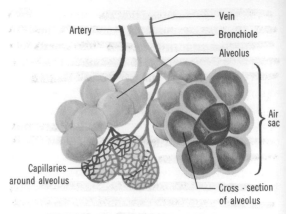

Figure 27-4. Diagram of microscopic portion of the lung of man showing bronchioles leading into air sacs. Each air sac consists of several alveoli.

overlie a rich network of capillaries and are admirably suited to function as a respiratory membrane. It has in fact been claimed that in some portions of the alveoli the membrane does not exist, and that the interchange of gases at these sites takes place directly between the capillaries and the air.

Gross Structure. The chest as a closed cavity is bounded at the sides by the ribs and body wall; at the rear by the spinal column, ribs, and body wall; in front by the ribs, breast bone, and body wall; above by the upper ribs and tissues of the body wall and neck; and at the bottom by the dome-shaped sheet of skeletal muscle, the *diaphragm*. The chest itself is divided vertically by a double wall within which lie the heart, the connecting large blood vessels, esophagus, and nerves, whereas the lungs are in the so-called *pleural cavities* on each side (Figure 27-3).

Each lung consists of its bronchial tree with its many air sacs and alveoli units together with associated structures such as blood vessels, nerves, and pleura. All are supported and attached to one another by a connective tissue framework. Both lungs are covered with a thin membrane called the *pleura* which extends from the point of entry of the bronchus into the lung to cover the interior surface of the chest cavity including the upper surface of the diaphragm. Thus the lungs are enclosed within a double sac consisting of the pleural membrane covering the lungs and its extension which lines the inside surface of the thoracic cavity (Figure 27-3). Under normal circumstances, during expansion of the lungs with air in the process of breathing, the pleura covering the lung and that lining the internal chest surface come in contact. There is usually just enough fluid between the two pleuras for lubrication to avoid friction and irritation during contact in the breathing process. When the pleura are inflamed the condition is known as *pleurisy* and is frequently accompanied by the accumulation of excess fluid between the two membranes.

The Physiology of Breathing

MECHANICS OF THE BREATHING PROCESS. Breathing is a mechanical process made up of two phases, the taking in of air, called *inspiration,* and the letting out of air, called *expiration.* Under placid or resting conditions the two phases occur alternately and rhythmically at a frequency of about 15 to 20 times per minute in the adult human. Inspiration takes place because of a passive expansion of the elastic lungs and expiration is due to a passive contraction of the lungs which follows expansion. The changes in volume experienced by the lungs during inspiration and expiration are solely the result of alternate changes in pressure within the closed thoracic cavity, compared to the outside air. They are caused by changes in volume of the chest cavity arising from the alternate contraction and relaxation of the diaphragm and muscles of the chest wall.

As a closed cavity with no external openings, the chest contains the two elastic, bag-like lungs which connect to the outside only by means of its air passageways or bronchial tree. Enlargement of the chest cavity is attained by contraction of the dome-shaped diaphragm, causing it to flatten and descend, and by simultaneous contraction of the wall muscles which raise the ribs and breastbone upward and forward. The resultant decrease in pressure within the chest cavity and therefore on the pleural surfaces of the elastic lungs causes the latter to expand. As a consequence the air pressure within the lungs is decreased, causing air to flow into the lungs from the outside (i.e., inspiration phase of breathing).

The subsequent relaxation of the diaphragm and chest wall muscles is responsible for a decrease in chest volume, a consequent increase in the internal pressure of the chest cavity, and therefore an increase in pressure on the lungs, causing air to be expelled (i.e., expiration phase of breathing).

The foregoing purely mechanical aspects of breathing can be illustrated by referring to a model system consisting of two balloons attached to a Y-shaped glass tubing (lungs and air passageways) enclosed within a bell jar (chest cavity) and bounded at the bottom by a rubber sheet (diaphragm) as shown in Figure 27-5. The Y-shaped tubing passes through a stopper in the bell jar so that the space within the bell jar, except for the insides of the balloons, is entirely closed off as is the thoracic cavity itself. When the rubber sheet representing the floor of the bell jar is pulled down, the volume within the jar is increased, and its pressure is therefore decreased with a concomitant lowering of pressure on the outside surface of the balloons. The inside of each balloon, however, is still subjected to the atmospheric pressure which is now relatively greater (compared to the pressure within the bell jar), resulting in a movement of air into the balloons and their inflation, a process which compares to inspiration in the process of breathing. By releasing the rubber diaphragm, the bell-jar volume is decreased. Its pressure is therefore increased, and air is thereupon squeezed out of the balloons thus resembling the expiration phase of breathing.

The model system illustrates two important aspects of breathing. First, the lungs play a passive role in the mechanical process of breathing. And second, the inspiration phase is caused by a decrease in pressure within the thorax as a result of an enlargement in its volume brought about by muscular contraction (of the diaphragm and chest wall muscles); the opposite effect, namely expiration, results from a reversal of these events.

It should be noted that in contrast to the balloons in the foregoing model, the lungs almost entirely fill the chest cavity (aside from the volume occupied by the heart and so on), so that only the narrow space between the two pleural membranes undergoes the pressure changes that cause inspiration and expiration.

Actually the absolute pressure changes that occur within the chest cavity and the interior of the lungs and account for inspiration and expiration are quite small. They are of the order of 1 to 3 mm of mercury of pressure (as compared to the 760 mm of mercury representing standard atmospheric pressure).

Under extreme conditions, such as great physical exertion, additional muscles may come into play to facilitate the respiratory movements. During forced expiration, for example, the contraction of the abdominal muscles will aid in a more rapid and extreme ascent of the diaphragm to increase the effect.

REGULATION OF BREATHING. As indicated, breathing depends on the rhythmic contraction and relaxation of the diaphragm muscle and several muscles of the chest wall. It is entirely under the control of the nervous system. The process of breathing is essentially involuntary in that it is performed automatically and usually not at the level of awareness. However, it can to a certain extent be placed under the control of the will. Thus we can voluntarily speed up or slow down and even halt the rate and depth of breathing movements for a limited period of time.

CENTRAL ROLE OF THE RESPIRATORY CENTER. In all instances, however, whether the breathing movements are voluntary or involuntary, the contraction and relaxation of the respiratory muscles depend on the arrival of nerve impulses originating from a group of nerve cells collectively called the *respiratory center* located in the *medulla oblongata* and the *pons* portions of the brain. The respiratory center in turn consists of several subdivisions—

an *inspiratory center* and *expiratory center* in the medulla, and a so-called *pneumotaxic* center in the pons.

The inspiratory center sends out nerve impulses which cause the contraction of the diaphragm and other respiratory muscles, thus accounting for the inspiration phase of the breathing cycle. Of themselves these nerve impulses would theoretically keep the chest in a constant state of inspiration. However, there are specialized stretch-sensitive nerve endings within the lung tissues which are stimulated when the expanding lungs reach a certain threshold tension, usually at the height of the inspiration phase. The nerve impulses thus initiated at the stretch-sensitive receptors arrive at the expiratory center which responds by sending out nerve impulses that inhibit the inspiratory center. The inspiratory center therefore ceases to discharge impulses to the respiratory muscles which consequently relax. The expiration phase of breathing follows. As the lungs deflate, the stretch receptors are no longer stimulated and the inhibitory effect of the expiratory center ceases. Within a few seconds the impulses from the inspiratory center which cause contraction of the respiratory muscles are resumed, and the breathing cycle starts again. In this manner the regular and alternating discharge of impulses from the inspiratory and expiratory centers account for the inspiration and expiration phases of the breathing cycle.

The role in the breathing process of the pneumotaxic center in the pons, which is connected by nerve tracts to the inspiratory center, is not entirely understood. It is believed to function at the instigation of the inspiratory center by sending impulses to the expiratory center in much the same way as do the stretch receptors in the lungs. The stimulated expiratory center in turn inhibits the activity of the inspiratory center as already indicated.

Voluntary control of breathing is mediated through the same nervous mechanisms as involuntary breathing. In the former situation impulses are transmitted from the higher

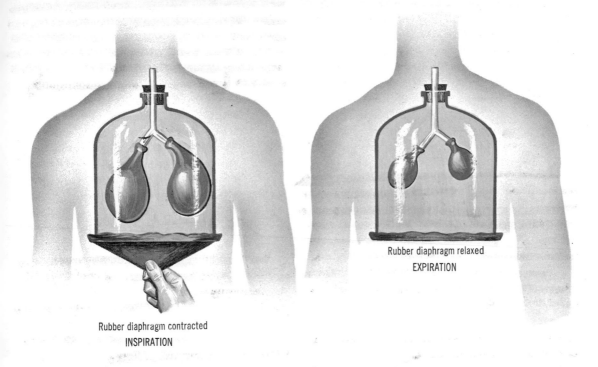

Rubber diaphragm contracted
INSPIRATION

Rubber diaphragm relaxed
EXPIRATION

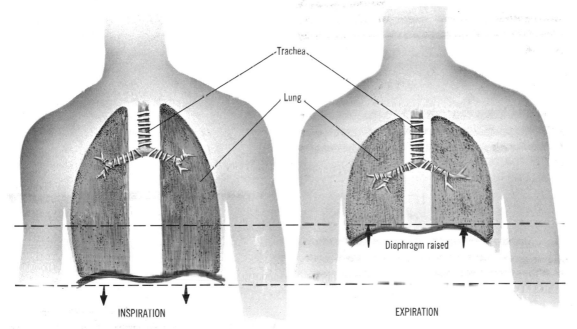

Trachea

Lung

Diaphragm raised

INSPIRATION

EXPIRATION

Figure 27-5. Mechanics of breathing illustrated by comparing the respiratory system with a model system containing two balloons attached to a Y-shaped glass tubing within a bell jar. See text for details.

centers of the brain (in this instance from the cerebral cortex) to the respiratory center. Similarly strong emotions, fright, excitement, and other mental factors also have a striking influence on the breathing process. Coughing and choking are reflex acts of protective value which are usually caused by stimulation of nerve endings in the lining of air passageways by chemicals or foreign particles. Coughing and choking generally result in expulsion of the irritating substances.

FACTORS AFFECTING THE RESPIRATORY CENTER. Several chemical and physical factors influence the respiratory center and therefore the rate and depth of the breathing process. The partial pressure of *carbon dioxide* in the blood is probably the most important. The respiratory center is highly sensitive to the partial pressure of carbon dioxide in *arterial* blood which remains more or less constant at about 40 mm of mercury. The slightest elevation in the carbon dioxide tension or concentration of arterial blood above this level, however, stimulates the respiratory center in the brain, resulting in an increased rate and depth of the breathing cycle. An increase of 1.5 mm of Hg in the partial pressure of arterial carbon dioxide, for example, results in a doubling of the volume of air breathed per minute.

Increased acidity or hydrogen ion concentration of the blood also has the same stimulating effect on the respiratory center as does carbon dioxide. The elevated concentrations of carbon dioxide and lactic acid as a result of muscular exercise are responsible for the accompanying increase in the rate and depth of breathing.

Under ordinary circumstances the normal variations in oxygen content are of little importance in the regulation of breathing. The greater sensitivity of the respiratory center to increased carbon dioxide and the subsequent stimulation of breathing during exercise is more than enough to maintain the partial pressures of oxygen in the alveoli and blood within the broad optimal range. Markedly lowered oxygen pressures, like increased arterial carbon dioxide pressures, stimulate the respiratory center in the brain by first stimulating certain chemoreceptors located within the walls of the *aorta* and the carotid arteries. For example, at high altitudes of 10,000 feet and more, the oxygen pressure of the atmosphere and therefore of the blood is greatly reduced. An increased rate of breathing occurs which cannot be ascribed to an increase in arterial carbon dioxide. At even higher altitudes where the partial pressure of oxygen in the atmosphere is so low that the stimulation in breathing can no longer compensate for the insufficiency of oxygen, altitude sickness results.

Body temperature and *blood pressure* also influence the breathing rate. A rise in body temperature during a siege of fever or muscular activity, for example, stimulates breathing, whereas a lowered body temperature has the opposite effect. A decrease in blood pressure increases the breathing rate; an increase in blood pressure causes a decrease. in the breathing rate.

Several factors are responsible for the initiation of breathing in a newborn infant. These include the accumulation of carbon dioxide and the decrease in oxygen pressures in the arterial blood when the connection between the infant's circulation and that of the mother is severed at the time of birth. Stimulation of skin receptors (e.g., by slapping the buttocks of the newborn) also serves to stimulate the respiratory center.

AIR CAPACITY OF THE RESPIRATORY SYSTEM. The maximal quantity of air that can fill the respiratory system—air passageways and lungs (i.e., alveoli)—is about 6000 ml in the average adult male. Of this amount only 150 ml occupies the air passageways (nasal cavities, pharynx, larynx, trachea, bronchi, and bronchioles) and is called the *dead space air* since it is not available for respiratory exchange. The large remainder in contact with the alveoli, the true respiratory portion of the lungs, is called *alveolar air.*

The volume of air inhaled and exhaled during normal restful breathing averages about 500 ml. Of this quantity only 350 ml reaches or leaves the alveoli since 150 ml occupies the air passageways as dead space air.

Therefore during normal breathing the last 150 ml of air that leaves the alveoli during expiration serves to line the air passageways. The subsequent inspiration returns this carbon dioxide-laden, oxygen-depleted air from the air passageways to the alveoli. In effect, therefore, the usual inhalation of 500 ml during quiet breathing brings only 350 ml of *fresh* air and 150 ml of *stale* air to the alveoli of the lungs. The maximal amount of air that can be expired by the most forceful effort after normal expiration of the above 500 ml is about 1000 to 1500 ml. Even after the most forceful expiration approximately 1200 ml of air remains in the lungs and can only be expelled by opening the pleural cavities to the atmosphere, thus collapsing the lungs. Even then a small quantity of air still remains in the collapsed lung, accounting for its buoyancy when placed in water (in contrast the lungs of an infant who has died before birth contain no air since they have never been expanded and will sink when placed in water). Therefore during the normal course of breathing there is a reserve of approximately 2500 ml of air in the lungs which mixes with the 500 ml that is inspired during each breathing cycle. The maximum amount of air which can be inhaled by the most forceful effort following the normal inspiration of the usual 500 ml is 3000 ml. The maximal capacity of the respiratory system is the sum of the 500 ml of air normally inhaled during each inspiration, the reserve of 2500 ml already in the lungs, and the extra 3000 ml that can be taken in by a most forceful inspiration to give a total of approximately 6000 ml.

GAS EXCHANGE BETWEEN BLOOD AND ALVEOLAR AIR. The uptake of oxygen and the release of carbon dioxide by blood passing through the capillaries of the alveoli can be fully accounted for by diffusion based on differences in the partial pressure of these gases.

The partial pressure of oxygen in alveolar air is approximately 100 mm of mercury (since oxygen constitutes only 13 per cent of alveolar air) compared to that of 152 mm of mercury for the oxygen in the atmosphere. The partial pressure of oxygen in blood entering the capillaries of the alveoli, however, is considerably lower, being only about 40 mm. Accordingly, oxygen will diffuse from the alveolar air into the blood. By the time the blood leaves the lungs its oxygen pressure has been raised to about 100 mm of Hg, the same as alveolar oxygen. Similarly, the higher partial pressure of carbon dioxide (46 mm) in the blood entering the alveoli compared to the partial pressure of carbon dioxide in the alveolar air (40 mm) accounts for the diffusion of carbon dioxide out of the blood into the alveoli. By the time the blood leaves the lungs its carbon dioxide pressure has been lowered to approximately 40 mm.

Although blood is pumped through the lungs at a rapid rate (approximately 5 liters per minute) several factors operate to assure adequate aeration during this relatively short period. First, within the rich network of capillaries surrounding the alveoli, blood is distributed in extremely thin layers and therefore exposed to a large alveolar surface equivalent to a total area of about 1000 square feet. Second, the red blood cells pass through the lung capillaries largely in single file so that each comes in close proximity to the alveolar air. Finally, the blood in the lungs is separated from the alveolar air by the extremely thin membranes of the capillaries and alveoli (estimated to be no more than 0.004 mm in thickness). As already mentioned it is even believed that the alveoli lack a complete lining.

TRANSPORT OF OXYGEN AND CARBON DIOXIDE BY THE BLOOD. *Oxygen Transport*. Oxygen is transported in the blood almost completely in a reversible physical combination with hemoglobin called *oxyhemoglobin*, already discussed in Chapter 25. Only 1 per cent of the total oxygen carried by the blood is present in solution in the blood plasma itself. The maximal amount of oxygen which normal human blood can absorb and carry is about 20 ml per 100 ml of blood, representing the maximal capacity of the hemoglobin for oxygen when it is fully oxygenated. Under normal conditions arterial blood which has been exposed to the alveoli of the lungs is not quite completely oxygenated. With an oxygen tension of 100 mm of mercury it is usually 98 per cent saturated and therefore contains 19.6 ml of oxygen (combined to hemoglobin) per 100 ml of blood. In addition to the 19.6 ml per 100 ml of blood there is about 0.2 to 0.3 ml of O_2 which is dissolved in the plasma.

As already indicated arterial blood has the same oxygen pressure as the alveoli (100 mm of mercury), having come into equilibrium with the alveolar air. In the proximity of most of the cells and tissues of the body where the oxygen tension is considerably lower (1 to 40 mm mercury), oxygen is accordingly liberated from the oxyhemoglobin and diffuses out from the blood through the thin capillary walls and eventually into the cells. This is made possible by the important fact that the combination between oxygen and hemoglobin in the red blood cells to yield oxyhemoglobin is a *reversible* one.

$$O_2 + Hb \rightleftharpoons Hb \cdot O_2$$

The liberation of oxygen from the blood to the tissues is just as important as its rapid absorption by the blood during its passage through the lungs. Hemoglobin would serve no useful purpose in the transportation of oxygen if it instead formed a union with oxygen that was not easily dissociable.

The Remarkable Oxygen-Hemoglobin Dissociation Curve. The actual relationship between the partial pressure of oxygen and the uptake as well as release of oxygen by blood is shown by the remarkable *oxygen-hemoglobin dissociation curve* (Figure 27-6). It summarizes the salient features concerning the uptake of oxygen by hemoglobin as well as the dissociation of oxygen from hemoglobin when blood is exposed to lower oxygen tensions. Increasing percentage oxygen saturation of hemoglobin is represented along the vertical axis, and increasing oxygen tension to which the blood is exposed along the horizontal axis. The unique S-shaped character of the oxygen-hemoglobin dissociation curve illustrates both the high oxygen-carrying capacity of hemoglobin and its ability to unload oxygen very rapidly where it is needed most by the cells and tissues of the body. Examination of the curve tells us that hemoglobin is almost completely oxygenated (approximately 95 per cent or more saturated) by an oxygen tension of 100 mm mercury which is the same as that in the lungs. This means that hemoglobin for all practical purposes can be as completely oxygenated by an oxygen pressure of 100 mm mercury as it can be by any higher oxygen pressure, say of 700 of more mm mercury which would be the case if we were breathing in pure oxygen.

The curve also tells us that when the oxygen pressure falls below 60 mm mercury (as it does in many of the cells and tissues of the body) the oxygen saturation of hemoglobin decreases very sharply. This is indicated by the steeper slope of the curve at the lower oxygen tensions; it means that oxyhemoglobin releases its oxygen very rapidly at partial pressures below 60 mm resulting in the liberation of relatively large quantities of oxygen from the hemoglobin. Thus, in the passage of blood through tissues where the oxygen tension is low, rapid dissociation of oxyhemoglobin occurs, yielding a comparatively large quantity of oxygen to the surrounding tissues and cells where it is most needed.

Two important factors, namely carbon dioxide or hydrogen ion concentration and temperature, affect the capacity of hemoglobin to combine with oxygen. The influence of increasing levels of carbon dioxide concentration in shifting the shape of the oxygen-hemoglobin dissociation curve to the right is also shown in Figure 27-6. This effect of carbon dioxide is ascribed largely to an increased acidity. It

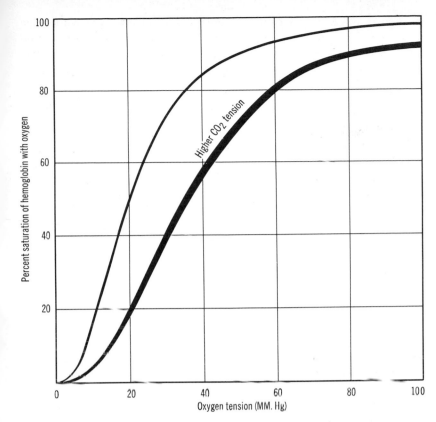

Figure 27-6. The oxygen-hemoglobin dissociation curves. Note that an increased carbon-dioxide concentration shifts the curve to the right, thereby favoring the greater liberation of oxygen from the blood to the tissues. See text for details.

tells us that the quantity of oxygen that hemoglobin will hold at any given oxygen tension decreases with increasing carbon dioxide pressures. That is, increased carbon dioxide tension favors the greater liberation of oxygen from the blood to the tissues. It means that more oxygen will be released to cells and tissues needing oxygen most, namely those respiring at a rapid rate as indicated by the higher levels of carbon dioxide production. Conversely, the uptake of oxygen and the formation of oxyhemoglobin in the blood coursing through the lungs greatly reduces the blood's carbon-dioxide-carrying capacity, thus facilitating the release of carbon dioxide to the alveoli.

A rise in temperature also causes a decrease in the oxygen-carrying capacity of blood. During increased muscle activity, for example, the elevation in acidity arising from carbon dioxide and lactic acid production and the localized increase in temperature results in a greater liberation of oxygen to these tissues.

Finally, it is apparent that the quantity of oxygen transported in blood will also depend on the hemoglobin content. Blood containing less hemoglobin, as in anemia, carries less oxygen to the cells and tissues.

Carbon Dioxide Transport. Carbon dioxide is transported in the blood in several different states. The means by which this is accomplished are quite complex and beyond the scope of this book. Arterial blood contains about 50 ml of carbon dioxide per 100 ml of blood, whereas venous blood has 54 ml per 100 ml. Therefore each 100 ml of blood as it passes through the tissues takes up 4 ml of CO_2, and in time gives off 4 ml of CO_2 per 100 ml blood as it passes through the lungs.

Approximately 85 per cent and more of the total carbon dioxide transported by the blood is present as the bicarbonate ion (HCO_3^-) largely as sodium and potassium bicarbonate ($NaHCO_3$ and $KHCO_3$, respectively). The manner of its formation is indicated below. Some 10 per cent of the total carbon dioxide, approximately 5 ml per 100 ml of blood, is combined directly with the amino groups of hemoglobin to form so-called *carbohemoglobin.* Only the small remaining fraction (about 5 per cent of the total, usually 2.5 ml per 100 ml of blood, occurs as carbon dioxide molecules in simple physical solution in the plasma.

Carbon dioxide is evolved in the body as a result of the varied metabolic activities of the cells and tissues. It diffuses largely as carbon dioxide molecules in simple aqueous solution across the capillary wall into the blood plasma. Under these circumstances it reacts chemically at only extremely slow rates with water (hydration reaction) to form carbonic acid, H_2CO_3. Upon entering the red blood cells, however, the foregoing reaction of carbon dioxide with water is rapidly catalyzed by *carbonic anhydrase,* a specific zinc-containing enzyme. The carbonic acid formed is rapidly converted to bicarbonate for the most part by reactions occurring in the red blood cells and the plasma. The enzyme is responsible in large part for the fact that most of the carbon dioxide in the blood is ultimately transformed to the form of bicarbonate ions. Carbonic anhydrase, like all other enzymes, also catalyzes the reversible reaction, in this case the splitting of carbonic acid to water and carbon dioxide. Thus it also accounts for the observed rapid release of carbon dioxide from the blood during its passage through the lungs.

The buffering action of the blood proteins maintains the pH of the blood at a relatively narrow range despite the changes in carbon dioxide content of the blood. This is due for the most part to hemoglobin itself (constituting three-fourths of the total blood protein) which binds with the hydrogen ions of carbonic acid to form the potassium and sodium bicarbonate salts. Thus practically all the carbonic acid (H_2CO_3) is converted to bicarbonate so that the amount of H_2CO_3 itself in the blood is very small. In the daily metabolism of an average adult male the 400 liters of carbon dioxide produced in terms of the acid H_2CO_3 is equivalent in acidity to approximately one-half liter of concentrated sulfuric acid. Because of the buffering ability of the blood to convert the carbonic acid to the bicarbonate salts, this amount of acid produced by the tissues and transported by way of the blood stream to the lungs where it is discharged as carbon dioxide causes little or no change in the pH of blood. The diminishing carbon dioxide tension and increasing oxyhemoglobin concentration in the blood as it passes through the lungs also causes a liberation of the carbon dioxide from the carbohemoglobin.

GAS EXCHANGE BETWEEN BLOOD AND BODY TISSUES. The movement of gases between the blood and the cells of the body is the reverse of those in the lungs since the partial pressure of oxygen in the tissues is low and that of carbon dioxide is high compared to that of the blood. Depending on the particular cells or tissues the oxygen tension may range from 40 mm of Hg downwards. The considerably higher pressure of oxygen (100 mm of mercury) in the arterial blood reaching the capillaries of these tissues results in a diffusion of oxygen from blood to tissues. As evidence, the venous blood leaving the capillaries has an oxygen pressure of only 40 mm of mercury. Simultaneously carbon dioxide diffuses out of the tissues from the region of its greater partial pressure (approximately 46 mm of Hg) to its lower concentration in the blood (40 mm), raising it to about 46 mm as measured in venous blood. The partial pressures of oxygen and carbon dioxide in the atmosphere, alveoli, blood, and tissues are summarized in Table 27-1.

Table 27-1. Partial Pressures of Oxygen and Carbon Dioxide in the Air and the Body

	pO_2, mm	pCO_2, mm
Atmosphere (inspired air)	158	0.3
Alveolar air	100	40
Venous blood	40	46
Arterial blood	100	40
Cells and tissues	1 to 40	52
Expired air	116	29

EFFICIENCY OF THE RESPIRATORY SYSTEM. In the metabolism of the average adult male on a normal daily diet of 2500 large calories about 500 liters of oxygen are used and about 400 liters of carbon dioxide are produced.

The respiratory system also plays an important role in the loss of water by evaporation and therefore in the loss of heat as well from the body. Under average conditions about 300 ml of water is vaporized daily from the lungs of a normal adult, whereas the skin loses about 500 ml. The vaporization or conversion of water from a liquid to a gaseous state (water vapor) requires about 0.6 of a large calorie per ml of water vaporized. Since water is lost from the lungs in its gaseous state, it also represents a heat loss of (300 × 0.6) 180 large calories per day.

Evolution of the Lungs

The lungs are essentially an outgrowth of the digestive tract. This is indicated by their embryonic origin from the tissues that develop into the digestive tract as well as by other evidence reflecting on their evolutionary history.

Surprisingly enough it seems likely that lungs in addition to gills were present in many if not all of the early bony fishes (the *Osteichthyes*, Chapter 20). Lungs probably originated in the primitive ancestors of these fishes as an evolutionary adaptation in the form of modified ventral pouches of the pharynx, favoring sur-

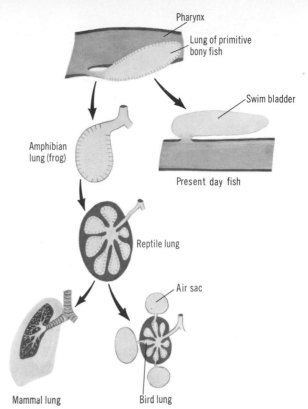

Figure 27-7. Probable evolution of lungs in the vertebrates.

vival in stagnant pools at a time in the earth's history (Devonian Period, Chapter 32) when climatic and geological events gave rise to such conditions. Stagnant water contains little oxygen, and gills as respiratory organs are of little use under these circumstances. The evolutionary development of lungs as organs for acquiring oxygen from air instead of water therefore permitted these fishes to obtain sufficient oxygen to meet their needs. Thus the lungs in these organisms served as a supplementary respiratory device when oxygen dissolved in water was deficient.

The evolution of the lung from these early bony fishes has followed several pathways (Figure 27-7). One line of bony fishes, now extinct, probably gave rise to the amphibia and subsequently to the land vertebrates with their functional lungs. The presence of lungs

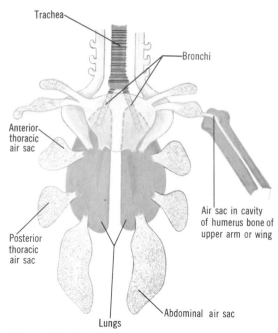

Trachea
Bronchi
Anterior thoracic air sac
Air sac in cavity of humerus bone of upper arm or wing
Posterior thoracic air sac
Abdominal air sac
Lungs

Figure 27-8. Respiratory system of birds including the air sacs which lay among the internal organs and extend even into the bones.

was of crucial significance in this path of development. Actually most members of the Osteichthyes evolved into the present-day bony fishes in which the lung has lost its respiratory function. Instead it has become the swim bladder, a gas-containing sac that influences the buoyancy of the fish, helping it to keep its position at different depths in water. The gases for the swim bladder, consisting of oxygen, carbon dioxide, and nitrogen, are derived from the blood stream to which they can be returned. In some fish the swim bladder also serves as a sound-producing organ, and in others it may be used to receive sound vibrations for transmission to the ear.

A few members of the Osteichthyes have even retained the primitive lung in its original function to this day. The present-day lungfishes found in Australia, Africa, and South America possess the primitive lung which functions in respiration as an accessory to the gills. In fact during periods of drought and stagnation of the water the lung functions

as the chief respiratory organ of these fishes. The African lungfish, for instance, inhabits the streams of central Africa which periodically are subjected to drought and drying-out. During such times the lungfish, which ordinarily respires by gills when aerated water is plentiful, resorts to the use of its paired lungs developed from the ventral side of the pharynx. Even in water it frequently rises to the surface at 10- to 15-minute intervals to empty its lungs and gulp fresh air which is passed into the lungs by swallowing. The lungfish hibernates in the mud during dry periods, surrounding itself by a capsule or cocoon-like structure which protects the fish from water loss. During this dormant period it breathes by means of its lungs. Air passes in and out of the lungs during infrequent intervals by means of an opening in the capsule to the mouth. In the Australian lungfish by contrast the lung is a single sac which lies dorsal to the digestive tract.

The lungs of amphibians and reptiles are more or less hollow sacs, in some cases possessing added respiratory surfaces furnished by ridges and separating membranes arising from the lung walls. In contrast, the lungs of mammals consist of a "respiratory tree" with branches finally terminating in the alveoli whose total surface is exceedingly large. The lungs of birds are unique and not completely understood. Although like mammals they have a "respiratory tree," they have several unusual features. These include so-called *air capillaries* in which gaseous exchange with the blood occurs through open tubules, and *air sacs* lying among the internal organs and even extending into the bones to which the lungs are connected (Figure 27-8).

The lungs of amphibians are filled by the swallowing of air. Those of reptiles are filled and emptied by volume changes in the body cavity as a result of rib movements brought about by the contractions and relaxation of the trunk muscles. In mammals, rib movements are secondary to the movements of the diaphragm in the inspiration and expiration of air by the lungs.

SUPPLEMENTARY REFERENCES

Amberkson, W. R., and D. C. Smith, *Outline of Physiology*, Appleton-Century-Crofts, New York, 1948.

Best, C.H., and N. B. Taylor, *The Physiological Basis of Medical Practise*, Williams and Wilkins, Baltimore, 1945.

Carlson, A. J., and V. Johnson, *The Machinery of the Body*, fifth edition, University of Chicago Press, Chicago, 1962.

Comroe, J. M., et al., *The Lung*, Year Book Medical Pubs., Chicago, 1955.

Fenn, W. O., "The Mechanism of Breathing," *Scientific American*, January 1960.

Gray, George W., "Life at High Altitudes," *Scientific American*, December 1955.

Krogh, A., *The Comparative Physiology of Respiratory Mechanisms*, University of Pennsylvania Press, Philadelphia, 1941.

Prosser, C. L., Editor, *Comparative Animal Physiology*, second edition, Saunders, Philadelphia, 1962.

Scheer, B. T., *Comparative Physiology*, Wiley, New York, 1948.

Chapter 28   Excretion

GENERAL CONSIDERATIONS

Definitions

Excretion is the general term applied to the processes by which the organism rids itself of metabolic wastes. The wastes may include any by-products of carbohydrate, fat, amino acid, protein, and nucleic-acid metabolism, various salts, and excess carbon dioxide and water.

Secretion refers to the discharging from particular cells or tissues of substances which in many cases are utilized in other parts of the body. For example, digestive enzymes and hormones are secretions. More basically the term secretion is often used to designate the energy-requiring processes whereby substances traverse a cell membrane. In all cases the driving energy is provided by the cell. At times it becomes difficult to distinguish between secretion and excretion, for, as we shall soon see, certain aspects of the urinary excretory process involve secretion.

Finally, the term *defecation* means the elimination of the undigested food and residue which has accumulated and passed through the digestive tract.

Types of Excretion in the Animal Kingdom

Several excretory devices have evolved for the removal of metabolic products from the animal body. In most unicellular organisms metabolic waste products are disposed of by diffusion into the external aqueous environment. In other unicellular organisms certain specialized structures (e.g., contractile vacuoles) function in the disposal of water which probably includes several dissolved substances.

Among the lower invertebrates, the sponges and coelenterates possess no specialized structures for excretion. As entirely water-dwelling animals whose every cell is near or adjacent to surrounding water, excretion to the external environment of carbon dioxide, salts, and their major nitrogenous waste product, ammonia, takes place by diffusion. However, the means by which surplus water is removed from these organisms, particularly from the fresh-water forms (e.g., *Hydra*) since the aquatic environment is clearly hypotonic, is not completely known.

In the flatworms such as *Planaria* excretion occurs by diffusion as well as by a specialized excretory system consisting of *flame cells* (Chapter 18) scattered throughout the mesoderm and connected to a branching system of fine tubules that open to the outside through small pores (Figure 28-1). The flame cells with their beating or "flickering" cilia somehow extract water and probably dissolved ammonia, carbon dioxide, and salts, which eventually pass out of the body through the tube pores.

In the annelids such as the earthworm the principal means of excretion is by specialized organs, the *nephridia* (Chapter 19), which occur in pairs in nearly every segment of the body. Each nephridium consists of a ciliated, funnel-shaped opening (located in the fluid-filled coelom or body cavity of the annelid) and a highly coiled tube which empties to the external surface of the succeeding segment of the body. The waste substances that collect in the coelomic fluid are in part removed and disposed of to the external environment through the functioning of the nephridia perhaps by mechanisms similar to that of the kidney tubules in higher animals. Water, ammonia and *urea* which constitute the principal nitrogenous wastes, and probably salts are excreted by the nephridia. Carbon dioxide is removed largely by the circulatory system.

In the arthropods such as the grasshopper the chief excretory organs are the long thin *Malpighian tubules* which extend from the large blood cavities of the body and empty into the digestive tract. Metabolic waste products (in which the chief nitrogen containing state is the purine *uric acid,*) are extracted

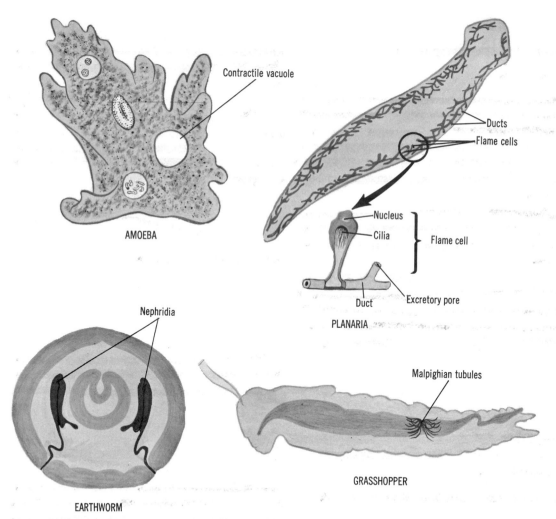

Figure 28-1. Comparison of excretory devices in several invertebrate organisms. See text for details.

from the blood and conveyed by the tubules to the digestive canal. They eventually are eliminated with undigested food materials through the anus.

The foremost organs of excretion in vertebrates are the kidneys which dispose of excess water (also an end product of oxidative metabolism), nitrogenous wastes, salts and other materials in the form of urine. *Urine* is an aqueous solution (95 per cent water) of organic nitrogenous wastes, inorganic salts, and certain other metabolic substances representing the major excretion products of the body. By virtue of their excretory function the kidneys are also largely responsible for maintaining the delicate balance of pH, water, salts, and other substances in the blood stream, and therefore indirectly in all the tissue fluids of the body. In effect the kidneys have a primary role in stabilizing internal environment of the body.

Although the kidneys are the key organs for the regulation of water balance in the body, the lungs, skin, and digestive tract of vertebrates above the level of fishes also function in this respect. The "average" quantity of water lost per day by a normal adult human, for example is usually about 1500 ml through the kidneys, 500 ml through the skin, 300 ml through the lungs, and 150 ml through defecation. These so-called "average" figures vary considerably depending on the inherent make-up of the individual, his water and salt intake, physical activity, hormonal balance, and other factors including environmental conditions.

The kidneys and associated organs which function in the production and elimination of urine are collectively called the *urinary system*. In man the urinary system accounts for the excretion of 75 per cent and more of the metabolic wastes of the body. The lungs serve to excrete carbon dioxide and water. The sweat glands of mammals including man also function in the elimination of salts, water, and some nitrogenous wastes in the form of *perspiration* whose composition resembles that of urine. Finally the liver, by disposing of certain hemoglobin breakdown products via the bile, also acts in an excretory capacity, as does the lining of the colon which excretes particular heavy metals into the feces.

In many marine fishes excess salts are eliminated through the gills. All marine birds (and probably all marine reptiles) that drink sea water dispose of their excess salt in large part by means of a *salt-eliminating organ* – a special gland in the head that removes salt from the blood more rapidly than any kidney (p. 660).

Comparative Biochemistry of Nitrogen Excretion

In virtually all animals either ammonia, urea, or uric acid is the predominating nitrogenous excretory substance, accounting for two-thirds or more of the total nitrogen excreted. The chief chemical state in which metabolic nitrogenous waste products are excreted by different members of the animal kingdom depends upon the given species and the evolutionary adaptations which it has made to the availability of water in its environment, especially during embryonic development.

Animals may be divided into the three following groups depending on their main nitrogenous excretory product: *ammonotelic* (ammonia), *ureotelic* (urea), and *uricotelic* (uric acid). Ammonia is the major and immediate nitrogenous product of protein and amino-acid metabolism for all organisms. It is a toxic but relatively easily diffusible substance. Most animals living in water are *ammonotelic*, for the ammonia is largely excreted as such without being further metabolized to the less toxic form of urea or uric acid. Aquatic and marine animals have at their disposal a vast environmental reservoir of water into which they can release waste ammonia without fear of self-intoxication. The great majority of invertebrates as aquatic or marine forms are ammonotelic in contrast to a few terrestrial forms such as insects which are *uricotelic*.

The uricotelic condition is best explained on the basis of an evolutionary adaptation to a limited environmental supply of water.

Under such conditions ammonia could not be disposed of fast enough from the body of the organism to avoid toxic or fatal effects. Its biological conversion to uric acid, an insoluble and comparatively harmless material, represents a biochemical means of surmounting the problem.

The animals that have evolved in an environment in which water availability and supply are intermediate between the extremes experienced by ammonotelics on the one hand and uricotelics on the other, tend to be *ureotelic*, that is, urea is the principal nitrogenous excretory product.

If the evolutionary choice, as some biologists believe, between ureotelism and uricotelism is determined by the conditions of water supply under which embryonic development occurs, then the picture is even more unified. Mammals are ureotelic. The mammalian embryo has the water supply of the mother at its disposal in contrast to uricoteles such as birds and reptiles whose embryos develop separately from the maternal tissue in eggs of limited water content. As further evidence the chick embryo in the course of its development is first ammonotelic, then ureotelic, and finally uricotelic, suggesting that this may well have been the course of the biochemical evolution of nitrogen excretion.

Among the vertebrates the fresh-water fishes are in general ammonotelic. They experience an osmotic force, in view of the lower osmotic concentration of the surrounding water as compared to their internal environment, which tends to drive water from their external aqueous surroundings into the organism. No accumulation of ammonia occurs in these animals since it escapes rapidly and readily by way of the urine. For many of the modern bony marine fishes in which the osmotic gradient is in the opposite direction, ammonia is still the prevalent nitrogenous excretory product and is excreted by diffusion across the gill membranes. A smaller proportion of the nitrogen is apparently excreted by the kidneys as the substance trimethylamine oxide [$(CH_3)_3NO$].

The marine cartilaginous fishes, however, have adapted to this situation in a different manner. They maintain instead an inordinately high concentration in their blood stream of urea (2-2.5 per cent) which raises the osmotic concentration of their blood to a level slightly higher than that of the surrounding sea water, thus reversing the osmotic gradient and therefore the outward flow of water. In these organisms, therefore, urea, which is considerably less poisonous than ammonia, serves to help maintain their water supply. The gill membranes are impermeable to urea which is excreted only by way of the kidneys. During conditions of adequate water supply the lungfish is ammonotelic, but during periods of limited water supply when it burrows in the mud the lungfish is ureotelic.

The amphibia are transitional between aquatic and terrestrial organisms. As a typical example, during the tadpole stage, when water is plentiful, the frog is ammonotelic; during the adult stage, in common with the adult forms of other amphibia, the frog is ureotelic. The remainder of the vertebrates—reptiles, birds, and mammals—are generally believed to have evolved from amphibian stock. Terrestrial reptiles living in moist environments are ureotelic, but in dry-living forms such as the snakes and lizards uric-acid excretion is the rule as it is in birds. In these organisms uric acid, the chief by-product of nitrogen metabolism, is excreted by the kidney tubules directly into the tubular urine. It precipitates out of solution, leaving the water free to be reabsorbed, and is finally released as a white paste (guano).

In summary, the chief nitrogenous excretory product of animals appears to be closely correlated with the supply of water, especially during embryonic development. Among the vertebrates the excretion of ammonia, the prin-

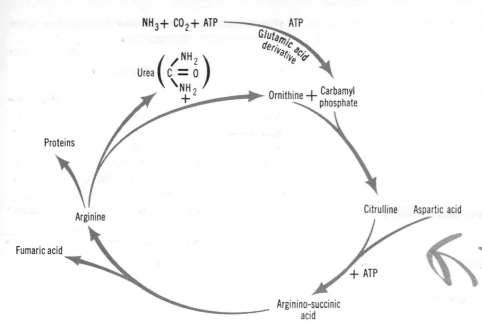

$$NH_3 + CO_2 + ATP \longrightarrow$$

ATP

Glutamic acid derivative

Urea $\left(\begin{array}{c} NH_2 \\ C = 0 \\ NH_2 \end{array}\right)$ +

Ornithine + Carbamyl phosphate

Proteins

Arginine

Citrulline   Aspartic acid

Fumaric acid

+ ATP

Arginino-succinic acid

Figure 28-2. The urea cycle. See text for details.

cipal excretory product of nitrogen metabolism, occurs in animals that are completely aquatic. In some of these animals, when water shortages occur, urea excretion takes place instead. With the evolutionary development of terrestrial animals, urea excretion predominated as in amphibia and mammals. Among the dry-living forms, reptiles and birds, uric acid is the major excretory product.

Urea Formation by the Urea Cycle

Urea formation is the process of converting the highly toxic ammonia, which is the major and immediate nitrogenous product of protein and amino-acid metabolism, to the considerably less poisonous state of urea. It constitutes 60 to 90 per cent of all nitrogenous material in the urine of man. In other animals, vertebrates and invertebrates, the major nitrogenous excretory products may be different depending on the species as described in the previous section.

Urea is formed principally in the liver (and to a lesser extent in the kidney) from ammonia, certain amino groups, and carbon dioxide in the presence of ATP by a cyclic sequence of enzymatic reactions called the *urea cycle* (Figure 28-2). Urea formation in higher animals depends in part on the immediate participation of the citric-acid cycle for certain intermediates including the amino acids aspartic and glutamic acids. The first step involves the enzymatic reaction whereby carbon dioxide, ammonia, and ATP in the presence of a certain derivative of glutamic acid are converted to the compound *carbamyl phosphate*. The latter in turn reacts with the amino acid *ornithine* in the presence of a suitable enzyme to form the amino acid *citrulline*.

The next two enzymatic steps lead to the formation of the amino acid *arginine* whereby citrulline and aspartic acid react in the presence of ATP to form first *arginino-succinic acid* which is then cleaved to yield arginine and fumaric acid. In effect, aspartic acid has provided one of its amino groups ($-NH_2$) to citrulline to form arginine. Some of the arginine may subsequently be used for protein synthesis, whereas some may be broken down by the hydrolyzing enzyme *arginase* to yield *urea* and one of the starting materials, ornithine, thus completing the urea cycle.

The net result of each complete turn of the energy-requiring urea cycle is that two nitrogen atoms (one from ammonia and one from aspartic acid) as well as carbon and oxygen (from carbon dioxide) have been combined in the liver to form urea. The latter enters the blood stream and is eventually excreted by the kidneys.

STRUCTURE AND FUNCTION OF THE URINARY SYSTEM IN MAN

Gross Structure

Each of the two kidneys in humans is in the general shape of a lima bean, but considerably larger, measuring in the adult about 4½ inches in length, 2 to 3 inches in width and 1 inch in thickness. Each kidney is embedded in a mass of fat and is located against the dorsal abdominal wall lateral to the vertebral column just above the waistline. The right kidney, which is immediately below the liver, lies a little lower than does the left. Both are anchored by connective tissue to surrounding structures and thus maintain their normal position.

The indentation on the medial side of each kidney (Figure 28-3) called the *hilus* is the site at which the main blood and lymph vessels and nerves connect to this organ. It is also the site at which the *ureter,* a tube measuring about 10 to 12 inches in length and one-fifth of an inch in diameter, emerges from each kidney and extends downward to the dorsal surface of the *urinary bladder.* The upper portion of the ureter is somewhat enlarged at its junction near a large space in the kidney called the *renal pelvis.* In longitudinal section the kidney consists of two general regions, an outer darker region, the *cortex,* and a considerably thicker inner region, the *medulla.* The cavity in the central portion is the previously mentioned *renal pelvis*, representing the enlarged end of the ureter within the kidney.

Each ureter is made up of three layers: an *inner* epithelial lining with an underlying coat of dense connective tissue, a *middle* layer of two coats of smooth muscle (inner longitudinal and outer circular muscle fibers), and an *outer* layer of fibrous connective tissue. At the separate site of entry of each ureter into the lower dorsal surface of the urinary bladder is a fold of epithelial tissue which acts as a valve to prevent the reentry or backflow of urine into the ureters as the bladder fills.

The *urinary bladder* is essentially an expandable or collapsible muscular bag made up of approximately the same three layers of tissue indicated for the ureters. The muscular layer of the bladder, however, is especially well developed and consists of three instead of two coats of muscle fibers. Because of the elasticity of its walls the urinary bladder is capable of considerable distention with a capacity that varies greatly among individuals.

Urine, which is continually being formed in the kidneys, drains into the pelvis and trickles down through the ureters into the bladder. Regular waves of muscular contraction and relaxation along the length of the ureters facilitate the movement of the urine droplets into the bladder.

The continuous production of urine soon results in its accumulation within the urinary bladder which increases readily in size. Urine is transported from the bladder to the outside of the body by a duct called the *urethra.* At the internal junction of the bladder with the urethra is a group of circularly arranged smooth muscle fibers called the *internal sphincter.* The first inch or so of the urethra as it leaves the bladder is controlled by striated muscle known as the *external sphincter.* As the urine continues to accumulate, the bladder distends until the stretch-sensitive receptors in its wall are stimulated. This usually occurs when the urine volume reaches approximately 300 ml, resulting in an awareness of pressure or fullness in the bladder region. In infants the

Figure 28-3. Urinary system of man including a longitudinal section of the kidney as well as a detailed microscopic representation of kidney tubule structure and orientation.

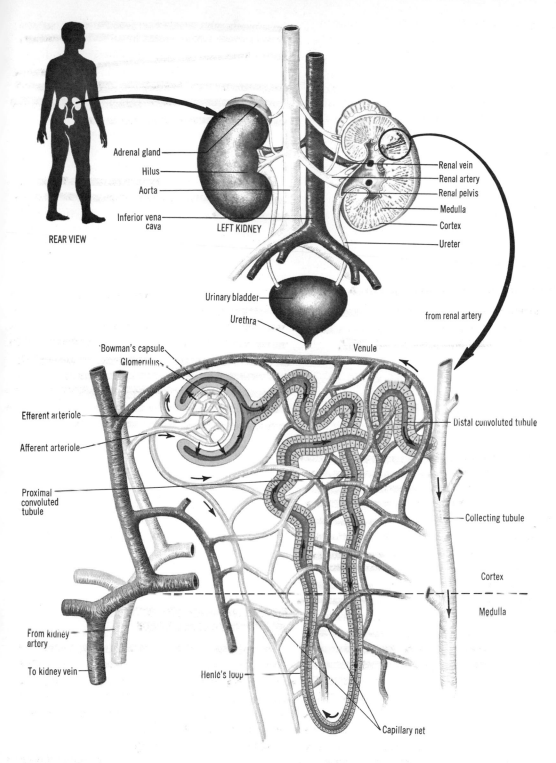

Adrenal gland

Hilus

Aorta

Inferior vena cava

REAR VIEW

LEFT KIDNEY

Renal vein

Renal artery

Renal pelvis

Medulla

Cortex

Ureter

Urinary bladder

Urethra

from renal artery

Bowman's capsule

Glomerulus

Venule

Efferent arteriole

Afferent arteriole

Distal convoluted tubule

Proximal convoluted tubule

Collecting tubule

Cortex

Medulla

From kidney artery

To kidney vein

Henle's loop

Capillary net

Figure 28-3.

urine is voided involuntarily and without restraint by reflex contraction of the bladder and relaxation of both the internal and external sphincters. In older children and adults inhibition of the reflexes of the bladder muscles and sphincters may occur at will, and urination can therefore be restrained until an appropriate time occurs for expelling the urine.

In the male, the urethra is not only the terminal portion of the urinary tract, but is also the terminal passageway of the reproductive tract (through the penis, Chapter 30) carrying sperm and accompanying fluid to the outside of the body. In females, the urethra opens to the outside of the body just anterior to the vaginal orifice and is exclusively excretory in function.

Microscopic Structure of the Nephron

The functional or excretory unit of the kidney is a relatively elongated and highly specialized tubule called *renal tubule* or *nephron.* Each human kidney contains approximately one million nephrons. A nephron is about $1\frac{1}{4}$ inches in length with thin walls of epithelial cells and consists of several differentiated regions showing distinctive structural and functional characteristics (Figure 28-3).

One end of the nephron, lying in the cortex of the kidney, is expanded into a double-walled, cup-like or funnel-like structure called *Bowman's capsule.* Each of its two walls is separated by a space or hollow and consists of a single layer of squamous epithelial cells. The concavity or cup-like portion of Bowman's capsule surrounds a thick cluster or sphere of capillaries called a *glomerulus.* The winding or convoluted portion of the tubule extending from Bowman's capsule toward the medulla region of the kidney is designated as the *proximal convoluted portion.* The next region of the nephron, called *Henle's loop,* consists of a relatively straight portion of tubule which extends into the medulla and loops back by means of a hairpin turn toward the cortex. The final portion of the tubule, termed the *distal convoluted portion,* which returns to the cortex of the kidney close to Bowman's capsule, is

also a winding and convoluted structure similar to the proximal convoluted portion. It joins, together with the distal convoluted tubules of several other nephrons, to larger ducts called *collecting tubules.* These ultimately conduct the urine formed in the nephrons to the renal pelvis of the kidney.

Arterial blood enters the kidney by way of the renal artery which subdivides into successively smaller and smaller arteries and finally to the so-called *afferent arterioles.* Each afferent arteriole leads into the capillaries of a glomerulus. Approximately one-fourth of the blood pumped by the heart enters the kidneys through the renal arteries and passes through the glomeruli (except for a small fraction which services the connective and other accessory tissues of the kidney). Blood is drained from each glomerulus by a single narrow blood vessel of arteriolar construction called the *efferent arteriole* (Figure 28-3). The considerably smaller diameter of the efferent arteriole as compared to that of the afferent arteriole makes for a relatively higher blood pressure within the capillaries of the glomerulus than in other capillary networks of the body. This is a significant factor in the efficient functioning of the nephron. The efferent arteriole continues for a short distance before leading into a second capillary network surrounding both convoluted portions of the tubule in the cortex of the kidney and Henle's loop in the medulla. Blood from these capillaries drains into various veins, eventually uniting to form the renal veins which return the blood to the general circulation.

Mechanism of Nephron Function in the Formation of Urine

Urine formation is the result of three processes that occur in each nephron: (1) *pressure filtration* through the glomerulus; (2) *reabsorption* of the filtrate as it passes through the various portions of the nephron tubule; and (3) *tubular secretion.*

PRESSURE FILTRATION. The first step in the formation of urine involves the separation of a cell-free and protein-free fluid by a simple mechanical process of pressure filtration of the circulating blood through the capillary walls of the glomerulus. The resulting initial aqueous *glomerular filtrate* which collects within the tubule of Bowman's capsule normally contains only those dissolved materials to which the capillary and tubule walls are permeable. Its composition except for the absence of the cellular elements (red blood cells, white blood cells, and platelets), plasma proteins, and fats is the same as that of blood. In addition to water as its main component, the glomerular filtrate contains sugars, amino acids, salts, nitrogenous wastes, and other dissolved substances in approximately the same concentrations as in the blood.

The unusually high blood pressure within the capillaries of the glomerulus provides the major force for the filtration process. In general, appreciable changes in the systemic blood pressure of individuals are usually not reflected by similar changes in the blood pressure of the glomeruli. By appropriate contraction and relaxation of the smooth muscles of the afferent and efferent arterioles of the glomeruli blood pressure within the kidney is maintained at a more constant level, thus permitting a more constant filtration rate despite fluctuations of pressure in other parts of the circulatory system.

Conclusive proof that the glomerular filtrate is the result of a filtration process was provided in 1921 by the work of A. N. Richards and his collaborators at the University of Pennsylvania. By inserting a fine glass micropipette into Bowman's capsule and withdrawing the fluid, they obtained a sample of the glomerular filtrate as it was produced in the frog and salamander. Analysis of the filtrate showed that it contained the same composition of dissolved substances including glucose, chloride, and so on as did plasma except for the absence of proteins.

It has been estimated that the total of two million glomeruli in both human kidneys provides a filtration surface of about 5000 sq mm

per gram of kidney. The average glomerular filtrate formed by a normal adult is approximately 125 ml per minute or 180 quarts per day, representing about 10 per cent of the normal blood passing through the kidneys, which is roughly 1200 ml per minute. Obviously the glomerular filtrate could not be equal to the amount of urine excreted, for the body would soon be dehydrated. Most of the filtrate volume must therefore be reabsorbed back into the blood stream, a process called *reabsorption*.

REABSORPTION. As the glomerular filtrate passes along the renal tubule from Bowman's capsule, most of its water and part of its dissolved materials are continuously reabsorbed through the walls of the tubule into the blood of the surrounding capillaries. The reabsorption process is a highly selective one since some substances such as water, glucose, and numerous other dissolved materials are returned to the blood stream to a greater extent than others such as urea and other products of protein metabolism. Thus, in passing along the proximal convoluted tubule alone, approximately 85 per cent of the water, sodium ions, chloride ions, most of the bicarbonate, and all the glucose of the glomerular filtrate is reabsorbed back into the blood stream. During its subsequent passage along Henle's loop and the distal convoluted tubule most of the remaining filtrate is further selectively reabsorbed so that only about 1 per cent of the volume of the original glomerular filtrate, now considerably different in composition, is finally excreted as urine. Of the 180 quarts of glomerular filtrate produced each day by the average adult only one or two quarts appear as urine.

Active Transport. Most of the reabsorption of water from the filtrate in the proximal convoluted tubule back to the blood stream occurs by a passive diffusion mechanism. An active transport mechanism (p. 112) is primarily responsible for the selective and specific reabsorption of various other substances (e.g., glucose, amino acids, sodium, calcium, and potassium ions) from the filtrate into the blood stream in both the proximal and distal tubules. Since it involves the transport of substances against a diffusion gradient, energy is required. The immediate energy source is probably ATP. The directional orientation as well as substrate specificity exhibited by the active transport mechanism suggests that the transport of a given substance, designated as A, across the tubule cell membrane is first preceded by combination with a carrier B to yield an enzyme-substrate type of complex AB. The latter then presumably moves to the opposite cell surface and discharges A, thus regenerating B so that it can be used again.

Reabsorption of sodium ions in the proximal convoluted tubule is due to an active transport process in which sodium ions are specifically removed from the tubular fluid. The negatively charged chloride ions are passively reabsorbed, moving with the electrical gradient established by the transfer of the positively charged sodium ions.

It is believed that in the distal convoluted tubule (and probably in Henle's loop) reabsorption of sodium ions by an active transport mechanism also occurs, and that it is stimulated by certain steroid hormones secreted into the blood stream by the adrenal cortex as indicated in a later section. It is the regulation of sodium reabsorption in these portions of the tubule that probably ultimately determines sodium balance in the body fluids and tissues.

The tubule cells obviously display remarkable characteristics of selectivity and specificity, reabsorbing most efficiently substances that the body vitally needs such as sodium, chloride, glucose, bicarbonate, and several other ions. In most instances, with the notable exception of water, the active transport mechanism largely accounts for reabsorption. Should the concentration of one of these substances in the blood and therefore in the glomerular filtrate exceed a certain threshold level, the active transport mechanism may not be adequate for complete reabsorption of the given material in the time that it takes for the filtrate to pass along the tubule. As a result the substance will appear in the urine. In the disease *Diabetes mellitus*, for example, the abnormal occurrence of glucose in the urine (Chapter 23) is precisely due to this type of situation.

Interestingly enough, urea is also reabsorbed from the filtrate but to a relatively small extent. The mechanism of its reabsorption appears to be one of diffusion, and not active absorption, since its concentration in the filtrate constantly increases as water is absorbed. The final concentration of urea in urine is about 60 to 80 times as great as that in the plasma or glomerular filtrate.

TUBULAR SECRETION. The energy-requiring active transport mechanism also accounts for the third and final step in urine formation whereby several substances are transported from the blood by the tubule cells into the filtrate, a process called *tubular secretion*. The active transport process in this instance is more or less similar to that occurring in reabsorption as previously indicated, except for differences in direction and specificity of the materials being transferred. Energy is expended in the process by the tubule cells, and specific enzymatic transport systems, as in the reabsorption process, are also apparently involved. Tubular secretion, by contributing to the excretory function of the nephron, increases the overall efficiency in extracting waste products from the blood.

The final changes in the composition and volume of urine occur in Henle's loop and the distal convoluted tubule. They are attained through further reabsorption of water and various dissolved substances and through tubular secretion into the filtrate of certain materials including potassium, ammonia, and hydrogen ions. In effect, the cells composing the walls of the tubule are responsible for a two-way traffic between the filtrate and the blood of the surrounding capillaries. On the one hand most of the water as well as essential food materials are reabsorbed from the tubular fluid and restored to the blood stream. On the other hand, additional substances, mostly wastes, are removed from the blood by tubular secretion and added to the concentrated filtrate which soon becomes the urine.

It is worth noting that in the overall formation of urine the glomeruli play a passive role since the energy of filtration is supplied by the heart via the pressure of blood. In the subsequent reabsorption and tubular secretion processes, energy (very likely as ATP) is provided by the metabolism of the tubule cells.

ACID-BASE BALANCE. The excretion of hydrogen ions and ammonia in varying amounts by the cells of both the proximal and distal convoluted tubules increases or decreases the acidity of urine. Thus it is an important mechanism in the control of the acidity and basicity of the body tissues and fluids. The kidney, in fact, rids the body of excess acid in several ways. Not only does it excrete a small amount of free hydrogen ions, but most of the excess acid is first neutralized in the kidney tissue itself before being excreted. This is accomplished through the formation of ammonium and phosphate salts.

HORMONAL EFFECTS ON KIDNEY FUNCTION. The distal convoluted tubule and probably Henle's loop, in contrast to the proximal convoluted tubule, is subjected to several hormone control mechanisms. The latter are part of a regulatory system which, by affecting the reabsorption function of the distal tubules, serves as a means of response for adjusting excesses or deficiencies in the internal environment.

The antidiuretic hormone (Chapter 23) secreted by the posterior pituitary gland promotes the reabsorption of water by the distal convoluted tubules and collecting tubules by somehow altering permeability. Like all other endocrine secretions the antidiuretic hormone reaches its target organ or tissue, in this case the kidney, by means of the blood stream. Its mechanism of action in altering permeability is an unsolved riddle. A decreased water supply to the body is reflected by an increased osmotic concentration of the blood. This in turn results in an increased secretion by the pituitary of the antidiuretic hormone. By stimulating tubular reabsorption of water through permeability changes, the hormone decreases the volume of urine formed. On the other hand, increased water intake by the body leads to a decreased secretion of the hormone. The overall effect, therefore, is a self-regulating mechanism for maintaining the water balance of the body. Individuals suffering from an insufficient secretion of the antidiuretic hormone, a condition called *Diabetes insipidus,* experience a less efficient reabsorption of water in the kidney tubules. The result is a urine volume increased as high as 20 liters per day (compared to a maximal output of 2500 ml in normal individuals). Although alcohol inhibits the secretion of the antidiuretic hormone and therefore causes an increased urine volume, the diuretic effects of beer drinking can be attributed mainly to the water consumed rather than to its alcohol content (only 4 per cent).

Other endocrine effects on kidney function include the action of several of the steroid hormones (mineral corticoids, Chapter 23), secreted by the adrenal cortex, which affect active transport by the tubular cells. Sodium reabsorption occurs mostly in the proximal convoluted tubule and to a lesser extent in the distal convoluted tubule. Nevertheless it is somehow stimulated, partly at the expense of a less complete reabsorption of potassium, by the adrenal mineral corticoid hormones (aldosterone, cortisone, and deoxycorticosterone).

Composition of Urine

The normal volume of urine voided by the average adult human may range from as little as 750 ml to as much as 2500 ml per 24 hours. The average is usually taken as 1500 ml. Its pH may vary between 4.6 and 8.0. The amount of urine formed is influenced by several factors including water intake, water lost through other means (skin, lungs, and bowels), diet, metabolic rate, muscular activity, and even emotional states. The remarkable variation in volume (and composition) of urine reflects in reality the wide range in the ability of the kidney to regulate the volume and composition of the blood and other tissue fluids.

Freshly voided urine is usually clear and straw-colored or amber in appearance. Its color is due to several pigments collectively called *urochrome* made up of a number of products of hemoglobin breakdown in the liver and intestinal tract. Urine ordinarily consists of 95 per cent water and 5 per cent dissolved solids. Of the 50 g or so of solids per liter of urine somewhat more than half consists of organic components and the remainder of inorganic salts. Urea accounts for about half of the solids in urine, being present in about 20 to 25 g per liter of urine. Its concentration in urine is about 60 to 70 times that of plasma. *Creatinine* as a by-product of muscle metabolism seems to be the next most prevalent organic compound of urine, but its concentration is about 1.5 g per liter of urine. Uric acid, the third principal organic component in urine, is an end product of purine metabolism, derived in part from the diet and from nucleic-acid metabolism of the body tissues. It averages about 0.5 g per liter of urine. Small quantities of other organic substances are also present, including several other breakdown products of hemoglobin, water-soluble vitamins, and certain hormones. Tests based on the presence of certain sex hormones in the urine of the female are used in the early diagnosis of pregnancy.

Sodium and potassium chlorides, the major inorganic salts of the diet, are also the major salts in human urine. They are excreted in varying amounts depending normally on the quantities ingested. Persons on low sodium diets, for example, excrete very little sodium. The average concentration of sodium chloride in urine is about 9.0 g per liter, whereas potassium chloride is second at approximately 2.5 g per liter. Progressively smaller quantities of sulfate, phosphate, ammonia, calcium, and magnesium are also present. In addition urine ordinarily contains trace amounts of copper, cobalt, zinc, manganese, iodine, fluorine, lead, and mercury.

ABNORMAL CONSTITUENTS OF URINE. Various abnormal constituents may appear in the urine depending on the condition of the individual. Glucose, which is normally completely reabsorbed in the proximal convoluted tubules by an active transport mechanism, can be present in the urine for several different reasons. The most common cause is *Diabetes mellitus,* the result of an insufficiency of the hormone insulin (Chapter 23). The consequent derangement in carbohydrate metabolism is reflected by an inordinately high concentration of sugar in the blood and therefore in the glomerular filtrate. The plasma concentration above which glucose appears in the urine (known as the *renal threshold* for glucose) varies between 150 and 190 mg per 100 ml blood as compared to the normal value of approximately 100 mg per 100 ml. The normal rate of active reabsorption of glucose as the filtrate traverses the length of the renal tubule is not adequate to remove completely the excessive quantities of glucose from the tubule filtrate. Glucose therefore appears in the urine, a diagnostic indication of the disease.

Diabetics characteristically excrete a greater volume of urine because of the resulting higher osmotic concentration of the filtrate which decreases the rate of water reabsorption from the tubules. Disorders of renal tubule function and extreme emotional states may also be responsible for the presence of glucose in the urine. Other sugars such as certain pentoses, galactose, fructose, and lactose may also appear in the urine depending on extent of dietary intake, genetic defects, and other factors. For example, in the hereditary disease *galactosemia* (Chapter 11), the normal metabolism of the hexose galactose is blocked. Galactose therefore appears in the urine as long as it is included in the diet.

Acetone and other ketone bodies (Chapter 7), which are normally absent from urine, will appear in the urine when their concentration becomes inordinately high in the blood. This occurs when excessive quantities of body fat are being incompletely metabolized as in diabetes and starvation. The presence in urine of detectable amounts of blood proteins (most commonly serum albumin and to a lesser extent globulins and fibrinogen) is usually an indication of increased glomerular permeability. It often accompanies several types of kidney disease. In fact, under normal conditions traces of protein are ordinarily present in the urine, but they are not detectable by the usual clinical tests for urinary protein.

A widespread hemolysis of red blood cells in the body, for whatever reasons (e.g., severe injury or aggregation and precipitation of red blood cells resulting from antibody-antigen reactions), may seriously impair kidney function and cause death. A portion of the hemoglobin and its breakdown products may appear in the glomerular filtrate and, upon concentration by the reabsorption process, precipitate, thus obstructing the tubules and destroying their function.

Other abnormal substances may occur in urine including degradation products of hemoglobin in certain blood diseases, particular amino acids in various renal diseases, and *homogentisic acid* in the genetic disease *alkaptonuria* (Chapter 11).

Resumé of the Role of the Kidney

In summary, the kidney exerts a major influence in stabilizing the constancy of the body's internal environment by maintaining the composition of the blood and therefore of the body and tissue fluids through (1) removal of the waste products of nitrogen metabolism; (2) elimination of excess inorganic salts; (3) regulation of the acid-base balance of the body; (4) elimination of excess water; and (5) excretion of substances present in blood in *excessive* amounts. These include not only normally occurring substances such as glucose (and other sugars as already indicated) and intermediate degradation products (e.g., ketone bodies), but frequently, foreign substances introduced into the body.

The contribution of the kidney to high blood pressure, which is so commonly associated with kidney disease, was indicated in Chapter 26.

EVOLUTION OF NEPHRON STRUCTURE AND FUNCTION IN VERTEBRATES

Relationship between Nephron Function and Availability of Water

The first vertebrates are generally thought to have been fresh-water forms whose invertebrate ancestors undoubtedly came from the sea. On the basis of osmotic considerations, fresh-water organisms would have tended to experience problems of excessive body water. Those who survived presumably did so because they were better adapted to cope with several problems, of which excessive hydration was undoubtedly one. Presumably the glomerulus and tubule evolved initially as devices that helped rid the body of excess water. The tubules probably acquired the added role of reabsorbing glucose, salts, and other essential dissolved materials that ordinarily would have been lost in the filtration process.

With the subsequent appearance of marine vertebrates and terrestrial vertebrates, suitable means of conserving rather than eliminating water became the problem. The modern marine bony fishes, whose skeletons are made up entirely of bone, have a decreased size and number of glomeruli and drink sea water, but are able to eliminate large quantities of salts through their gills. Urine volume is kept at a low level, and urine formation occurs mainly by tubular excretion. On the other hand, the marine cartilaginous fishes, as represented by sharks and certain other fishes, retained their large glomeruli but evolved nephrons which reabsorb urea. Their blood attains urea concentrations as high as 2.0 to 2.5 per cent, thus raising the osmotic pressure to a slightly greater level than sea water. As a consequence there is an osmotic flow of water into the organism through the gills and oral membranes. Like the fresh-water forms, they take in large quantities of water and excrete excessive amounts of dilute urine. Amphibians, as illustrated by the modern-day frog, toad, and salamander, surely evolved from a fresh-water, air-breathing fish. They spend most of their lives in fresh water or in very moist environments; and their kidney tubules, as devices for eliminating excess body water, function in essentially the same manner as indicated for fresh-water fishes.

In terrestrial vertebrates such as reptiles and birds, the tendency, as in marine bony fishes, has been for a reduced glomerular system. Accessory body structures such as waterproof scales (in snakes and lizards) and the development of a waterproof egg shell to prevent drying out of the embryo also evolved, serving to prevent excess water loss by evaporation. In addition, in birds a portion of the nephron reabsorbs water. Finally, it has recently been demonstrated that marine birds (e.g., sea gulls) and certain marine reptiles (e.g., marine turtles) drink sea water and are capable of desalting it by means of specialized salt glands located in the head. The salt glands, containing a rich supply of capillaries, consist of thousands of branching tubules which remove salt from the blood and drain the resulting concentrated salt solution into the nasal cavities or directly to the exterior (Figure 28-4).

In mammals, reabsorption of water from the tubule filtrate is a principal evolutionary device for water conservation. Not only are the processes of glomerular filtration and tubular reabsorption appreciably accelerated over those of the lower forms but they are under a more precise and more delicate system of control by known pituitary and adrenal cortical hormones as indicated previously.

Types of Kidney Tubules

The structure of the nephron or renal tubule as described for the human kidney is essentially the same, with some variations, in the kidneys of all vertebrates. It has even been identified in the fossil imprints of the oldest known vertebrates.

Figure 28-4. Location of the salt glands in the sea gull and a reptile, the marine iguana. (*Adapted from Scient. American.*)

The renal tubule or nephron in vertebrates has itself undergone a series of changes in the course of evolution. The most primitive form of vertebrate kidney tubule is believed to be the so-called *holonephros* tubule occurring in the embryos of certain lower fish. The tubule extends from the region of the heart to near the end of the digestive tract into which it drains. This type of kidney presumably evolved to the next stage known as the *pronephros*, consisting of three to five kidney tubules near the region of the heart. With the exception of some fishes, where it persists throughout life, the pronephros kidney exists for only a brief period during the early embryonic development of most vertebrates. For many lower vertebrates it is the functional kidney of the early embryo. With subsequent embryonic development the pronephros tubules begin to degenerate, but another set of more complex tubules, more posterior in location opposite the intestine, called the *mesonephros,* which have been developing, now take over to become the functional and final kidney of the late embryo and adult of most fishes and amphibians.

Finally, in the subsequent embryonic development of reptiles, birds, and mammals, another kidney called the *metanephros* appears in a still more posterior position. The metanephros as the most advanced of the kidney types functions together with the mesonephros during the latter stages of embryonic life. The mesonephros gradually degenerates and the metanephros kidney becomes the functional kidney of the embryo and of the adult.

In the human embryo the pronephros forms in the third week of embryonic development and begins to degenerate during the fourth. In mammals and birds it never functions as an excretory organ. The mesonephros, however, is functional, beginning to form during the fourth week, developing for a month, and then degenerating. The metanephros begins to make its appearance during the fifth week of development.

It has been generally considered that the three types of kidneys developing successively during the embryonic development of reptiles, birds, and mammals show a gradually increasing complexity that reflects the successive steps in the evolution of the kidney in these vertebrates. The importance of the pronephros in development, even though it appears to be functionless, is shown by the failure of a mesonephros or metanephros to develop in the chick embryo when the pronephros is removed.

SUPPLEMENTARY REFERENCES

Carlson, A. J., and V. Johnson, *The Machinery of the Body,* fifth edition, University of Chicago Press, Chicago, 1962.

Robinson, J. R., *Reflections on Renal Function,* Blackwell, Oxford, England, 1954.

Smith, H. W., *Studies on the Physiology of the Kidney,* University of Kansas Press, Lawrence, Kan., 1939.

Smith, H. W., *From Fish to Philosopher,* Little, Brown, Boston, 1953.

Smith, H. W., "The Kidney," *Scientific American,* January 1953.

Chapter 29   Locomotion and Protection:

Muscle, Skeleton, and Skin

GENERAL CONSIDERATIONS

The muscles, skeleton, and skin represent three separate organ systems which perform a variety of different functions. In a broad sense, however, they share several common roles. First, they serve to protect and support the soft and more delicate organs within the body. Second, they obviously help determine the shape and form of the body. And, finally, in certain species the muscles, skeleton, and skin (or its derivatives) together account for the locomotion of the body, a function ordinarily attributed to the skeleton and its associated muscles. For example, in the action of the wing of a bat or the webbed feet of ducks and frogs, the skin is an important adjunct to the appropriate skeletal parts and muscles. In birds, the feathers as derivatives of the skin are essential in the tail and wings for normal flight. For these reasons as well as for convenience, the muscles, skeleton, and skin have been grouped in the same chapter.

THE MUSCULAR SYSTEM

General Features

The capacity for movement is called *contractility* and is one of the basic characteristics of living things. Biological contractility may occur in one or more of several ways. Depending on the species a living cell may show only intracellular movement by some of its component parts, such as chromosome migration during cell division and cytoplasmic streaming. Other cells may also undergo locomotion or independent movement relative to its surroundings.

In many unicellular organisms and larval forms locomotion or contractility relative to the surroundings occurs by amoeboid, ciliary, or flagellar movements. In most green plants independent movements relative to the external environment take place almost entirely by growth or by turgor changes (except for the flagellate gametes of some species). In virtually all multicellular animals above the level of sponges, locomotion of the whole organism is achieved by muscular movement or contraction. However, within all multicellular animals extending from sponges to man, certain cells also clearly exhibit independent movement as in the instances of white blood cells, macrophages, ciliated epithelial cells, gametes, and numerous embryonic cells during the early development of the individual.

Amoeboid movement, as illustrated by the characteristic motion of amoeba and white blood cells, is not well understood and is generally attributed to a reversible gel-sol transformation (Chapter 6) of the protoplasm. There is some evidence that it may be due to a contractile protein similar to the contractile proteins of higher animal muscles. Energy is required for contraction to occur and is probably supplied as ATP. In addition, there are several reports that added ATP promotes the beating action of extracted cilia and flagella.

Muscle tissue is unique in that it is the most highly developed of all cells and tissues with regard to the property of contractility. It also has the secondary properties of *extensibility* (ability to be stretched) and *elasticity* (ability to return to its original length after being stretched). Muscle is thus the best endowed of all tissues for accomplishing the movement of the whole multicellular animal and its component parts. It is in fact the primary effector tissue of the body in all multicellular animals starting with the phylum Coelenterata. Within the animal kingdom as a whole, muscle tissue can be classified into two general types: (*a*) those associated with the viscera or internal organs; and (*b*) those associated with other body parts (e.g., the muscles of the body wall and the appendages) which account for the movement or behavior of the organism in response to changes in the external environment. These would correspond in mammals to the involuntary muscle (smooth and cardiac) and the voluntary (skeletal) muscle, respectively. In an earthworm, for example, the muscular tissue of the digestive canal and circulatory system including the ten "hearts" are of the visceral type, whereas that of the body wall and bristles responsible for the accordian-like movement of the animal are of the second type.

Finally it should be noted that the evolution of both a skeleton and elaborate appendages have together provided distinct advantages by permitting the development of more rapid locomotion and complicated motions. In all animals possessing skeletons, whether they are external skeletons (*exoskeletons*) as in arthropods, or internal skeletons (*endoskeletons*) as in vertebrates, nearly all skeletal muscles are attached to the skeletal parts, hence their name. Muscular contraction accounts for the movement of the skeletal parts. Appendages in these organisms are levers which are moved by muscles and are responsible for locomotion. They are most effective when they are stiff, a characteristic they possess by virtue of their skeletal parts.

Vertebrates, including man, possess three distinctly different types of muscle called *skeletal or voluntary muscle, smooth* muscle, and *cardiac* muscle, together representing 40 per cent of the weight of the human body. The cellular structure and other fundamental characteristics of the three types of muscle have been described in Chapter 5. All three types account for the various movements performed by the different body parts.

Skeletal muscle is principally associated with the skeleton and comprises the large bulk of the musculature. Although most skeletal muscles are attached from bone to bone, a few such as those of the face are connected from one part of the skin to the other, and several are attached to cartilage or to other muscles. They operate not as individual muscles but as groups of muscles under the integrated control of the central nervous system. The coordinated movements of groups of skeletal muscles are a conscious action. They are responsible for movement of the bones, body locomotion, and posture. Skeletal muscles are also a major source of heat production in the body.

Smooth muscle, which is generally regulated by the visceral nervous system, is included in most of the organ systems of the body. It is a major component of the walls of the internal organs such as the digestive tract, urinary bladder, and nearly all tubular structures, including those of the circulatory system, respiratory system, urinary system, and reproductive system. Smooth muscle, like cardiac muscle, frequently exhibits an inherent rhythmic contraction independent of its innervation. For example, excised pieces of intestinal or uterine smooth muscle will contract and relax rhythmically for varying periods of time when placed in a suitable nutrient solution. It is slower acting than skeletal muscle. Cardiac muscle is exclusively associated with the heart, and by its action propels blood through the circulatory system. Like skeletal muscle it is striated, but

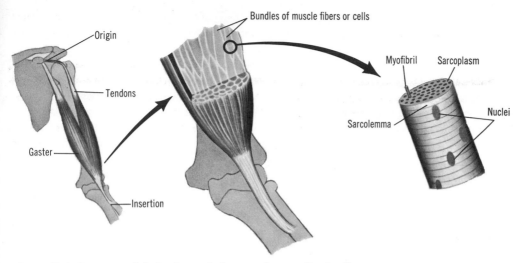

Figure 29-1. Structure of skeletal muscle in man. See text for details.

like smooth muscle it is under involuntary control. It thus appears to be intermediate between skeletal muscle and smooth muscle.

Strictly speaking the term muscular system should include all the muscles—skeletal, smooth, and cardiac—of the body. It is used most commonly, however, to refer to the skeletal muscles only, in part because skeletal muscle is assembled and organized as entities or organs (the muscles themselves) just as any other organs of the body. Moreover, we probably know more about the voluntary muscles than the other types. The more detailed functioning and additional characteristics of heart muscle have been discussed in Chapter 26, whereas those of smooth muscle have been considered together with the appropriate organ systems in which they occur or with which they are closely associated. For these various reasons the following sections therefore are devoted to an account of the skeletal muscles only.

Form and Function of the Skeletal Musculature

GROSS STRUCTURE AND ORGANIZATION. Skeletal muscles show a wide variation in size, shape, and mode of attachment to bones and other structures. Some are long and tapering,

others are short and blunt. Some are flat, others bulky; many have definite but different shapes whereas others are irregular.

In gross appearance each muscle consists of a main portion called the *gaster* or *belly*, and two ends by which it is anchored, usually to bones, and less frequently to skin, cartilage, or other connective tissue. By convention, the end of the muscle attached nearer to the central portion of the body is called its *origin* which remains relatively fixed when the muscle contracts, whereas the other more distant point of attachment is called the *insertion* (Figure 29-1).

All skeletal muscles consist of innumerable muscle cells called *muscle fibers* which vary in number depending on the muscle. The muscle fibers of each muscle are bound together by an intricate framework of connective tissue to constitute collectively a skeletal muscle. More precisely, each muscle fiber is encased in a delicate connective tissue sheath which is part of a larger connective tissue membrane enclosing different sized bundles of muscle fibers. Groups of such muscle-fiber bundles are in turn finally wrapped together and invested in a common outer connective tissue envelope, an integral part of the smaller underlying connective tissue encasements, to make up the skeletal muscle. It is by means of this complex system of connective tissue that the nerves and blood vessels are distributed throughout each muscle. For most skeletal muscles the connective tissues usually extend from the insertion end of the muscle to form a tough, white, fibrous cord called a *sinew* or *tendon* by which the muscle is attached to the bone. Tendons display a wide variation in length depending on the muscle, ranging in man from a fraction of an inch to as much as 12 inches or more. Some muscles have tendons at both extremities.

From another point of view skeletal muscle fibers consist of two major types, dark red and light. A familiar example is the dark and light meat of fowl. The red color is due to the presence of the oxygen-carrying pigment *myoglobin* which resembles hemoglobin. Thus the myoglobin maintains a small reservoir of oxygen in the muscle. Both types of fibers can be found in the same muscle with one type of fiber predominating frequently, depending on the muscle. The dark red muscle fibers are rich in lipids, fatigue less easily, have consistently more mitochondria, and have less dense sarcoplasm than the white fibers.

GROSS MUSCLE ACTION. Muscles perform work by their ability to exert force by contraction. Therefore, they never push but only pull by contracting. In this manner, they apply power at the insertion just as the shortening of marionette strings produces movements by pulling on the puppet's body parts. The different movements that result depend on the nature of the joint and the relationship of the muscles to the bones. In effect, the bones act as levers, the joints as the fulcrums for these levers, and contracting muscles as the source of power for the movement of the bones.

As a rule, muscles act in groups or teams rather than singly, usually exerting opposite or antagonistic effects. This is well illustrated in the bending of the arm at the elbow which is caused by the contraction of the *biceps* (Figure 29-2). For bending to occur, however, the oppositely acting muscles, the *triceps,* must relax. Since the actual bending movement is produced by contraction of the biceps this muscle is referred to as the *prime mover* in this particular operation. In order to execute the reverse movement, namely the straightening or extending of the arm, the triceps as the oppositely acting or antagonist muscle must contract, now becoming the prime mover, while the biceps simultaneously relax.

The bending and straightening of the arm serves to illustrate another generalization concerning muscle arrangement and function. The origin and belly of many skeletal muscles are usually located on one side of the joint whereas the insertion is on the other. Thus muscular contraction moves body parts at the joint by pulling from one bone across the joint to the other bone. One of the bones remains relatively stationary (in this instance that of the upper

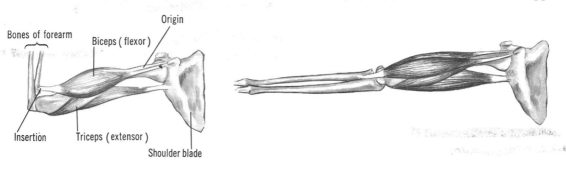

Bones of forearm
Biceps (flexor)
Origin
Insertion
Triceps (extensor)
Shoulder blade

BENDED ARM

EXTENDED ARM

Figure 29-2. Gross muscle action as illustrated by the bending and extending of the arm. See text for details.

Figure 29-3. Electron micrographs of longitudinal sections showing myofibrils and sarcosomes from (A) rat diaphragm muscle, magnification, 50,000X (*courtesy of Dr. M. L. Watson, J. Biophys. Biochem. Cytol.*); and (B) *Drosophila* flight muscle, magnification, 40,000X (*courtesy of Dr. S. A. Shafiq, J. Cell Biol.*).

arm), acting as an anchor point for the contracting muscle as it pulls the other bones (those of the forearm) to it. The origin of the muscle, therefore, usually remains comparatively stationary as the muscle contracts, whereas the insertion experiences relatively more movement.

TYPES OF MUSCLES. The different skeletal muscles of the body may be classified in several ways. One common system of classification is based on the type of principal movement which they execute. For example, the biceps bend or flex the arm over an angle and is accordingly called a *flexor.* The triceps is referred to as an *extensor* muscle since it extends or straightens the forearm, decreasing the angle of the joint. Muscles that raise body parts are called *levators,* those that lower them *depressors. Sphincters* decrease the size of an opening and *dilators* enlarge them. *Pronators* rotate body parts downward or backward as in turning the palm of the hand downward, and *supinators* turn them upward or foreward. *Abductors* move parts away from the central axis of the body and *adductors* move them toward the central axis. *Tensors* tense a body part, making it more rigid.

MICROSCOPIC STRUCTURE AND ORGANIZATION. The phase contrast microscope and electron microscope have proved to be important tools in elucidating the fine microscopic structure of skeletal (and cardiac) muscle and in understanding the contractile process. The skeletal muscle fiber as the unit of muscle structure may be considered to be an elongated multinucleate cell. It consists of a semifluid cytoplasm called *sarcoplasm* which uniquely contains numerous longitudinal fibrils called *myofibrils.* The latter range from 1 to 3 microns in diameter and possess alternating light and dark bands. The cell membrane enclosing each muscle fiber is called the *sarcolemma,* and the mitochondria-like bodies in the sarcoplasm are referred to as the *sarcosomes.* The many nuclei scattered throughout the fiber are generally located immediately under the sarcolemma in mammalian skeletal muscles.

Skeletal muscle fibers range in diameter from 10 to 100 microns and may extend through the entire length of the muscle joining with the tendons at its ends. The myofibrils are the actual contractile elements of the muscle fiber, and it is the coincidence of the light and dark bands of the many myofibrils which gives the muscle fiber its characteristically striated appearance (Figure 29-3).

The striations or repeating pattern of light and dark bands are similar for each myofibril and have been designated by letters as shown

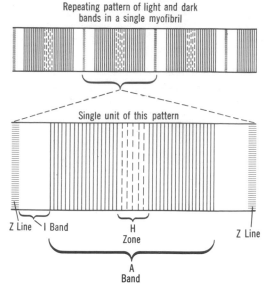

Repeating pattern of light and dark bands in a single myofibril

Single unit of this pattern

Z Line   I Band   H   Z Line
                        Zone

A
Band

Figure 29-4. Diagram of striated muscle structure at different levels of organization including that of the myofibrils (*adapted from Dr. H. E. Huxley, Endeavour*).

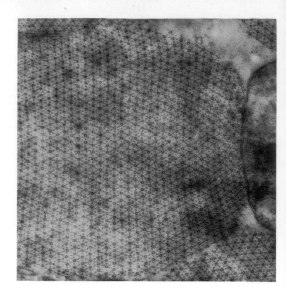

Figure 29-5. Electron micrograph of cross-section of *Drosophila* flight muscle showing the two types of filaments (primary and secondary) of the myofibrils. Magnification, 170,000X. (*Courtesy of Dr. S. A. Shafiq, J. Cell Biol.*)

in Figure 29-4. The dense bands are called A bands and the lighter bands are called I bands. A typical pattern unit consists of an A band bounded on each side by an I band; it is separated from the adjacent unit by a thin dark band known as a Z line. The least dense portion of the A band is in the central region and is called the H zone. Its width tends to decrease upon contraction.

Electron microscopic studies of cross sections of the myofibril have established that each myofibril is composed of an ordered arrangement of two types of filaments. One type is referred to as the *primary filament* and has a diameter of about 100 angstrom units whereas the thinner type known as the *secondary filament* has a diameter of approximately 50 angstrom units (Figure 29-5). Each myofibril is constructed of several hundred of each type of filament arranged so that each primary filament is surrounded by 6 secondary filaments which are in turn "shared" with 6 surrounding primary filaments as depicted in Figure 29-6. The repeating band pattern is due to the alter-

nate overlapping of the primary and secondary filaments, the dark bands occurring where both kinds of filaments overlap and the light bands where only one kind of filament overlaps. The dense Z lines are continuous across the width of each muscle fiber, somehow serving to hold the myofibrils together. In this manner it accounts for the coincidence of the A and I bands of the many myofibrils to give the whole muscle fiber its typically striated appearance.

ACTION AND COMPOSITION OF MYOFIBRILS. It is this new understanding of the fine structure of the myofibrils as the contractile units of the muscle fiber that has formed the basis for our present-day view of the process of muscular contraction and relaxation. The changes in length of a muscle fiber during contraction and relaxation are now principally attributed to a sliding past one another of the two types of filaments of the myofibrils. This modern viewpoint is based in large part on the observations that during contraction and relaxation the length of the A bands remains constant, whereas that of I bands and H zone changes in accordance

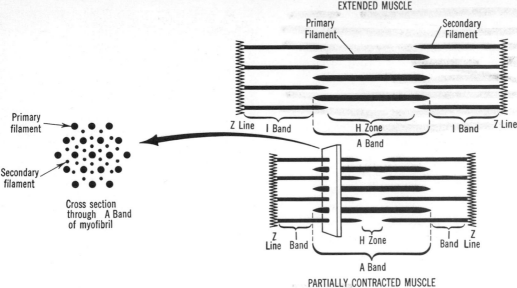

Figure 29-6. Diagram of the arrangement of the primary and secondary filaments in myofibrils and the relationships of the two types of filaments in muscular contraction and relaxation (*adapted from Dr. H. E. Huxley, Endeavour*).

with the length of the muscle. An increase or decrease of the I bands is accompanied by a corresponding increase or decrease in the H zone as diagrammed in Figure 29-6. This proposal does have its limitations. The older concept that muscular contraction results from the extensive folding or coiling of the filaments is no longer favored. It may well be that a combination of both concepts will be proved correct.

The myofibrils themselves are made up almost entirely of three types of protein called *myosin, actin,* and *tropomyosin.* Myosin is the most abundant, representing approximately half of the dry weight of the myofibril. By selective extraction procedures it has been possible to show that the primary or thick filaments of the myofibril consist of myosin whereas the secondary or thin filaments are composed of actin (molecular weight 40,000) and very likely tropomyosin. For example, after treatment of muscle with an appropriate salt solution which is known to remove myosin, the A bands are found to be no longer present. This is confirmed by the observation that similar treatment of myofibrils results in the re-

moval of the primary filaments. On the other hand, extraction of actin from the myofibrils results in the removal of a large part, but not all, of the thin filaments and I bands. The remaining fragments of I bands are probably made up of tropomyosin.

Physiology of Muscle Contraction

THE NERVE IMPULSE AND MUSCULAR CONTRACTION. Each muscle fiber has both a sensory and motor innervation. Under normal circumstances skeletal muscles within the body contract only in response to nerve impulses arriving via the motor neurons. This is in contrast to the inherent rhythmic contractility of cardiac and smooth muscle. It should be noted, however, that an isolated skeletal muscle removed from the body can also be made to contract by directly applying either an electrical or mechanical stimulus.

As it leads to a skeletal muscle a motor nerve fiber divides into numerous small branches. Each branch terminates in a specially organized flattened muscle fiber structure called the *motor end plate* located at the membrane surface of the muscle fiber. The junction between the motor neuron terminal and the motor end plate is called the *neuromuscular junction* and resembles in several respects the synapse between neurons (Figure 29-7). The arrival of the motor neuron impulse at the motor end plate causes the muscle fiber to undergo a *single contraction* or *twitch*. In the skeletal muscles of crustaceans there are many neuromuscular junctions. Some are excitatory, evoking a twitch, whereas others are inhibitory, preventing the occurrence of a twitch.

A resting muscle fiber like a resting nerve cell is electrically polarized as its membrane surface. The inner surface is negatively charged as compared to the outer surface to the extent that a potential difference of about 0.1 of a volt exists between the two. The arrival of the nerve impulse at the motor end plate presumably produces acetycholine, initiating a wave of depolarization or action potential along the muscle fiber similar to that described for nerve impulse transmission (Chapter 21). The wave of depolarization that sweeps along the muscle fiber temporarily alters the permeability of the membrane to sodium ions. This excitation somehow results in the contraction of the muscle fiber. The drug curare, originally used by South American Indians as a poison for their blow-pipe darts, blocks the transmission of the nerve impulse across the neuromuscular junction by preventing response to acetylcholine, and thus leads to paralysis.

ALL-OR-NONE LAW. When it contracts, a muscle fiber always contracts maximally despite the intensity of the stimulus, as long as the stimulus is sufficient to initiate the contraction process. This phenomenon is known as the all-or-none principle. You will remember that a similar principle applies to the initiation of the nerve impulse (Chapter 21). In other words a muscle fiber contracts maximally or not at all. A whole muscle or fragment of a muscle, however, may contract partially in contrast to the all-or-none behavior of its component muscle fibers, depending on the strength of the stimulus. This is explained by the fact that in a

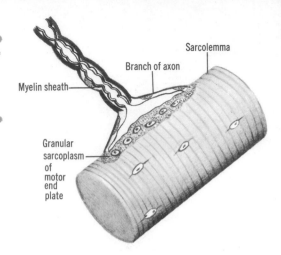

Neuromuscular junction, profile view

Figure 29-7. Diagram of neuromuscular junction, the junction between the axon endings of the motor neuron, and the specially organized skeletal muscle fiber structure (motor end plate) at the membrane surface of the muscle fiber. The granular sarcoplasm beneath the motor end plate contains several nuclei.

partially contracted muscle some muscle fibers are completely contracted while others are not contracted at all. A stronger stimulus in contrast to a weaker stimulus initiates nerve impulses to a greater number of neuromuscular junctions and therefore to a greater number of muscle fibers. They in turn contract to their fullest extent thereby resulting in a greater degree of contraction of the whole muscle. Under normal physiological conditions skeletal muscles usually contract to about 85 per cent and at most 65 per cent of their resting length. They ordinarily stretch to about 120 per cent and not more than 140 per cent of their resting length.

FORCE OF CONTRACTION. Two important general relationships have been established with regard to the force exerted by a contracting muscle. First, the force that a muscle can exert depends on its initial length. Within a certain range the greater the initial length of the muscle the more forceful will be its contraction. However, progressive increases in the length of muscle beyond a certain point result

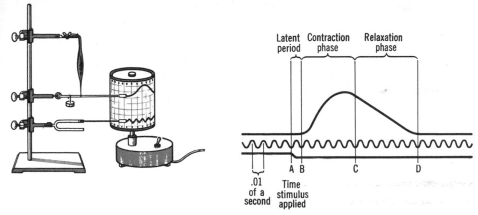

Figure 29-8. Diagram of a kymograph and the tracing of a typical time course of a single muscle twitch showing the latent period, contraction phase, and relaxation phase.

in progressively less forceful contractions. In actuality the greatest force of contraction is exerted by the muscle at the length in which it exists in its natural state in the body. Shorter or longer initial lengths result in less forceful contractions. Second, the heavier the load (or the more stretched the muscle), the more slowly is the maximum force attained by the contracting muscle, or the longer it takes to shorten a given distance.

THE SINGLE MUSCLE TWITCH. A single stimulus applied to a muscle ordinarily causes a single simple muscular contraction called a *muscle twitch.* It is due to a contraction of numerous muscle fibers of the muscle and is best described by observing the rate of contraction and subsequent relaxation of a single excised muscle. As an illustration, the calf muscle of a frog's leg and its nerve supply, the sciatic nerve, together with a portion of the attached thigh bone (femur) are removed from the organism. The muscle is suspended in such a way that the upper end is held in a clamp and the lower end is connected to a sensitive lever as shown in Figure 29-9. The opposite end of the lever is in turn attached to a modified pen point in contact with a cylinder of graph paper covering the surface of a vertical drum which revolves at a constant speed. The

apparatus is called a *kymograph.* A single stimulation of the excised muscle (usually by applying a single electric shock to its nerve, or to the muscle directly) results in a single rapid muscle twitch lasting a total of about 0.1 second. The movements experienced by the stimulated muscle in the course of a single twitch are transmitted as movements to the attached lever pen which inscribes a record on the graph paper of the rotating drum.

The typical curve traced by a single muscle twitch (as shown in Figure 29-8) consists of three successive phases known as the *latent period,* the *contraction phase,* and the *relaxation phase.* The abscissa of the graph is in units of time, whereas the ordinate represents the distance by which the muscle shortens (the extent of contraction). The *latent period,* as its name implies, is the lag period or time interval between the application of the stimulus and the actual beginning of visible muscle contraction. It is indicated by the distance from A to B and lasts about 0.01 second. The *contraction phase,* as indicated by the portion of the curve extending from B to the peak C is the time interval in which the muscle attains maximal contraction and performs work. It has a duration of approximately 0.04 second. The *relaxation phase,* as the final phase of a muscle twitch, is the interval in which the muscle returns to its original length and relaxed state and is represented by the portion of the curve between *C* and *D*. It is the longest of the three phases, having a duration of about 0.05 second.

SUMMATION AND TETANUS. With the exception perhaps of the eye-winking movement a single isolated muscle twitch ordinarily does not occur under normal circumstances within the body of the intact animals. If a second stimulus is applied to a muscle that is still in the contraction phase, further contraction will occur. The second contraction adds to the first and results in a greater shortening of the muscle than that caused by a single stimulus, a phenomenon known as *summation*. Subsequent stimuli or nerve impulses arriving at the contracted muscle at the correct intervals will cause an even greater summation effect to produce a greater total shortening of the muscle.

If the successive stimuli arrive at the muscle with sufficiently long time intervals between them, the individual contractions can still be distinguished since some degree of relaxation occurs between them to give a curve with a wavy plateau as shown in Figure 29-9. This condition is called *incomplete tetanus*. If the successive stimuli are applied closer and closer together, the summated contractions are completely fused or blended together to give a sustained maximal contraction (Figure 29-9) called *tetanus*, which is considerably greater than that caused by a single stimulus. The frequency of stimuli or nerve impulses required to produce tetanus varies with the muscle and its physiological condition. Actually the normal frequency of muscle stimulation is slow, resulting in incomplete and unfused tetanus. Smoothness of muscle contraction is achieved by asynchronous arrival of nerve impulses to different neuromuscular junctions. As a result some fibers are relaxing while others are contracting.

Unfortunately the term tetanus is also used to refer to the disease commonly called "lockjaw" which results from an infection by the anaerobic bacterium *Clostridium tetani*. The

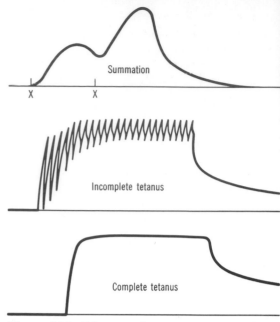

Figure 29-9. Diagram of summation, incomplete tetanus, and tetanus. See text for details.

disease is characterized by a complete spasmic tetanus or "locking" of the jaw muscles making it impossible for the patient to relax these muscles at will, the result of powerful nerve poison or toxin produced by the infecting bacteria.

MUSCLE FATIGUE. The condition or state whereby a muscle experiences diminished ability to contract as a result of prolonged stimulation is known as *muscle fatigue*. It rarely occurs in intact muscles of the body but can be readily demonstrated with excised muscles. Several factors are responsible for muscle fatigue. One of these is a decreased level of *phosphocreatine* (p. 674).

REFRACTORY PERIOD. Skeletal muscle, like nerves, exhibits a *refractory period*, an extremely short time interval lasting about 0.002 to 0.005 seconds, during which it will not respond to a second stimulus. It is thought to represent the time necessary for the occurrence of physical and chemical changes which will permit subsequent muscular contraction. The refractory period of cardiac muscle is considerably longer (approximately 100-fold) than that of skeletal muscle and occurs during the interval of contraction; it therefore lasts during the entire period of systole which means that cardiac muscle will not respond to a second stimulus while it is contracting. By contrast, skeletal muscle with a much shorter refractory period will contract to a second stimulus while it is still contracting in response to the first stimulus. The second contraction is super-imposed upon the first to give the aforementioned summation effect.

Biochemistry of Muscular Contraction

Muscle fibers or cells are unique in their highly developed capability for utilizing chemically stored energy derived from metabolism to perform mechanical work. The basic question as to how the molecular machinery of muscle transforms chemical energy to mechanical work is still unanswered despite extensive and prolonged research efforts. Nevertheless important progress has been made in this area in recent years.

CHEMICAL COMPOSITION OF MUSCLE. In terms of its chemical composition skeletal muscle consists of 75 per cent water and nearly 20 per cent protein, a considerable portion of which includes the *myosin, actin,* and *tropomyosin* proteins of the myofibrils. Other proteins present in muscle include the enzymes necessary for catalyzing the reactions that ultimately release the energy stored in the chemical bonds of glycogen to form ATP (from ADP and inorganic phosphate). The remaining 5 per cent includes 0.5 to 1 per cent glycogen, small amounts of salts, free amino acids, and a variety of other organic substances including the compound called *phosphocreatine* which has an important function in muscular contraction, as described in a later section.

ATP AS AN ENERGY SOURCE FOR MUSCULAR CONTRACTION. The ultimate source of energy for muscle contraction is delivered by the blood in the form of glucose and stored in the muscle as glycogen. The integrated and successive series of enzymatic reactions collectively known as *glycolysis* or the *Embden-Meyerhoff pathway* (Chapter 8) by which the glycogen is metabolized to pyruvate and lactic acid yields the energy-rich ATP. Most of the present evidence indicates that it is the ATP derived from the metabolism of muscle glycogen and from two other known sources (as described below) that is the immediate energy source for muscle contraction. Lipid may be a major alternate energy source to carbohydrate.

The behavior of actin and myosin as the principal protein components of the myofibrils in the presence of ATP appears to be the basis for muscular contraction. Several strong lines of evidence support this viewpoint. First, actin and myosin (as the principal protein components of the myofibrils or contractile units) can be extracted from muscle, combined into so-called *actomyosin* fibers or threads, and made to contract upon addition of ATP (presumably by forming an actin-myosin-ATP system) in the presence of potassium and magnesium ions in concentrations similar to those in muscle fiber fluid. The contraction is accompanied by a hydrolysis of ATP to yield ADP and inorganic phosphate. This has also been demonstrated with intact myofibrils and with specially treated muscle fibers soaked for some time in a glycerol solution. Second, it has been established that myosin itself is also an enzyme which catalyzes the breakdown of ATP to ADP (and inorganic phosphate) and energy. Thus it has been demonstrated that (a) there is a requirement for ATP in order that the closely connected contractile proteins actin and myosin undergo shortening, and (b) myosin is an enzyme for the dephosphorylation of ATP, which process is in turn closely linked with the release of energy for contraction.

OTHER ENERGY SOURCES. The quantity of ATP present in skeletal muscle at any one time, although adequate to meet the requirements of resting muscle, is not sufficient to supply the needs of the contracting muscle. Obviously, if ATP is to meet the energy demands of contracting muscle other sources must be available.

At least two systems are now known to be present in muscle which supplement the ATP supply. One is the so-called *phosphocreatine system* which consists of the high energy-containing compound phosphocreatine and the enzyme *creatine kinase*. Phosphocreatine is present in resting muscle in amounts approximately fivefold as much as ATP. Although it cannot serve as an immediate source of energy for contraction, phosphocreatine through the action of creatine kinase acts to transform ADP into ATP (and reversibly the enzyme catalyzes the conversion of ATP and creatine into phosphocreatine and ADP).

Phosphocreatine + ADP ⇌ Creatine + ATP

Thus phosphocreatine is an energy reservoir which contributes ATP for muscular contraction. (In invertebrates the compound *phosphoarginine* generally occurs in place of phosphocreatine.)

The second additional energy-supplying system for actively contracting muscle is the glycolytic (or Embden-Meyerhoff) pathway which is responsible for the stepwise breakdown of glycogen to lactic acid to give a net yield of three moles of ATP per mole of glucose equivalent (Chapter 8). We know that if an isolated muscle is constantly stimulated under anaerobic conditions it will contract and persist in tetanus until all its glycogen and phosphocreatine have been consumed with the resultant accumulation of lactic acid, creatine, and inorganic phosphate. Under aerobic conditions in which the supply of oxygen is abundant, large quantities of lactic acid still accumulate. In the intact animal, however, lactic acid is carried by the blood from the muscle to the liver where most of it is resynthesized to glycogen. This synthesis occurs at the expense of ATP which is necessary to push lactic acid up the energy hill to glycogen. The ATP is provided by the aerobic oxidation of about one-sixth of the quantity of lactic

acid to carbon dioxide and water via the Krebs cycle and the terminal respiratory chain (Chapter 8). Liver glycogen is ultimately released as glucose to the blood stream and is resynthesized to glycogen in the muscle to be used in due course for muscular contraction.

Intermittent stimulation aerobically of *isolated excised* muscle results in the liberation during contraction of lactic acid, which is then resynthesized during the relaxation phase within the muscle itself. As in the instance of glycogen resynthesis in the liver, the energy for resynthesis is derived from the simultaneous aerobic oxidation of a small portion of lactic acid to carbon dioxide and water. It should be noted that the transformation of lactic acid to glycogen in the *intact animal* occurs in the liver and not in the muscle. It can be demonstrated to occur to a certain extent in the muscle only when the latter has been excised from the body. Some ATP for muscular contraction is also undoubtedly provided by aerobic oxidation of a portion of the lactic acid to carbon dioxide and water.

In summary, the immediate energy source for muscular contraction is ATP, which is present only in small quantities at any given time in the muscle. ATP must therefore be generated to account for contraction. ATP is formed in muscle by at least three important processes: (1) by enzymatic interaction of the high-energy reservoir compound *phosphocreatine* and ADP which is mediated by creatine kinase; (2) by glycolysis or anaerobic oxidation of muscle glycogen. The latter is synthesized from glucose delivered by the blood stream; and (3) by aerobic oxidation of some of the lactic acid in muscle.

Interestingly enough resting skeletal muscle in contrast to contracting muscle, obtains a large portion of its energy in the resting state from the oxidation of fatty acids and acetoacetate. Cardiac muscle derives its ATP for contraction principally by aerobic oxidation of lactic acid, acetoacetate and probably fatty acids. Smooth muscle experiences relatively slow contractions and obtains its energy from the oxidation of fatty acids and acetoacetate and secondarily from glucose.

MECHANISM OF CONTRACTION. The arrival of the nerve impulse via the motor neuron at the muscle fiber serves to depolarize the muscle fiber sarcolemma, temporarily altering the permeability of the membrane to certain ions. This is believed to activate somehow the enzymatic properties of the myosin (of the actin-myosin-ATP system of the myofibrils) to split away the terminal phosphate group of the ATP to yield ADP and a concomitant release of energy. The net result is a contraction of the muscle fibers which is accomplished by a shortening of the myofibrils. The means by which this shortening is attained is not yet known. It is at present presumed to occur by a sliding of the primary and secondary filaments past one another, powered by the energy released from ATP, possibly by a reattachment of the myosin cross bridges to the actin filaments. The fundamental nature of this proposed mechanism is still not clear. It is assumed that relaxation or lengthening of the myofibrils occurs by a reverse process during which time ATP is reformed from ADP, inorganic phosphate and energy to restore the original actin-myosin-ATP system.

Of great significance is the fact that an appreciable release of heat takes place when skeletal muscle undergoes contraction depending on the extent of muscle shortening. Heat production is one of the important functions performed by the muscles for the body as a whole. In fact the heat produced whenever a muscle contracts represents a major portion of the energy released by the chemical changes of contraction.

OXYGEN DEBT. During strenuous physical exercise sufficient oxygen is not delivered fast enough to metabolize completely glycogen to carbon dioxide and water (and ATP) since large quantities of lactic acid accumulate and spill over into the blood stream. Nevertheless, the muscles are still able to sustain maximal activity under these essentially anaerobic con-

ditions. The muscles, under these circumstances, are said to have accumulated a so-called *oxygen debt.* Eventually enough oxygen must be provided for the liver to oxidize sufficient lactic acid to transform the remaining lactic acid to glycogen (and to restore eventually the normal phosphocreatine concentration as indicated earlier).

In effect some of the energy for muscular work is derived through oxidation performed in the liver. This can be illustrated by the example of the sprinter who runs the 100-yard dash in 10 seconds. Approximately 6 liters of oxygen would be necessary to produce enough ATP by complete oxidation of glycogen to carbon dioxide and water for the energy used during the dash. Actually, however, the sprinter only consumes about a liter of oxygen during the race; but he continues to breathe heavily for some time after he has stopped running. Thus he obtains the 5 more liters of oxygen which represents the oxygen debt necessary for the oxidation of enough lactic acid to convert the remaining lactic acid to glycogen and to restore the normal phosphocreatine level of muscle.

THE SKELETON

General Features

The term skeleton usually refers to the hard supportive connective tissues of the animal, around or within which the organism is built.

Animal skeletons are usually classified into two main groups: the exterior *exoskeleton* as in arthropods and molluscs, and the interior *endoskeleton* characteristic of the vertebrates. The vertebrate endoskeleton includes all the bones of the body, the joints formed by the attachment of bones to one another, and associated cartilage and connective tissue or ligaments that connect bone to bone. Not only does the skeleton support and protect the softer and more delicate organs of the body, but it also serves as a mechanical framework for locomotion. In addition it functions in many vertebrates in other important roles. For example,

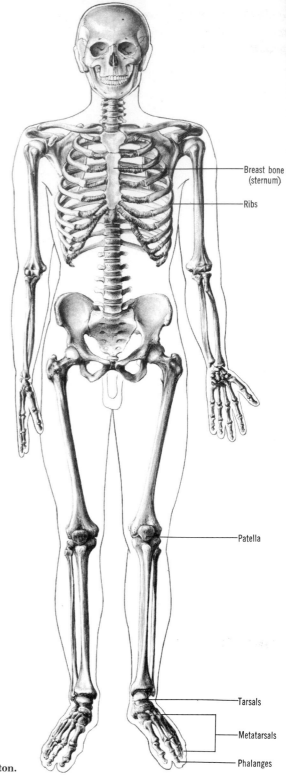

Breast bone
(sternum)

Ribs

Patella

Tarsals

Metatarsals

Phalanges

Figure 29-10. Front and rear views of the human skeleton.

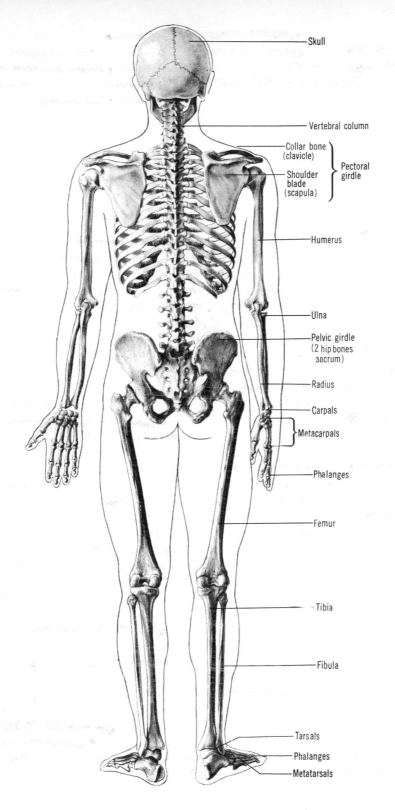

Skull

Vertebral column

Collar bone
(clavicle)

Shoulder
blade
(scapula)

Pectoral
girdle

Humerus

Ulna

Pelvic girdle
(2 hip bones
sacrum)

Radius

Carpals

Metacarpals

Phalanges

Femur

Tibia

Fibula

Tarsals

Phalanges

Metatarsals

it is the all-important body reservoir of calcium and phosphorous, and the site of formation of red blood cells and certain white blood cells by particular tissues of the bone marrow (Chapter 25).

Vertebrates that also have plates and scales as derivatives of the skin may be considered to have both an exoskeleton and endoskeleton since plates and skin constitute a type of exoskeleton. In fact several observers believe that a number of bones, particularly those of the head, have evolved from plates in the skin.

Human Skeleton

For all practical purposes the human skeleton (Figure 29-10) is an endoskeleton consisting of two main subdivisions: (a) the *axial skeleton* representing the main axis of the body, and (b) the attached *appendicular skeleton* consisting of the bones in the shoulders, hips, arms, and legs. The bones of the body are usually classified into four general types according to their shapes: *long bones* as in the arms and legs, *short bones* as in the wrists and ankles, *flat bones* as in the skull and rib basket, and *irregular bones* as in the vertebral column.

AXIAL SKELETON. The axial skeleton in man is composed of some 80 bones and consists of the *skull, vertebral column, ribs,* and *breast bone.* The skull itself, which is formed from 28 irregular-shaped bones including those of the middle ear, consists of the brain case or *cranium* (containing small openings for the passage of the cranial nerves and blood vessels) and the bones of the face. All the skull bones with the exception of the lower jawbone are so united with each other as to be immovable. Several bones of the cranium have not yet fused at the time of birth, thus allowing for greater plasticity of the head and therefore greater facility during passage through the narrow birth canal. Fusion of these bones is almost entirely completed within the first two years of life.

The *vertebral column, spinal column,* or *backbone* composes the longitudinal axis of the body on which the head is balanced. It consists of 33 irregular-shaped bones, the *vertebrae,* so connected or *articulated* to one another as to allow forward, backward, and sideways movement. Some regions of the column are more flexible than others. As shown in Figure 29-11 the vertebral column in man is curved, a characteristic associated with greater carrying strength and balance in the upright animal.

Although the vertebrae differ in size and shape at different sites along the backbone they share certain common structural features. The main portion of a typical vertebra is called the *centrum* from whose dorsal surface there projects a ring of bone called the *neural arch.* The latter surrounds and protects the spinal cord. Bony projections from the neural arch singly lock each vertebra to the one above and the one below. In addition the vertebrae are securely tied together by numerous ligaments. Different vertebrae have a variety of other bony projections for the attachment of ribs and muscles. A small pad of tough gristle or cartilage called a *disc* lies between each of the vertebrae. Pairs of small openings occur between the vertebrae from which the spinal nerves emerge.

The first or anterior 7, so-called *cervical* vertebrae make up the skeletal framework of the neck. The next 12 *thoracic vertebrae* are located behind (or dorsal to) the thoracic cavity. The 5 *lumbar* vertebrae follow, supporting the small of the back. Below these are the *sacrum* and *coccyx* regions of the backbone, in that order. In man the sacrum is a single solid bone which has resulted from the fusion of 5 separate vertebrae. It is joined to one of the bones of the *pelvic girdle* which attaches the legs to the spine. The coccyx in man is also a single bone which has resulted from the fusion of 4 tiny bones. In many vertebrates it gives support to the tail, but in man the coccyx is now a useless vestigial structure.

The bony *chest cage* or *basket* consists of the 12 *thoracic vertebrae, 12 pairs of ribs* which are joined dorsally to the thoracic vertebrate (each rib from its vertebral attachment curves outward, then forward and downward), and the ventrally located *breast bone* or *sternum* (Figure 29-10). Ten of the 12 rib pairs are directly fused or indirectly attached by means of cartilage to the breast bone. The eleventh and twelfth pairs of ribs have no attachments whatsoever to the breast bone and for this reason are called "the floating ribs."

APPENDICULAR SKELETON. The appendicular skeleton in man is composed of 126 bones. It consists of the bones of the arms and legs called the *appendages,* and the bones composing the so-called *girdles* which attach these appendages to the axial skeleton. Each of the two *pectoral girdles* is made up of a collar bone (*clavicle*) and a shoulder blade (*scapula*) to which the arm is attached. Each clavicle forms a bony joint to the breast bone at one end, whereas at its other end it articulates with a scapula. The latter in turn connects to the ribs, not by a joint but by muscles and ligaments, an arrangement which accounts for the flexibility and freedom of movement of the shoulders and arms. In effect the girdles resemble flattened loops (two pectoral girdles and one pelvic girdle) to which the limbs are joined (Figure 29-10).

The socket formed by the union of clavicle and scapula is the site to which the arm is attached. The bone of the upper arm is called the *humerus* and articulates with the shoulder socket by means of ligaments. The 2 bones of the lower arm or forearm are the *radius* and the narrower and smaller *ulna.* The 8 small bones composing the wrist are called the *carpals* (Figure 29-10), bound together by ligaments into two rows of four. The hand consists of the 5 slender bones or *metacarpals* of the palm and the 14 finger bones or *phalanges* of the fingers—3 phalanges for each finger except for the thumb which only has 2.

The single *pelvic girdle,* in contrast to the 2 pectoral girdles, consists of 2 *hip bones* and the so-called *sacrum bone,* firmly bound together to form a stable circular foundation that supports the trunk and attaches the legs to it

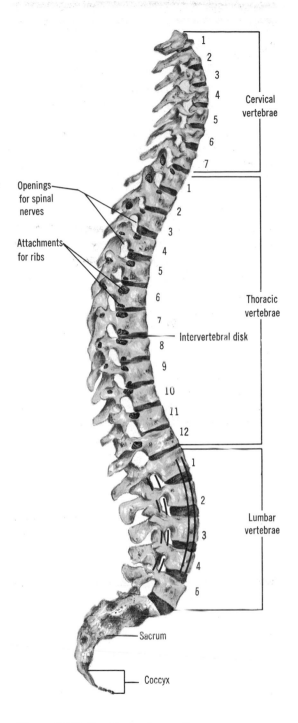

Figure 29-11. Vertebral column of man.

Openings for spinal nerves

Attachments for ribs

Cervical vertebrae

Thoracic vertebrae

Intervertebral disk

Lumbar vertebrae

Sacrum

Coccyx

(Figure 29-10). Each hip bone in reality is made up of 3 separate bones which have fused into a single large, irregular-shaped bone. The adult human male skeleton is in general larger and heavier than that of the female. However the pelvic girdle in the female is broader and more flaring with a wider arch in contrast to the narrower corresponding structure in the male, thus accommodating the child-bearing function.

The bone of the upper leg or thigh is called the *femur* and is the longest and heaviest in the body. Its end nearest the torso fits into a deep socket in one of the hip bones of the pelvic girdle but does not have quite as much freedom of movement as the upper arm bone (humerus) in the shoulder socket. The lower leg or shank comprises two bones, the *tibia* or shin bone and the narrower and smaller *fibula*. The tibia is articulated to the femur by a hinge-like attachment, the knee joint. The latter is protected by a small separate bone called the *kneecap* or *patella*, which has no counterpart in the arm.

The structure of the foot is somewhat similar to that of the hand but with certain modifications which adapt it for supporting weight. The arch of the foot is constructed of some of the 7 ankle bones or *tarsals* and the 5 *metatarsals* which correspond to the metacarpals of the palm. The arched position of the footbones, consisting of a transverse arch and longitudinal arch (Figure 29-10), is due to the strong ligaments and leg muscle tendons. Each foot, like the hand, has 14 phalanges, 3 for each toe except for the large toe which has only 2.

BONE JOINTS. Bones are joined to one another in a number of ingenious ways. The region of articulation or attachment of one bone to another is called a *joint*. Although movement of bone depends on the activity of the attached skeletal muscle, the type of movement or the degree of freedom of the bone movement will be largely determined by the articulation or nature of the joint or connection between the bones and the shape of the articulating ends of the bones.

In general, joints may be classified into the following three principal types depending on the degree of movement that they permit: (1) those that allow no movement as in the bones of the cranium which become dove-tailed or sutured to one another early in life by small bony projections interlocking like the teeth of a zipper; (2) those that permit only very slight movement between the bones as in many of the vertebrae of the spine; and (3) those that permit in varying degrees free movement between the bones. These include several types such as the shoulder and hip joints which enjoy the widest range of movements, the elbow and knee joints which have movement in one plane, and so on (Figure 29-12).

Different structural devices which exist at different joints determine the degree and kind of movement. At the one extreme in those joints where free movement prevails, a small space normally occurs between the articulating ends of the two bones. A thin layer of cartilage covers the articulating end of each bone, and the joint is encased within a fibrous capsule (possessing an inner lubricating lining) to form a true joint cavity. Several ligaments (made up of tough connective tissue) provide added strength by attaching the bones together. Small fluid-filled sacs called *bursae* are often found wherever pressure is exerted over moving parts. They serve as cushions to relieve pressure between moving parts and occur between bones, muscles, ligaments, between skin and bone and between tendons and bone. When they become inflamed the condition is known as *bursitis*. At the other extreme where little or no movement occurs the space between the two articulating ends of the bones may be filled with either cartilage or a dense connective tissue as in the cranial bones in early life before they fuse.

Various kinds of joint structures intermediate between these two extremes exist. For example, in the vertebral joints where only slight movement occurs, the fibrous-like cartilaginous disc is present between the articulating surfaces of the bones which are held together by ligaments. In the ball-and-socket joint (as in the

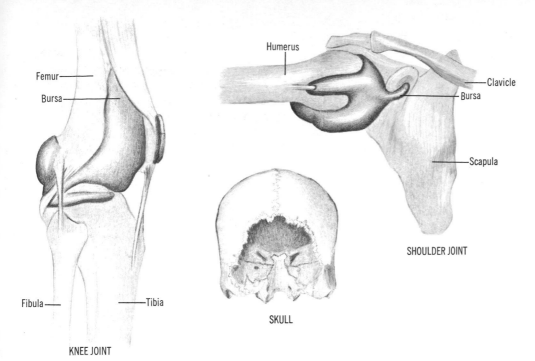

Femur
Bursa

Fibula
Tibia

KNEE JOINT

Humerus
Clavicle
Bursa

Scapula

SHOULDER JOINT

SKULL

Figure 29-12. Examples of several types of bone joints.

hip joint), a ball-shaped end of the bone (femur) fits into a concave socket permitting movement in all possible planes. In a hinge joint (as at the knee) a convex end surface of one bone (tibia) fits into a concave end surface of the other bone (femur) with bone movement occurring in only one plane.

FORMATION, GROWTH, AND PHYSIOLOGY OF BONE. The skeleton of the embryo when first formed is made up principally of cartilage shaped like bones. Cartilage is in fact the most prominent skeletal material of all vertebrates. In higher vertebrates including man most of the cartilage is slowly destroyed and its place taken by bone, a process known as *ossification*. As a result the adult skeleton is predominantly bony. Only in certain fishes (Chondrichthyes, Chapter 20) which include the sharks does cartilage persist as the major skeletal material of adults.

The typical gross anatomy and growth of a bone can be illustrated by referring to a long bone such as the thigh bone or femur (Figure 29-13). The main shaft of the long bone is called the *diaphysis* and consists of a hard outer cylindrical bony matrix enclosing a central cavity occupied by *marrow*. Each end of bone is called the *epiphysis* and consists in general of a more spongy type of bone matrix interspersed with the marrow tissue responsible for blood cell formation. Increase in bone length occurs by a continual formation of new cartilage at the epiphyseal ends followed by subsequent ossification. Growth in bone diameter takes place as a result of two general processes: (*a*) destruction of bone cells within the interior of the diaphysis, thus increasing the hollow marrow cavity; and (*b*) the simultaneous deposition of new bony tissue around the outside of the bone. The attainment of adult bone size is apparently under the control of several chemical mechanisms (as are bone repair and maintenance) including hormonal factors and vitamins.

Bone is not a static substance but is in a constant state of flux, old bone matrix being destroyed and new material being formed. The steady breakdown and resorption of bone is the result of a poorly understood process carried out by certain bone-destroying cells. The phenomenon is under hormonal regulation—specifically under the control of the parathyroid hormone (Chapter 23)—and is directly correlated with the requirements of the body. A deficiency of calcium in the other tissues of the body somehow causes an increased secretion of the parathyroid glands (Chapter 23), resulting in an increased activity of the bone-destroying cells. As a consequence calcium ions are released to the blood. Conversely an increase in the calcium level of the body by a reverse process leads to increased formation of bone matrix. Thus the skeleton serves as a reservoir for calcium which is as an essential nutrient element for a variety of functions including blood clotting and general cell metabolism. In addition bone is a storage site for phosphate whose all-important role in metabolism and energy transfer was described earlier (Chapter 8). In birds, bone also provides the mineral supply for egg-shell formation, and in deer for the periodic formation of antlers.

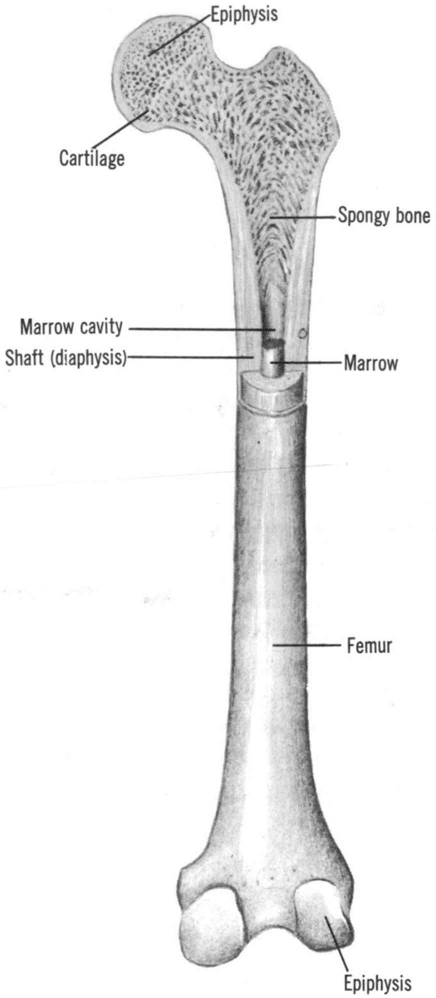

Radioactive strontium 90 as a product of atomic "fallout" in our present age has a strong affinity for bony tissue. Upon entering the body, usually by way of the digestive and respiratory tracts, strontium 90 is concentrated in the bony matrix much like calcium. It has a direct deleterious effect on bone structure because of its radioactivity. The latter may also seriously affect the blood-forming tissues in the marrow as well as other parts of the body, producing damage and inducing malignancies.

THE SKIN OR INTEGUMENT

Functions

The *skin* or *integument* as the outermost covering of the body performs a number of diverse functions.

First, it has a highly important role in *protection*. It protects the underlying tissues and organs against (*a*) mechanical injury, (*b*) invasion by bacteria and other infective agents, (*c*) excessive loss of moisture, (*d*) chemical damage, (*e*) extreme temperature changes in the external environment, and (*f*) overexposure to ultraviolet irradiation from the sun. In other animals it has an additional protective role by virtue of the adaptations it has made in coping with enemies and predators. Especially noteworthy in this respect are the numerous instances of protective coloration afforded by hair, feather, and pigment patterns, the hard external, armor-like tissues, and the poison- and odor-producing glands (which are derived

Figure 29-13. Anatomy of the long bone.

Epiphysis

Cartilage

Spongy bone

Marrow cavity

Shaft (diaphysis)

Marrow

Femur

Epiphysis

from the integument) observed in a variety of animals.

Second, in warm-blooded animals such as birds and mammals, where the body temperature is kept fairly constant, the skin is involved in the *regulation of heat loss*. This is attained by changes in the blood supply of the skin, by evaporation of sweat produced by mammalian skin, and by the insulation afforded by the oil and hair of mammalian skin and the feathers of birds. The diameters of the arteries and capillaries in the skin, and therefore the volume of blood flowing through the skin, are controlled by the autonomic nervous system according to the needs of the organism. Dilation of these blood vessels brings more blood to the skin thus favoring a greater loss of heat by radiation from the surface of the body, whereas constriction of the blood vessels reduces heat loss by radiation. Increased perspiration by the sweat glands promotes greater heat loss or cooling by evaporation.

Third, the skin has an *excretory* function which supplements the role of the kidneys. In addition to its large content of water (about 99 per cent), sweat contains a variety of substances (including inorganic salts, urea, uric acid, ammonia, and creatinine) whose composition resembles that of urine.

Fourth, by housing a vast number of nerve endings or receptors concerned with the senses of touch, pressure, temperature, and pain (Chapter 22), the skin serves in a *sensory capacity*. Thus it is one of several means by which the organism is informed of some of the activities occurring in its immediate external environment.

Fifth, the skin has a *secretory role*. In mammals, including man, oil is secreted to the surface by special glands. The oil prevents the skin from drying out and cracking, protects against excessive ultraviolet irradiation from the sun, and aids in suitable maintenance of the hair. The milk-secreting or mamary glands of mammals as specialized derivatives of the skin have an obviously important secretory function.

Finally, the skin also has a *nutritional function* for it contains the steroid 7-dehydrocholesterol which is transformed to vitamin D upon exposure to ultraviolet light (Chapter 9).

It should be noted that in many vertebrates, especially in fishes and amphibians, the skin makes a significant *respiratory* contribution by mediating an appreciable proportion of the gas exchange (oxygen uptake and carbon dioxide release) between the organism and its environment. Some gaseous exchange through the skin even takes place in such terrestrial vertebrates as the turtle, pigeon, and man.

Structure

The skin is made up of two principal parts—the outer layers of epithelial cells, called the *epidermis*, and the inner and considerably thicker *dermis* of loose connective tissue containing the blood vessels, nerves, and other specialized structures (Figure 29-14). The dermis is attached to the underlying tissue by a layer of connective tissue called the *subcutaneous layer*, containing varying amounts of fat.

In human adults the skin covers a total area of some 20 square feet and has a weight of about 7 pounds. It is from one-eighth to one-thirty-second of an inch thick and is laced with nerve receptors in which are initiated the sensations of touch, pain, and temperature. The skin and central nervous system both originate from the outer embryonic layer of cells (*ectoderm*, Chapter 31) of the embryo.

EPIDERMIS. The epidermis has no blood vessels of its own and depends on the rich supply in the dermis. The innermost or deepest layer of the epidermis, which lies adjacent to the upper surface of the dermis, is composed of columnar epithelial cells. These are the only cells of the epidermis that undergo cell multiplication or mitosis. The new cells they produce are pushed outwards toward the surface of the body away from the necessary blood supply, become progressively more flattened, and soon die. In the course of these events the outer cell layers of the epidermis attain a tough, horny, water-resistant quality because of the deposition of the hard protein-aceous substance *keratin,* the same material found in the fingernails and toenails. The outer horny cells of the epidermis are being continually sloughed off and worn away, but they are steadily replaced at a more or less equal rate by the above-mentioned multiplying innermost epidermal layer of columnar epithelial cells. The occurrence of dandruff is a more obvious example of the shedding or flaking process in man, particularly so because the presence of hair tends to retain the flakes Although in mammals the sloughing off of the horny epidermal cells is a constant and piece-meal or flaking process, in other animals as in amphibians and lizards large portions are shed at one time at intervals of a few days. Snakes in fact periodically shed the entire outer layer as a whole.

The thickness of the epidermis, although it varies in different parts of the human body and under different circumstances, remains fairly constant at any one site. It usually thickens or becomes calloused wherever there is continual pressure or rubbing, as on the soles of the feet and the palms of the hands. The epidermis of fishes in contrast to that of amphibians, reptiles, birds, and mammals consists in its entire thickness of live cells.

DERMIS. The bulk of the dermis is composed more of a matrix of connective tissue fibers than of the cells that produced it. It is this fibrous connective tissue matrix that is con-verted to leather by the tanning process. Scat-tered within the dermis is an abundance of blood vessels, lymphatics, nerve endings, sense organs, fat deposits, smooth muscle, essentially two types of glands, and other structures. The dermis also contains numer-ous elastic fibers. With age the loss in elasticity together with the decrease in subcutaneous fat accounts for the appearance of wrinkles.

SKIN GLANDS. Of the two general types of glands present in the human skin, one type called *sebaceous glands* secretes oil, and the other, the *sweat glands,* produces sweat or perspiration. Although both kinds of glands occur well within the dermis they are actually derivatives of the epidermis, having formed as ingrowths from the multiplying innermost epithelial cell layer of the epidermis. Sebaceous glands are tiny glands whose oil secretions are beneficial for both the hair and skin. There are at least two sebaceous glands associated with each hair. They may also occur in areas of the skin where hair is absent. The oil which they secrete passes out through an opening in the epidermis to the surface of the skin. It keeps the hair supple, the skin soft and pliant, and is responsible in part for an animal's individual scent or odor.

Sweat glands are small, coiled, tubular glands whose ducts lead to the surface of the body (Figure 29-14). In man, sweat glands are plenti-fully distributed in the skin over the entire surface of the body. They are especially pro-fuse in the palms, soles, forehead, and arm-pits. Their distribution in mammals varies with the species. Sweat glands in the horse and the bear, as in man, are also widely distributed over the body. Moles, on the other hand, have no sweat glands at all. In cats and rats sweat glands, are found only on the undersides of the paws; in cattle and sheep they are restricted to the muzzle and snout, and in dogs they occur only on the tongue. The function of the sweat glands in excretion and in the regulation of heat loss has already been indicated. The mammary or milk-producing glands are essen-tially highly specialized and modified sweat glands. Other modified sweat glands in the external ear secrete a waxy, pigmented material instead of the usual aqueous sweat.

Most of the glands in the skin of fishes secrete a protective layer of mucus. The skin of amphibians contains in addition to mucus-secreting glands so-called *granular* glands whose secretions may be irritating and even highly toxic to other animals. In contrast, the skin of reptiles and birds as a rule have few or no glands.

HAIR, SCALES, AND FEATHERS. Hair is dis-tinctive of the mammal. In man it is more or less

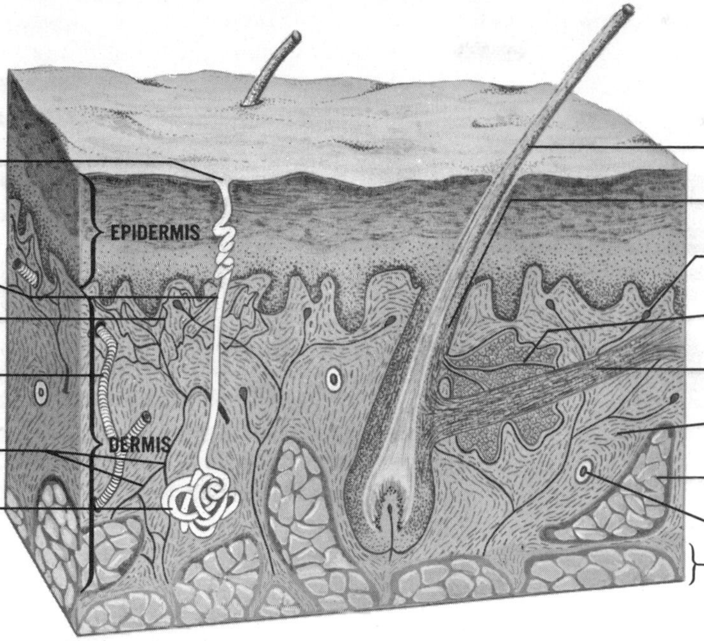
Pore of sweat gland
Duct of sweat gland
Capillaries
Artery
Nerve fibers
Sweat gland
EPIDERMIS
DERMIS
Hair shaft
Hair follicle
Tactile corpuscle
Sebaceous gland
Hair muscle
Loose connective tissue
Fat cell
Blood vessel
Subcutaneous layer

Figure 29-14. Diagram of microscopic section illustrating anatomy of the skin in man.

distributed over the entire body except the palms and soles, and is more heavily concentrated in some areas than in others. Although hairs are anchored deep within the dermis they are in fact essentially derived from inpocketings of the epidermis. A hair typically consists of two portions—the *shaft,* the visible portion projecting above the surface of the skin, and the *root,* the portion buried within the skin and extending well into the dermis. The hollow tube sunken into the dermis within which the root is located is called the *hair follicle.* The expanded hollow bulbous end of the root at the bottom of the hair follicle encloses some capillaries and nerves collectively called the *papilla.* The epithelial cells within the bulbous end of the root nearest the papilla are the only living cells of the hair. These cells are constantly dividing, pushing new cells upward which soon die and eventually become the cells of the shaft.

In cross section a hair is seen to have a complex structure, being made up of several cell layers, some of which contain pigment, and often containing air spaces. Hairs having a circular cross section tend to be straight, whereas those that are flat or oval show waviness or curliness. To each hair follicle is attached one or more delicate bundles of smooth muscle whose contraction is under the control of the autonomic nervous system. When these muscles contract the hair is pulled into a more upright position, raising the skin immediately around the hair to produce the familiar "goose pimples."

In most mammals, hair serves in insulation. Some mammals display a dense coat of hair or fur during the cold months and shed a large portion of it in the spring. Hair may also have specialized uses as in the eyebrows, eyelashes, and the hairs of the nose and ears (for keeping out dust and insects), the tactile whiskers of cats and dogs, and the protective quills of the porcupine.

The *fingernails* and *toenails* of man and other primates are modified horny epidermal cells which grow from the epithelial cells lying under the white crescent at the proximal or beginning end of each nail. Somewhat similar horny epidermal tissue constitutes the *claws* in reptiles, some amphibians, and many mammals, and the *hoofs* in cattle, horses, deer, and so on. The beaks or bills of birds consist of the bones of the upper and lower jaws ensheathed by layers of horny epidermal cells. The horns of cattle and goats are composed of bone enclosed in a case of modified epidermal tissue.

Epidermal scales, as their name implies, are derivatives of the epidermis, largely of the horny or keratinized outer layers. They are exceptionally well developed in reptiles and are present to a limited extent in birds and in some mammals. In birds they are usually found only on the legs and feet. In certain mammals such as the beaver and rat they occur on the tail. On the other hand the scaly anteater of Africa and Asia has a complete coat of horny scales.

Feathers as derivative of the epidermis are the distinctive feature of birds and are believed to have evolved from the epidermal scales of reptilian ancestors. Feathers have several roles including heat insulation, flight, protective coloration, and sexual display. They are replaced throughout the life of the bird, in some species according to season and in others gradually throughout the year. The tremendous range in colors and color patterns is due to chemical pigments as well as to the physical structure of the feathers. The latter feature produces its color effects in part through the physical phenomena of *diffraction* and *reflection* of light. The deposition of some pigments are controlled by several endocrine secretions including the sex hormones.

Other Features of the Skin

COLOR. The characteristic colors of vertebrates are determined in large part by the presence of pigment in the skin and its derivatives. In mammals, including man, the color of the skin (and hair) is due principally to the presence in the epidermis of a pigment known as *melanin*. Melanin pigments consist of fine granules ranging in color from pale yellow through various shades of red-brown to black. The pigment is believed to be a polymer or group of polymers formed from the amino acid tyrosine in certain cells, called *melanophores* or *melanoblasts*. These cells are present as part of the innermost multiplying epithelial cells of the epidermis. Since the melanin-synthesizing cells, like the other cells of the multiplying layer, proliferate to build up all the overlying epidermal layers, melanin is therefore distributed throughout the epidermis and hair. The greater the deposits and distribution of melanin in the epidermis—characteristics controlled by both genetic and environmental factors—the darker the skin. Certain hormones, vitamins, and light are known to influence the amount of pigment produced. The sun-tanning of human skin, for example, is the result of increased multiplication of the melanophores under the stimulus of ultraviolet light. In albinos, melanin-forming cells are entirely absent from the tissues.

In man, skin color also depends in part on the blood supply to the dermis. When the capillaries of the skin, especially in the upper portion of the dermis, are dilated and the blood flow is rapid the skin becomes reddish in color. When the vessels are constricted the skin is pale. If the blood flow is unusually slow most of its oxygen is given up to the tissues by the blood within the capillaries. Blood devoid of its oxygen is relatively blue and the skin under these circumstances acquires a bluish tint.

Brilliant and varied body color patterns are well displayed by the bony fishes, amphibians, and some reptiles as a result of different pigment-containing cells, melanophores, and certain cells possessing guanine crystals which effectively reflect and disperse light. The pigment-containing cells in bony fishes and reptiles are most abundant in the dermis, and in amphibians they are found largely between the epidermis and dermis. Many fishes and amphibians and some reptiles can change their colors and color patterns in response to certain environmental conditions, especially light and temperature, by means of hormonal and nervous mechanisms. The color of bird feathers is due largely to melanin supplemented by other pigments as well as the physical structure of the feathers.

PRINTS. All primates display on the skin at the finger-tips and toetips and on certain areas of the palms and soles various fixed patterns of narrow epidermal ridges and valleys. The patterns, which originate in corresponding ridges and valleys in the underlying multiplying epidermal cell layer and upper surface of the dermis, are distinctive to each individual and serve as the basis for personal identification by fingerprinting and footprinting.

SUPPLEMENTARY REFERENCES

Bainbridge, F. A., A. V. Bock, and D. B. Dill, *The Physiology of Muscular Exercise,* third edition, Longmans, Green, London, 1931.

Carlson, A. J., and V. Johnson, *The Machinery of the Body,* fifth edition, University of Chicago Press, Chicago, 1962.

Huxley, H. E., "The Contraction of Muscle," *Scientific American,* November 1958.

Katchalsky, A., and S. Lifson, "Muscle as a Machine," *Scientific American,* March 1954.

Szent-Gyorgi, A., "Muscle Research," *Scientific American,* June 1949.

Chapter 30   Reproduction

GENERAL CONSIDERATIONS

Reproduction is the self-directed process by which every kind of living thing produces new individuals of its own kind. It is nature's way of perpetuating life, and it is the vital process that links the past, present, and future. This universal ability of organisms to produce new living entities like themselves is a kind of immortality that surmounts the relatively short life span of the individual. Although reproduction is accomplished in several different ways depending on the organism, its most essential feature is the separation from the parent organism of a suitable complement of its DNA (accompanied by a portion of other protoplasmic constituents) to form eventually one or more new individuals. In the extreme example of viruses the introduction of DNA (or RNA in the viruses that have no DNA) into an appropriate host cell eventually leads to the production of new virus particles. In such instances the nucleic-acid complement of the infecting virus redirects and utilizes the metabolic machinery of the host protoplasm toward the single purpose of forming new but similar virus particles (Chapter 11).

Sexual and Asexual Reproduction

Reproduction is classified into two main types, *sexual* and *asexual*. In *sexual reproduction* the nuclei of two cells called *gametes* must first unite to form one cell in order to produce offspring. Each of the gametes frequently comes from a different parent so that in many instances sexual reproduction requires the participation of two parents. This, however, is not always the case as in the example of certain animals and numerous self-fertilizing flowering plants where a single organism forms the two types of gametes that undergo fusion. In brief, sexual reproduction is often biparental but may also be uniparental depending on the species.

In *asexual reproduction*, described below, no gametes are required and the process is nearly always accomplished by cell division or mitosis. Only a single parent is involved.

ASEXUAL REPRODUCTION

Binary Fission

Several types of asexual reproduction are recognized. In many but not all unicellular organisms asexual reproduction is attained simply by cell division or mitosis and is frequently called *binary fission* (Figure 30-1). The two new daughter cells have identical nuclei and more or less equal amounts of cytoplasm and cytoplasmic structures. In the process the single parent cell has been transformed into two daughter cells. If motile, such as most protozoa and free-swimming algae, the two cells formed by binary fission soon separate and go their separate ways. If nonmotile the cells often adhere to each other and, upon

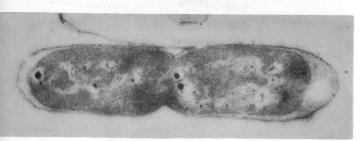

Figure 30-1. Electron micrograph of a dividing bacterial cell (*Escherichia coli*). The cell wall and cell membrane are indenting opposite sides of the parent cell. Magnification, 65,000X. (*Courtesy Dr. K. Smith, Jr., J. Ultrastructure Res.*)

further reproduction by binary fission, form clusters or colonies.

Budding

Budding is another form of asexual reproduction occurring in several types of organisms. In unicellular organisms it is a type of binary fission involving the formation of two identical nuclei. The cytoplasm, however, is unequally divided so that the two daughter cells differ markedly in size. The smaller cell or "bud" often remains temporarily attached to the larger one as illustrated by the yeasts (Figure 30-2). In multicellular organisms, budding is often referred to as *vegetative reproduction* and is described below.

Spore Formation

Spore formation is a common form of asexual reproduction which is widely distributed among simple organisms. It consists of a series of cell divisions giving rise to several small cells called *spores* which temporarily remain within the confines of the original cell membrane or cell wall of the parent cell. They are eventually liberated by rupture of the parental membrane or wall and under favorable conditions resume growth. In general, spores are able to withstand unfavorable environmental conditions such as dryness, extreme heat or cold, and harmful chemicals. Yeast cells, for example, under certain conditions reproduce by spore formation (Figure 30-3) instead of by budding.

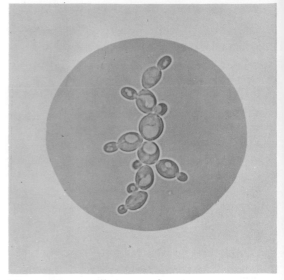

Figure 30-2. Budding in bakers' yeast (*Saccharomyces cerevisiae*). (*Courtesy of Fleischmann Laboratories, Standard Brands, Inc.*)

Vegetative Reproduction

The term *vegetative reproduction* is frequently used to designate the asexual process by which a portion or segment of a multicellular plant or animal body is separated and developed into a new individual. In the lower multicellular animals such as the coelenterate *Hydra*, a small swelling or "bud" appears on the surface of the body of the animal and eventually develops most of the structures of the body (See Figure 18-6). It may remain permanently connected to the maternal tissue or become completely separated as an entirely independent entity. The process is also frequently referred to as *budding* and resembles the budding process indicated for unicellular organisms.

Many higher plants reproduce asexually by vegetative reproduction in addition to sexual means. The small embryonic cell clusters in potato tubers, called buds or "eyes," the bulbs of onions, gladioli, and similar plants, and the horizontal runner stems of strawberries are examples of a type of asexual reproduction that is classified under vegetative reproduction.

Parthenogenesis

The development of an egg cell into a new individual without benefit of fertilization by a sperm cell is called *parthenogenesis*. It is considered to be a form of asexual reproduction since it does not involve the fusion of two gametes. Parthenogenesis is a naturally occurring phenomenon among several invertebrate groups, principally insects, crustaceans, and rotifers.

In the honeybee, an example of natural parthenogenesis, the male or drones all have their origin from unfertilized eggs and are therefore haploid. The females, who are the workers, and the queen develop from fertilized eggs and are therefore diploid. The queen is apparently only inseminated once but can store the sperm for as long as five years or more using it for fertilizing eggs, apparently at will, during this time. In nearly all other animals the eggs under natural conditions must be fertilized in order for them to develop into embryos.

In the laboratory a variety of artificial treatments have proved to be highly successful in activating or stimulating unfertilized egg cells to develop into an embryo, a process called *artificial parthenogenesis*. Exposure of sea urchin egg cells, and to a much less extent frog egg cells, to numerous chemical and physical agents (including inorganic salts, organic solvents and acids, osmotic shock, temperature shock, electric shocks, ultraviolet light, and shaking) has been sufficient to start embryo development. In sea urchins and frogs artificial parthenogenesis has led to the full devel-

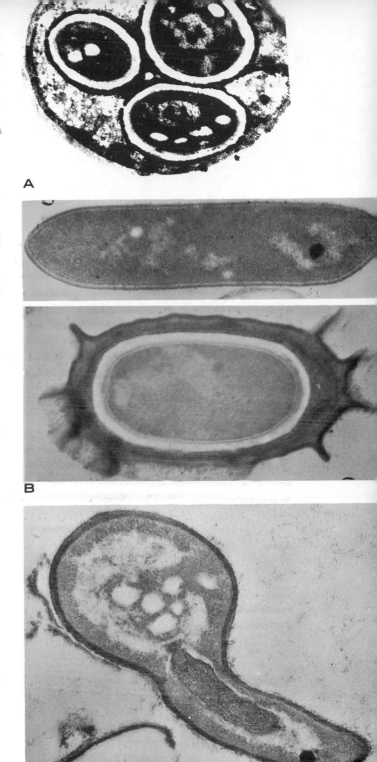

Figure 30-3. Electron micrograph of (A) a final stage of spore formation in a yeast cell (*Saccharomyces cerevisiae*). Three mature ascospores are seen in this section, magnification, 21,000X (*courtesy of Dr. S. F. Conti, J. Biophys. Biochem. Cytol.*); (B) longitudinal sections of the bacterium *Bacillus polymyxa* in its vegetative stage (*above*), and in its spore stage (*below*), magnification, 65,000X (*courtesy of Dr. P. E. Holbert, J. Biophys. Biochem. Cytol.*); (C) germinating spore of *Streptomyces violaceoruber*, magnification, 120,000X (*courtesy of Dr. A. M. Glauert, J. Cell. Biol.*).

opment of new individuals. Notable success has been obtained in producing artificial parthenogenesis in turkeys to yield adults. There are also reports of the development of mammalian eggs by artificial parthenogenesis, but only through the early stages of embryonic development.

The long list and wide variety of effective agents in causing artificial parthenogenesis suggest that these treatments probably act by triggering off within the egg an unidentified reaction or reaction whose nature is determined by factors within the egg itself. In parthenogenesis there is a tendency for the diploid number to be restored, and complete or advanced embryological development can only occur if diploidy is attained. This can take place by fusion of the nuclei of the egg cell and a polar body prior to embryonic development, by fusion of haploid nuclei in the early stages of development before cell division, or by mitosis without cytoplasmic division.

Polyembryony

The development of two or more individuals from an originally single, sexually produced embryo as a result of certain changes occurring at an early developmental stage of the embryo is called *polyembryony*. In a remote sense it can be regarded as a type of asexual reproduction, although this is not important. Polyembryony is scattered throughout the animal kingdom and in humans is manifested as identical twins, triplets, quadruplets, and, in rare cases, quintuplets. It is a regular occurrence in the armadillo, a mammal where four identical offspring are produced at a single birth.

SEXUAL REPRODUCTION
Significance of Sex

Sexual reproduction is of widespread occurrence, appearing in a tremendous diversity of living forms ranging from the simplest to the most complex. It is apparently not essential for the propagation of life in several unicellular species and some multicellular forms since it has not been found thus far among these living systems. The fact that the sexual process is so extensively distributed in different organisms in such a vast variety of forms suggests that it serves in a role of broad biological significance in addition to its function in reproduction.

It is now apparent that the greatest significance of sex resides in (1) its maintenance of the diploid condition, thereby providing certain distinct advantages in survival, and (2) its important role in promoting genetic variability by mixing and reassorting the genes in the offspring of each generation (Chapter 13). In this respect the two most fundamental events in any sexual process are *meiosis* for reassorting different genes in the formation of gametes, and the fusion of two gametes or nuclei, a phenomenon known as *fertilization*, which is the means for combining or mixing different genes in the production of offspring. The single cell resulting from fertilization is called a *zygote* and gives rise to the new individual. Thus sexual reproduction permits the combining within a single individual of the best genes of its parents. It is true by the same token that at the other extreme it also allows for the combining of the most unfavorable parental genes within a single offspring. The latter individual, however, because of the resulting detrimental characteristics, will be placed at a distinct disadvantage in survival. The chances are, therefore, that eventually he will be eliminated by the inexorable selection process of evolution.

It has been discovered in recent years that even viruses and bacteria, heretofore regarded as asexual forms, possess mechanisms for recombining genes. They therefore have sexuality. Of the major groups of living organisms only the blue-green algae have not yet been shown to have a means for recombining genes (i.e., sexual reproduction), possibly because they have not yet been extensively studied along these lines.

Evolution of Sex

The process of sexual reproduction has undoubtedly originated and evolved from the more primitive process of asexual reproduction. Among many of the lower organisms, as in the case of certain protozoa and algae, the gametes are the ordinary cells of the organism, whereas in others they are small specialized flagellate cells which cannot be distinguished from one another.

In all higher organisms, both plants and animals, and in multicellular algae two types of gametes have evolved—the *female gamete* or *ovum* consisting of a typically large, non-motile egg cell usually containing relatively larger amounts of stored food material, and the *male gamete* or *sperm cell*, a small motile, free-swimming flagellate cell. Both gametes are haploid, despite their difference in size, and therefore contain equivalent amounts of DNA. The difference between female and male gametes in multicellular organisms is part of the general pattern of specialization and division of labor in the structural and functional organization of these living systems. By contrast, in numerous unicellular organisms capable of sexual reproduction every cell may under suitable environmental conditions act as a gamete.

Sexual reproduction in all multicellular animals and nearly all multicellular plants consists of the union of two dissimilar gametes —an egg nucleus with a sperm nucleus—to yield a single-celled diploid zygote which eventually develops into a multicellular organism resembling the parents. Asexual reproduction of widely divergent types also occurs among some of the lower multicellular animals but is absent or rare among many of the higher animals.

The organs in which the gametes are formed are called the *gonads*. The male gonads produce sperm cells and are called the *testes* (singular, *testis*); the female gonads which produce the egg cells are called the *ovaries*.

In the coelenterates as represented by *Hydra* the gonads are temporary structures appearing at the period of sexual reproduction as small swellings on the outer surface of the body. In all multicellular animals above the coelenterates the gonads are developed within the body.

Hermaphroditism vs. Bisexuality

An organism that possesses both male and female gonads is said to be *hermaphroditic* or *monoecious*. A *dioecious organism*, on the other hand, has only one type of gonad, either male or female, so that two different sexes or the *bisexual condition* exists. Many invertebrates as well as a majority of flowering plants are hermaphrodites. A flower contains the gonads of higher plants. A hermaphroditic plant has flowers containing female parts that produce the egg cells and male parts that give rise to the male gametes or *sperm nuclei* (Chapter 16). The probable course of events in the evolution of sexual reproduction in plants is discussed in Chapter 16. Among the higher animals there are considerably more dioecious species than monoecious ones.

Actually many hermaphrodites have evolved in such a way as to avoid self fertilization or inbreeding. In some invertebrate hermaphrodites (e.g., snails and slugs) each individual has a single hermaphrodite gonad which produces eggs and sperm at the same time. However, the ducts which transport the eggs and sperm to the outside are separate, as are the female and male copulatory organs. Self-fertilization is a rare phenomenon among this group. Instead, two hermaphroditic slugs mate or copulate so that the eggs of each are fertilized by the sperm of the other. In some plant and animal hermaphrodites the male reproductive organs develop either before or after the female organs do. In others, self-sterility exists so that inbreeding is impossible. Several, however, are capable of self-fertilization in addition to being able to mate with other individuals of the species.

All vertebrates (with the exception of certain

fishes which first develop and function as one sex and later change into the other) and nearly all insects are dioecious. Hermaphroditism in animals is considered to be the primitive condition since it occurs chiefly in lower animals and not at all in higher forms. Bisexuality, or the separation of sexes, presumably evolved at a later time. It assures that fertilization will take place by a union of gametes from different individuals, and thus has the obvious evolutionary attribute of rendering certain the main advantage of sexual reproduction, namely the formation of new gene combinations. By also permitting a division of labor among the two sexes, bisexuality provides additional advantages compared to hermaphroditism. In most animals the male often proves to be more active than the female in terms of mobility, procurement of food, and protection.

Transitional stages between hermaphroditism and bisexuality are seen in some plants. For example, the corn plant as a whole is a hermaphrodite since the flowers at the top of the tassel are exclusively male whereas the lateral flowers of the ear are exclusively female. Certain plants may possess three types of flowers—male flowers, female flowers, and hermaphroditic ones—all on the same individual.

Sexual Behavior and Breeding Patterns

One of the primary requirements imposed by bisexuality is a means for bringing the opposite sexes together in order for mating and subsequent fertilization to occur. There seems to be little question that the evolution of a highly developed nervous system must have played an important role in this respect. Sexual behavior is markedly influenced by all kinds of sensory stimuli, including visual, auditory, olfactory, tactual, and chemical. The important role of the steroid hormones in the development and maintenance of sexual behavior has already been discussed. The development of both the endocrine and nervous systems has been accompanied by the evolution of complex sexual behavior patterns on the part of both the male and female animals, leading not only to the ultimate bringing together of sperm and egg but to the care of the resulting young.

The external secondary sexual characteristics have the principal function of serving as a visual, olfactory, mechanical, or auditory stimulus to attract the opposite sex and to elicit a mating response. Thus they indirectly further the chances of a union of egg cell and sperm. The secondary sexual characteristics of vertebrates manifest themselves in various ways including voice, features of muscle and skeleton, and pigment patterns or specialized skin structures such as particular groups of feathers or hairs, combs, horns, and so on. Some female fishes release a substance to the water and thereby notify the males that they are reproductively active. Color and scent probably are significant factors among the reptiles for attracting male to female.

Breeding in most mature vertebrates is generally restricted to a specific period and does not take place throughout the year. Several environmental factors exert an important effect in determining the onset of breeding in most species. Of these, light is probably the most critical in controlling the development and periodicity of reproduction. Increasing temperature and rainfall also serve to stimulate reproductive activity. In the temperate zones the period of greatest breeding for most vertebrates occurs at such a time as to assure birth in the springtime when chances for survival are maximal. Exceptions occur in all vertebrate groups. The role of the endocrine system and the cyclic nature of breeding patterns are discussed in later sections on the *estrus* and *menstrual cycles.*

The pattern of courtship and pairing among the vertebrates also varies considerably. On the one hand some vertebrates carry on a polygamous, casual, and promiscuous sexual relationship after which there is no further relationship between the male and female as in the instance of many rodents and birds. At the other extreme some vertebrate species display a strong monogamous system of mating in which pairing-off between individual males and females occurs, and is maintained for many years, perhaps for life, as in wolves (ironically) and some species of geese. In some animals during the breeding season—for instance, certain fishes, birds, deer, and antelope—the male designates and physically defends against intrusion by other males an area or territory for mating purposes. In many vertebrates a tendency to migrate or wander marks the beginning of the sexual cycle, for example, the migration of fishes to their breeding grounds. For certain fishes (e.g., salmon), spawning after reaching the breeding grounds is followed shortly afterwards by the natural death of the spawners.

Fertilization

Depending on the particular vertebrate group, fertilization (the union of the egg cell and sperm) may be either *internal*, occurring within the female body, or *external*, occurring outside it. Fertilization among fishes may be either internal or external according to the species. Some species of fish bear live offspring as a result of internal fertilization and embryonic development. Among others, such as trout and salmon, the male and female without experiencing physical contact simultaneously release eggs and sperm into the water where fertilization (of the external type) and subsequent embryonic development take place.

In amphibians such as frogs and toads fertilization is external, but close physical contact during the sexual act occurs between male and female. The male clasps the body of the female from the back with his forelegs, and, as he exerts pressure on the female abdomen, both simultaneously release sperm and eggs, respectively, to the surrounding water where fertilization ensues. In contrast to frogs and toads most tailed amphibians such as salamanders undergo internal fertilization, although the sperm are never directly deposited within the female by a male copulatory organ.

In reptiles internal fertilization is the rule, the sperm being deposited in most cases within the female by an erectile copulatory organ of the male. In birds internal fertilization is also the rule but in most species the male lacks a copulatory organ or penis. During copulation the male balances himself on the back of the female so that the opening called the *cloaca* near the base of the tail on the underside of the body of each comes in contact with one another. During this brief period sperm is transferred from male to female. In other species of birds —for example, ducks—an erectile male organ emerges from the cloaca and is used during copulation to deposit the sperm within the female.

In mammals fertilization is always internal. Copulation essentially involves the insertion of the male copulatory organ, the penis, into the vagina of the female with the liberation of sperm.

Parental Care of Eggs and Young

Parental care of the eggs is almost nonexistent for most species of fishes and amphibians and for some reptiles. Once the eggs are laid they are completely ignored. A few species of fish and amphibians, however, do look after their eggs. Care usually consists of fanning movements by the fins in the vicinity of the eggs thus generating localized water currents which help to replenish the needed oxygen supply. Although many species of reptiles deposit their eggs in the mud and leave them unattended, some lizards and snakes remain with their eggs during their development into offspring (Figure 30-4).

Birds, like mammals, are warm-blooded animals and their fertilized eggs often require a temperature higher than that of the external environment in order to undergo successfully embryonic development. By sitting on the eggs the parent provides the additional necessary heat. In some species of birds only the female performs the incubation whereas in others both the male and female participate. Many species of birds build an individual nest dur-

Figure 30-4. Female fox snake (*Coluber vulpinus*) and her eggs. (*Courtesy of Amer. Mus. Nat. Hist.*).

ing the breeding period and lay their eggs in it. The most common pattern is for the female to build the nest alone. In mammals the fertilized egg cell is maintained throughout embryonic development within the body of the female (with the exception of the *monotremes* who are egg layers) and is thus assured of protection, nutrition, and other essential care.

Nest building or shelter building by mammals is not necessarily associated with breeding behavior, and in general occurs all year around. Some fishes also display nest-building tendencies during the breeding season, although most do not.

Elaborate patterns for care of the young (following birth) have evolved among birds and mammals, whereas virtually none exist for fishes, amphibians, and reptiles.

THE REPRODUCTIVE SYSTEM OF MAN

General Features

The basic function of the reproductive system of all sexual organisms is to accomplish fertilization—the union of the nuclei of two appropriate gametes with one another. In most higher animals fertilization is attained by the fusion of the nucleus of the egg cell with that of the sperm. In virtually all mammals including man the reproductive system has the added role of insuring the successful development of the embryo into a new individual within the body of the female.

The reproductive system in vertebrates is the only system of the body that exists in two morphologically and functionally different states thus accounting for two different types of individuals, male and female. It is essentially composed of the gonads or sex glands (which produce sex cells or gametes) and the ducts or passageways which permit the transfer of the gametes. An additional primary sexual structure, the copulatory organ or penis, has evolved in the males of some animals, such as the mammals, permitting the deposition of sperm within the ducts of the female reproductive system.

The Female Reproductive Organs

The reproductive system of the human female (Figure 30-5) consists primarily of two *ovaries* (or the female gonads) which produce the female gametes or egg cells, and associated ducts and structures. The latter include the *Fallopian tubes* or *oviducts, uterus, vagina,* and *vulva.*

THE OVARIES. Each of the two adult ovaries is about the size and shape of a large almond and is separately located in the lower or pelvic region of the abdominal cavity (Figure 30-5). The surface of the ovary consists of a layer of columnar epithelial cells which at various intervals penetrate deeply as columns of cells into the underlying connective tissue. During embryonic development of the female small groups of cells separate from these columns and become arranged into definite structures known as primordial *Graafian* or *ovarian follicles,* each consisting essentially of a larger single cell surrounded usually by a single layer of cells. At the time of birth the newborn female infant contains several thousand primordial ovarian follicles in each of its ovaries. With the onset some dozen years later of sexual development, called *puberty,* a single ovarian follicle under the influence of the follicle-stimulating hormone (FSH) of the anterior pituitary gland begins to undergo maturation. It is followed periodically by successive maturation of other individual follicles

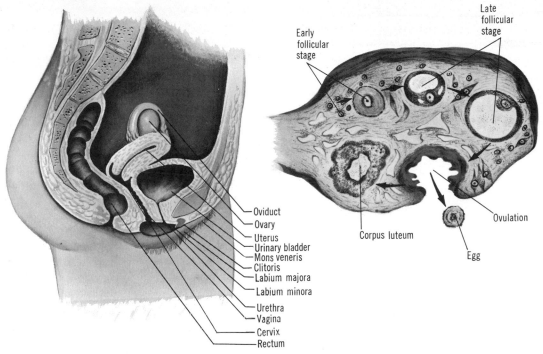

Figure 30-5. Diagram of a sagittal section showing the reproductive system of an adult human female. The separate schematic diagram of the ovary depicts the changes that occur in the maturation of an ovarian follicle, the release of the egg cell, and the formation of the corpus luteum.

(about once every 28 days) throughout the sexually mature life of the female. The details of this process and its control by various hormones are discussed in later sections on the *estrus* and *menstrual cycles*.

THE OVIDUCTS. In close proximity to each ovary is a large funnel-shaped fringed opening of a duct called the *oviduct* which is about one-half inch long. At its opposite or lower end each oviduct opens into the upper part of the uterus or womb. The inner lining of the tubes consists of ciliated epithelial cells which together with the peristaltic action of the duct walls facilitate the passage of the egg cell received from a ruptured ovarian follicle. At the time of ovulation the released egg cell is not yet mature and is in fact only in the early steps of oögenesis (Chapter 12), usually in the secondary oöcyte stage. It is during the course

of its passage along the oviduct that the second meiotic division occurs to yield ultimately a mature egg cell with the haploid number of chromosomes.

THE UTERUS OR WOMB. The uterus or womb to which the oviducts lead is a hollow, muscular, somewhat flattened, pear-shaped organ about the size of a clenched fist in the adult nonpregnant woman. It is located between the bladder and rectum and is essentially a Y-shaped structure (Figure 30-5) whose arms are continuous with the oviducts. The uterine cavity is somewhat triangular in shape and is comparatively small due to the thickness of its walls. The walls are made up of a thick coat of smooth muscle fibers and are lined on the inner surface by a mucous membrane called the *endometrium*, which is composed of columnar epithelial, glandular, and connective tissues. The main stem of the Y constitutes the principal portion of the uterus. Its lower end, the *cervix* (which is smaller and narrower than the main body of the organ), opens into the vagina. During pregnancy the uterus undergoes a 200-fold increase in size.

THE VAGINA. The vagina as the copulatory organ of the female is a sheath-like tube composed mostly of smooth muscle and lined with mucous membrane. It leads from the cervix of the uterus to the outside of the body and in sexual intercourse receives the erect male copulatory organ or penis. At birth the vagina also serves as part of the canal through which the embryo or *fetus* passes enroute to becoming a newborn infant. In females who have not had sexual intercourse the lower or external end of the vagina is partially closed or constricted by a fold of mucous membrane called the *hymen*. Ordinarily a sufficient opening is present which allows the escape of the menstrual flow. The hymen is generally ruptured during the first act of sexual intercourse.

THE VULVA. The external structures or organs of the reproductive tract in the adult female are collectively designated as the *vulva*. It consists of the region called the *vestibule*, in which the external openings of the urethra and vagina are located, and several surrounding structures including the *labia majora, labia minora, clitoris,* and *mons veneris* (Figure 30-5). Within the vestibule the opening of the urethra is anterior to that of the vagina. The vestibule itself is enclosed by two pairs of fleshy, lip-like skin structures—the outer and larger hair-covered *labia majora* and the inner and smaller hair-free *labia minora*. The lips of each pair join at the anterior and posterior ends of the vestibule. The *clitoris* is a small pea-like mass of erectile tissue which is analogous to the penis in the male, but unlike the latter it does not include the urethra. It is located near the anterior junction of the labia minora. The clitoris, like the penis, becomes engorged with blood during sexual excitement and apparently functions as an excitatory organ during sexual relations. The *mons veneris* is

a skin-covered pad of fat with pubic hair located in the ventral, lowermost region of the torso just anterior to the clitoris.

THE ESTRUS CYCLE. The mature females of nearly all mammalian species experience a distinct rhythm (or series of cyclic changes) in ovulation and reproductive activities. Breeding in most, but not all, sexually mature vertebrates is usually restricted to a particular period of the year depending upon the specie. This is believed to be in part of a consequence of natural selection because it confines the appearance of the newborn to a season of the year, usually spring, that is most favorable for the birth and subsequent care of the young. Some animals experience one breeding season during the year (for example, deer and sheep), others have several, whereas still others such as man may breed throughout the year.

The relatively brief periods within the breeding season when the female of most mammalian species, with the exception of the higher primates, undergoes spontaneous ovulation and is most receptive of the male is known as the "heat" or *estrus*. The rhythmic or cyclic changes in the development, release, and maturation of the egg cell, together with the accompanying structural and physiological changes in the reproductive system as well as behavorial changes, periodically prepare the female for mating, and are collectively termed the *estrus cycle*.

The estrus itself is that part of the cycle during which the female is physiologically and psychologically prepared for mating. Sexual desire is at its height and reproductive activity is maximal. Maturation and growth of an ovarian follicle represent some of the important changes occurring prior to the estrus. The onset of estrus coincides with the rupture of the follicle and the release of its egg cell. Thus the egg cell is ready for fertilization at the very same time that the female reaches the peak of readiness for accepting the male. With the release of the egg cell, the ruptured follicle collapses and is soon replaced by the growth of a small mass of cells, the *corpus luteum*, which secretes the female sex hormone progesterone.

The *endometrium,* consisting of a thin uterine epithelium and the underlying highly vascularized glandular mucosa of the uterus, experiences a marked transformation during the estrus cycle. At the beginning of the estrus the relatively thin endometrium progressively thickens, its blood supply increases, and its uterine glands deepen as follicular maturation proceeds. With the release of the egg cell and the subsequent appearance of the corpus luteum, the endometrium continues to thicken and build up even more rapidly. If fertilization occurs the fertilized egg cell implants itself in the endometrium where it develops into a new individual. The corpus luteum is maintained through most of the duration of pregnancy. If fertilization does not occur the egg cell degenerates, the corpus luteum begins to disappear, and the endometrium regresses, returning to its original thin state. The endometrium does not build up again until the beginning of the next estrus cycle. If pregnancy is absent the estrus cycle will be regularly repeated according to the mating pattern of the species.

Depending on the species a mature female may experience one or several estrus cycles within a breeding season. The silver fox, for example, like most wild animals has one breeding season per year. It lasts for about 5 days in February during which time only a single estrus cycle occurs. The mare, on the other hand, may have several estrus periods in a single breeding season, the time of estrus lasting 4 to 9 days and the frequency of estrus occurring every 21 days if breeding does not take place. In cats and dogs two estrus periods occur per year, whereas in the mouse and rat the female has an estrus cycle about every 4 or 5 days. In some mammals such as the rabbit, mink, and cat ovulation does not normally occur unless it is first stimulated by the act of sexual intercourse or coitus.

Although all female mammals show sexual cycles of one type or another, the *males* of some species (e.g., man, dog, cat, and rat, to name a few) do not display cycles and are fertile throughout the year.

THE MENSTRUAL CYCLE. In the female of the human and other higher primates the estrus cycle is still present but less distinct. Reception of the male by the female is no longer confined to certain intervals but is more or less continuous. Moreover, regression of the endometrium is a more extreme process. The uterine lining rapidly deteriorates resulting in the rupture of its blood vessels, the flow of blood and other fluid, and the sloughing away of most of the endoterium, phenomena collectively called *menstruation.* The cycle is thus uniquely marked by regularly occurring periods of menstruation. The period of menstruation, which lasts about 4 days, occurs between the periods of ovulation and therefore does not correspond to the estrus (it is ovulation which coincides with the estrus). The cycle is accordingly called the *menstrual cycle* and in humans averages about 28 days (may range from 21 to 35 days) from start to end, before the next cycle begins. Repair of the uterine lining follows, and with the beginning of the next cycle the endometrium begins to thicken progressively once more. If fertilization takes place, the endometrium is maintained and in fact experiences further changes as indicated in the later discussion of human embryonic development (Chapter 31).

The striking dependency of reproductive activity on the gonadotropic hormones of the anterior pituitary gland and the hormones of the gonads are illustrated by the description of the menstrual cycle in the human female. In the human female the beginning of sexual development, or puberty, may occur between the ages of 10 to 14 and is often marked by the onset of menstruation, the first definite sign that the menstrual cycle has been initiated. The menstrual cycle is henceforth successively repeated throughout the reproductive life of the female, except for periods of pregnancy and lactation. The cessation of the menstrual cycles, marking the end of the reproductive period of the woman, usually occurs between 45 and 50 years of age and is known as the *menopause.* It is characteristically accompanied by certain changes in the ovaries and other sex organs and

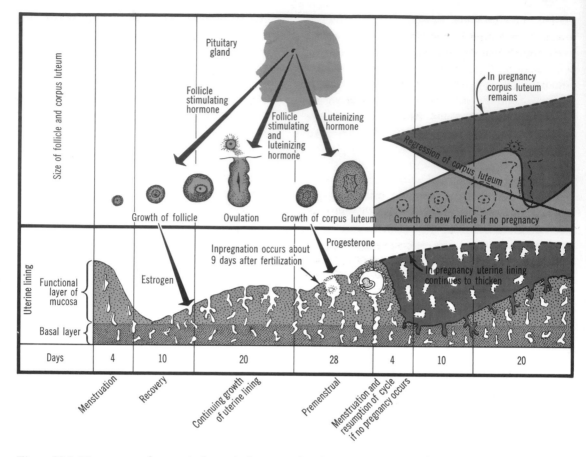

Figure 30-6. Time course of events in the typical menstrual cycle of the adult human female.

frequently by typical physiological and psychological reactions including hot flushes, depression, irritability, and so on.

Menstruation, as the periodic shedding of the rich uterine lining and accompanying blood flow, normally occurs when fertilization fails to take place. In a typical menstrual cycle the 10 days or so immediately following the cessation of menstrual flow are characterized by the progressive development and maturation of an ovarian follicle in one of the ovaries. The initiation and maintenance of the maturing ovarian follicle is controlled by an increased secretion of the *follicle-stimulating hormone* (FSH) from the anterior pituitary gland at this

time (Figure 30-6). As it develops the follicle secretes increasing quantities of the female sex hormone *estrogen*, which promotes the redevelopment of the uterine lining in preparation for the possible arrival within the next few days of a fertilized egg cell. Maturation of the follicle consists of growth and proliferation of the follicular cells accompanied by the accumulation of fluid near the center of the follicle which causes it to distend and move outward toward the surface of the ovary. The continued distension of the maturing follicle causes it to project from the ovary surface like a small swelling or cyst until it eventually bursts to discharge its egg cell.

The development of the follicle and its rupture, resulting in the liberation of the egg cell approximately 10 days after the *cessation* of menstrual flow (or 14 days after the *start* of menstrual flow), involves the necessary participation of the *leuteinizing hormone* (LH) of the anterior pituitary gland. Almost immediately following ovulation, or the discharge of the egg cell, the cavity of the ruptured follicle under the influence of LH begins to fill with a mass of developing yellowish cells, the *corpus luteum*, which produce the hormone progesterone. Progesterone promotes even greater growth and proliferation of the uterine lining, especially of its glandular tissue, thus providing a favorable environment for the implantation of a fertilized egg. At the same time progesterone inhibits the development of any other ovarian follicles as well as uterine contraction, and stimulates further development of the mammary glands in preparation for milk formation after birth. The *lactogenic hormone* secreted by the anterior pituitary gland also participates together with the LH hormone in maintaining the corpus luteum and therefore progesterone secretion.

If fertilization has not occurred by the twenty-seventh or twenty-eighth day after the start of the previous menstrual flow, the corpus luteum undergoes degeneration with a consequent cessation in progesterone secretion, probably the result of decreased gonadotrophic secretions by the anterior pituitary gland. Because of a lack of progesterone and a minimum production of estrogen the thickened uterine lining can somehow no longer be maintained. It shortly begins to degenerate and slough off with accompanying hemorrhaging, thus marking the beginning of menstruation and another menstrual cycle. The frequent premenstrual emotional irritability and tension on the part of the female is believed to be associated with the low level of sex hormones in the body at this time.

If fertilization takes place, the corpus luteum and its secretion of progesterone are maintained for approximately the first five months or more of pregnancy. If for any reason the corpus luteum is removed or destroyed during this time, pregnancy ceases with the occurrence of a miscarriage or abortion. The developing placenta (Chapter 31) secretes increasing quantities of progesterone and by the fourth or fifth month of pregnancy produces sufficient quantities to maintain pregnancy. It is about this time that the corpus luteum regresses and ceases its hormone secretion. The corpus luteum is therefore a temporary gland of internal secretion in the female, degenerating after two weeks if the animal does not become pregnant within the given cycle, but remaining for a considerably longer time if fertilization occurs.

Ovulation ordinarily occurs between the fourteenth and sixteenth days of the menstrual cycle, or midway between menstrual periods, if the beginning of the cycle is taken as the time that menstruation commences. The released egg cell is thought to be viable or capable of fertilization for about 24 to possibly 48 hours. This interval, often called the *fertile period*, therefore represents the time when fertilization is most likely to take place. Sperm liberated within the reproductive tract of the female are capable of fertilizing an egg cell for about the same interval of time. Some authorities claim that the fertile period in females may be as much as 4 to 6 days.

The Male Reproductive System

The male reproductive system in humans consists of two primary sex glands, the *testes*, which produce the sperm, and a series of ducts, accessory glands, and supporting structures.

THE TESTES. Each of the two testes in the adult male is an ovoid body about the size of a walnut. Both are located outside the body cavity within skin-covered pouch called the *scrotum* or *scrotal sac* (Figure 30-7). In other vertebrates such as fish, frogs, reptiles, and birds the testes are located within the abdominal cavity. In man, as in most mammals, they are formed within the abdomen close to the kidneys and lie there until shortly before, or soon after, birth. Thereupon they normally descend through an opening in the abdominal wall called the *inguinal canal* into the scrotal sac. The slightly lower temperature of the scrotum (about 3° to 5° C less) compared to the abdominal cavity is believed to be essential for the formation of sperm. In many mammals who are seasonal breeders the testes are found in the scrotum only during the breeding season and are largest just before that time.

The two principal functions of the testes are the formation of sperm cells and the production of the male sex hormone testosterone. The wall of each testis consists largely of connective tissue which is continuous with wall-like partitions dividing the interior of of the testis into approximately 250 small compartments called *lobules*. Each lobule contains from one to three tiny convoluted tubes called *seminiferous tubules* within which the sperm are formed (Figure 30-8). The special cells situated among the seminiferous tubules are collectively called the *interstitial*

tissue, which performs the important function of producing and secreting testosterone. Starting at puberty, under the stimulation of the follicle-stimulating hormone secreted by the anterior pituitary gland, and continuing throughout the reproductive life of the male, specialized cells lining the interior of each seminiferous tubule undergo spermatogenesis to form ultimately the mature sperm.

The mature human sperm cell (Figure 30-9) is enveloped by the cell membrane and consists of three principal regions—the *head, middlepiece,* and *tail*. The head is made up mostly of the haploid nucleus and a small amount of golgi material. In many animals, including mammals, there is also a structure called the *acrosome*, located beneath the cell membrane of the headpiece, which varies in size and appearance. For example, the acrosome is quite large in the sperm of the guinea pig but relatively small in the human sperm. It is known to be essential for the sperm's penetration of the egg cell, and recent evidence has

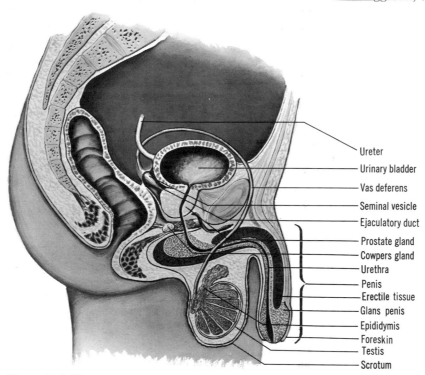

Ureter
Urinary bladder
Vas deferens
Seminal vesicle
Ejaculatory duct
Prostate gland
Cowpers gland
Urethra
Penis
Erectile tissue
Glans penis
Epididymis
Foreskin
Testis
Scrotum

Figure 30-7. Diagrammatic representation of a sagittal section of the reproductive system of an adult human male.

established that it functions in two ways in this respect. First, the acrosome discharges a filament that joins the sperm head to the surface of the egg; and second, it releases hydrolyzing enzymes which digest a portion of the egg membrane, thus allowing for penetration of the sperm. The middlepiece possesses a pair of centrioles and a rich concentration of mitochondria arranged in a loose spiral around a central core of fibrils that extends the length of the tail. The mitochondria apparently provide the energy responsible for the mobility of the sperm. The tail is the longest part of the sperm (about 0.045 mm in length) and accounts for the motility of the gamete. It displays the typical structure of flagella or cilia, consisting of a core of ten pairs of fibrils arranged so that nine pairs constitute a circle about a single central pair (see Figure 4-10). A second type of cell also composing the inner lining of the seminiferous tubule is believed to have a role in providing nourishment to the developing sperm.

ACCESSORY DUCTS AND GLANDS. Within the testes the sperm pass from the convoluted seminiferous tubules successively through straight tubules and a system of connected spaces ultimately emptying into a single large convoluted tube called the *epididymis*. One epididymis lies along the side and top of each testis. The epididymis stores sperm prior to their ejaculation in the sexual act. When uncoiled it measures 15 to 20 feet in length. The end or tail of the epididymis is continuous with a duct, the *vas deferens*. The latter passes upward from the testis through the inguinal canal into the abdominal cavity (where it is enclosed in a fibrous connective tissue cylinder called the *spermatic cord*), and extends upward over the top and down the posterior surface of the urinary bladder. Here each vas deferens (one from each testis) joins with a duct from a separate gland, the *seminal vesicle*, to form the so-called *ejaculatory* duct (Figure 30-7).

The *paired seminal vesicles* are hollow glands about 2 inches in length which lie at the lower back surface of the urinary bladder.

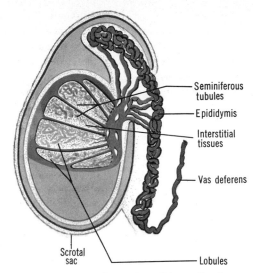

Figure 30-8. Diagram of a section of the testis of man.

Labels: Seminiferous tubules; Epididymis; Interstitial tissues; Vas deferens; Scrotal sac; Lobules

They secrete a thick, viscous, seminal fluid containing some nutrients. The seminal fluid together with the sperm arriving from the testes and lesser secretions by other glands are collectively called *semen*. The earlier belief that the seminal vesicles are receptacles or storage places for the sperm has been discarded.

The two ejaculatory ducts drain into the urethra which in turn is surrounded close to its origin from the urinary bladder by the *prostate gland*. The gland secretes by way of numerous ducts leading into the urethra an alkaline fluid which is believed to activate or increase the motility of the sperm and to neutralize the acid condition of the urethra and the female reproductive tract. In older men the prostate gland frequently becomes enlarged, thus constricting the urethra and making urination difficult. Surgical removal of the gland is often used as a remedy for this condition. Slightly below the prostate gland is a pair of small glands each about the size and shape of a small pea collectively called *Cowper's glands*. The mucous secretions of Cowper's glands drain into the urethra, serving as a lubricant. They also help to counteract acidity as do the prostatic secretions.

THE PENIS. The main body of the penis or male copulatory organ is constituted of sponge-like, so-called *erectile* tissue arranged in three longitudinal, cylindrical columns held together by fibrous connective tissue and covered with skin. The urethra passes through one of the erectile tissue columns and empties at the conical tip of the penis called the *glans penis*. The latter is covered completely or in part by a double fold of skin called the *foreskin* (Figure 30-5). *Circumcision* is the surgical removal of a portion of the foreskin. During sexual excitement the sponge-like spaces of the erectile tissue become engorged with blood under pressure due to dilation of the tissue's arteries and constriction of its veins. The resulting turgidity causes the penis to become enlarged, hard, and erect.

Sexual Intercourse

Sexual intercourse (also called *mating, coitus,* or *copulation*) consists of the coordinated body activities of the male and female which make possible the bringing together of the egg cell and sperm. In mammals, the penis of the male becomes erect in the course of sexual excitement and is inserted into the vagina of the female. In the male, stimulation of sensory nerve endings in the penis as a result of friction against the lubricated walls of the vagina culminates in a short period of heightened paroxysmal sexual excitement called the *orgasm*. The orgasm is accompanied almost simultaneously by *ejaculation*, the forceful ejection of semen from the penis.

Ejaculation is the result of several coordinated involuntary muscular contractions including those of the walls of the epididymis and vas deferens, propelling the sperm from their place of storage, the epididymis, through the ducts into the urethra. At the same time the seminal vesicles, and to a lesser extent the prostate and Cowper's glands, release their secretions which mix with the sperm to constitute the semen. This occurs almost concurrently with the expulsion of the semen with some force by contractions largely of urethral and other muscles to complete the act of ejaculation. The sperm are usually not motile until ejaculated, as a result of mixing with the secretions of the prostate gland. Human mature sperm cells average about 0.05 mm in length but only have about 1/100,000 of the volume of the egg cell. The mature human egg cell is probably the largest cell produced by the body, averaging about 0.14 mm in diameter.

In the female the friction of the erect penis on the vaginal walls during coitus ordinarily culminates in an orgasm which is accompanied by involuntary rhythmic contractions of the vaginal and uterine walls. No special discharge or ejaculation of fluid occurs during the orgasm of the female other than the stimulated secretion by the many glands in the lining of the reproductive tract as a result of sexual excitement.

The average volume of semen ejaculated during coitus is about 3 to 5 milliliters and contains about 300 million sperm. The sperm are usually released in the upper region of the vagina near the cervix, and are moved principally by muscular contractions of the female reproductive tract into the uterus and then into the oviducts.

FERTILIZATION. Fertilization or the union of the nuclei of the egg cell and sperm cell ordinarily takes place in the upper third of the

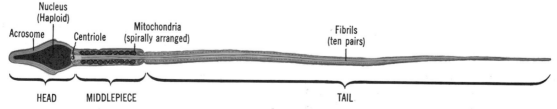

Figure 30-9. Diagram of longitudinal section of a mature human sperm (*adapted from Dr. D. W. Fawcett, Int. Rev. Cytol*).

oviducts. It always occurs in a fluid medium, the sperm being suspended in glandular secretions of the male reproductive system and the eggs in fluid within the female reproductive passages. The mammalian egg cell at the time prior to fertilization is usually surrounded by an accompanying layer of follicle cells called the *corona radiata* which in the ovary was nearest to the egg (Figure 30-10). In order for fertilization to occur the *corona radiata* must be penetrated or dissolved. This is accomplished by enzymatic hydrolysis of the cementing mucopolysaccharide material composed of hyaluronic acid polymers which hold the cells of the corona radiata together. The many sperm which come in contact with this cell layer possess a hydrolyzing enzyme called *hyaluronidase* (probably arising from the acrosome) which contributes to the dissolution of the cementing material. Once the corona radiata cells have been parted and the egg cell membrane penetrated, a single sperm cell enters the egg cell. Subsequent changes in the egg cell membrane somehow prevent the entry of any other sperm. However, the entry of more than one sperm cell into the eggs of birds, reptiles, and some amphibia is a usual occurrence, but only one sperm nucleus will fuse with the egg-cell nucleus. Actually, oögenesis, or egg-cell formation, at this time has not yet been completed. Most vertebrate eggs during oögenesis experience a halt in development after the first meiotic division and at this stage the "egg cell" is released from the ovary. Ordinarily only a single human egg cell is released at a time in contrast to several in the mammals that give birth to litters. The activation induced by sperm penetration or other appropriate stimulus causes the "egg cell" to undergo its second meiotic division and subsequent maturation so that fusion of the egg-cell nucleus and sperm-cell nucleus can occur.

The nuclei of the sperm and mature egg egg cell now meet, become one, and undergo the first mitotic division to produce two daughter cells, Successive mitotic divisions continue as the young embryo moves down the oviduct. Within 10 days, as an embryo already consisting

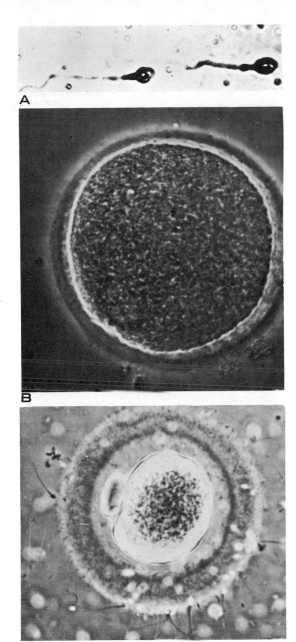

Figure 30-10 Micrographs of (A) human sperm, magnification, 1000X (*courtesy of Dr. L. B. Shettles, Columbia-Presbyterian Medical Center, N.Y.C.*). (B) Human egg cell recovered during an operation, with its surrounding layer of *corona radiata* cells, magnification, 400X. (C) Human egg cell (and corona radiata) and impinging human sperm cells, magnification, 400X (*courtesy of Dr. L. B. Shettles, Ovum Humanum, Hafner Publ. Co., N.Y.C.*).

of several hundred cells, it finally is implanted in the uterus, becoming completely covered by the rich mucosa lining or endometrium.

Fertilization as the process of fusion of the nuclei of egg cell and sperm cell accomplishes two very significant and distinct events. First, by uniting the haploid nuclei of the two gametes it not only restores the diploid chromosome number, but brings together the hereditary composition furnished by the parents to form that of a new individual. It provides a means of combining half the genes of both parents within a single offspring. Thus it is an important mechanism for attaining gene variability in progeny—a fundamental factor operating in the process of evolution. Second, fertilization is the process for activating the egg, causing it to start cell divisions and development into a new individual of the type predestined by its genetic make-up contributed by both parents. The mechanism by which fertilization transforms a quiescent egg cell into one undergoing numerous rapid changes as indicated by its successive cell divisions and development into an embryo is not known. The fact that a wide variety of artificial chemical and physical agents can induce parthenogenesis strongly suggests that the egg cell already possesses most, if not all, of the capabilities to develop into an embryo. All that is required is a means for activating it or starting it on its development. Activation of the egg cell by fertilization is the initiation or triggering of a series of well-ordered reactions in space and time which progressively transform the egg cell and its descendants into an embryo and eventually a new individual.

SUPPLEMENTARY REFERENCES

Allen, R. D. "The Moment of Fertilization," *Scientific American*, July 1959.
Bullough, W. S., *Hormones and Reproduction*, Methuen, London, 1952.
Corner, G. W., *The Hormones in Human Reproduction*, revised edition, Princeton University Press, Princeton, N.J., 1947.
Hartman, C. G., *Science and the Safe Period*, Williams and Wilkens, Baltimore, 1962.
Pincus, G., "Fertilization in Mammals," *Scientific American*, March 1951.

Chapter 31   Embryonic Development

GENERAL CONSIDERATIONS

Embryology and Genetics

Embryology is the study of the development of the organism from the zygote or fertilized egg. All multicellular animals—including vertebrates and invertebrates—ultimately arise from a single fertilized egg cell. Therefore each has an embryonic history. In all instances the events of embryonic development are under the ultimate regulation of the hereditary factors, the genes, which direct and control the steps in the transformation of a single fertilized egg to a fully formed embryo. Although embryology is ostensibly concerned with the patterns and means of development, and genetics as a "separate" discipline is concerned with the mechanism of inheritance of these patterns, both are inextricably intertwined. The embryologist and the geneticist are primarily concerned with the mechanisms by which these patterns are put into effect. In essence, embryology is one important aspect of the study of *developmental genetics*.

Major Processes of Development

How does a single fertilized egg cell manage to develop along predesignated and directed lines to form a whole and complex organism composed of billions upon billions of cells? At least three major processes are involved in the development of a single fertilized egg cell into a completed multicellular organism.

The first is the ability to form other cells. This is accomplished by *mitosis* or regular cell division. The second involves *growth*—the increase in size of an organism or its parts due to a *net formation or synthesis of protoplasm*. It is the net result of a greater rate of synthetic metabolic reactions as compared to the rate of degradative metabolic processes. When both rates happen to be the same no apparent growth takes place, although both synthetic and degradative types of reactions are continuously occurring. Growth is usually measured by determining the mass or weight of an organism. By plotting the weight of a growing animal, taken at regular intervals, against time, a *growth curve* (Chapter 10) is obtained demonstrating the increase of mass with time. The third process is *differentiation*—the poorly understood, complex biological chain of events by which cell diversity, namely, specialization of structure and function occurs.

Several fundamental features are common to the embryology of most multicellular animals. In all cases the early stages of development, of the vertebrates, and to some extent of the invertebrates, display certain common characteristics indicative of a basic pattern of development.

BASIC PATTERNS AND PRINCIPLES OF EMBRYONIC DEVELOPMENT

Blastula Formation

Strictly speaking the start of embryonic development is taken as the time at which fertilization occurs. Among the first visible events following fertilization is a series of mitotic cell divisions called *cleavage*. It occurs in rapid succession at the very beginning of development in which the fertilized or activated egg cell first divides into 2 cells, then 4 cells, 8 cells, and so on (Figure 31-1). The resulting cells, called *blastomeres*, decrease in size as their number increases and tend to have different quantities of cytoplasm. There is little or no increase in the total cytoplasmic mass. Cleavage usually produces a single-layered hollow ball of several hundred smaller cells known as the *blastula* (Figure 31-1) whose hollow center called the *blastocoel* is filled with a lymph-like fluid. By definition the cleavage stage is ended with the formation of the blastula. The notable absence of growth during cleavage accounts for the fact that the cells are smaller than the original fertilized egg cell. The increase in nuclear material (a new nucleus for each blastomere), consisting principally of DNA and protein, occurs largely at the expense of cytoplasmic substances.

Several types of cleavage patterns occur depending on a number of factors including the species and the quantity and distribution in the egg cell of the food reserves (proteins, lipids, and carbohydrates), collectively called *yolk*. The egg cells of vertebrates fall into two main types (Figure 31-2): (*a*) the primitive *isolecithal* egg cells in which the yolk is present in small quantities and scattered more or less evenly throughout the cytoplasm; and (*b*) the *telolecithal* egg cells having a considerably greater quantity of yolk which tends to be concentrated in part of the cell. As an example, the egg cell of reptiles and birds are telolecithal, tending to have huge quantities of yolk with respect to cytoplasm. In telolecithal cells the region of the cell where the concentration of yolk is greatest is called the *vegetal pole* and where it is least is called the *animal pole*. Cell division proceeds more slowly in the vegetal pole region of the cell. As a result the vegetal pole region gives rise to larger but fewer blastomeres in contrast to that of the animal pole (Figure 31-1). If the quantity of yolk is very great, as in the instance of bird eggs, cleavage is restricted to the animal pole, cell divisions failing to occur in the region of heavy yolk concentrations.

A still more important factor, in addition to yolk concentration and distribution, affects the cleavage pattern. It is some kind of organizational influence, as yet unidentified, which

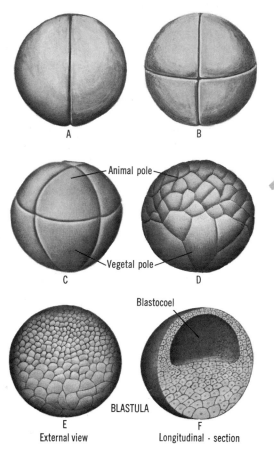

BLASTULA FORMATION

Figure 31-1. Early mitotic divisions or cleavage of the fertilized egg cell to form the blastula stage in the embryonic development of the frog.

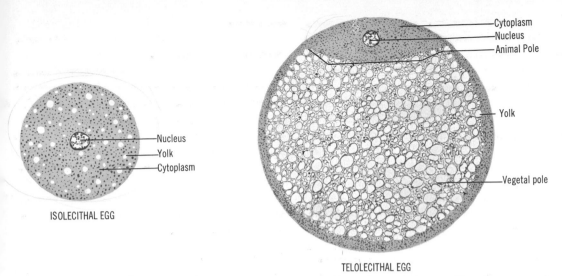

Figure 31-2. Diagram of a typical *isolecithel* egg cell and typical *teliolecithel* egg cell.

becomes evident in certain egg cells such as those of mammals where the cleavage pattern is completely contrary to that expected on the basis of its yolk.

Gastrula Formation

The next series of changes experienced by the embryo is called *gastrulation.* It involves primarily a rearrangement of the cells of the blastula by movement of cells and folding of various cell regions to form the three primary germ layers. The resulting embryo at this stage of development is termed a *gastrula.* It is fundamentally a hollow cylinder whose walls in vertebrates (and all other multicellular animals above the level of the flatworms) consist of three primary germ layers—the *ectoderm* or outermost layer, the *mesoderm* or middle layer, and the *endoderm* or innermost layer (Figure 31-3). The hollow center of the gastrula is called the *archenteron.* The opening leading into the archenteron is called the *blastopore.* It is from these three layers that all the tissues and organs of the fully formed animal will develop. The most basic feature of gastrulation is the movements and folding by which these cell layers are brought into position.

Cell divisions do occur during gastrulation but at a slower pace than during blastula formation and growth is also still significantly small, if it occurs at all. The fact that mitotic cell division continues (but at a slower rate) throughout gastrulation must mean that the increase in nuclear material, notably DNA and protein, occurs at the expense of cytoplasmic substances. Studies of frog and sea-urchin embryos have indicated that oxygen consumption is significantly increased during gastrulation as compared with that of blastula formation. This would be expected in view of the predictably greater energy expenditure that is made by the cell movements during gastrulation. Most of the substances utilized in respiration during this time are carbohydrates, as indicated by the respiratory quotient of one (Chapter 9), with little or no breakdown of proteins occurring. In fact new proteins are being synthesized during gastrulation at the expense of the yolk as shown in the sea urchin. These changes in protein composition are of course accompanied by changes in enzyme constitution. Some enzymes remain unaltered whereas certain others such as malic dehydrogenase (of the Krebs cycle, Chapter 8) show a definite increase starting at the early gastrula stage.

In brief, gastrulation consists essentially of an

irreversible cell migration (and multiplication) to yield a hollow embryo whose walls consist of three primary cell layers. Like cleavage it displays a great many variations. The movements of cells which characterize gastrulation, as indicated by unfolding, spreading, or other kinds of displacement, are essentially a mass flow of cells from one region to another. The mechanisms and forces by which these directed cell movements occur have thus far remained elusive despite the many research efforts in this field.

The gastrula ectoderm is in reality the embryonic skin. In the course of subsequent embryonic development it will give rise to the epidermis and its derivatives as well as to the nervous system. The archenteron will become the cavity of the digestive tract, and the endoderm will form its future epithelial lining. The mesoderm, located as it is between the embryonic skin and embryonic digestive tract, will split into two cell layers (in schizocoelic animals such as vertebrates), and the space appearing between the two will become the future body cavity or coelom. The outer portion of mesoderm will develop into the muscles and other structures of the body walls, whereas the inner mesoderm sheet will give rise to the muscles of the digestive tract walls. In fact the mesoderm in higher animals is the major source of cells in the developing organism for the connective tissues, blood, muscle, skeleton, kidney, and reproductive organs.

Differentiation

Shortly after gastrulation has occurred the cells of the embryo begin to show the first visible signs of specialized structural and functional changes, the result of a process known as *differentiation*. The more or less uniform appearing cells of the gastrula stage now evince local structural differences and diversification. Certain groups of cells begin to acquire the features of specialized cells such as nervous tissue or muscle fibers, and at the same time arrange themselves with other newly forming tissues to form organs. Several important simultaneously occurring phenomena are involved in differentiation, including cell division, migration and arrangement of individual cells and groups of cells into tissues and organs, greater localized growth of particular portions of the embryo, splitting of certain cell layers into two or more layers as indicated for the mesoderm of schizocoelic animals, and folding of particular cell layers or tissues. *Differentiation* is the entire complex of changes whereby the 3 original germ layers give rise to structurally and functionally specialized tissues and organs.

The mechanisms of cell differentiation are as yet unknown and are still among the great unsolved riddles of modern-day biology. There is no doubt that particular biochemical modifications are taking place in the cells concerned prior to their differentiation into heart tissue,

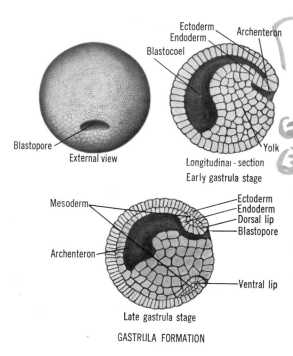

Figure 31-3. Conversion of the blastula to the gastrula stage in the embryonic development of the frog.

Labels for Figure 31-3:

Early gastrula stage — External view: Blastopore; Longitudinal-section: Ectoderm, Endoderm, Blastocoel, Archenteron, Yolk

Late gastrula stage: Mesoderm, Archenteron, Ectoderm, Endoderm, Dorsal lip, Blastopore, Ventral lip

GASTRULA FORMATION

muscle tissue, nerve tissue, or whatever else. These progressive biochemical changes in the composition, metabolism, and organization of the cells probably determine the type and course of differentiation in different regions of the embryo. Nevertheless our basic knowledge of the biochemical steps involved is almost nonexistant. We do know, however, that several factors have important roles. These include genetic make-up and the influence of neighboring regions of the embryo. The latter phenomenon, known as *embryonic induction*, is discussed in greater detail below.

Effect of Genetic Make-up

That the genetic make-up exercises a fundamental control of embryonic development is made obvious from the fact that the unique features (including growth, structure, form, and function) characteristic of the organism or species are inherited. We know that the onset of structural and functional differentiation is preceded by metabolic changes long before the first signs of differentiation become evident. These prior biochemical changes are mediated by enzymes and are very probably responsible for the subsequent appearance of structural and physiological differentiation. In effect differentiation is ultimately determined by unique enzyme patterns in cells. We know that genes control biochemical changes by determining protein synthesis—and, therefore, enzyme synthesis (Chapter 11). Accordingly it is quite likely that at particular times in embryonic development particular biochemical changes under the control of genes occur in certain cells or regions of the embryo, thus determining and directing the course of development that these cells will follow. The basis for differentiation appears to reside largely in gene-determined biochemical changes which ultimately express themselves in terms of the structural and functional specialization of given cells and tissues.

But the genetic constitutions of all adult cells of most multicellular organisms have arisen from a single fertilized egg and are presumably identical. If this is so, and genes control differentiation, how can we explain the seeming paradox that in the process of differentiation cells of the same genotype (i.e., all the cells of the embryo) develop into cells of different phenotype? The answer is not yet really known. Since the consequences of gene function are modified by environment, one possibility is that cells, even though they are part of the same organism, have different physical and chemical environments in relationship to one another in terms of nutrient supply, disposal of metabolic wastes, and so on. Such different environments might bring about differential gene function and hence produce the various specialized cells of the adult. The control of differentiation by chemical substances is dramatically illustrated by the effect of added vitamin A in transforming embryonic chick skin in tissue culture into a nonkeratinized mucus-secreting epithelial type despite an identical genetic constitution.

Embryonic Induction

Although the course of development that a particular region of the embryo will follow is determined by specific chemical properties, gene control, and interaction between genes and cytoplasm, it is also influenced and directed in its development and differentiation by adjacent or neighboring parts of the embryo. This important phenomenon in embryonic development whereby neighboring cells exert an influence in differentiation is called *embryonic induction*. It is apparently effected by interactions between neighboring regions of the embryo, their positions in the embryo in relation to the other cells, and undoubtedly other factors. Embryonic induction usually operates during a limited and specific period of embryonic development, and is in part the result of gastrulation which places cells in close contact with adjacent cell layers. In the developing embryos of some animals certain cells may be influenced by adjacent cells to form tissues which they would not form if these neighboring cells were absent. As an illustration, lens formation in the salamander's eye from the external ectoderm requires the presence of a particular underlying layer of cells which later becomes the retina. If this underlying layer is removed lens formation by the overlying cells does not occur. Should these cells be transplanted at a sufficiently early stage in their development from one part of an embryo to another, they would now differentiate not as lens tissue but along new lines in accordance with their new environment.

At least two types of cells are involved in embryonic induction, those undergoing differentiation and those in the immediate vicinity whose presence is essential for differentiation along given lines. The latter cells are usually also embryonic cells which are simultaneously developing into other tissues and organs. For example, the development in vertebrates of the future nervous system from the ectoderm is known to be induced or determined in part by the underlying mesodermal layer. Experiments have indicated that the mechanism of induction can in part be ascribed to a transfer of chemical substances, possibly nucleoproteins, from the cells of the underlying layer. It seems quite clear that in the development of several vertebrate organ systems (such as the central nervous system, kidney, and lung) an induction effect in cell differentiation, presumably by the transfer of substances from cell to cell, is definitely involved. The details and possible mechanisms of embryonic induction are discussed more fully in a later section dealing with the *organizer theory*.

It should be noted, however, that not all regions of the vertebrate embryo are affected by embryonic induction. Some areas of the embryo already possess the ability to develop into a particular tissue even before gastrulation has occurred.

Autonomous and Dependent Types of Embryonic Development

Although embryonic induction is an important process in the differentiation of many tissues and organs in the embryos of vertebrates and several invertebrates, it has little or no influence on differentiation in the embryos of certain invertebrates. For example, the embryonic cells of molluscs and annelids differentiate only along a predetermined and fixed course even when placed in abnormal surroundings. Isolated blastomeres or embryonic cells obtained from the blastula stage of molluscs and annelids tend to develop as if they were still part of the intact embryo despite the imposed absence of adjacent or neighboring cells. In these invertebrate embryos removal or destruction of blastomeres gives rise to radical changes in the course of development. The tissues or organs that usually arise from the absent blastomere or blastomeres fail to develop and a defective individual results. In such organisms the role of one blastomere can obviously not be assumed by another since the blastomeres appear to possess an inherent capacity to differentiate in a predetermined direction. This fixed kind of development or organization is spoken of as a *mosaic* or *autonomous* type. Embryos of this type, during their early stages of development, are regarded as a mosaic of cells, each cell being capable of producing only specific tissues or parts of the body.

At the other extreme is the kind of development known as the *regulative* or *dependent* type in which the fate of the blastomeres is not irrevocably determined. This can be readily illustrated with embryos of echinoderms and amphibia. The blastomeres of these animals are capable of different types of development and are able to make up for the defects incurred by removal or destruction during development. For example, in the sea urchin, an echinoderm, separation of the blastomeres from one another in the four-cell embryo stage can result in the formation of four perfectly formed larva although each will be one-fourth the normal size. In later stages of cleavage the removal of particular blastomeres will not radically alter embryo development, and even bisection of the cell mass in a suitable plane could yield two perfectly formed embryos.

It should be noted that various intermediate gradations between these two extreme types of differentiation exist depending on the organism and the stage of embryonic development.

Moreover, no animal embryo possesses exclusively the characteristics of one type and not the other. For example, although the sea-urchin egg is mostly regulative in its properties, it also exhibits some mosaic characteristics. In general, regulative ability is gradually lost by the later stages of development. The embryo in its later development is very clearly of the mosaic type.

The blastula stage of embryonic development in most animals can be divided into regions corresponding to the parts which in the normal course of events will develop into the future organs of the animal. Starting from an early stage of embryonic development the probable fate of each cell can be mapped with a good degree of accuracy. A map of this sort showing the fate of the blastula regions is called a *fate map*. In annelid worms and certain molluscs, for example, the cells of the blastula formed during the early stages of development can be numbered. The cells formed from them are predestined to go into the formation of specific organs or tissues. The surface of the blastula of an amphibian can also be mapped into various areas which are destined to become specific body parts. A particular area will develop into the nervous system of the embryo, another will give rise to certain anterior parts of the digestive tract, and so on.

As a rule differentiation, once it has been accomplished and whether of the mosaic or regulative types, is an irreversible and stable state. Only under unusual circumstances such as during regeneration of injured tissues or growth in tissue culture is it known that differentiated cells may revert back to an embryonic-like state. In general the more highly differentiated a tissue or organ, the slower its growth. The brain and spinal cord as the most highly differentiated tissue of the vertebrate body display the slowest rate of growth. Most cells of the higher animal body become differentiated by the adult stage. They do not normally divide, which accounts in large part for the observed cessation in growth. A few tissues, however, such as the skin, for example, have residual growth centers of relatively un-

differentiated or partially differentiated proliferating cells (Chapter 29) throughout the life of the animal. Other growth centers may entirely disappear at adulthood as in the case of the long bones whose growth centers cease to exist at about the time of sexual maturity, resulting in a cessation of growth in length. Thus progressive differentiation and a decline in growth rate of animals go hand in hand.

Theories of Embryonic Development

The important theories of embryonic development are given below. As we shall see, all emphasize certain unique aspects and none are necessarily mutually exclusive of the others.

PREFORMATION THEORY. The *preformation theory* as one of the major concepts of embryonic development in the seventeenth and eighteenth centuries postulated that a tiny perfectly formed body was already present in the sperm or egg cell. Accordingly, embryonic development simply involved an increase in size of the already preformed adult parts. The only major difference of opinion for a time was whether the minute preformed body was present in the sperm cell or the egg cell. Several microscopists actually reported that they had observed the presence of tiny fully formed individuals in the egg cell or sperm cell. Supporters of the preformation theory included such great scientists as Leuwenhoek, Malpighi, and Swammerdam.

A logical extension of the theory would imply that each preformed tiny body contained still smaller preformed individuals in its gametes which in turn contained even smaller individuals in its reproductive cells and so on ad infinitum, comparable to an infinite series of boxes, one within the other. Some even believed that Adam or Eve originally had all the future generations of the human race within their gonads.

EPIGENESIS. During this period proponents of a rival concept, known as *epigenesis*, argued that the adult parts of the individual were not already preformed in the gametes. This was a belief that was held in the late seventeenth century by Harvey, the discoverer of blood circulation, and by Aristotle, the famous philosopher of ancient Greece, some 2000 years earlier. It was only during the first half of the nineteenth century that the concept of epigenesis finally gained wide acceptance by biologists as a result of careful studies by numerous workers who demonstrated that the body parts only formed during embryonic development. The general concept of epigenesis is, of course, the view that is established and accepted today.

In terms of its details the old preformation theory of transmission of preformed adult parts appears to be ridiculous. In terms of principles, however, from the viewpoint of modern genetics, it is quite obvious that something determinitive or preformed is indeed transmitted from parent to embryo. For otherwise how do the embryos develop into the same type of individuals as the parents? It is evident that the genes are precisely these preformed entities which ultimately direct and determine the course of embryonic development. What is preformed is the genetic constitution and hence the potentiality for development, not the adult structures themselves.

THE ORGANIZER THEORY. The next major advance in the field of differentiation, after the proposals in the late nineteenth century of the *mosaic* and *regulative* theories of development, was initiated by the German embryologist Hans Spemann in the early 1900's and by others as a result of studies on the differentia-

tion of the nervous system in the amphibian embryo. It gave rise to the so-called *organizer theory* which is recognized as one of the most significant concepts of embryonic development put forth in the twentieth century.

If the ectoderm cells which normally give rise to the *neural tube* (the structure that later develops into the brain and spinal cord) are surgically removed at an early stage of gastrulation in the frog and continued in isolated tissue culture, they fail to differentiate into neural tissue. If the same experiments are instead performed toward the end of gastrulation the cells now undergo differentiation into a neural tube. Obviously during the interval between the beginning and end of gastrulation one or more important changes have endowed these cells with the capacity to develop into neural tissue. Additional experiments performed by Spemann and other embryologists strongly indicated that differentiation of particular ectodermal cells to form neural tissues is stimulated by the presence of certain other neighboring cells of the embryo. This is the phenomenon of *embryonic induction* discussed in the previous section.

By the 1920's Spemann and his coworkers could show that the *dorsal lip*, a particular region in the mesoderm at the edge of the archenteron roof in the early or middle invaginating gastrula stage of the frog embryo (Figure 31-4), was responsible for inducing the overlying ectoderm cells to form the neural tube. They called this embryonic structure represented by the dorsal lip the *organizer*. The organizer somehow acts on certain ectoderm cells directing their development into neural tissue. The transfer of these ectoderm cells during the early gastrula stage when the organizer has not yet exercised its influence results in their development into epidermal cells and not neural tissue. Transfer during the later stages of gastrulation, however, results in their development into neural tissue because the organizer has already exerted its effect. The action of the organizer in altering and directing the differentiation of embryonic cells is thus responsi-

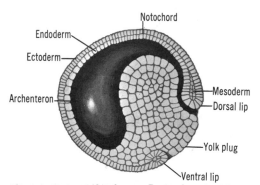

Figure 31-4. Middle invaginating gastrula stage of the frog embryo showing the dorsal lip region in the mesoderm at the edge of the archenteron roof.

Figure 31-5. Formation of an extra eye on the head and abdominal regions of the frog by transplantation of the optic cup at a suitable time during embryonic development. (*Courtesy Dr. C. L. Markert.*)

ble for embryonic induction. According to the organizer theory a portion of the ectoderm in normal embryonic development goes on to form neural tissue because it has been acted upon by the organizer. The remainder of the ectoderm gives rise to epidermal cells because it has not been in contact with the organizer. The latter has the same function in development in all vertebrates in inducing the nervous system and the sense organs. It has also been shown that the dorsal lip of the blastopore not only induces the formation of the neural tube from the ectoderm, but in addition exercises an important influence on the mesoderm and endoderm in the development of the whole embryo. For this reason the dorsal lip is also referred to as the *primary organizer*.

The presence of other organizers responsible for the differentiation of embryonic cells into specialized tissues and organs such as the heart, lens of the eye, and mouth has also been demonstrated. In the development of the lens of the eye, for example, the organizer happens to be certain outgrowths of the neural folds called the *optic cups*. The latter somehow influence the adjacent epidermal cells to differentiate into the lens. If the cells which form the optic cup of a frog embryo are removed or destroyed early enough in gastrulation, the lens which normally develops from the overlying ectoderm cells will not appear. On the other hand, if the optic cup is excised from an embryo at a suitable time and transplanted to another

part of the body, for example, to a slit beneath the dorsal or abdominal region of the embryo or to the head region, a lens will develop from the overlying epidermal cells that would ordinarily form the outer skin layer. Thus an extra eye is formed on the abdominal region or on the head region (Figure 31-5); but it will not be functional since it does not have suitable nerve connections to the brain.

Transplantation of tissues at the proper stage between different species has demonstrated that the reacting tissue responds according to its own specific genetic constitution. For example, the interchange of frog and salamander ectoderm which forms the mouth results in the development of a frog mouth on the salamander and a salamander mouth on the frog, even though they are induced by salamander organizer and frog organizer, respectively.

What is the nature of the organizer? The contact between the cells of the roof of the archenteron as the organizer or inductor and the overlying ectoderm which is induced to become the neural tube is a very intimate one. The insertion of a thin layer of cellophane or even a thin porous membrane between inducing and reacting cells suppresses induction. Experiments with organizer tissues killed by heat or chemical treatments are still capable of inducing differentiation, indicating that chemical substances are involved. The general assumption is that specific inducing substances probably pass from the roof of the archenteron into the overlying ectoderm cells, thus influencing the metabolism and directing them to differentiate as neural tissue. Thus far, however, no major break-through has occurred in isolating or identifying the substances concerned. Moreover, to confuse matters further, it has been observed that almost any tissue (e.g., liver, kidney, and muscle) of the adult animal, even from different animal species, can induce a neural tube when placed under the presumptive ectoderm of an embryo in the early gastrula stage. Some tissues are better inductors in the killed state than in the fresh state; and remarkably enough certain tissues that are not inductors in the living state are inductors in the killed state. Certain chemical substances such as steroids and several weak organic acids have proved to be good inductors. More recent evidence based on the examination of inducing substance released by inductor tissues into tissue culture medium tentatively indicates that the naturally occurring inductor of the amphibian blastopore may well be a nucleoprotein.

Ontogeny and Phylogeny

ONTOGENY. The sequence of transformations or changes representing the development of the individual or its parts is called *ontogeny*. It refers to the individual's entire developmental history through the embryonic stages as well as those that lead to adulthood following birth. Ontogeny, in particular of the embryonic stages, has proved to be a powerful tool in determining evolutionary relationships among different animals. In brief, a comparison of embryonic development among various animals has established that the features of ancient origin become evident early in embryonic development, whereas those of relatively more recent origin appear later. The basic characteristics common to a large group of animals manifest themselves earlier during ontogeny (e.g., brain and spinal cord, axial skeleton in the form of a notochord, and other features that typify all vertebrate animals) as compared to the more specialized characteristics (e.g., hair in mammals, feathers in birds) which distinguish the different members of the group. It logically follows that the sequence in which various body parts develop during successive embryonic stages very probably reflects the sequence in which they probably evolved over many millions of years in the development of the species or race.

The Gill Pouches. The great value of ontogeny in elucidating the relationships of contemporary animals is illustrated by the example of gill-pouch formation in all vertebrates during embryonic development. In aquatic vertebrates such as fishes the gill pouches give rise in the adult to the gill clefts (or gills) which serve as respiratory organs. In amphibians the gill pouches become functional respiratory gill clefts only during the aquatic larval stages (e.g., in the tadpole stage of frog development) and then become modified and nonfunctional during the adult or terrestrial stage. In terrestrial vertebrates such as the reptiles, birds, and mammals the gill pouches as such are only evident during a period of embryonic development. By the time the adult state has been reached the gill pouches have either disappeared or become almost unrecognizably modified to provide parts of the ear, tongue, throat, and several glands, with the respiratory function having been assumed by the lungs. Such evidence clearly implies that terrestrial vertebrates have evolved from aquatic forms with functional gills, a view strongly supported by other types of evidence.

PHYLOGENY. The history of the evolution or development of any group, species, or race of organisms is called *phylogeny*. In certain respects ontogeny during the *embryonic state* reflects or repeats phylogeny in a modified way. It is important to note that different animal species resemble one another more at the early stages of their embryonic development than at the adult stage. As they become more fully formed, the embryos become more dissimilar. In other words, the developing animal in its *early* embryonic stages appears to pass through the *early* embryonic stages of lower animals but diverges from them as it approaches the fully formed state. Undoubtedly several evolutionary stages which occurred in the original course of evolutionary development (phylogeny) have been eliminated in the course of embryonic development (ontogeny). In some instances the sequence of events in the ontogeny of a body part is the reverse of its known phylogenetic history. For example, the skull of the developing mammal is at first cartilaginous and is subsequently replaced by bone. Nevertheless, the phylogeny of skull development indicates that the skulls of the first vertebrates were for the most part bony and have remained so in most cases of subsequent evolution.

In certain important respects ontogeny exercises a striking influence on phylogeny. One of the basic mechanisms determining the course of evolution centers about the passing on from one generation to another of mutations experienced during the ontogeny of the individual. It is therefore these genetically changing ontogenies that determine phylogeny. From one viewpoint evolution results essentially from the passing on from one generation to the next of developmental mechanisms which have been successively mutated or genetically modified over the many millions of years, accounting for the progressive succession from fish to man. In brief, *phylogeny is a succession of modified ontogenies.*

DEVELOPMENT OF THE HUMAN EMBRYO

The details of early embryonic development among the various mammals differ so considerably that no single form can be used to typify the group. In particular our information on humans is still quite restricted. Most of our knowledge of the early steps in the development of the human embryo has in fact been derived from studies of the rhesus monkey, whose reproductive cycle and embryonic development are much like that of man.

Early Stages

Fertilization normally occurs in the oviduct,

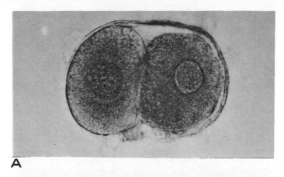

A

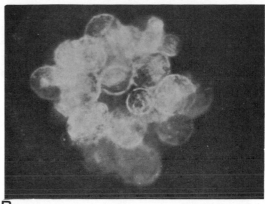

B

Figure 31-6. Early stages in the development of the human embryo: (A) two-cell stage—an infrared photomicrograph, magnification, 500X (*courtesy Dept. of Embryology, Carnegie Inst., Washington*); (B) the morula stage at about the third or fourth day following fertilization (*courtesy of Dr. L. B. Shettles, Ovum Humanum, Hafner Publ. Co., N.Y.C.*).

and has been described in detail in the preceding chapter. The fertilized egg begins to develop shortly after fusion of the two gametes, the first division of the fertilized egg probably occurring about 24 hours after ovulation. Although the human egg has very little yolk and therefore is ostensibly of the isolecithal type, its subsequent behavior in embryonic development in terms of cleavage (production of unequal blastomeres) and migration and formation of tissues strongly suggests the former presence of yolk. Cleavage occurs during the passage of the fertilized egg cell through the oviduct. By 48 and 96 hours the embryo consists of 4 and 16 cells respectively.

Once in the uterus, where it arrives at about the fourth day, the total number of cells of the

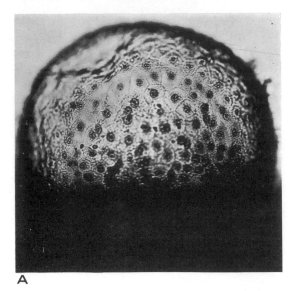
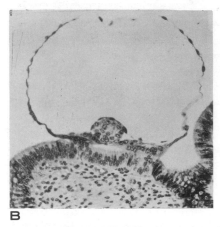

A

B

Figure 31-7. (A) Transilluminated monkey blastocyst illustrating character of trophoblast (wall of blastocyst), magnification, 300X; (B) longitudinal section through a monkey blastocyst (ninth day) showing beginning of union of trophoblast cells with epithelial cells of uterine lining. The embryonic disc is at the lower side of the hollow, fluid-filled spherical cavity, magnification, 300X. (*Courtesy of Dept. of Embryology, Carnegie Inst., Washington.*)

embryo as well as the embryonic mass increases rapidly to approximately 100 to form a solid mulberry-like mass of cells called the *morula* (Figure 31-6). A cavity filled with fluid soon begins to form in its midst to yield the next mammalian embryo stage called the *blastocyst*—a hollow, fluid-filled, spherical-shaped body with an inner mass of cells at one side (Figure 31-7). The enveloping single layer of cells composing the sphere of the blastocyst is called the *trophoblast,* and the inner cell mass which will develop into the embryo proper is called the *formative cells.* Although the trophoblast is an embryonic structure, it does not enter into the formation of the embryo itself. Instead it remains external to the developing embryo, giving rise to the so-called *chorion* and *amnion,* two of the three extraembryonic membranes which function in the care and maintenance of the embryo. The third extraembryonic membrane is known as the *allantois.* Despite superficial resemblances

the blastocyst stage of mammals does not compare to the blastula stage of other vertebrates.

Soon after entering the uterus the embryo begins to implant itself in its lining or endometrium. The cells of the trophoblast, usually that portion overlying the inner cell mass, which have made contact with the endometrium embed themselves by multiplying and spreading into the mucosa of the uterine lining. By about the ninth or tenth day after fertilization the entire sphere of embryonic cells lies completely beneath the uterine epithelium, fully implanted in the richly supplied mucosa (Figure 31-8). Gastrulation occurs only after implantation.

Formation of the Three Primary Germ Layers and Accompanying Structures

While implantation is occurring the inner cell mass continues to develop. Certain cells have arranged themselves into a flattened

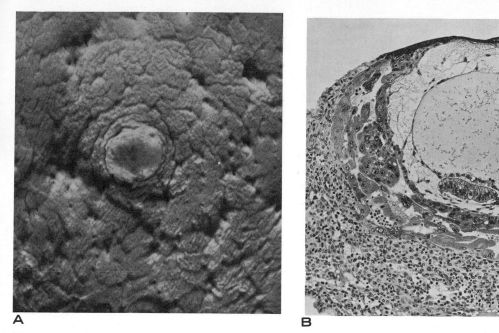

A **B**

Figure 31-8. (A) Twelve-day-old human embryo implanted in the uterine lining. (B) A section through a 13-day human embryo. The entire sphere of embryonic cells now lies fully implanted beneath the uterine epithelium, magnification, 500X. (*Courtesy of Dept. of Embryology, Carnegie Inst., Washington.*)

embryonic disc. Above the disc and beneath the outer cells forming the hollow sphere a narrow space develops which marks the beginning of the *amniotic cavity.*

In the 9- to 10-day-old human embryo the amniotic cavity is definitely established and is lined with a single layer of cells, the *ectoderm*, one of the three primary germ layers. Beneath the lower border of the amniotic cavity at this stage is the disc or plate of cells, composed of an *outer ectoderm* cell layer and the second of the primary germ layers, the *inner ectoderm* (Figure 31-7). It is the embryonic disc that develops into the embryo proper. The endoderm has in fact become so extended as to encompass most of the blastocyst cavity and is called the *yolk sac*. The yolk sac in humans is a vestigial structure which does not contain yolk and serves no apparent function. In summary, the human embryo at approximately the 10-day stage is a blastocyst essentially consisting of a two-layered disc enclosed

by the trophoblast. The upper layer is made up of ectoderm which is continuous with the lining of the overlying amniotic cavity; the lower layer consists of endoderm which is continuous with the yolk sac.

Within the next 10 days or less several important developments take place. The trophoblast develops complex villi-like structures over its entire surface which grow deeper into the uterine wall. The trophoblast and its villi, which soon contain blood vessels, are now collectively called the *chorion*. The yolk sac becomes constricted and the distal end disintegrates, whereas the remainder remains intact and still contains the endoderm. In time the endoderm lining of the yolk sac develops into the epithelial lining of most of the digestive tract. A finger-like projection of the endoderm extends laterally from the yolk sac and is called the rudimentary *allantois.* The embryonic disc at its posterior end is seen to be suspended from the chorion by a mass of cells known as the *body stalk* (Figure 31-9 and Figure 31-11A).

The *mesoderm* as the third germinal layer develops between the ectoderm and endoderm of the embryonic disc. It arises in mammals, including man, from migratory cells that move between the endoderm and ectoderm where they proliferate and develop. In the human the mesoderm first appears at the mid-line of the early flat-like embryo between the ectoderm and endoderm, which collectively form a central longitudinal thickened strip called the *primitive streak* coinciding with the primary axis of the embryo. The primitive streak in the human embryo is formed initially as a thickened band of ectoderm and endoderm. Some of the cells that it produces migrate out between the ectoderm and endoderm to form the mesoderm and *notochord* as indicated later. Ectoderm, endoderm, and mesoderm cells are apparently produced at the primitive streak and move out laterally to give rise to the different parts of the embryo.

Formation of the Embryo Parts

All the structures of the body are ultimately formed from the three primary germ layers. The skin, the nervous system, most of the eye, the salivary glands, and the epithelial lining of the nose and a portion of the mouth arise mainly from the *ectoderm*.

The skeleton, muscles, heart, blood vessels, lymphatic system and blood, the kidneys, and connective tissues originate chiefly from the *mesoderm*.

The epithelial lining of nearly all of the digestive tract and respiratory tract, the liver, pancreas, and thyroid and parathyroid glands are formed from the *endoderm*.

Actually no structure in the animal body is exclusively derived from any of the three primary germ layers. In many cases the basically functional portion of the organ may have its origin from a single germ layer but products of the other two germ layers nevertheless contribute. For example, the intestinal lining which is of endodermal origin, is the principal functional structure of the digestive tract, acting

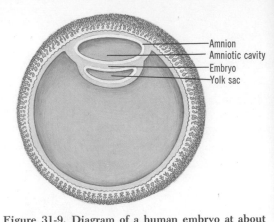

Figure 31-9. Diagram of a human embryo at about the 20-day stage.

in secretion of digestive juices and absorption of digested materials. However, the muscles, connective tissue, blood vessels, nerves, and outer lining, which make up the bulk of the intestines, are derived from mesoderm and ectoderm.

Formation of the Neural Tube, Notochord, and Vertebral Column

With subsequent development of the embryo, the primitive streak gradually disappears. The embryo at approximately the 20-day stage is more or less still a longitudinal disc, forming the floor of the amniotic cavity above and the roof of the yolk cavity below (Figure 31-9).

In the development which follows, the mesoderm spreads laterally from the primitive streak, the embryo tending to become more quickly organized in the anterior or head region. The nervous system is one of the earliest systems to make its appearance. It originates initially as a thickening of the ectoderm along the mid-dorsal long axis of the disc-like embryo to form the *neural plate*. The subsequent depression of the center of the neural plate and the appearance of ridges on either side results in the formation of the *neural groove*, whose neural crests soon fuse to form a *neural tube* along the mid-line of the embryo beneath the now continuous ectoderm (Figure 31-10). The anterior portion of the neural tube gives rise to the brain, and the remainder forms the spinal cord.

At about the same time as the mesoderm grows and spreads out laterally, a portion of the mesoderm at approximately the same dorsal longitudinal axis rounds itself off to form a temporary unsegmented structure called *the notochord,* which lies underneath and parallel to the developing neural tube (Figure 31-10). The notochord is a stiff, pliant connective tissue rod which provides support for the embryo body and is present at one time or another in the embryos of all vertebrates (and all other chordates) (Chapter 20). In vertebrates (and most other chordates) it has a temporary existence. It is eventually replaced during embryonic development by the vertebral column or backbone. In some chordates, however, the notochord persists throughout the entire life of the organism.

Formation of the Tubular Body and Digestive Tract

Meanwhile the spreading mesoderm, which extends laterally and ventrally as a sheet, splits into two layers with a cavity between them in the region of the embryo that is to become the trunk. The two mesodermal layers eventually meet and fuse at the ventral midline to form a tube-like body. The space between the two mesodermal sheets becomes the body cavity or coelom (Figure 31-10). The inner mesodermal layer ultimately develops into the muscular wall of the digestive tract, whereas the outer mesodermal layer becomes associated with the ectoderm and develops largely into the musculature of the body wall. The outward and downward growth of the rest of the embryonic disc together with a movement of certain tissues and newly forming organs toward the ventral surface eventually yield the cylindrically shaped body of the vertebrate. In this fashion the characteristic "tube-within-a-tube" body plan of higher animals arises.

Subsequent growth and development causes many rapid modifications to yield a changing embryo that increasingly comes to resemble a human being. The more rapid growth of the

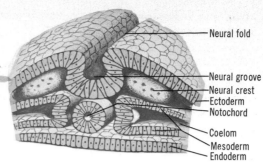

Figure 31-10. Diagram of formation of the neural tube, notochord, and coelom. See text for details.

Labels: Neural fold, Neural groove, Neural crest, Ectoderm, Notochord, Coelom, Mesoderm, Endoderm

anterior and posterior regions at this stage as compared to the other parts of the embryonic disc results in elongation of the embryo and formation of the head and tail, respectively.

As the anterior portion of the embryonic disc expands laterally and turns in ventrally, it constricts a portion of the yolk sac folding in its endoderm to form the so-called *foregut,* which becomes eventually the anterior region of the digestive tract. Similarly the posterior portion of the yolk sac forms the *hindgut,* which develops eventually into the posterior portion of the digestive tract. Meanwhile the continued rapid expansion of the amnion progressively encloses the body stalk, the rudimentary allantois, and a portion of the remaining yolk sac that connects the foregut and hindgut to form by the end of four weeks of embryonic development a cord-like structure called the *umbilical cord,* containing arteries and veins (Figure 31-11). The pancreas, most of the liver, and the lining of the lungs arise from evagination of the wall of the foregut.

Formation of the Heart, Gill Pouches, and Kidneys

At the same time the heart has been developing from two tubes hollowed out of mesoderm in the body cavity surrounding the foregut. The two tubes fuse to form a double-walled structure which undergoes a series of changes to become the heart.

In the anterior region of the foregut, where the pharynx develops, five paired gill pouches appear as outpocketings of the endoderm, which coincide with a corresponding set of inpocketings from the endoderm. In higher vertebrates the pouches either disappear or give rise to other structures such as the middle ear and Eustachian tube, the tonsils, and several glands. In the fish as lower vertebrates the corresponding outpocketings and inpocketings have actually joined to form a more or less continuous passage known as the *gill slits* or gills for breathing purposes.

In mammals three different progressively advanced kidneys appear during embryonic

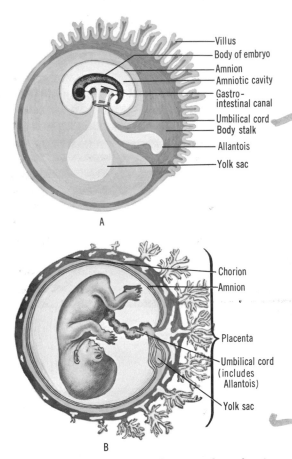

Figure 31-11. (A) Diagram of human embryo showing formation of digestive tract, umbilical cord, and various embryonic membranes. (B) Considerably later stage in human embryonic development illustrating subsequent development of the embryonic membranes.

development. These have been discussed in Chapter 28. The first and most primitive is the nonfunctional *pronephros kidney* characteristic of primitive fish. It degenerates at about the fourth week of human embryonic development, at which time the *mesonephros kidney* begins forming. The latter functions for a month or so, degenerating at the end of the sixteenth week. Its excretory role is finally taken over by the developing *metanephros kidney* which becomes the functional kidney of the older embryo and adult mammal and bird.

The more or less transitory appearance of certain vestigial structures such as the notochord and pronephros kidney during embryonic development of the mammal might suggest that these parts serve no function in higher animals. It should be noted, however, that the particular cells of the archenteron roof which give rise to the notochord are the very same ones that compose the organizer responsible for inducing the overlying ectoderm cells to form a neural tube. Similarly the importance of the pronephros kidney, although never functional as an excretory organ in the embryo of birds or mammals, is indicated by the fact that if removed from a chick embryo, subsequent successive normal development of the functional mesonephros and metanephros kidneys does not occur.

The Extraembryonic Structures

Every vertebrate in the course of its embryonic development produces certain tissues or structures which themselves are not part of the embryo proper but function in the care and maintenance of the embryo. These parts are referred to as the *extraembryonic* membranes and in the mammal include the *amnion, chorion, placenta, yolk sac, allantois,* and *umbilical cord* (Figure 31-11).

AMNION. The *amnion* is the membrane that originates from the ectoderm in the early stages of embryonic development as the wall enclosing the amniotic cavity. It is later supplemented by mesoderm tissue, increasing in size with the enlarging amniotic cavity which it encloses until it comes to surround the entire embryo proper except for a small abdominal area which is the site of attachment to the umbilical cord. The *amniotic cavity* is therefore the space between the embryo proper and the amnion and is filled with a clear lymph-like fluid called *amniotic fluid* in which the embryo is suspended. Thus the amnion membrane or sac with its contained fluid comes to form a protective fluid envelope, particularly in the late months of pregnancy, surrounding the embryo. It serves as a protective, shock-absorbing cushion allowing for growth and freedom of movement of the embryo. At birth the amniotic sac under pressure of the contracting uterus aids in dilating the cervix in preparation for the passage of the fully formed embryo (or *fetus*) outward through the vagina. At about this time in the birth process the amnion usually ruptures, releasing amniotic fluid which serves to lubricate and disinfect the vagina or birth canal.

CHORION AND PLACENTA. The *chorion* originates largely from the ectoderm (and in part from the mesoderm) of the trophoblast, the surrounding single layer of cells composing the sphere of the blastocyst in early embryonic development. The chorion is therefore the outermost extraembryonic membrane enclosing the amnion and all its contents, including the embryo proper as well as the yolk sac and allantois. In reptile and bird eggs the chorion is represented by the outermost membrane in contact with the inner surface of the shell.

In mammals, following implantation of the young embryo in the lining of the uterus, villi develop over the entire outer surface of the chorion, penetrating into the uterine mucosa. Soon afterwards the villi begin to atrophy with the exception of those in the area immediately beneath the blastocyst. The latter villi instead continue to enlarge and branch. By the fourth month of pregnancy most of the surface area of the chorion is almost smooth except for its site of attachment to the uterine wall where the villi (which fit into corresponding depressions

in the uterine wall), containing blood vessels and connective tissue, have extensively developed. It is this area of attachment of the embryo to the uterine wall that develops into the so-called *placenta*. The latter consists essentially of the villi of the chorion and the maternal tissue of the uterine lining which it penetrates.

In the subsequent course of pregnancy the spaces surrounding the villi in the developing placenta become filled with maternal blood, bathing the villi like soil water bathing the roots of plants. The villi themselves contain numerous capillaries receiving blood via arteries extending from the embryo proper through the umbilical cord and returning to the embryo via the umbilical vein (Figure 31-11). It should be emphasized that the maternal blood circulation and the embryo blood circulation in the placenta are separate and distinct. Normally only the slightest intermixing of these two bloods occurs. The maternal blood in the spaces of the placenta surrounding the villi is apparently separated from the embryo blood by the walls of the capillaries in the villi. It is here that the exchange of materials takes place between the two bloods. Metabolic waste materials such as carbon dioxide and urea diffuse from villi capillaries to the surrounding maternal blood, whereas oxygen, nutritive substances, hormones, and antibodies are transferred in the opposite direction. The placenta, consisting of both fetal and maternal tissues in close contact, therefore, performs the important function during embryonic life of serving as both an excretory and nutritive organ for the embryo.

The placenta is also the structure that permits the transfer of antibodies from maternal to embryonic circulation. In this way the newborn infant temporarily acquires some of his mother's immunity to tide him over for the first few months of life until he produces his own antibodies in response to various foreign agents in his environment.

Finally, the placenta also serves as an endocrine gland, furnishing, among other hormones, sufficient quantities of progesterone after the fourth or fifth month of pregnancy when progesterone secretion by the corpus luteum declines. As indicated earlier progesterone is essential for the maintenance and successful completion of embryonic development.

The mature placenta at birth is usually a disc-like structure about 6 to 7 inches in diameter and about an inch thick.

YOLK SAC AND ALLANTOIS. The *yolk sac* in reptiles and birds contains yolk and is the principal organ of nutrition for the developing embryo. It originates early in embryonic development from the endoderm (on the future abdominal side of the embryo) which grows around the yolk and digests it. The endoderm of the yolk eventually forms the epithelial lining of a major portion of the digestive tract. In mammals the yolk sac is small and collapsed, contains no yolk, and is of little functional importance. It is eventually incorporated into the umbilical cord and soon loses its connection to the gut (Figure 31-11).

The *allantois*, like the yolk sac, is attached to the abdominal region of the embryo, arising as a small outpocketing of the hindgut. It is located between the chorion and the amnion, and in egg-laying vertebrates such as reptiles and birds it completely encloses the embryo, forming the inner lining of the shell. In these organisms the allantois actually fuses with the chorion to form a compound membrane. It is well ramified with blood vessels which take up oxygen and give off carbon dioxide. These gases readily diffuse through the porous egg shell. Thus the allantois serves as an embryonic respiratory device until the time of hatching. In addition the sac-like allantois membrane in reptiles and birds also serves as a depository for urinary wastes. The wastes accumulate (largely as water-insoluble deposits of uric acid) in the allantois sac during embryonic development and are finally eliminated at hatching when the membranes are discarded.

In mammals, the allantois is small, collapses, and no longer functions in respiration or in the accumulation of urinary wastes. It does, however, possess blood vessels, and when it be-comes incorporated into the umbilical cord its blood vessels become the umbilical arteries and vein connecting the blood circulation of the embryo proper with that of the placenta (Figure 31-11). A small portion of the allantois also contributes to the formation of part of the urinary bladder.

UMBILICAL CORD. The umbilical cord is a tubular, spirally twisted structure which at birth is about 2 feet long and three-fourths of an inch in diameter (Figures 31-11 and 31-13). It connects the embryo proper and the placenta and possesses two umbilical arteries and one vein which account for blood circulation between embryo and placenta. The umbilical cord is in part actually an extension of the body wall of the embryo, having formed by a growing together of the edges of the amniotic sac on the ventral side of the embryo. The umbilical cord consists of an outer epithelial covering of ectoderm surrounding connective tissue in which are embedded two arteries, a vein, the remains of the yolk sac, allantois, and body stalk. The *umbilicus* or *navel* is the site on the abdomen of all individuals representing the remains of the attachment of the umbilical cord.

Time Table of Human Embryonic Development

The period of development of the young within the female reproductive system of mammals is called *pregnancy* or *gestation*. It begins at fertilization and ends at birth. In humans the normal period of gestation is approximately 266 days as compared to 16 days for the hamster, 335 days for the horse, and 22 months for the elephant.

By the time of implantation into the rich, spongy lining of the uterus, usually 8 to 10 days after fertilization, the human embryo has already undergone rapid successive cell divisions and is in the blastocyst stage. It consists of the primary germ layers and several extra-embryonic structures which include the tropho-blast, amnion, and yolk sac.

By the end of the first month the embryo proper (Figure 31-12), protected and supported within the amniotic fluid, is less than half an inch in length and has the beginnings of brain, eyes, stomach, vestigial kidneys, and heart. The heart is beating (at approximately 60 times per minute) and the embryo has already experienced a 10,000-fold weight increase when compared to the egg cell from which it originated. The primitive umbilical cord has formed by constriction of yolk sac, body stalk, and allantois as a result of growth and folding of the embryo and amnion. The embryo at this stage displays gill pouches and a tail-like appendage. The entire exterior surface of the enclosing chorion is fringed with root-like villi which anchor and draw nourishment from the maternal tissues. Some of the villi will soon be incorporated into the placenta, whereas the remainder will atrophy and disappear.

Between the fifth and eighth weeks the principal parts of the face and neck develop through modifications of the gill pouches and adjoining structures. The limbs have begun to appear, first as "buds" or paddle-like protuberances, and soon develop and differentiate into arms and legs (Figure 31-12). The tail becomes most prominent about the sixth week and subsequently retrogresses and disappears.

By the end of the second month the embryo possesses most of the features and internal organs of the future adult, and from this stage until birth it is usually referred to as a *fetus* rather than an embryo. The arms and fingers including thumbs are already formed by the seventh week. The slower-growing legs display recognizable knees, ankles, and toes. The fetus at the end of two months is no longer than two inches and weighs about one twenty-fifth of an ounce. The nervous and muscular systems have developed to the extent that the fetus can move its arms and turn its body slightly. The eyes and ears have considerably progressed in their development.

During the third month the limbs become longer, nails begin to make their appearance, and the external sex organs differentiate sufficiently so that male and female can be distinguished. Some movements of body and limbs occur but the fetus's total length of approximately three inches is so small that the mother does not yet feel his presence. Most of the subsequent development of the fetus in the remaining six months or so of gestation has to do largely with an increase in size and to a lesser extent with the final steps in the formation of some organs.

In the fourth month hair appears on the head and body, and the facial features become more distinct. By this time the placenta is firmly established and the entire uterine cavity is occupied by the fetus. After the fourth month with increasing size the uterus pushes up towards the abdominal cavity displacing several of the internal organs. In the fifth month the fetus is about a foot long and blood formation in the bone marrow commences. By the sixth month the movements of the fetus in the uterus are quite vigorous and extensive. His presence is very clearly felt by the mother. He experiences intervals of sleep and of wakefulness similar to that of a newborn infant. At the end of the seventh month the body of the fetus has attained better proportions but is somewhat wrinkled (Figure 31-12).

It is in the final two or three months of gestation that the fetus gains most of his birth weight and becomes increasingly able to survive if born prematurely. Approximately five pounds are added to the weight of the fetus during this period, his body becoming smoother and plumper with the deposition of subcutaneous fat. Most of the antibodies which he receives from his mother are transmitted at this time. It will provide him with some measure of protection from infectious agents for the first six months after he is born.

During the course of gestation the uterus has increased in size approximately 200 fold, from a weight of about 50 g and a capacity of approximately 5 ml in the nonpregnant state to a weight of about 1000 g by the end of gestation.

The human fetus toward the latter part of pregnancy normally assumes a position with its head directed downward.

CHILDBIRTH OR PARTURITION

The process by which the fetus is expelled from the body of the mother to terminate the

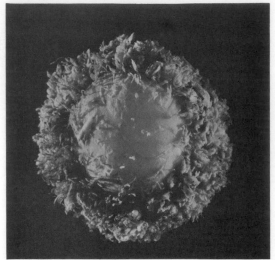

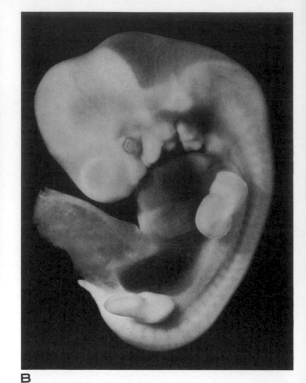

B

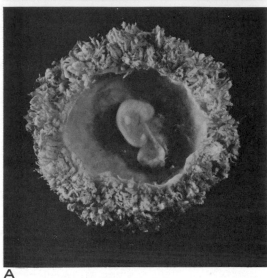

A

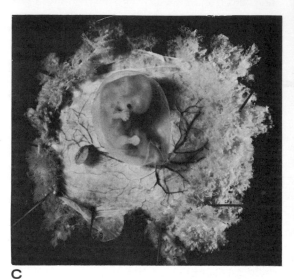

Figure 31-12. Further development of the human embryo. (A) A 28-day embryo: (*above*) with chorion intact; (*below*) with chorion opened to show embryo within amniotic cavity, magnification, 3X. (B) A 34-day embrvo, actual length 11.6 mm, magnification, 10X. (C) A 39-day embryo. Chorion is opened and pinned back to show embryo in intact amnion, magnification, 2X. (D) A 44-day embryo, actual length 23 mm, magnification, 7X. (E) A 56-day embryo, actual length 37 mm, magnification, 5X. (F) A 10-week embryo within the amnion. Uterus is opened to show embryo and fetal membranes, magnification, 0.8X. (G) A 28-week human embryo. (*Courtesy Dept. of Embryology, Carnegie Inst. Washington.*)

C

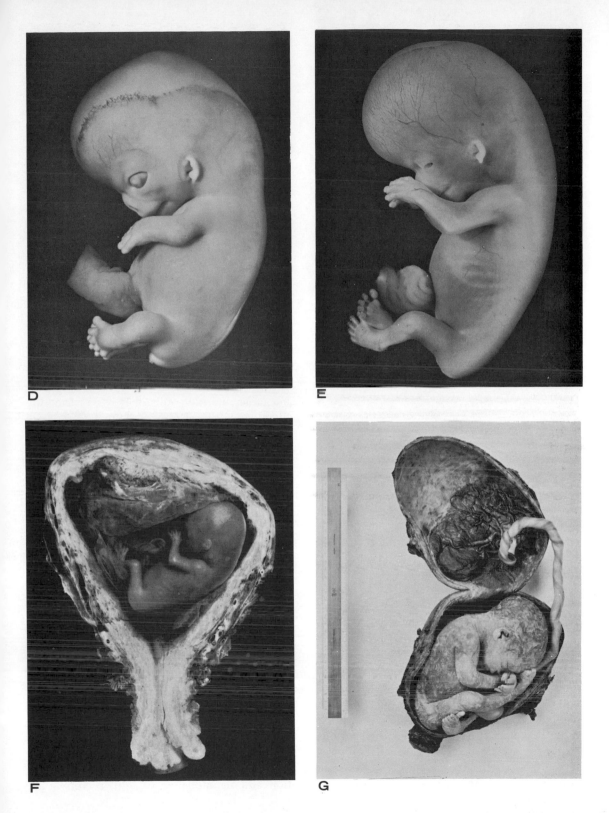

D

E

F

G

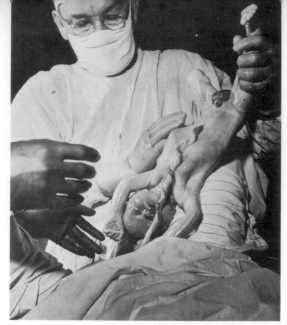

Figure 31-13. Birth, the beginning of life. (*Courtesy of Wayne Miller, Magnum.*)

period of gestation is called *birth* or *parturition*. The factors which initiate and control the remarkable process of birth are still obscure. Several hormonal changes, particularly a decreased secretion of progesterone relative to that of estrogen, occur in the body of the mother prior to the onset of childbirth. They are undoubtedly in part responsible for the softening of the ligaments and certain other structures of the pelvic joints rendering them more pliable for childbirth. Although the means by which these hormonal changes are brought into play are not yet known, their eventual effect is to increase the contractibility and irritability of the uterus.

Birth begins with the onset of involuntary contractions of the uterine walls called *labor pains*. They are at first somewhat weak and of short duration but become progressively stronger and more prolonged. The contractions of the uterus force the fetus, especially the head, against the cervix, causing it to dilate. Dilation of the cervix normally takes several hours. The still intact amniotic sac with its enclosed fluid enveloping the fetus at this time begins to bulge into the vagina. It usually ruptures shortly afterward, liberating the quart or so of amniotic fluid which drains out through the vagina. Meanwhile the vagina itself has become more pliable and distensible. The birth process is culminated by powerful contractions of the uterus aided by voluntary contractions of the abdominal muscles which are sufficient to expel the fetus head first through the maximally enlarged cervix and vagina to the exterior (Figure 31-13).

The umbilical cord which still connects the newborn infant to the uterus by way of the placenta is tied off by the physician soon after birth and cut close to the baby's body. Within the next 15 to 30 minutes further contractions of the uterine wall serve to loosen and expel the placenta and other attached extraembryonic structures, collectively called the *afterbirth*, from the body of the mother. At parturition in humans and other primates the placenta, which includes part of the uterine wall, is torn away, leaving an open, hemorrhaging wound on the wall of the uterus. The bleeding is ordinarily controlled by the same means which served to expel the newborn, namely contraction of the muscular uterine walls which constrict the blood vessels, thus impeding the flow of blood. Clotting finally terminates the bleeding entirely. In other mammals such as the horse, pig, and cow only the fetal portion of the placenta is detached at parturition, the villi being pulled out of the pockets of the uterine wall in which they have been embedded. The surface of the uterine wall remains intact and no bleeding, unlike the case of the primates, occurs at birth.

The duration of the birth process, or *labor*, averages about 16 to 20 hours for women pregnant with their first child. For those women who have already given birth in the past to one or more children the duration of labor averages about 12 hours.

The rapid changes in the circulatory and respiratory systems of the newborn infant which occur shortly after birth have already been described in Chapter 26 on blood circulation.

Lactation

The term *lactation* includes not only initiation and maintenance of milk secretion but also delivery of milk to the young. Mammary development and function are highly complex phenomena. They are controlled and influenced directly and indirectly by a variety of hormones (Chapter 23) including estrogen, progesterone, adrenal corticoids, lactogenic hormone, follicle-stimulating hormone, lutenizing hormone, and oxytocin (also called the *milk let-down* or *ejection factor*).

According to our present knowledge the following primary events occur. During the later stages of pregnancy, progesterone secreted by the placenta aids in the further development of the mammary gland for future lactation. The relatively high level of estrogen at this time, also secreted by the placenta, inhibits secretion of the lactogenic hormone from the adenohypophysis. The expulsion of the placenta during parturition is responsible for a sudden decrease in the estrogen level of the mother, resulting in an increased secretion of the lactogenic hormone and subsequent synthesis of milk. Soon after birth the ejection of milk from the mammary glands is stimulated by the suckling action of the newborn at the nipples of the mother's breast. The suckling stimulus apparently gives rise to afferent nerve impulses to the hypothalamus, resulting in the release from the posterior pituitary gland of oxytocin. The latter in turn stimulates the ejection of milk from the mammary glands. Oxytocin is also responsible for stimulating contraction of the uterus. It thus aids in restoring this organ to its normal nonpregnant size and position as well as decreasing the loss of blood from the torn area of the uterus by constricting the blood vessels.

The first milk secreted after parturition is a watery fluid called *colostrum* with a high content of the mother's antibodies. The antibodies can be absorbed through the infant's intestine to confer a passive immunity to common infectious disease during the first six months or so of life. Suckling or removal of milk is essential for the continued formation of milk by the breast and for its secretion. Milk therefore will continue to be secreted as long as the infant suckles, and ordinarily lasts for a period of eight or nine months. Milk secretion will progressively decrease and finally cease, with the breasts decreasing in size, if the milk is not removed.

SUPPLEMENTARY REFERENCES

Balinsky, B. I., *An Introduction to Embryology*, Saunders, Philadelphia, 1960.
Barth, L. G., *Embryology*, revised edition, Dryden, New York, 1953.
Heuttner, A. F., *Fundamentals of Comparative Embryology of the Vertebrates*, revised edition, Macmillan, New York, 1949.
Moog, F., "Up From the Embryo," *Scientific American*, February 1950.
Waddington, C. H., "How Do Cells Differentiate?," *Scientific American*, September 1953.
Willier, B. N., P. A. Weiss, and V. Hamburger, *Analysis of Development*, Saunders, Philadelphia, 1955.

SEVEN

EVOLUTIONARY INTERRELATIONSHIPS

The vast variety of shapes, sizes, and other features that different living forms display would make it appear at first glance that they are entirely unrelated in form, function, and origin. Closer and more careful examination, however, from several different viewpoints including comparative embryonic development, cellular and subcellular characteristics, physiological activities, biochemical composition, metabolic patterns, and known and deduced histories of the various groups have made it clear that all living systems are related.

This basic resemblance among all forms of life provides strong support for the widely held *theory of organic evolution*. The theory declares that all different kinds of plants and animals that exist today and have existed in the past are related, having arisen from preexisting kinds by relatively slow changes. It refutes the so-called *theory of special creation*, which contends that each type or species of plant or animal had been specially or separately created, and once created could never give rise to any other kind. According to the theory of organic evolution, if we could trace the ancestory of the present-day different kinds or species of living things far enough back, their origins would converge like the branches of a tree into fewer but larger branches which would ultimately fuse into a main trunk representing the single primitive ancestoral stock of all life. Some organisms have arisen from a common ancestor in the relatively recent past. Others are obviously more distantly related having shared a common ancestor in the deeper past of biological history.

The following chapters deal with the evolutionary interrelations existing among living things as well as with the evidence and mechanisms that bear on evolution.

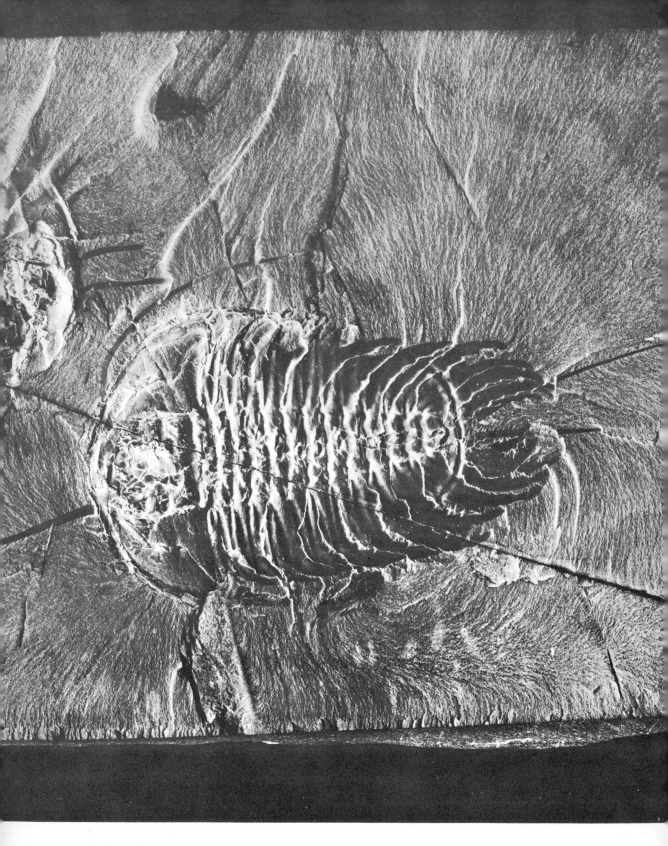

Trilobite fossils (courtesy of Smithsonian Institution).

Chapter 32   Evolution: History and Evidence

INTRODUCTION AND HISTORICAL DEVELOPMENT

The Fact of Evolution

The concept that change, not immutability, is the rule of the universe is one of the fundamental unifying principles of nature perceived by the mind of man. *Evolution* as a gradual and continuous orderly succession of changes is the underlying theme that ties together a vast welter of facts and information into a broad, cohesive, and unified picture of nature—its past, its present, and to a certain extent its future. Its effects are seen in every field of human knowledge and thought. Matter and energy are the basic components of the universe (Chapter 2) and by their very interchangeability and dynamic nature make change or evolution inevitable. The principle of change, or evolution, therefore, applies to all forms of mass and energy whether they occur as inanimate systems extending from the infinitesimally small cosmos of subatomic particles to the infinitely vast cosmos of outer space, or as living systems extending from the relatively simple virus particle to the incredibly complex organism, man. According to our present views biological evolution is simply one aspect of the overall evolution of the cosmos. We conceive of evolution as having started from the nonbiological state with the origin of the expanding universe (if, indeed, the universe did have a beginning) as described in Chapter 2; and that inanimate systems evolved by many steps over billions of years into living systems and thence to contemporary organisms as described in Chapter 3.

For convenience we subdivide the field of evolution into two general areas, *nonbiological* or *inorganic evolution* and *biological* or *organic evolution,* with the implicit understanding that they are inextricably intertwined with one another, often exerting mutual effects. *Nonbiological evolution* is a fundamental concept in the physical sciences (physics, astronomy, chemistry, and geology) and concerns itself with the succession of changes which have occurred over vast periods of time in mass and energy from various points of view, including changes in climate, the surface of the earth, and so on. *Biological evolution* is concerned with the origin of life and its subsequent development and diversification over the billions of years into the plants, animals, and microorganisms of the present day. As a concept it contends that all contemporary species of life did not come into existence in the same form which they exhibit today, but have originated and gradually changed from other now extinct species. They are the descendants of primordial, and in most instances, simpler ancestors.

In general the major biological evolutionary tendency has been toward increased specialization and complexity of structure and function, although in some organisms simplification from more complex ancestors has occurred. Those species whose offspring possess inherited variations that are well suited to a given environment tend to survive in succeeding generations, whereas those that are not well adapted are eliminated, a phenomenon commonly known as *natural selection*. The evolutionary process, both biological and non-biological, still continues, but is generally so slow for higher animals and plants in their natural environments as to be almost undetectable over the few centuries that man has recorded his observations. Evolution for most organisms under natural circumstances is a process which at its most rapid rate requires several hundred years before changes can be detected.

Many types of evidence have firmly established evolution as a demonstrated fact. The main lines of such evidence for the occurrence of evolution in living systems are discussed in the following sections. The principal mechanisms involved are described in the next chapter. Actually many of the evolutionary aspects of form and function including metabolism have already been highlighted throughout the previous chapters of the book. In particular, the surveys of the plant and animal kingdoms (Chapters 15, 16, 18–20) were designed to show how the members of the living world, as we know them today, emerged from more primitive ancestors through various lines of descent. Similarly the central role of gene mutations and of sexual reproduction, as the mainsprings of evolution by providing a vast increase in possible gene combinations (and therefore new biological variations), have also been indicated in earlier chapters. Their roles in these respects will also be described in greater detail in the following chapter.

Early History

Faint glimmerings of the idea of organic evolution have appeared at various times in the history of human thought, as far back as the ancient civilizations. The myths and beliefs created by the Greek philosophers Anaximander (sixth century B.C.) and Empedocles (fifth century B.C.), the Roman poet Lucretius (first century B.C.), and others extending well into the sixteenth and seventeenth centuries often centered about bizarre and ludicrous transformations of different species into one another—men into animals, higher plants into higher animals, and so on.

The great Greek philosopher and naturalist Aristotle (fourth century B.C.) proposed a classification of living things that bordered on the very edge of organic evolution. He suggested that nature "advances by small steps from inanimate things to animate..." like a single ladder of progress with the simpler and less complex organisms at the bottom ranging in a single line to the more complex and more "perfect" forms at correspondingly higher rungs of the ladder to culminate with man at the very top. Whether Aristotle meant that life had evolved in this pattern or had been created as such by a higher force is not clear and has in fact been the subject of various scholarly interpretations.

Although it had already become increasingly clear by the end of the seventeenth century that plants and animals fall into natural groups or species, it was commonly accepted that they were unchangeable, and that each species was the result of an act of special creation. The view had originally been embodied in the book of Genesis of the Old Testament: God bade the earth and waters to bring forth living creatures —first the plants, then fishes, birds, land animals, and finally man.

By the eighteenth century several biologists seriously began to question the concept that species were unchangeable. Studies with cultivated plants and domestic animals, and the many new discoveries and detailed studies of an increasingly vast number of plants and animals during this period, as a consequence of world explorations, soon made it evident that there was no clear distinction between species and varieties or races.

It was Jean Lamarck (1744-1829) who made

the first great pioneering step toward the development of our modern theory of organic evolution. With a boldness and vision which bordered on genius he perceived that species and varieties were subject to change. He declared that change, not immutability, of species was the basis for the diversification of life, and that the more complex organisms have in reality evolved from the simpler ones. His views, which for the first time presented a somewhat reasonable account of organic evolution, also asserted that evolution had not ceased but was still occurring. Despite the greatness of Lamarck's idea of organic evolution, it was unacceptable for several reasons. First, Lamarck unfortunately believed in a single line of evolutionary development from the less perfect to the more perfect organisms much like the idea of the single ladder of progress proposed by Aristotle some 2000 years earlier. He was soon easily refuted on this point by the great anatomist and paleontologist Cuvier (1768-1833). Second, Lamarck erroneously contended that evolution was caused by changes in traits acquired during the lifetime of an organism as a result of use or disuse according to its needs. He believed that such acquired traits were somehow incorporated into the heredity of the individual and thus transmitted from generation to generation. The latter proposal was at first accepted in many quarters, but has since been refuted by an overwhelming number of experiments performed by scientists in various parts of the world.

Probably the nearest predecessor to Lamarck in evolutionism was the naturalist Buffon (1707–1788) who believed that organisms could be changed by environment and that these changes were inherited. Buffon's views were soon obscured, in part because they were too contrary at that time to the entrenched dogma of special creation. The proposal in the mid-twentieth century by the Russian agriculturalist Lysenko that a plant strain or species may be transformed into another by environmental influences is the most recent claim that has been made along these lines, but it has failed to receive confirmation by other researchers. It is now clearly established that the effects of use or disuse of an organ or body part are not transmitted by inheritance; stated in other words, the environment is not responsible for specific and directed genetic changes.

THE CONTRIBUTIONS OF CHARLES DARWIN. It was at about this time in the history of biology that the English naturalist Charles Darwin (1809–1882) began his famous studies that laid the foundations for the modern concept of organic evolution. Not only did Darwin provide for the first time a mass of detailed and extensive evidence and reasonable explanations to show that biological evolution had taken place, but he also presented a proposal known as the *theory of natural selection* to account for its operation.

The Voyage of the Beagle. In the year 1831 Darwin at the age of 22 embarked on a five-year trip around the world as a naturalist on the British ship *H.M.S. Beagle*. He had no grounds at this time for doubting the immutability of species and the concept that each existing species had been created by divine power. The voyage proved to be of great significance not only to Darwin but to the history of human thought. For it was primarily his observations and studies of nature during the course of this trip, especially in South America and the Galapagos Islands located in the Pacific Ocean about 600 miles west of Ecuador, that led to his well-founded proposal a quarter century later of the *theory of organic evolution by natural selection*. On the basis of his studies of nature in the field Darwin returned to England at the end of his voyage a confirmed evolutionist. His detailed observations and findings of animal life, plant life, and geology which provided the first extensive proof of biological evolution, together with his theory of natural selection to explain how evolution worked, were published some 20 years later in 1859 as the famous volume *On the Origin of Species by Means of Natural Selection, or the Preservation of Favoured Races in the Struggle for Life* (henceforth referred to as *Origin of Species*).

Figure 32-1. Darwin finches, arranged to show evolutionary tree of their development. (*Courtesy of Amer. Mus. of Natural History.*)

Darwin's Observations. What were the key observations that led Darwin to the theory of organic evolution? Essentially three sets of findings started him on his revolt against the concept of immutability of species. First, in his studies of the species of plants and animals on the Galapagos Islands he found that although the species of the birds called finches (Figure 32-1) differed slightly from island to island, they still showed strong similarities to one another as well as to several species in the adjacent mainland of South America. This was also true for many other species of plants and animals examined. Was each species on each island specially created or did they arise from a common stock by evolution? Moreover, why was the bird life so different on the Galapagos Islands as compared with that on the Cape

Verde Islands (located some 500 miles west of Dakar, Africa) despite the resemblance in the volcanic nature and physical conditions of the islands. The birds of the Galapagos bear close relationship to particular South American species, whereas the birds of the Cape Verde Islands show a marked similarity to those of Africa.

Second, examination of living forms, especially along the eastern coast of South America where the Beagle had occasion to make numerous stops, soon revealed particular patterns to Darwin. For example, certain species such as hares occupying a particular locality, were often different but nevertheless still closely related to a somewhat similar species occupying a corresponding locality several hundred miles away. It seemed to Darwin that the greater the distance between the localities the greater the diversity between obviously related species. Could this apparent geographical succession of related species best be explained by acts of special creation, one for each area, or was it possible that species are after all not immutable?

The third principal set of observations was also made in South America. In the pampas Darwin came upon the fossil remains of large extinct mammals covered with armor and resembling contemporary armadillos (Figure 32-2). The extinct armadillo-like animal (now designated as a member of the genus *Glyptodon*) and the living armadillo (both types are found only in the western hemisphere), although distinctly different in several respects, have the same body plan and are obviously related. Inevitably the same question arose. Did the present-day armadillo descend from the extinct form, or were both created separately by an act of divine power?

Darwin's Conclusions. What were the most reasonable answers to the questions raised by the important observations made during the voyage of the Beagle? Darwin could no longer be satisfied with the "explanation" offered by the idea of special creation that species are immutable. Science had matured to the stage of seeking answers to natural phenomena in terms of cause-and-effect relationships. Darwin was inexorably drawn by his observations to the simple and satisfactory working hypothesis that species were subject to change during descent, diverging into different species and different lines of descent in the course of time. According to this view species have therefore experienced evolution by modification from ancestral species shared in common with other species, a process which continues incessantly. The important observations of Darwin could now be simply and satisfactorily answered by a common and reasonable explanation. The finches of the Galapagos are basically similar to one another and to those of South America because they evolved along different lines from a common ancestor. They differ from the birds of the Cape Verde Islands, for the latter birds together with related species of Africa must have descended from a different common ancestor. Similarly the various species of South American hares bearing strong resemblances to one another must have descended from a common ancestor, as did the living armadillo and the fossil *Glyptodon*. The use of fossil evidence was especially significant, for it emphasized the importance of fossils and other paleontological records in the study of evolution.

By the time the Beagle had completed its round-the-world voyage in 1836, Darwin had accumulated a formidable array of evidence in support of the idea of organic evolution. This was an outstanding contribution in itself, but Darwin was not yet entirely satisfied. In the 20 years that followed he not only reassembled and organized the voluminous notes of his voyage, but studied at least two other aspects of the evolution problem. First, in order to fortify further his contention that evolution has occurred, Darwin turned elsewhere for additional evidence. He searched the entire field of biological knowledge, both zoological and botanical, for facts and other information reflecting on his view of evolution. The biological literature at the time bearing on such areas as comparative anatomy of plants and animals,

Figure 32-2. Comparison of contemporary armadillos with the skeleton of a glyptodont (*below*). (*Courtesy of Fish and Wildlife Service, U.S. Dept. Interior, N. Y. Zoological Soc. and Amer. Mus. of Natural History.*)

embryology, paleontology, taxonomy, interbreeding among organisms, and the commercial production of divergent lines of plants and animals provided him with additional support for his now irrefutable claim that evolution—the changing of species and their origin from other species—is a reality. The total evidence furnished from all these sources stands today as a milestone in biology and human thought. It has been repeatedly confirmed as well as extended to many new branches of science. Second, Darwin sought an explanation or mechanism to account for the manner in which the evolutionary process operated in both plants and animals. By the 1850's he had formulated his *Theory of Natural Selection* which was published as a scientific paper in 1858 jointly with another English naturalist, Alfred Wallace. As we shall see in the following section Wallace had independently arrived at the same conclusions as Darwin concerning evolution and the means by which it occurred. In the following year, 1859, Darwin published his great volume *Origin of Species* which contained in detail his theory of evolution by natural selection together with the vast array of evidence in support of it.

The Darwin-Wallace Theory of Evolution by Natural Selection. All living things are more or less adapted to the external environment in which they live, for otherwise they could not exist. Stated in another way, different species possess different characteristics which seem to be well suited to their mode of existence. Seals, for example, are mammals that live in the sea. Unlike most mammals, which are terrestrial, seals possess flippers instead of arms or legs, an adaptation well fitted for life in water. As another example, *xerophytes* (Figure 32-3), or plants that live under arid conditions, are admirably adapted to an environment of limited water supply by their possession of deep widespread roots, a reduced and heavily cutinized leaf and stem area, and often reserves of water in their tissues. How did these adaptations arise in the course of evolution? And how were these adaptations, once they appeared,

selected for by nature so that they best fitted a plant or animal to its particular mode of existence? Variations appearing in the many characteristics of a species have been used by man for centuries as a basis for selecting desirable traits in the breeding of plants and domestic animals. If variations are the basis for adaptations in the course of evolution, what is the mechanism by which variations seem to be preferentially selected?

Darwin's solution was in part inspired by the English economist Thomas Malthus (Chapter 10). In his *Essay on Population* Malthus contended that more children are born than reach maturity, and that such factors as limited food sources, war, and disease are important influences in the "struggle for existence" restricting the size of the human population. Darwin realized that these principles could also apply to any other living species. Darwin reasoned that under the competitive conditions in which all organisms live, selection in nature works automatically because the inherited variations that favored an organism's existence and ability to produce fertile offspring would be maintained from generation to generation. By contrast, the variations that were disadvantageous in these respects would be eliminated sooner or later by elimination of the organisms and their offspring which possessed these features. Thus an automatic or natural selection process was constantly in operation, tending to perpetuate the existence of the variations that in a given environment conferred an advantage in terms of survival and production of fertile offspring.

It was during this period in the late 1850's that another English naturalist, Alfred Russel Wallace (1823–1913), working entirely independently and without any knowledge of Darwin's studies, arrived at the same theory of organic evolution and natural selection to account for the changeability of species. Wallace's conclusions were based upon observations of animal and plant life and their fossils in Indonesia (then called the Malay Archipelago) and upon examination of the distribution of the different classes of known organisms over the world. Like Darwin he was also stimulated by Malthus's *Essay on Population* to suggest an explanation of the workings of evolution on the basis of survival of the best fitted, or natural selection. Unaware that Darwin had reached the same conclusions and that these were being prepared together with the supporting evidence for publication as a book (the now famous *Origin of Species*), Wallace in 1858 sent a manuscript from the Far East describing his theory to Darwin in England. In the true spirit of science Darwin presented Wallace's as well as his own identical views on the theory and explanation of organic evolution a month later in July 1858 before a meeting of the Linnaean Society in London.

In the following year Darwin's *Origin of Species* was published. It revoked the widely accepted idea of divine creation and replaced it with the concept of organic evolution that inevitably related different living organisms to one another. Darwin's book inspired a storm of intellectual and emotional controversy among the civilized peoples of the world that rocked the latter half of the nineteenth century and extended well into the first three decades of the twentieth century. Although the concept of organic evolution still encounters resistance from certain segments of the population, the impartial evaluation of Darwin's voluminous evidence as well as many new lines of supporting knowledge in the 100 years or so since the publication of the *Origin of Species* have led to its general acceptance by the scientific community. However, the theory of natural selection, as the means by which evolution has come about, has met with considerably more disagreement in scientific circles. And as we shall see in the next chapter it has necessarily been modified and modernized as a result of important findings, especially in genetics, the new biological science which was founded almost a half-century after the appearance of Darwin's *Origin of Species*.

Although Darwin and Wallace independently and simultaneously proposed the theories of

Figure 32-3. Cactus, a xerophyte. (*Courtesy of Amer. Mus. of Natural History.*)

organic evolution and natural selection, most of the credit and honors have been accorded to Darwin, largely because he provided the wealth of irrefutable evidence in its favor. Nevertheless a share of the glory belongs to Wallace as well.

The essential features of evolution and its causes as presented by Darwin and Wallace in the late 1850's can be summarized as follows.

1. *Overproduction.* Organisms, because of their prodigious reproduction capacities, produce far more offspring than can ever survive or reach maturity.

2. *Constancy of Population Size.* Despite the tendency for a species to increase in population at a geometric or exponential rate, the population of a species remains more or less constant over long periods of time. There must, therefore, be an appreciable death rate which is in part due to limited food and space.

3. *Variation.* All members of a given species are not alike but show variations in many of their characteristics.

4. *Natural Selection.* Those variations that better fit organisms in the competition for survival in a given environment will favor their existence as compared to organisms and their progeny that possess less suited variations. In this manner there will be a natural selection among individuals of the species in favor of those members whose variations more effectively adapt them to the conditions of their environment.

5. *Inheritance.* Since inheritance is a fact as indicated by the resemblance between parents and progeny, surviving individuals will pass on their variations, or adaptations, for the most part the more favorable ones because of natural selection, to succeeding generations. In this manner adaptations in the course of many generations will become increasingly modified, better suiting the species to its environment.

In effect the theory was based on the established facts of overproduction, the constancy of population size, the occurrence of variations, and the hereditary resemblance between parent and progeny. From these Darwin and Wallace deduced that there is a competition for survival—a struggle for existence among living things—resulting in the elimination of organisms with less favorable variations, and in the persistence of those individuals possessing the most advantageous variations for a given environment. These variations were presumably transmitted by inheritance from generation to generation, thus gradually modifying and better adapting the species to its environment.

It can be seen from the foregoing points that environment is a central force in the process of natural selection, for it serves to determine which variations are favorable and which are unfavorable. A change in environment could modify the significance of certain variations, conferring them now with favorable or unfavorable attributes, as the case may be, and thus changing to a new direction the entire course of evolution for organisms. With the passage of time and numerous generations the accumulation of many new variations as a result of natural selection could modify the characteristics of a group of organisms sufficiently to warrant their classification as a new species.

THE EVIDENCE FOR EVOLUTION

Since Darwin's time there has accured a vast and overwhelming volume of evidence in support of organic evolution—that it has occurred in the past and is in operation today. The main lines of evidence which have convinced biologists that evolution is a demonstrated fact are derived from: (1) the study of fossils (called *paleontology*); (2) *taxonomy* or classification; (3) *homology or comparative studies* of physiology and biochemistry, anatomy, and embryonic development; (4) *geographical distribution*; and (5) *genetics.*

Evidence from Fossils

Fossils are the remains or impressions of ancient plants and animals which are usually preserved in rocks (Figure 32-4). They represent only an infinitesimally small record of life of the past ages and are the most direct evidence that evolution has occurred. It is from fossil remains that the paleontologists attempt to reconstruct a picture of the ancient extinct organisms as they actually existed and the environment in which they lived.

FOSSIL FORMATION. When organisms die their bodies are usually decomposed by microorganisms, and in time completely eradicated. In a relatively few instances plants or animals that have died and fallen into the sediments that later became a portion of the stratified rocks of the earth's crust were preserved in one form or other. As a rule only their hard parts, specifically their skeletal structures, which are more resistant to decay, were preserved, whereas their soft parts disappeared through the normal processes of decay. In many cases of fossil formation the skeletons of animals, invertebrate and vertebrate, and the cellulose and wood of plants were infiltrated with ground water containing high concentrations of minerals including silica, calcium, and magnesium to form hard resistant *petrifactions.* Silicified or petrified wood is an example of a petrifaction. Petrifaction is considered to be a gradual filling of the cell cavities and intercellular spaces of the hard tissue with mineral matter. It is not a replacement process of organic matter by mineral material as formerly believed.

Figure 32-4. Various types of fossils. (A) Fossil frog. (B) Fossil cycad which lived about 200 million years ago (Triassic Period), from the Petrified Forest of Arizona. (C) Fossil cephalopod (about 150 million years old, Jurassic Period), resembling present-day nautilus. (D) Well-preserved fly in amber. (*Courtesy of Amer. Mus. of Natural History and Smithsonian Institution.*)

In other instances the accidental burial of plants and animals in the soft sediment which subsequently hardened into rock have left *impressions or casts,* including at times many detailed and fine features of body structure, despite the subsequent disappearance by decay long since of all the tissues. Footprints of certain ancient vertebrates such as the dino-saurs and the tracks left by certain vertebrates have also been found in rocks which at one time made up the mud and sand in and near the primitive oceans. Fossil remains of soft-bodied organisms are rare with the exception of impressions as just described. On particular occasions the viscous gums exuded by ancient trees have trapped insects and other terrestrial

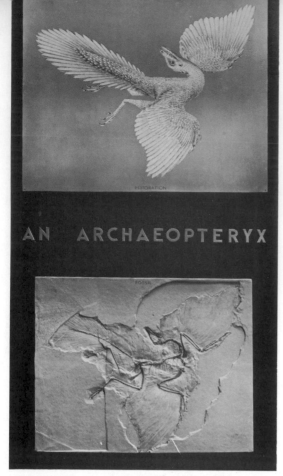

AN ARCHAEOPTERYX

Figure 32-5. Fossil (*below*) of the primitive bird *Archaeopteryx*, and a restoration (*above*) or model depicting the actual appearance of this primitive animal. (*Courtesy Amer. Mus. Natural History.*)

invertebrates, and in the course of time several of these gums were transformed into a hard translucent amber within which the intact bodies of these organisms have been beautifully preserved.

It should be emphasized that the number of fossils formed from the vast number of ancient plants and animals who once lived in times gone by has been infinitesimally small. An appreciable number of fossils have undoubtedly been destroyed by the forces of nature, including erosion and the high pressures and high temperatures which accompanied volcanic eruptions, mountain building, and other upheavals of the earth's structure. Moreover, only an extremely small number of the remain-

ing preserved fossils have been studied. Nevertheless, the increasing and painstaking efforts of paleontologists, especially since the time of Darwin, have provided us with a record of ancient life, in some cases grossly incomplete, and in other instances remarkably abundant and detailed. Thus it has furnished us not only with the most direct evidence in our possession that evolution has occurred but in certain instances has actually indicated the steps by which it did occur. A series of fossil horses found in certain rock strata of western North America has indicated the sequence of changes in the evolution of the horse (Chapter 33). Other successions of fossils apparently represent the remains of connecting links between larger groups of organisms. An outstanding example was the discovery of fossils of a primitive bird, *Archaeopteryx* (Figure 32-5), with numerous reptilian characteristics such as reptilian teeth, tail vertebrae, and wings with claws, thus strongly supporting the theory that birds evolved from reptiles.

FORMATION AND SEQUENCE OF SEDIMENTARY ROCKS. The earth's crust is made up in part of various layers or strata of so-called *sedimentary rocks*. These were formed over vast periods of time in the distant past by the slow settling out and compaction of sediments or deposits of sand, silt, mud, and volcanic ash from the seas, lakes, rivers, and the air. The lowermost rock layers are in general the first deposits and therefore the oldest, whereas the succeeding upper strata reflect the sequence of their deposition very much like the bricks of a house, the topmost layer being the most recent. The exposed stratified rock walls of the Grand Canyon (Figure 32-6) are a good example of such a time sequence.

It should be noted, however, that in various regions of the earth's crust the geologist has been able to show numerous exceptions to the chronological order of rock stratification as a result of certain geologic events. In some instances localized shiftings in the earth's crust have caused tremendous foldings in the rock strata (for example, during periods of mountain formation), so that the older and earlier layers may now be located on top of the later and more recent ones. At times the appearance of breaks in the rock strata, known as *faults*, and subsequent horizontal slippage may cause the same effect. In other cases the erosion of the upper rock layers followed by a change in geologic conditions, such as submergence beneath a shallow sea which favors resumed deposition, may be responsible for the close proximity of recent layers to ancient ones.

THE GEOLOGIC TIME TABLE. *General Features.* The sequence of rock strata in the earth's crust serves as a time clock of the ancient past in the study of primitive life. It has provided us with valuable information of the approximate ages of the different fossils found in the various strata as well as with important clues about the succession and relationship of changes in the evolution of organisms. The fossil record often shows the succession of animals and plants from the relatively simple aquatic types of older geologic times to the progressively more complex and better adapted terrestrial forms of the more recent geologic eras. It has also given us important clues about the relationships between extinct and living forms. In addition it has been useful to the geologist in establishing the ages of rocks in which the fossils are found, for once the geologic time range of a fossil group has been determined elsewhere in rock strata of known ages, the occurrence of the same fossil group in other rocks is indicative of a similarity in age.

Certain fossils have also provided us with important clues of past environmental conditions as well as the past distribution of lands and seas. If fossils can be shown to be related to specific present-day living forms of restricted habitat, it is a reasonable assumption that the fossils had similar limitations. Invertebrate fossils such as reef corals, for example, indicate warm marine temperatures. The occurrence of fossil palms and magnolias in

Figure 32-6. Stratified walls of the Grand Canyon. (*Courtesy of Union Pacific Railroad.*)

particular rock strata of southern Alaska suggests the occurrence of subtropical humid conditions there in the distant past. The finding of marine fossils in inland regions points to the past existence of inland seas.

Geologists have been able to relate the sequence of the formation or sedimentation of the rock strata of the earth to a record of geologic history often spoken of as the *geologic time table*. The ages of the different sedimentary rock strata have been approximated by several methods including the order of their arrangement from the oldest strata at the bottom to the progressively more recent ones at the top, and measurements of the extents of decay of certain long-lived radioactive elements contained within them as indicated for uranium and lead (Chapters 2 and 6).

The geologic time table of the earth is based on the five major sedimentary rock strata which compose a significant portion of the earth's crust. Accordingly the geologic history of the earth is divided into five major time intervals, called *eras*, which in turn are progressively subdivided in *periods* and *epochs*. The oldest geologic era is the *Archeozoic* and is followed in order by the progressively younger *Proterozoic, Paleozoic, Mesozoic,* and *Cenozoic* eras (Table 32-1). The Cenozoic as the most recent is presently in existence. The biologist often pools together the Archeozoic and Proterozoic eras into a collective and single so-called *Precambrian* Era because of the virtual lack of fossils in their rock strata. We can therefore only guess as to the course of biological evolution during that time.

The changes in structure and climate experienced by the earth's surface during the course of geologic time have not always proceeded in a uniform manner or at a steady rate. At times there were widespread and intense intervals of mountain building called *revolutions,* the result of tremendous geologic disturbances whereby vast portions of the earth's crust were shifted and raised, causing enormous modifications in the distribution of lands, oceans, and climates and the death of many organisms. The particular revolution that gave rise to the Appalachian Mountains marked the end of the Paleozoic Era and the beginning of the Mesozoic Era. The more recent revolution which formed the Rockies, Andes, Alps, and Himalayas is the transition between the end of the Mesozoic Era and the start of the Cenozoic Era. The erosion which eventually leveled mountains and decreased the size of continents proceeded at varying rates, at times quite rapidly and at other times more slowly.

DISTRIBUTION OF FOSSILS IN THE GEOLOGIC TIME TABLE. *General Features.* According to

Table 32-1   The Geological Time Table

Era	Period	Epoch	Millions of years ago[*]	Duration in millions of years	
Cenozoic	Quaternary	Recent	.025	.025	1
		Pleistocene	1.0	1.0	
	Tertiary	Pliocene	10	9	
		Miocene	25	15	
		Oligocene	40	15	75
		Eocene	60	20	
		Paleocene	75	15	
Mesozoic	Cretaceous		130	65	
	Jurassic		165	25	125
	Triassic		200	35	
Paleozoic	Permian		230	30	
	Carboni- ⌠Pennsylvanian		250	20	
	ferous ⌡Mississippian		280	30	
	Devonian		325	40	325
	Silurian		360	35	
	Ordovician		425	65	
	Cambrian		525	100	
Precambrian ⎰Protero- zoic ⎱Archeo- zoic ?			3000 (?)	3000 (?)	2500 (?)

[*]Taken from beginning of indicated era, period, or epoch.

angiosperms : Characteristics

1. Flowers
   microsporophylls - stamens
   megasporophylls - carpels

2. Ovules and seeds in ovary

3. Vessels in xylem

4. double fertilization

5. pollination by insects, birds, wind

6. herbaceous - 1 or 2 years
   woody - perennials

7. dependent gametophytes

8. large, almost independent sporophytes

9. heterospory

10. seed, true roots, stems, leaves

unlike gymnosperms (1 through 6)

like gymnosperms (7 through 10)

see Weisz
Soph. notes

Comparisons

	monocot (more advanced)	dicot
Leaves	|| veins	branched veins
Stem	herbaceous (palm - exception)	woody, herbaceous
Vb	scattered	in rings
	1 cotyledon	2 cotyledons
	no cambium	cambium
flowers	multiples of 3	multiples of 4 or 5

no mobile ♂ gametophytes

alternation of generations

double fertilization {
pollentube → (via) micropyle (embryo sac) → ♂ nucleus + ♀ ~~nucleus~~ egg =
zygote 2n (veg. sporo. gen.)
♂ nucleus + 2 polar nuclei = 3n nucleus (endosperm)
antipodals & synergids disintegrate

ovule → seed
ovary (with seeds) → fruit

embryo:
1 or 2 cotyledons
epicotyl ~~[illegible]~~ (plumule) (above the attachment)
hypocotyl – below the
radicle – lower end of h root

~~Stems~~
woody

our latest estimates the earth originated some 5 billion years ago (Chapter 2). Fossils have been found in relatively reasonable abundance as far back as the beginning of the Cambrian Period of the Paleozoic Era approximately half a billion years ago. Few or no fossils have been discovered in Precambrian rocks for two principal reasons. First, the living forms of that era were presumably very small and composed chiefly of soft tissues, features which are unfavorable for preservation as fossils. Second, these rock layers under the enormous weight of all the other overlying strata have been greatly modified or "metamorphosed" by great pressures and high temperatures which have also undoubtedly been responsible for the loss of any contained fossils. The fact that the rocks of the early Cambrian Period include diverse fossils representative of most of the modern sea animals (with the notable exception of the vertebrates) must mean that the origin of life took place considerably earlier. We can also deduce that the latter stages of the Precambrian Era were surely inhabited by some aquatic animals of relatively advanced body structure even though we have few or no fossils for corroboration. The few doubtful plant fossils which have been found to be associated with the Precambrian Era suggest the possible existence of bacteria and algae. On the other hand, the rocks of the Cambrian Period have yielded a succession of fossils indicative of the existence of a thriving population of blue-green, green, and even brown algae similar to our present-day brown algae.

All of the earliest fossils found reflect the existence of solely aquatic animals and plants during the Cambrian Period (and the Precambrian Era), a most important line of evidence for the inference that life originated in the sea. In fact the first fossils of land-dwelling organisms show up subsequently in rock strata that were deposited some 200 million years later. We now believe that the first life on our planet originated some two billion years ago in the primitive seas (Chapter 3), or approximately one and one-half billion years before our earliest fossil record. The three billion years between the presumed time of the origin of the earth and first appearance of life is believed to have been a period of molecular evolution which laid the groundwork for the beginnings of life (Chapter 3).

By far the vast majority of the ancient living forms of the past—100 million years ago and earlier—have become extinct. The organisms of today are the descendants of only a handful of the hundred of thousands of species that existed in the Mesozoic Era. Studies thus far of the fossil remains of animals and plants have permitted us to make interpretations of the past history of the major phyla in terms of their abundance, distribution, relationships with one another, habits of growth, and climates in which they lived.

THE FOSSIL RECORD OF ANIMAL LIFE. One of the more favored schemes based on the fossil record which has been suggested for the history of the major groups of animals is shown in Figure 32-7. It indicates the principal animal groups of the past and present in terms of relative abundance and approximate time. The important events and relationships of animals in the biologic past may be summarized as follows.

The Invertebrates. The Cambrian Period of the Paleozoic Era, which in effect is as far back as the usable fossil record extends, already contained most of the modern major invertebrate phyla living in the seas today. These included many of the marine representatives of protozoa, sponges, coelenterates, echinoderms, molluscs, annelids, and arthropods (Figure 32-8). The latter were especially well represented by the *trilobites* (also see p. 730), a very primitive and now extinct group of arthropods. The *Bryozoa* were notably absent and did not appear until the following Ordovician Period some 50 to 100 million years later.

The Vertebrates. The Fishes. The principal biologic event of the Ordovician Period was the origin of the vertebrates, most likely from a preceding tunicate-like ancestor. The oldest verte-

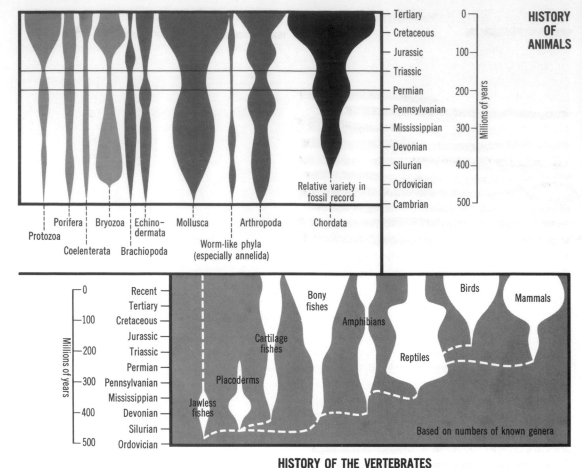

HISTORY OF THE VERTEBRATES

Figure 32-7. Schematic representation of the history of the major animal phyla. The widths of the pathways are proportional to the relative abundance of species of the various phyla. (*Adapted from G. G. Simpson, The Meaning of Evolution, Yale University Press, 1950.*)

brate fossils discovered thus far are those of the jawless fishes. These are also the most primitive of the living vertebrates whose best known modern representatives are the lampreys and the hagfish (Chapter 20). In the course of geologic time certain ancient *jawless fishes* must have given rise to the now extinct *jawed fishes* or *placoderms* (Chapter 20), the only known extinct class of vertebrates. Certain ancestral descendants of the placoderms in turn probably evolved independently into the cartilaginous fishes or chondrichthyans and the bony fishes or osteichthyans. The placoderms arose during the early Silurian Period

and became most abundant during the Devonian Period, spreading from the fresh waters, in which they probably first appeared, into the seas. They rapidly began to disappear with the closing of the Devonian and the beginning of the Mississippian periods, being replaced by the relatively newly evolved cartilaginous fishes and bony fishes. All the evidence indicates that the placoderms were entirely extinct by the end of the Permian Period.

The cartilaginous fishes as represented by the present-day sharks, skates, and rays are for the most part marine types which have shown few fluctuations in abundance during

Figure 32-8. Representation of marine life during the Cambrian Period. The organism at the lower middle region of the photograph is a trilobite (an arthropod); above it is another arthropod (*Sidneyia*). At the left can be seen a jellyfish floating in front of an alga. Standing diagonally below it to the right is a sea cucumber, beside which is an annelid worm. (*Courtesy of Amer. Mus. of Natural History.*)

their long evolutionary history. By contrast, the ancient bony fishes gave rise to three main lines (1) the *paleoniscoids*, from which the vastly abundant modern bony fishes, both fresh-water and marine types, ascended; (2) the *lungfishes* (Chapter 27) consisting at present of only three remaining living genera; and (3) the *lobe-finned fishes* (see Figure 20-10), now also virtually extinct, from which the amphibians are believed to have evolved sometime during the Devonian Period.

The Amphibians. The most primitive amphibian fossils known thus far have been found in certain Devonian deposits of Greenland. The development of lungs for breathing air and of fins for traveling over land were the two principal adaptations in the evolution of fish to amphibians. They were presumably selected for in an environment where a periodic drying out of pools and streams occurred, perhaps as the result of alternate rainy and dry seasons. The amphibians attained their peak in number and diversity during the Pennsylvanian and Permian periods (the insects as terrestrial invertebrates were also rapidly becoming abun-

dant during this same interval). The later portion of the Paleozoic Era extending from the Mississippian through the Permian and part of the Triassic periods is often called the "Age of Amphibians." At the height of their development the amphibians were probably predominantly large-bodied types, resembling somewhat the present-day crocodiles. Their sudden and near extinction, perhaps because of the appearance of the reptiles, during the Jurassic Period was followed by the evolution of new amphibian groups—the frogs and toads.

The Reptiles. The amphibians were then eclipsed by a group of newly evolved organisms, the earliest known reptiles, the *Cotylosaurs*, which apparently arose as an offshoot of certain primitive amphibians during the later Mississippian or early Pennsylvanian periods. The reptiles, as the first truly terrestrial vertebrates (in contrast to the amphibians which require an aquatic habitat during the larval or tadpole stages), rapidly became abundant during the Permian Period. They decreased somewhat during the subsequent Triassic Period and then increased during

Figure 32-9. Fossil remains of *Ichthyosaurus guadriscissus* (170 cm long), an ancient marine reptile (resembling sharks and porpoises) which was most abundant during the Jurassic Period some 165 million years ago. It became extinct well before the end of the Cretaceous Period. (*Courtesy of the American Museum of Natural History.*)

the Jurassic and Cretaceous periods. It was in the latter period that they achieved their climax in terms of abundance. They adapted to an existence in the water (Figure 32-9), on the land, and in the air with correspondingly different body structures and ways of life. They were probably the most successful of all the terrestrial animals living in the past. The Mesozoic Era is usually referred to as the "Age of Reptiles." During their peak the reptiles consisted of at least five distinct principal lines or stocks, all having evolved from the single primitive reptilian line, the above-mentioned cotylosaurs. The most famous were of course the dinosaurs (Figure 32-10), some of which attained lengths of nearly 100 feet and weights of approximately 25 tons. But then relatively suddenly, for reasons which are not entirely clear, many of the larger forms such as the dinosaurs disappeared and were replaced by the birds and mammals. Lizards and snakes as the most successful of the modern reptiles are of more recent origin than the crocodiles and the turtles. Fossil studies indicate that the latter two orders have experienced no major evolutionary changes from the time that they were first known to exist in the Triassic and Permian periods, some 200 million years ago.

Birds and Mammals. Birds and mammals evolved independently and separately from two of the five different main reptilian lines. It was during the Triassic Period that one of the five main reptilian stocks, the so-called *thecodonts*, evolved in a radiating fashion into several separate smaller groups. These in the course of time independently led to the ancestral birds, to the ancestors of the modern crocodiles, lizards, and snakes, to the turtle, to the dinosaurs, and so forth. The evolutionary transition during the Jurassic Period of one of these radiating thecodont lines to birds is strongly supported by the fossil of the remarkable primitive bird, the *Archaeopteryx* (Figure 32-5), with its numerous reptilian characteristics.

The fossil record shows that the first mammal-like reptiles, animals possessing a mixture of mammalian and reptilian characteristics as represented by the so-called *therapsids*, had already arisen by the time of the late Permian or early Triassic periods some 125 million years ago. During the succeeding Jurassic Period at least four different orders of mammals, all now extinct, were in existence. It was in the early Tertiary Period, some 70 million years ago, that the mammals evolved into the numerous diversified lines with different body structures and modes of existence representing

Figure 32-10. A giant amphibious dinosaur (*Brontosaurus*) from the upper Jurassic Period. These giant dinosaurs (weighing as much as 25 tons) probably spent most of their existence in lagoons where the buoyancy of the water offset the burden of their great weight. Some primitive crocodiles are shown in the foreground. (*From a mural by Charles R. Knight, courtesy of Field Museum of Natural History, Chicago.*)

every mammalian order alive today including several that are extinct. Although the number of species has shown a regular decline, the time span from the beginning of the Tertiary Period to the present, representing the Cenozoic Era, is known as the "Age of Mammals."

The very definite decrease in abundance of nearly all phyla during the Permian and Triassic periods fits in well with the geologic evidence for great upheavals of the earth's crust at that time, namely the Appalachian revolution, accompanied by radical changes in climate. The Appalachian revolution marked the end of the Paleozoic Era and the beginning of the Mesozoic Era.

THE FOSSIL RECORD AND THE EVOLUTION OF THE HORSE.

In certain instances studies of closely related fossils, which have been fortuitously preserved in a more or less continuous succession of rock strata, have permitted us to trace in some detail the evolutionary progression of a species (and related species) as it occured over a period of several millions of years. An outstanding example is the sequence of fossil horses found in the Cenozoic rock strata of western North America showing progressive modifications from a three-toed to a one-toed condition. Extensive studies of these remains have led to a detailed reconstruction of the evolution of the horse family (and certain other large herbivorous mammals, often referred to as the Ungulates) as described below.

The gradual transformation of the horse family from its earliest known representative, the small, cat-sized *Eohippus*, existing some 60 million years ago (in the Eocene Epoch of the Cenozoic Era), to the modern horse of today is often cited as a classic illustration of the fact of evolution and the mechanisms by which it has taken place. *Eohippus* fossils indicate that this mammal, among its other characteristics, possessed a short neck, a tooth structure adapted for chewing soft, succulent leaves of the forest (i.e., browsing) instead of the tougher grasses (i.e., grazing), front legs with four functional toes, and hind legs with three toes each ending in a separate hoof. In the course of the next 60 million years there ensued many evolutionary changes among the descendants of *Eohippus* which culminated in the modern horse, the genus *Equus*, in addition to several other types. The principal evolutionary changes displayed by the modern horse in contrast to *Eohippus* are a considerable increase in overall size, a longer neck, feet with a single modified toe or hoof, and teeth with higher crowns, deep roots, and other features admirably suited for feeding on the tough and hard grasses.

More recent studies of the evolution of the horse family, especially of the well-documented intermediate stages, have made it increasingly clear that the evolution of *Eohippus* to the modern horse *Equus* did not proceed in a straight, unbranched line of progressive changes involving a gradual and constant increase in size, decreased toes, and more advanced teeth. Instead descendants of *Eohippus* have branched out, or *radiated*, into numerous evolutionary lines of many genera, most of which are now extinct. The variety of indicated evolutionary changes in characteristics did not occur at a steady rate but somewhat sporadically, sometimes quite rapidly and at other times hardly at all. The genus *Equus* which includes several species of the modern horse, donkeys, and zebras therefore represents one of the few remaining lines of descent of the many branches that arose from *Eohippus* and its intermediary types.

Like that of the horse family the detailed evolutionary histories of several other species of organisms (e.g., the elephant family and certain cephalopod molluscs) have been equally well reconstructed. In general they illustrate quite clearly the basic rule that evolution has not proceeded at a steady rate in any single direction. Instead it has followed a complicated branching course leading to many diverse organisms. Man happens to be the end of one of these branches, whereas other existing living systems, plants, animals, and bacteria, are the ends of other branches. Together they have strongly suggested that evolution is in general attained by the mechanism of mutations and various gene combinations.

"LIVING FOSSILS." Further evidence of evolution is seen in the existence of a few living but almost extinct species often called "living fossils," bearing strong resemblances to certain ancient transitional animals. For example, the existing lungfishes (Figure 10-8) are regarded as being closely related to a connecting link between aquatic and terrestrial vertebrates. The discovery since 1939 of several living representatives of the lobe-finned fishes, the coelacanths (Figure 20-10), which had only been known from their fossil remains and thought to have been extinct, is another instance. The extant duckbill, or platypus (Figure 20-13), an egg-laying mammal, can also be described as a "living fossil," for in terms of its structural and reproductive characteristics it can be considered to be not too distantly related to the egg-laying reptilian stock that gave rise to the mammals.

THE FOSSIL RECORD OF PLANT LIFE. The fossil record of plants, like that of animals, also clearly demonstrates that evolution is a fact; that it has in general proceeded from simpler to progressively more complex groups; and that many plant species have become extinct as indicated by the relatively few fossil remains. The history of the major groups of plants is summarized in Figure 32-11.

Ancient Algae. As in the case of animals the earliest reliable plant fossils date back to the Cambrian Period of the Paleozoic Era. They indicate that the marine algae were the predominant form of plant life, including the blue-green algae, the green algae, and even certain brown algae resembling those of our present day. The most common marine algae fossils in the Cambrian and Ordovician periods are the calcareous or lime-secreting types which were probably more resistant to destruction and decay than the other algae.

First Land Plants. Fossils of the first known land plants, the now extinct *psilophytales* (Chapter 16), appear in the Silurian Period, approximately 100 million years before the appearance of the first land animals (although the algae were still the dominant form of plant life), and suggest that they may have initially arisen in the preceding Ordovician Period. Numerous fossils of the psilophytales have been found in the Silurian rocks of Australia, Britain, New England, and Germany.

Although there is not complete agreement concerning the evolutionary significance of the psilophytales the more favored view at

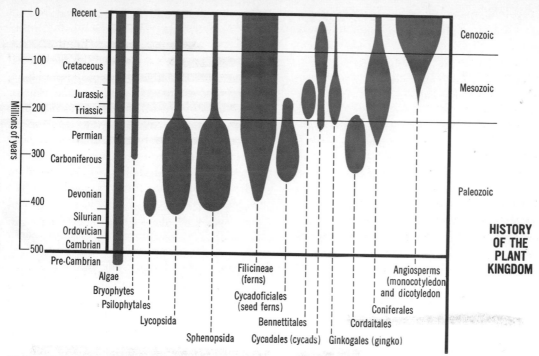

Figure 32-11. Schematic representation of the history of the major plant groups. The widths of the pathways are proportional to the relative abundance of species of the various groups. (*Adapted from C. A. Arnold, An Introduction to Paleobotany, McGraw-Hill, 1947*).

present is that they and the bryophytes evolved independently of one another from certain ancient green algae. This is apparent from the consistent findings of bryophyte fossils in rock layers formed later than those containing the psilophytales. The psilophytales as vascular plants are believed to be the ancestors of the more recent groups of tracheophytes (Chapter 16). In the ensuing Devonian Period the psilophytales increased in abundance and distribution. Other types of plants also began to appear including primitive lycopods, horsetails, and so-called "seed-ferns" resembling ferns in their general structure but bearing ovules that developed into seeds like those of living cycad types of living gymnosperms (Chapter 16).

Swamp Forests and Coal Beds. The Mississippian and Pennsylvanian periods which followed witnessed the development of dense, widespread, lowland or swamp forests made up of large tree-like lycopods, horsetails, seed-ferns, and other primitive gymnosperms. These are the ancient swamp forests (Figure 32-12) whose remains were gradually transformed into the major coal beds of the world. For this reason the Mississippian and Pennsylvanian periods are often collectively called the *Carboniferous Period* or the *Coal Age*. Many of these plants, in falling to the watery and swampy ground, were soon covered with mud and silt. The overlying sediments which accumulated in the millions of years that followed created great and crushing pressures, resulting eventually in the gradual conversion of the plant remains to coal deposits.

The Gymnosperm Forests. With the closing of the Permian Period, which marked the end of the Paleozoic Era, many ancient and dominant plants of the Carboniferous Period declined into extinction and were replaced by extensive forests of gymnosperms more closely resembling those of our present day. Thus in the course of a time span of some 350 million years representing the entire Paleozoic Era the early dominant aquatic plant life of our planet, consisting of fungi and well-developed algae, was progressively succeeded by the first land plants (the psilophytales) and then the lycopods, horsetails, ferns, and seed-ferns, culminating finally in extensive forests of gymnosperms. The most important series of evolutionary changes were undoubtedly those that made possible the successful existence of plants in a terrestrial environment. They occurred during the early Paleozoic Era.

In the Mesozoic Era which followed, the earlier periods consisting of the Triassic and Jurassic were characterized by a wider distribution and diversification of the gymnosperms and the final decline into extinction of the giant lycopods, giant horsetails, and seed-ferns. The conifers were soon to become the dominant vegetation of the earth.

The Rise of the Flowering Plants. Another momentous evolutionary advance made itself evident in the early Mesozoic, for it is in the Jurassic Period that we note the first fossil remains of angiosperms or flowering plants. They are believed to have evolved from an ancient group of cycad-like seed-ferns independently of the origin of the higher gymnosperms. The remarkably rapid rise, development, and distribution of the angiosperms during the ensuing Cretaceous Period resulted in their ascendancy as the dominant terrestrial vegetation (mostly woody plants) of the earth in the closing years of the Mesozoic Era. During this time the once prevalent gymnosperms began to dwindle.

The Cenozoic Era which extends to the present has witnessed an even greater diversification and distribution of the flowering plants ranging over virtually all parts of the earth. The prevalent woody types of angiosperms (now found in the tropics, subtropics, and generally mild climates), making up a large part of the forests of the late Mesozoic and early Cenozoic, began to give way to herbaceous plants. This has been chiefly attributed to a change from the warm, mild, relatively moist climate then prevailing over most of the planet to cooler and drier conditions particularly at the poles and the higher latitude zones. The Great Ice Age of one and a half million years ago was responsible for the extinction of many warm-adapted woody plants in the higher latitudes. At the same time it provided the cooler and drier environmental conditions which herbaceous plants could better withstand than woody ones. Herbaceous plants as annuals often grow sufficiently rapidly from seed within a short growing season to produce another generation of seeds before they are killed off by unfavorable weather; and thus the species survives. Alternatively, perennial herbaceous plants, whose aerial parts may be destroyed by winter weather, have underground stems and roots which are sufficiently insulated and protected by the surrounding soil to survive and sprout into a new plant during the growing season of the following year.

Evidence from Classification or Taxonomy

Numerous features of living organisms, and of fossils, have permitted us to construct highly reasonable schemes of natural classification for plants and animals among both the living forms of the present and extinct forms of the past (Chapters 14 to 20). They indicate the natural relationships and the probable paths of the evolution of living things.

Evidence from Comparative Structure and Function

The structure and function of a living form at all levels—subcellular, cellular, and the whole organism—are ultimately determined by its molecular organization and the physical and chemical reactions which it carries out. The evidence for evolution from comparative structure and function can be conveniently subdivided into *comparative biochemistry* and *physiology, comparative microscopic anatomy, comparative gross anatomy,* and *comparative growth and development.*

COMPARATIVE BIOCHEMISTRY AND PHYSIOLOGY. There is a fundamental resemblance in chemical composition and structure, metab-

Figure 32-12. Restoration of a swamp forest of the Carboniferous Period. (*Courtesy of the Chicago Nat. Hist. Museum.*)

olism, and physiological action in all living forms extending from microorganisms to man. At the molecular level all living systems are composed of similar substances— nucleic acids, proteins, lipids, carbohydrates, mineral salts, water, and so on. Without exception organisms are governed by the same biochemical principles and are known to possess, with some variations, essentially similar or related types of enzymatic reactions and metabolic pathways (Chapter 8). For example, ATP is the universal and key intermediate in the energy metabolism of all organisms examined in this respect. Its formation, whether in bacteria, plants, or animals, serves as the means for trapping a portion of the useful energy liberated in metabolic reactions. Its subsequent utilization represents the immediate energy source for all cell activities including biosynthesis, movement, osmotic work, and so on (and therefore growth and reproduction). Additional examples of the common basis and, therefore, the broad evolutionary relationships shared by all organisms include: (1) the general occurrence and metabolism in all living systems of the same vitamins, coenzymes, fatty acids, 20 or so amino acids, and so on; (2) the presence of almost identical respiratory pathways; and (3) the same central role in heredity

and metabolism of the nucleic acids through their established functions of transmitting information from generation to generation, and determining and directing molecular activities and therefore cell activities at all higher levels of organization, by controlling protein synthesis (Chapter 11).

Certain biochemical phenomena have proved to be highly useful tools in determining the degree of interrelationship between organisms. For example, the degree of specificity of certain proteins which each organism produces can be compared with that of other animals by the antigen-antibody reaction (Chapter 25). Repeated injections of cow serum proteins into a laboratory animal such as a rabbit will induce the formation of antibodies in the rabbit's blood. The mixing of such rabbit antibodies with cow serum results in a visible precipitation as a result of an antigen-antibody reaction. The same rabbit antibodies when mixed with the serum of other animal species such as the sheep, goat, or even man show varying degrees of precipitation depending on the closeness of common ancestry between the species. Extensive experimentation along these lines has firmly established that the degree of similarity between the proteins of different organisms—for plants as well as animals—determined by the foregoing immunological technique is the same as that demonstrated by other types of evidence. Thus the immunological technique has proved to be a useful semiquantitative method for resolving relative evolutionary relationships among organisms. For example, it has shown that man is more closely related to the primates than to any other group of mammals, that the chordates have a stronger similarity to the echinoderms than to most other invertebrates, and that certain plant groups are more closely related to one another than heretofore believed.

Similarities in physiological processes at higher levels of organization such as those of the digestive, nervous, reproductive, excretory, respiratory, and endocrine systems of animals are further evidences of the evolutionary resemblances and therefore the closeness of ancestry among organisms. In green plants, the ability to carry on photosynthesis, for example, suggests a common descent of all plants bearing chlorophyll.

COMPARATIVE MICROSCOPIC ANATOMY. The structure of the cell as the unit of life with its basic subcellular components is another source of evidence for evolution. The organization of the nuclear material, the absence, presence, similarities, and differences in mitochondria, ribosomes, and endoplasmic reticulum, chloroplasts, Golgi apparatus, cell wall, and so forth indicate a sharing of ancestry and therefore of common evolutionary relationships.

COMPARATIVE GROSS ANATOMY. Homology (Chapter 14) as one of the criteria for the natural classification of living things has been an important source of evidence for the facts of evolution. A classic example is the general similarity in structure of the arm of man, the fin of a fish, the wing of a bat or a bird, and the forelimb of a frog (see Figure 14-3). In higher plants, for example, such features as the basic similarity of flower structure and vascular tissue anatomy, despite numerous and varying degrees of modification, are important indications of evolutionary proximity.

Vestigial structures, or those body parts that are reduced or degenerate and no longer have an apparent function, represent important evidences for the facts of evolution. In humans, for example, the coccyx or fused tail vertebrae as one of many vestigial structures is homologous to the tail of other mammals and reptiles. It is reasonably explained on the basis of inheritance in the distant past from an ancestor which possessed a functional tail. In man the nonfunctional final set of molars (wisdom teeth) and the muscles for moving the pinna of the outer ears in various directions are other well-known examples of vestigial structures which in many other mammals serve a useful role.

COMPARATIVE GROWTH AND DEVELOPMENT. Embryology has been useful in two important ways as a means of determining evolutionary relationships. First, it has provided a firm basis in establishing the homology of certain structures among different kinds of organisms by demonstrating identity of embryonic origin. It has been particularly useful in instances in which no fossil records exist, especially of soft tissues such as the kidneys and the circulatory system. Second, the general resemblance of embryos during the early stages of development within many groups of organisms is considered to be another important source of evidence for the occurrence of evolution. For example, in plants the occurrence of the algallike protonema stage of mosses and the filamentous prothallus of ferns is regarded as evidence that the remote ancestors of these plant groups were filamentous green algae. This aspect in animals has already been discussed in Chapter 31 on embryonic development.

Evidence from Geographical Distribution

Studies of the distribution of the plants and animals of today and of the past over the surface of the earth furnish additional supporting evidence for the occurrence of evolution. Many species of plants and animals are found in different parts of the world, whereas others such as marsupial animals (Chapter 20) are restricted to particular areas even though climatic conditions of other regions are excellently suited for their existence. In some instances there is an extremely discontinuous distribution of a particular species or related species such as camels in Asia and Africa and the related llama in South America; lungfish in the widely separated areas of Australia, Africa, and South America; magnolias in eastern United States, China, and Japan; and alligators in southeastern United States and the Yangtze River of China.

These phenomena are usually best explained by relating the present distribution of plants and animals to the fossil record of the past. For example, the restriction of a particular species to certain areas is best understood on the basis of a *geographical isolation* (Chapter 33), the result of certain physical barriers such as large bodies of water or high mountains, which have prevented their spread to other regions having a suitable environment. Organisms that dwell in isolated regions tend to evolve along divergent lines, often with distinctive characteristics. The extreme effects of a long time isolation are found in Australia where numerous lines of marsupials (instead of the placental mammals) have evolved, such as the kangaroos living on the plain, the tree-dwelling koala bear, and the marsupial wolf. The characteristic and limited plant life of oceanic islands such as the Hawaiian Islands and Fiji Islands are other examples of prolonged periods of geographic isolation. The somewhat different but related species of finches observed by Darwin on the Galapagos Islands are examples of the effects of a relatively short time geographic isolation.

In the instances of discontinuous distribution, such as those just cited, the fossil record frequently indicates that these organisms or their closely related ancestors were at one time continuously distributed over a vast area territory; but that as a result of subsequent geological changes and accompanying climatic changes many of the organisms in certain of the areas could no longer survive and thus became extinct. Magnolias and associated plants, for example, were at one time widely and continuously spread out over an enormous warm-climate territory. The occurrence of glaciers in the Pleistocene Epoch radically changed the environmental conditions and accounts in large part for the present-day discontinuous distribution of these plants.

Finally, mention should be made of those frequent situations in which neighboring areas are populated by similar but somewhat differing varieties or species (e.g., the hares studies by Darwin in South America), at times constituting a series or chain of related forms extending across a continent. This is explained by evolutionary changes in a living form as it distributes itself into adjacent areas of differing environmental conditions in the course of long periods of time.

Evidence from Genetics

Actual *experimental* evidence for the occurrence of evolution has been obtained from several sources. The oldest of these is undoubtedly the selection and breeding practices used by man in the past few thousand years for obtaining new and more desirable varieties of domestic animals and cultivated plants. Long before he knew any of the facts of genetics man took advantage of the occurrence of heritable variations to develop numerous varieties, lines, or races of cultivated plants and domestic animals.

Microorganisms have been especially useful in experimentally demonstrating the occurrence of evolution. Experiments with bacteria based on the alteration or mutation of one or a few genes followed by a simple selection process can readily result in the development of a new population or bacterial strain. For example, infection of a pure culture of bacteria containing hundreds of millions of cells with bacteriophages may result in the destruction of the entire bacterial population with the possible exception of just a few mutated cells which happen to be resistant. The few resistant cells may survive and under suitable conditions reproduce and give rise to a new bacteriophage-resistant strain of bacteria. A somewhat similar experiment can be performed using an antibiotic (e.g., penicillin) as the selecting agent instead of bacteriophage. The surviving penicillin-resistant mutants will reproduce and give rise to an antibiotic-resistant population of bacteria. Such evolutionary changes based on the mutation of a single gene, or a small number of genes, are called *microevolutionary*.

Another type of experimental evidence is seen in the apparently new species of cultivated plants caused by polyploidy (Chapter 13).

SUPPLEMENTARY REFERENCES

Andrews, H. N., *Ancient Plants and the World They Lived In,* Comstock, Ithaca, N.Y., 1947.
Arnold, C. A., *An Introduction to Paleobotany,* McGraw-Hill, New York, 1947.
Carter, G. S., *Animal Evolution,* Sedgwick & Jackson, London, 1951.
Colbert, E. H., *Evolution of the Vertebrates,* Wiley, New York, 1955.
Darwin, C., *The Origin of Species,* Modern Library, New York, 1948.
Rower, A. S., *Vertebrate Paleontology,* University of Chicago Press, Chicago, 1945.
Simpson, G. G., *The Meaning of Evolution,* Yale University Press, New Haven, Conn., 1950.
Simpson, G. G., *Life of the Past,* Yale University Press, New Haven, Conn., 1953.
Smith, H. W., *From Fish to Philosopher,* Little, Brown, Boston, 1953.

Chapter 33

Evolution:

Modern Theory and Mechanisms;

Evolution of Man

MODERN THEORY OF EVOLUTION AND NATURAL SELECTION

Modifications and Essential Features of the Modern Theory

GENETICS AND ENVIRONMENT. The modern theory of evolution and natural selection places major emphasis on the mechanisms and means by which evolution takes place. It is a modified version of the theory originally proposed by Darwin and Wallace, and has necessarily evolved to its present form in the light of the remarkable advances made in biology, especially in the area of genetics and biochemistry, since the publication of the *Origin of Species* in 1859. Any understanding of modern evolution is necessarily based on an understanding of genetics. The original theory was all the more unusual, for at the time that it was formulated by Darwin and Wallace virtually nothing was known about the laws of heredity. The latter only first came to light in 1900 with the rediscovery of Mendel's principles. All that could really be said of inheritance in the nineteenth century was that progeny tended to resemble both parents. Darwin failed to distinguish between inherited and noninherited variations. He in fact erroneously believed in the Lamarckian proposal that variations in tissues and organs arose from use and disuse and were inherited. This is the only major point of the Darwinian theory that has had to be abandoned.

In the light of present-day knowledge it is now clear that recombinations of genes (by sexual reproduction) and mutations are the source of variations for natural selection and resultant evolution. Sexual reproduction as a means for creating a variety of gene combinations may in this manner also be responsible for the appearance of an almost infinite diversity of genotypes (and therefore phenotypes). With the exception of identical siblings (e.g., identical twins, triplets, and so forth) no two individuals in a sexually reproducing population are of the same genotype. In effect, sexuality provides a vast quantity of permutations in the determination of individual characteristics, thus representing a means for effecting gradual and continuous changes or variations in characteristics.

The modern theory recognizes the role of environment as a factor which *directs* but *does not cause* evolutionary change. Environment is not the causative factor in producing inherited variations but the directive factor in determining which variations will survive and which will become extinct. This is accomplished by *natural selection*, the natural elimination of organisms with variations less suited to the environment and the perpetuation of those with the more favorable ones. Darwin was fully aware of the selective function of the environment, since it was the very foundation for his theory of natural selection. However, he incorrectly attributed a causative effect to environment (that it was also responsible for the variations themselves) in the process of evolutionary change, as indicated previously by his acceptance of the Lamarckian concept of use and disuse as the cause of inherited variations. Stated in other words, natural selection is the isolation procedure for sorting out the genotypes that better fit the organism for existence in a given environment. Adaptations occur in the process of evolution by means of natural selection of those genotypes which are relatively better suited to live and reproduce in a given range of environments, making possible their continued successful existence. In other words, living things become adapted to their environments as a result of a long sequence of evolutionary transformations through the natural selection of inherited variations and not through conscious foresight or desire.

The modern theory of evolution offers a unified and satisfactory explanation of many of the phenomena of evolutionary change. The theory is by no means perfected, and like any other concept it is subject to change and revision in accordance with new data and new interpretations.

"STRUGGLE FOR EXISTENCE." Unfortunately the use of such terms as "struggle for existence," "competition," and "survival of the fittest" in describing natural selection by Darwin and the writers of his day (as well as by other scientists) has imparted a melodramatic and distorted view of the evolutionary process. Such terms are misused if they conjure up a picture of fierce and mortal physical combat between organisms to account for the natural selection process. "Struggle for existence" and "survival of the fittest" include the abilities to obtain adequate nutrition and to withstand and cope with various physical and chemical factors in the environment such as heat or cold, desiccation, and poisonous substances, as well as with disease, predators, and parasites. Competition for food and space among plants and animals often proves to be

passive, involving no aggressive physical struggle. Xerophytes such as desert plants have deeper roots, water storage tissues, and a heavily cutinized epidermis as adaptions which better fit them to cope with an arid environment without necessarily involving them in a competition with other organisms. In several instances cooperation or mutualism instead of competition between different species has evolved (e.g., lichens) as an adaptation to the environment.

THE MECHANISMS OF EVOLUTION. The key to our present-day understanding of the mechanisms of evolution resides in the science of genetics, for genes are the "raw material of evolution." The modern theory of evolution is based on two principal phenomena: (1) *diversification* or the *formation of inherited variations* by mutation and gene recombination, and (2) *natural selection.*

Genes as the Basis for Diversification. Genes in modified forms (i.e., *mutations*) and in different combinations are responsible for the occurrence of the inherited variations and diversities that are "filtered, sifted, and tested" in the course of natural selection to constitute evolutionary change. Most mutations are harmful in any one environment. However, a mutation or genotype that is harmful in a particular environment could prove to be highly advantageous when the surroundings are changed. Under the new environmental circumstances a formerly unfavorable mutation may now endow the organism with a better chance to survive. Although individual genes may be associated with particular characteristics, the control of these characteristics is also influenced by other genes which together constitute an organized gene complex. The almost infinite possibilities for different gene combinations to occur at fertilization may often bring about gradual or small changes under the main control of individual genes.

Sexual forms have a tremendous potential reservoir of genetic variability available for recombination from the many genes present in the species (i.e., the gene pool, p. 760). It has in fact been estimated that if mutations were to cease the vast number of possible gene recombinations alone in most sexually reproducing populations including man would account for a virtually unaltered and continuing rate of evolution for many generations to come.

In an asexually reproducing population mutation is the only source of inherited variation since gene recombination, the result of sexual reproduction, is ruled out. By its very nature asexual reproduction does not permit the combination within the same individual of favorable genes or mutations from the common gene pool of the species. For this reason asexual forms are less adaptable than sexual forms. The evolution of sexual from asexual means of reproduction obviously gave the sexual organisms decided advantages, for it endowed them with the increased possibilities for evolutionary adaptation.

The Basic Role of Natural Selection. Although there are differences of opinion among evolutionists with respect to the mechanisms involved in particular aspects of evolution—but not with the fact of evolution—it is becoming increasingly apparent that these differences can be explained in terms of natural selection in different environments. For example, an old disputed view has contended that there are unexplained directed and predetermined trends in evolution leading in some instances to overspecialization, the evolution of certain variations to such an extreme that they actually impede or hinder the survival of a species, as in the development of the gigantic and unwieldy antlers in the males of the Irish elk (Figure 33-1). Another area of disagreement has been the presence in many plants and animals of so-called nonadaptive traits, characteristics that have little or no significant survival value. However, the existence of overspecialized traits and nonadaptive traits very likely had distinct survival value in a different environment at one time in the past. They must have lost their worth as a result of subsequent changes in the environment.

There is little doubt that natural selection

Figure 33-1. Irish elk (giant deer). (*Painting by Charles R. Knight, courtesy of Amer. Mus. of Natural History.*)

has brought about a vast increase in the diversity of living things and the types of environments in which they can exist and propagate. This is borne out by the fossil record which alone demonstrates the gradual transformation in the course of geologic time from the limited primordial life originally and totally confined to a watery existence to an almost infinite spectrum of different land-inhabiting forms.

MOLECULAR BASIS OF EVOLUTION. The molecular basis of organic evolution resides primarily in DNA, for it is the key substance of the gene and therefore the substance of heredity. The role of nucleic acids as the master molecules of living systems which direct and control all life activities by directing and controlling protein synthesis has already been discussed earlier (Chapter 11). In essence proteins are an expression of the information carried by the genes since the genes are the determinants of protein structure. The molecular basis of evolution, which rests primarily on the evolution of nucleic acids, therefore resides by extension in the evolution of the various proteins of the cell.

Molecular evolution, specifically of proteins, is governed by the same principles that apply to evolution of the whole organism. The production of a new or modified enzyme (i.e., a protein), for example, with new or different catalytic properties as a result of a mutation could confer on the organism under suitable environmental conditions an advantage in its existence. As an illustration one could visualize that a new enzyme participating in melanin formation might result in a marked increase in skin pigmentation. Such a trait could possibly tip the balance between survival and extinction by protecting against ultraviolet light irradiation damage in regions of intense and prolonged sunlight such as at the equator. Conversely the genetic modification of a catalytic protein could impose an unfavorable trait on the organism, which is more often the case. In humans the genetic disease *galactosemia* (Chapter 11) is a clear example of an inherited variation in one of the thousands of kinds of protein molecules in the cell, conferring a distinct disadvantage on the existence of the organism. Another outstanding example is seen in the nutritional requirement for vitamin C (ascorbic acid) by the guinea pig and primates including man, the effect of a modified gene which has resulted in the loss of one of the enzymes in the metabolic pathway responsible for the formation of the vitamin from certain carbohydrates (Chapter 9).

At the molecular level therefore evolution can be viewed as consisting of the same two principal steps of *diversification* and *natural selection* applied to protein molecules. A comparison of organic or biological evolution at the molecular and whole organism level is shown in Figure 33-2.

Formation of New Races (Subspecies) and Species

POPULATIONS AND GENE POOLS. A population of organisms rather than the individual is the unit of study in evolution. All the genes and their alleles (including their mutations) that are collectively present within a population or species of organisms are collectively called a *gene pool.* The environment is the primary directing force, selecting from the gene pools of a population those particular mutations and gene combinations already present which best adapt organisms to their given existence.

ISOLATION. What are the steps by which mutations and new combinations of genes within a given population give rise to new species? A variety of factors are involved. One of the most significant is *isolation*. We know that inherited variations (through the formation of different gene combinations by sexual reproduction and mutation) occur at random and in all directions. Thus in the course of successive generations and in accordance with the laws of chance organisms possessing numerous variations would be expected to appear in a given population. By natural selection those organisms with inherited variations that best adapt them to survival and

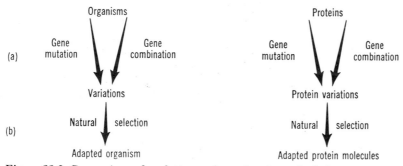

Figure 33-2. Comparison of evolution at the molecular and whole organism level.

efficient reproduction in the existing environment would tend to be perpetuated, whereas the others would tend to be eliminated. However, in order for these new variations to become established and thus constitute an evolutionary change a certain degree of *isolation* of the population is necessary, since free interbreeding tends to promote a relative homogeneity or uniformity among the individuals of a population.

Isolation in nature may be attained in several ways. If a population is split into smaller populations by natural physical barriers (e.g., by migration of several individuals and their subsequent isolation by mountains, glaciers, deserts, or bodies of water), *geographic isolation* is the result. Each of the geographically isolated populations originally possessing the same pool of genes continues to experience, although independently of one another, random mutations and gene combinations in all directions in the course of successive generations. It can be expected on the basis of chance that the gene pools and, therefore, the inherited variations of the isolated populations will gradually become different from one another. Thus the chances are that the isolated populations, even though they were originally identical at one time, will in the course of time evolve in different directions. Moreover, the divergences in evolution will be appreciably influenced if the environmental conditions are different for each of the isolated populations, since different environments as the primary directing forces in the evolutionary process will tend to select for different variations. The finches and a few other species of land animals on the Galapagos Islands (created by volcanoes in the Pacific Ocean more than a million years ago), as compared to the corresponding species on the South American mainland, almost ideally reflect the effects of geographic isolation on the course of evolutionary development over a time interval of thousands of years.

Races or *subspecies* are populations within the same species which have become different in one or a few of their genes as a result of geographic isolation. In general the differences between races are mostly quantitative rather than qualitative. They usually differ in gene frequencies rather than in the presence or absence of genes. If the geographical barriers between two or more races of a species are removed, interbreeding will usually occur, they will soon share a common gene pool, and in time thus become a single race or population. If the barriers remain, the isolated populations may tend with the passage of time to become gradually and increasingly different until a point is reached where the members of one population may now be unable to breed with those of the others, should they come in contact with one another. This inability to produce offspring is called *reproductive isolation* and is one of the important criteria for distinguishing separate species (Chapter 14). Should these populations now be mixed, they would in reality still be isolated or separate and distinct groups, not geographically but in the reproductive sense, since gene exchange between them could not take place. The great majority of present-day organisms reproduce by sexual means. Once a species is established it is principally maintained by frequent interbreeding which produces fertile offspring. Such a process is responsible for the sharing of a common genetic pool that leads to the unity and continuity typical of a species. Different species inhabiting the same territory thus retain their identity because of reproductive isolation, one of the key factors which affects the process of new species formation from existing races.

Reproductive isolation, or the inability to interbreed, may be due to one or more causes. These include structural, physiological, and biochemical factors which are responsible for (1) preventing copulation, fertilization, or both; (2) differences in mating behavior; (3) production of nonviable offspring; and (4) production of sterile progeny. One might expect that by the continued and independent evolution of these isolated populations further differences would accumulate that could lead successively to the establishment of new genera, families, orders, and so on. Geographic isolation in many instances precedes the development of reproductive isolation, and is one of the most important types of isolation responsible for the origination of species.

MICROEVOLUTION AND MACROEVOLUTION. Most biologists agree that the early phases of evolution lead first to differences that account for the appearance of several races or strains within a given species. These in turn may lead progressively by further alterations in genotype to the formation of new species, genera, families, and so forth. The term *microevolution* is used to designate the evolutionary changes that account for the formation of races or subspecies, often as a result of alterations in a single gene or a small number of genes. The examples cited in the previous chapter of the conversion of a bacteriophage-susceptible bacterial population or an antibiotic-sensitive bacterial population to a strain or race now resistant to these agents as a result of a gene mutation and consequent selection are illustrative of microevolution.

Macroevolution involves evolutionary changes in many of the genes or most of the genotype, and it is equated with the evolution of new species and progressively larger groups of species, including genera, families, orders, and so on. The evolution of the modern horse *Equus* from its ancestor *Eohippus* is an example of macroevolution.

ADAPTIVE RADIATION OR DIVERGENT EVOLUTION. Several different species and larger groups of species with diverse body structure and habit may evolve in the course of time from a common ancestor, a phenomenon known as *adaptive radiation* or *divergent evolution*. For example, if some organisms of a given population should experience different changes in environment because of migration or geologic phenomena, natural selection operating in the new and different environments would favor mutations and gene combinations different from those that were advantageous in the original environment. With the passage of time

one would therefore expect differences to appear among the populations in the diverse environments which could lead to the evolution of several new species and larger groups of species.

Many examples of adaptive radiation are known. One of these is seen in the many orders of mammals now living, most of which evolved relatively rapidly in the course of some 35 million years (during the Paleocene and Eocene epochs of the Tertiary Period, p. 748) from just a few primitive ancestors. As another example one can point to the marsupials, the most characteristic mammals of Australia. In addition to the kangaroo they consist of many kinds of animals such as the rodent-like, squirrel-like, wolf-like, and mole-like marsupials, which incidentally resemble corresponding kinds of placental mammals living outside Australia (Figure 33-3). There is little question that these diverse marsupial types have arisen from a common primitive ancestor.

CONVERGENT EVOLUTION AND PARALLEL EVOLUTION. The phenomenon in nature whereby unrelated groups of organisms (of less similar ancestry) living in similar kinds of environments, or having similar ways of life, frequently tend to evolve similar characteristics is called *convergent evolution* (see Chapter 14). In other words, two or more originally diverse groups have tended to become more alike in the course of evolution.

Examples of convergent evolution are seen in the unusual similarity between the molluscan and vertebrate eye (Chapter 22), the development of wings in at least four groups of animals — the insects, the flying reptiles or so-called *pterosaurs*, the birds, and bats (Figure 33-4) — and the adaptive formation to aquatic life of flipper-like appendages (Figure 33-4) as seen in the primitive reptile *Ichthyosaurus* (Figure 32-9), the present-day sea turtle (Figure 20-11), the penguin, a bird, and the walrus, a mammal.

The phenomenon of *parallel evolution* involves the independent evolution of one or more similar characteristics by *related* groups of organisms (of more similar ancestry). The main difference between convergent evolution and parallel evolution is that in the latter, one or more similar features evolve in groups of organisms that have arisen from a *common* or at least relatively recent ancestor, whereas in convergent evolution it occurs in organisms that are more distantly related. At times these two types of evolution are hardly distinguishable from one another. Both types are due in large part to the selective influence of a similar environment.

THE HARDY-WEINBERG LAW. Most large sexually reproducing populations exhibit a tendency toward genetic stability in the sense that inherited characteristics (and, therefore, genes) are maintained in more or less the same proportions from generation to generation. During the early history of genetics it had seemed puzzling to some geneticists that dominant characteristics did not continue to increase in the population and eventually replace the recessive ones, thus making for an increasingly "purer" population with time. The explanation was independently arrived at in 1908 by Weinberg and Hardy (Chapter 11). They proved by mathematical formulations that the gene frequencies or ratios of genes (e.g., the proportions of dominants to recessives) remained constant in succeeding generations, provided that certain conditions were met, a phenomenon now called the *Hardy-Weinberg Law.*

At first glance it would appear that the Hardy-Weinberg Law contradicts modern evolutionary theory, for it implies that large sexually reproducing populations are in genetic equilibrium, that is, their rates of evolution are at a standstill. But we know that evolution in most large sexually reproducing populations has occurred and is still occurring. What are the causes for the apparent contradiction? The answer is that the Hardy-Weinberg Law declaring that gene frequencies remain constant from one generation to the other is valid only under certain circumstances. Genetic equilibrium (or the constancy of gene frequencies)

Figure 33-3. An adult female kangaroo (*Marcropus major*) and its offspring. The latter is about 9 months old and just about ready to leave the pouch permanently. (*Courtesy of Australian News and Information Bureau.*)

is maintained provided all three of the following conditions are satisfied: (1) mating is random, (2) mutations do not occur, and (3) the population is large.

If the foregoing conditions are not met, genetic equilibrium will be disturbed and evolution will occur. In other words evolution is the result of a change in gene frequencies. This is in keeping with all that we have already said about evolution, and is simply another way of looking at the same mechanisms and processes, as we shall soon see.

Random Mating. Mating in most populations is random in the sense that mates do not necessarily select each other for special characteristics; but it is not truly random in the statistical sense, for all genotypes do not contribute equally to the gene pool of the next generation. Some genotypes may be more fertile, others may be sterile, and other may fail to maintain the viability of individuals to the reproductive age, thus resulting in a statistically nonrandom mating. This inevitably results in a natural

A

B

selection for at least those genotypes which are viable and better suited for reproduction. In this manner it leads to a change of gene frequencies in successive generations and therefore in the occurrence of evolution.

Occurrence of Mutations. The occurrence of mutations and their subsequent natural selection in favoring or handicapping, as the case may be, the existence and reproduction of the organism can lead to a change in the frequencies or ratios of the genes in the population and therefore to evolutionary change.

Small Populations. Small populations tend to experience greater percentages of fluctuations in gene frequencies purely on a chance basis. This leads to definite changes in the proportions of genes in the population, a phenomenon known as *genetic drift.* The situation is comparable to performing breeding experiments with a small number of individuals. In such an instance the statistically expected ratios of genotypes (and therefore of phenotypes) will not result because of the greater "sampling error" arising from too few individuals. Just as we could not hope to detect the expected $9:3:3:1$ ratio in the F_2 generation of a dihybrid cross (Chapter 12) using only 10 progeny (but we could with 1000 progeny), so would the fluctuations in small populations tend to indicate changed gene frequencies as a result of chance fluctuations. Genetic drift has no regular trends, decreasing gene frequencies in some generations and increasing them in others, in disagreement with the Hardy-Weinberg Law. The degree of importance of the role of genetic drift in the evolutionary process of nature is uncertain.

Mathematical Formulation of the Hardy-Weinberg Law. The frequencies of a gene and its alleles in a large population can be readily calculated from the known ratios or proportions of genotypes in the population. Suppose that by sampling a given population of plants or animals we determine that the proportions of the three possible genotypes with respect to the gene A and its only allele a are as follows:

AA	aa	Aa
25% (or .25)	25% (or .25)	50% (or .5)

The frequencies for genes A and a in the given population are equivalent to the frequencies of the gametes bearing each gene. If we assume that all organisms of the population produce approximately the same quantity of gametes, then AA individuals representing 25 per cent of the total population will produce 25 per cent of all gametes formed, each containing the A gene. In like fashion aa individuals also making up 25 per cent of the total population will produce 25 per cent of the total gametes, each possessing an a gene. On the other hand the Aa individuals making up 50 per cent of the total population produce two kinds of gametes in equal numbers, half or 25 per cent bearing A genes and the other half or 25 per cent with a genes. Thus the proportions of the gametes with respect to genes A and a, and therefore of the frequencies of these genes in the population, adds up to 50 per cent (or .5) for A and 50 per cent (or .5) for a as shown below:

Population:
25% (or .25) AA   25% (or .25) aa   50% (or .50) Aa
Gametes:
25% (or .25) A   25% (or .25) a   25% (or .25) A
                                    25% (or .25) a

Overall gamete proportions   { 50% (or .5) A
and therefore gene frequencies: { 50% (or .5) a

Figure 33-4. Examples of convergent evolution are seen in: (A) The development of wings in insects (monarch butterfly in flight, *courtesy of L. M. Chace*), reptiles (restoration of an ancient flying reptile or pterosaur, Jurassic Period, *courtesy of Amer. Mus. of Natural History*), birds (sea gull, *courtesy of Rapho Guillumette*), and mammals (Wagner's short-faced bat, *Phyllostoma pusillum, courtesy of Amer. Mus. of Natural History*). (B) The adaptive formation to aquatic life of flipper-like appendages in reptiles (see Figures 20-11 and 32-9), birds (the King Penguin, *courtesy of N. Y. Zool. Society*), and mammals (walrus, *courtesy of Rapho Guillumette*).

Figure 33-5. Opossum and young (*courtesy of L. M. Chace*).

If we assume that random mating occurs, then the proportions or frequencies of genotypes in the next generation with respect to A and a will therefore be as follows:

	.5 A ♀	.5 a
.5 A ♂	.25 AA	.25 Aa
.5 a	.25 Aa	.25 aa

or .25 AA, .25 aa, .50 Aa

These are exactly the same proportions (and therefore the same gene frequencies) as in the previous generation. If the previous generation were made up of other proportions of genotypes such as .36 AA, .16 aa, and .48 Aa (and therefore a gene frequency of .6 A and .4 a), then the succeeding generations would have shown the same unchanged genotype proportions (i.e., .36 AA, .16 aa, and .48 Aa).

Hardy and Weinberg mathematically formulated the foregoing relationship in terms of the equation

$$p^2 + 2pq + q^2 = 1$$

where p represents the proportion or frequency of gene A, and q of its allele a in a large population of organisms. The equation is in reality an expression of the binominal $(p + q)^2$ where $p + q = 1$. By comparing the genotype proportions used in the foregoing examples with the Hardy-Weinberg equation it can readily be recognized that p^2 represents the frequency for one of the homozygous genotypes (e.g., AA), q^2 for that of the other (aa), and $2pq$ for that of the heterozygous one (Aa). Aside from its basic importance in elucidating our understanding of evolution, and explaining the tendency of a sexually reproducing population to continue for successive generations without significant change in its gene frequencies, the Hardy-Weinberg Law has also proven to be a highly useful tool in studies of population genetics. It has been especially helpful in human genetics, where controlled test matings do not exist, for clarifying the mode of inheritance of certain traits.

Rates of Evolution

Evolution has not proceeded at a steady rate. Instead its pace has varied considerably in the course of time—spurting forward, slowing down, pausing, and ceasing—depending on the particular groups of organisms, their relationships to changing environments, and other factors.

At the one extreme are several types of living organisms which we know by comparison with the fossil record to have remained virtually at a standstill for many millions of years. They are often aptly referred to as "living fossils." For example, the present-day horseshoe crab, *Limulus* (see Figure 19-32) appears to be almost entirely the same as its ancestors of some 200 million years ago. Other examples of "living fossils" are the opossum (Figure 33-5) (which has experienced little or no evolutionary modifications within the last 75 million years), the recently discovered living coelacanth fish (which is more or less the same as its ancestors of some 125 million years ago, Figure 20-10), and the primitive lizard-like reptile the *Sphenodon* (which is only a slightly modified version of its ancestors of 135 million years ago).

At the other extreme are the organisms that have experienced radically rapid evolutionary changes. Outstanding instances of rapid evolutionary rates are seen in the birds and mammals. The human species in particular has evolved at an extremely fast pace. On the basis of various kinds of data it has been estimated that in birds and mammals as a whole an average of at least 10,000 years has been necessary for a subspecies to evolve, about a million years for a species, and several million years for a genus. One of the best known examples of the evolution of a living group is the horse (Chapter 32), of which 8 successive genera evolved in nearly 50 million years, an average of some 6 million years per genus.

Differences in rates of evolution of various groups of organisms at various times (and the fact that certain groups become extinct whereas others evolve extensively along diverse lines) are still best explained on the basis of natural selection in response to changes in environment. Where highly specialized adaptations by a group of organisms have evolved in response to a particular and narrow type of environment, there is a greater risk of extinction. For should this environment undergo certain changes, the organisms under consideration may be placed at so decided a disadvantage in exploiting environmental opportunities as to lead to their extinction.

EVOLUTION OF MAN

The Classification of Man and Other Primates

With the advent of the Darwinian theory of evolution, man's realization that man has descended in the relatively recent past from ancestors who were nonhumans was at first poorly received in many quarters. Although it is now accepted by scientists as a whole and by a large portion of the civilized world, this evolutionary view is still not held in high favor on purely emotional grounds among particular segments of the population. Nevertheless, the facts of biology are that man, like any other organism, is the product of a long evolution that inevitably extends from simpler and less complex forms. The evidence in favor of the interpretation is overwhelming: (1) the fossil record of prehuman and early human types; (2) man's structure, physiology, and embryonic development which are fundamentally like those of other mammals; (3) the occurrence of primitive features (e.g., gill pouches, primitive kidneys and heart, tail, and so on) in the developing embryo; (4) and vestigial structures in the adult body.

Modern man, or *Homo sapiens*, is presently classified in the family *Hominidae*, of the super family *Hominoidea*, of the suborder *Anthropoidea*, of the order *Primates*, of the subclass *Theria*, of the class *Mammalia*, of the subphylum *Vertebrata*, and of the phylum *Chordata*. *Homo sapiens* is the only species within the family Hominidae. The most closely related living group of animals are the so-called *anthropoid apes* constituting the family *Pongidae* consisting of the chimpanzee, gorilla, gibbon, and orangutan (Figure 33-6). In contrast to man, who lives and walks erect on the ground, the anthropoid apes (except for the adult gorilla) are tree-dwellers. The marked resemblance between living man and the anthropoid apes is seen in the similarities of brain and skull structure, absence of a tail, nearly identical reproductive features including menstruation and embryonic development, and numerous other anatomical and physiological characteristics.

Included within the suborder Anthropoidea in addition to man and the anthropoid apes are the superfamily *Cercopithecoidea* or the so-called *Old World monkeys* (Figure 33-7) occurring in tropical Asia, and Africa, and the superfamily *Ceboidea* or the *New World monkeys* found in the tropics of Central and South America (Figure 33-8). Some species have tails and others are without tails depending on whether they dwell in trees or on the ground. In addition to the suborder Anthro-

[handwritten margin notes:] Chordata / SP Vertebrata / C Mammalia / SC Theria / O Primates / SO Anthropoidea / SF Hominoidea / F Hominidae

A

B

C

D

Figure 33-6. The anthropoid apes (family Pongidae), the most closely related living animals to man. (A) Chimpanzee (*courtesy of Rapho Guillumette*); (B) gorilla (*courtesy of N. Y. Zool. Society*); (C) gibbon (*courtesy of Rapho Guillumette*); (D) orangutan, male (larger) and female (*courtesy of N. Y. Zool. Society*).

A

B

C

D

Figure 33-7. Examples of Old World monkeys (superfamily Cercopithecoidea). (A) Rhesus monkey (India); (B) baboon; (C) wanderoo or lion-tailed monkey (India); (D) mandrill (West Africa). (*Courtesy of Rapho Guillumette.*)

Figure 33-8. A New World monkey (superfamily Ceboidea). The old organ grinder monkey or hooded capuchine (*Cebus apella*) from South America. (*Courtesy of N. Y. Zool. Society.*)

poidea the order primates includes the suborder *Prosimii* or "pre-monkeys" consisting of tree shrews, lemurs, and tarsiers with elongated snouts and movable large ears in contrast to the reduced size of these structures in apes and monkeys (Figure 33-9).

The primates as a group share several characteristics, although exceptions exist. Their teeth are adapted for handling a variety of foods of both animal and vegetable origin. They are virtually all tropical or subtropical animals with the notable exception of man who ranges over the entire globe. Many live in trees and have both eyes directed forward which endows them with stereoscopic or three-dimensional vision, a feature of great value in estimating distances. The ability of most primates to grasp and handle objects has reached its highest state of development in man. Although unlike most other primates

he no longer has the use of his feet for grasping, man, like most other primates, possesses the unusual ability to manipulate his hands. This primate facility, together with the possession of a highly developed brain, accounts for his unique success in understanding and coping with the environment.

The Races of Mankind

Present-day man, although he has spread to nearly all parts of the globe, consists of the single species *Homo sapiens*, comprising several races or subspecies. The major races of mankind are not fixed and definite units that are entirely isolated, geographically or culturally. They not only fail to experience reproductive isolation but are in fact undergoing an even greater mixing of genes despite social and cultural barriers. The races are constantly shifting and to a certain extent interbreeding with one another, thus experiencing an exchange of genes. Our ever-increasing mobility, the result of our ever-improving means of transportation and communications, continues to reduce the chances of geographic isolation among human races and thus precludes the possibility of their evolution into new species.

There is no common agreement among anthropologists as to the number of different races of mankind. Various classification systems have been proposed, ranging from only a few human races to as many as several hundred. Many of these systems are based on physical criteria including skin pigmentation, type of hair, skull structure, and facial characteristics. The numerous gradations or degrees of difference in these features and their dynamic and continually changing status as a result of greater mixing and intermarriage are some of the reasons for the different views of the races of mankind. One classification system places the races of mankind into three major divisions: (1) *White* or *Caucasoid race,* consisting of light-skinned peoples, frequently with straight or wavy (but not woolly) hair and long noses; (2) *Negroid race,* consisting of dark-skinned peoples with broad flat noses, woolly hair, and long heads; and (3) *Mongoloid race*, consisting of yellow- or yellowish-brown-skinned peoples with coarse black hair and the "slant-eye" caused by an overlapping skin fold that extends from the upper eyelid, and flattened nose (Figure 33-10). Another system of classification consisting of six divisions includes the foregoing three races but places the Australian native, the American Indian, and the Polynesian into their own separate divisions. Still another classification system recognizes 30 different races of mankind, and so on.

Origin of the Primates

EARLY HISTORY. The limited fossil record of primates has been in part responsible for the disagreement among authorities about the evolutionary history of the primates as a group as well as of the origin of man. According to one of the more favored theories, the primates are presumed to have originated from a prosimian ancestor of the present-day *tree shrew* during the early Tertiary Period some 50 to 75 million years ago. Oddly enough, the ancient prosimians as the earliest of the primates apparently evolved from the most primitive of the placental mammals, namely the early *Insectivora* or "insect eaters," as represented by the present-day shrew and mole. Certain structural features of the living tree shrew (such as its larger brain and more facile digits) are suggestive of this relationship. One of its now extinct forebears presumably gave rise to the first primitive primate prosimians, represented by ancient lemurs and tarsoids which are believed to have existed by the time of the Eocene Epoch. The change of conditions in Europe and North America from a tropical to a cooler climate during the subsequent Oligocene and Miocene Epochs was accompanied by a disappearance of the prosimian primates from those regions of the world and their restriction to warmer areas such as Southern Asia, East Africa, and Madagascar.

LATER HISTORY. The hypothesis that the members of the suborder *Anthropoidea*, which includes man, the apes, the Old World mon-

A

B

Figure 33-9. Examples of the Prosimii suborder of primates, or "pre-monkeys." (A) Ringtailed lemur (*courtesy of Rapho Guillumette*); (B) adult male tarsier (*Tarsius tarsier*) (*courtesy of N. Y. Zool. Society*).

keys, and the New World monkeys with their typically flattened faces and reduced snouts, descended from prosimian stock is supported by some highly limited fossil record. The Old World monkeys and New World monkeys probably arose from separate but closely related prosimian ancestors. Certain definite similarities between the anthropoid apes and the Old World monkeys suggest that the apes may well have arisen from an ancient branch of the Old World monkeys, or that they share a common ancestry. The oldest fossil record of primitive apes indicates their presence during the Oligocene Epoch in northern Africa. By the latter part of the succeeding Miocene Epoch some 15 to 25 million years later a rapid adaptive radiation had occurred, as indicated by the variety of primitive apes resembling the present-day gibbon, chimpanzee, gorilla, and orangutan known to be in existence at that time in certain parts of Asia and southwest Europe as well as Africa.

Origin of Man

NEAR-HUMAN ANCESTORS. The continuing rapid adaptive radiation of the anthropoid apes during the latter Tertiary and early Quaternary periods, especially in South Africa as indicated by the more extensive fossil record, is believed to have given rise to the more immediate forebears of man. The discovery of certain fossil skulls possessing characteristics of both the ape family (*Pongidae*) and the family of man (*Hominidae*) with a brain capacity of some 600 cc like that of the chimpanzee or gorilla but with more human-like teeth, forehead, and posture has led some authorities to consider these extinct ape-men-like individuals (often called *Australopithecus*) with ape-sized brains and essentially man-like bodies as possible ancestors of man (presumably as one of the intermediate stages between ancient apes and early man). They appear to be the earliest of the near-human fossils found thus far. Their precise age, however, is not certain. Current estimates place them as far back as the late Pliocene

Epoch, some two or three million years in the past, to as recently as the middle Pleistocene Epoch approximately half a million years ago. They apparently lived in caves and hunted animals. In contrast, other specialists in the field regard *Australopithecus* as a contempory of ancient man and in no way directly involved in his evolutionary descent. There is therefore no common agreement as to some of the stages by which early man descended from primitive anthropoid apes.

JAVA MAN AND PEKING MAN — HOMO ERECTUS. Several types of early human fossils, but nevertheless possessing certain ape-like features, have been found and studied which shed some light on the more recent evolution of man himself. None date back before the Pleistocene Epoch, which means that they can be no older than a million years. In fact, most appear to be less than 500,000 years in age. The oldest of these are the skulls and other bone fragments found first in Java in 1891 and originally called *Java Man* or *Pithecanthropus* (Figure 33-11), and from 1929 onward in caves near Peking, China, and originally called *Peking Man* or *Sinanthropus* (Figure 33-11). Both date from the Pleistocene Epoch, 500,000 or more years ago, and are sufficiently similar to warrant their reclassification as simply different races or subspecies of a single species with the proposed name *Homo erectus*. His brain size ranged from about 750 to 1200 cc (as compared to the 600 cc of *Australopithecus* and the 1350 cc of modern man), and he possessed thick skull bones, prominent ridges at the eyebrows, and protruding jaws (smaller than those of *Australopithecus*) and teeth. He walked erect, probably attained an average height of five feet, inhabited caves, hunted wild animals, used fire, rough stone tools and weapons, and was probably cannibalistic.

The Pleistocene Epoch experienced several great glaciations when the great ice glaciers slowly moved southward on the nothern continents and then slowly retreated northward. Four separate glaciations are known to have occurred between 1,000,000 and 15,000

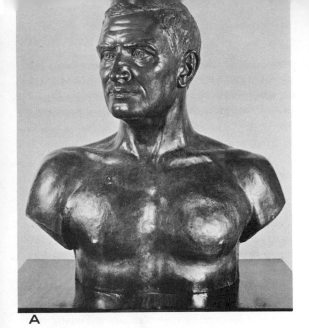

A

Figure 33-10. The races of man according to one system of classification: (A) White or Caucasoid race, Basque male from Northern Spain; (B) Negroid race, male from Senegal, West Africa; (C) Mongoloid race, female from Canton, South China. (*Courtesy of the Chicago Nat. Hist. Museum; Malvina Hoffman, sculptress.*)

B.C. *Homo erectus* may have first appeared in the warm period following the first of those glaciations and eventually must have migrated to Europe and other parts of the Old World.

NEANDERTHAL MAN. Relatively numerous and more recent fossil remains have been found in many locations in Europe, western Asia, and North Africa of a race of man called *Neanderthal man* (Figure 33-12) and often designated as *Homo neanderthalensis*, but more properly termed *Homo sapiens neanderthalensis*. They were a powerfully built race averaging about five feet in height with short legs and moderately long arms. Their brain size was fully as large as that of modern man, while the structure of their skull and face with its thick bones, brow ridges, protruding jaw, and receding forehead and chin were somewhat similar to but less extreme than that of Java Man and Peking Man. They inhabited Europe, western Asia, and North Africa in the warm period

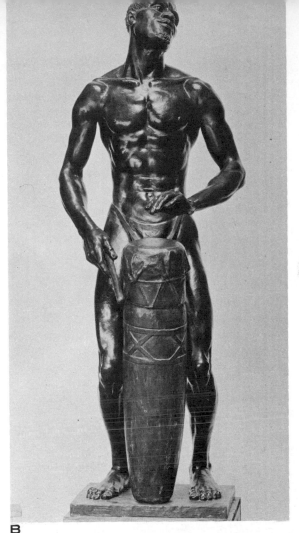

B

C

A

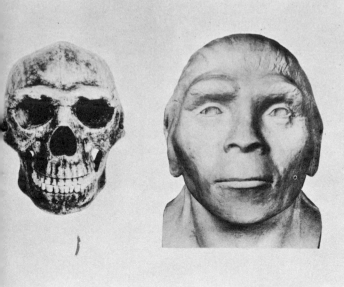

B

Figure 33-11. Early man. (A) Reconstructed head of "Java Man" (*Pithecanthropus*); (B) skull and reconstructed head of "Peking Man" (*Sinanthropus*). Both date from the Pleistocene Epoch and are sufficiently similar to warrant their reclassification as different races or subspecies of the single proposed species *Homo erectus*. (*Courtesy Amer. Mus. of Nat. History.*)

following the recession of the third great glacier during the Pleistocene Epoch through part of the fourth glacial age which began 125,000 years ago. They were quite intelligent, lived in caves, used a variety of stone tools, hunted large game including mammoths which were then found in that part of the world, and at times buried their dead with ritual offerings suggestive of religious practices. They probably became extinct some 50-75,000 years ago.

CRO-MAGNON MAN. The earliest known fossils of modern man, *Homo sapiens*, who were clearly like ourselves were first found in a cave in Cro-Magnon, France. They are representative of a race of modern man, now called *Cro-Magnon man* (Figure 33-12), which dates back approximately 25 to 50 thousand years ago. They were tall and erect, attaining heights of six feet or more. They were also intelligent, possessing brain sizes that were the same as present-day man, and quite advanced culturally. Their caves in southern Europe are decorated with an artistic display of painting and carving of the men and animals of the time. Their tools, utensils, and weapons were more advanced and they very likely engaged in religious rituals. It is quite possible that Cro-Magnon man originated in western Asia and migrated to southern Europe, replacing Neanderthal man in the process, in part by interbreeding.

MODERN MAN. The intermediate stages in the evolutionary progression of modern man from his ape-like ancestors are not entirely clear. Fossil remains of other primitive men have been found in addition to the principal ones described. Together they indicate one indisputable fact, namely that man did not evolve through an unbranched, straight-line sequence of evolutionary events. The findings in England and Germany, for example, of certain fossil skulls clearly older than the Neanderthals, but nevertheless showing a closer similarity in several respects to that of modern man, have been interpreted to suggest that Neanderthal man was probably not a direct intermediate type in the evolution of modern

A   **B**

Figure 33-12. Reconstructed heads of (A) Neanderthal Man; (B) Cro-Magnon Man. (*Courtesy of Amer. Mus. of Nat. History.*)

man from the Pithecanthropus line. It seems more likely that Neanderthal man was one of several lines, probably arising from a Pithecanthropus-like ancestor (the result possibly of adaptive radiation), which eventually became extinct. Presumably one of the other lines or variants, perhaps those represented by the above-mentioned fossils from England and Germany, was an intermediate form in the advance to modern man.

The anthropologist, Dr. Carleton S. Coon, has recently suggested that *Homo sapiens*, or modern man, evolved independently from five different races or subspecies of *Homo erectus* in five different areas or territories of the world. This is in sharp contrast to the generally accepted idea that *Homo sapiens* originated only once and then distributed himself around the world east and west and north and south. According to Coon's view the five principal geographical races of *Homo erectus* evolved from *Australopithecus*-like ancestors which had spread from Africa to various parts of the world. Coon contends that the evolutionary transition from *Homo erectus* to *Homo sapiens* occurred independently in Java some 40,000 years ago, in two places in China to yield the Mongoloid race (about 350,000 years ago) and the ancestors of the American Indian (about 150,000 years ago), in western Europe some 250,000 years ago to yield the Caucasoid race, and in Africa some 5000 to 8000 years ago to yield the Negroid race by a blending of four different racial lines.

Modern Europeans are probably descended from a mixture of different races of *Homo sapiens* including certain Asiatic races and Cro-Magnon man. The first humans to reach

North America are believed to have arrived from Asia during the late Pleistocene Epoch (prior to the fourth glaciation via narrow land connections at Bering Strait). With the passage of time they moved southward and by 25,000 B.C. were apparently well established in both North and South America.

The most significant developments in the evolution of man have been those parts of the brain that confer intelligence. For it is man's intelligence that has been the most instrumental factor in his phenomenal success in controlling and dealing with his living and nonliving environment. It has endowed man with adaptive powers that permit him to live and thrive in virtually every naturally occurring environment in our planet, and perhaps in the not too distant future on other planets. The relationship of brain development to the accompanying development of manual dexterity, erect posture, and stereoscopic vision have gone hand in hand.

Man is the culmination within the animal kingdom, just as flowering plants are the culmination within the plant kingdom, of one of the most advanced and complex states in the incredibly long sequence of the evolutionary organization of energy and matter—a chain of events that started with the beginning of the expanding universe and evolved by steps from nonliving to living systems and thence to contemporary living organisms.

Many wonders there be, but naught more wondrous than man.
SOPHOCLES, 5TH CENTURY B.C.

SUPPLEMENTARY REFERENCES

Blum, H. *Time's Arrow and Evolution*, Princeton University Press, Princeton, N.J., 1951.
Dobzhansky, T., *Evolution, Genetics, and Man*, Wiley, New York, 1955.
Dobzhansky, T., "The Genetic Basis of Evolution," *Scientific American,* January 1950.
Hooton, E. A., *Up from the Ape*, Macmillan, New York, 1945.
Huxley, J., *Evolution in Action*, Harper, New York, 1953.
Huxley, J. S., *Evolution, The Modern Synthesis*, Allen-Unwin, London, 1942.
Moore, R., *Man, Time and Fossils*, Knopf, New York, 1953.
Simpson, G. G., *The Meaning of Evolution*, Yale University Press, New Haven, Conn., 1950.
Simpson, G. G., *This View of Life: The World of an Evolutionist*, Harcourt, Brace and World, New York, 1964.

The index is also intended to serve as a glossary. **Bold-face numbers** indicate an illustration, a chemical formula, or the main definition (or description) when more than one entry is given. *Italics* indicate a scientific name (genus and species).

Oligosaccharides, 148
Omasum, 569
"One gene, one enzyme," 277
Ontogeny, 716
Onychophora, 458
Oögenesis, 305-306
Oögonia, **305**, 351
Oparin, I. A., 33
Operculum, 475
Ophiuroidea, 469
  basket star, 470
Opisthorchis sinensis, 252
Opossum, 479, **766**
Opsin, 223, **534**
Opsonization, 598
Optic chiasma, 533
Optic cup, 715
Optic nerve, 531
Optical activity, 144-146
Optical isomers, 144
Oral groove, 423
Orangutan, 767, **768**
Orders (taxonomic), 341
Ordovician period, 744
Organic acids, 139-140
Organic chemistry, 136-157
Organic compounds, functional groups,
  138-141
Organic nutrients, absorption of, from
  the digestive tract, 576-577
Organic substances, evolution of, 31
Organisms, effect of physical environ-
  ment on, 246-250
Organizer, 714
Organizer theory, 714-716
Organs, 85
Organ system, 85
Orgasm, 704
Origin of life, modern evolutionary
  theory, 29-36
Origin of moon, 20
Origin of muscle, 665
Origin of planets, 20-21
Origin of Species (by Charles Darwin),
  735, 738
Origin of universe, 18-20
Ornithine, in urea formation, 651
Ornithine transcarbamylase, 288
Ornithology, 9
Oscillatoria, 349
Osmosis, 109-112
Osmotic concentration (Osmotic
  pressure) 109-112
"Osmotic shock," 271
Ossification, 681
Osteichthyes (bony fishes), 475-476
Ostriches, 478
Otoliths, 526
Oxaloacetic acid, in citric acid cycle,
  182, 183, **185, 187**
  in transamination reactions, 199
Oxalosuccinic acid, 186
Oxidase, 162
Oxidation-reduction reactions, 126-127
Oxidative decarboxylation, of alpha-
  ketoglutaric acid to succinic acid,
  186
  of isocitric acid, 185
  of pyruvic acid, 185
Oxidative phosphorylation, 189
  uncoupling of, 543

Oxidizing agent, 126
Oxygen, 119
  effect of evolution, 37
  isotopes, 120
  in respiration, see aerobic respiration
Oxygen cycle, 223-224
Oxygen debt, 675
Oxygen-hemoglobin dissociation curve,
  640-641
Oxygen transport, 639-641
Oxyhemoglobin, 639
Oxyntic cell, 567
Oxytocin, 556-557
Ova, *see* Egg cell
Oval opening (of heart), 626
Oval window (of ear), **521**, 522
Ovarian follicle, 696
Ovaries of higher animals, 557
  of man, 696-697
  of plants, 383
Oviducts, of man, 697
Ovipositor, of grasshopper, 461
Ovulation, 700
Ovules, 379
  in angiosperms, 383, 384, **385**
  in pine, 380

P_1 generation, *see* Parental generation
"Pacemaker" (sino-atrial (S-A) node),
  609
Pain, referred, 520
Painter, T., 268, 315
Pairing of DNA polynucleotides, 168
Palate, 563
Paleocene epoch, 744
Paleoniscoids, 747
Paleontology, 9
Paleozoic era, 744
Palisade layer, 393
Palmitic acid, 150
Pancreas, in digestion, 570-572
  Islets of Langerhans, 546-548
Pancreatic juice secretion, control of, 577
Pancreozymin, 578
Panthothenic acid, 220
Papulae, of starfish, 468
Para-aminobenzoic acid, **163**, 221
Parallel evolution, 762
Paramecium, 81-82, **422-423**
Paramylum, 349
Parapodia, of *Nereis*, 447
Parasites, 251
Parasitism, 250, **251-253**
  evolutionary aspects, 251-252
  versus predation, 253
Parasitology, 9
Parasympathetic nervous system, 491,
  503-506
Parathyroid glands, 544, 546
Parenchyma, 93
Parental generation (P_1), 296
Parotid salivary glands, 565
Parthenogenesis, 691-692
Partial pressures, of gases, 629
Parturition (birth), 728
Passive immunity, 601
Pasteur, L., 29
Pasteurization, 360
Patella (kneecap), 680
Pathogenic agents, 590
Pavlov, I., 499, 568

Pearl (in oyster), 441
Pectic acids, 149
Pectoral girdle, 676, 677, **679**
Pedicellariae, of starfish, 467
Pedigree histories, 330
Pedipalps, of Arachnida, 464
"Peking man" (*Sinanthropus*), **772, 774**
Pelecypoda, 441, **443-444**
Pelvic girdle, 676, 677, 678, **679**
Pellagra, 219
Pellicle, 61
  in *Paramecium*, 422
Penquin, 478, **765**
Penicillin, 363
Penis, of man, 704
Pennsylvanian Period, 744
Pentose oxidative pathway, 174, **193-194**
Pentoses, 146
Pepsin, 567
Pepsinogen, 567
Peptidases, in indigestion, 573
Peptide bonds, 152-153
Perennials, **382**, 387
Pericardium, 606
Perilymph, 522
Periods (geologic), 743, **744**
Peripatus ("walking worm"), 458
Peripheral nervous system, 490, **502-506**
Periopods, of lobster, 456
Perissodactyla, 481
Peristalsis, of esophagus, 566
  of large intestine, 575
  of small intestine, 573
Permanent tissues (of plants), 92
Permeability of protoplasm, 110
Permeases, 288
Permian Period, 744
Pernicious anemia, 222, **588**
Peroxidase, 169
Perspiration, 649
Perutz, M. F., 154
Petals, 383, **384**
Petiole, 392
Petrification, 740
Petromyzon, (lamprey), 474
pH, **125, 126**
Phaeophyta (brown algae), 355-357
Phages, 77, **78, 270, 271**, 273
Phagocytosis, 590, **591, 595**
Phalanges, **676, 677**, 679, 680
Phanerogamic botany, 9
Pharyngeal gill slits, 471
Pharynx, in amphioxus, 473
  in earthworm, 450
  in man, 565
  in nematodes, 436
  in *Nereis*, 447, **448**
  in planaria, 431-432
  in tunicates, 472
Phase (colloidal), 113
Phase-contrast microscope, 44
Phase of accelerating multiplication, 254
Phase of decelerating multiplication, 255
Phaseolus vulgaris (common bean),
  germination of, 387
Phenotype, 297
Phenylalanine, 142
Phenylketonuria, 289
Phenylpyruvic acid, 289
Phloem, 96
  in root, 391-392